The calculus with analytic geometry

Louis Leithold

DEPARTMENT OF MATHEMATICS

CALIFORNIA STATE COLLEGE AT LOS ANGELES

THE CALCULUS
with analytic geometry

HARPER & ROW, PUBLISHERS

NEW YORK, EVANSTON, AND LONDON

THE CALCULUS WITH ANALYTIC GEOMETRY

LIBRARY OF CONGRESS CATALOG CARD NUMBER: 67-12547

To my son GORDON MARC LEITHOLD

Contents

Preface

During the last ten years, in the colleges and universities of this country, there have been many significant changes in the teaching of calculus. The tendency has been to present elementary calculus from a more rigorous approach, instead of the older, intuitive and computational point of view. In this book I have attempted to achieve a healthy balance between the two approaches. The text can be used for courses designed for prospective mathematics majors, as well as for those having students whose primary interest is in engineering, the physical sciences, or nontechnical fields. It is assumed that the reader has completed courses in algebra and trigonometry.

A textbook should be written for the student. With this in mind, I have attempted to keep the presentation geared to a beginner's experience and maturity and to leave no steps unexplained or omitted. I desire that the reader be aware that proofs of theorems are necessary and that these proofs be well motivated and carefully explained so that they are understandable to the student who has achieved an average mastery of the preceding sections of the book. If a theorem is stated without proof, I have generally augmented the discussion by both figures and examples, and in such cases I have always stressed that what is presented is an illustration of the content of the theorem and is not a proof.

The first chapter contains basic facts about the real-number system. I have avoided presenting sophisticated, tricky arguments merely for the purpose of showing that some of the properties can be derived from others. It has been my experience that few students of beginning calculus are capable of appreciating such discussions and that these considerations belong to a course in abstract algebra. Chapter 2 gives an introduction to analytic geometry, and it includes the traditional material on straight lines as well as a discussion of the circle and the parabola. This chapter may be omitted by those who have already had a course in analytic geometry.

Chapters 3, 4, and 5 are the heart of any first course in calculus. I have defined a function as a set of ordered pairs and have used this idea to point up the concept of a function as a correspondence between sets of real numbers. The notion of a limit of a function is first given a step-by-step motivation, which brings the reader from computing the value of a function near a number, through an intuitive discussion of the limiting process, up to a rigorous epsilon-delta definition. A sequence of examples progressively graded in difficulty is included. All the limit theorems are stated, and some proofs are presented in the text, while other proofs have been outlined in the exercises. In the chapter on continuity, I have used as examples and counterexamples "common, everyday" functions and have avoided those that would have little intuitive meaning for the reader.

In Chapter 6, before giving the formal definition of a derivative, I have defined the tangent line to a curve and instantaneous velocity on a straight line in order to demonstrate in advance that the concept of a derivative is of wide application, both geometrical and physical. Theorems on differentiation are proved and illustrated by examples in Chapter 7, and Chapter 8 gives the traditional applications of the derivative to problems involving related rates, maxima and minima, and curve sketching. The antiderivative is treated in Chapter 9. I use the term "antidifferentiation" instead of "indefinite integration," but the standard notation $\int f(x)\,dx$ is retained, so that the reader will not be given a bizarre new notation that would make the reading of standard references difficult. This notation will suggest to the student that some relation must exist between definite integrals, introduced in Chapter 10, and antiderivatives, but I see no harm in this as long as he is presented with the theoretically proper view of the definite integral as the limit of sums. Exercises involving the evaluation of definite integrals by finding limits of sums are given in Chapter 10, to impress upon the reader that this is how they are calculated. The introduction of the definite integral follows the definition of the area under a curve as a limit of sums. Elementary properties of the definite integral are derived and the fundamental theorem of integral calculus is proved. It is emphasized that this is a theorem, and an important one, because it provides us with an alternative to computing limits of sums. It is also emphasized that the definite integral is in no sense some special type of antiderivative. In Chapter 11, I have given numerous applications of definite integrals. The presentation stresses not only the manipulative techniques but also the fundamental principles involved. In each application, the definitions of the new terms are intuitively motivated and explained.

The treatment of logarithmic and exponential functions in Chapter 12 is the modern approach. The natural logarithm is defined as an integral, and after a discussion of the inverse of a function, the exponential function is defined as the inverse of the natural logarithm function. An irrational power of a real number is then defined. A brief review of trigonometry, in which the functional nature of the trigonometric functions is emphasized, is given in the first part of Chapter 13. This is followed by sections on the differentiation and integration of these functions as well as of the inverse trigonometric functions.

Chapter 14, on techniques of integration, involves one of the most important computational aspects of the calculus. I have explained the theoretical backgrounds of each different method after an introductory motivation. The mastery of integration techniques depends upon the examples, and I have used as illustrations problems that the student will certainly meet in practice, those which require patience and persistence to solve. The material on the approximation of definite integrals, given in Chapter 15, includes the statement of theorems for computing the bounds of the error involved in these approximations. The theorems and the problems that go with them, being self-contained, may be omitted from a course if the instructor so wishes.

Polar coordinates and some of their applications are given in Chapter 16. In Chapter 17, conics are treated as a unified subject, to impress upon the reader their natural and close relationship to each other. Equations of the conics in polar coordinates are treated first, and the cartesian equations are derived from the polar equations.

The first six sections of Chapter 18 on vectors in the plane may be taken up after Chapter 7 if it is desired to introduce vectors earlier in the course. The approach to vectors is modern, and it serves both as a preview of the viewpoint of linear algebra and of that of classical vector analysis. The applications are to physics and geometry. Chapter 21 treats vectors in three-dimensional space and, if desired, the topics in the first three sections of this chapter may be studied concurrently with the corresponding topics of Chapter 18. In Chapter 21, the treatment of solid analytic geometry by the use of vectors is also a modern one, and it provides the reader with an immediate application of vector analysis.

Chapter 19 is a self-contained treatment of hyperbolic functions. The first two sections may be studied immediately following the discussion of the circular trigonometric functions in Chapter 13, if so desired. However, the geometric interpretation of the hyperbolic functions, given in the third section of Chapter 19, involves the use of parametric equations, which appear for the first time in Chapter 18. The topics of indeterminate forms and improper integrals and the computational techniques involved are presented in Chapter 20.

Limits, continuity, and differentiation of functions of several variables are treated in Chapter 22. The discussion and examples are limited mainly to functions of two and three variables; however, statements of most of the definitions and theorems are extended to functions of n variables. The double integral of a function of two variables and the triple integral of a function of three variables, along with some applications to physics and geometry, are considered in Chapter 23.

I have attempted in Chapter 24 to give as complete a treatment of infinite series as is feasible in an elementary calculus text. In addition to the customary computational material, I have included the proof of the equivalence of convergence and boundedness of monotonic sequences based on the completeness property of the real numbers and the proofs of the computational processes involving differentiation and integration of power series.

The exercises throughout are graded to provide a challenge to students having a wide range of abilities. They are designed to give the student drill on computational processes as well as to bring out the significance of the theoretical results obtained.

The format of the book is such that definitions and theorems are displayed for easy reference. For example, the number 6.2.3 refers to the third definition or theorem in section two of Chapter 6. Important formulas or equations are indicated by two boldfaced left-hand parentheses in the left margin. The figures were drawn by the Imperial Drafting Service, Arcadia, California.

The material in this book was used in a prepublication version in a course for freshman and sophomore students at California State College at Los Angeles and for a course for adults in the evening division of Santa Monica City College. To these students I wish to express my thanks for their suggestions and their patience with the dittoed copies.

I am very grateful for the valuable suggestions for improving the manuscript that were made by Professors Phillip Clarke of Los Angeles Valley College, James Hurley of the University of California at Riverside, and Richard Chamberlain of California State College at Los Angeles, who reviewed the prepublication version. Thanks are also due to Mrs. Robert Watson, who typed the final version, and to Carol Terry, Dennis Spuck, Alex Adjemian, and David Nellis, who helped with numerous tasks.

LOUIS LEITHOLD

1 Some properties of the real numbers

(1.1)   Real numbers

In elementary calculus we are concerned with the real-number system. It is assumed that the reader is familiar with the algebraic operations of addition, subtraction, multiplication, and division of real numbers, as well as with the algebraic concepts of solving equations, factoring, and so forth. In this chapter we shall be concerned with properties of the real numbers that are important to the study of calculus.

A *real number* is either a positive number, a negative number, or zero, and any real number may be classified as a *rational number* or an *irrational number*. A rational number is any number that can be expressed as the ratio of two integers. That is, a rational number is a number of the form p/q, where p and q are integers and $q \neq 0$. The rational numbers consist of the following:

1. The *integers* (positive, negative, and zero)

$$\ldots, -5, -4, -3, -2, -1, 0, 1, 2, 3, 4, 5, \ldots$$

2. The positive and negative *fractions*, such as

$$\frac{2}{7} \qquad \frac{-4}{5} \qquad \frac{83}{5}$$

3. The positive and negative *terminating decimals*

$$2.36 = \frac{236}{100} \qquad -0.003251 = -\frac{3251}{1,000,000}$$

4. The positive and negative *nonterminating repeating decimals*

$$0.333\ldots = \frac{1}{3} \qquad -0.549549549\ldots = -\frac{61}{111}$$

The real numbers that are not rational numbers are called *irrational numbers*. These are the positive and negative *nonterminating, nonrepeating* decimals; for example,

$$\sqrt{3} = 1.732\ldots \qquad \pi = 3.14159\ldots \qquad \tan\frac{8\pi}{9} = -0.364\ldots$$

The fundamental properties of the operations of addition and multiplication include the following, where a, b, and c are real numbers:

1.1.1 COMMUTATIVE LAWS $a + b = b + a$ $ab = ba$

1.1.2 ASSOCIATIVE LAWS $a + (b + c) = (a + b) + c$ $a(bc) = (ab)c$

1.1.3 DISTRIBUTIVE LAW $a(b + c) = ab + ac$

1.1.4 EXISTENCE OF IDENTITY ELEMENTS   There exist two distinct real numbers 0 and 1 such that for every real number a

$$a + 0 = a \quad \text{and} \quad a \cdot 1 = a$$

1.1.5 EXISTENCE OF NEGATIVES   Every real number a has a negative, denoted by $-a$, such that

$$a + (-a) = 0$$

1.1.6 EXISTENCE OF RECIPROCALS   Every real number $a \neq 0$ has a reciprocal, denoted by $1/a$, such that

$$a \cdot \frac{1}{a} = 1$$

From these properties, other laws of algebra may be derived. One such property is

$$ab = 0 \quad \text{if and only if} \quad a = 0 \text{ or } b = 0$$

Another property is that the sum and product of two positive numbers is positive.

The real numbers may be represented geometrically as points on a horizontal line which extends indefinitely to the right and to the left. We shall call this line the *real line*. With each point on the real line is associated a real number, and with each real number is associated a point on the real line. This is illustrated in Fig. 1.1.1 and is described below.

Figure 1.1.1

A point on the line is chosen to represent the number 0 (zero). A unit of distance is selected. Then each positive number n is represented by the point at a distance of n units to the right of the point 0. Each negative number n is represented by the point at a distance of $-n$ to the left of the point 0. (It should be noted that if n is negative then $-n$ is positive.) The points on the line are identified with the numbers they represent.

(1.2)   Inequalities

There is an order relation for real numbers.

1.2.1 DEFINITION   The symbols $<$ ("is less than") and $>$ ("is greater than") are defined as follows:

(i) $a < b$ *if and only if* $b - a$ *is positive*

(ii) $a > b$ *if and only if* $a - b$ *is positive*

Expressions such as $a < b$ and $a > b$ are called *inequalities*. For example,

$$3 < 5, \quad -1 < 2, \quad -5 < -3, \quad 7 > 4, \quad 3 > -4, \quad -2 > -7$$

1.2.2 DEFINITION   The symbols $\leq$ ("is less than or equal to") and $\geq$ ("is greater than or equal to") are defined as follows:

(i) $a \leq b$ if and only if   either $a < b$ or $a = b$

(ii) $a \geq b$ if and only if   either $a > b$ or $a = b$

We shall now consider properties of the order relation which we need in order to work with inequalities.

1.2.3 PROPERTY   If $a < b$ and $b < c$, then $a < c$.

EXAMPLE: $2 < 5$ and $5 < 7$; so $2 < 7$.

1.2.4 PROPERTY   If $a < b$, then $a + c < b + c$, if c is any real number.

EXAMPLE: $3 < 8$; so $3 + 2 < 8 + 2$; and $3 - 5 < 8 - 5$.

1.2.5 PROPERTY   If $a < b$ and $c < d$, then $a + c < b + d$.

EXAMPLE: $2 < 5$ and $-1 < 4$; so $2 + (-1) < 5 + 4$.

1.2.6 PROPERTY   If $a < b$, and c is any positive number, then $ac < bc$.

EXAMPLE: $3 < 5$; so $3 \cdot 2 < 5 \cdot 2$.

1.2.7 PROPERTY   If $a < b$, and c is any negative number, then $ac > bc$.

EXAMPLE: $3 < 5$; so $3(-2) > 5(-2)$.

It should be noted that Property 1.2.6 states that if both sides of an inequality are multiplied by a positive number, the direction of the inequality remains unchanged, whereas Property 1.2.7 states that if both sides of an inequality are multiplied by a negative number, the direction of the inequality is reversed.

Properties 1.2.6 and 1.2.7 also hold for division, since dividing both sides of an inequality by a number d is the same as multiplying both sides by $1/d$.

These five properties may be proved by using the properties of the real numbers and Definition 1.2.1. For example, the proof of Property 1.2.5 is as follows:

Since $a < b$, $b - a$ is positive (by 1.2.1).

Since $c < d$, $d - c$ is positive (by 1.2.1).

Therefore $(b - a) + (d - c)$ is positive, since the sum of two positive numbers is positive.

Therefore $(b + d) - (a + c)$ is positive, using properties of the real numbers.

Therefore $a + c < b + d$ (by 1.2.1).

The proofs of Properties 1.2.3, 1.2.4, 1.2.6, and 1.2.7 are left for the reader (see Exercises 32 through 34 at the end of this section).

We have corresponding properties if we reverse the direction of each inequality. These are stated below.

1.2.8 PROPERTY   If $a > b$ and $b > c$, then $a > c$.

EXAMPLE: $8 > 4$ and $4 > -2$; so $8 > -2$.

1.2.9 PROPERTY   If $a > b$, then $a + c > b + c$, if c is any real number.

EXAMPLE: $3 > -5$; so $3 - 4 > -5 - 4$.

1.2.10 PROPERTY   If $a > b$ and $c > d$, then $a + c > b + d$.

EXAMPLE: $7 > 2$ and $3 > -5$; so $7 + 3 > 2 + (-5)$.

1.2.11 PROPERTY   If $a > b$ and if c is any positive number, then $ac > bc$.

EXAMPLE: $-3 > -7$; so $(-3)4 > (-7)4$.

1.2.12 PROPERTY   If $a > b$ and if c is any negative number, then $ac < bc$.

EXAMPLE: $-3 > -7$; so $(-3)(-4) < (-7)(-4)$.

Before solving inequalities, we shall interpret the order relation geometrically and introduce the concept of an *interval*.

Geometrically, we see that $a < b$ if and only if the point representing a on the real line is to the left of the point representing the number b. Similarly, $a > b$ if and only if the point representing a on the real line is to the right of the point representing the number b. In the discussion that follows, we shall use the same symbol for both the number and the point representing that number on the real line. So the number $2 <$ the number 5, since the point 2 is to the left of the point 5.

A number x is between a and b if $a < x$ and $x < b$. We may write this as a continued inequality as follows:

(1) $$a < x < b$$

The continued inequality (1) denotes an *open interval*.

1.2.13 DEFINITION   The *open interval* from a to b, denoted by (a,b), is the set of all real numbers x such that $a < x < b$.

The *closed interval* from a to b consists of all numbers between a and b as well as a and b.

1.2.14 DEFINITION   The *closed interval* from a to b, denoted by $[a,b]$, is the set of all real numbers x such that $a \leq x \leq b$.

Figure 1.2.1 illustrates the open interval (a,b) and Fig. 1.2.2 illustrates the closed interval $[a,b]$.

Figure 1.2.1   Figure 1.2.2

The interval half-open on the left consists of all numbers between a and b as well as b, but not a.

1.2.15 DEFINITION   The *interval half-open on the left*, denoted by $(a,b]$, is the set of all real numbers x such that $a < x \leq b$.

Similarly, we define an interval half-open on the right.

1.2.16 DEFINITION   The *interval half-open on the right*, denoted by $[a,b)$, is the set of all real numbers x such that $a \leq x < b$.

Figure 1.2.3 illustrates the interval $(a,b]$, and Fig. 1.2.4 illustrates the interval $[a,b)$.

Figure 1.2.3   Figure 1.2.4

We shall use the symbol $+\infty$ ("positive infinity") and the symbol $-\infty$ ("negative infinity"); however, care must be taken not to confuse these symbols with real numbers, for they do not obey the properties of the real numbers.

We use the notation $(a, +\infty)$ to denote the set of all numbers greater than a. One may also say that $(a, +\infty)$ is the set of all real numbers x such that $x > a$.

Similarly, $(-\infty, b)$ denotes the set of all numbers less than b; or, $(-\infty, b)$ is the set of all real numbers x such that $x < b$.

Figure 1.2.5 illustrates the interval $(a, +\infty)$, and Fig. 1.2.6 illustrates the interval $(-\infty, b)$.

Figure 1.2.5   **Figure 1.2.6**

$[a, +\infty)$ is the set of all real numbers x such that $x \geq a$; and $(-\infty, b]$ is the set of all real numbers x such that $x \leq b$.

Finally, $(-\infty, +\infty)$ denotes the set of all real numbers.

We shall now solve some inequalities and express the solutions as intervals.

EXAMPLE 1: Find all real numbers satisfying the inequality

$$2 + 3x < 5x + 8$$

Solution: If x is a number such that

$$2 + 3x < 5x + 8$$

then $\quad 2 + 3x - 2 < 5x + 8 - 2 \quad$ by 1.2.4

or $\quad\quad 3x < 5x + 6$

Then, adding $-5x$ to both sides of this inequality, we have

$$-2x < 6 \quad \text{by 1.2.4}$$

Dividing both sides of this inequality by -2 and reversing the direction of the inequality, we get

$$x > -3 \quad \text{by 1.2.7}$$

What we have proved is that if

$$2 + 3x < 5x + 8$$

then $\quad x > -3$

Each of the steps is reversible; that is, if we start with

$$x > -3$$

we multiply each side by -2 and reverse the direction of the inequality, and get

$$-2x < 6$$

Then add $5x$ and 2 to both sides of the inequality, and we get

$$2 + 3x < 5x + 8$$

Therefore, we may conclude that

$$2 + 3x < 5x + 8 \quad \textit{if and only if} \quad x > -3$$

So the interval solution of the given inequality is $(-3, +\infty)$, which is illustrated in Fig. 1.2.7.

EXAMPLE 2: Find all real numbers satisfying the inequality

$$4 < 3x - 2 \leq 10$$

Solution: Adding 2 to each member of the inequality, we get

$$6 < 3x \leq 12$$

Dividing each member by 3, we get

$$2 < x \leq 4$$

Each step is reversible; so the interval solution is (2,4], as is illustrated in Fig. 1.2.8.

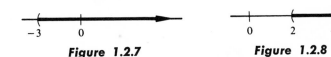

$$\text{\textbf{\textit{Figure 1.2.7}}} \qquad\qquad \text{\textbf{\textit{Figure 1.2.8}}}$$

EXAMPLE 3: Find all real numbers satisfying the inequality

$$\frac{7}{x} > 2 \qquad x \neq 0$$

Solution: We wish to multiply both sides of the inequality by x. However, the direction of the inequality that results will depend upon whether x is positive or negative. So we must consider two cases.

Case 1: x is positive; that is, $x > 0$.

Multiplying both sides by x, we get

$$7 > 2x$$

Dividing both sides by 2, we get

$$\frac{7}{2} > x \qquad \text{or, equivalently,} \qquad x < \frac{7}{2}$$

Therefore, since the above steps are reversible, the solution of Case 1 is the set of all numbers x such that $x > 0$ and $x < 7/2$; that is, $0 < x < 7/2$, which is the interval (0,7/2).

Case 2: x is negative; that is, $x < 0$.

Multiplying both sides by x, we get, reversing the direction of the inequality,

$$7 < 2x$$

Dividing both sides by 2, we get

$$\frac{7}{2} < x \qquad \text{or, equivalently,} \qquad x > \frac{7}{2}$$

Therefore, since the above steps are reversible, the solution of Case 2 is the set of all numbers x such that $x < 0$ and $x > 7/2$. But it is impossible to find a value for x satisfying both of these inequalities.

From cases 1 and 2 we conclude that the solution of the given inequality is the open interval (0,7/2), which is illustrated in Fig.1.2.9.

Figure 1.2.9

EXAMPLE 4: Find all real numbers satisfying the inequality

$$\frac{x}{x-3} < 4 \qquad x \neq 3$$

Solution: Since we wish to multiply both sides of the inequality by $x - 3$, we must consider two cases, as in the previous example.

Case 1: $x - 3 > 0$; that is, $x > 3$.

Multiplying both sides of the inequality by $x - 3$, we get

$$x < 4x - 12$$

Adding $-4x$ to both sides, we get

$$-3x < -12$$

Dividing both sides by -3 and reversing the direction of the inequality, we get

$$x > 4$$

Therefore, the solution of Case 1 is the set of all numbers x such that $x > 3$ and $x > 4$. This is the set of all x such that $x > 4$, or the interval $(4, +\infty)$.

Case 2: $x - 3 < 0$; that is, $x < 3$.

Multiplying both sides by $x - 3$ and reversing the direction of the inequality, we get

$$x > 4x - 12$$

or $\qquad -3x > -12$

or $\qquad x < 4$

Therefore x must be less than 4 and also less than 3. So the solution of Case 2 is the interval $(-\infty,3)$.

If we combine the solutions for Case 1 and Case 2, we get all numbers x in the two intervals $(-\infty,3)$ and $(4,+\infty)$ — or more simply, all numbers x *not* in the closed interval [3,4]. The solution is illustrated in Fig. 1.2.10.

Figure 1.2.10

EXAMPLE 5: Find all real numbers satisfying the inequality

$$(x + 3)(x + 4) > 0$$

Solution: The inequality will be satisfied when both factors have the same sign; that is, if $x + 3 > 0$ and $x + 4 > 0$, or if $x + 3 < 0$ and $x + 4 < 0$. We consider the two cases.

Case 1: $x + 3 > 0$ and $x + 4 > 0$.
That is,

$$x > -3 \quad \text{and} \quad x > -4$$

So, both inequalities hold if $x > -3$, which is the interval $(-3, +\infty)$.

Case 2: $x + 3 < 0$ and $x + 4 < 0$.
That is,

$$x < -3 \quad \text{and} \quad x < -4$$

Both inequalities hold if $x < -4$, which is the interval $(-\infty, -4)$. Therefore, if we combine the solutions for Case 1 and Case 2, we get the two intervals $(-\infty, -4)$ and $(-3, +\infty)$; or, equivalently, all x *not* in the closed interval $[-4, -3]$.

Exercises 1.2

In Exercises 1 through 26, find all real numbers satisfying the given inequality. Give the interval solution, and illustrate the solution on the real line.

1. $5x + 2 > x - 6$

2. $3 - x < 5 + 3x$

3. $\dfrac{2x}{3} - \dfrac{1}{2} < 0$

4. $3x - 5 < \dfrac{3x}{4} + \dfrac{1 - x}{3}$

5. $13 \geq 2x - 3 \geq 5$

6. $8 < 5x + 4 \leq 10$

7. $2 \leq 5 - 3x < 11$

8. $2 > -3 - 3x \geq -7$

9. $\dfrac{5}{x} < \dfrac{3}{4}$

10. $\dfrac{4}{x} - 3 > \dfrac{2}{x} - 7$

11. $\dfrac{x}{x - 1} > \dfrac{1}{4}$

12. $\dfrac{2}{1 - x} \leq 1$

13. $x^2 > 4$

14. $x^2 \leq 9$

15. $(x - 3)(x + 5) > 0$

16. $x^2 - 3x + 2 > 0$

17. $1 - x - 2x^2 \geq 0$

18. $2x^2 + x < 3$

19. $4x^2 + 9x < 9$

20. $x^2 + 3x + 1 > 0$

21. $2x^2 - 6x + 3 < 0$

22. $\dfrac{x + 1}{2 - x} < \dfrac{x}{3 + x}$

23. $\dfrac{1}{x + 1} < \dfrac{2}{3x - 1}$

24. $\dfrac{3}{x + 4} < \dfrac{2}{x - 5}$

25. $\dfrac{1}{3x - 7} \geq \dfrac{4}{3 - 2x}$

26. $x^3 + 1 > x^2 + x$

27. Find all the values of x for which $\sqrt{2 - 3x}$ is a real number. HINT: The number $\sqrt{2 - 3x}$ is real if and only if $2 - 3x \geq 0$.

In Exercises 28 through 31, find all the values of x for which the number is real.

28. $\sqrt{8x - 5}$

29. $\sqrt{x^2 - 16}$

30. $\sqrt{x^2 - 5x + 4}$

31. $\sqrt{x^2 + 2x - 1}$

32. Prove Property 1.2.3.

33. Prove Property 1.2.4.

34. Prove Properties 1.2.6 and 1.2.7.

35. If $a > b > 0$, prove that $a^2 > b^2$.

36. Prove that if $a \geq 0$ and $b \geq 0$, then $a^2 = b^2$ if and only if $a = b$.

37. Prove that if $b > a > 0$ and $c > 0$, then $\dfrac{a + c}{b + c} > \dfrac{a}{b}$.

(1.3) Absolute value

1.3.1 DEFINITION   The absolute value of x, denoted by $|x|$, is defined as follows:

$$|x| = \quad x \qquad \text{if } x > 0$$
$$|x| = -x \qquad \text{if } x < 0$$
$$|0| = 0$$

Thus, the absolute value of a positive number or zero is equal to the number itself. The absolute value of a negative number is the corresponding positive number, since the negative of a negative number is positive. For example,

$$|3| = 3 \qquad |-5| = -(-5) = 5 \qquad |8 - 14| = |-6| = -(-6) = 6$$

We see from the definition that the absolute value of a number is either a positive number or zero; that is, it is nonnegative.

Geometrically, the absolute value of a number x is its distance from 0, without regard to direction. In general, $|a - b|$ is the distance between a and b without regard to direction: that is, without regard to which is the larger number. This is illustrated in Fig. 1.3.1.

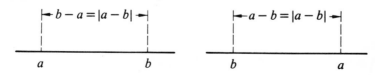

Figure 1.3.1

We have the following properties of absolute values.

1.3.2 THEOREM $|x| < a$ if and only if $-a < x < a$, where $a > 0$.

1.3.3 COROLLARY $|x| \leq a$ if and only if $-a \leq x \leq a$, where $a > 0$.

1.3.4 THEOREM $|x| > a$ if and only if $x > a$ or $x < -a$, where $a > 0$.

1.3.5 COROLLARY $|x| \geq a$ if and only if $x \geq a$ or $x \leq -a$, where $a > 0$.

The proof of a theorem that has an "if and only if" qualification requires two parts, as illustrated in the following proof of Theorem 1.3.2.

PART 1: Prove that $|x| < a$ if $-a < x < a$, where $a > 0$.
We consider two cases: $x \geq 0$ and $x < 0$.
Case 1: $x \geq 0$.
Then $|x| = x$. Therefore, since $x < a$, we conclude that $|x| < a$.
Case 2: $x < 0$.
Then $|x| = -x$. Since $-a < x$, we apply Property 1.2.7 and obtain $a > -x$; or, equivalently, $-x < a$. But since $-x = |x|$, this gives us $|x| < a$.
In both cases, thus,

$$|x| < a \qquad \text{if} \qquad -a < x < a, \text{ where } a > 0$$

PART 2: Prove that $|x| < a$ only if $-a < x < a$, where $a > 0$. Here we must show that whenever the inequality $|x| < a$ holds, then the inequality $-a < x < a$ also holds.
Assume $|x| < a$ and consider the two cases $x \geq 0$ and $x < 0$.
Case 1: $x \geq 0$.
Then $|x| = x$. So, since $|x| < a$, we conclude $x < a$. Also, since $a > 0$, it follows from Property 1.2.12 that $-a < 0$. So we have $-a < 0 \leq x < a$, or $-a < x < a$.
Case 2: $x < 0$.
Then $|x| = -x$. Since $|x| < a$, we conclude that $-x < a$. Also, since $x < 0$, it follows from Property 1.2.7 that $0 < -x$. Therefore, we have $-a < 0 < -x < a$, or $-a < -x < a$, which by applying 1.2.7 gives us $-a < x < a$.
In both cases,

$$|x| < a \qquad \text{only if} \qquad -a < x < a, \text{ where } a > 0$$

The proof of Theorem 1.3.4 is left for the reader (see Exercise 25 below).

The following examples illustrate the solution of equations and inequalities involving absolute values.

EXAMPLE 1: Solve for x: $|3x + 2| = 5$.
Solution: This equation will be satisfied either if

$$3x + 2 = 5 \qquad \text{or if} \qquad 3x + 2 = -5$$

So, considering each equation separately, we have

$$x = 1 \quad \text{and} \quad x = -\frac{7}{3}$$

which are the two solutions to the given equation.

EXAMPLE 2: Solve for x: $|2x - 1| = |4x + 3|$.
  Solution: This equation will be satisfied either if

$$2x - 1 = 4x + 3 \quad \text{or if} \quad 2x - 1 = -(4x + 3)$$

Solving the first equation, we get $x = -2$; solving the second, we get $x = -1/3$, thus giving us two solutions to the original equation.

EXAMPLE 3: Solve for x: $|5x + 4| = -3$.
  Solution: Since the absolute value of a number may never be negative, this equation has no solution.

EXAMPLE 4: Find all real numbers satisfying the inequality $|x - 5| < 4$.
  Solution: If x is a number such that

$$|x - 5| < 4$$

$$\text{then} \quad -4 < x - 5 < 4 \quad \text{by 1.3.2}$$

Adding 5 to each member of the preceding inequality, we obtain

$$1 < x < 9$$

Since each step is reversible, we may conclude that

$$|x - 5| < 4 \quad \text{if and only if} \quad 1 < x < 9$$

So, the interval solution of the given inequality is (1,9), which is illustrated in Fig. 1.3.2.

Figure 1.3.2

EXAMPLE 5: Find all real numbers satisfying the inequality

$$\left|\frac{3 - 2x}{2 + x}\right| \le 4$$

  Solution: By Corollary 1.3.3, the given inequality is equivalent to

$$-4 \le \frac{3 - 2x}{2 + x} \le 4$$

If we multiply by $2 + x$, we must consider two cases, depending upon whether $2 + x$ is positive or negative.

Case 1: $2 + x > 0$ or $x > -2$.

Then, we have

$$-4(2 + x) \le 3 - 2x \le 4(2 + x)$$

$$\text{or} \qquad -8 - 4x \le 3 - 2x \le 8 + 4x$$

So, if $x > -2$, then also $-8 - 4x \le 3 - 2x$ and $3 - 2x \le 8 + 4x$. We solve the latter two inequalities. Considering the first of these, we have

$$-8 - 4x \le 3 - 2x$$

Adding $2x + 8$ to both members gives us

$$-2x \le 11$$

Dividing both members by -2 and reversing the inequality sign, we obtain

$$x \ge -\frac{11}{2}$$

From the other inequality, we have

$$3 - 2x \le 8 + 4x$$

Adding $-4x - 3$ to both members gives us

$$-6x \le 5$$

Dividing both members by -6 and reversing the inequality sign, we obtain

$$x \ge -\frac{5}{6}$$

Therefore if $x > -2$, the original inequality holds if and only if $x \ge -11/2$ and $x \ge -5/6$.

Since all three inequalities $x > -2$, $x \ge -11/2$, and $x \ge -5/6$ must be satisfied by the same x, we have $x \ge -5/6$, or the interval $[-5/6, +\infty)$.

Case 2: $2 + x < 0$ or $x < -2$.

Thus, we have

$$-4(2 + x) \ge 3 - 2x \ge 4(2 + x)$$

$$\text{or} \qquad -8 - 4x \ge 3 - 2x \ge 8 + 4x$$

Considering the left inequality, we have

$$-8 - 4x \ge 3 - 2x$$

$$\text{or} \qquad -2x \ge 11$$

$$\text{or} \qquad x \le -\frac{11}{2}$$

From the right inequality we have

$$3 - 2x \ge 8 + 4x$$

$$\text{or} \qquad -6x \ge 5$$

$$\text{or} \qquad x \le -\frac{5}{6}$$

Therefore, if $x < -2$, the original inequality holds if and only if $x \leq -11/2$ and $x \leq -5/6$.

Since all three inequalities must be satisfied by the same value of x, we have $x \leq -11/2$, or the interval $(-\infty, -11/2]$.

Combining the solutions of Case 1 and Case 2, we have as the solution the two intervals $(-\infty, -11/2]$ and $[-5/6, +\infty)$: or more simply, all x not in the interval $(-11/2, -5/6)$.

EXAMPLE 6: Find all real numbers satisfying the inequality

$$|3x + 2| > 5$$

Solution: By Theorem 1.3.4, the given inequality is equivalent to

(1) $$3x + 2 > 5 \quad \text{or} \quad 3x + 2 < -5$$

That is, the given inequality will be satisfied if either of the inequalities in (1) is satisfied.

Considering the first inequality, we have

$$3x + 2 > 5$$

$$\text{or} \quad x > 1$$

Therefore the interval $(1, +\infty)$ is a solution.

From the second inequality, we have

$$3x + 2 < -5$$

$$\text{or} \quad x < -\frac{7}{3}$$

Therefore the interval $(-\infty, -7/3)$ is a solution.

The solution of the given inequality consists of the two intervals $(-\infty, -7/3)$ and $(1, +\infty)$ — or, equivalently, all x *not* in the closed interval $[-7/3, 1]$.

The reader will recall from algebra that the symbol $\sqrt{a}$, where $a \geq 0$, is defined to be the unique nonnegative number x such that $x^2 = a$. We read $\sqrt{a}$ as "the principal square root of a."

For example,

$$\sqrt{4} = 2 \qquad \sqrt{0} = 0 \qquad \sqrt{\frac{9}{25}} = \frac{3}{5}$$

NOTE: $\sqrt{4} \neq -2$; -2 is a square root of 4, but $\sqrt{4}$ denotes only the positive square root of 4.

Since we are concerned only with real numbers in this book, $\sqrt{a}$ is not defined if $a < 0$.

From the definition of $\sqrt{a}$, it follows that

$$\sqrt{x^2} = |x|$$

For example: $\qquad \sqrt{5^2} = 5 \qquad \text{and} \qquad \sqrt{(-3)^2} = 3$

Case 1: $2 + x > 0$ or $x > -2$.

Then, we have

$$-4(2 + x) \leq 3 - 2x \leq 4(2 + x)$$

or $\qquad -8 - 4x \leq 3 - 2x \leq 8 + 4x$

So, if $x > -2$, then also $-8 - 4x \leq 3 - 2x$ and $3 - 2x \leq 8 + 4x$. We solve the latter two inequalities. Considering the first of these, we have

$$-8 - 4x \leq 3 - 2x$$

Adding $2x + 8$ to both members gives us

$$-2x \leq 11$$

Dividing both members by -2 and reversing the inequality sign, we obtain

$$x \geq -\frac{11}{2}$$

From the other inequality, we have

$$3 - 2x \leq 8 + 4x$$

Adding $-4x - 3$ to both members gives us

$$-6x \leq 5$$

Dividing both members by -6 and reversing the inequality sign, we obtain

$$x \geq -\frac{5}{6}$$

Therefore if $x > -2$, the original inequality holds if and only if $x \geq -11/2$ and $x \geq -5/6$.

Since all three inequalities $x > -2$, $x \geq -11/2$, and $x \geq -5/6$ must be satisfied by the same x, we have $x \geq -5/6$, or the interval $[-5/6, +\infty)$.

Case 2: $2 + x < 0$ or $x < -2$.

Thus, we have

$$-4(2 + x) \geq 3 - 2x \geq 4(2 + x)$$

or $\qquad -8 - 4x \geq 3 - 2x \geq 8 + 4x$

Considering the left inequality, we have

$$-8 - 4x \geq 3 - 2x$$

or $\qquad -2x \geq 11$

or $\qquad x \leq -\frac{11}{2}$

From the right inequality we have

$$3 - 2x \geq 8 + 4x$$

or $\qquad -6x \geq 5$

or $\qquad x \leq -\frac{5}{6}$

Therefore, if $x < -2$, the original inequality holds if and only if $x \leq -11/2$ and $x \leq -5/6$.

Since all three inequalities must be satisfied by the same value of x, we have $x \leq -11/2$, or the interval $(-\infty, -11/2]$.

Combining the solutions of Case 1 and Case 2, we have as the solution the two intervals $(-\infty, -11/2]$ and $[-5/6, +\infty)$: or more simply, all x not in the interval $(-11/2, -5/6)$.

EXAMPLE 6: Find all real numbers satisfying the inequality

$$|3x + 2| > 5$$

Solution: By Theorem 1.3.4, the given inequality is equivalent to

(1) $$3x + 2 > 5 \quad \text{or} \quad 3x + 2 < -5$$

That is, the given inequality will be satisfied if either of the inequalities in (1) is satisfied.

Considering the first inequality, we have

$$3x + 2 > 5$$

$$\text{or} \quad x > 1$$

Therefore the interval $(1, +\infty)$ is a solution.

From the second inequality, we have

$$3x + 2 < -5$$

$$\text{or} \quad x < -\frac{7}{3}$$

Therefore the interval $(-\infty, -7/3)$ is a solution.

The solution of the given inequality consists of the two intervals $(-\infty, -7/3)$ and $(1, +\infty)$ — or, equivalently, all x *not* in the closed interval $[-7/3, 1]$.

The reader will recall from algebra that the symbol $\sqrt{a}$, where $a \geq 0$, is defined to be the unique nonnegative number x such that $x^2 = a$. We read $\sqrt{a}$ as "the principal square root of a."

For example,

$$\sqrt{4} = 2 \qquad \sqrt{0} = 0 \qquad \sqrt{\frac{9}{25}} = \frac{3}{5}$$

NOTE: $\sqrt{4} \neq -2$; -2 is a square root of 4, but $\sqrt{4}$ denotes only the positive square root of 4.

Since we are concerned only with real numbers in this book, $\sqrt{a}$ is not defined if $a < 0$.

From the definition of $\sqrt{a}$, it follows that

$$\sqrt{x^2} = |x|$$

For example: $\qquad \sqrt{5^2} = 5 \qquad \text{and} \qquad \sqrt{(-3)^2} = 3$

The following theorems about absolute value will be useful later.

1.3.6 THEOREM   If a and b are any numbers,

$$|ab| = |a| \cdot |b|$$

Expressed in words, this equation signifies that the absolute value of the product of two numbers is the product of the absolute values of the two numbers.

Proof:
$$\begin{aligned} |ab| &= \sqrt{(ab)^2} \\ &= \sqrt{a^2 b^2} \\ &= \sqrt{a^2} \cdot \sqrt{b^2} \\ &= |a| \cdot |b| \end{aligned}$$
                                                                Q.E.D

1.3.7 THEOREM   If a is any number and b is any number except 0,

$$\left|\frac{a}{b}\right| = \frac{|a|}{|b|}$$

That is, the absolute value of the quotient of two numbers is the quotient of the absolute values of the two numbers.

The proof of Theorem 1.3.7 is left to the reader (see Exercise 26 below).

1.3.8 THEOREM   (*The Triangle Inequality*)   If a and b are any numbers, then

$$|a + b| \leq |a| + |b|$$

Proof: We consider four cases.

Case 1: $a \geq 0$ and $b \geq 0$.
Then $|a| = a$, $|b| = b$, and $|a + b| = a + b$.
Hence, $|a + b| = |a| + |b|$
and so the theorem holds.

Case 2: $a < 0$ and $b < 0$.
Then $|a| = -a$, $|b| = -b$, and $|a + b| = -(a + b)$.
Hence, $|a + b| = |a| + |b|$
and so the theorem holds.

Case 3: $a \geq 0$ and $b < 0$.
Then $|a| = a$, $|b| = -b$.

Therefore, $|a + b| = a + b$ if $a + b \geq 0$
or $|a + b| = -(a + b)$ if $a + b < 0$

But, $a + b < a + (-b) = |a| + |b|$, since $b < 0$ and $a \geq 0$; also, $-(a + b) = (-a) + (-b) \leq a + (-b) = |a| + |b|$, since $b < 0$ and $a \geq 0$.
In either case, $|a + b| \leq |a| + |b|$, and the theorem holds.

Case 4: $a < 0$ and $b \geq 0$.
The proof of this case is identical with the proof of Case 3. So, for all cases we have

$$|a + b| \leq |a| + |b|$$
                                                                Q.E.D.

Exercises 1.3

In Exercises 1 through 10, solve for x.

1. $|4x + 3| = 7$

2. $|3x - 8| = 4$

3. $|5 - 2x| = 11$

4. $|4 + 3x| = 1$

5. $|5x - 3| = |3x + 5|$

6. $|x - 2| = |3 - 2x|$

7. $|7x| = 4 - x$

8. $2x + 3 = |4x + 5|$

9. $\left|\dfrac{x + 2}{x - 2}\right| = 5$

10. $\left|\dfrac{3x + 8}{2x - 3}\right| = 4$

In Exercises 11 through 24, find all real numbers satisfying the given inequality; give the interval solution; illustrate the solution on the real line.

11. $|x + 4| < 7$

12. $|2x - 5| < 3$

13. $|3x - 4| \leq 2$

14. $|3 + 5x| \leq 9$

15. $|2x - 5| > 3$

16. $|6 - 2x| \geq 7$

17. $|x + 4| \leq |2x - 6|$

18. $|3 + 2x| < |4 - x|$

19. $|9 - 2x| \geq |4x|$

20. $|3x| > |6 - 3x|$

21. $\left|\dfrac{x + 2}{2x - 3}\right| < 4$

22. $\left|\dfrac{6 - 5x}{3 + x}\right| \leq \dfrac{1}{2}$

23. $\left|\dfrac{2 - 3x}{3 + x}\right| \geq \dfrac{1}{4}$

24. $\left|\dfrac{5}{2x - 1}\right| \geq \left|\dfrac{1}{x - 2}\right|$

25. Prove Theorem 1.3.4.

26. Prove Theorem 1.3.7.

27. Prove Theorem 1.3.8 by adding corresponding members of the inequalities $-|a| \leq a \leq |a|$ and $-|b| \leq b \leq |b|$, and then applying Corollary 1.3.3.

28. *Prove:* If a and b are any numbers, then $|a - b| \leq |a| + |b|$. HINT: Write $a - b$ as $a + (-b)$ and use Theorem 1.3.8.

29. *Prove:* If a and b are any numbers, then $|a| - |b| \leq |a - b|$. HINT: Let $|a| = |(a - b) + b|$, and use Theorem 1.3.8.

30. What single inequality is equivalent to the following two inequalities: $a > b + c$ and $a > b - c$?

2 Introduction to analytic geometry

Rectangular cartesian coordinates

In order to determine the position of a point in a plane, we establish a one-to-one correspondence between the points in the plane and ordered pairs of real numbers. There are various methods of establishing this correspondence, but the one most frequently used is the one attributed to the French mathematician René Descartes (1596–1650), who is credited with the invention of analytic geometry in 1637.

We select a horizontal line in the plane; this line, extending indefinitely to the left and to the right, is called the *x axis*. A vertical line is chosen; extending indefinitely up and down, it is called the *y axis*. The point of intersection of the *x* axis and the *y* axis is called the *origin*, and this point is denoted by the letter O. A unit of length is chosen (usually, the unit length on each axis is the same). We establish the positive direction on the *x* axis to the right of the origin, and the positive direction on the *y* axis above the origin.

We now associate an ordered pair of real numbers (x,y) with a point P in the plane. The distance of P from the *y* axis (considered as positive if P is to the right of the *y* axis and negative if P is to the left of the *y* axis) is called the *abscissa* of P and is denoted by x. The distance of P from the *x* axis (considered as positive if P is above the *x* axis and negative if P is below the *x* axis) is called the *ordinate* of P and is denoted by y. The abscissa and the ordinate of a point are called the *rectangular cartesian coordinates* of the point. There is a one-to-one correspondence between the points in a plane and the rectangular cartesian coordinates. That is, with each point there corresponds a unique ordered pair (x,y), and with each ordered pair (x,y) there is associated only one point. Figure 2.1.1 illustrates the rectangular cartesian coordinate system with some points plotted.

The two axes divide the plane into four parts, called *quadrants*. The first quadrant is the one in which the abscissa and the ordinate are both positive: that is, the upper right quadrant. The other quadrants are numbered in the counterclockwise direction, with the fourth, for example, being the lower right quadrant.

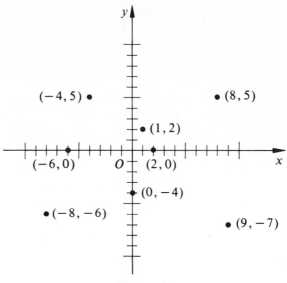

Figure 2.1.1

(2.2)   Directed distances

If A is the point (x_1, y) and B is the point (x_2, y) — that is, A and B have the same ordinate but different abscissas — then the directed distance from A to B, denoted by $\overline{AB}$, is defined as $x_2 - x_1$. Following are some examples, which are illustrated in Figs. 2.2.1a, b, and c.

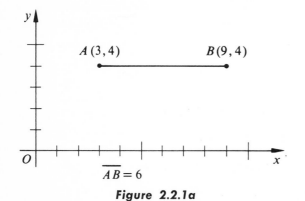

$$\overline{AB} = 6$$

Figure 2.2.1a

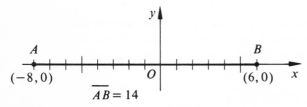

$$\overline{AB} = 14$$

Figure 2.2.1b

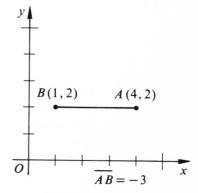

$$\overline{AB} = -3$$

Figure 2.2.1c

If A is the point $(3,4)$ and B is the point $(9,4)$, then $\overline{AB} = 9 - 3 = 6$.

If A is the point $(-8,0)$ and B is the point $(6,0)$, then $\overline{AB} = 6 - (-8) = 14$.

If A is the point $(4,2)$ and B is the point $(1,2)$, then $\overline{AB} = 1 - 4 = -3$.

We see that $\overline{AB}$ is positive if B is to the right of A, and $\overline{AB}$ is negative if B is to the left of A.

If C is the point (x,y_1) and D is the point (x,y_2), then the directed distance from C to D, denoted by $\overline{CD}$, is defined as $y_2 - y_1$. The following examples are illustrated in Figs. 2.2.2*a* and *b*.

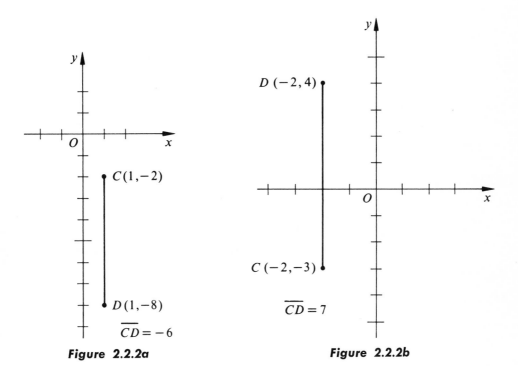

Figure 2.2.2a   **Figure 2.2.2b**

If C is the point $(1,-2)$ and D is the point $(1,-8)$, then

$$\overline{CD} = -8 - (-2) = -6$$

If C is the point $(-2,-3)$ and D is the point $(-2,4)$, then

$$\overline{CD} = 4 - (-3) = 7$$

$\overline{CD}$ is positive if D is above C, and $\overline{CD}$ is negative if D is below C.

We may consider a directed distance $\overline{AB}$ as the signed distance traveled by a particle that starts at A and travels to B. In such a case, the abscissa of the particle changes from x_1 to x_2, and we use the notation Δx ("delta x") to denote this change; that is,

$$\Delta x = x_2 - x_1$$

Therefore $\overline{AB} = \Delta x$.

It is important to note that the symbol Δx denotes the difference between the abscissa of B and the abscissa of A, and it does not mean "delta multiplied by x."

Similarly, if we consider a particle moving along a line parallel to the y axis from a point $C(x,y_1)$ to a point $D(x,y_2)$, then the ordinate of the particle changes from y_1 to y_2. We denote this change by Δy; or,

$$\Delta y = y_2 - y_1$$

Thus $\overline{CD} = \Delta y$.

Now let $P_1(x_1,y_1)$ and $P_2(x_2,y_2)$ be any two points in the plane. We wish to obtain a formula for finding the nonnegative distance between these two points. We shall denote this distance by $|\overline{P_1P_2}|$. We use absolute-value signs because we are concerned only with the length of the line segment between the two points P_1 and P_2, which is a nonnegative number. To derive the formula, we note $|\overline{P_1P_2}|$ is the length of the hypotenuse of a right triangle P_1MP_2. This is illustrated in Fig. 2.2.3 for P_1 and P_2 both in the first quadrant.

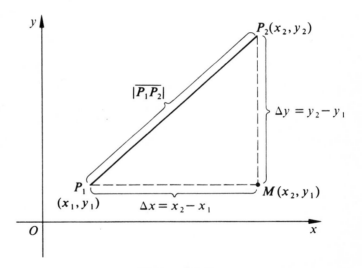

Figure 2.2.3

Using the pythagorean theorem, we have

$$|\overline{P_1P_2}|^2 = |\Delta x|^2 + |\Delta y|^2$$

So,

$$|\overline{P_1P_2}| = \sqrt{|\Delta x|^2 + |\Delta y|^2}$$

or

(1)
$$|\overline{P_1P_2}| = \sqrt{(x_2 - x_1)^2 + (y_2 - y_1)^2}$$

Formula (1) holds for all possible positions of P_1 and P_2 in all four quadrants. The length of the hypotenuse will always be $|\overline{P_1P_2}|$, and the lengths of the two legs will always be $|\Delta x|$ and $|\Delta y|$ (see Exercises 18 and 19 below).

EXAMPLE 1: If a point $P(x,y)$ is such that its distance from $A(3,2)$ is always twice its distance from $B(-4,1)$, find an equation that the coordinates of P must satisfy.

Solution: From the statement of the problem,

$$\overline{|PA|} = 2\overline{|PB|}$$

Using formula (1), we have

$$\sqrt{(x-3)^2 + (y-2)^2} = 2\sqrt{(x+4)^2 + (y-1)^2}$$

Squaring both sides, we have

$$x^2 - 6x + 9 + y^2 - 4y + 4 = 4(x^2 + 8x + 16 + y^2 - 2y + 1)$$

or $3x^2 + 3y^2 + 38x - 4y + 55 = 0$

EXAMPLE 2: Show that the triangle with vertices at $A(-2,4)$, $B(-5,1)$, and $C(-6,5)$ is isosceles.

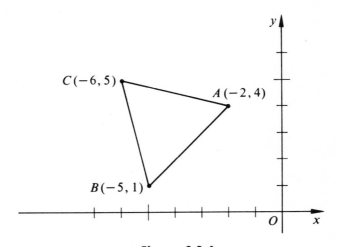

Figure 2.2.4

Solution: The triangle is shown in Fig. 2.2.4.

$$\overline{|BC|} = \sqrt{(-6+5)^2 + (5-1)^2} = \sqrt{1+16} = \sqrt{17}$$

$$\overline{|AC|} = \sqrt{(-6+2)^2 + (5-4)^2} = \sqrt{16+1} = \sqrt{17}$$

$$\overline{|BA|} = \sqrt{(-2+5)^2 + (4-1)^2} = \sqrt{9+9} = 3\sqrt{2}$$

Therefore, $\overline{|BC|} = \overline{|AC|}$

Therefore, triangle ABC is isosceles.   Q.E.D.

EXAMPLE 3: Prove analytically that the lengths of the diagonals of a rectangle are equal.

Solution: Draw a general rectangle. Since we may choose the coordinate axes anywhere in the plane, and since the choice of the position of the axes does not affect the truth of the theorem, we take the origin at one vertex, the x axis along one side, and the y axis along another side. This simplifies the coordinates of the vertices on the two axes. Refer to Fig. 2.2.5.

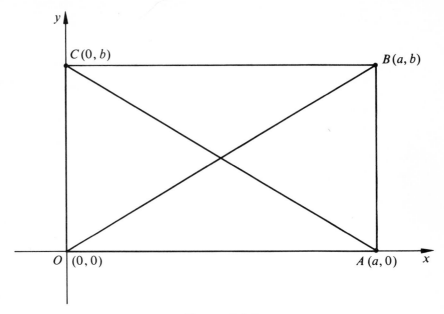

Figure 2.2.5

The hypothesis and the conclusion of the theorem may now be stated. *Hypothesis:* $OABC$ is a rectangle with diagonals OB and AC. *Conclusion:* $|\overline{OB}| = |\overline{AC}|$.

Proof: $|\overline{OB}| = \sqrt{(a-0)^2 + (b-0)^2} = \sqrt{a^2 + b^2}$

$|\overline{AC}| = \sqrt{(0-a)^2 + (b-0)^2} = \sqrt{a^2 + b^2}$

Therefore, $|\overline{OB}| = |\overline{AC}|$

Q.E.D.

Exercises 2.2

In Exercises 1 through 6, plot the given point P and such of the following points as may apply:

(a) The point Q such that the line through Q and P is perpendicular to the x axis and is bisected by it. Give the coordinates of Q.

(b) The point R such that the line through P and R is perpendicular to and is bisected by the y axis. Give the coordinates of R.

(c) The point S such that the line through P and S is bisected by the origin. Give the coordinates of S.

(d) The point T such that the line through P and T is perpendicular to and is bisected by the 45° line through the origin bisecting the first and third quadrants. Give the coordinates of T.

1. $P(1,-2)$ 4. $P(-2,-2)$

2. $P(-2,2)$ 5. $P(-1,-3)$

3. $P(2,2)$ 6. $P(0,-3)$

7. A straight line is drawn through the point $A(1,2)$ and the point $B(2,4)$. Find $\tan \alpha$, where α is the acute angle that this line makes with the horizontal line through A.

8. The line through the pair of points $(2,3)$ and $(1,1)$ intersects the y axis at the point $(0,b)$. Find b by using similar triangles.

9. Prove that the triangle with vertices $A(3,-6)$, $B(8,-2)$, and $C(-1,-1)$ is a right triangle. Find the area of the triangle.

10. Prove that the points $A(6,-13)$, $B(-2,2)$, $C(13,10)$, and $D(21,-5)$ are the vertices of a square. Find the length of a diagonal.

11. By using the distance formula (1), prove that the points $(-3,2)$, $(1,-2)$, and $(9,-10)$ lie on a line.

12. Determine whether or not the points $(14,7)$, $(2,2)$, and $(-4,-1)$ lie on a line by using the distance formula (1).

13. The abscissa of a point is -6 and its distance from the point $(1,3)$ is $\sqrt{74}$. Find the ordinate of the point.

14. If two vertices of an equilateral triangle are $(-4,3)$ and $(0,0)$, find the third vertex.

15. Find the radius of a circle with center at $(-5,1)$ and which passes through the point $(-4,-3)$.

16. Find an equation that must be satisfied by the coordinates of any point that is equidistant from the two points $(-3,2)$ and $(4,6)$.

17. Find an equation that must be satisfied by the coordinates of any point whose distance from the point $(5,3)$ is always two units greater than its distance from the point $(-4,-2)$.

18. Derive the distance formula (1) if P_1 is in the third quadrant and P_2 is in the second quadrant. Draw a figure.

19. Derive the distance formula (1) if P_1 is in the second quadrant and P_2 is in the fourth quadrant. Draw a figure.

20. Prove analytically that the lengths of the diagonals of a square are equal.

21. Prove analytically that the sum of the squares of the distances of any point from two opposite vertices of any rectangle is equal to the sum of the squares of its distances from the other two vertices.

(2.3)   Midpoint of a line segment

Let $P_1(x_1,y_1)$ and $P_2(x_2,y_2)$ be the end points of a line segment. We shall denote this line segment by P_1P_2. This is not to be confused with the notation $\overline{P_1P_2}$, which denotes the directed distance from P_1 to P_2. That is, $\overline{P_1P_2}$ denotes a number, whereas P_1P_2 is a line segment. Let $P(x,y)$ be the midpoint of the line segment P_1P_2. Refer to Fig. 2.3.1.

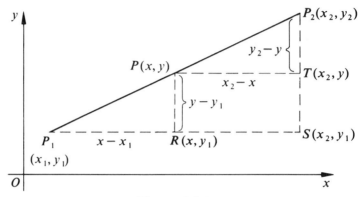

Figure 2.3.1

In Fig. 2.3.1 we see that triangles P_1RP and PTP_2 are congruent. Therefore $|\overline{P_1R}| = |\overline{PT}|$, and so $x - x_1 = x_2 - x$, giving us

《 (1) $$x = \frac{x_1 + x_2}{2}$$

Similarly, $|\overline{RP}| = |\overline{TP_2}|$. Then $y - y_1 = y_2 - y$, and therefore

《 (2) $$y = \frac{y_1 + y_2}{2}$$

Hence, the coordinates of the midpoint of a line segment are, respectively, the average of the abscissas and the average of the ordinates of the end points of the line segment.

In the derivation of formulas (1) and (2) it was assumed that $x_2 > x_1$ and $y_2 > y_1$. The same formulas are obtained using any orderings of these numbers (see Exercises 1 and 2 below).

EXAMPLE 1: Prove analytically that the diagonals of a parallelogram bisect each other.

Solution: Draw a general parallelogram. Take the origin at one vertex and the x axis along one side. This simplifies the coordinates of the two vertices on the x axis. Refer to Fig. 2.3.2.

Hypothesis: OABC is a parallelogram with diagonals *OB* and *AC*.

Conclusion: OB and *AC* bisect each other.

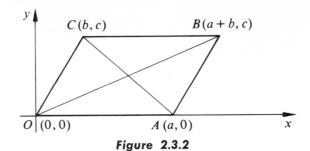

Figure 2.3.2

Proof: In order to prove that two lines bisect each other, we prove they have the same midpoint.

The abscissa of the midpoint of OB is $\frac{1}{2}[(a + b) + 0]$.
The ordinate of the midpoint of OB is $\frac{1}{2}(c + 0)$.
Therefore the midpoint of OB is the point $[\frac{1}{2}(a + b), \frac{1}{2}c]$.
The abscissa of the midpoint of AC is $\frac{1}{2}(a + b)$.
The ordinate of the midpoint of AC is $\frac{1}{2}(c + 0)$.
Therefore the midpoint of AC is the point $[\frac{1}{2}(a + b), \frac{1}{2}c]$.
Thus the midpoint of OB is the same point as the midpoint of AC.
Therefore OB and AC bisect each other.   Q.E.D.

Exercises 2.3

1. Derive the midpoint formulas (1) and (2) if P_1 is in the first quadrant and P_2 is in the third quadrant.

2. Derive the midpoint formulas (1) and (2) if $P_1(x_1, y_1)$ and $P_2(x_2, y_2)$ are both in the second quadrant, and $x_2 > x_1$ and $y_1 > y_2$.

3. Find the length of the medians of the triangle having vertices $A(2,3)$, $B(3, -3)$, and $C(-1, -1)$.

4. Find the midpoints of the diagonals of the quadrilateral whose vertices are $(0,0)$, $(0,4)$, $(3,5)$, and $(3,1)$.

5. The two points $A(-2, -2)$ and $B(4,1)$ are the end points of a diameter of a circle. Find the coordinates of the center of the circle and the length of the radius of the circle.

6. If one end of a line segment is the point $(-4,2)$ and the midpoint is $(3, -1)$, find the coordinates of the other end of the line segment.

7. Find the coordinates of the three points that divide the line segment from $A(-5,3)$ to $B(6,8)$ into four equal parts.

8. Given the two points $A(-3,4)$ and $B(2,5)$, find the coordinates of a point P on the line through A and B such that P is (*a*) twice as far from A as from B; (*b*) twice as far from B as from A.

9. If r_1 and r_2 are positive integers, prove that the coordinates of the point $P(x,y)$, which divides the line segment P_1P_2 in the ratio r_1/r_2 — that is, $|\overline{P_1P}|/|\overline{P_1P_2}| = r_1/r_2$ — are given by

$$x = \frac{(r_2 - r_1)x_1 + r_1x_2}{r_2} \quad \text{and} \quad y = \frac{(r_2 - r_1)y_1 + r_1y_2}{r_2}$$

10. Prove analytically that the line segments joining the midpoints of the opposite sides of any quadrilateral bisect each other.

11. Prove analytically that the line segment joining the midpoints of two opposite sides of any quadrilateral and the line segment joining the midpoints of the diagonals of the quadrilateral bisect each other.

12. Prove analytically that the midpoint of the hypotenuse of any right triangle is equidistant from each of the three vertices.

(2.4)   Slope of a straight line

2.4.1 DEFINITION   If $P_1(x_1,y_1)$ and $P_2(x_2,y_2)$ are any two distinct points on line l, which is not parallel to the y axis, then the *slope* of l, denoted by m, is given by

(((1)
$$m = \frac{y_2 - y_1}{x_2 - x_1}$$

In equation (1), $x_2 \neq x_1$ since l is not parallel to the y axis.

The value of m computed from equation (1) is independent of the choice of the two points P_1 and P_2 on l. To show this, suppose we choose two different points, $\overline{P}_1(\overline{x}_1,\overline{y}_1)$ and $\overline{P}_2(\overline{x}_2,\overline{y}_2)$, and compute a number m from (1).

$$\overline{m} = \frac{\overline{y}_2 - \overline{y}_1}{\overline{x}_2 - \overline{x}_1}$$

We shall show that $\overline{m} = m$. Refer to Fig. 2.4.1. Triangles $\overline{P}_1\overline{R}\overline{P}_2$ and P_1RP_2

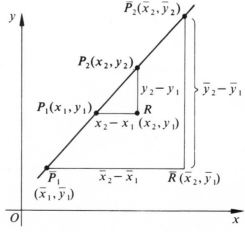

Figure 2.4.1

are similar, so that the lengths of corresponding sides are proportional. There-fore,

$$\frac{\bar{y}_2 - \bar{y}_1}{\bar{x}_2 - \bar{x}_1} = \frac{y_2 - y_1}{x_2 - x_1}$$

or $\bar{m} = m$

Hence we conclude that the value of m computed from equation (1) is the same number no matter what two points on l are selected.

In Fig. 2.4.1, $x_2 > x_1$, $y_2 > y_1$, $\bar{x}_2 > \bar{x}_1$, and $\bar{y}_2 > \bar{y}_1$. The discussion above is valid for any ordering of these pairs of numbers, since Definition 2.4.1 holds for any ordering.

In Sec. 2.2 we defined $\Delta y = y_2 - y_1$ and $\Delta x = x_2 - x_1$. Substituting these values into equation (1), we have

$$m = \frac{\Delta y}{\Delta x}$$

If we multipy both sides of this equation by Δx, we obtain

(2) $\Delta y = m\, \Delta x$

We see from equation (2) that if we consider a particle moving along line l, the change in the ordinate of the particle is proportional to the change in the abscissa, and the constant of proportionality is the slope of the line.

Note that if the line is parallel to the x axis, then $y_2 = y_1$ and so $m = 0$.

If the line is parallel to the y axis, $x_2 = x_1$, and so equation (1) is meaning-less, since we cannot divide by zero. This is the reason that lines parallel to the y axis, or vertical lines, are excluded in Definition 2.4.1. We say that a vertical line does not have a slope.

EXAMPLE 1: Let l be the line through the points $P_1(2,3)$ and $P_2(4,7)$. Find the slope of l.

Solution: The slope of l, by Definition 2.4.1, is given by

$$m = \frac{7 - 3}{4 - 2} = 2$$

Refer to Fig. 2.4.2. If $P(x,y)$ and $Q(x + \Delta x, y + \Delta y)$ are any two points on l, then

$$\frac{\Delta y}{\Delta x} = 2$$

or $\Delta y = 2\Delta x$

Thus, if a particle is moving along the line l, the change in the ordinate is twice the change in the abscissa. That is, if the particle is at $P_2(4,7)$ and the abscissa is increased by 1 unit, then the ordinate is increased by 2 units, and the particle is then at the point $P_3(5,9)$. Similarly, if the particle is at $P_1(2,3)$ and the abscissa is decreased by 3 units, then the ordinate is decreased by 6 units, and the par-ticle is then at the point $P_4(-1,-3)$.

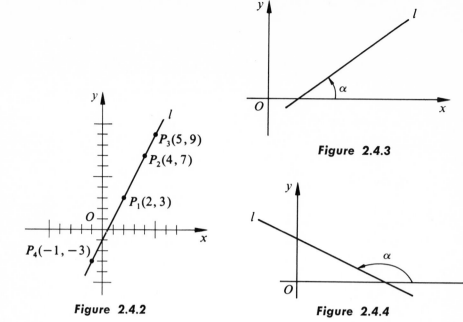

Figure 2.4.3

Figure 2.4.2

Figure 2.4.4

2.4.2 DEFINITION   The *inclination* of a line not parallel to the x axis is the smallest angle measured counterclockwise from the positive direction of the x axis to the line. The inclination of a line parallel to the x axis is defined to be zero.

If α denotes the inclination of a line, α may be any angle in the interval, $0 \le \alpha < \pi$. (See Figs. 2.4.3 and 2.4.4.)

2.4.3 THEOREM   If α is the inclination of line l, not parallel to the y axis, then the slope m of l is given by

$$m = \tan \alpha$$

Proof: We shall give the proof for $0 \le \alpha < \pi/2$.

Let $P_1(x_1,y_1)$ and $P_2(x_2,y_2)$ be any two distinct points on l, and consider the three cases $y_1 < y_2$, $y_2 < y_1$, and $y_1 = y_2$.

Case 1: $y_1 < y_2$.

In this case P_2 is above P_1. See Fig. 2.4.5.

Draw a line through P_1 parallel to the x axis and a line through P_2 parallel to the y axis, with the two lines intersecting at point R. Then the inclination of l is the same as the angle at P_1 in the right triangle P_1RP_2. Therefore,

$$\tan \alpha = \frac{|\overline{RP_2}|}{|\overline{P_1R}|} = \frac{y_2 - y_1}{x_2 - x_1}$$

So, from Definition 2.4.1, $\tan \alpha = m$.

Case 2: $y_2 < y_1$.

Here P_1 is above P_2. So, if we interchange P_1 and P_2, x_1 and x_2, and y_1 and y_2, then from Case 1, we have

$$\tan \alpha = \frac{y_1 - y_2}{x_1 - x_2} = \frac{y_2 - y_1}{x_2 - x_1} = m$$

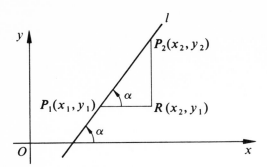

Figure 2.4.5

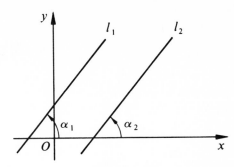

Figure 2.4.6

Case 3: $y_1 = y_2$.

In this case $\alpha = 0$ and $m = 0$. Therefore $m = \tan \alpha$.

The proof of Theorem 2.4.3 for $\pi/2 < \alpha < \pi$ is left for the reader (see Exercise 15 below).

In Fig. 2.4.3, $0 < \alpha < \pi/2$; so m is positive.

In Fig. 2.4.4, $\pi/2 < \alpha < \pi$; so m is negative.

If line l is parallel to the y axis, the inclination of l is $\pi/2$, and $\tan \pi/2$ does not exist. However, if the inclination of l is close to $\pi/2$, the slope of the line has a large absolute value.

In Fig. 2.4.6 are seen two nonvertical lines l_1 and l_2, which are parallel. These two lines have the same inclination; that is,

$$\alpha_1 = \alpha_2$$

Hence $\tan \alpha_1 = \tan \alpha_2$

and so $m_1 = m_2$

Thus it is seen that if two lines are parallel, they have the same slope. Conversely, if two nonvertical lines l_1 and l_2 have the same slope, then

$$m_1 = m_2$$

So $\tan \alpha_1 = \tan \alpha_2$

and $0 \leq \alpha_1 < \pi$ and $0 \leq \alpha_2 < \pi$

Therefore $\alpha_1 = \alpha_2$

and hence l_1 is parallel to l_2. We shall state these results as a theorem.

2.4.4 THEOREM   Two nonvertical lines are parallel if and only if their slopes are equal. That is, if m_1 is the slope of l_1 and m_2 is the slope of l_2, then l_1 is parallel to l_2 if and only if

$$m_1 = m_2$$

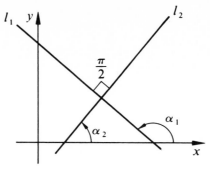

Figure 2.4.7

In Fig. 2.4.7, the two lines l_1 and l_2 are perpendicular. We state and prove the following theorem regarding the slopes of two perpendicular lines.

2.4.5 THEOREM If neither line l_1 nor line l_2 is vertical, then l_1 and l_2 are perpendicular if and only if the product of their slopes is -1. That is, if m_1 is the slope of l_1 and m_2 is the slope of l_2, then l_1 and l_2 are perpendicular if and only if

$$m_1 m_2 = -1$$

Proof: The proof consists of two parts. We shall first prove that l_1 is perpendicular to l_2 only if $m_1 m_2 = -1$.

With l_1 assumed perpendicular to l_2, then if α_1 is the inclination of l_1 and α_2 is the inclination of l_2, α_1 and α_2 differ by $\pi/2$. It may be assumed without loss of generality that α_1 is the greater inclination; hence,

$$\alpha_1 = \alpha_2 + \frac{\pi}{2}$$

$$\text{So,} \quad \tan \alpha_1 = \tan\left(\alpha_2 + \frac{\pi}{2}\right)$$

$$= -\cot \alpha_2$$

$$= -\frac{1}{\tan \alpha_2}$$

Since $\tan \alpha_1 = m_1$ and $\tan \alpha_2 = m_2$, we obtain from the above

$$m_1 = -\frac{1}{m_2}$$

$$\text{Therefore} \quad m_1 m_2 = -1$$

Now we prove the converse; that is, if $m_1 m_2 = -1$, then l_1 and l_2 are perpendicular.

If $m_1 m_2 = -1$, then either m_1 or m_2 is positive. We assume m_2 to be positive; so, m_1 is negative, and $\pi/2 < \alpha_1 < \pi$. Thus $\pi < \alpha_1 + \pi/2 < 3\pi/2$.

Since $m_2 = \tan \alpha_2$ and $m_1 = \tan \alpha_1$, this gives us

$$\tan \alpha_2 = -\frac{1}{\tan \alpha_1}$$

$$\tan \alpha_2 = -\cot \alpha_1$$

(3) $$\tan \alpha_2 = \tan\left(\alpha_1 + \frac{\pi}{2}\right)$$

Now, since $m_2 > 0$, α_2 is an acute angle, and so $0 < \alpha_2 < \pi/2$. Since α_1 is the inclination of a line, $0 < \alpha_1 < \pi$, and therefore $\pi/2 < \alpha_1 + \pi/2 < 3\pi/2$. Hence we may conclude from (3) that

$$\alpha_2 = \left(\alpha_1 + \frac{\pi}{2}\right) - \pi$$

which gives us

$$\alpha_1 = \alpha_2 + \frac{\pi}{2}$$

Therefore, l_1 and l_2 are perpendicular. This completes the proof of Theorem 2.4.5.

Theorem 2.4.5 states that if two lines are perpendicular and neither one is vertical, the slope of one of the lines is the negative reciprocal of the slope of the other line. For example, if line l_1 is perpendicular to line l_2 and the slope of l_1 is $2/3$, then the slope of l_2 must be $-3/2$.

EXAMPLE 2: Prove by means of slopes that the four points $A(6,2)$, $B(8,6)$, $C(4,8)$, and $D(2,4)$ are the vertices of a rectangle.
Solution: See Fig. 2.4.8.

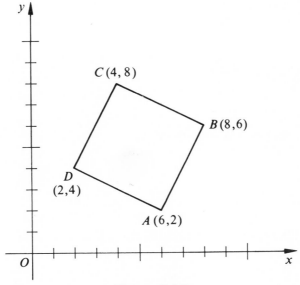

Figure 2.4.8

Let m_1 = the slope of $AB = \dfrac{6-2}{8-6} = 2.$

Let m_2 = the slope of $BC = \dfrac{8-6}{4-8} = -\dfrac{1}{2}.$

Let m_3 = the slope of $DC = \dfrac{8-4}{4-2} = 2.$

Let m_4 = the slope of $AD = \dfrac{4-2}{2-6} = -\dfrac{1}{2}.$

Since $m_1 = m_3$, $AB \parallel DC$.

Since $m_2 = m_4$, $BC \parallel AD$.

Since $m_1 m_2 = -1$, $AB \perp BC$.

Therefore quadrilateral $ABCD$ has opposite sides parallel and two adjacent sides perpendicular, and we conclude that $ABCD$ is a rectangle. Q.E.D.

Exercises 2.4

In Exercises 1 through 4, find the slope of the line through the given points.

1. $(2, -3)$, $(-4, 3)$

2. $(5, 2)$, $(-2, -3)$

3. $\left(\dfrac{1}{3}, \dfrac{1}{2}\right)$, $\left(\dfrac{-5}{6}, \dfrac{2}{3}\right)$

4. $(-2.1, 0.3)$, $(2.3, 1.4)$

5. Show by means of slopes that the points $(-4, -1)$, $(3, 8/3)$, $(8, -4)$, and $(2, -9)$ are the vertices of a trapezoid.

6. Three consecutive vertices of a parallelogram are $(-4, 1)$, $(2, 3)$, and $(8, 9)$. Find the coordinates of the fourth vertex.

7. For each of the following sets of three points, determine by means of slopes if the points are on a line: (a) $(2, 3)$, $(-4, -7)$, $(5, 8)$; (b) $(-3, 6)$, $(3, 2)$, $(9, -2)$; (c) $(2, -1)$, $(1, 1)$, $(3, 4)$; (d) $(4, 6)$, $(1, 2)$, $(-5, -4)$.

8. Prove by means of slopes that the three points $A(3, 1)$, $B(6, 0)$, and $C(4, 4)$ are the vertices of a right triangle, and find the area of the triangle.

9. A line through $(1, -2)$ and $(3, 1)$ is perpendicular to a line through $(2, y)$ and $(1, -2)$. Find the value of y.

10. Prove analytically that the line segment joining the midpoints of any two sides of a triangle is parallel to the third side and that its length is one-half the length of the third side.

11. Prove analytically that the diagonals of a rhombus are perpendicular.

12. Prove analytically that if the diagonals of a rectangle are perpendicular, the rectangle is a square.

13. Prove analytically that the line segments joining consecutive midpoints of the sides of any quadrilateral form a parallelogram.

14. Prove analytically that if the diagonals of a quadrilateral bisect each other, the quadrilateral is a parallelogram.

15. Prove Theorem 2.4.3 if $\pi/2 < \alpha < \pi$.

(2.5)   Graphs of Equations

Consider the equation

(1) $$y = x^2 - 2$$

By a solution of this equation, we mean an ordered pair of numbers, one for x and one for y, which satisfies the equation. For example, if x is replaced by 3 in equation (1), we see that $y = 7$; thus $x = 3$ and $y = 7$ constitutes a solution of this equation. If any number is substituted for x in the right-hand side of (1), we obtain a corresponding value for y. It is seen, then, that equation (1) has infinitely many solutions. Table 2.5.1 gives a few such solutions.

Table 2.5.1

x	0	1	2	3	4	-1	-2	-3	-4
$y = x^2 - 2$	-2	-1	2	7	14	-1	2	7	14

If we plot the points having as coordinates the number pairs (x,y) satisfying equation (1), we have a sketch of the graph of the equation. In Fig. 2.5.1, we have plotted points whose coordinates are the number pairs obtained from Table 2.5.1, and these points are connected by a smooth curve. Any point (x,y) on this curve has coordinates satisfying equation (1). Also, the coordinates of any point not on this curve do not satisfy the equation. We have the following general definition.

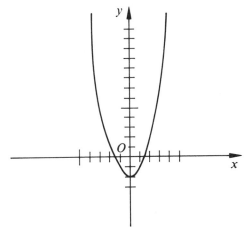

Figure 2.5.1

2.5.1 DEFINITION   The *graph of an equation* involving x and y is the set of all points (x,y) whose coordinates are numbers satisfying the equation.

We sometimes call the graph of an equation the *locus* of the equation. The graph is also called a *curve*.

EXAMPLE 1: Draw a sketch of the graph of the equation

(2) $$y^2 - x - 2 = 0$$

Solution: Solving equation (2) for y, we have

(3) $$y = \pm\sqrt{x + 2}$$

Equation (3) is equivalent to the two equations

(4) $$y = \sqrt{x + 2}$$

(5) $$y = -\sqrt{x + 2}$$

The coordinates of all points that satisfy equation (3) will satisfy either equation (4) or (5), and the coordinates of any point that satisfies either (4) or (5) will satisfy equation (3). Table 2.5.2 gives some of these values of x and y.

Table 2.5.2

x	0	0	1	1	2	2	3	3	-1	-1	-2
y	$\sqrt{2}$	$-\sqrt{2}$	$\sqrt{3}$	$-\sqrt{3}$	2	-2	$\sqrt{5}$	$-\sqrt{5}$	1	-1	0

Note that for any value of $x < -2$, there is no real value for y. Also for each value of $x > -2$, there are two values for y. A sketch of the graph of equation (2) is shown in Fig. 2.5.2. The graph is a *parabola*.

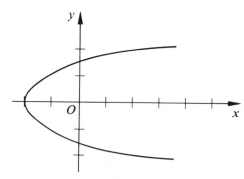

Figure 2.5.2

EXAMPLE 2: Draw a sketch of the graph of the equation

(6) $$y = \sqrt{x + 2}$$

Solution: Equation (6) is the same as equation (4). The value of y is non-negative; hence the graph of equation (6) is the upper half of the graph of equation (3). This is shown in Fig. 2.5.3.

Similarly, the graph of the equation

$$y = -\sqrt{x + 2}$$

a sketch of which is shown in Fig. 2.5.4, is the lower half of the parabola of Fig. 2.5.2.

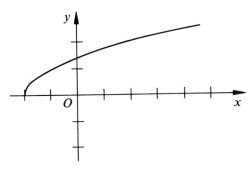

Figure 2.5.3   **Figure 2.5.4**

EXAMPLE 3: Draw a sketch of the graph of the equation

(7) $y = |x + 3|$

Solution: From the definition of the absolute value of a number, we have

$y = x + 3$ if $x + 3 \geq 0$ and $y = -(x + 3)$ if $x + 3 < 0$

or equivalently,

$y = x + 3$ if $x \geq -3$ and $y = -(x + 3)$ if $x < -3$

Table 2.5.3 gives some values of x and y satisfying equation (7).

Table 2.5.3

x	0	1	2	3	-1	-2	-3	-4	-5	-6	-7	-8	-9
y	3	4	5	6	2	1	0	1	2	3	4	5	6

A sketch of the graph of equation (7) is shown in Fig. 2.5.5.

EXAMPLE 4: Draw a sketch of the graph of the equation

(8) $(x - 2y + 3)(y - x^2) = 0$

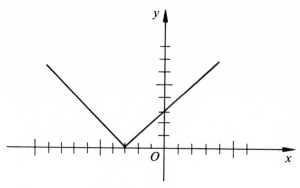

Figure 2.5.5

Solution: By the property of real numbers that $ab = 0$ if and only if $a = 0$ or $b = 0$, we have from (8)

$$(9) \qquad\qquad x - 2y + 3 = 0$$

and

$$(10) \qquad\qquad y - x^2 = 0$$

The coordinates of all points that satisfy equation (8) will satisfy either equation (9) or equation (10), and the coordinates of any point that satisfies either (9) or (10) will satisfy (8). Therefore the graph of equation (8) will consist of the graph of (9) and the graph of (10). Table 2.5.4 gives some values of x and y satisfying equation (9), and Table 2.5.5 gives some values of x and y satisfying equation (10).

Table 2.5.4

x	0	1	2	3	-1	-2	-3	-4	-5
y	3/2	2	5/2	3	1	1/2	0	$-1/2$	-1

Table 2.5.5

x	0	1	2	3	-1	-2	-3
y	0	1	4	9	1	4	9

A sketch of the graph of equation (8) is shown in Fig. 2.5.6.

2.5.2 DEFINITION   An *equation of a graph* is an equation which is satisfied by the coordinates of those, and only those, points on the graph.

EXAMPLE 5: Find an equation whose graph consists of all points whose distance from (8,0) is always twice the distance from (0,4).

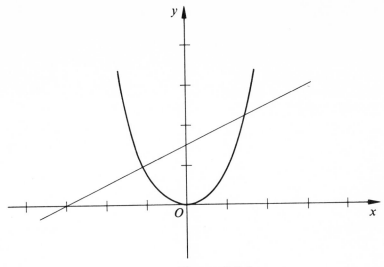

Figure 2.5.6

Solution: Let $P(x,y)$ be any point on the graph of the equation desired. If we denote the point (8,0) by A and the point (0,4) by B, then

$$|\overline{AP}| = 2|\overline{BP}|$$

Applying the distance formula, we have

$$\sqrt{(x-8)^2 + (y-0)^2} = 2\sqrt{(x-0)^2 + (y-4)^2}$$

Squaring both sides of this equation, we obtain

$$x^2 - 16x + 64 + y^2 = 4(x^2 + y^2 - 8y + 16)$$

Combining terms, we have the resulting equation,

$$3x^2 + 3y^2 + 16x - 32y = 0$$

Exercises 2.5

In Exercises 1 through 22, draw a sketch of the graph of the equation.

1. $y = 2x + 5$

2. $y = 4x - 3$

3. $y = \sqrt{x-3}$

4. $y = -\sqrt{x-3}$

5. $y^2 = x - 3$

6. $y = 5$

7. $x = -3$

8. $x = y^2 + 1$

9. $y = |x - 5|$

10. $y = -|x + 2|$

11. $y = |x| - 5$

12. $y = -|x| + 2$

13. $4x^2 + 9y^2 = 36$

14. $4x^2 - 9y^2 = 36$

15. $y = 4x^3$

16. $y^2 = 4x^3$

17. $4x^2 - y^2 = 0$

18. $3x^2 - 13xy - 10y^2 = 0$

19. $4x^2 + y^2 = 0$

20. $(2x + y - 1)(4y + x^2) = 0$

21. $x^4 - 5x^2y + 4y^2 = 0$

22. $(y^2 - x + 2)(y + \sqrt{x - 4}) = 0$

23. Draw a sketch of the graph of each of the following equations:
    (a) $y = \sqrt{2x}$ (b) $y = -\sqrt{2x}$ (c) $y^2 = 2x$

24. Draw a sketch of the graph of each of the following equations:
    (a) $y = \sqrt{-2x}$ (b) $y = -\sqrt{-2x}$ (c) $y^2 = -2x$

25. Draw a sketch of the graph of each of the following equations:
    (a) $x + 3y = 0$ (b) $x - 3y = 0$ (c) $x^2 - 9y^2 = 0$

26. (a) Write an equation whose graph is the x axis.
    (b) Write an equation whose graph is the y axis.
    (c) Write an equation whose graph is the set of all points on either the x axis or the y axis.

27. (a) Write an equation whose graph consists of all points having an abscissa of 4.
    (b) Write an equation whose graph consists of all points having an ordinate of -3.

28. (a) Find an equation whose graph consists of all points that are at a distance of 4 units from the point (1,3).
    (b) Draw a sketch of the graph of the equation found in (a).

29. (a) Find an equation whose graph consists of all points on the line through the points $A(-1,2)$ and $B(3,4)$. HINT: If $P(x,y)$ is any point on this line, the slope of the line through A and P is the same as the slope of the line through A and B.
    (b) Find an equation whose graph consists of all points equidistant from the points A and B in (a).
    (c) On the same set of coordinate axes draw sketches of the graphs of the equations found in (a) and (b).

(2.6)   Equations of a straight line

We shall now consider equations whose graphs are straight lines.

Since two points $P_1(x_1,y_1)$ and $P_2(x_2,y_2)$ determine a unique line, we should be able to obtain an equation of the line through these two points. Consider $P(x,y)$ any point on the line. We want an equation that is satisfied by x and y if and only if $P(x,y)$ is on the line through $P_1(x_1,y_1)$ and $P_2(x_2,y_2)$. We distinguish two cases.

Case 1: $x_2 = x_1$.

In this case the line through P_1 and P_2 is parallel to the y axis, and all points on this line have the same abscissa. So $P(x,y)$ will be any point on the line if and only if

(1) $x = x_1$

Equation (1) is an equation of a line parallel to the y axis. Note that this equation is independent of y; that is, the ordinate may have any value whatsoever, and the point $P(x,y)$ will be on the line whenever the abscissa is x_1.

Case 2: $x_2 \neq x_1$.

The slope of the line through P_1 and P_2 is given by

(2) $$m = \frac{y_2 - y_1}{x_2 - x_1}$$

If $P(x,y)$ is any point on the line except (x_1,y_1), the slope is also given by

(3) $$m = \frac{y - y_1}{x - x_1}$$

P will be on the line through P_1 and P_2 if and only if the value of m from equation (2) is the same as the value of m from (3); that is, if and only if

$$\frac{y - y_1}{x - x_1} = \frac{y_2 - y_1}{x_2 - x_1}$$

Multiplying both sides of this equation by $(x - x_1)$, we obtain

(((4) $$y - y_1 = \frac{y_2 - y_1}{x_2 - x_1}(x - x_1)$$

Equation (4) is satisfied by the coordinates of P_1 as well as by the coordinates of any other point on the line through P_1 and P_2.

Equation (4) is called the *two-point* form of an equation of the line. It gives an equation of the line if two points on the line are known.

If in (4) we replace $(y_2 - y_1)/(x_2 - x_1)$ by m, we get $(y - y_1)/(x - x_1) = m$, or

(((5) $$y - y_1 = m(x - x_1)$$

Equation (5) is called the *point-slope* form of an equation of the line. It gives an equation of the line if a point $P_1(x_1,y_1)$ on the line and the slope m of the line are known.

If we choose the particular point $(0,b)$ — that is, the point where the line intersects the y axis — for the point (x_1,y_1) in equation (5), we have

$$y - b = m(x - 0)$$

or

(((6) $$y = mx + b$$

The number b, which is the ordinate of the point where the line intersects the y axis, is called the *y intercept* of the line. Consequently, equation (6) is called the *slope-intercept* form of an equation of the line. This form is especially important since it enables us to find the slope of a line from its equation. It is also important since it expresses the y coordinate explicitly in terms of the x coordinate.

EXAMPLE 1: Given the line having the equation $3x + 4y = 7$, find the slope of the line.

Solution: Solving the equation for y, we have

$$y = -\frac{3}{4}x + \frac{7}{4}$$

Comparing this equation with equation (6), we see that $m = -3/4$ and $b = 7/4$. Therefore, the slope is $-3/4$.

Another form of an equation of a line is the one involving the intercepts of a line. We define the x *intercept* of a line as the abscissa of the point at which the line intersects the x axis. We denote the x intercept by a. If we are given the x intercept a and the y intercept b, we have two points $(a,0)$ and $(0,b)$ on the line. Applying equation (4), the two-point form, we have

$$y - 0 = \frac{b - 0}{0 - a}(x - a)$$

or $\qquad -ay = bx - ab$

or $\qquad bx + ay = ab$

Dividing by ab, if $a \neq 0$ and $b \neq 0$, we obtain

(((7) $\qquad\qquad\qquad \dfrac{x}{a} + \dfrac{y}{b} = 1$

Equation (7) is called the *intercept* form of an equation of the line. Obviously it does not apply to a line through the origin, since for such a line both a and b are zero.

2.6.1 THEOREM   The graph of the equation

(8) $\qquad\qquad\qquad Ax + By + C = 0$

where A, B, and C are constants and where not both A and B are zero, is a straight line.

Proof: Consider the two cases $B \neq 0$ and $B = 0$.

Case 1: $B \neq 0$.

Since $B \neq 0$, we divide equation (8) by B and obtain

(9) $\qquad\qquad\qquad y = -\dfrac{A}{B}x - \dfrac{C}{B}$

Equation (9) is an equation of a straight line since it is in the slope-intercept form, where $m = -A/B$ and $b = -C/B$.

Case 2: $B = 0$.

Since $B = 0$, we may conclude that $A \neq 0$ and thus have

$$Ax + C = 0$$

or

(10) $\qquad\qquad\qquad x = -\dfrac{C}{A}$

Equation (10) is in the form of equation (1), and so the graph is a straight line parallel to the y axis. This completes the proof.

Because the graph of equation (8) is a straight line, it is called a *linear equation*. Equation (8) is the general equation of the first degree in x and y.

EXAMPLE 2: Given the line l having the equation $2x + 3y - 5 = 0$, find an equation of the line perpendicular to line l and passing through the point $A(-1,3)$.

Solution: Since the required line is perpendicular to line l, its slope must be the negative reciprocal of the slope of l. We find the slope of l by putting its equation into the slope-intercept form. Solving the given equation for y, we obtain

$$y = -\frac{2}{3}x + \frac{5}{3}$$

Therefore the slope of l is $-2/3$, and the slope of the required line is $3/2$. Since we also know that the required line contains the point $(-1,3)$, we use the point-slope form, which gives

$$y - 3 = \frac{3}{2}(x + 1)$$

or $2y - 6 = 3x + 3$

or $3x - 2y + 9 = 0$

EXAMPLE 3: The point $(2,3)$ bisects that portion of a line which is cut off by the coordinate axes. Find an equation of the line.

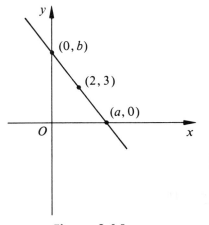

Figure 2.6.1

Solution: Refer to Fig. 2.6.1. If a is the x intercept of the line and b is the y intercept of the line, then the point $(2,3)$ is the midpoint of the line segment joining $(a,0)$ and $(0,b)$. By the midpoint formulas, we have

$$2 = \frac{a + 0}{2} \quad \text{and} \quad 3 = \frac{0 + b}{2}$$

Then $a = 4$ and $b = 6$

The intercept form, equation (7), gives us

$$\frac{x}{4} + \frac{y}{6} = 1$$

or $3x + 2y = 12$

Since two points determine a line, in order to draw a sketch of the graph of a straight line from its equation, it is only necessary to determine the coordinates of two points on the line, plot the two points, and then draw the line. Any two points will suffice, but it is usually convenient to plot the two points where the line intersects the two axes (which are given by the intercepts).

EXAMPLE 4: Given line l_1, having the equation $2x - 3y = 12$, and line l_2, having the equation $4x + 3y = 6$, draw a sketch of each of the lines. Then find the coordinates of the point of intersection of l_1 and l_2.

Solution: In order to draw a sketch of the graph of l_1, we find the intercepts a and b. In the equation of l_1, we substitute 0 for x and get $b = -4$. In the equation of l_1, we substitute 0 for y and get $a = 6$. Similarly, we obtain the intercepts a and b for l_2, and for l_2 we have $a = 3/2$ and $b = 2$. The two lines are plotted in Fig. 2.6.2.

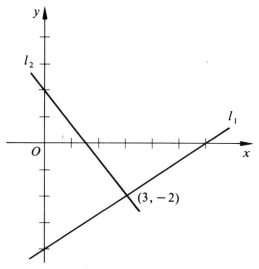

Figure 2.6.2

In order to find the coordinates of the point of intersection of l_1 and l_2, we solve the two equations simultaneously. Since the point must lie on both lines, its coordinates must satisfy both equations. If we put both equations in the slope-intercept form we have

$$y = \frac{2}{3}x - 4 \quad \text{and} \quad y = -\frac{4}{3}x + 2$$

$m = -\frac{a}{b}$ $y \text{ intercept} = -\frac{c}{B}$

Eliminating y gives us

$$\frac{2}{3}x - 4 = -\frac{4}{3}x + 2$$

or $2x - 12 = -4x + 6$

or $6x = 18$

or $x = 3$

So that $y = \frac{2}{3}(3) - 4$

or $y = -2$

Therefore the point of intersection is $(3, -2)$.

Exercises 2.6

In Exercises 1 through 10, find an equation of the line satisfying the given conditions.

1. Slope is 4, and through the point $(2, -3)$.
2. Through the two points $(3,1)$ and $(-5,4)$.
3. Through the point $(-3, -4)$ and parallel to the y axis.
4. Through the point $(1, -7)$ and parallel to the x axis.
5. x intercept is -3, and y intercept is 4.
6. Through $(1,4)$ and parallel to the line whose equation is $2x - 5y + 7 = 0$.
7. Through $(-2, -5)$ and having an inclination of $60°$.
8. Through the origin and bisecting the angle between the axes in the first and third quadrants.
9. Through the origin and bisecting the angle between the axes in the second and fourth quadrants.
10. Slope is -2, and x intercept is 4.

11. Find an equation of the line through the points $(1,3)$ and $(2, -2)$, and put the equation in the intercept form.

12. Find an equation of the line through the points $(3, -5)$ and $(1, -2)$, and put the equation in the slope-intercept form.

13. Find equations of the three medians of the triangle having vertices $A(3, -2)$, $B(3,4)$, and $C(-1,1)$, and prove that they meet in a point.

14. Find an equation of the line which has equal intercepts and which passes through the point $(8, -6)$.

15. Find an equation of each of the lines through the point $(3,2)$, which forms with the coordinate axes a triangle of area 12.

16. Find equations of the perpendicular bisectors of the sides of the triangle having vertices $A(-1, -3)$, $B(5, -3)$, and $C(5,5)$, and prove that they meet in a point.

17. Given the line l having the equation $2y - 3x = 4$ and the point $P(1,-3)$, find:
    (a) an equation of the line through P and perpendicular to l.
    (b) the shortest distance from P to line l

18. Find equations of the lines passing through the origin that are tangent to the circle having its center at $(2,1)$ and a radius of 2.

19. Given the line l, having the equation $Ax + By + C = 0$, $B \neq 0$, find:
    (a) the slope
    (b) the y intercept
    (c) the x intercept
    (d) an equation of the line through the origin perpendicular to l

20. If A, B, C, and D are constants, show that:
    (a) the lines $Ax + By + C = 0$ and $Ax + By + D = 0$ are parallel.
    (b) the lines $Ax + By + C = 0$ and $Bx - Ay + D = 0$ are perpendicular.

21. Let l_1 be the line having the equation $A_1x + B_1y + C_1 = 0$, and let l_2 be the line having the equation $A_2x + B_2y + C_2 = 0$. If l_1 is not parallel to l_2 and if k is any constant, the equation

$$A_1x + B_1y + C_1 + k(A_2x + B_2y + C_2) = 0$$

represents infinitely many lines. Prove that each of these lines contains the point of intersection of l_1 and l_2.

22. Given an equation of l_1 is $2x + 3y - 5 = 0$ and an equation of l_2 is $3x + 5y - 8 = 0$, by using Exercise 21 and without finding the coordinates of the point of intersection of l_1 and l_2, find an equation of the line through this point of intersection and
    (a) passing through the point $(1,3)$
    (b) parallel to the x axis
    (c) parallel to the y axis
    (d) having slope -2
    (e) perpendicular to the line having the equation $2x + y = 7$
    (f) forming an isosceles triangle with the coordinate axes

23. Find an equation of each straight line which is perpendicular to the line having the equation $5x - y = 1$ and which forms with the coordinate axes a triangle having an area equal to 5.

24. Prove analytically that the three altitudes of any triangle intersect in a point.

25. Prove analytically that the three medians of any triangle intersect in a point.

(2.7) Angle between two lines

If two lines intersect, two angles are formed at their point of intersection, the two angles being supplementary. To distinguish these two angles, let l_2 be the line with the greater inclination α_2, and let l_1 be the line with the smaller inclination α_1. Then the angle θ between the two lines is defined by

(1) $$\theta = \alpha_2 - \alpha_1$$

If l_1 and l_2 are parallel, $\alpha_1 = \alpha_2$, and the angle between the two lines is 0°. Thus if l_1 and l_2 are two distinct lines, $0° \leq \theta < 180°$. Refer to Figs. 2.7.1 and 2.7.2.

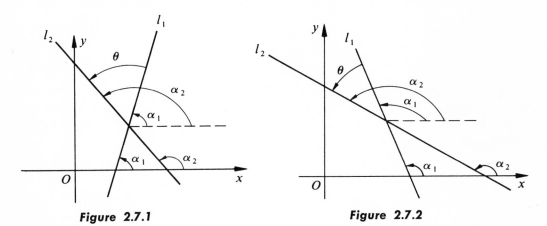

Figure 2.7.1   **Figure 2.7.2**

The following theorem enables us to find θ when the slopes of l_1 and l_2 are known.

2.7.1 THEOREM   If l_1 and l_2 are two intersecting, nonperpendicular lines, with slopes m_1 and m_2, and if l_2 has the greater inclination, then

❮❮ (2) $$\tan \theta = \frac{m_2 - m_1}{1 + m_1 m_2}$$

Proof: If α_1 is the inclination of l_1 and if α_2 is the inclination of l_2, from equation (1) we have

$$\theta = \alpha_2 - \alpha_1$$

Taking the tangent of both sides gives

$$\tan \theta = \tan (\alpha_2 - \alpha_1)$$
$$= \frac{\tan \alpha_2 - \tan \alpha_1}{1 + \tan \alpha_2 \tan \alpha_1}$$
$$= \frac{m_2 - m_1}{1 + m_1 m_2} \qquad \text{Q.E.D.}$$

The formula does not hold when $1 + m_1 m_2 = 0$. In this case, however, $m_1 m_2 = -1$, and the two lines are perpendicular; so that $\theta = 90°$.

EXAMPLE 1: Find to the nearest degree the interior angles of the triangle having vertices $B(-2,1)$, $C(2,2)$, $D(-3,4)$.

Solution: Let β, γ, and δ be the interior angles of the triangle at vertices B, C, and D, respectively. Let u denote the line through B and C, v the line through C and D, w the line through B and D, and m_u, m_v, and m_w their respective slopes. Refer to Fig. 2.7.3.

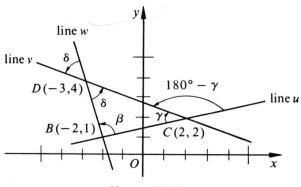

Figure 2.7.3

Using the formula for the slope of a line through two given points, we get

$$m_u = \frac{1}{4} \qquad m_v = -\frac{2}{5} \qquad m_w = -3$$

To determine β, we observe that line w has a greater inclination than line u, so that in formula (2), $m_2 = m_w = -3$ and $m_1 = m_u = 1/4$. β is the angle between lines u and v. Thus, from formula (2), we have

$$\tan \beta = \frac{-3 - (1/4)}{1 + (1/4)(-3)}$$

$$= -13$$

Therefore $\beta = 94°$

To determine γ, since line v has a greater inclination than line u, $m_2 = m_v = -2/5$ and $m_1 = m_u = 1/4$. The angle between lines u and v is, by definition, $180° - \gamma$. Applying formula (2), then, gives us

$$\tan (180° - \gamma) = \frac{(-2/5)-(1/4)}{1 + (1/4)(-2/5)}$$

$$= -\frac{13}{18}$$

Therefore $180° - \gamma = 144°$

So that $\gamma = 36°$

To determine δ, since line v has a greater inclination than line w, $m_2 = m_v = -2/5$ and $m_1 = m_w = -3$. The angle between lines v and w is then δ. Applying formula (2), we obtain

$$\tan \delta = \frac{-2/5 - (-3)}{1 + (-2/5)(-3)}$$

$$= \frac{13}{11}$$

Therefore $\delta = 50°$

Check: $\beta + \gamma + \delta = 94° + 36° + 50°$

$$= 180°$$

Exercises 2.7

1. Find the tangent of the angle between the lines whose slopes are:
   (*a*) 1 and 1/3; (*b*) 5 and $-5/3$; (*c*) $-2/3$ and 1/2; (*d*) $-1/3$ and $-1/10$; (*e*) $-4/3$ and $-5/2$; (*f*) 2.6 and -1.7.

2. Find, to the nearest degree, the angle between the lines whose slopes are:
   (*a*) 5 and $-7/9$; (*b*) -3 and 2; (*c*) 3/2 and 1/4; (*d*) $-3/2$ and $-1/4$.

3. Find, to the nearest degree, the interior angles of the triangle formed by the lines that have equations $2x + y - 6 = 0$, $3x - y - 4 = 0$, and $3x + 4y + 8 = 0$.

4. Find, to the nearest degree, the interior angles of the triangle having vertices (1,0), (-3,2), and (2,3).

5. Find, to the nearest degree, the interior angles of the triangle having vertices (2,-2), (3,2), and (-5,4).

6. Find, to the nearest degree, the interior angles of the triangle having vertices (6,5), (-5,4), and (-1,2).

7. Find an equation of a line through the point (-1,4) making an angle of 45° with the line having the equation $2x + y - 5 = 0$ (two solutions).

8. Find an equation of a line through the point ($-3, -2$) making an angle of 60° with the line having the equation $3x - 2y - 7 = 0$.

9. Using Theorem 2.7.1, prove that the triangle having vertices (2,3), (6,2), and (3,-1) is isosceles.

10. Using Theorem 2.7.1, prove that the triangle having vertices (-3,0), (-1,0), and ($-2,\sqrt{3}$) is equilateral.

11. Find the four interior angles of the quadrilateral having vertices (5,6), (-2,4), (-2,1), and (3,1), and prove that their sum is 360°.

12. If two lines have slopes 1 and 7, respectively, find the slopes of the two lines that bisect the angles at their intersection.

13. Find the slope of the bisector of the angle at A in the triangle having the vertices: $A(4,1)$; $B(6,5)$; and $C(-1,8)$.

14. Find the slope of the bisector of the angle at A in the triangle having the vertices: $A(-3,5)$; $B(2,-4)$; and $C(-1,7)$.

15. Let A, B, and C be the vertices of an oblique triangle (no right angle), and let α, β, and γ be the interior angles at vertices A, B, and C, respectively. Prove that $\tan \alpha + \tan \beta + \tan \gamma = \tan \alpha \tan \beta \tan \gamma$.

16. Find the tangents of the interior angles of the triangle having vertices $(-3,-2)$, $(-6,3)$, and $(5,1)$, and check by applying the result of Exercise 15.

(2.8) The circle

2.8.1 DEFINITION A *circle* is the set of all points in a plane equidistant from a fixed point. The fixed point is called the *center* of the circle, and the constant equal distance is called the *radius* of the circle.

2.8.2 THEOREM The circle with center at the point $C(h,k)$ and radius r has as an equation

(1) $$(x - h)^2 + (y - k)^2 = r^2$$

Proof: The point $P(x,y)$ lies on the circle if and only if

$$|\overline{PC}| = r$$

that is, if and only if

$$\sqrt{(x - h)^2 + (y - k)^2} = r$$

This is true if and only if

$$(x - h)^2 + (y - k)^2 = r^2$$

which is equation (1).

Equation (1) is satisfied by the coordinates of those and only those points which lie on the given circle. Hence (1) is an equation of the circle.

From Definition 2.5.1, it follows that the graph of equation (1) is the circle with center at (h,k) and radius r.

If the center of the circle is at the origin, then $h = k = 0$, and therefore its equation is $x^2 + y^2 = r^2$.

EXAMPLE 1: Find an equation of the circle with center at $(2,-3)$ and radius equal to 4.

Solution: The circle is shown in Fig. 2.8.1. In this example, $h = 2$, $k = -3$, $r = 4$. Substituting into equation (1), we have

$$(x - 2)^2 + [y - (-3)]^2 = 4^2$$
$$\text{or} \quad (x - 2)^2 + (y + 3)^2 = 16$$

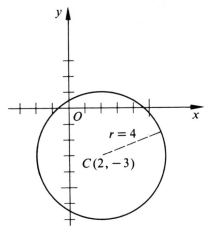

Figure 2.8.1

Squaring and then combining terms, we have

$$x^2 - 4x + 4 + y^2 + 6y + 9 = 16$$

or $$x^2 + y^2 - 4x + 6y - 3 = 0$$

EXAMPLE 2: Given the equation

$$x^2 + y^2 + 6x - 2y - 15 = 0$$

prove that the graph of this equation is a circle, and find its center and radius.

Solution: The given equation may be written as

$$(x^2 + 6x) + (y^2 - 2y) = 15$$

Completing the squares of the terms in parentheses by adding 9 and 1 to both sides of the equation, we have

$$(x^2 + 6x + 9) + (y^2 - 2y + 1) = 15 + 9 + 1$$
or $$(x + 3)^2 + (y - 1)^2 = 25$$

Comparing this equation with equation (1), we see this is an equation of a circle with its center at $(-3,1)$ and a radius of 5.

In equation (1), removing parentheses and combining terms gives

(2) $$x^2 + y^2 - 2hx - 2ky + (h^2 + k^2 - r^2) = 0$$

Equation (2) is of the form

(3) $$x^2 + y^2 + Dx + Ey + F = 0$$

where $D = -2h$, $E = -2k$, and $F = h^2 + k^2 - r^2$.

Equation (3) is called the *general form* of an equation of a circle, while equation (1) is called the *center-radius form*. Since every circle has a center and a radius, its equation may be put in the center-radius form, and hence into the general form.

We shall now consider the question of whether or not the graph of every equation of the form

$$x^2 + y^2 + Dx + Ey + F = 0$$

is a circle. To determine this, we shall attempt to write this equation in the center-radius form. We rewrite the equation as

$$(x^2 + Dx) + (y^2 + Ey) = -F$$

and complete the squares of the terms in parentheses by adding $D^2/4$ and $E^2/4$ to both sides, giving us

$$\left(x^2 + Dx + \frac{D^2}{4}\right) + \left(y^2 + Ey + \frac{E^2}{4}\right) = -F + \frac{D^2}{4} + \frac{E^2}{4}$$

or

(4)
$$\left(x + \frac{D}{2}\right)^2 + \left(y + \frac{E}{2}\right)^2 = \frac{D^2 + E^2 - 4F}{4}$$

Equation (4) will be of the form of equation (1) if and only if

$$(D^2 + E^2 - 4F)/4 = r^2.$$

We shall now consider three cases, namely, $(D^2 + E^2 - 4F)/4$ as positive, zero, and negative.

Case 1: $(D^2 + E^2 - 4F)/4 > 0$.

Then $r^2 = (D^2 + E^2 - 4F)/4$, and so equation (4) is an equation of a circle having a radius equal to $\sqrt{D^2 + E^2 - 4F}/2$ and its center at $(-D/2, -E/2)$.

Case 2: $(D^2 + E^2 - 4F)/4 = 0$.

Equation (4) is then of the form

(5)
$$\left(x + \frac{D}{2}\right)^2 + \left(y + \frac{E}{2}\right)^2 = 0$$

Since the only real values of x and y satisfying equation (5) are $x = -D/2$ and $y = -E/2$, the graph is the point $(-D/2, -E/2)$. Comparing equation (5) with equation (1), we see $h = -D/2$, $k = -E/2$, and $r = 0$. This point may thus be called a *point-circle*.

Case 3: $(D^2 + E^2 - 4F)/4 < 0$.

Then equation (4) has a negative number on the right-hand side and the sum of the squares of two real numbers on the left-hand side. There are no real values of x and y that satisfy such an equation; consequently we say there is no real locus.

Before stating the results of these three cases as a theorem, we observe that an equation of the form

(6) $Ax^2 + Ay^2 + Dx + Ey + F = 0$ where $A \neq 0$

can be written in the form of equation (3) by dividing by A, thereby obtaining

$$x^2 + y^2 + \frac{D}{A}x + \frac{E}{A}y + \frac{F}{A} = 0$$

Equation (6) is a special case of the general equation of the second degree:

$$Ax^2 + Bxy + Cy^2 + Dx + Ey + F = 0$$

in which the coefficients of x^2 and y^2 are equal and which has no xy term. We have, then, the following theorem.

2.8.3 THEOREM   The graph of any second degree equation in x and y in which the coefficients of x^2 and y^2 are equal and in which there is no xy term is either a circle, a point-circle, or no real locus.

EXAMPLE 3: Determine the graph of the equation

$$2x^2 + 2y^2 + 12x - 8y + 31 = 0$$

Solution: The equation is of the form (6), and therefore the graph is either a circle, a point-circle, or no real locus. If the equation is put in the form of equation (1), we have

$$x^2 + y^2 + 6x - 4y + \frac{31}{2} = 0$$

$$(x^2 + 6x) + (y^2 - 4y) = -\frac{31}{2}$$

$$(x^2 + 6x + 9) + (y^2 - 4y + 4) = -\frac{31}{2} + 9 + 4$$

$$(x + 3)^2 + (y - 2)^2 = -\frac{5}{2}$$

Therefore, there is no real locus.

EXAMPLE 4: Find an equation of the circle through the three points $A(4,5)$, $B(3,-2)$, and $C(1,-4)$.

Solution: The general form of an equation of the circle is

$$x^2 + y^2 + Dx + Ey + F = 0$$

Since the three points A, B, and C must lie on the circle, the coordinates of these points must satisfy the equation. So we have

$$16 + 25 + 4D + 5E + F = 0$$
$$9 + 4 + 3D - 2E + F = 0$$
$$1 + 16 + D - 4E + F = 0$$

$$\text{or} \quad 4D + 5E + F = -41$$
$$3D - 2E + F = -13$$
$$D - 4E + F = -17$$

Solving these three equations simultaneously, we get

$$D = 7 \quad E = -5 \quad F = -44$$

Thus, an equation of the circle is

$$x^2 + y^2 + 7x - 5y - 44 = 0$$

EXAMPLE 5: Find an equation of the circle with its center at the point $C(1,6)$ and tangent to the line l having the equation $x - y - 1 = 0$.

   Solution: See Fig. 2.8.2. Being given $h = 1$ and $k = 6$, if we find r we can obtain an equation of the circle by using the center-radius form.

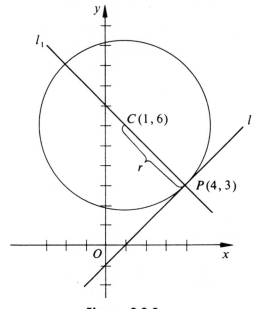

Figure 2.8.2

   Let l_1 be the line through C and the point P, which is the point of tangency of line l with the circle.

$$r = |\overline{PC}|$$

Hence, we must find the coordinates of P. We do this by finding an equation of l_1 and then finding the point of intersection of l_1 with l. Since l_1 is along a diameter of the circle, and l is tangent to the circle, l_1 is perpendicular to l. Since the slope of l is 1, the slope of l_1 is -1. Therefore, using the point-slope form of an equation of a line, we obtain as an equation of l_1

$$y - 6 = -1(x - 1)$$

or $x + y - 7 = 0$

Solving this equation simultaneously with the given equation of l, namely,

$$x - y - 1 = 0$$

we get $x = 4$ and $y = 3$. Thus P is the point $(4,3)$.

Therefore,

$$r = |\overline{PC}| = \sqrt{(4-1)^2 + (3-6)^2}$$

or $r = \sqrt{18}$

So, an equation of the circle is

$$(x-1)^2 + (y-6)^2 = (\sqrt{18})^2$$

or $x^2 + y^2 - 2x - 12y + 19 = 0$

Exercises 2.8

In Exercises 1 through 4, find an equation of the circle with center at C and radius r. Write the equation in both the center-radius form and the general form.

1. $C(4,-3)$, $r = 5$
2. $C(0,0)$, $r = 8$
3. $C(-5,-12)$, $r = 3$
4. $C(-1,1)$, $r = 2$

In Exercises 5 through 10, find an equation of the circle satisfying the given conditions.

5. Center is at $(1,2)$ and through the point $(3,-1)$.
6. Center is at $(-2,5)$ and tangent to the line $x = 7$.
7. Center is at $(-3,-5)$ and tangent to the line $12x + 5y - 4 = 0$.
8. Through the three points $(2,8)$, $(7,3)$, and $(-2,0)$.
9. Tangent to the line $3x + y + 2 = 0$ at $(-1,1)$ and through the point $(3,5)$.
10. Tangent to the line $3x + 4y - 16 = 0$ at $(4,1)$ and with a radius of 5. (Two possible circles.)

In Exercises 11 through 14, find the center and radius of each circle, and draw a sketch of the graph.

11. $x^2 + y^2 - 6x - 8y + 9 = 0$
12. $2x^2 + 2y^2 - 2x + 2y + 7 = 0$
13. $3x^2 + 3y^2 + 4y - 7 = 0$
14. $x^2 + y^2 - 10x - 10y + 25 = 0$

In Exercises 15 through 20, determine whether the graph is a circle, a point-circle, or no real locus.

15. $x^2 + y^2 - 2x + 10y + 19 = 0$
16. $4x^2 + 4y^2 + 24x - 4y + 1 = 0$
17. $x^2 + y^2 - 10x + 6y + 36 = 0$
18. $x^2 + y^2 + 2x - 4y + 5 = 0$
19. $36x^2 + 36y^2 - 48x + 36y - 119 = 0$
20. $9x^2 + 9y^2 + 6x - 6y + 5 = 0$

21. Find an equation of the common chord of the two circles $x^2 + y^2 + 4x - 6y - 12 = 0$ and $x^2 + y^2 + 8x - 2y + 8 = 0$. HINT: If the coordinates

of a point satisfy two different equations, then the coordinates also satisfy the difference of the two equations.

22. Find the points of intersection of the two circles in Exercise 21.

23. Find an equation of the line that is tangent to the circle $x^2 + y^2 - 4x + 6y - 12 = 0$ at the point $(5,1)$.

24. Find an equation of each of the two lines having slope $-4/3$ that are tangent to the circle $x^2 + y^2 + 2x - 8y - 8 = 0$.

25. Prove analytically that a line from the center of any circle bisecting any chord is perpendicular to the chord.

26. Prove analytically that an angle inscribed in a semicircle is a right angle.

27. Given the line $y = mx + b$ tangent to the circle $x^2 + y^2 = r^2$, find an equation involving m, b, and r.

(2.9)   The parabola

A *conic section* is a curve of intersection of a plane with a right circular cone of two nappes. There are three types of curves that occur in this way: the parabola, the ellipse, and the hyperbola. The resulting curve depends upon the inclination of the axis of the cone to the cutting plane. In this section we shall study the parabola; the ellipse and the hyperbola will be discussed in a later chapter.

When the cutting plane is parallel to an element of the cone, a parabola is obtained. Following is the analytic definition of a parabola.

2.9.1 DEFINITION   A *parabola* is the set of all points in a plane equidistant from a fixed point and a fixed line. The fixed point is called the *focus*, and the fixed line is called the *directrix*.

We shall now derive an equation of a parabola from the definition. In order for this equation to be as simple as possible, we choose the x axis as perpendicular to the directrix and containing the focus. The origin is taken at the point on the x axis midway between the focus and the directrix. It should be stressed that we are choosing the axes (*not* the parabola) in a special way (see Fig. 2.9.1).

Let p be the directed distance $\overline{OF}$. The focus is the point $F(p,0)$, and the directrix is the line having the equation $x = -p$. Let $P(x,y)$ be any point on the parabola. Then point P is equidistant from the point F and the directrix. From P draw a line perpendicular to the directrix, and let $Q(-p,y)$ be the foot of this perpendicular. Then,

$$|\overline{FP}| = |\overline{QP}|$$

Since $\qquad\qquad |\overline{FP}| = \sqrt{(x - p)^2 + y^2}$

and $\qquad\qquad |\overline{QP}| = \sqrt{(x + p)^2 + (y - y)^2}$

we have $\qquad \sqrt{(x - p)^2 + y^2} = \sqrt{(x + p)^2}$

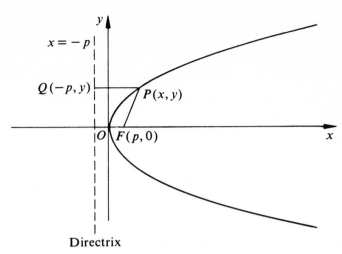

Figure 2.9.1

Squaring both sides of the equation, we get

$$x^2 - 2px + p^2 + y^2 = x^2 + 2px + p^2$$

$$\text{or} \quad y^2 = 4px$$

This result is stated as a theorem.

2.9.2 THEOREM   An equation of the parabola having its focus at $(p,0)$ and as its directrix the line $x = -p$ is

(1) $y^2 = 4px$

In Fig. 2.9.1, p is positive; p may be negative, however, since it is the directed
distance $\overline{OF}$. In Fig. 2.9.2 is shown a parabola for $p < 0$.

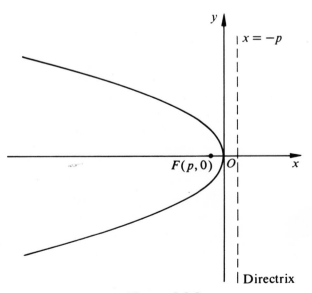

Figure 2.9.2

From Figs. 2.9.1 and 2.9.2, we see that for the equation $y^2 = 4px$ the parabola opens to the right if $p > 0$ and to the left if $p < 0$. The point midway between the focus and the directrix on the parabola is called the *vertex*. The vertex of the parabolas in Figs. 2.9.1 and 2.9.2 is the origin. The line through the vertex and the focus is called the *axis* of the parabola. The axis of the parabolas in Figs. 2.9.1 and 2.9.2 is the x axis.

In the above derivation, if the x axis and the y axis are interchanged, then the focus is at the point $F(0,p)$, and the directrix is the line having the equation $y = -p$. An equation of this parabola is $x^2 = 4py$, and the result is stated as a theorem.

2.9.3 THEOREM An equation of the parabola having its focus at $(0,p)$ and as its directrix the line $y = -p$ is

(2) $$x^2 = 4py$$

If $p > 0$, the parabola opens upward as shown in Fig. 2.9.3; and if $p < 0$, the parabola opens downward as shown in Fig. 2.9.4. In each case the vertex is at the origin, and the y axis is the axis of the parabola.

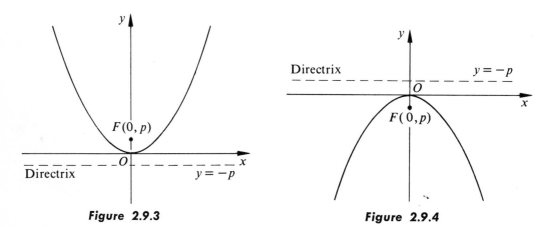

Figure 2.9.3   **Figure 2.9.4**

When one draws a sketch of the graph of a parabola, it is helpful to draw the chord through the focus, perpendicular to the axis of the parabola. This chord is called the *latus rectum* of the parabola. The length of the latus rectum is $|4p|$. (See Exercise 17 below.)

EXAMPLE 1: Find an equation of the parabola having its focus at $(0,-3)$ and as its directrix the line $y = 3$. Draw a sketch of the graph.

Solution: Since the focus is on the y axis and is also below the directrix, the parabola opens downward, and $p = -3$. Hence an equation of the parabola is

$$x^2 = -12y$$

The length of the latus rectum is

$$|4(-3)| = 12$$

A sketch of the graph is shown in Fig. 2.9.5.

   Any point on the parabola is equidistant from the focus and the directrix. In Fig. 2.9.5, three such points (P_1, P_2, and P_3) are shown, and we have

$$\overline{|FP_1|} = \overline{|P_1Q_1|} \qquad \overline{|FP_2|} = \overline{|P_2Q_2|} \qquad \overline{|FP_3|} = \overline{|P_3Q_3|}$$

EXAMPLE 2: Given the parabola having the equation

$$y^2 = 7x$$

find the coordinates of the focus, the equation of the directrix, and the length of the latus rectum. Draw a sketch of the graph.

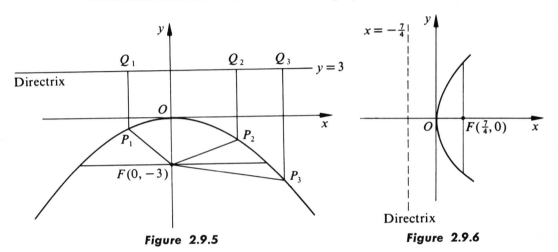

Figure 2.9.5   **Figure 2.9.6**

Solution: The given equation is of the form of equation (1); so,

$$4p = 7$$

$$\text{or} \qquad p = \frac{7}{4}$$

Since $p > 0$, the parabola opens to the right. The focus is at the point $F(7/4, 0)$. An equation of the directrix is $x = -7/4$. The length of the latus rectum is 7. A sketch of the graph is shown in Fig. 2.9.6.

Exercises 2.9

   For each of the parabolas in Exercises 1 through 8, find the coordinates of the focus, an equation of the directrix, and the length of the latus rectum. Draw a sketch of the curve.

1. $x^2 = 4y$
2. $y^2 = 6x$
3. $y^2 = -8x$
4. $x^2 = -16y$

5. $x^2 + y = 0$
6. $y^2 - 5x = 0$
7. $2y^2 - 9x = 0$
8. $3x^2 + 4y = 0$

In Exercises 9 through 16, find an equation of the parabola having the given properties.

9. Focus, (5,0); directrix, $x = -5$.
10. Focus, (0,4); directrix, $y = -4$.
11. Focus, (0,−2); directrix, $y - 2 = 0$.
12. Focus, (−5/3,0); directrix, $5 - 3x = 0$.
13. Focus, (1/2,0); directrix, $2x + 1 = 0$.
14. Focus, (0,2/3); directrix, $3y + 2 = 0$.
15. Vertex, (0,0); opens to the left; length of latus rectum = 6.
16. Vertex, (0,0); opens upward; length of latus rectum = 3.

17. Prove that the length of the latus rectum of a parabola is $|4p|$.

18. Find an equation of the parabola having its vertex at the origin, the x axis as its axis, and passing through the point (2,−4).

19. Find an equation of the parabola having its vertex at the origin, the y axis as its axis, and passing through the point (−2,−4).

20. A parabolic arch has a height of 20 ft and a width of 36 ft at the base. If the vertex of the parabola is at the top of the arch, at what height above the base is it 18 ft wide?

21. The cable of a suspension bridge hangs in the form of a parabola when the load is uniformly distributed horizontally. The distance between two towers is 1500 ft, the points of support of the cable on the towers are 220 ft above the roadway, and the lowest point on the cable is 70 ft above the roadway. Find the distance to the cable from a point in the roadway 150 ft from the foot of a tower.

22. Assume that water issuing from the end of a horizontal pipe, 25 ft above the ground, describes a parabolic curve, the vertex of the parabola being at the end of the pipe. If, at a point 8 ft below the line of the pipe, the flow of water has curved outward 10 ft beyond a vertical line through the end of the pipe, how far beyond this vertical line will the water strike the ground?

23. Using Definition 2.9.1, find an equation of the parabola having as its directrix the line $x = -3$ and as its focus the point (2,5).

24. Using Definition 2.9.1, find an equation of the parabola having as its directrix the line $y = 4$ and as its focus the point (−3,8).

25. Find an equation of the circle passing through the vertex and the end points of the latus rectum of the parabola $x^2 = -8y$.

26. Prove analytically that the circle having as its diameter the latus rectum of a parabola is tangent to the directrix of the parabola.

27. Prove that if θ is the angle between the line segments joining the end points of the latus rectum of a parabola to its vertex, then $\tan \theta/2 = 2$.

28. Find all points on the parabola $y^2 = 8x$ such that the foot of the perpen-

dicular drawn from the point to the directrix, the focus, and the point itself are vertices of an equilateral triangle.

29. A focal chord of a parabola is a line segment through the focus and with its end points on the parabola. If *A* and *B* are the end points of a focal chord of a parabola, and if *C* is the point of intersection of the directrix with a line through the vertex and point *A*, prove that the line through *C* and *B* is parallel to the axis of the parabola.

(2.10) Translation of axes

The shape of a curve is not affected by the position of the coordinate axes; however, an equation of the curve is affected. For example, if a circle with a radius of 3 has its center at the point $(4,-1)$, then an equation of this circle is

$$(x - 4)^2 + (y + 1)^2 = 9$$

$$\text{or} \quad x^2 + y^2 - 8x + 2y + 8 = 0$$

However, if the origin is at the center, the same circle has a simpler equation, namely,

$$x^2 + y^2 = 9$$

If we may take the coordinate axes as we please, they are generally chosen in such a way that the equations will be as simple as possible. If the axes are given, however, we often wish to find a simpler equation of a given curve referred to another set of axes.

In general, if in the plane with given x and y axes new coordinate axes are chosen parallel to the given ones, we say that there has been a *translation of axes* in the plane.

In particular, let the given x and y axes be translated to the x' and y' axes, having origin (h,k) with respect to the given axes. Also, assume the positive numbers are on the same side of the origin on the x' and y' axes as they are on the x and y axes (see Fig. 2.10.1).

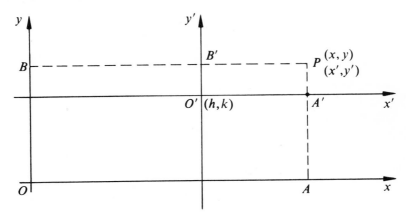

Figure 2.10.1

A point P in the plane, having coordinates (x,y) with respect to the given coordinate axes, will have coordinates (x',y') with respect to the new axes. To obtain relationships between these two sets of coordinates, we draw a line through P parallel to the x axis and the x' axis, and also a line through P parallel to the y axis and the y' axis. Let the first line intersect the x axis at the point A and the x' axis at the point A', and the second line intersect the y axis at the point B and the y' axis at the point B'.

With respect to the x and y axes, the coordinates of P are (x,y), the coordinates of A are $(x,0)$, and the coordinates of A' are (x,k). Since, $\overline{A'P} = \overline{AP} - \overline{AA'}$, we have

$$y' = y - k$$
$$\text{or} \quad y = y' + k$$

With respect to the x and y axes, the coordinates of B are $(0,y)$, and the coordinates of B' are (h,y). Since $\overline{B'P} = \overline{BP} - \overline{BB'}$, we have

$$x' = x - h$$
$$\text{or} \quad x = x' + h$$

These results are stated as a theorem.

2.10.1 THEOREM If (x,y) represents a point P with respect to a given set of axes, and (x',y') is a representation of P after the axes are translated to a new origin having coordinates (h,k) with respect to the given axes, then

(1)
$$x = x' + h \quad \text{and} \quad y = y' + k$$
or
(2)
$$x' = x - h \quad \text{and} \quad y' = y - k$$

Equations (1) or (2) are called the *equations of translating the axes.*

If an equation of a curve is given in x and y, then an equation in x' and y' is obtained by replacing x by $(x' + h)$ and y by $(y' + k)$. The graph of the equation in x and y, with respect to the x and y axes, is exactly the same set of points as the graph of the corresponding equation in x' and y' with respect to the x' and y' axes.

EXAMPLE 1: Given the equation $x^2 + 10x + 6y + 19 = 0$, find an equation of the graph with respect to the x' and y' axes after a translation of axes to the new origin $(-5,1)$.

Solution: A point P, represented by (x,y) with respect to the old axes, has the representation (x',y') with respect to the new axes. Then by equations (1), with $h = -5$ and $k = 1$, we have

$$x = x' - 5 \quad \text{and} \quad y = y' + 1$$

Substituting these values of x and y into the given equation, we obtain

$$(x' - 5)^2 + 10(x' - 5) + 6(y' + 1) + 19 = 0$$
$$\text{or} \quad x'^2 - 10x' + 25 + 10x' - 50 + 6y' + 6 + 19 = 0$$
$$\text{or} \quad x'^2 = -6y'$$

The graph of this equation with respect to the x' and y' axes is a parabola with its vertex at the origin, opening downward, and with $4p = -6$. The graph with respect to the x and y axes is, then, a parabola having its vertex at $(-5,1)$, its focus at $(-5,-1/2)$ and as its directrix the line $y = 5/2$ (see Fig. 2.10.2).

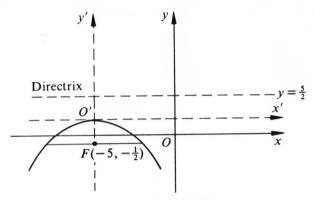

Figure 2.10.2

The above example illustrates how an equation may be reduced to a simpler form by a suitable translation of axes. In general, equations of the second degree which contain no term involving xy may be simplified by a translation of axes. This is illustrated in the following example.

EXAMPLE 2: Given the equation $9x^2 + 4y^2 - 18x + 32y + 37 = 0$, translate the axes so that the equation of the graph with respect to the x' and y' axes will contain no first-degree terms.

Solution: We rewrite the given equation:

$$9(x^2 - 2x) + 4(y^2 + 8y) = -37$$

Completing the squares of the terms in parentheses by adding $(9 \cdot 1)$ and $(4 \cdot 16)$ to both sides of the equation, we have

$$9(x^2 - 2x + 1) + 4(y^2 + 8y + 16) = -37 + 9 + 64$$
$$\text{or} \quad 9(x - 1)^2 + 4(y + 4)^2 = 36$$

Then, if we let $x' = x - 1$ and $y' = y + 4$, we obtain

$$9x'^2 + 4y'^2 = 36$$

From equation (2), we see that the substitutions of $x' = x - 1$ and $y' = y + 4$ result in a translation of axes to a new origin of $(1,-4)$. In Fig. 2.10.3, we have a sketch of the graph of the equation in x' and y' with respect to the x' and y' axes.

We shall now apply the translation of axes to finding the general equation of a parabola having its directrix parallel to a coordinate axis and its vertex at the point (h,k). In particular, let the directrix be parallel to the y axis. If the vertex is at point $V(h,k)$, then the directrix has the equation $x = h - p$, and the focus is at the point $F(h + p,k)$.

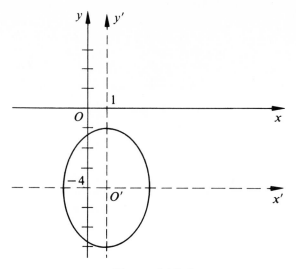

Figure 2.10.3

Let the x' and y' axes be such that the origin O' is at $V(h,k)$(see Fig. 2.10.4).

An equation of the parabola in Fig. 2.10.4 with respect to the x' and y' axes is

$$y'^2 = 4px'$$

To obtain an equation of this parabola with respect to the x and y axes, we replace x' by $(x - h)$ and y' by $(y - k)$ from equations (2), which gives us

$$(y - k)^2 = 4p(x - h)$$

The axis of this parabola is parallel to the x axis.

Similarly, if the directrix of a parabola is parallel to the x axis and the vertex is at $V(h,k)$, then its focus is at $F(h,k + p)$ and the directrix has the equation $y = k - p$, and an equation of the parabola with respect to the x and y axes is

$$(x - h)^2 = 4p(y - k)$$

The axis of this parabola is parallel to the y axis. We have proved, then, the following theorem.

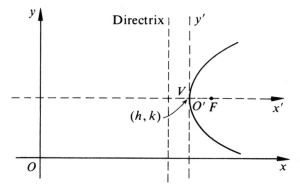

Figure 2.10.4

2.10.2 THEOREM   If p is the directed distance from the vertex to the focus, an equation of the parabola with its vertex at (h,k) and with its axis parallel to the x axis is

(3) $$(y - k)^2 = 4p(x - h)$$

A parabola with the same vertex and with its axis parallel to the y axis has for an equation

(4) $$(x - h)^2 = 4p(y - k)$$

EXAMPLE 3: Find an equation of the parabola having as its directrix the line $y = 1$ and as its focus the point $F(-3,7)$.

Solution: Since the directrix is parallel to the x axis, the axis will be parallel to the y axis, and the equation will have the form (4).

Since the vertex V is halfway between the directrix and the focus, V has coordinates $(-3, 4)$. The directed distance from the vertex to the focus is p, so that

$$p = 7 - 4 = 3$$

Therefore, an equation is

$$(x + 3)^2 = 12(y - 4)$$

Squaring and simplifying, we get

$$x^2 + 6x - 12y + 57 = 0$$

A sketch of the graph of this parabola is shown in Fig. 2.10.5.

EXAMPLE 4: Given the parabola having the equation

$$y^2 + 6x + 8y + 1 = 0$$

find the vertex, the focus, an equation of the directrix, an equation of the axis, and the length of the latus rectum, and draw a sketch of the graph.

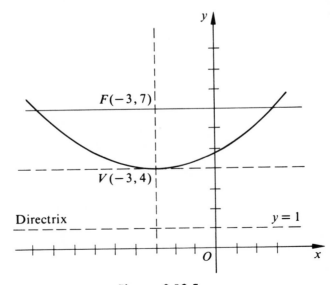

Figure 2.10.5

Solution: Rewrite the given equation as

$$y^2 + 8y = -6x - 1$$

Completing the square of the terms involving y on the left-hand side of this equation by adding 16 to both sides, we obtain

$$y^2 + 8y + 16 = -6x + 15$$

or $$(y + 4)^2 = -6\left(x - \frac{5}{2}\right)$$

Comparing this equation with (3), we let

$$k = -4 \qquad h = \frac{5}{2}$$

and $$4p = -6 \qquad \text{or} \qquad p = -\frac{3}{2}$$

Therefore, the vertex is at $(5/2, -4)$; an equation of the axis is $y = -4$; the focus is at $(1, -4)$; an equation of the directrix is $x = 4$; and the length of the latus rectum is 6. A sketch of the graph is shown in Fig. 2.10.6.

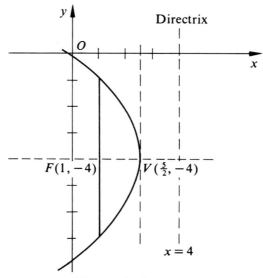

Figure 2.10.6

Exercises 2.10

In Exercises 1 through 8, find a new equation of the graph of the given equation after a translation of axes to the new origin as indicated. Draw the original and the new axes and a sketch of the graph.

1. $x^2 + y^2 + 6x + 4y = 0$; $(-3, -2)$
2. $x^2 + y^2 - 10x + 4y + 13 = 0$; $(5, -2)$
3. $y^2 - 6x + 9 = 0$; $(3/2, 0)$
4. $y^2 + 3x - 2y + 7 = 0$; $(-2, 1)$

5. $x^2 + 4y^2 + 4x + 8y + 4 = 0$; $(-2,-1)$
6. $25x^2 + y^2 - 50x + 20y - 500 = 0$; $(1,-10)$
7. $y - 4 = 2(x - 1)^3$; $(1,4)$
8. $(y + 1)^2 = 4(x - 2)^3$; $(2,-1)$

In Exercises 9 through 12, translate the axes so that an equation of the graph with respect to the new axes will contain no first-degree terms. Draw the original and the new axes and a sketch of the graph.

9. $x^2 + 4y^2 - 16x + 24y + 84 = 0$
10. $16x^2 + 25y^2 - 32x - 100y - 284 = 0$
11. $3x^2 - 2y^2 + 6x - 8y - 11 = 0$
12. $x^2 - y^2 + 14x - 8y - 35 = 0$

In Exercises 13 through 18, find the vertex, the focus, an equation of the axis, and an equation of the directrix of the given parabola. Draw a sketch of the graph.

13. $x^2 + 6x + 4y + 8 = 0$
14. $4x^2 - 8x + 3y - 2 = 0$
15. $y^2 + 6x + 10y + 19 = 0$
16. $3y^2 - 8x - 12y - 4 = 0$
17. $2y^2 = 4y - 3x$
18. $y = 3x^2 - 3x + 3$

In Exercises 19 through 28, find an equation of the parabola having the given properties. Draw a sketch of the graph.

19. Vertex at $(2,4)$; focus at $(-3,4)$.
20. Vertex at $(1,-3)$; directrix, $y = 1$.
21. Focus at $(-1,7)$; directrix, $y = 3$.
22. Focus at $(-3/4,4)$; directrix, $x = -5/4$.
23. Vertex at $(3,-2)$; axis, $x = 3$; length of the latus rectum is 6.
24. Axis parallel to the x axis; through the points $(1,2)$, $(5,3)$, and $(11,4)$.
25. Vertex at $(-4,2)$; axis, $y = 2$; through the point $(0,6)$.
26. Directrix, $x = -2$; axis, $y = 4$; length of the latus rectum is 8.
27. Directrix, $x = 4$; axis, $y = 4$; through the point $(9,7)$.
28. End points of the latus rectum are $(1,3)$ and $(7,3)$.

29. Given the parabola having the equation $y = ax^2 + bx + c$, with $a \neq 0$, find the coordinates of the vertex.

30. Find the coordinates of the focus of the parabola in Exercise 29.

31. Find an equation of every parabola containing the points $A (-3,-4)$ and $B (5,-4)$, such that points A and B are each 5 units from the focus.

32. Given the equation $4x^3 - 12x^2 + 12x - 3y - 10 = 0$, translate the axes so that the equation of the graph with respect to the new axes will contain no second-degree term and no constant term. Draw a sketch of the graph and the two sets of axes. HINT: Let $x = x' + h$ and $y = y' + k$ in the given equation.

33. Given the equation $x^3 + 3x^2 - y^2 + 3x + 4y - 3 = 0$, translate the axes so that the equation of the graph with respect to the new axes will contain no first-degree term and no constant term. Draw a sketch of the graph and the two sets of axes (see hint for Exercise 32).

3 Functions

(3.1)   Functions and their graphs

A quantity y is a function of another quantity x if there is some rule by which a unique value is assigned to y by a corresponding value of x. Familiar examples of such relationships are given by equations such as

(1) $$y = 2x^2 + 5$$

and

(2) $$y = \sqrt{x^2 - 9}$$

It is not necessary that x and y be related by an equation in order for a functional relationship to exist between them. For example, if y is the number of cents in the postage of a first-class letter and if x is the number of ounces in the weight of the letter, then y is a function of x. For this functional relationship, there is no equation involving x and y; however, the relationship between x and y may be given by means of a table, such as Table 3.1.1.

Table 3.1.1

x: number of ounces in the weight of the letter	$0 < x \le 1$	$1 < x \le 2$	$2 < x \le 3$	$3 < x \le 4$	$4 < x \le 5$	$5 < x \le 6$	$6 < x \le 7$
y: number of cents in first-class postage	5	10	15	20	25	30	35

3.1.1 DEFINITION   A *function* is a set of ordered pairs of numbers (x,y), in which no two distinct ordered pairs have the same first number. The totality of all possible values of x is called the *domain* of the function, and the totality of all possible values of y is called the *range* of the function.

In the above definition, the restriction that no two distinct ordered pairs may have the same first number assures us that y is unique for a specific value of x.

Equation (1) defines a function. Let us call this function f. The equation gives us the rule by which we can determine a unique value of y whenever x is given: that is, multiply the number x by itself, then multiply that product by 2, and add 5. The function f is the set of all ordered pairs (x,y) such that x and y satisfy equation (1). x and y are called *variables*. Since for the function f we assign values to x and since the value of y is dependent upon the choice of x, we call x the *independent variable* and y the *dependent variable*. The domain of the function is the totality of all possible values of the independent variable, and the range of the function is the totality of all possible values of the dependent variable. For the function f, under consideration, the domain is the set of all real numbers, which we may denote with interval notation as $(-\infty,+\infty)$. The smallest value that y may assume is 5 (when $x = 0$). The range of f is then the set of all positive numbers greater than or equal to 5, which is $[5,+\infty)$.

Now, let g be the function which is the set of all ordered pairs (x,y) defined by equation (2): $y = \sqrt{x^2 - 9}$. Because we are confining ourselves to real numbers, y is a function of x only for $x \geq 3$ and $x \leq -3$ (or simply $|x| \geq 3$), since for any x satisfying either of these inequalities a unique value of y is determined; however, if x is in the interval $-3 < x < 3$, we obtain a square root of a negative number, and hence no real number y exists. Therefore, we must restrict x, and we may say that the function g is the set of all ordered pairs (x,y) such that

$$y = \sqrt{x^2 - 9} \quad \text{and} \quad |x| \geq 3$$

The domain of g is $(-\infty,-3]$ and $[3,+\infty)$, and the range of g is $[0,+\infty)$.

If P is the function which is the set of all ordered pairs (x,y) defined by a table similar to Table 3.1.1, then the domain of P will be the set of all positive numbers up to a certain maximum allowed by postal regulations. This maximum being 320, the domain of P is $(0,320]$. The range of P is the set of all positive integers which are multiples of 5 and which are less than or equal to 1,600.

It should be stressed that, in order to have a function, there must be *exactly one value* of the dependent variable for a value of the independent variable in the domain of the function.

If the ordered pairs of numbers (x,y) for a specific function are plotted as the cartesian coordinates of a point in the plane, the totality of all such points is called the *graph* of the function. Since for each value of x in the domain of the function there corresponds a unique value of y, no vertical line can intersect the graph of the function in more than one point. Following are some examples of functions and their graphs.

EXAMPLE 1: Let f be the function that is the set of all ordered pairs (x,y) such that

$$y = \sqrt{5 - x}$$

Find the domain and range of f, and draw a sketch of the graph of f.

Solution: A sketch of the graph of f is shown in Fig. 3.1.1. The domain of f is the set of all real numbers less than or equal to 5, which is $(-\infty, 5]$, and the range of f is the set of all nonnegative real numbers, which is $[0, +\infty)$.

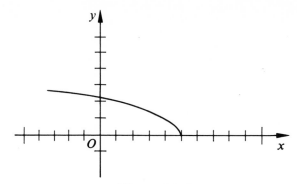

Figure 3.1.1

EXAMPLE 2: Let g be the function which is the set of all ordered pairs (x,y) such that

$$y = \begin{cases} -3 & \text{if } x \le -1 \\ 1 & \text{if } -1 < x \le 2 \\ 4 & \text{if } 2 < x \end{cases}$$

Find the domain and range of g, and draw a sketch of the graph of g.

Solution: The domain of g is $(-\infty, +\infty)$, while the range of g consists of the three numbers -3, 1, and 4. A sketch of the graph is shown in Fig. 3.1.2.

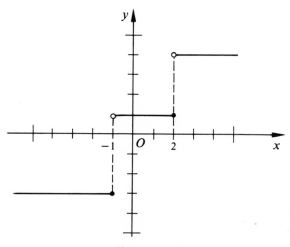

Figure 3.1.2

Note in Figure 3.1.2 that there is a break at $x = -1$ and another at $x = 2$. g is said to be discontinuous at -1 and 2. We shall consider continuous and discontinuous functions in the next chapter.

EXAMPLE 3: Let h be the function which is the set of all ordered pairs (x,y) such that

$$y = |x|$$

Find the domain and range of h, and draw a sketch of the graph of h.

Solution: The domain of h is $(-\infty, +\infty)$, and the range of h is $[0, +\infty)$. A sketch of the graph of h is shown in Fig. 3.1.3.

EXAMPLE 4: Let F be the function which is the set of all ordered pairs (x,y) such that

$$y = \begin{cases} 3x - 2 & \text{if } x < 1 \\ x^2 & \text{if } 1 \le x \end{cases}$$

Find the domain and range of F, and draw a sketch of the graph of F.

Solution: A sketch of the graph of F is shown in Fig. 3.1.4. The domain of F is $(-\infty, +\infty)$, and the range of F is $(-\infty, +\infty)$.

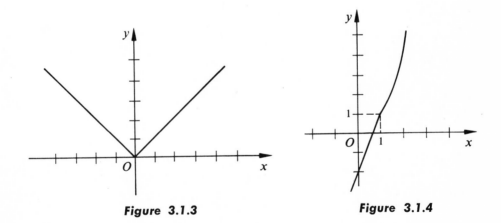

Figure 3.1.3   **Figure 3.1.4**

EXAMPLE 5: Let G be the function which is the set of all ordered pairs (x,y) such that

$$y = \frac{x^2 - 9}{x - 3}$$

Find the domain and range of G, and draw a sketch of the graph of G.

Solution: A sketch of the graph is shown in Fig. 3.1.5. Since a value for y is determined for each value of x except $x = 3$, the domain of G consists of all real numbers except 3. When $x = 3$, both the numerator and denominator are zero, and $0/0$ is undefined.

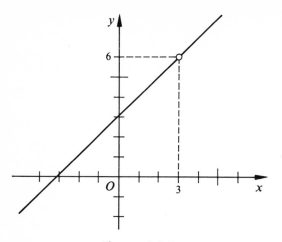

Figure 3.1.5

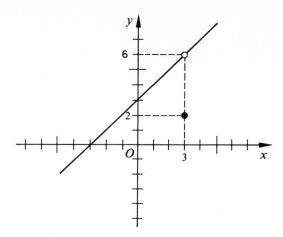

Figure 3.1.6

Factoring the numerator into $(x - 3)(x + 3)$, we get

$$y = \frac{(x - 3)(x + 3)}{(x - 3)}$$

or $y = x + 3$, provided that $x \neq 3$. In other words, the function G consists of all ordered pairs (x,y) such that

$$y = x + 3 \qquad \text{and} \qquad x \neq 3$$

The range of G consists of all real numbers except 6. The graph consists of all points on the line $y = x + 3$ except the point $(3,6)$.

EXAMPLE 6: Let H be the function which is the set of all ordered pairs (x,y) such that

$$y = \begin{cases} x + 3 & \text{if } x \neq 3 \\ 2 & \text{if } x = 3 \end{cases}$$

Find the domain and range of H, and draw a sketch of the graph of H.

   Solution: A sketch of the graph of this function is shown in Fig. 3.1.6. The graph consists of the point $(3,2)$ and all points on the line $y = x + 3$ except the point $(3,6)$. Function H is defined for all values of x, and therefore the domain of H is $(-\infty, +\infty)$. The range of H consists of all real numbers except 6.

EXAMPLE 7: Let ϕ be the function which is the set of all ordered pairs (x,y) such that

$$y = \frac{(x^2 + 3x - 4)(x^2 - 9)}{(x^2 + x - 12)(x + 3)}$$

Find the domain and range of ϕ, and draw a sketch of the graph of ϕ.

   Solution: A sketch of the graph of this function is shown in Fig. 3.1.7. Factoring the numerator and denominator, we obtain

$$y = \frac{(x + 4)(x - 1)(x - 3)(x + 3)}{(x + 4)(x - 3)(x + 3)}$$

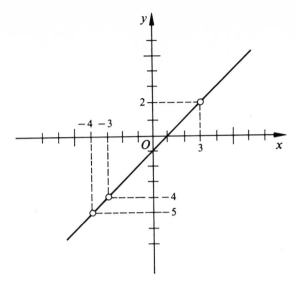

Figure 3.1.7

We see that the denominator is zero for $x = -4, -3$, and 3; therefore, ϕ is undefined for these three values of x. For values of $x \neq -4, -3$, or 3, we may divide numerator and denominator by the common factors and obtain

$$y = x - 1 \qquad \text{if } x \neq -4, -3, \text{ or } 3$$

Therefore, the domain of ϕ is the set of all real numbers except $-4, -3$, and 3, and the range of ϕ is the set of all real numbers except those values of $(x - 1)$ obtained by replacing x by $-4, -3$, or 3; that is, all real numbers except $-5, -4$, and 2. The graph of this function is the straight line $y = x - 1$, with the points $(-4, -5), (-3, -4)$, and $(3, 2)$ deleted.

EXAMPLE 8: Let f be the function which is the set of all ordered pairs (x,y) such that

$$y = \begin{cases} x^2 & \text{if } x \neq 2 \\ 7 & \text{if } x = 2 \end{cases}$$

Find the domain and range of f, and draw a sketch of the graph of f.

Solution: A sketch of the graph of f is shown in Fig. 3.1.8. The graph consists of the point $(2,7)$ and all points on the parabola $y = x^2$, except the point $(2,4)$. Function f is defined for all values of x, and so the domain of f is $(-\infty, +\infty)$. The range of f consists of all nonnegative real numbers.

EXAMPLE 9: Let h be the function which is the set of all ordered pairs (x,y) such that

$$y = \begin{cases} x - 1 & \text{if } x < 3 \\ 2x + 1 & \text{if } 3 \leq x \end{cases}$$

Find the domain and range of h, and draw a sketch of the graph of h.

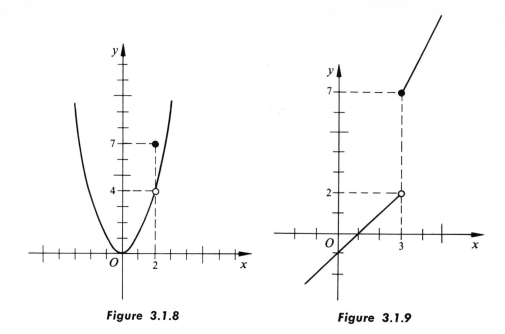

Figure 3.1.8   **Figure 3.1.9**

Solution: A sketch of the graph of h is shown in Fig. 3.1.9. The domain of h is $(-\infty, +\infty)$. The values of y are either less than 2 or greater than or equal to 7. So, the range of h is $(-\infty, 2)$ and $[7, +\infty)$, or equivalently, all real numbers not in $[2, 7)$.

Exercises 3.1

In each of the following exercises, the function is the set of all ordered pairs (x, y) satisfying the given equation. Find the domain and range of the function, and draw a sketch of the graph of the function.

1. f: $y = 3x - 1$

2. g: $y = x^2 + 2$

3. F: $y = 3x^2 - 6$

4. G: $y = \sqrt{x + 1}$

5. h: $y = \sqrt{3x - 4}$

6. f: $y = \sqrt{4 - x^2}$

7. g: $y = \sqrt{x^2 - 4}$

8. H: $y = |x - 3|$

9. ϕ: $y = |3x + 2|$

10. F: $y = \dfrac{4x^2 - 1}{2x + 1}$

11. G: $y = \begin{cases} -2 & \text{if } x \le 3 \\ 2 & \text{if } 3 < x \end{cases}$

12. h: $y = \begin{cases} -4 & \text{if } x < -2 \\ -1 & \text{if } -2 \le x \le 2 \\ 3 & \text{if } 2 < x \end{cases}$

13. f: $y = \begin{cases} 2x - 1 & \text{if } x \ne 2 \\ 0 & \text{if } x = 2 \end{cases}$

14. ϕ: $y = \begin{cases} \sqrt{25 - x^2} & \text{if } x \le 5 \\ x - 5 & \text{if } 5 < x \end{cases}$

15. H: $y = \begin{cases} x^2 - 4 & \text{if } x < 3 \\ 2x - 1 & \text{if } 3 \le x \end{cases}$ 16. g: $y = \begin{cases} 6x + 7 & \text{if } x \le -2 \\ 4 - x & \text{if } -2 < x \end{cases}$

17. F: $y = \dfrac{(x + 1)(x^2 + 3x - 10)}{x^2 + 6x + 5}$

18. G: $y = \dfrac{(x^2 + 3x - 4)(x^2 - 5x + 6)}{(x^2 - 3x + 2)(x - 3)}$

19. f: $y = \sqrt{x^2 - 3x - 4}$

20. h: $y = \sqrt{6x^2 - 5x - 4}$

21. g: $y = \dfrac{x^3 - 2x^2}{x - 2}$

22. f: $y = \dfrac{x^3 - x^2 - 13x - 3}{x + 3}$

23. h: $y = \dfrac{x^3 + 9x^2 + 27x + 35}{x + 5}$

24. F: $y = \dfrac{x^4 - 3x^3 - 11x^2 + 23x + 6}{x^2 + x - 6}$

(3.2)   Function notation and operations on functions

If f is the function having as its domain the values of x and as its range the values of y, we shall use the symbol $f(x)$ (read "f of x") to denote the particular value of y that corresponds to the value of x. Therefore, in Example 1 of Sec. 3.1, we may write $f(x) = \sqrt{5 - x}$; since when $x = 1$, $\sqrt{5 - x} = 2$, we write $f(1) = 2$. Similarly, $f(-6) = \sqrt{11}$, $f(0) = \sqrt{5}$, etc. In Example 2 of Sec. 3.1, since the function is denoted by g, we would use the symbol $g(x)$ to denote the function value corresponding to x, and thus we have $g(-5) = -3$, $g(0) = 1$, $g(2) = 1$, $g(17) = 4$, etc.

When defining a function, the domain of the independent variable must be given, either explicitly stated, or implied. For example, if we are given

$$f(x) = 3x^2 - 5x + 2$$

it is implied that x may be any real number. However, if we are given

$$f(x) = 3x^2 - 5x + 2 \qquad 1 \le x \le 10$$

then the domain of f consists of all real numbers between and including 1 and 10.

Similarly, if g is defined by the equation

$$g(x) = \frac{5x - 2}{x + 4}$$

it is implied that $x \ne -4$, since the quotient is undefined for $x = -4$; hence the domain of g is the set of all real numbers except -4.

If we are given

$$h(x) = \sqrt{9 - x^2}$$

it is implied that x is in the closed interval $-3 \le x \le 3$, since $\sqrt{9 - x^2}$ is undefined (i.e., not a real number) for $x > 3$ or $x < -3$. So, the domain of h is $[-3, +3]$, and the range of h is $[0,3]$.

EXAMPLE 1: Given that f is the function defined by $f(x) = x^2 + 3x - 4$, find:

(a) $f(0)$ (e) $f(2x)$
(b) $f(2)$ (f) $f(x + h)$
(c) $f(h)$ (g) $f(x) + f(h)$
(d) $f(2h)$

Solution:

(a) $f(0) = 0^2 + 3 \cdot 0 - 4 = -4$
(b) $f(2) = 2^2 + 3 \cdot 2 - 4 = 6$
(c) $f(h) = h^2 + 3h - 4$
(d) $f(2h) = (2h)^2 + 3(2h) - 4 = 4h^2 + 6h - 4$
(e) $f(2x) = (2x)^2 + 3(2x) - 4 = 4x^2 + 6x - 4$
(f) $f(x + h) = (x + h)^2 + 3(x + h) - 4 = x^2 + 2hx + h^2 + 3x + 3h - 4$
$$= x^2 + (2h + 3)x + (h^2 + 3h - 4)$$
(g) $f(x) + f(h) = (x^2 + 3x - 4) + (h^2 + 3h - 4) = x^2 + 3x + (h^2 + 3h - 8)$

EXAMPLE 2: Given $g(x) = \sqrt{3x - 1}$, find:

$$\frac{g(x + h) - g(x)}{h} \qquad h \ne 0$$

Solution:

$$\frac{g(x + h) - g(x)}{h} = \frac{\sqrt{3(x + h) - 1} - \sqrt{3x - 1}}{h}$$

$$= \frac{(\sqrt{3x + 3h - 1} - \sqrt{3x - 1})(\sqrt{3x + 3h - 1} + \sqrt{3x - 1})}{h(\sqrt{3x + 3h - 1} + \sqrt{3x - 1})}$$

$$= \frac{(3x + 3h - 1) - (3x - 1)}{h(\sqrt{3x + 3h - 1} + \sqrt{3x - 1})}$$

$$= \frac{3h}{h(\sqrt{3x + 3h - 1} + \sqrt{3x - 1})}$$

$$= \frac{3}{\sqrt{3x + 3h - 1} + \sqrt{3x - 1}}$$

In the second step of the above solution, we multiplied numerator and denominator by the conjugate of the numerator in order to rationalize the numerator, and this gave us a common factor of h in the numerator and the denominator.

We shall now consider operations (i.e., addition, subtraction, multiplication, division) on functions. The functions obtained from these operations — called the sum, the difference, the product, and the quotient of the original functions — are defined as follows.

3.2.1 DEFINITION   Given the two functions f and g:

    (i)   Their *sum*, denoted by $(f + g)$, is the function defined by $(f + g)(x) = f(x) + g(x)$.

    (ii)   Their *difference*, denoted by $(f - g)$, is the function defined by $(f - g)(x) = f(x) - g(x)$.

    (iii)   Their *product*, denoted by $(f \cdot g)$, is the function defined by $(f \cdot g)(x) = f(x) \cdot g(x)$.

    (iv)   Their *quotient*, denoted by (f/g), is the function defined by $(f/g)(x) = f(x)/g(x)$.

In each case the *domain* of the resulting function consists of those values of x common to the domains of f and g, with the exception that in case (iv) the values of x for which $g(x) = 0$ are excluded.

EXAMPLE 3: Given that f is the function defined by $f(x) = \sqrt{x + 1}$ and g is the function defined by $g(x) = \sqrt{x - 4}$, find:

    (a) $(f + g)(x)$ (c) $(f \cdot g)(x)$

    (b) $(f - g)(x)$ (d) $(f/g)(x)$

In each case, determine the domain of the resulting function.

Solution:

    (a) $(f + g)(x) = \sqrt{x + 1} + \sqrt{x - 4}$

    (b) $(f - g)(x) = \sqrt{x + 1} - \sqrt{x - 4}$

    (c) $(f \cdot g)(x) = \sqrt{x + 1} \cdot \sqrt{x - 4}$

    (d) $(f/g)(x) = \dfrac{\sqrt{x + 1}}{\sqrt{x - 4}}$

The domain of f is $[-1, +\infty)$, and the domain of g is $[4, +\infty)$. So, in parts (a), (b), and (c) the domain of the resulting function is $[4, +\infty)$. In part (d) the denominator is zero when $x = 4$; thus 4 is excluded from the domain, and the domain is therefore $(4, +\infty)$.

To indicate the product of a function f multiplied by itself, or $f \cdot f$, we write f^2. For example, if f is defined by $f(x) = 3x$, then f^2 is the function defined by $f^2(x) = (3x)(3x) = 9x^2$.

In addition to combining two functions by the operations given in Definition 3.2.1, we shall consider the *composite function* of two given functions.

3.2.2 DEFINITION   Given the two functions f and g, the *composite function*, denoted by $f \circ g$, is defined by

$$(f \circ g)(x) = f(g(x))$$

and the domain of $f \circ g$ is the set of all numbers x in the domain of g, such that $g(x)$ is in the domain of f.

EXAMPLE 4: Given that f is defined by $f(x) = \sqrt{x}$ and g is defined by $g(x) = 2x - 3$, find $F(x)$ if $F = f \circ g$, and find the domain of F.

Solution:
$$F(x) = (f \circ g)(x) = f(g(x))$$
$$= f(2x - 3)$$
$$= \sqrt{2x - 3}$$

The domain of g is $(-\infty, +\infty)$, and the domain of f is $[0, +\infty)$. So the domain of F is the set of real numbers for which $2x - 3 \geq 0$, or equivalently, $[3/2, +\infty)$.

EXAMPLE 5: Given that f is defined by $f(x) = \sqrt{x}$ and g is defined by $g(x) = x^2 - 1$, find: (a) $f \circ f$; (b) $g \circ g$; (c) $f \circ g$; (d) $g \circ f$. Also find the domain of the composite function in each part.

Solution: The domain of f is $[0, +\infty)$, and the domain of g is $(-\infty, +\infty)$.

(a) $(f \circ f)(x) = f(f(x)) = f(\sqrt{x}) = \sqrt{\sqrt{x}} = \sqrt[4]{x}$
   The domain of $f \circ f$ is $[0, +\infty)$.

(b) $(g \circ g)(x) = g(g(x)) = g(x^2 - 1) = (x^2 - 1)^2 - 1 = x^4 - 2x^2$
   The domain of $g \circ g$ is $(-\infty, +\infty)$.

(c) $(f \circ g)(x) = f(g(x)) = f(x^2 - 1) = \sqrt{x^2 - 1}$
   The domain of $f \circ g$ consists of the two intervals $(-\infty, -1]$ and $[1, +\infty)$, or equivalently, all x not in $(-1, 1)$.

(d) $(g \circ f)(x) = g(f(x)) = g(\sqrt{x}) = (\sqrt{x})^2 - 1 = x - 1$
   The domain of $g \circ f$ is $[0, +\infty)$. Note that even though $x - 1$ is defined for all values of x, the domain of $g \circ f$, by Definition 3.2.2, is the set of all numbers x in the domain of f such that $f(x)$ is in the domain of g.

Exercises 3.2

1. Given $f(x) = 2x^2 + 5x - 3$, find:

   (a) $f(-2)$

   (b) $f(-1)$

   (c) $f(0)$

   (d) $f(3)$

   (e) $f(h + 1)$

   (f) $f(2x^2)$

   (g) $f(x^2 - 3)$

   (h) $f(x + h)$

   (i) $f(x) + f(h)$

   (j) $\dfrac{f(x + h) - f(x)}{h}, h \neq 0$

2. Given $g(x) = 3x^2 - 4$, find:

   (a) $g(-4)$

   (b) $g(\frac{1}{2})$

   (c) $g(x^2)$

   (d) $g(3x^2 - 4)$

   (e) $g(x - h)$

   (f) $g(x) - g(h)$

   (g) $\dfrac{g(x + h) - g(x)}{h}, h \neq 0$

3. Given $F(x) = \sqrt{2x + 3}$, find:

   (a) $F(-1)$ (d) $F(30)$

   (b) $F(4)$ (e) $F(2x + 3)$

   (c) $F(\tfrac{1}{2})$ (f) $\dfrac{F(x + h) - F(x)}{h}, h \neq 0$

4. Given $G(x) = \sqrt{2x^2 + 1}$, find:

   (a) $G(-2)$ (d) $G(4/7)$

   (b) $G(0)$ (e) $G(2x^2 - 1)$

   (c) $G(1/5)$ (f) $\dfrac{G(x + h) - G(x)}{h}, h \neq 0$

In Exercises 5 through 10, the functions f and g are defined. In each problem define the following functions and determine the domain of the resulting function: $(a) f + g$; $(b) f - g$; $(c) f \cdot g$; $(d) f/g$; $(e) g/f$; $(f) f \circ g$; $(g) g \circ f$.

5. $f(x) = x - 5$; $g(x) = x^2 - 1$

6. $f(x) = \sqrt{x}$; $g(x) = x^2 + 1$

7. $f(x) = \dfrac{x + 1}{x - 1}$; $g(x) = \dfrac{1}{x}$

8. $f(x) = \sqrt{x - 2}$; $g(x) = \dfrac{1}{x}$

9. $f(x) = \sqrt{x^2 - 1}$; $g(x) = \sqrt{x - 1}$

10. $f(x) = |x|$; $g(x) = |x - 3|$

11. g is the function defined by $g(x) = x^2$. (a) If $x \geq 0$, define a function f such that $(f \circ g)(x) = x$. (b) If $x < 0$, define a function f such that $(f \circ g)(x) = x$.

Use the following definition for Exercises 12 through 16: A function f is said to be an *even* function if for every x in the domain of f, $f(-x) = f(x)$; and f is said to be an *odd* function if for every x in the domain of f, $f(-x) = -f(x)$ — it being understood that $-x$ is in the domain of f whenever x is.

12. For each of the following functions, determine whether f is even, odd, or neither.

   (a) $f(x) = 2x^4 - 3x^2 + 1$ (e) $f(x) = 5x^7 + 1$

   (b) $f(x) = 5x^3 - 7x$ (f) $f(x) = |x|$

   (c) $f(x) = x^2 + 2x + 2$ (g) $f(x) = \dfrac{x^3 - x}{x^2 + 1}$

   (d) $f(x) = x^6 - 1$ (h) $f(x) = \dfrac{x - 1}{x + 1}$

13. Prove that if f and g are both odd functions, then $(f + g)$ and $(f - g)$ are also odd functions.

14. Prove that if f and g are both odd functions, then $f \cdot g$ and f/g are both even functions.

15. Determine whether the composite function $f \circ g$ is odd or even in each of the following cases: *(a)* f and g are both even; *(b)* f and g are both odd; *(c)* f is even and g is odd; *(d)* f is odd and g is even.

16. There is one function that is both even and odd. What is it?

$$f(x) = 0$$

(3.3)   Types of functions and some special functions

If the range of a function f consists of only one number, then f is called a *constant function.* So if $f(x) = c$, and if c is any real number, then f is a constant function and its graph is a straight line parallel to the x axis at a directed distance of c units from the x axis.

If a function f is defined by

$$f(x) = a_0x^n + a_1x^{n-1} + a_2x^{n-2} + \cdots + a_{n-1}x + a_n$$

where n is a nonnegative integer, and $a_0, a_1, \ldots, a_n$ are real numbers, $a_0 \neq 0$, then f is called a *polynomial function* of degree n. Thus the function f defined by

$$f(x) = 3x^5 - x^2 + 7x - 1$$

is a polynomial function of degree 5.

If the degree of a polynomial function is 1, then the function is called a *linear function;* if the degree is 2, the function is called a *quadratic function;* and if the degree is 3, the function is called a *cubic function.* So the function f defined by

$$f(x) = 3x + 4$$

is a linear function. The function g defined by

$$g(x) = 5x^2 - 8x + 1$$

is a quadratic function. The function h defined by

$$h(x) = 8x^3 - x + 4$$

is a cubic function. If the degree of a polynomial function is zero, the function is a constant function.

The general linear function is defined by

$$f(x) = mx + b$$

where m and b are constants and $m \neq 0$. The graph of this function is a straight line having m as its slope and b as its y intercept.

The particular linear function defined by

$$f(x) = x$$

is called the *identity function.* The general quadratic function is defined by

$$f(x) = ax^2 + bx + c$$

where a, b, and c are constants and $a \neq 0$. The graph of the quadratic function is a parabola, which opens upward if $a > 0$ and downward if $a < 0$.

If a function can be expressed as the quotient of two polynomial functions, the function is called a *rational function*. For example, the function f defined by

$$f(x) = \frac{x^3 - x^2 + 5}{x^2 - 9}$$

is a rational function, for which the domain is the set of all real numbers except 3 and -3.

An *algebraic function* is a function formed by a finite number of algebraic operations on the identity function and the constant function. These algebraic operations include addition, subtraction, multiplication, division, raising to powers, and extracting square roots. An example of an algebraic function is the function f defined by

$$f(x) = \frac{(x^2 - 3x + 1)^3}{\sqrt{x^4 + 1}}$$

In addition to algebraic functions, we consider *transcendental functions* in elementary calculus. Examples of transcendental functions are trigonometric functions, inverse trigonometric functions, logarithmic functions, and exponential functions. These functions will be discussed in later chapters. The following examples illustrate some special functions.

EXAMPLE 1: Given the function f defined by

$$f(x) = 5n \qquad \text{if } n - 1 < x \leq n$$

where n is a positive integer. This function is called the *postage function*. Draw a sketch of the graph of this function.

Solution: The graph of function f is the graph of $y = 5n$, if $n - 1 < x \leq n$, where n is a positive integer. Therefore,

$$\begin{aligned}
y &= 5 && \text{if } 0 < x \leq 1 \\
y &= 10 && \text{if } 1 < x \leq 2 \\
y &= 15 && \text{if } 2 < x \leq 3 \\
y &= 20 && \text{if } 3 < x \leq 4 \qquad \text{etc.}
\end{aligned}$$

The graph is sketched in Fig. 3.3.1.

In the following example, the symbol $[\![x]\!]$ is used. $[\![x]\!]$ is defined to be the greatest integer which is less than or equal to x. Therefore, $[\![1]\!] = 1$, $[\![1.3]\!] = 1$, $[\![1/2]\!] = 0$, $[\![-4.2]\!] = -5$, $[\![-8]\!] = -8$, $[\![9.8]\!] = 9$. The function F defined by $F(x) = [\![x]\!]$ is called the *greatest integer function*.

EXAMPLE 2: F is the greatest integer function, defined by $F(x) = [\![x]\!] = n$, if $n \leq x < n + 1$, where n is an integer. Draw a sketch of the graph of F. State the domain and range of F.

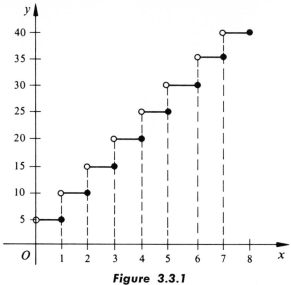

Figure 3.3.1

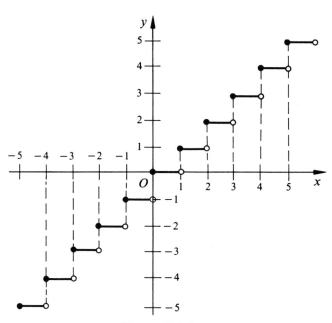

Figure 3.3.2

Solution: A sketch of the graph is shown in Fig. 3.3.2, where $y = [\![x]\!]$.

$$-5 \leq x < -4 \qquad [\![x]\!] = -5$$
$$-4 \leq x < -3 \qquad [\![x]\!] = -4$$
$$-3 \leq x < -2 \qquad [\![x]\!] = -3$$
$$-2 \leq x < -1 \qquad [\![x]\!] = -2$$

$$-1 \leq x < 0 \qquad [\![x]\!] = -1$$
$$0 \leq x < 1 \qquad [\![x]\!] = 0$$
$$1 \leq x < 2 \qquad [\![x]\!] = 1$$
$$2 \leq x < 3 \qquad [\![x]\!] = 2$$
$$3 \leq x < 4 \qquad [\![x]\!] = 3$$
$$4 \leq x < 5 \qquad [\![x]\!] = 4$$

The domain of F is the set of all real numbers. The range of F consists of all the integers.

EXAMPLE 3: G is the function defined by $G(x) = [\![x]\!] - x$. Draw a sketch of the graph of G. State the domain and range of G.
Solution:

If $0 \leq x < 1$, $[\![x]\!] = 0$; so $G(x) = -x$.

If $1 \leq x < 2$, $[\![x]\!] = 1$; so $G(x) = 1 - x$.

If $2 \leq x < 3$, $[\![x]\!] = 2$; so $G(x) = 2 - x$.

If $-1 \leq x < 0$, $[\![x]\!] = -1$; so $G(x) = -1 - x$.

etc.

A sketch of the graph is shown in Fig. 3.3.3. The domain of G is the set of all real numbers, and the range of G is $(-1,0]$.

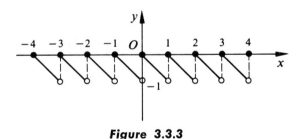

Figure 3.3.3

Exercises 3.3

For each of the functions in the following exercises, draw a sketch of the graph and state the domain and range. In Exercises 2 through 7, the function U is the unit step function defined in Exercise 1.

1. U is the function defined by $U(t) = \begin{cases} 0 & \text{if } t < 0 \\ 1 & \text{if } t \geq 0 \end{cases}$

This function U is called the *unit step function.*

2. $f(x) = U(x - 1)$

3. $g(x) = U(x) - U(x - 1)$

4. $F(t) = U(t^2 - 9)$

5. $h(x) = x \cdot U(x)$

6. $f(t) = (t + 1) \cdot U(t + 1)$

7. $G(t) = (t + 1) \cdot U(t + 1) - t \cdot U(t)$

8. $f(x) = |x| + |x - 1|$

9. $g(x) = |x| \cdot |x - 1|$

10. $F(x) = [[x + 2]]$

11. $G(x) = x - [[x]]$

12. $H(x) = |x| + [[x]]$

13. $h(x) = [[x^2]]$

14. $f(x) = (x - [[x]])^2$

15. $g(x) = \dfrac{[[x]]}{|x|}$

16. $h(x) = \dfrac{|x|}{[[x]]}$

17. $f(x) = 2 + (-1)^n$, where $n = [[x]]$

4 Limits

(4.1)   The limit of a function

Let us consider the function f defined by the equation

(1) $$f(x) = \frac{(2x + 3)(x - 1)}{(x - 1)}$$

The function f is defined for all values of x except $x = 1$. Furthermore, if $x \neq 1$, we may divide numerator and denominator by $(x - 1)$ and obtain

(2) $$f(x) = 2x + 3 \qquad x \neq 1$$

Let us investigate the function values, $f(x)$, when x is close to 1 but not equal to 1. First, let x take on the values 0, 0.25, 0.50, 0.75, 0.9, 0.99, 0.999, 0.9999, etc. We are taking values of x closer and closer to 1, but less than 1; in other words, the variable x is approaching 1, through values that are less than 1. We illustrate this in Table 4.1.1.

Table 4.1.1

x	0	0.25	0.5	0.75	0.9	0.99	0.999	0.9999	0.99999
$f(x) = 2x + 3$ $(x \neq 1)$	3	3.5	4	4.5	4.8	4.98	4.998	4.9998	4.99998

Now, let the variable x approach 1, through values that are greater than 1; that is, let x take on the values 2, 1.75, 1.5, 1.25, 1.1, 1.01, 1.001, 1.0001, 1.00001, etc. This is illustrated in Table 4.1.2.

Table 4.1.2

x	2	1.75	1.5	1.25	1.1	1.01	1.001	1.0001	1.00001
$f(x) = 2x + 3$ $(x \neq 1)$	7	6.5	6.0	5.5	5.2	5.02	5.002	5.0002	5.00002

We see from both tables that as x gets closer and closer to 1, $f(x)$ gets closer and closer to 5; and the closer x is to 1, the closer $f(x)$ is to 5. For instance, from Table 4.1.1, when $x = 0.9$, $f(x) = 4.8$; that is, when x is 0.1 less than 1, $f(x)$ is 0.2 less than 5. When $x = 0.999$, $f(x) = 4.998$; or when x is 0.001 less than 1, $f(x)$ is 0.002 less than 5. Furthermore, when $x = 0.9999$, $f(x) = 0.49998$; or when x is 0.0001 less than 1, $f(x)$ is 0.0002 less than 5.

From Table 4.1.2, we see that when $x = 1.1$, $f(x) = 5.2$; or when x is 0.1 greater than 1, $f(x)$ is 0.2 greater than 5. When $x = 1.001$, $f(x) = 5.002$; or when x is 0.001 greater than 1, $f(x)$ is 0.002 greater than 5. When $x = 1.0001$, $f(x) = 5.0002$; or when x is 0.0001 greater than 1, $f(x)$ is 0.0002 greater than 5.

Therefore, from the two tables, we see that when x differs from 1 by ± 0.001 (that is, $x = 0.999$ or $x = 1.001$), then $f(x)$ differs from 5 by ± 0.002 [that is, $f(x) = 4.998$ or $f(x) = 5.002$]. And when x differs from 1 by ± 0.0001, $f(x)$ differs from 5 by ± 0.0002.

Now, looking at the situation another way, we consider the values of $f(x)$ first. We see that we can make the value of $f(x)$ as close to 5 as we please by taking x close enough to 1. Another way of saying this is that we can make the absolute value of the difference between $f(x)$ and 5 as small as we please by making the absolute value of the difference between x and 1 small enough. That is, $|f(x) - 5|$ can be made as small as we please by making $|x - 1|$ small enough.

A more precise way of noting this is by using two symbols for these small differences. The symbols usually used are ϵ (epsilon) and δ (delta). So, we state: $|f(x) - 5|$ will be less than ϵ whenever $|x - 1|$ is less than δ and $|x - 1| \neq 0$ (since $x \neq 1$). It is important to realize that in general the size of δ will depend upon the size of ϵ. Still another way of phrasing this is: Given any positive number ϵ, we can make $|f(x) - 5| < \epsilon$ by taking $|x - 1|$ small enough; that is, there is some sufficiently small positive number δ such that

(3) $\qquad |f(x) - 5| < \epsilon \qquad$ whenever $\qquad 0 < |x - 1| < \delta$

We see from the two tables that $|f(x) - 5| = 0.2$ when $|x - 1| = 0.1$. So, given $\epsilon = 0.2$, we take $\delta = 0.1$ and say that

$$|f(x) - 5| < 0.2 \qquad \text{whenever} \qquad 0 < |x - 1| < 0.1$$

This is statement (3), with $\epsilon = 0.2$ and $\delta = 0.1$.

Also, $|f(x) - 5| = 0.002$ when $|x - 1| = 0.001$. Hence if $\epsilon = 0.002$, we take $\delta = 0.001$, and then

$$|f(x) - 5| < 0.002 \qquad \text{whenever} \qquad 0 < |x - 1| < 0.001$$

This is statement (3), with $\epsilon = 0.002$ and $\delta = 0.001$.

Similarly, if $\epsilon = 0.0002$, we take $\delta = 0.0001$ and state that

$$|f(x) - 5| < 0.0002 \qquad \text{whenever} \qquad 0 < |x - 1| < 0.0001$$

This is statement (3), with $\epsilon = 0.0002$ and $\delta = 0.0001$.

We could go on and give ϵ any small positive value, and find a suitable value for δ such that $|f(x) - 5|$ will be less than ϵ whenever $|x - 1|$ is less than δ and

$x \neq 1$ (or $|x - 1| > 0$). Now, since for any $\epsilon > 0$, we can find a $\delta > 0$ such that $|f(x) - 5| < \epsilon$ whenever $0 < |x - 1| < \delta$, we say that the limit of $f(x)$ as x approaches 1 is equal to 5, or expressed in symbols:

(4) $$\lim_{x \to 1} f(x) = 5$$

You will note that we state $0 < |x - 1|$. This condition is imposed since we are concerned only with values of $f(x)$ for x close to 1, but not for $x = 1$. As a matter of fact, this function is not defined for $x = 1$.

Let us see what this means geometrically for the particular function defined by equation (1). Figure 4.1.1 illustrates the geometrical significance of ϵ and δ.

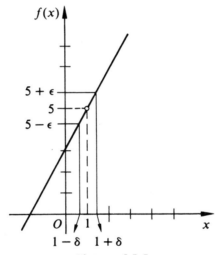

Figure 4.1.1

We see that $f(x)$ on the vertical axis will lie between $5 - \epsilon$ and $5 + \epsilon$ whenever x on the horizontal axis lies between $1 - \delta$ and $1 + \delta$;

or $|f(x) - 5| < \epsilon$ whenever $0 < |x - 1| < \delta$

Another way of stating this is: $f(x)$ on the vertical axis may be restricted to lie between $5 - \epsilon$ and $5 + \epsilon$ by restricting x on the horizontal axis to lie between $1 - \delta$ and $1 + \delta$.

It should be noted that the values of ϵ are chosen arbitrarily and may be as small as desired, and that the value of a δ is dependent upon the ϵ chosen. It also should be pointed out that the smaller the value of ϵ, the smaller will be the corresponding value of δ.

Summing up for this example, we say that $\lim_{x \to 1} f(x) = 5$, since for any $\epsilon > 0$, however small, there exists a $\delta > 0$, such that

$$|f(x) - 5| < \epsilon \qquad \text{whenever} \qquad 0 < |x - 1| < \delta$$

We are now in a position to define the limit of a function in general.

4.1.1 DEFINITION   Let f be a function which is defined at every number in some open interval I containing a, except possibly at the number a itself. The limit of $f(x)$ as x approaches a is L, written as

(5)
$$\lim_{x \to a} f(x) = L$$

if for any $\epsilon > 0$, however small, there exists a $\delta > 0$ such that

(6) $|f(x) - L| < \epsilon$ whenever $0 < |x - a| < \delta$

In words, Definition 4.1.1 states: the function values $f(x)$ approach a limit L as x approaches a number a, if the absolute value of the difference between $f(x)$ and L can be made as small as we please by taking x sufficiently near a, but not equal to a.

It is important to realize that in the above definition nothing is said about the value of the function when $x = a$. That is, it is not necessary that the function be defined for $x = a$ in order for the $\lim_{x \to a} f(x)$ to exist. This was seen in our example, where

$$\lim_{x \to 1} \frac{(2x + 3)(x - 1)}{(x - 1)} = 5$$

$$\text{but} \quad \frac{(2x + 3)(x - 1)}{(x - 1)}$$

is not defined for $x = 1$. However, the first sentence in Definition 4.1.1 requires that the function f be defined at all numbers except 1 in some open interval containing 1.

We shall now consider some examples of finding a δ which corresponds to a specific ϵ in some simple cases.

EXAMPLE 1: Let the function f be defined by the equation

$$f(x) = 4x - 1$$

Given $\lim_{x \to 3} f(x) = 11$, find a δ for $\epsilon = 0.01$, such that $|f(x) - 11| < 0.01$ whenever $0 < |x - 3| < \delta$.

Solution: $|f(x) - 11| = |(4x - 1) - 11|$

$$= |4x - 12|$$

$$= 4|x - 3|$$

Therefore, we want

$$4|x - 3| < 0.01 \quad \text{whenever} \quad 0 < |x - 3| < \delta$$

or $|x - 3| < 0.0025$ whenever $0 < |x - 3| < \delta$

If we take $\delta = 0.0025$, we have

(7) $|(4x - 1) - 11| < 0.01$ whenever $0 < |x - 3| < 0.0025$

It is important to realize that in this example, any positive number less than 0.0025 may be used in place of 0.0025 as the required δ. That is, if $0 < \gamma < 0.0025$ and statement (7) holds, then

$$|(4x - 1) - 11| < 0.01 \qquad \text{whenever} \qquad 0 < |x - 3| < \gamma$$

since every number x satisfying the inequality $0 < |x - 3| < \gamma$ also satisfies the inequality $0 < |x - 3| < 0.0025$.

The solution of the above example consisted of finding a δ for a specific ϵ. If we find a δ that will work for *any* ϵ, we shall have established that the value of the limit is 11. We do this in Example 2.

EXAMPLE 2: Let the function f be defined by the equation $f(x) = 4x - 1$ and, using Definition 4.1.1, prove that

$$\lim_{x \to 3} (4x - 1) = 11$$

Solution: We wish to show, that for any $\epsilon > 0$, there exists a $\delta > 0$ such that

$$|(4x - 1) - 11| < \epsilon \qquad \text{whenever} \qquad 0 < |x - 3| < \delta$$

From the previous example, we note that

$$|(4x - 1) - 11| = |4x - 12|$$
$$= 4|x - 3|$$

Therefore, we want

$$4|x - 3| < \epsilon \qquad \text{whenever} \qquad 0 < |x - 3| < \delta$$

So, if we take $\delta = \epsilon/4$, we have

$$4|x - 3| < 4\delta \qquad \text{whenever} \qquad 0 < |x - 3| < \delta$$

$$\text{or} \qquad 4|x - 3| < 4\frac{\epsilon}{4} \qquad \text{whenever} \qquad 0 < |x - 3| < \delta$$

$$\text{or} \qquad 4|x - 3| < \epsilon \qquad \text{whenever} \qquad 0 < |x - 3| < \delta$$

giving us

$$|(4x - 1) - 11| < \epsilon \qquad \text{whenever} \qquad 0 < |x - 3| < \delta$$

if $\delta = \epsilon/4$. This proves that $\lim_{x \to 3} (4x - 1) = 11$.

In particular, if $\epsilon = 0.01$, then we take $\delta = 0.01/4$, or 0.0025, which corresponds to our result in Example 1.

Any positive number $\delta' < \epsilon/4$ may be used in place of $\epsilon/4$ as the required δ in Example 2.

EXAMPLE 3: Using Definition 4.1.1, prove that

$$\lim_{x \to 2} x^2 = 4$$

$f \quad |x^2 - 4| < \epsilon \quad \text{when} \quad |x - 2| < \delta$

Solution: We must show that, for any $\epsilon > 0$, there exists a $\delta > 0$ such that

$$|x^2 - 4| < \epsilon \qquad \text{whenever} \qquad 0 < |x - 2| < \delta$$

Factoring, we get

$$|x^2 - 4| = |x - 2| \cdot |x + 2|$$

We want to show that $|x^2 - 4|$ is small when x is close to 2. To do this, we first find an upper bound for the factor $|x + 2|$. If x is close to 2, we know that the factor $|x - 2|$ is small, and that the factor $|x + 2|$ is close to 4.

Since we are considering values of x close to 2, it may be safely assumed that $|x - 2| < 1$; that is, we are requiring the δ, for which we are looking, to be less than or equal to 1.

The inequality

$$|x - 2| < 1$$

is equivalent to

$$-1 < x - 2 < 1$$

which is equivalent to

$$1 < x < 3$$

$$\text{or} \qquad 3 < x + 2 < 5$$

This says that if $|x - 2| < 1$, then $3 < |x + 2| < 5$, and therefore we have

$$|x^2 - 4| = |x - 2| \cdot |x + 2| < |x - 2| \cdot 5 \qquad \text{whenever} \qquad |x - 2| < 1$$

Now, we want

$$|x - 2| \cdot 5 < \epsilon \qquad \text{or, equivalently,} \qquad |x - 2| < \epsilon/5$$

Thus we take δ as the smaller of 1 and $\epsilon/5$; then, whenever

$$|x - 2| < \epsilon/5 \text{ and } |x + 2| < 5, \text{ we have } |x^2 - 4| < (\epsilon/5) \cdot (5)$$

Therefore,

$$|x^2 - 4| < \epsilon \qquad \text{whenever} \qquad 0 < |x - 2| < \delta$$

if $\delta = \min(1, \epsilon/5)$.

EXAMPLE 4: Using Definition 4.1.1, prove that

$$\lim_{t \to 7} \frac{8}{t - 3} = 2$$

Solution: We must show that, for any $\epsilon > 0$, there exists a $\delta > 0$ such that

$$\left| \frac{8}{t - 3} - 2 \right| < \epsilon \qquad \text{whenever} \qquad 0 < |t - 7| < \delta$$

$$\left| \frac{8}{t - 3} - 2 \right| = \left| \frac{8 - 2(t - 3)}{t - 3} \right|$$

$$= \left| \frac{14 - 2t}{t - 3} \right|$$

$$= \frac{2 \cdot |7 - t|}{|t - 3|}$$

$$= |t - 7| \cdot \frac{2}{|t - 3|}$$

We wish to show that $|8/(t - 3) - 2|$ is small when t is close to 7. We proceed to find some upper bound for the fraction $2/|t - 3|$. If t is close to 7, the factor $|t - 7|$ is small. Since t is close to 7, we take $|t - 7| < 1$, which requires that δ be less than or equal to 1.

$|t - 7| < 1$ is equivalent to $-1 < t - 7 < 1$, or $6 < t < 8$, or $3 < t - 3 < 5$, or $|t - 3| > 3$. Therefore, we have $|8/(t - 3) - 2| = |t - 7| \cdot (2/|t - 3|) < |t - 7| \cdot (2/3)$ whenever $|t - 7| < 1$ (since then $|t - 3| > 3$). Now, we want

$$|t - 7| \cdot (2/3) < \epsilon \qquad \text{or} \qquad |t - 7| < (3/2) \epsilon$$

Consequently, we take δ as the minimum of 1 and $(3/2) \epsilon$, which assures us that whenever $|t - 7| < \delta$, then $|t - 7| < (3/2) \epsilon$ and $|t - 3| > 3$ (since this is true when $|t - 7| < 1$). This gives us

$$\left| \frac{8}{t - 3} - 2 \right| < |t - 7| \cdot \frac{2}{3} < \frac{3}{2}\epsilon \cdot \frac{2}{3}$$

$$\text{or} \qquad \left| \frac{8}{t - 3} - 2 \right| < \epsilon$$

whenever $0 < |t - 7| < \delta$, and where $\delta = \min [1, (3/2)\epsilon]$. We have therefore proved that $\lim_{t \to 7} [8/(t - 3)] = 2$.

Exercises 4.1

In Exercises 1 through 8, we are given $f(x)$, a, and L, as well as $\lim_{x \to a} f(x) = L$. Determine a number δ for the given ϵ such that $|f(x) - L| < \epsilon$ whenever $0 < |x - a| < \delta$.

1. $\lim_{x \to 3} (2x + 4) = 10;\ \epsilon = 0.01$

2. $\lim_{x \to 2} (4x - 5) = 3;\ \epsilon = 0.001$

3. $\lim_{x \to -1} (3 - 4x) = 7;\ \epsilon = 0.02$

4. $\lim_{x \to -2} (2 + 5x) = -8;\ \epsilon = 0.002$

5. $\lim_{x \to 3} x^2 = 9;\ \epsilon = 0.005$

6. $\lim_{x \to 4} \sqrt{x} = 2;\ \epsilon = 0.005$

7. $\lim_{x \to -2} \dfrac{x^2 - 4}{x + 2} = -4;\ \epsilon = 0.01$

8. $\lim_{x \to 1/3} \dfrac{9x^2 - 1}{3x - 1} = 2;\ \epsilon = 0.01$

In Exercises 9 through 27, establish the limit by using Definition 4.1.1; that is, for any $\epsilon > 0$, find a $\delta > 0$, such that

$$|f(x) - L| < \epsilon \qquad \text{whenever} \qquad 0 < |x - a| < \delta$$

9. $\lim_{x \to 1} (5x - 3) = 2$

10. $\lim_{x \to -2} (7 - 2x) = 11$

11. $\lim_{x \to 3} \dfrac{x^2 - 9}{x - 3} = 6$

12. $\lim_{x \to 4} \dfrac{\sqrt{x} - 2}{x - 4} = \dfrac{1}{4}$

13. $\lim_{x \to 1} x^2 = 1$

14. $\lim_{x \to -3} x^2 = 9$

15. $\lim\limits_{x \to 3} \dfrac{4}{x-1} = 2$

16. $\lim\limits_{x \to 6} \dfrac{x}{x-3} = 2$

17. $\lim\limits_{x \to 5} \dfrac{2}{x-4} = 2$

18. $\lim\limits_{x \to -4} \dfrac{1}{x+3} = -1$

19. $\lim\limits_{x \to 5} (x^2 - 3x) = 10$

20. $\lim\limits_{x \to 2} (x^2 + 2x - 1) = 7$

21. $\lim\limits_{x \to -3} (5 - x - x^2) = -1$

22. $\lim\limits_{x \to 1/2} \dfrac{3 + 2x}{5 - x} = 8/9$

23. Prove that $\lim\limits_{x \to a} x^2 = a^2$ if a is any positive number.

24. Prove that $\lim\limits_{x \to a} x^2 = a^2$ if a is any negative number.

25. Prove that $\lim\limits_{x \to a} \sqrt{x} = \sqrt{a}$ if a is any positive number.

26. Prove that $\lim\limits_{x \to a} \dfrac{1}{x} = \dfrac{1}{a}$ if a is any positive number.

27. Prove that $\lim\limits_{x \to a} \dfrac{1}{x} = \dfrac{1}{a}$ if a is any negative number.

(4.2) Theorems on limits of functions

In order to find limits of functions in a straightforward manner, we shall need some theorems. The proofs of the theorems are based upon Definition 4.1.1. These theorems, as well as other theorems on limits of functions appearing in later sections of this chapter, will be labeled "limit theorems" and will be so designated as they are presented.

4.2.1 LIMIT THEOREM 1   If m and b are any constants,

$$\lim_{x \to a} (mx + b) = ma + b$$

Proof: In order to prove this theorem, we make use of Definition 4.1.1 from the preceding section. For any $\epsilon > 0$, we must prove that there exists a $\delta > 0$ such that

(1) $|(mx + b) - (ma + b)| < \epsilon$ whenever $0 < |x - a| < \delta$

Case 1: $m \neq 0$.

Since, $|(mx + b) - (ma + b)| = |mx - ma| = |m| \cdot |x - a|$, we want to find a $\delta > 0$, for any $\epsilon > 0$, such that

$$|m| \cdot |x - a| < \epsilon \quad \text{whenever} \quad 0 < |x - a| < \delta$$

or, since $m \neq 0$,

(2) $|x - a| < \dfrac{\epsilon}{|m|}$ whenever $0 < |x - a| < \delta$

Statement (2) will hold if we take $\delta = \epsilon/|m|$. So, we conclude that

$$|(mx + b) - (ma + b)| < \epsilon \qquad \text{whenever} \qquad 0 < |x - a| < \delta, \text{ if } \delta = \frac{\epsilon}{|m|}$$

This proves the theorem for Case 1.

Case 2: $m = 0$.

If $m = 0$, then $|(mx + b) - (ma + b)| = 0$ for all values of x. So we take δ to be any positive number, and statement (1) holds. This proves the theorem for Case 2.

4.2.2 LIMIT THEOREM 2   If c is a constant, then for any number a,

$$\lim_{x \to a} c = c$$

Proof: This follows immediately from Limit Theorem 1, by taking $m = 0$ and $b = c$.

4.2.3 LIMIT THEOREM 3 $\lim\limits_{x \to a} x = a.$

Proof: This also follows immediately from Limit Theorem 1, by taking $m = 1$ and $b = 0$.

4.2.4 LIMIT THEOREM 4   If $\lim\limits_{x \to a} f(x) = L$ and $\lim\limits_{x \to a} g(x) = M$, then

$$\lim_{x \to a} [f(x) \pm g(x)] = L \pm M$$

Proof: We shall prove this theorem using the "$+$" sign. Given

(3) $$\lim_{x \to a} f(x) = L$$

and

(4) $$\lim_{x \to a} g(x) = M$$

we wish to prove that

(5) $$\lim_{x \to a} [f(x) + g(x)] = L + M$$

In order to prove equation (5), we must use Definition 4.1.1; that is, for any $\epsilon > 0$, we must prove that there exists a $\delta > 0$ such that

(6) $|(f(x) + g(x)) - (L + M)| < \epsilon \qquad \text{whenever} \qquad 0 < |x - a| < \delta$

Since we are given equation (3), we know from the definition of a limit that for $\epsilon/2 > 0$ there exists a $\delta_1 > 0$ such that

$$|f(x) - L| < \frac{\epsilon}{2} \qquad \text{whenever} \qquad 0 < |x - a| < \delta_1$$

Similarly, from equation (4), for $\epsilon/2 > 0$ there exists a $\delta_2 > 0$ such that

$$|g(x) - M| < \frac{\epsilon}{2} \qquad \text{whenever} \qquad 0 < |x - a| < \delta_2$$

Now, let δ be the smaller of the two numbers δ_1 and δ_2. Therefore $\delta \leq \delta_1$ and $\delta \leq \delta_2$. So we can say

$$|f(x) - L| < \frac{\epsilon}{2} \qquad \text{whenever} \qquad 0 < |x - a| < \delta$$

and

$$|g(x) - M| < \frac{\epsilon}{2} \qquad \text{whenever} \qquad 0 < |x - a| < \delta$$

Hence we have

$$
\begin{aligned}
|(f(x) + g(x)) - (L + M)| &= |(f(x) - L) + (g(x) - M)| \\
&\leq |f(x) - L| + |g(x) - M| \\
&< \frac{\epsilon}{2} + \frac{\epsilon}{2} = \epsilon \qquad \text{whenever} \qquad 0 < |x - a| < \delta
\end{aligned}
$$

In this way, we have obtained statement (6), thereby proving that

$$\lim_{x \to a} [f(x) + g(x)] = L + M$$

The proof of Limit Theorem 4 using the minus sign is left for the reader (see Exercise 24 below).

Limit Theorem 4 may be extended to any finite number of functions.

4.2.5 LIMIT THEOREM 5   If $\lim_{x \to a} f_1(x) = L_1$, $\lim_{x \to a} f_2(x) = L_2$, $\ldots$, and $\lim_{x \to a} f_n(x) = L_n$, then

$$\lim_{x \to a} [f_1(x) \pm f_2(x) \pm \cdots \pm f_n(x)] = L_1 \pm L_2 \pm \cdots \pm L_n$$

This theorem may be proved by applying Limit Theorem 4 and mathematical induction (see Exercise 25 below).

4.2.6 LIMIT THEOREM 6   If $\lim_{x \to a} f(x) = L$ and $\lim_{x \to a} g(x) = M$, then

$$\lim_{x \to a} f(x) \cdot g(x) = L \cdot M$$

The proof of this theorem is more sophisticated than those of the preceding theorems, and it is often omitted from a beginning calculus text. We have outlined the proof in Exercises 27 and 28 below, with some steps left to be supplied by the reader.

Limit Theorem 6 may also be extended to any finite number of functions by applying mathematical induction.

4.2.7 LIMIT THEOREM 7   If $\lim_{x \to a} f_1(x) = L_1$, $\lim_{x \to a} f_2(x) = L_2$, $\ldots$, and $\lim_{x \to a} f_n(x) = L_n$, then

$$\lim_{x \to a} [f_1(x) \cdot f_2(x) \cdot \ldots \cdot f_n(x)] = L_1 \cdot L_2 \cdot \ldots \cdot L_n$$

The proof is left for the reader (see Exercise 29 below).

4.2.8 LIMIT THEOREM 8   If $\lim\limits_{x \to a} f(x) = L$ and $\lim\limits_{x \to a} g(x) = M$, and $M \neq 0$, then

$$\lim_{x \to a} \frac{f(x)}{g(x)} = \frac{L}{M}$$

The proof, based on Definition 4.1.1, is also frequently omitted from a beginning calculus text. However, a proof is given in Sec. 5.2 of the next chapter. Although we are postponing the proof, we shall apply this theorem when necessary.

4.2.9 LIMIT THEOREM 9   If $\lim\limits_{x \to a} f(x) = L$, then

$$\lim_{x \to a} \sqrt[n]{f(x)} = \sqrt[n]{L}$$

if n is a positive odd integer, or if n is a positive even integer and $L > 0$.

A proof of this theorem is given in Sec. 5.2, and as is the case with the preceding theorem we shall apply it when necessary.

Following are some examples illustrating the application of the above theorems. To indicate the limit theorem being used, we shall write "L.T." followed by the theorem number: for example, "L.T. 2" refers to Limit Theorem 2.

EXAMPLE 1: Find $\lim\limits_{x \to 3} (x^2 + 7x - 5)$, and when applicable indicate the limit theorems which are being used.

Solution:

$$\lim_{x \to 3} (x^2 + 7x - 5) = \lim_{x \to 3} x^2 + \lim_{x \to 3} 7x - \lim_{x \to 3} 5 \qquad \text{(L.T. 5)}$$

$$= \lim_{x \to 3} x \cdot \lim_{x \to 3} x + \lim_{x \to 3} 7 \cdot \lim_{x \to 3} x - \lim_{x \to 3} 5 \quad \text{(L.T. 6)}$$

$$= 3 \cdot 3 + 7 \cdot 3 - 5 \qquad \text{(L.T. 3 and L.T. 2)}$$

$$= 9 + 21 - 5 = 25.$$

It is important, at this point, that the reader realize that this limit was evaluated by direct application of the theorems on limits. For the function f defined by the equation $f(x) = x^2 + 7x - 5$, we see that $f(3) = 3^2 + 7 \cdot 3 - 5 = 25$, which is the same as $\lim\limits_{x \to 3} (x^2 + 7x - 5)$. It is not always true that we have $\lim\limits_{x \to a} f(x) = f(a)$ (see Example 4 below). In Example 1 above, $\lim\limits_{x \to 3} f(x) = f(3)$, because the function f is continuous at $x = 3$. We shall discuss the meaning of continuous functions in the next chapter.

EXAMPLE 2: Find $\lim\limits_{x \to 2} \sqrt{(x^3 + 2x + 3)/(x^2 + 5)}$, and when applicable indicate the limit theorems being used.

Solution:

$$\lim_{x \to 2} \sqrt{\frac{x^3 + 2x + 3}{x^2 + 5}} = \sqrt{\lim_{x \to 2} \frac{x^3 + 2x + 3}{x^2 + 5}} \qquad \text{(L.T. 9)}$$

$$= \sqrt{\frac{\lim_{x \to 2} (x^3 + 2x + 3)}{\lim_{x \to 2} (x^2 + 5)}} \qquad \text{(L.T. 8)}$$

$$= \sqrt{\frac{\lim_{x \to 2} x^3 + \lim_{x \to 2} 2x + \lim_{x \to 2} 3}{\lim_{x \to 2} x^2 + \lim_{x \to 2} 5}} \qquad \text{(L.T. 5)}$$

$$= \sqrt{\frac{\lim_{x \to 2} x \cdot \lim_{x \to 2} x \cdot \lim_{x \to 2} x + \lim_{x \to 2} 2 \cdot \lim_{x \to 2} x + \lim_{x \to 2} 3}{\lim_{x \to 2} x \cdot \lim_{x \to 2} x + \lim_{x \to 2} 5}}$$

$$\text{(L.T. 7)}$$

$$= \sqrt{\frac{2 \cdot 2 \cdot 2 + 2 \cdot 2 + 3}{2 \cdot 2 + 5}} \qquad \text{(L.T. 3 and L.T. 2)}$$

$$= \sqrt{\frac{8 + 4 + 3}{9}} = \frac{\sqrt{15}}{3}$$

EXAMPLE 3: Find $\lim\limits_{x \to 3} \dfrac{x^3 - 27}{x - 3}$, and when applicable indicate the limit theorems being used.

Solution: Here we have a more difficult problem, since we cannot apply Limit Theorem 8 to the quotient $(x^3 - 27)/(x - 3)$ because $\lim\limits_{x \to 3} (x - 3) = 0$. However, factoring the numerator, we get

$$\frac{x^3 - 27}{x - 3} = \frac{(x - 3)(x^2 + 3x + 9)}{x - 3}$$

This quotient is $(x^2 + 3x + 9)$ if $x \neq 3$ [since if $x \neq 3$ we may divide the numerator and denominator by $(x - 3)$].

When evaluating $\lim\limits_{x \to 3} \dfrac{x^3 - 27}{x - 3}$, we are considering values of x close to 3, but not equal to 3. Therefore, it is possible to divide numerator and denominator by $(x - 3)$. Our solution to this problem takes the following form:

$$\lim_{x \to 3} \frac{x^3 - 27}{x - 3} = \lim_{x \to 3} \frac{(x - 3)(x^2 + 3x + 9)}{x - 3}$$

$$= \lim_{x \to 3} (x^2 + 3x + 9) \qquad \text{dividing numerator and denominator by } (x - 3) \text{ since } x \neq 3$$

$$= \lim_{x \to 3} x^2 + \lim_{x \to 3} (3x + 9) \qquad \text{(L.T. 4)}$$

$$= \lim_{x \to 3} x \cdot \lim_{x \to 3} x + 18 \qquad \text{(L.T. 6 and L.T. 1)}$$

$$= 3 \cdot 3 + 18 = 27 \qquad \text{(L.T. 3)}$$

Note that in this example $(x^3 - 27)/(x - 3)$ is not defined when $x = 3$, but $\lim\limits_{x \to 3} \dfrac{x^3 - 27}{x - 3}$ exists and is equal to 27.

EXAMPLE 4: Given that f is the function defined by

$$f(x) = \begin{cases} x - 3 & \text{if } x \neq 4 \\ 5 & \text{if } x = 4 \end{cases}$$

find $\lim\limits_{x \to 4} f(x)$.

Solution: When evaluating $\lim\limits_{x \to 4} f(x)$, we are considering values of x close to 4, but not equal to 4. Thus we have

$$\lim_{x \to 4} f(x) = \lim_{x \to 4} (x - 3)$$
$$= 1 \qquad\qquad \text{(L.T. 1)}$$

In this example, $\lim\limits_{x \to 4} f(x) = 1$ but $f(4) = 5$; therefore, $\lim\limits_{x \to 4} f(x) \neq f(4)$.

This is an example of a function which is discontinuous at $x = 4$. Geometrically this means that there is a break in the graph of the function at the point where $x = 4$. This may be seen in Fig. 4.2.1. The graph of the function consists of the isolated point $(4,5)$ and the straight line whose equation is $y = x - 3$, with the point $(4,1)$ deleted.

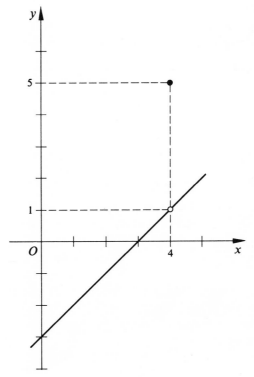

Figure 4.2.1

In Exercises 1 through 17, find the value of the limit, and when applicable indicate the limit theorems being used.

1. $\lim\limits_{x \to 2} (x^2 + 2x - 1)$

2. $\lim\limits_{y \to -1} (y^3 - 2y^2 + 3y - 4)$

3. $\lim\limits_{t \to 2} \dfrac{t^2 - 5}{2t^3 + 6}$

4. $\lim\limits_{x \to -1} \dfrac{2x + 1}{x^2 - 3x + 4}$

5. $\lim\limits_{y \to -2} \dfrac{y^3 + 8}{y + 2}$

6. $\lim\limits_{s \to 1} \dfrac{s^3 - 1}{s - 1}$

7. $\lim\limits_{x \to -3} \dfrac{x^2 + 5x + 6}{x^2 - x - 12}$

8. $\lim\limits_{x \to 4} \dfrac{3x^2 - 17x + 20}{4x^2 - 25x + 36}$

9. $\lim\limits_{r \to 1} \sqrt{\dfrac{8r + 1}{r + 3}}$

10. $\lim\limits_{x \to 2} \sqrt{\dfrac{x^2 + 3x + 4}{x^3 + 1}}$

11. $\lim\limits_{y \to -3} \sqrt{\dfrac{y^2 - 9}{2y^2 + 7y + 3}}$

12. $\lim\limits_{t \to 3/2} \sqrt{\dfrac{8t^3 - 27}{4t^2 - 9}}$

13. $\lim\limits_{x \to 0} \dfrac{\sqrt{x + 2} - \sqrt{2}}{x}$
   HINT: Rationalize the numerator.

14. $\lim\limits_{t \to 0} \dfrac{2 - \sqrt{4 - t}}{t}$

15. $\lim\limits_{h \to 0} \dfrac{\sqrt[3]{h + 1} - 1}{h}$

16. $\lim\limits_{x \to -2} \dfrac{x^3 - x^2 - x + 10}{x^2 + 3x + 2}$

17. $\lim\limits_{x \to 3} \dfrac{2x^3 - 5x^2 - 2x - 3}{4x^3 - 13x^2 + 4x - 3}$

18. If $f(x) = x^2 + 5x - 3$, show that $\lim\limits_{x \to 2} f(x) = f(2)$.

19. If $F(x) = 2x^3 + 7x - 1$, show that $\lim\limits_{x \to -1} F(x) = F(-1)$.

20. If $g(x) = (x^2 - 4)/(x - 2)$, show that $\lim\limits_{x \to 2} g(x) = 4$ but that $g(2)$ is not defined.

21. If $h(x) = (\sqrt{x + 9} - 3)/x$, show that $\lim\limits_{x \to 0} h(x) = 1/6$ but that $h(0)$ is not defined.

22. Given that f is the function defined by

$$f(x) = \begin{cases} 2x - 1 & \text{if } x \neq 2 \\ 1 & \text{if } x = 2 \end{cases}$$

   (a) Find $\lim\limits_{x \to 2} f(x)$, and show that $\lim\limits_{x \to 2} f(x) \neq f(2)$.
   (b) Draw a sketch of the graph of f.

23. Given that f is the function defined by

$$f(x) = \begin{cases} x^2 - 9 & \text{if } x \neq -3 \\ 4 & \text{if } x = -3 \end{cases}$$

(a) Find $\lim\limits_{x \to -3} f(x)$, and show that $\lim\limits_{x \to -3} f(x) \neq f(-3)$

(b) Draw a sketch of the graph of f.

24. Using Definition 4.1.1, prove that if

$$\lim_{x \to a} f(x) = L \qquad \text{and} \qquad \lim_{x \to a} g(x) = M$$

$$\text{then} \qquad \lim_{x \to a} [f(x) - g(x)] = L - M$$

25. Prove Limit Theorem 5 by applying Limit Theorem 4 and mathematical induction.

26. Prove that if $\lim\limits_{x \to a} f(x) = L$, then $\lim\limits_{x \to a} [f(x) - L] = 0$.

27. Using Definition 4.1.1, prove that if

$$\lim_{x \to a} f(x) = L \qquad \text{and} \qquad \lim_{x \to a} g(x) = 0$$

$$\text{then} \qquad \lim_{x \to a} f(x) \cdot g(x) = 0$$

HINT: In order to prove that $\lim\limits_{x \to a} f(x) \cdot g(x) = 0$, we must show that for any $\epsilon > 0$, there exists a $\delta > 0$ such that $|f(x) \cdot g(x)| < \epsilon$ whenever $0 < |x - a| < \delta$. First show that there is a $\delta_1 > 0$ such that $|f(x)| < 1 + |L|$ whenever $0 < |x - a| < \delta_1$, by applying Definition 4.1.1 to $\lim\limits_{x \to a} f(x) = L$, with $\epsilon = 1$ and $\delta = \delta_1$, and then use the triangle inequality. Then show that there is a $\delta_2 > 0$ such that $|g(x)| < \epsilon/(1 + |L|)$ whenever $0 < |x - a| < \delta_2$, by applying Definition 4.1.1 to $\lim\limits_{x \to a} g(x) = 0$. By taking δ as the smaller of the two numbers δ_1 and δ_2, the theorem is proved.

28. Prove Limit Theorem 6: If $\lim\limits_{x \to a} f(x) = L$ and $\lim\limits_{x \to a} g(x) = M$, then

$$\lim_{x \to a} [f(x) \cdot g(x)] = L \cdot M.$$

HINT: Write $f(x) \cdot g(x) = [f(x) - L]g(x) + L[g(x) - M] + L \cdot M$. Apply Limit Theorem 5 and the results of Exercises 26 and 27.

29. Prove Limit Theorem 7 by applying Limit Theorem 6 and mathematical induction.

30. Prove that, if $f(x) = g(x)$ for all values of x except $x = a$, then $\lim\limits_{x \to a} f(x) = \lim\limits_{x \to a} g(x)$ if the limits exist.

(4.3)   One-sided limits

When considering $\lim\limits_{x \to a} f(x)$, the values of x are taken sufficiently close to a, and these values of x may be greater than a or less than a. Specifically, in the example in Sec. 4.1, when considering $\lim\limits_{x \to 1} f(x)$ we let x approach 1 through values less than 1, and also through values greater than 1.

Sometimes, the independent variable x is restricted to values greater than a; in this case, we say that x approaches a from the right and thus write

$$\lim_{x \to a^+} f(x)$$

This is called the *one-sided limit from the right*, or the *right-hand limit*.

4.3.1 DEFINITION Let f be a function which is defined at every number in some open interval (a,c). Then, the limit of $f(x)$, as x approaches a from the right, is L, written

$$\lim_{x \to a^+} f(x) = L$$

if for any $\epsilon > 0$, however small, there exists a $\delta > 0$, such that

(1) $|f(x) - L| < \epsilon$ whenever $0 < x - a < \delta$

You will note that in statement (1) there are no absolute value bars around $x - a$, since $x - a > 0$, because $x > a$.

If the independent variable x is restricted to values less than a, we say that x approaches a from the left and thus write

$$\lim_{x \to a^-} f(x)$$

This is called the *one-sided limit from the left*, or the *left-hand limit*.

4.3.2 DEFINITION Let f be a function which is defined at every number in some open interval (d,a). Then, the limit of $f(x)$, as x approaches a from the left, is L, written

$$\lim_{x \to a^-} f(x) = L$$

if for any $\epsilon > 0$, however small, there exists a $\delta > 0$, such that

$|f(x) - L| < \epsilon$ whenever $-\delta < x - a < 0$

We may refer to $\lim_{x \to a} f(x)$ as the *two-sided limit*, or the *undirected limit*, to distinguish it from the one-sided limits.

EXAMPLE 1: Let f be defined by the equation

$$f(x) = \sqrt{x - 4}$$

(*a*) Draw a sketch of the graph of f.

(*b*) Determine $\lim_{x \to 4^+} f(x)$ if it exists.

(*c*) Determine $\lim_{x \to 4^-} f(x)$ if it exists.

Solution: A sketch of the graph of f is shown in Fig. 4.3.1.

$$\lim_{x \to 4^+} f(x) = \lim_{x \to 4^+} \sqrt{x - 4} = 0$$

$$\lim_{x \to 4^-} f(x) = \lim_{x \to 4^-} \sqrt{x - 4}$$

which does not exist since $\sqrt{x - 4}$ is not a real number if x is less than 4.

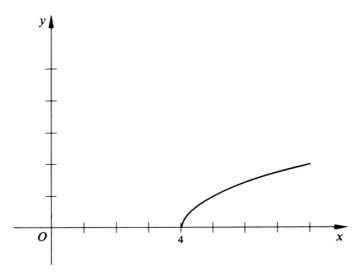

Figure 4.3.1

EXAMPLE 2: Let f be defined as follows:

$$f(x) = \begin{cases} -1 & \text{if } x < 0 \\ 0 & \text{if } x = 0 \\ 1 & \text{if } 0 < x \end{cases}$$

(a) Draw a sketch of the graph of f.
(b) Determine $\lim\limits_{x \to 0^-} f(x)$ if it exists.
(c) Determine $\lim\limits_{x \to 0^+} f(x)$ if it exists.

   Solution: A sketch of the graph is shown in Fig. 4.3.2. $\lim\limits_{x \to 0^-} f(x) = -1$ since, if x is any number less than 0, $f(x)$ has the value -1. Similarly $\lim\limits_{x \to 0^+} f(x) = +1$.

   In the above example $\lim\limits_{x \to 0^-} f(x) \neq \lim\limits_{x \to 0^+} f(x)$. Because the left-hand limit and

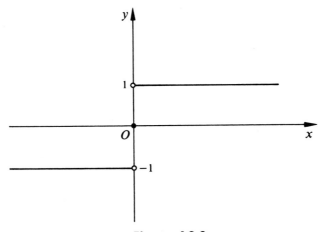

Figure 4.3.2

the right-hand limit are not equal, we say that the two-sided limit, $\lim\limits_{x \to 0} f(x)$, does not exist. The concept of the two-sided limit failing to exist because the two one-sided limits are unequal is true in general, and it is stated in the following theorem.

4.3.3 THEOREM $\lim\limits_{x \to a} f(x)$ exists and is equal to L if and only if $\lim\limits_{x \to a^-} f(x)$ and $\lim\limits_{x \to a^+} f(x)$ both exist and both are equal to L.

The proof of this theorem is left for the reader (see Exercise 13 below).

In Example 1 above, we saw that $\lim\limits_{x \to 4^+} \sqrt{x - 4} = 0$ and that $\lim\limits_{x \to 4^-} \sqrt{x - 4}$ does not exist. Therefore, by Theorem 4.3.3 the two-sided limit, $\lim\limits_{x \to 4} \sqrt{x - 4}$, does not exist.

EXAMPLE 3: Let g be defined by

$$g(x) = \begin{cases} |x| & \text{if } x \neq 0 \\ 2 & \text{if } x = 0 \end{cases}$$

(*a*) Draw a sketch of the graph of g.
(*b*) Find $\lim\limits_{x \to 0} g(x)$ if it exists.

Solution: A sketch of the graph is shown in Fig. 4.3.3.

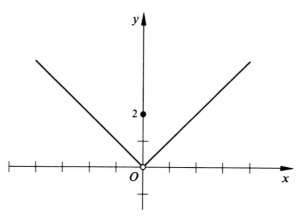

Figure 4.3.3

$$\lim\limits_{x \to 0^-} g(x) = \lim\limits_{x \to 0^-} (-x) = 0 \quad \text{and} \quad \lim\limits_{x \to 0^+} g(x) = \lim\limits_{x \to 0^+} x = 0$$

Therefore, by Theorem 4.3.3 $\lim\limits_{x \to 0} g(x)$ exists and is equal to 0. You will note that $g(0) = 2$, which has no effect on $\lim\limits_{x \to 0} g(x)$.

EXAMPLE 4: Let h be defined by

$$h(x) = \begin{cases} 4 - x^2 & \text{if } x \leq 1 \\ 2 + x^2 & \text{if } 1 < x \end{cases}$$

(*a*) Draw a sketch of the graph of h.

(*b*) Find each of the following limits if they exist: $\lim\limits_{x \to 1^-} h(x)$; $\lim\limits_{x \to 1^+} h(x)$; $\lim\limits_{x \to 1} h(x)$.

Solution: A sketch of the graph is shown in Fig. 4.3.4.

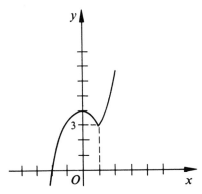

Figure 4.3.4

$$\lim_{x \to 1^-} h(x) = \lim_{x \to 1^-} (4 - x^2) = 3$$

$$\lim_{x \to 1^+} h(x) = \lim_{x \to 1^+} (2 + x^2) = 3$$

Therefore, by Theorem 4.3.3 $\lim\limits_{x \to 1} h(x)$ exists and is equal to 3. Note that $h(1) = 3$.

Exercises 4.3

For each of the following functions, draw a sketch of the graph. Find the indicated limit if it exists; if the limit does not exist, give the reason.

1. $f(x) = \sqrt{x + 3}$ *Find:* (*a*) $\lim\limits_{x \to -3^+} f(x)$; (*b*) $\lim\limits_{x \to -3^-} f(x)$; (*c*) $\lim\limits_{x \to -3} f(x)$

2. $g(x) = \sqrt{2x - 1}$ *Find:* (*a*) $\lim\limits_{x \to 1/2^+} g(x)$; (*b*) $\lim\limits_{x \to 1/2^-} g(x)$; (*c*) $\lim\limits_{x \to 1/2} g(x)$

3. $F(t) = \sqrt{6 - 3t}$ *Find:* (*a*) $\lim\limits_{t \to 2^+} F(t)$; (*b*) $\lim\limits_{t \to 2^-} F(t)$; (*c*) $\lim\limits_{t \to 2} F(t)$

4. $G(r) = 4 + \sqrt{-r - 3}$ *Find:* (*a*) $\lim\limits_{r \to -3^+} G(r)$; (*b*) $\lim\limits_{r \to -3^-} G(r)$; (*c*) $\lim\limits_{r \to -3} G(r)$

5. $f(x) = \begin{cases} 2, & \text{if } x < 1 \\ -1, & \text{if } x = 1 \\ -3, & \text{if } 1 < x \end{cases}$ *Find:* (*a*) $\lim\limits_{x \to 1^+} f(x)$; (*b*) $\lim\limits_{x \to 1^-} f(x)$; (*c*) $\lim\limits_{x \to 1} f(x)$

6. $g(s) = \begin{cases} s + 3, & \text{if } s \leq -2 \\ 3 - s, & \text{if } -2 < s \end{cases}$ *Find:* (*a*) $\lim\limits_{s \to -2^+} g(s)$; (*b*) $\lim\limits_{s \to -2^-} g(s)$; (*c*) $\lim\limits_{s \to -2} g(s)$

7. $h(x) = \begin{cases} 2x + 1, & \text{if } x < 3 \\ 10 - x, & \text{if } 3 \leq x \end{cases}$ *Find:* (a) $\lim\limits_{x \to 3^+} h(x)$; (b) $\lim\limits_{x \to 3^-} h(x)$; (c) $\lim\limits_{x \to 3} h(x)$

8. $F(x) = \begin{cases} x^2, & \text{if } x \leq 2 \\ 8 - 2x, & \text{if } 2 < x \end{cases}$ *Find:* (a) $\lim\limits_{x \to 2^+} F(x)$; (b) $\lim\limits_{x \to 2^-} F(x)$; (c) $\lim\limits_{x \to 2} F(x)$

9. $f(r) = \begin{cases} 2r + 3, & \text{if } r < 1 \\ 2, & \text{if } r = 1 \\ 7 - 2r, & \text{if } 1 < r \end{cases}$ *Find:* (a) $\lim\limits_{r \to 1^+} f(r)$; (b) $\lim\limits_{r \to 1^-} f(r)$; (c) $\lim\limits_{r \to 1} f(r)$

10. $g(t) = \begin{cases} 3 + t^2, & \text{if } t < -2 \\ 0, & \text{if } t = -2 \\ 11 - t^2, & \text{if } -2 < t \end{cases}$ *Find:* (a) $\lim\limits_{t \to -2^+} g(t)$; (b) $\lim\limits_{t \to -2^-} g(t)$; (c) $\lim\limits_{t \to -2} g(t)$

11. $F(x) = |x - 5|$ *Find:* (a) $\lim\limits_{x \to 5^+} F(x)$; (b) $\lim\limits_{x \to 5^-} F(x)$; (c) $\lim\limits_{x \to 5} F(x)$

12. $f(x) = 3 + |2x - 4|$ *Find:* (a) $\lim\limits_{x \to 2^+} f(x)$; (b) $\lim\limits_{x \to 2^-} f(x)$; (c) $\lim\limits_{x \to 2} f(x)$

13. Prove Theorem 4.3.3.

(4.4) Limits involving infinity

Let us consider the function f defined by the equation

$$f(x) = \frac{2x^2}{x^2 + 1}$$

A sketch of the graph of this function is shown in Fig. 4.4.1.

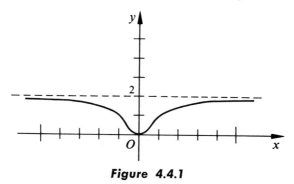

Figure 4.4.1

Let x take on the values $0, .1, 2, 3, 4, 5, 10, 100, 1,000$, etc., allowing x to increase without bound. The corresponding function values are given in Table 4.4.1.

Table 4.4.1

x	0	1	2	3	4	5	10	100	1,000
$f(x) = \dfrac{2x^2}{x^2 + 1}$	0	1	$\dfrac{8}{5}$	$\dfrac{18}{10}$	$\dfrac{32}{17}$	$\dfrac{50}{26}$	$\dfrac{200}{101}$	$\dfrac{20,000}{10,001}$	$\dfrac{2,000,000}{1,000,001}$

When the independent variable x is increasing without bound through positive values, as in Table 4.4.1, we say that x is approaching positive infinity and write

$$x \to +\infty$$

We see from Table 4.4.1 that as $x \to +\infty$ the function values $f(x)$ get closer and closer to 2, or $f(x) \to 2$. In particular, when $x = 4$,

$$2 - \frac{2x^2}{x^2 + 1} = 2 - \frac{32}{17} = \frac{2}{17}$$

Therefore, the difference between 2 and $f(x)$ is 2/17 when $x = 4$. When $x = 100$,

$$2 - \frac{2x^2}{x^2 + 1} = 2 - \frac{20,000}{10,001} = \frac{2}{10,001}$$

Hence the difference between 2 and $f(x)$ is 2/10,001 when $x = 100$.

Continuing on, we see that we can make the value of $f(x)$ as close to 2 as we please by taking x large enough. In other words, we can make the difference between 2 and $f(x)$ as small as we please by taking x large enough; or going a step further, for any $\epsilon > 0$, however small, we can find a number $N > 0$ such that $|f(x) - 2| < \epsilon$ whenever $x > N$.

Because of this, we say

$$\lim_{x \to +\infty} \frac{2x^2}{x^2 + 1} = 2$$

In general, we have the following definition.

4.4.1 DEFINITION   The limit of $f(x)$ as x approaches positive infinity is L, written

$$\lim_{x \to +\infty} f(x) = L$$

if for any $\epsilon > 0$, however small, there exists a number $N > 0$ such that

$$|f(x) - L| < \epsilon \qquad \text{whenever} \qquad x > N$$

Now, let us consider the same function and let x take on the values 0, -1, -2, -3, -4, -5, -10, -100, $-1,000$, etc., allowing x to decrease through negative values without bound. In this case, we say that x is approaching negative infinity and write

$$x \to -\infty$$

Table 4.4.2 gives the corresponding function values, $f(x)$.

Table 4.4.2

x	0	-1	-2	-3	-4	-5	-10	-100	$-1,000$
$f(x) = \dfrac{2x^2}{x^2 + 1}$	0	1	$\dfrac{8}{5}$	$\dfrac{18}{10}$	$\dfrac{32}{17}$	$\dfrac{50}{26}$	$\dfrac{200}{201}$	$\dfrac{20,000}{10,001}$	$\dfrac{2,000,000}{1,000,001}$

We note that the function values are the same for the negative numbers as for the corresponding positive numbers. So, we can see that as $x \rightarrow -\infty$, $f(x) \rightarrow 2$; or for any $\epsilon > 0$, however small, we can find a number $N < 0$ such that $|f(x) - 2| < \epsilon$ whenever $x < N$. Accordingly, we say

$$\lim_{x \rightarrow -\infty} \frac{2x^2}{x^2 + 1} = 2$$

In general, we have the following definition.

4.4.2 DEFINITION   The limit of $f(x)$ as x approaches negative infinity is L, written

$$\lim_{x \rightarrow -\infty} f(x) = L$$

if for any $\epsilon > 0$, however small, there exists a number $N < 0$ such that

$$|f(x) - L| < \epsilon \qquad \text{whenever} \qquad x < N$$

If $|x|$ increases without bound, we say that x approaches unsigned infinity and write

$$x \rightarrow \infty$$

For the function for which $f(x) = 2x^2/(x^2 + 1)$ we see that, as $|x|$ increases without bound, $f(x)$ approaches 2; therefore, as $x \rightarrow \infty$, $f(x) \rightarrow 2$, and we write

$$\lim_{x \rightarrow \infty} \frac{2x^2}{x^2 + 1} = 2$$

We have the following definition.

4.4.3 DEFINITION   The limit of $f(x)$ as x approaches unsigned infinity is L, written

$$\lim_{x \rightarrow \infty} f(x) = L$$

if for any $\epsilon > 0$, however small, there exists a number $N > 0$ such that

$$|f(x) - L| < \epsilon \qquad \text{whenever} \qquad |x| > N$$

Limit Theorems 2, 4, 5, 6, 7, 8, and 9 given in Sec. 4.2 remain unchanged when a is replaced by ∞, $+\infty$, or $-\infty$. We have the following additional limit theorem.

4.4.4 LIMIT THEOREM 10   If r is any positive integer, then

(i) $\displaystyle \lim_{x \rightarrow \infty} \frac{1}{x^r} = 0$

(ii) $\displaystyle \lim_{x \rightarrow +\infty} \frac{1}{x^r} = 0$

(iii) $\displaystyle \lim_{x \rightarrow -\infty} \frac{1}{x^r} = 0$

Proof of (i): In order to prove part (i), we must show that Definition 4.4.3 holds for $f(x) = 1/x^r$ and $L = 0$; that is, we must show that for any $\epsilon > 0$ there exists a number $N > 0$ such that

$$\left|\frac{1}{x^r} - 0\right| < \epsilon \qquad \text{whenever} \qquad |x| > N$$

or equivalently,

$$|x|^r > \frac{1}{\epsilon} \qquad \text{whenever} \qquad |x| > N$$

or equivalently, since $r > 0$,

$$|x| > \left(\frac{1}{\epsilon}\right)^{1/r} \qquad \text{whenever} \qquad |x| > N$$

In order for the above to hold, take $N = (1/\epsilon)^{1/r}$. Thus, we may conclude that

$$\left|\frac{1}{x^r} - 0\right| < \epsilon \qquad \text{whenever} \qquad |x| > N, \text{ if } N = \left(\frac{1}{\epsilon}\right)^{1/r}$$

This proves part (i).

The proofs of parts (ii) and (iii) are analogous.

EXAMPLE 1: Find $\displaystyle\lim_{x \to \infty} \frac{4x - 3}{2x + 5}$, and when applicable indicate the limit theorems being used.

Solution: In order to use Limit Theorem 10, we divide the numerator and the denominator by x, giving us

$$\lim_{x \to \infty} \frac{4x - 3}{2x + 5} = \lim_{x \to \infty} \frac{4 - 3/x}{2 + 5/x}$$

$$= \frac{\displaystyle\lim_{x \to \infty} (4 - 3/x)}{\displaystyle\lim_{x \to \infty} (2 + 5/x)} \qquad \text{(L.T. 8)}$$

$$= \frac{\displaystyle\lim_{x \to \infty} 4 - \lim_{x \to \infty} (3/x)}{\displaystyle\lim_{x \to \infty} 2 + \lim_{x \to \infty} (5/x)} \qquad \text{(L.T. 4)}$$

$$= \frac{\displaystyle\lim_{x \to \infty} 4 - \lim_{x \to \infty} 3 \cdot \lim_{x \to \infty} (1/x)}{\displaystyle\lim_{x \to \infty} 2 + \lim_{x \to \infty} 5 \cdot \lim_{x \to \infty} (1/x)} \qquad \text{(L.T. 6)}$$

$$= \frac{4 - 3 \cdot 0}{2 + 5 \cdot 0} = 2 \qquad \text{(L.T. 2 and L.T. 10)}$$

EXAMPLE 2: Find $\displaystyle\lim_{x \to \infty} \frac{2x^2 - x + 5}{4x^3 - 1}$, and when applicable indicate the limit theorems being used.

Solution: In this problem, in order to use Limit Theorem 10, we divide the numerator and the denominator by the highest power of x, occurring in either the numerator or denominator, which in this case is x^3. So, we have

$$\lim_{x \to \infty} \frac{2x^2 - x + 5}{4x^3 - 1} = \lim_{x \to \infty} \frac{2/x - 1/x^2 + 5/x^3}{4 - 1/x^3}$$

$$= \frac{\displaystyle\lim_{x \to \infty} (2/x - 1/x^2 + 5/x^3)}{\displaystyle\lim_{x \to \infty} (4 - 1/x^3)} \qquad \text{(L.T. 8)}$$

$$= \frac{\displaystyle\lim_{x \to \infty} (2/x) - \lim_{x \to \infty} (1/x^2) + \lim_{x \to \infty} (5/x^3)}{\displaystyle\lim_{x \to \infty} 4 - \lim_{x \to \infty} (1/x^3)} \qquad \text{(L.T. 5)}$$

$$= \frac{\displaystyle\lim_{x \to \infty} 2 \cdot \lim_{x \to \infty} (1/x) - \lim_{x \to \infty} (1/x^2) + \lim_{x \to \infty} 5 \cdot \lim_{x \to \infty} (1/x^3)}{\displaystyle\lim_{x \to \infty} 4 - \lim_{x \to \infty} (1/x^3)}$$
$$\text{(L.T. 6)}$$

$$= \frac{2 \cdot 0 - 0 + 5 \cdot 0}{4 - 0} = 0 \qquad \text{(L.T. 2 and L.T. 10)}$$

EXAMPLE 3: Find $\displaystyle\lim_{x \to +\infty} \frac{3x + 4}{\sqrt{2x^2 - 5}}$, and when applicable indicate the limit theorems being used.

Solution: We divide the numerator and the denominator of the fraction by x. In the denominator we may let $x = \sqrt{x^2}$, since we are considering only positive values of x.

$$\lim_{x \to +\infty} \frac{3x + 4}{\sqrt{2x^2 - 5}} = \lim_{x \to +\infty} \frac{3 + 4/x}{\sqrt{2x^2 - 5}/\sqrt{x^2}}$$

$$= \frac{\displaystyle\lim_{x \to +\infty} (3 + 4/x)}{\displaystyle\lim_{x \to +\infty} \sqrt{2 - 5/x^2}} \qquad \text{(L.T. 8)}$$

$$= \frac{\displaystyle\lim_{x \to +\infty} (3 + 4/x)}{\sqrt{\displaystyle\lim_{x \to +\infty} (2 - 5/x^2)}} \qquad \text{(L.T. 9)}$$

$$= \frac{\displaystyle\lim_{x \to +\infty} 3 + \lim_{x \to +\infty} (4/x)}{\sqrt{\displaystyle\lim_{x \to +\infty} 2 - \lim_{x \to +\infty} (5/x^2)}} \qquad \text{(L.T. 4)}$$

$$= \frac{\displaystyle\lim_{x \to +\infty} 3 + \lim_{x \to +\infty} 4 \cdot \lim_{x \to +\infty} (1/x)}{\sqrt{\displaystyle\lim_{x \to +\infty} 2 - \lim_{x \to +\infty} 5 \cdot \lim_{x \to +\infty} (1/x^2)}} \qquad \text{(L.T. 6)}$$

$$= \frac{3 + 4 \cdot 0}{\sqrt{2 - 5 \cdot 0}} = \frac{3}{\sqrt{2}} \qquad \text{(L.T. 2 and L.T. 10)}$$

We shall now consider infinite limits. Let f be the function defined by

$$f(x) = \frac{3}{(x - 2)^2}$$

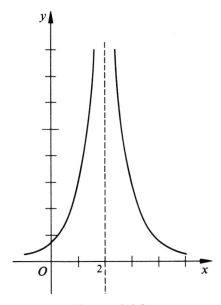

Figure 4.4.2

A sketch of the graph of this function is shown in Fig. 4.4.2.

We shall investigate the function values $f(x)$ when x is close to 2. Letting x approach 2 from the right, we have the values of $f(x)$ given in Table 4.4.3.

Table 4.4.3

x	3	$\dfrac{5}{2}$	$\dfrac{7}{3}$	$\dfrac{9}{4}$	$\dfrac{21}{10}$	$\dfrac{201}{100}$	$\dfrac{2{,}001}{1{,}000}$
$f(x) = \dfrac{3}{(x-2)^2}$	3	12	27	48	300	30,000	3,000,000

From Table 4.4.3, we see that as x gets closer and closer to 2, $f(x)$ increases without bound; or in other words, we can make $f(x)$ as large as we please by taking x close enough to 2. So we say that

$$\lim_{x \to 2^+} \frac{3}{(x-2)^2} = +\infty$$

If we let x approach 2 from the left, we have the values of $f(x)$ given in Table 4.4.4.

Table 4.4.4

x	1	$\dfrac{3}{2}$	$\dfrac{5}{3}$	$\dfrac{7}{4}$	$\dfrac{19}{10}$	$\dfrac{199}{100}$	$\dfrac{1{,}999}{1{,}000}$
$f(x) = \dfrac{3}{(x-2)^2}$	3	12	27	48	300	30,000	3,000,000

We see from Table 4.4.4 that as x gets closer and closer to 2, through values less than 2, $f(x)$ increases without bound; so we say that

$$\lim_{x \to 2^-} \frac{3}{(x-2)^2} = +\infty$$

Therefore the right-hand limit and the left-hand limit as x approaches 2 are $+\infty$; and so we say that

$$\lim_{x \to 2} \frac{3}{(x-2)^2} = +\infty$$

We have the following definition.

4.4.5 DEFINITION   The limit of $f(x)$ as x approaches a is positive infinity, written

$$\lim_{x \to a} f(x) = +\infty$$

if for any number $N > 0$, there exists a $\delta > 0$ such that $f(x) > N$ whenever $0 < |x - a| < \delta$.

In words, Definition 4.4.5 says: we can make $f(x)$ as large as we please (that is, greater than any positive number N) by taking x sufficiently close to a.

Analogously, we can define a limit that is negative infinity. To lead up to this, we consider the function g defined by the equation

$$g(x) = \frac{-3}{(x-2)^2}$$

A sketch of the graph of this function is shown in Fig. 4.4.3.

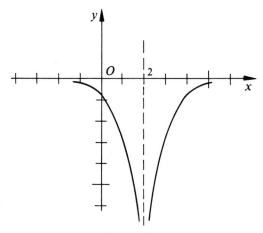

Figure 4.4.3

The function values given by $g(x) = -3/(x-2)^2$ are the negatives of the function values given by $f(x) = 3/(x-2)^2$. So for the function g as x approaches 2, either from the right or the left, $g(x)$ decreases without bound and we write

$$\lim_{x \to 2} \frac{-3}{(x-2)^2} = -\infty$$

In general we have the following definition.

4.4.6 DEFINITION   The limit of $f(x)$ as x approaches a is negative infinity, written

$$\lim_{x \to a} f(x) = -\infty$$

if for any number $N < 0$, there exists a $\delta > 0$ such that $f(x) < N$ whenever $0 < |x - a| < \delta$.

We shall also be concerned with a limit that is unsigned infinity.

4.4.7 DEFINITION   The limit of $f(x)$ as x approaches a is unsigned infinity, written

$$\lim_{x \to a} f(x) = \infty$$

if $\lim\limits_{x \to a} |f(x)| = +\infty$.

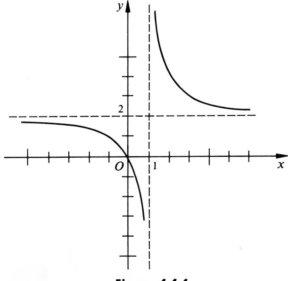

Figure 4.4.4

Consider the function f defined by the equation

$$f(x) = \frac{2x}{x-1}$$

A sketch of the graph of this function is shown in Fig. 4.4.4. Since

$$\lim_{x \to 1} \left| \frac{2x}{x-1} \right| = +\infty$$

we have, from Definition 4.4.7,

$$\lim_{x \to 1} \frac{2x}{x - 1} = \infty$$

Note that $\lim\limits_{x \to 1^+} \dfrac{2x}{x - 1} = +\infty$ and $\lim\limits_{x \to 1^-} \dfrac{2x}{x - 1} = -\infty$.

The reader must remember that ∞ cannot be treated as a number; therefore, the limit theorems do not hold when the limit is infinite. However, we do have the following properties regarding infinite limits. The proofs are left for the reader (see Exercises 21 to 23 below).

4.4.8 THEOREM   If $\lim\limits_{x \to a} f(x) = \infty$ and $\lim\limits_{x \to a} g(x) = c$, where c is a constant, then

$$\lim_{x \to a} [f(x) + g(x)] = \infty.$$

Theorem 4.4.8 also holds if ∞ is replaced by $+\infty$ or $-\infty$.

4.4.9 THEOREM   If $\lim\limits_{x \to a} f(x) = +\infty$ and $\lim\limits_{x \to a} g(x) = c$, where c is a constant $\neq 0$, then

(i)   If $c > 0$, $\lim\limits_{x \to a} f(x) \cdot g(x) = +\infty$

(ii) If $c < 0$, $\lim\limits_{x \to a} f(x) \cdot g(x) = -\infty$

4.4.10 THEOREM   If $\lim\limits_{x \to a} f(x) = -\infty$ and $\lim\limits_{x \to a} g(x) = c$, where c is a constant $\neq 0$, then

(i)   If $c > 0$, $\lim\limits_{x \to a} f(x) \cdot g(x) = -\infty$

(ii) If $c < 0$, $\lim\limits_{x \to a} f(x) \cdot g(x) = +\infty$

NOTE: If $\lim\limits_{x \to a} f(x) = \infty$, $+\infty$, or $-\infty$, and if $\lim\limits_{x \to a} g(x) = 0$, then nothing can be said regarding $\lim\limits_{x \to a} f(x) \cdot g(x)$ until additional work is performed.

Also, it should be pointed out that if $\lim\limits_{x \to a} f(x) = +\infty$ and $\lim\limits_{x \to a} g(x) = -\infty$, nothing can be said regarding $\lim\limits_{x \to a} [f(x) + g(x)]$ until additional work is performed.

We have some further properties that will be stated as limit theorems.

4.4.11 LIMIT THEOREM 11   If r is any positive integer, then

(i) $\lim\limits_{x \to 0} \dfrac{1}{x^r} = \infty$

(ii) $\lim\limits_{x \to 0^+} \dfrac{1}{x^r} = +\infty$

(iii) $\lim\limits_{x \to 0^-} \dfrac{1}{x^r} = \begin{cases} -\infty, \text{ if } r \text{ is odd} \\ +\infty, \text{ if } r \text{ is even} \end{cases}$

Proof: According to Definition 4.4.7, part (i) will be true if

(1)
$$\lim_{x \to 0} \left| \frac{1}{x^r} \right| = +\infty$$

If parts (ii) and (iii) are true, then equation (1) follows and thus (i) will be true.

Therefore, we prove part (ii) first. We must show that Definition 4.4.5 holds for $f(x) = 1/x^r$ and $x \to 0^+$; that is, we must show that for any $N > 0$ there exists a $\delta > 0$ such that

$$\frac{1}{x^r} > N \qquad \text{whenever} \qquad 0 < x < \delta$$

or, equivalently, since $x > 0$ and $N > 0$,

$$x^r < \frac{1}{N} \qquad \text{whenever} \qquad 0 < x < \delta$$

or, equivalently, since $r > 0$,

$$x < \left(\frac{1}{N} \right)^{1/r} \qquad \text{whenever} \qquad 0 < x < \delta$$

The above statement will hold if $\delta = (1/N)^{1/r}$. We conclude that

$$\frac{1}{x^r} > N \qquad \text{whenever} \qquad 0 < x < \delta, \text{ if } \delta = \left(\frac{1}{N} \right)^{1/r} \qquad \text{Q.E.D.}$$

The proof of (iii) is analogous and is left for the reader (see Exercise 24 below).

4.4.12 LIMIT THEOREM 12   If a is a real number, ∞, $+\infty$, or $-\infty$, and if $\lim_{x \to a} f(x) = 0$ and $\lim_{x \to a} g(x) = c$, where c is a constant $\neq 0$, then

(i)   if $c > 0$ and if $f(x) \to 0$ through positive values of $f(x)$,

$$\lim_{x \to a} \frac{g(x)}{f(x)} = +\infty$$

(ii)   if $c > 0$ and if $f(x) \to 0$ through negative values of $f(x)$,

$$\lim_{x \to a} \frac{g(x)}{f(x)} = -\infty$$

(iii)   if $c < 0$ and if $f(x) \to 0$ through positive values of $f(x)$,

$$\lim_{x \to a} \frac{g(x)}{f(x)} = -\infty$$

(iv)   if $c < 0$ and if $f(x) \to 0$ through negative values of $f(x)$,

$$\lim_{x \to a} \frac{g(x)}{f(x)} = +\infty$$

NOTE: If $c = 0$, nothing can be said about $\lim_{x \to a} g(x)/f(x)$ without further work.

4.4.13 LIMIT THEOREM 13   If a is a real number, ∞, $+\infty$, or $-\infty$, and if $\lim\limits_{x\to a} f(x) = +\infty$, $-\infty$, or ∞ and $\lim\limits_{x\to a} g(x) = c$, where c is any constant, then

$$\lim_{x\to a} \frac{g(x)}{f(x)} = 0$$

EXAMPLE 4: Find $\lim\limits_{x\to+\infty} \dfrac{2x - x^2}{3x + 5}$, and when applicable indicate the limit theorems being used.

Solution:

$$\lim_{x\to+\infty} \frac{2x - x^2}{3x + 5} = \lim_{x\to+\infty} \frac{2/x - 1}{3/x + 5/x^2} \qquad \text{dividing numerator and denominator by } x^2$$

We shall consider the limits of the numerator and the denominator separately.

$$\lim_{x\to+\infty} \left(\frac{2}{x} - 1\right) = \lim_{x\to+\infty} \frac{2}{x} - \lim_{x\to+\infty} 1 \qquad \text{(L.T. 4)}$$

$$= 0 - 1 = -1 \qquad \text{(L.T. 13 and L.T. 2)}$$

$$\lim_{x\to+\infty} \left(\frac{3}{x} + \frac{5}{x^2}\right) = \lim_{x\to+\infty} \frac{3}{x} + \lim_{x\to+\infty} \frac{5}{x^2} \qquad \text{(L.T. 4)}$$

$$= 0 + 0 = 0 \qquad \text{(L.T. 13)}$$

Therefore, we have the limit of a fraction in which the limit of the numerator is -1 and the limit of the denominator is 0. By Limit Theorem 12(iii), we have

$$\lim_{x\to+\infty} \frac{2x - x^2}{3x + 5} = -\infty$$

EXAMPLE 5: Find (a) $\lim\limits_{x\to3^+} \dfrac{x^2 + x + 2}{x^2 - 2x - 3}$; (b) $\lim\limits_{x\to3^-} \dfrac{x^2 + x + 2}{x^2 - 2x - 3}$; and (c) $\lim\limits_{x\to3} \dfrac{x^2 + x + 2}{x^2 - 2x - 3}$.

Solution: (a) $\lim\limits_{x\to3^+} \dfrac{x^2 + x + 2}{x^2 - 2x - 3} = \lim\limits_{x\to3^+} \dfrac{x^2 + x + 2}{(x - 3)(x + 1)}$

The limit of the numerator is $+14$, which may easily be verified.

$$\lim_{x\to3^+} (x - 3)(x + 1) = \lim_{x\to3^+} (x - 3) \cdot \lim_{x\to3^+} (x + 1)$$

$$= 0 \cdot 4 = 0$$

The limit of the denominator is 0, and the denominator is approaching 0 through positive values. Applying Limit Theorem 12(i), we get

$$\lim_{x\to3^+} \frac{x^2 + x + 2}{x^2 - 2x - 3} = +\infty$$

(b) $\lim\limits_{x\to3^-} \dfrac{x^2 + x + 2}{x^2 - 2x - 3} = \lim\limits_{x\to3^-} \dfrac{x^2 + x + 2}{(x - 3)(x + 1)}$

As in part (*a*), the limit of the numerator is $+14$.

$$\lim_{x \to 3^-} (x - 3)(x + 1) = \lim_{x \to 3^-} (x - 3) \cdot \lim_{x \to 3^-} (x + 1)$$

$$= 0 \cdot 4 = 0$$

In this case, the limit of the denominator is zero, but the denominator is approaching zero through negative values. Applying Limit Theorem 12(ii) we obtain

$$\lim_{x \to 3^-} \frac{x^2 + x + 2}{x^2 - 2x - 3} = -\infty$$

(c) $\lim_{x \to 3} \dfrac{x^2 + x + 2}{x^2 - 2x - 3} = \infty$ because $\lim_{x \to 3} \left| \dfrac{x^2 + x + 2}{x^2 - 2x - 3} \right| = +\infty$

EXAMPLE 6: Find $\lim_{x \to +\infty} \dfrac{x^2}{x + 1}$.

Solution: Dividing the numerator and the denominator by x^2, we obtain

$$\lim_{x \to +\infty} \frac{x^2}{x + 1} = \lim_{x \to +\infty} \frac{1}{1/x + 1/x^2}$$

Let us evaluate the limit of the denominator. We have

$$\lim_{x \to +\infty} \left(\frac{1}{x} + \frac{1}{x^2} \right) = \lim_{x \to +\infty} \frac{1}{x} + \lim_{x \to +\infty} \frac{1}{x^2} = 0 + 0 = 0$$

Therefore the limit of the denominator is 0, and the denominator is approaching 0 through positive values.

The limit of the numerator is 1, and so by Limit Theorem 12(i) we have

$$\lim_{x \to +\infty} \frac{x^2}{x + 1} = +\infty$$

Exercises 4.4

In Exercises 1 through 8, find the limits, and when applicable indicate the limit theorems being used.

1. $\lim_{x \to \infty} \dfrac{2x + 1}{5x - 2}$

2. $\lim_{x \to \infty} \dfrac{4x^2 + 3}{2x^2 - 1}$

3. $\lim_{x \to \infty} \dfrac{x + 4}{3x^2 - 5}$

4. $\lim_{x \to \infty} \dfrac{x^2 - 2x + 5}{7x^3 + x + 1}$

5. $\lim_{x \to +\infty} \dfrac{\sqrt{x^2 + 4}}{x + 4}$

6. $\lim_{x \to -\infty} \dfrac{\sqrt{x^2 + 4}}{x + 4}$

7. $\lim_{x \to +\infty} \dfrac{5 - x^2}{2x + 4}$

8. $\lim_{x \to +\infty} \dfrac{2x^2 - x + 3}{x + 6}$

In Exercises 9 through 20, evaluate the limits.

9. $\lim\limits_{x\to 4} \dfrac{x}{x-4}$

10. $\lim\limits_{x\to 3} \dfrac{4x^2}{9-x^2}$

11. $\lim\limits_{x\to 2^+} \dfrac{x+2}{x^2-4}$

12. $\lim\limits_{x\to 2^-} \dfrac{x+2}{x^2-4}$

13. $\lim\limits_{x\to 3^+} \dfrac{\sqrt{x^2-9}}{x-3}$

14. $\lim\limits_{x\to 4^-} \dfrac{\sqrt{16-x^2}}{x-4}$

15. $\lim\limits_{x\to\infty} \dfrac{4x^3+2x^2-5}{8x^3+x+2}$

16. $\lim\limits_{x\to\infty} \dfrac{3x^4-7x^2+2}{2x^4+1}$

17. $\lim\limits_{x\to 0} \left(\dfrac{1}{x}-\dfrac{1}{x^2}\right)$

18. $\lim\limits_{x\to 2} \left(\dfrac{1}{x-2}-\dfrac{3}{x^2-4}\right)$

19. $\lim\limits_{x\to +\infty} (\sqrt{x^2+1}-x)$

20. $\lim\limits_{x\to +\infty} (\sqrt{x^2+x}-x)$

21. Prove Theorem 4.4.8.

22. Prove Theorem 4.4.9.

23. Prove Theorem 4.4.10.

24. Prove Theorem 4.4.11(iii).

25. Analogous to Definitions 4.4.1, 4.4.2, 4.4.5, and 4.4.6, give a definition for each of the following: (a) $\lim\limits_{x\to +\infty} f(x) = +\infty$; (b) $\lim\limits_{x\to +\infty} f(x) = -\infty$; (c) $\lim\limits_{x\to -\infty} f(x) = +\infty$; (d) $\lim\limits_{x\to -\infty} f(x) = -\infty$.

26. Prove that $\lim\limits_{x\to +\infty} \dfrac{x}{x-1} = 1$ by applying Definition 4.4.1; that is, for any $\epsilon > 0$, show that there exists a number $N > 0$ such that
$$\left|\frac{x}{x-1} - 1\right| < \epsilon \qquad \text{whenever} \qquad x > N$$

27. Prove that $\lim\limits_{x\to 2} \dfrac{3}{(x-2)^2} = +\infty$ by applying Definition 4.4.5.

28. Prove that $\lim\limits_{x\to -1} \dfrac{-5}{(x+1)^2} = -\infty$ by applying Definition 4.4.6.

(4.5)   Horizontal and vertical asymptotes

Let f be the function defined by

(1)
$$f(x) = \frac{1}{(x-a)^2}$$

A sketch of the graph of f is shown in Fig. 4.5.1. Any line parallel to and above the x axis will intersect this graph in two points: one point to the left of the line $x = a$ and one point to the right of this line. Thus, for any $k > 0$, no matter how large, the line $y = k$ will intersect the graph of f in two points; the distance of these two points from the line $x = a$ gets smaller and smaller as k gets larger

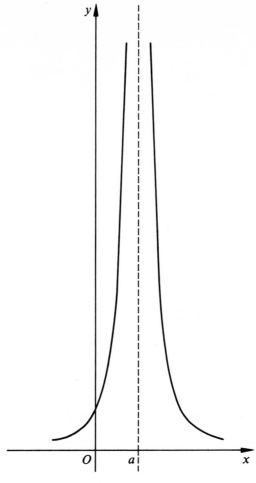

Figure 4.5.1

and larger. The line $x = a$ is called a *vertical asymptote* of the graph of f. Following is the definition of a vertical asymptote.

4.5.1 DEFINITION   The line $x = a$ is said to be a *vertical asymptote* of the graph of the function f if at least one of the following statements is true:

(i) $\lim\limits_{x \to a^+} f(x) = +\infty$

(ii) $\lim\limits_{x \to a^+} f(x) = -\infty$

(iii) $\lim\limits_{x \to a^-} f(x) = +\infty$

(iv) $\lim\limits_{x \to a^-} f(x) = -\infty$

For the function defined by equation (1), both parts (i) and (iii) of the above definition are true.

If *g* is the function defined by

$$g(x) = \frac{-1}{(x-a)^2}$$

then both parts (ii) and (iv) are true, and so the line $x = a$ is a vertical asymptote of the graph of *g*. This is shown in Fig. 4.5.2.

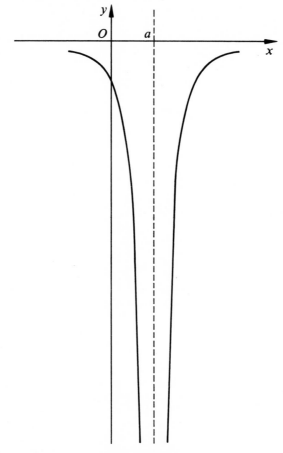

Figure 4.5.2

A *horizontal asymptote* of a graph is a line parallel to the *x* axis.

4.5.2 DEFINITION   The line $y = b$ is said to be a *horizontal asymptote* of the graph of the function *f* if at least one of the following statements is true:

(i) $\lim\limits_{x \to +\infty} f(x) = b$

(ii) $\lim\limits_{x \to -\infty} f(x) = b$

EXAMPLE 1: Find the horizontal asymptotes of the graph of the function f defined by

$$f(x) = \frac{x}{\sqrt{x^2 + 1}}$$

and draw a sketch of the graph.

Solution: First we consider $\lim_{x \to +\infty} f(x)$, and we have

$$\lim_{x \to +\infty} f(x) = \lim_{x \to +\infty} \frac{x}{\sqrt{x^2 + 1}}$$

To evaluate this limit we write $x = \sqrt{x^2}$ ($x > 0$, since $x \to +\infty$) and then divide the numerator and the denominator, under the radical sign, by x^2.

$$\lim_{x \to +\infty} \frac{x}{\sqrt{x^2 + 1}} = \lim_{x \to +\infty} \frac{\sqrt{x^2}}{\sqrt{x^2 + 1}}$$

$$= \lim_{x \to +\infty} \sqrt{\frac{1}{1 + 1/x^2}}$$

$$= \sqrt{\frac{1}{1 + \lim_{x \to +\infty} (1/x^2)}} = 1$$

Therefore, by Definition 4.5.2(i), the line $y = 1$ is a horizontal asymptote.

Now, we consider $\lim_{x \to -\infty} f(x)$; and in this case we write $x = -\sqrt{x^2}$, since if $x \to -\infty$, $x < 0$. So, we have

$$\lim_{x \to -\infty} f(x) = \lim_{x \to -\infty} \frac{-\sqrt{x^2}}{\sqrt{x^2 + 1}}$$

$$= \lim_{x \to -\infty} -\sqrt{\frac{1}{1 + 1/x^2}}$$

$$= -\sqrt{\frac{1}{1 + \lim_{x \to -\infty} (1/x^2)}} = -1$$

Accordingly, by Definition 4.5.2(ii), the line $y = -1$ is a horizontal asymptote. A sketch of the graph is shown in Fig. 4.5.3.

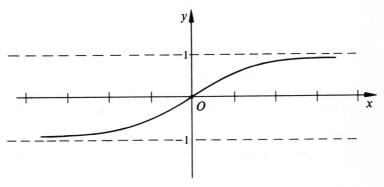

Figure 4.5.3

EXAMPLE 2: Find the vertical and horizontal asymptotes of the graph of the equation $xy^2 - 2y^2 - 4x = 0$, and draw a sketch of the graph.

Solution: Solving the given equation for y, we obtain

$$(2) \qquad\qquad y = \pm 2\sqrt{\dfrac{x}{x-2}}$$

Equation (2) defines two functions:

$$y = f_1(x) \text{ where } f_1 \text{ is defined by } f_1(x) = +2\sqrt{\dfrac{x}{x-2}}$$

and

$$y = f_2(x) \text{ where } f_2 \text{ is defined by } f_2(x) = -2\sqrt{\dfrac{x}{x-2}}$$

The graph of the given equation will be made up of the graphs of the two functions f_1 and f_2.

First we consider f_1. Since

$$\lim_{x \to 2^+} f_1(x) = \lim_{x \to 2^+} 2\sqrt{\dfrac{x}{x-2}} = +\infty$$

by Definition 4.5.1(i) the line $x = 2$ is a vertical asymptote of the graph of f_1.

$$\lim_{x \to +\infty} f_1(x) = \lim_{x \to +\infty} 2\sqrt{\dfrac{x}{x-2}} = \lim_{x \to +\infty} 2\sqrt{\dfrac{1}{1 - 2/x}} = 2$$

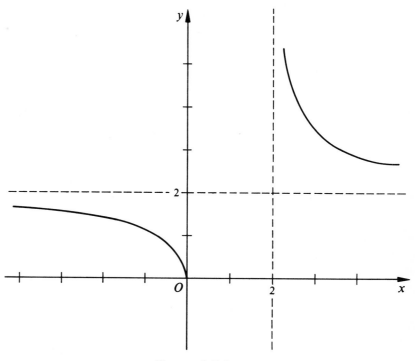

Figure 4.5.4

So by Definition 4.5.2(i), the line $y = 2$ is a horizontal asymptote of the graph of f_1.

Similarly, $\lim\limits_{x \to -\infty} f_1(x) = 2$. A sketch of the graph of f_1 is shown in Fig. 4.5.4.

$$\lim_{x \to 2^+} f_2(x) = \lim_{x \to 2^+} \left[-2\sqrt{\frac{x}{x-2}} \right] = -\infty$$

Hence by Definition 4.5.1(ii) the line $x = 2$ is a vertical asymptote of the graph of f_2.

$$\lim_{x \to +\infty} f_2(x) = \lim_{x \to +\infty} \left[-2\sqrt{\frac{x}{x-2}} \right] = \lim_{x \to +\infty} \left[-2\sqrt{\frac{1}{1-\frac{2}{x}}} \right] = -2$$

So by Definition 4.5.2(i) the line $y = -2$ is a horizontal asymptote of the graph of f_2.

$\lim\limits_{x \to -\infty} f_2(x) = -2$, also. A sketch of the graph of f_2 is shown in Fig. 4.5.5.

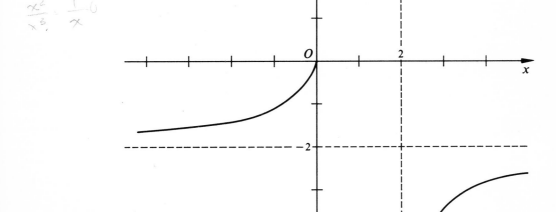

Figure 4.5.5

The graph of the given equation consists of the graphs of f_1 and f_2 and a sketch is shown in Fig. 4.5.6.

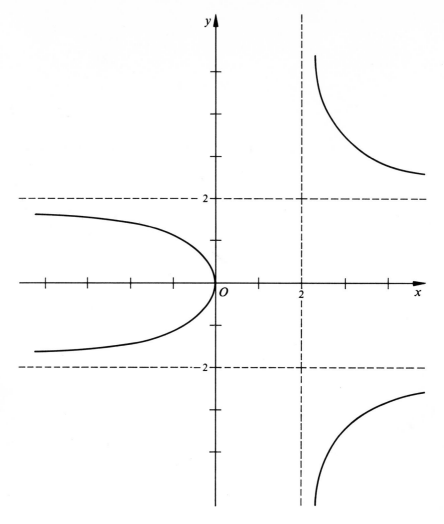

Figure 4.5.6

Exercises 4.5

In Exercises 1 through 14, find the horizontal and vertical asymptotes of the graph of the given function, and draw a sketch of the graph.

1. $f(x) = \dfrac{4}{x - 5}$

2. $f(x) = \dfrac{-2}{x + 3}$

3. $g(x) = \dfrac{-3}{(x + 2)^2}$

4. $F(x) = \dfrac{5}{x^2 + 8x + 16}$

5. $f(x) = \dfrac{1}{x^2 + 5x - 6}$

6. $G(x) = \dfrac{2x}{6x^2 + 11x - 10}$

7. $h(x) = \dfrac{4x^2}{x^2 - 9}$

8. $f(x) = \dfrac{x^2}{4 - x^2}$

　　　　ADDITIONAL THEOREMS ON LIMITS OF FUNCTIONS　

9. $f(x) = \dfrac{2}{\sqrt{x^2 - 4}}$　　　　12. $h(x) = \dfrac{x}{\sqrt{x^2 - 9}}$

10. $g(x) = \dfrac{-1}{\sqrt{x^2 + 5x + 6}}$　　13. $f(x) = \dfrac{4x^2}{\sqrt{x^2 - 2}}$

11. $F(x) = \dfrac{-3x}{\sqrt{x^2 + 3}}$　　　14. $f(x) = \dfrac{-3x^2}{\sqrt{x^2 + 7x + 10}}$

In Exercises 15 through 21, find the horizontal and vertical asymptotes of the graph of the given equation, and draw a sketch of the graph.

15. $3xy - 2x - 4y - 3 = 0$　　　18. $2xy^2 + 4y^2 - 3x = 0$

16. $2xy + 4x - 3y + 6 = 0$　　　19. $(y^2 - 1)(x - 3) = 6$

17. $x^2y^2 - x^2 + 4y^2 = 0$　　　20. $xy^2 + 3y^2 - 9x = 0$

21. $x^2y + 6xy - x^2 + 2x + 9y + 3 = 0$

(4.6)　　Additional theorems on limits of functions

We shall need to make use of the following theorems on limits of functions in later chapters.

4.6.1 THEOREM　　If $\lim\limits_{x \to a} f(x)$ exists and is positive, then there is an open interval containing a such that $f(x) > 0$ for every $x \neq a$ in the interval.

Proof: Let $L = \lim\limits_{x \to a} f(x)$. By hypothesis, $L > 0$. Applying Definition 4.1.1 and taking $\epsilon = L/2$, there exists a $\delta > 0$ such that

(1)　　　　$|f(x) - L| < \dfrac{L}{2}$　　whenever　　$0 < |x - a| < \delta$

Also, $|f(x) - L| < L/2$ is equivalent to $-L/2 < f(x) - L < L/2$, which in turn is equivalent to

(2)　　　　　　$\dfrac{L}{2} < f(x) < \dfrac{3}{2}L$

Also, $0 < |x - a| < \delta$ is equivalent to $-\delta < x - a < \delta$ but $x \neq a$, which in turn is equivalent to

$$a - \delta < x < a + \delta \qquad \text{but} \qquad x \neq a$$

which is equivalent to saying

(3)　　　　　x is in the open interval $(a - \delta, a + \delta)$, but $x \neq a$

From statements (2) and (3), we may replace (1) by the statement $L/2 < f(x) < 3L/2$ when x is in the open interval $(a - \delta, a + \delta)$, but $x \neq a$.

Since $L > 0$, we have the conclusion

$$f(x) > 0 \text{ for every } x \neq a \text{ in the open interval } (a - \delta, a + \delta) \qquad \text{Q.E.D.}$$

The following theorem is similar to the above theorem.

4.6.2 THEOREM   If $\lim_{x \to a} f(x)$ exists and is negative, there is an open interval containing a such that $f(x) < 0$ for every $x \neq a$ in the interval.

The proof is left for the reader (see Exercise 1 below).

4.6.3 THEOREM   Suppose the function f is defined on some open interval I containing a, except possibly at a. Also suppose that there is some number M such that $f(x) \leq M$ when $|x - a|$ is sufficiently small. Then, if $\lim_{x \to a} f(x)$ exists and is equal to L, $L \leq M$.

The proof is left for the reader (see Exercise 3 below).

4.6.4 THEOREM   Suppose the function f is defined on some open interval I containing a, except possibly at a. Also suppose that there is some number M such that $f(x) \geq M$ when $|x - a|$ is sufficiently small. Then, if $\lim_{x \to a} f(x)$ exists and is equal to L, $L \geq M$.

The proof is left for the reader (see Exercise 4 below).

Exercises 4.6

1. Prove Theorem 4.6.2.

2. Suppose the functions f, g, and h are defined on some open interval I containing a, except possibly at a itself, and that $f(x) \leq g(x) \leq h(x)$ for all x in I for which $x \neq a$. Also suppose that $\lim_{x \to a} f(x)$ and $\lim_{x \to a} h(x)$ both exist and are equal to L. Prove that $\lim_{x \to a} g(x)$ also exists and is equal to L. HINT: First show that when $|x - a|$ is sufficiently small, and $\epsilon > 0$, the following inequalities must hold: $L - \epsilon < f(x) < L + \epsilon$, and $L - \epsilon < h(x) < L + \epsilon$.

3. Prove Theorem 4.6.3. HINT: Assume $M < L$, and show that this assumption leads to a contradiction.

4. Prove Theorem 4.6.4.

5 Continuity

(5.1) Continuity of a function at a number

In Sec. 4.1 we considered the function f defined by the equation

$$f(x) = \frac{(2x + 3)(x - 1)}{x - 1}$$

We noted that f is defined for all values of x except 1. A sketch of the graph consisting of all points on the line $y = 2x + 3$ except $(1,5)$ is shown in Fig. 5.1.1. There is a break in the graph at the point $(1,5)$, and we say that the function f is *discontinuous* at the number 1.

If we define $f(1) = 2$, the function is defined for all values of x, but there is still a break in the graph, and the function is still discontinuous at 1. However, if we define $f(1) = 5$, there is no break in the graph, and the function f is said to be *continuous* at all values of x. We have the following definition.

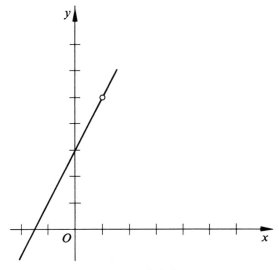

Figure 5.1.1

123

5.1.1 DEFINITION   The function *f* is said to be *continuous* at the number *a* if and only if the following three conditions are satisfied:

(i) $f(a)$ exists

(ii) $\lim\limits_{x \to a} f(x)$ exists

(iii) $\lim\limits_{x \to a} f(x) = f(a)$

If one or more of these three conditions fails to hold at *a*, the function *f* is said to be *discontinuous* at *a*.

Let us apply the three conditions in Definition 5.1.1 at the number 1 to the function *f* defined by

$$f(x) = \begin{cases} \dfrac{(2x + 3)(x - 1)}{x - 1} & \text{if } x \neq 1 \\ 2 & \text{if } x = 1 \end{cases}$$

$f(1) = 2$; therefore condition (i) is satisfied.
$\lim\limits_{x \to 1} f(x) = 5$; therefore condition (ii) is satisfied.
However, $\lim\limits_{x \to 1} f(x) \neq f(1)$; therefore condition (iii) is not satisfied.

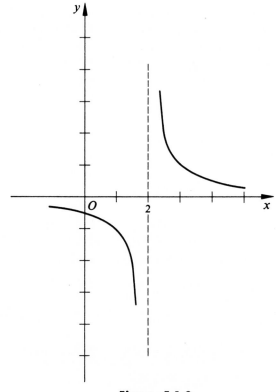

Figure 5.1.2

We conclude that the function f is discontinuous at 1.

You will note, however, that if we had defined $f(1) = 5$, then $\lim\limits_{x \to 1} f(x) = f(1)$, and f would be continuous at 1.

We shall now consider some examples of discontinuous functions. In each example we shall draw a sketch of the graph, determine the points where there is a break in the graph, and show which of the three conditions in Definition 5.1.1 fails to hold at each discontinuity.

EXAMPLE 1: Let f be defined as follows:

$$f(x) = \frac{1}{x - 2}$$

A sketch of the graph of this function is given in Fig. 5.1.2. We see that there is a break in the graph at the point where $x = 2$. So, we investigate there the conditions of Definition 5.1.1.

$f(2)$ is not defined; therefore condition (i) is not satisfied.

We conclude that f is discontinuous at 2.

EXAMPLE 2: Let g be defined by

$$g(x) = \begin{cases} \dfrac{1}{x - 2} & \text{if } x \neq 2 \\ 3 & \text{if } x = 2 \end{cases}$$

A sketch of the graph of this function is shown in Fig. 5.1.3. Investigating the conditions at 2, we have:

$g(2) = 3$; therefore condition (i) is satisfied.

$\lim\limits_{x \to 2^-} g(x) = -\infty$, and $\lim\limits_{x \to 2^+} g(x) = +\infty$; therefore condition (ii) is not satisfied.

Thus g is discontinuous at 2.

EXAMPLE 3: Let h be defined as follows:

$$h(x) = \begin{cases} 3 + x & \text{if } x \leq 1 \\ 3 - x & \text{if } 1 < x \end{cases}$$

A sketch of the graph is shown in Fig. 5.1.4. Because there is a break in the graph at the point where $x = 1$, we investigate the conditions at 1. We have:

$h(1) = 4$; therefore condition (i) is satisfied.

$$\lim\limits_{x \to 1^-} h(x) = \lim\limits_{x \to 1^-} (3 + x) = 4.$$

$$\lim\limits_{x \to 1^+} h(x) = \lim\limits_{x \to 1^+} (3 - x) = 2.$$

Since $\lim\limits_{x \to 1^-} h(x) \neq \lim\limits_{x \to 1^+} h(x)$, we conclude that $\lim\limits_{x \to 1} h(x)$ does not exist; therefore condition (ii) fails to hold at 1.

Hence, h is discontinuous at 1.

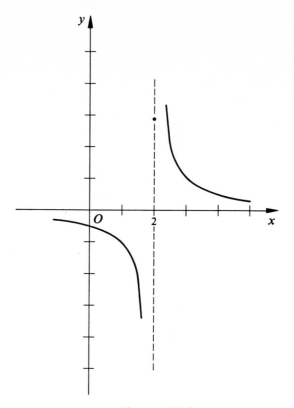

Figure 5.1.3

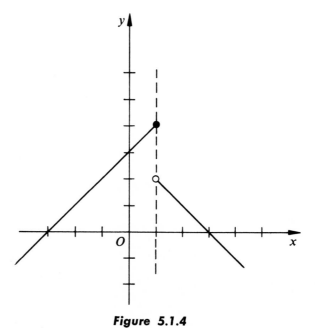

Figure 5.1.4

EXAMPLE 4: Let F be defined by

$$F(x) = \begin{cases} |x - 3| & \text{if } x \neq 3 \\ 2 & \text{if } x = 3 \end{cases}$$

A sketch of the graph of this function is shown in Fig. 5.1.5. We investigate the three conditions at the point where $x = 3$. We have:

$F(3) = 2$; therefore condition (i) is satisfied.

$\lim\limits_{x \to 3^-} F(x) = 0$ and $\lim\limits_{x \to 3^+} F(x) = 0$. So, $\lim\limits_{x \to 3} F(x)$ exists and $= 0$; therefore condition (ii) is satisfied.

$\lim\limits_{x \to 3} F(x) = 0$ but $F(3) = 2$. Therefore, condition (iii) is not satisfied.

This proves that F is discontinuous at 3.

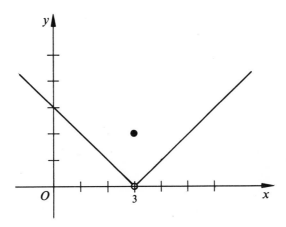

Figure 5.1.5

EXAMPLE 5: Let G be defined as follows:

$$G(x) = \sqrt{x - 4}$$

A sketch of the graph is shown in Fig. 5.1.6. There is a break at the point where $x = 4$. We investigate the conditions at 4.

$G(4) = 0$; therefore condition (i) is satisfied.

$\lim\limits_{x \to 4^+} \sqrt{x - 4} = 0$, but $\lim\limits_{x \to 4^-} \sqrt{x - 4}$ does not exist since $\sqrt{x - 4}$ is not a real number for values of x less than 4. Therefore condition (ii) is not satisfied at 4.

We conclude that G is discontinuous at 4.

It should be apparent that the geometric notion of a break in the graph at a certain point is synonymous with the analytic concept of a function being discontinuous at a certain value of the independent variable.

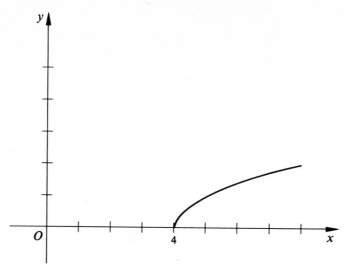

Figure 5.1.6

Exercises 5.1

In Exercises 1 through 18 draw a sketch of the graph of the function; then by observing where there are breaks in the graph, determine the values of the independent variable at which the function is discontinuous and show why Definition 5.1.1 is not satisfied at each discontinuity.

1. $f(x) = \begin{cases} \dfrac{5}{x-4} & \text{if } x \neq 4 \\ 1 & \text{if } x = 4 \end{cases}$

8. $f(x) = 3 - \sqrt{x+4}$

2. $g(x) = \begin{cases} \dfrac{1}{x+2} & \text{if } x \neq -2 \\ 0 & \text{if } x = -2 \end{cases}$

9. $h(x) = \dfrac{x+3}{x^2 + x - 6}$

3. $F(x) = \dfrac{x^2 + x - 6}{x+3}$

10. $g(x) = \dfrac{x^2 - 4}{x^4 - 16}$

4. $h(x) = \dfrac{x^4 - 16}{x^2 - 4}$

11. $f(x) = \begin{cases} -1 & \text{if } x < 0 \\ 0 & \text{if } x = 0 \\ 1 & \text{if } 0 < x \end{cases}$

5. $g(x) = \begin{cases} \dfrac{x^2 + x - 6}{x+3} & \text{if } x \neq -3 \\ 1 & \text{if } x = -3 \end{cases}$

12. $H(x) = \begin{cases} 1 + x & \text{if } x \leq -2 \\ 2 - x & \text{if } -2 < x \leq 2 \\ 2x - 1 & \text{if } 2 < x \end{cases}$

6. $f(x) = \dfrac{x^3 - 2x^2 - 11x + 12}{x^2 - 5x + 4}$

13. $f(x) = |2x + 5|$

7. $G(x) = \sqrt{2x + 3}$

14. $G(x) = \begin{cases} |2x + 5| & \text{if } x \neq -\dfrac{5}{2} \\ 3 & \text{if } x = -\dfrac{5}{2} \end{cases}$

15. $f(x) = \dfrac{x - 3}{|x - 3|}$

17. $g(x) = \begin{cases} 2x + 3 & \text{if } x \le 1 \\ 8 - 3x & \text{if } 1 < x < 2 \\ x + 3 & \text{if } 2 \le x \end{cases}$

16. $F(x) = \begin{cases} \dfrac{x - 3}{|x - 3|} & \text{if } x \ne 3 \\ 0 & \text{if } x = 3 \end{cases}$

18. $f(x) = \begin{cases} \dfrac{x^2 + x - 2}{x + 2} & \text{if } x \ne -2 \\ -3 & \text{if } x = -2 \end{cases}$

19. If F is the greatest integer function, at what numbers is F discontinuous? What condition in Definition 5.1.1 is not satisfied at each discontinuity? HINT: See Example 2 in Sec. 3.3.

20. If U is the unit step function, at what number or numbers is U discontinuous? What condition in Definition 5.1.1 is not satisfied at each discontinuity? HINT: See the first problem in Exercises 3.3.

21. Let f be the function defined by $f(x) = \begin{cases} |x - [\![x]\!]| & \text{, \quad if } [\![x]\!] \text{ is even} \\ |x - [\![x + 1]\!]|, & \text{if } [\![x]\!] \text{ is odd} \end{cases}$
Draw a sketch of the graph of f. At what numbers is f found to be discontinuous?

22. Let f be a function which is discontinuous at the number a but for which $\lim_{x \to a} f(x)$ exists and is finite. Then either $f(a) \ne \lim_{x \to a} f(x)$ or $f(a)$ does not exist. Such a discontinuity is called a *removable discontinuity*, since if f were redefined at a so that $f(a) = \lim_{x \to a} f(x)$, f becomes continuous at a.

For each of the following functions, define $f(a)$ so that the discontinuity is removed at the given value of a:

(a) $f(x) = \dfrac{9x^2 - 4}{3x - 2}; a = \dfrac{2}{3}$ $(3x - 2)(3x + 2)$

(b) $f(x) = \begin{cases} |x - 3| & \text{if } x \ne 3 \\ 2 & \text{if } x = 3 \end{cases}; a = 3$

(c) $f(x) = \dfrac{\sqrt{x + 5} - \sqrt{5}}{x}; a = 0$

(d) $f(x) = \dfrac{\sqrt{2 + \sqrt[3]{x}} - 2}{x - 8}; a = 8$

(e) $f(x) = \dfrac{\sqrt[3]{x + 1} - 1}{x}; a = 0$

23. f is the function defined by

$$f(x) = \lim_{n \to +\infty} \left(\frac{2nx}{1 - nx} \right)$$ $\dfrac{1/n}{1/n} = \dfrac{2x}{1/n - x}$

Draw a sketch of the graph of f. At what values of x is f discontinuous?

(5.2) Continuity of a function on an interval and theorems on continuity

By applying Definition 5.1.1 and limit theorems, we have the following theorem about functions that are continuous at a number.

5.2.1 THEOREM   If f and g are two functions that are continuous at the number a, then

(i) $f + g$ is continuous at a

(ii) $f - g$ is continuous at a

(iii) $f \cdot g$ is continuous at a

(iv) f/g is continuous at a, provided that $g(a) \neq 0$

To illustrate the kind of proof required for each part of this theorem, we shall prove part (i):

Since f and g are continuous at a, from Definition 5.1.1 we have

(1)
$$\lim_{x \to a} f(x) = f(a)$$

and

(2)
$$\lim_{x \to a} g(x) = g(a)$$

Therefore, from equations (1) and (2) and Limit Theorem 4, we have

(3)
$$\lim_{x \to a} [f(x) + g(x)] = f(a) + g(a)$$

Equation (3) is the condition that $f + g$ is continuous at a, which furnishes the proof of (i).

The proofs of parts (ii), (iii), and (iv) are left for the reader (see Exercises 1 through 3 below).

5.2.2 THEOREM   A polynomial function is continuous at every number.

To prove this theorem, consider the polynomial function f defined by

$$f(x) = b_0 x^n + b_1 x^{n-1} + b_2 x^{n-2} + \cdots + b_{n-1} x + b_n \qquad b_0 \neq 0$$

where n is a nonnegative integer, and $b_0, b_1, \ldots, b_n$ are real numbers. By successive applications of limit theorems it can be shown that if a is any number,

$$\lim_{x \to a} f(x) = b_0 a^n + b_1 a^{n-1} + b_2 a^{n-2} + \cdots + b_{n-1} a + b_n$$

from which it follows that

$$\lim_{x \to a} f(x) = f(a)$$

thus establishing the theorem. The details of the proof are left to the reader (see Exercise 4 below).

5.2.3 THEOREM   A rational function is continuous at every number in its domain.

Proof: If f is a rational function, it may be expressed as the quotient of two polynomial functions. So f may be defined by

$$f(x) = \frac{g(x)}{h(x)}$$

where g and h are two polynomial functions, and the domain of f consists of all numbers except those for which $h(x) = 0$.

If a is any number in the domain of f, then $h(a) \neq 0$; and so by Limit Theorem 8,

(4)
$$\lim_{x \to a} f(x) = \frac{\lim_{x \to a} g(x)}{\lim_{x \to a} h(x)}$$

Since g and h are polynomial functions, by Theorem 5.2.2 they are continuous at a, and so $\lim_{x \to a} g(x) = g(a)$ and $\lim_{x \to a} h(x) = h(a)$. Consequently, from equation (4) we have

$$\lim_{x \to a} f(x) = \frac{g(a)}{h(a)}$$

and so we may conclude that f is continuous at every number in its domain.

Definition 5.1.1 states that the function f is continuous at the number a if $f(a)$ exists, if $\lim_{x \to a} f(x)$ exists and is finite, and if

(5)
$$\lim_{x \to a} f(x) = f(a)$$

Definition 4.1.1 states that $\lim_{x \to a} f(x) = L$ if for any $\epsilon > 0$ there exists a $\delta > 0$ such that

$$|f(x) - L| < \epsilon \qquad \text{whenever} \qquad 0 < |x - a| < \delta$$

Applying this definition to equation 5, we have $\lim_{x \to a} f(x) = f(a)$ if for any $\epsilon > 0$ there exists a $\delta > 0$ such that

(6)
$$|f(x) - f(a)| < \epsilon \qquad \text{whenever} \qquad 0 < |x - a| < \delta$$

If f is continuous at a, we know that $f(a)$ exists; thus in statement (6) it is not necessary that $|x - a| > 0$, since when $x = a$, statement (6) obviously holds. We have then the following definition of continuity of a function, using ϵ and δ notation.

5.2.4 DEFINITION   The function f is said to be continuous at the number a if f is defined on some open interval containing a and if for any $\epsilon > 0$ there exists a $\delta > 0$ such that

$$|f(x) - f(a)| < \epsilon \qquad \text{whenever} \qquad |x - a| < \delta$$

This alternate definition is used in proving the following important theorem regarding the limit of a composite function.

5.2.5 THEOREM   If $\lim\limits_{x \to a} g(x) = b$ and if the function f is continuous at b, then

$$\lim_{x \to a} (f \circ g)(x) = f(b)$$

or equivalently,

$$\lim_{x \to a} f(g(x)) = f(\lim_{x \to a} g(x))$$

Proof: Since f is continuous at b, we have the following from Definition 5.2.4: for any $\epsilon_1 > 0$ there exists a $\delta_1 > 0$ such that

(7) $|f(y) - f(b)| < \epsilon_1$ whenever $|y - b| < \delta_1$

Since $\lim\limits_{x \to a} g(x) = b$, for any $\delta_1 > 0$ there exists a $\delta_2 > 0$ such that

(8) $|g(x) - b| < \delta_1$ whenever $0 < |x - a| < \delta_2$

Whenever $0 < |x - a| < \delta_2$, we replace y in statement (7) by $g(x)$ and obtain the following: for any $\epsilon_1 > 0$ there exists a $\delta_1 > 0$ such that

(9) $|f(g(x)) - f(b)| < \epsilon_1$ whenever $|g(x) - b| < \delta_1$

From statements (9) and (8), we may conclude that for any $\epsilon_1 > 0$ there exists a $\delta_2 > 0$ such that

$$|f(g(x)) - f(b)| < \epsilon_1 \quad \text{whenever} \quad 0 < |x - a| < \delta_2$$

from which it follows that

$$\lim_{x \to a} f(g(x)) = f(b)$$

or, equivalently,

$$\lim_{x \to a} f(g(x)) = f(\lim_{x \to a} g(x)) \qquad \text{Q.E.D.}$$

An immediate application of this theorem is in proving Limit Theorems 8 and 9, the proofs of which were deferred until now. We shall now restate these theorems and prove them.

LIMIT THEOREM 8   If $\lim\limits_{x \to a} f(x) = L$ and if $\lim\limits_{x \to a} g(x) = M$ and $M \neq 0$, then

$$\lim_{x \to a} \frac{f(x)}{g(x)} = \frac{L}{M}$$

Proof: Let h be the function defined by $h(x) = 1/x$. Then, the composite function $h \circ g$ is defined by $h(g(x)) = 1/g(x)$.

Hence $\lim\limits_{x \to a} \dfrac{1}{g(x)} = \lim\limits_{x \to a} h(g(x))$

$\qquad\qquad\qquad = h\,(\lim\limits_{x \to a} g(x))$ by Theorem 5.2.5

$\qquad\qquad\qquad = h(M)$

$\qquad\qquad\qquad = \dfrac{1}{M}$

Applying Limit Theorem 6 (limit of a product) and the above result, we have

$$\lim_{x \to a} \frac{f(x)}{g(x)} = \lim_{x \to a} f(x) \cdot \lim_{x \to a} \frac{1}{g(x)}$$

$$= L \cdot \frac{1}{M}$$

$$= \frac{L}{M} \qquad \qquad \text{Q.E.D.}$$

LIMIT THEOREM 9   If $\lim_{x \to a} f(x) = L$, then

$$\lim_{x \to a} \sqrt[n]{f(x)} = \sqrt[n]{L}$$

if n is a positive odd integer, or if n is a positive even integer and $L > 0$.

Proof: Let h be the function defined by $h(x) = \sqrt[n]{x}$. Then the composite function $h \circ f$ is defined by $h(f(x)) = \sqrt[n]{f(x)}$.
Consequently,

$$\lim_{x \to a} \sqrt[n]{f(x)} = \lim_{x \to a} h(f(x))$$

$$= h(\lim_{x \to a} f(x)) \qquad \text{by Theorem 5.2.5}$$

$$= \sqrt[n]{\lim_{x \to a} f(x)}$$

$$= \sqrt[n]{L} \qquad \qquad \text{Q.E.D.}$$

5.2.6 DEFINITION   A function is said to be continuous on an open interval if it is continuous at every number in the open interval.

For example, the function f defined by $f(x) = 1/(x - 2)$ is continuous on any open interval that does not contain the number 2.

Suppose the domain of a function is a closed interval. For example, if f is defined by

(10) $$f(x) = \sqrt{16 - x^2}$$

the domain of f is the closed interval $[-4,4]$. To define continuity of a function on a closed interval, we must first define *right-hand continuity and left-hand continuity.*

5.2.7 DEFINITION   The function f is said to be *continuous from the right* at the number a if and only if the following three conditions are satisfied:

(i) $f(a)$ exists

(ii) $\lim_{x \to a^+} f(x)$ exists

(iii) $\lim_{x \to a^+} f(x) = f(a)$

5.2.8 DEFINITION   The function f is said to be *continuous from the left* at the number a if and only if the following three conditions are satisfied:

(i) $f(a)$ exists

(ii) $\lim\limits_{x \to a^-} f(x)$ exists

(iii) $\lim\limits_{x \to a^-} f(x) = f(a)$

5.2.9 DEFINITION   The function f, whose domain includes the closed interval $[a,b]$, is said to be continuous on $[a,b]$ if and only if it is continuous on the open interval (a,b), as well as continuous from the right at a and continuous from the left at b.

The function defined by equation (10) is then continuous on the closed interval $[-4,4]$, since it is continuous on the open interval $(-4,4)$ and

$$\lim_{x \to -4^+} \sqrt{16 - x^2} = 0 = f(-4)$$

and

$$\lim_{x \to 4^-} \sqrt{16 - x^2} = 0 = f(4)$$

Another application of Theorem 5.2.5 is in proving that *a continuous function of a continuous function is continuous*. We shall state this as a theorem and prove it.

5.2.10 THEOREM   If the function g is continuous on the closed interval $[a,b]$ and if the function f is continuous on the closed interval $[g(a),g(b)]$ (or $[g(b),g(a)]$ if $g(b) < g(a)$) and at all numbers $g(c)$ if c is in (a,b), then the composite function $f \circ g$ is continuous on the closed interval $[a,b]$.

Proof: Let c be any number in (a,b). Since g is continuous on $[a,b]$,

(11) $$\lim_{x \to c} g(x) = g(c)$$

Then, $\lim\limits_{x \to c} (f \circ g)(x) = \lim\limits_{x \to c} f(g(x))$

$\qquad\qquad = f(\lim\limits_{x \to c} g(x)) \qquad$ by Theorem 5.2.5

$\qquad\qquad = f(g(c)) \qquad\qquad$ by equation (11)

$\qquad\qquad = (f \circ g)(c)$

Therefore, $f \circ g$ is continuous at c, and since c is any number in (a,b) it follows that $f \circ g$ is continuous on (a,b).

In the above proof if c is an end point of the interval $[a,b]$, then if $\lim\limits_{x \to c}$ is replaced by $\lim\limits_{x \to c^+}$ when $c = a$ and by $\lim\limits_{x \to c^-}$ when $c = b$, we shall have proved that $f \circ g$ is continuous from the right at a and continuous from the left at b. This proves the theorem.

Theorem 5.2.10 enables us to conclude that particular functions are continuous without having to apply the definition of continuity. For example, if h is the function defined by $h(x) = \sqrt{x-4}$ we can conclude that h is continuous on the interval $[4,+\infty)$ because of the following reasoning:

If $g(x) = x - 4$ and if $f(x) = \sqrt{x}$, then $(f \circ g)(x) = \sqrt{x-4}$. g is continuous on $[4,+\infty)$, and f is continuous on $[0,+\infty)$. Therefore, $f \circ g$ is continuous on $[4,+\infty)$.

EXAMPLE 1: Given f is the function defined by $f(x) = \sqrt{(2-x)/(3+x)}$, determine whether f is continuous or discontinuous on each of the following intervals: $(-3,2)$, $[-3,2]$, $[-3,2)$, $(-3,2]$.

Solution: We first determine the domain of f. The domain of f consists of all numbers for which $(2-x)/(3+x)$ is nonnegative. Thus, any values of x for which the numerator and the denominator of this fraction have opposite signs are excluded from the domain of f. The numerator changes sign when $x = 2$, and the denominator changes sign when $x = -3$. We make use of the following table to determine whether the fraction is "+", "−", 0, or undefined, from which we are able to determine the values of x for which $f(x)$ exists. The do-

Table 5.2.1

	$2-x$	$3+x$	$\dfrac{2-x}{3+x}$	$f(x)$
$x < -3$	$+$	$-$	$-$	does not exist
$x = -3$	5	0	undefined	does not exist
$-3 < x < 2$	$+$	$+$	$+$	$+$
$x = 2$	0	3	0	0
$2 < x$	$-$	$+$	$-$	does not exist

main of f is then the interval half-open on the left $(-3,2]$. f is continuous on the open interval $(-3,2)$. f is continuous from the left at 2 because

$$\lim_{x \to 2^-} \sqrt{\frac{2-x}{3+x}} = 0 = f(2)$$

However, f is not continuous from the right at -3 because

$$\lim_{x \to -3^+} \sqrt{\frac{2-x}{3+x}} = +\infty$$

We conclude that f is continuous on $(-3,2]$ and discontinuous on $[-3,2]$ and $[-3,2)$.

1. Prove Theorem 5.2.1(ii).

2. Prove Theorem 5.2.1(iii).

3. Prove Theorem 5.2.1(iv).

4. Prove Theorem 5.2.2, showing step by step which limit theorems are used.

In Exercises 5 through 16 determine whether the function f is continuous or discontinuous on each of the indicated intervals.

5. $f(x) = \dfrac{2}{x+5}$; $(3,7)$, $[-6,4]$, $(-\infty,0)$, $(-5,+\infty)$, $[-5,+\infty)$, $[-10,-5)$

6. $f(x) = \dfrac{x+3}{x^2-4}$, $(0,4]$, $(-2,2)$, $(-\infty,-2]$, $(2,+\infty)$, $[-4,4]$, $(-2,2]$

7. $f(x) = \sqrt{x^2-9}$; $(-\infty,-3)$, $(-\infty,-3]$, $(3,+\infty)$, $[3,+\infty)$, $(-3,3)$

8. $f(x) = [\![x]\!]$; $(-\frac{1}{2},\frac{1}{2})$, $(\frac{1}{4},\frac{1}{2})$, $(1,2)$, $[1,2)$, $(1,2]$

9. $f(x) = \dfrac{|x-1|}{x-1}$; $(-\infty,1)$, $(-\infty,1]$, $[-1,1]$, $(-1,+\infty)$, $(1,+\infty)$

10. $f(x) = \begin{cases} 2x-3 & \text{if } x < -2 \\ x-5 & \text{if } -2 \le x \le 1 \\ 3-x & \text{if } 1 < x \end{cases}$; $(-\infty,1)$, $(-2,+\infty)$, $(-2,1)$, $[-2,1)$

11. $f(x) = \sqrt{4-x^2}$; $(-2,2)$, $[-2,2]$, $[-2,2)$, $(-2,2]$, $(-\infty,-2]$, $(2,+\infty)$

12. $f(x) = \sqrt{\dfrac{2+x}{2-x}}$; $(-2,2)$, $[-2,2]$, $[-2,2)$, $(-2,2]$, $(-\infty,-2)$, $[2,+\infty)$

13. $f(x) = \dfrac{1}{\sqrt{3+2x-x^2}}$; $(-1,3)$, $[-1,3]$, $[-1,3)$, $(-1,3]$

14. $f(x) = \sqrt{3+2x-x^2}$; $(-1,3)$, $[-1,3]$, $[-1,3)$, $(-1,3]$

15. $f(x) = \sqrt{\dfrac{9-x^2}{4-x}}$; $(-\infty,-3)$, $(-3,3)$, $[-3,3]$, $[-3,3)$, $[3,4]$, $(3,4]$, $[4,+\infty)$, $(4,+\infty)$

16. $f(x) = \sqrt{\dfrac{2+x}{25-x^2}}$; $(-\infty,-5)$, $(-\infty,-5]$, $[-5,-2]$, $[-2,5]$, $[-2,5)$, $(-2,5]$, $(-2,5)$, $[5,+\infty)$, $(5,+\infty)$

In Exercises 17 through 20, find the values of the constants c and k that make the function continuous on $(-\infty,+\infty)$ and draw a sketch of the graph of the resulting function.

17. $f(x) = \begin{cases} 3x+7 & \text{if } x \le 4 \\ kx-1 & \text{if } 4 < x \end{cases}$

18. $f(x) = \begin{cases} kx-1 & \text{if } x < 2 \\ kx^2 & \text{if } 2 \le x \end{cases}$

19. $f(x) = \begin{cases} x & \text{if } x \le 1 \\ cx+k & \text{if } 1 < x < 4 \\ -2x & \text{if } 4 \le x \end{cases}$

20. $f(x) = \begin{cases} x+2c & \text{if } x < -2 \\ 3cx+k & \text{if } -2 \le x \le 1 \\ 3x-2k & \text{if } 1 < x \end{cases}$

21. Given that f is defined by $f(x) = \begin{cases} g(x) & \text{if } a \le x < b \\ h(x) & \text{if } b \le x \le c \end{cases}$

    If g is continuous on $[a,b)$, and h is continuous on $[b,c]$, can we conclude that f is continuous on $[a,c]$? If your answer is yes, prove it. If your answer is no, what additional condition or conditions would assure continuity of f on $[a,c]$?

    In Exercises 22 through 31, determine all values of x for which the given function is continuous. Indicate which theorems you apply.

22. $f(x) = x^2(x + 3)^3$

27. $H(x) = \sqrt{\dfrac{x + 4}{x - 4}}$ $(-\infty,-4] \ (4,\infty)$

23. $g(x) = \sqrt{x^2 + 4}$

28. $G(x) = \left(\dfrac{x^2}{x^2 - 4} - \dfrac{1}{x}\right)^{1/3}$

24. $F(x) = \sqrt{x^2 - 16}$

29. $f(x) = x^2(x^{-2} + x^{-1/2})^3$

25. $f(x) = \sqrt{16 - x^2}$

30. $g(x) = [\![\sqrt{1 - x^2}]\!]$

26. $h(x) = \sqrt{\dfrac{4 - x}{4 + x}}$

31. $F(x) = 1 - x + [\![x]\!] - [\![1 - x]\!]$

    In Exercises 32 through 39, functions f and g are defined. In each exercise define $f \circ g$, and determine all values of x for which $f \circ g$ is continuous.

32. $f(x) = x^2$; $g(x) = x^2 - 3$

36. $f(x) = \sqrt[3]{x}$; $g(x) = \sqrt{x + 1}$

33. $f(x) = x^3$; $g(x) = \sqrt{x}$

37. $f(x) = \dfrac{1}{x - 2}$; $g(x) = \sqrt{x}$

34. $f(x) = \sqrt{x}$; $g(x) = x + 1$

38. $f(x) = \sqrt{x + 1}$; $g(x) = \sqrt[3]{x}$

35. $f(x) = \sqrt{x}$; $g(x) = \dfrac{1}{x - 2}$

39. $f(x) = \dfrac{x + 1}{x - 1}$; $g(x) = \sqrt{x}$

40. If f is the function defined by $f(x) = \sqrt[n]{x^m}$, where m and n are positive integers, prove that f is continuous on the interval $[0, +\infty)$.

41. If f is the function defined by $f(x) = |x - 5|$, prove that f is continuous for all values of x.

42. Prove that if the function f is continuous at x, then $\lim_{h \to 0} f(x - h) = f(x)$.

⑥ The derivative

(6.1) The tangent line

Many of the important problems in calculus depend upon the problem of finding the tangent line to a given curve at a specific point on the curve. If the curve is a circle, we know from plane geometry that the tangent line at a point P on the circle is defined as the line intersecting the circle at only one point P. This definition will not suffice for a curve in general. For example, in Fig. 6.1.1, the tangent line to the curve at point P intersects the curve at another point Q.

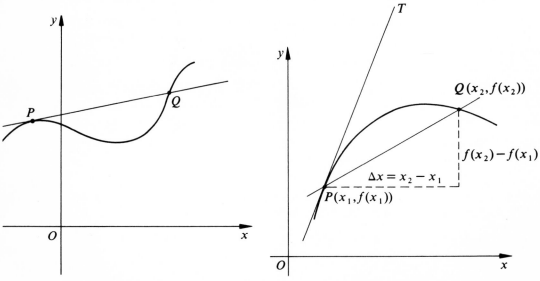

Figure 6.1.1   Figure 6.1.2

In this section we shall arrive at a suitable definition of the tangent line to the graph of a function at a point on the graph. We shall proceed by considering how we should define the slope of the tangent line at a point, since if we know the slope of a line and a point on the line, the line is determined.

Let the function f be continuous at x_1, and let f be defined on some open interval I containing x_1. We wish to define the slope of the tangent line to the graph of f at $P(x_1, f(x_1))$. Let $Q(x_2, f(x_2))$ be another point on the graph of f, such that x_2 is also in I. Draw a line through P and Q. Any line through two points on a curve is called a *secant line;* therefore the line through P and Q is a secant line (see Fig. 6.1.2).

Let us denote the difference of the abscissas of Q and P by Δx, so that

$$\Delta x = x_2 - x_1$$

The slope of the secant line PQ then is given by

$$m_{PQ} = \frac{f(x_2) - f(x_1)}{\Delta x}$$

Since $x_2 = x_1 + \Delta x$, we may write the above as

(1) $$m_{PQ} = \frac{f(x_1 + \Delta x) - f(x_1)}{\Delta x}$$

Now think of the point P as being fixed, and move point Q along the curve toward P; that is, Q approaches P. This is equivalent to saying that Δx approaches zero. As this occurs, the secant line turns about the fixed point P, and if this secant line has a limiting position, it is this limiting position that we wish to be the tangent line to the graph at P. So, we shall want the slope of the tangent line to the graph at P to be the limit of m_{PQ} as Δx approaches zero, if this limit exists. If $\lim_{\Delta x \to 0} m_{PQ}$ does not exist but equals ∞, then the inclination of PQ approaches $\pi/2$ as Δx approaches zero. In this case we would want the tangent line to the graph at P to be the line $x = x_1$. The preceding discussion leads us to the following definition.

6.1.1 DEFINITION   If the function f is continuous at x_1 and if f is defined on some open interval I containing x_1, then the *tangent line* to the graph of f at the point $P(x_1, f(x_1))$ is

(i)   the line through P having slope $m(x_1)$, given by

❨❨ (1) $$m(x_1) = \lim_{\Delta x \to 0} \frac{f(x_1 + \Delta x) - f(x_1)}{\Delta x}$$

if this limit exists; or

(ii)   the line $x = x_1$ if $\lim_{\Delta x \to 0} \dfrac{f(x_1 + \Delta x) - f(x_1)}{\Delta x} = \infty$

If neither (i) nor (ii) of Definition 6.1.1 holds, then there is no tangent line to the graph of f at the point $P(x_1, f(x_1))$.

EXAMPLE 1: Find the slope of the tangent line to the curve $y = x^2 - 4x + 3$ at the point (x_1, y_1).

Solution: $f(x) = x^2 - 4x + 3$; therefore, $f(x_1) = x_1^2 - 4x_1 + 3$, and $f(x_1 + \Delta x) = (x_1 + \Delta x)^2 - 4(x_1 + \Delta x) + 3$. From equation (1), we have

$$m(x_1) = \lim_{\Delta x \to 0} \frac{f(x_1 + \Delta x) - f(x_1)}{\Delta x}$$

$$= \lim_{\Delta x \to 0} \frac{[(x_1 + \Delta x)^2 - 4(x_1 + \Delta x) + 3] - [x_1^2 - 4x_1 + 3]}{\Delta x}$$

$$= \lim_{\Delta x \to 0} \frac{x_1^2 + 2x_1 \Delta x + (\Delta x)^2 - 4x_1 - 4\Delta x + 3 - x_1^2 + 4x_1 - 3}{\Delta x}$$

$$= \lim_{\Delta x \to 0} \frac{2x_1 \Delta x + (\Delta x)^2 - 4\Delta x}{\Delta x}$$

Since $\Delta x \neq 0$, we may divide the numerator and the denominator by Δx and obtain

$$m(x_1) = \lim_{\Delta x \to 0} (2x_1 + \Delta x - 4)$$

or

(2) $$m(x_1) = 2x_1 - 4$$

Let us now draw a sketch of the graph. We shall plot some points and a segment of the tangent line at some points. We shall take values of x arbitrarily and compute the corresponding value of y from the given equation, as well as the value of m from equation (2). The results are given in Table 6.1.1, and a sketch of the graph is shown in Fig. 6.1.3. It is important to determine the points where the graph has a horizontal tangent. We find these points by setting $m(x_1) = 0$ and solving for x_1. Doing this for this example, we have $2x_1 - 4 = 0$ which gives $x_1 = 2$. Therefore at the point having an abscissa of 2, the tangent line will be parallel to the x axis.

Table 6.1.1

x	y	m
2	−1	0
1	0	−2
0	3	−4
−1	8	−6
3	0	2
4	3	4
5	8	6

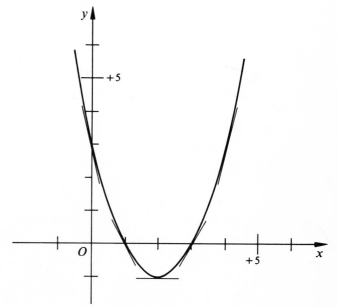

Figure 6.1.3

EXAMPLE 2: Find an equation of the tangent line to the curve of Example 1 at the point (4,3).

  Solution: Since the slope of the tangent line at any point (x_1, y_1) is given by

$$m(x_1) = 2x_1 - 4$$

the slope of the tangent line at the point (4,3) is 4. Therefore an equation of the desired line, using the point-slope form, is

$$y - 3 = 4(x - 4)$$

$$\text{or} \qquad 4x - y - 13 = 0$$

6.1.2 DEFINITION   The *normal line* to a curve at a given point is the line perpendicular to the tangent line at that point.

EXAMPLE 3: Find an equation of the normal line to the curve $y = \sqrt{x - 3}$ which is parallel to the line $6x + 3y - 4 = 0$.

  Solution: Let l be the given line. To find the slope of l, we write its equation in the slope-intercept form, which is

$$y = -2x + \frac{4}{3}$$

Therefore the slope of l is -2, and the slope of the desired normal line is also -2, since the two lines are parallel.

   To find the slope of the tangent line to the given curve at any point (x_1, y_1), we apply Definition 6.1.1 with $f(x) = \sqrt{x - 3}$, and we have

$$m(x_1) = \lim_{\Delta x \to 0} \frac{\sqrt{x_1 + \Delta x - 3} - \sqrt{x_1 - 3}}{\Delta x}$$

To evaluate this limit, we rationalize the numerator.

$$m(x_1) = \lim_{\Delta x \to 0} \frac{(\sqrt{x_1 + \Delta x - 3} - \sqrt{x_1 - 3})(\sqrt{x_1 + \Delta x - 3} + \sqrt{x_1 - 3})}{\Delta x(\sqrt{x_1 + \Delta x - 3} + \sqrt{x_1 - 3})}$$

$$= \lim_{\Delta x \to 0} \frac{\Delta x}{\Delta x(\sqrt{x_1 + \Delta x - 3} + \sqrt{x_1 - 3})}$$

Dividing numerator and denominator by Δx (since $\Delta x \neq 0$), we obtain

$$m(x_1) = \lim_{\Delta x \to 0} \frac{1}{\sqrt{x_1 + \Delta x - 3} + \sqrt{x_1 - 3}}$$

$$= \frac{1}{2\sqrt{x_1 - 3}}$$

   Since the normal line at a point is perpendicular to the tangent line at that point, the product of their slopes is -1. Hence the slope of the normal line at (x_1, y_1) is given by

$$-2\sqrt{x_1 - 3}$$

As shown above, the slope of the desired line is -2. So, we solve the equation

$$-2\sqrt{x_1 - 3} = -2$$

giving us

$$x_1 = 4$$

Therefore, the desired line is the line through point (4,1) on the curve and has a slope of -2. Using the point-slope form of an equation of a line, we obtain

$$y - 1 = -2(x - 4)$$

or $\quad 2x + y - 9 = 0$

Refer to Fig. 6.1.4, which shows a sketch of the curve together with the line *l*, the normal line *PN* at (4,1), and the tangent line *PT* at (4,1).

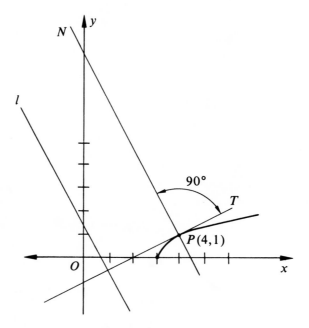

Figure 6.1.4

Exercises 6.1

In Exercises 1 through 8, find the slope of the tangent line to the graph at the point (x_1, y_1). Make a table of values of x, y, and m at various points on the graph, and include in the table all points where the graph has a horizontal tangent. Draw a sketch of the graph.

1. $y = 9 - x^2$

2. $y = x^2 - 6x + 9$

3. $y = 7 - 6x - x^2$

4. $y = \frac{1}{4}x^2$

5. $y = x^3 - 3x$

6. $y = x^3 - x^2 - x + 10$

7. $y = 4x^3 - 13x^2 + 4x - 3$

8. $y = \sqrt{x + 1}$

In Exercises 9 through 18, find an equation of the tangent line and an equation of the normal line to the given curve at the indicated point. Draw a sketch of the curve, together with the resulting tangent line and normal line.

9. $y = x^2 - 4x - 5$; $(-2,7)$

10. $y = x^2 + 2x + 1$; $(1,4)$

11. $y = \frac{1}{8}x^3$; $(4,8)$

12. $y = 2x - x^3$; $(-2,4)$

13. $y = \sqrt{9 - 4x}$; $(-4,5)$

14. $y = \sqrt{4x - 3}$; $(3,3)$

15. $y = \frac{6}{x}$; $(3,2)$

16. $y = -\frac{8}{\sqrt{x}}$; $(4,-4)$

17. $y = \sqrt[3]{x}$; $(8,2)$

18. $y = \sqrt[3]{5 - x}$; $(-3,2)$

19. Find an equation of the tangent line to the curve $y = 2x^2 + 3$ which is parallel to the line $8x - y + 3 = 0$.

20. Find an equation of the normal line to the curve $y = x^3 - 3x$ which is parallel to the line $2x + 18y - 9 = 0$.

21. Find an equation of the tangent line to the curve $y = \sqrt{4x - 3} - 1$ which is perpendicular to the line $x + 2y - 11 = 0$.

22. Find an equation of each line through the point $(3,-2)$ which is tangent to the curve $y = x^2 - 7$.

23. Find an equation of each line through the point $(2,-6)$ which is tangent to the curve $y = 3x^2 - 8$.

24. Prove analytically that there is no line through the point $(1,2)$ which is tangent to the curve $y = 4 - x^2$.

(6.2)   Instantaneous velocity in rectilinear motion

Consider a particle moving along a straight line. Such a motion is called *rectilinear motion*. One direction will be chosen arbitrarily as positive, and the opposite direction will then be negative. For simplicity, let us assume that the motion of the particle is along a horizontal line; with distance to the right as positive, and distance to the left as negative. Select some point on the line and denote it by the letter O. Let f be the function determining the directed distance of the particle from O at any particular time.

To be more specific, let s be the number of feet in the distance of the particle from O at t seconds of time. Then f is the function defined by the equation

(1) $s = f(t)$

which gives the directed distance from the point O to the particle at a particular instant of time. Equation (1) is called the *equation of motion* of the particle.

In particular, let

$$s = t^2 + 2t - 3$$

Then, when $t = 0$, $s = -3$; therefore the particle is 3 ft to the left of point O when $t = 0$. When $t = 1$, $s = 0$; so the particle is at point O at 1 sec. When $t = 2$, $s = 5$; so the particle is 5 ft to the right of point O at 2 sec. When $t = 3$, $s = 12$; so the particle is 12 ft to the right of point O at 3 sec.

Figure 6.2.1 illustrates the various positions of the particle for specific values of t.

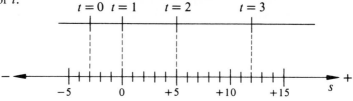

Figure 6.2.1

Between time $t = 1$ and $t = 3$, the particle moves from the point where $s = 0$ to the point where $s = 12$, and thus travels a distance of 12 ft in the 2-sec interval. The average velocity of the particle is the ratio of the distance traveled to the time elapsed. So, the number of feet per second in the average velocity of the particle from $t = 1$ to $t = 3$ is $12/2 = 6$. From $t = 0$ to $t = 2$, the distance the particle travels is 8 ft, and so the number of feet per second in the average velocity of the particle in this 2-sec interval is $8/2 = 4$.

Obviously, the average velocity of the particle is not constant; and the average velocity gives us no specific information about the motion of the particle at any particular instant. For example, if a person is driving a car a distance of 70 miles, and it takes him 2 hours, we say his average velocity in traveling that distance is 35 miles/hr. However, from this information we cannot conclude anything about the speedometer reading of the car at any particular time in the 2-hr period. The speedometer reading at a specific time is referred to as the *instantaneous velocity*. The following discussion will enable us to arrive at a definition of what is meant by "instantaneous velocity."

Let equation (1) define the distance s of the particle from point O as a function of the time t. When $t = t_1$, $s = s_1$. The particle travels a distance of $(s - s_1)$ over the interval of time $(t - t_1)$, and the average velocity of the particle over this interval of time is given by

$$\frac{s - s_1}{t - t_1}$$

or, since $s = f(t)$ and $s_1 = f(t_1)$, the average velocity is given by

$$\frac{f(t) - f(t_1)}{t - t_1}$$

Now, the shorter the time interval is from t_1 to t, the closer the average velocity will be to what we would intuitively think of as the instantaneous velocity at time t_1.

For example, if the speedometer reading of a car as it passes a point P_1 is 40 miles/hr and if a point P is, say, 100 ft from P_1, then the average velocity of the car as it travels this 100 ft will very likely be close to 40 miles/hr, since the variation of the velocity of the car along this short stretch is probably very little. Now, if the distance from P_1 to P were shortened to 50 ft, the average velocity of the car in this interval would be even closer to the speedometer reading of the car as it passes P_1. We can continue this process, and the speedometer reading at P_1 may be represented as the limit of the average velocity between P_1 and P, as P approaches P_1. We have then the following definition.

6.2.1 DEFINITION   If f is the function given by the equation

(1) $$s = f(t)$$

and a particle is moving along a straight line so that s is the number of units in the directed distance of the particle from a fixed point at t units of time, then the *instantaneous velocity* $v(t_1)$ of the particle at time t_1 is defined by the equation

(((2) $$v(t_1) = \lim_{t \to t_1} \frac{f(t) - f(t_1)}{t - t_1}$$

if this limit exists.

Since $t \neq t_1$, we may write

(3) $$t = t_1 + \Delta t$$

and we may conclude that

(4)   "$t \to t_1$" is equivalent to "$\Delta t \to 0$"

From equations (2) and (3) and statement (4), we get the following expression for the instantaneous velocity at t_1:

(((5) $$v(t_1) = \lim_{\Delta t \to 0} \frac{f(t_1 + \Delta t) - f(t_1)}{\Delta t}$$

if this limit exists.

Formula (5) may be substituted for formula (2) in the definition of instantaneous velocity.

The instantaneous velocity may be either positive or negative, depending upon whether the particle is moving along the line in the positive or the negative direction. When the instantaneous velocity is zero, the particle is at rest.

The *speed* of a particle at any time t_1 is defined to be the absolute value of the instantaneous velocity. The speed then is a nonnegative number. The terms "speed" and "instantaneous velocity" are often confused. It should be noted that the speed tells us only how fast the particle is moving, whereas the instantaneous velocity also tells us the direction of motion.

EXAMPLE 1: A particle is moving along a straight line according to the equation of motion

$$s = 2t^3 - 4t^2 + 2t - 1$$

Determine the intervals of time when the particle is moving to the right and when it is moving to the left. Also determine the instant when the particle reverses its direction.

Solution: $f(t) = 2t^3 - 4t^2 + 2t - 1$.

Applying formula (2) for the instantaneous velocity of the particle at t_1, we have

$$v(t_1) = \lim_{t \to t_1} \frac{f(t) - f(t_1)}{t - t_1}$$

$$= \lim_{t \to t_1} \frac{(2t^3 - 4t^2 + 2t - 1) - (2t_1^3 - 4t_1^2 + 2t_1 - 1)}{t - t_1}$$

$$= \lim_{t \to t_1} \frac{2(t^3 - t_1^3) - 4(t^2 - t_1^2) + 2(t - t_1)}{t - t_1} \quad {\scriptstyle 4(t-t_1)(t+t_1)+2(t-t}$$

$$\qquad\qquad\qquad\qquad\qquad\qquad = {\scriptstyle 2(t-t_1)(2t+t}$$

$$= \lim_{t \to t_1} \frac{2(t - t_1)[(t^2 + tt_1 + t_1^2) - 2(t + t_1) + 1]}{t - t_1}$$

Dividing the numerator and the denominator by $t - t_1$ (since $t \neq t_1$), we obtain

$$v(t_1) = \lim_{t \to t_1} 2(t^2 + tt_1 + t_1^2 - 2t - 2t_1 + 1)$$

$$= 2(t_1^2 + t_1^2 + t_1^2 - 2t_1 - 2t_1 + 1)$$

$$= 2(3t_1^2 - 4t_1 + 1)$$

$$= 2(3t_1 - 1)(t_1 - 1)$$

The instantaneous velocity is zero when $t_1 = \frac{1}{3}$ and $t_1 = 1$. Therefore the particle is at rest at these two times. The particle is moving to the right when $v(t_1)$ is positive, and it is moving to the left when $v(t_1)$ is negative. We determine the sign of $v(t_1)$ for various intervals of t_1, and the results are given in Table 6.2.1.

Table 6.2.1

	$3t_1 - 1$	$t_1 - 1$	Conclusion
$t_1 < \dfrac{1}{3}$	−	−	$v(t_1)$ is positive, and the particle is moving to the right.
$t_1 = \dfrac{1}{3}$	0	−	$v(t_1)$ is zero, and the particle is changing direction from right to left.
$\dfrac{1}{3} < t_1 < 1$	+	−	$v(t_1)$ is negative, and the particle is moving to the left.
$t_1 = 1$	+	0	$v(t_1)$ is zero, and the particle is changing direction from left to right.
$1 < t_1$	+	+	$v(t_1)$ is positive, and the particle is moving to the right.

The motion of the particle, indicated in Fig. 6.2.2, is along the horizontal line; however, the behavior of the motion is indicated above the line. The accompanying Table 6.2.2 gives values of s and v for specific values of t.

Table 6.2.2

t	s	v
-1	-9	18
0	-1	2
$\frac{1}{3}$	$\frac{19}{27}$	0
1	-1	0
2	3	10

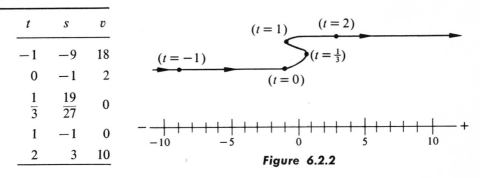

Figure 6.2.2

In the above example, $v(t_1)$ may also be found by applying formula (5). (See Exercise 1 below.)

EXAMPLE 2: A ball is thrown vertically upward from the ground with an initial velocity of 64 ft/sec. The equation of motion is

$$s = -16t^2 + 64t$$

If t is the number of seconds in the time that has elapsed since the ball was thrown, and s is the number of feet in the distance of the ball from the starting point at t sec, find:

    (a)   the instantaneous velocity of the ball at the end of 1 sec
    (b)   the instantaneous velocity of the ball at the end of 3 sec
    (c)   how many seconds it takes the ball to reach its highest point
    (d)   how high the ball will go
    (e)   the speed of the ball at the end of 1 sec and at the end of 3 sec
    (f)   how many seconds it takes the ball to reach the ground
    (g)   the instantaneous velocity of the ball when it reaches the ground

At the end of 1 sec is the ball rising or falling? At the end of 3 sec is the ball rising or falling?

Solution: $v(t_1) =$ the number of feet per second in the instantaneous velocity of the ball at t_1 sec.

$$s = f(t) \qquad \text{where} \qquad f(t) = -16t^2 + 64t$$

Applying formula (2), we find that

$$v(t_1) = \lim_{t \to t_1} \frac{f(t) - f(t_1)}{t - t_1}$$

$$= \lim_{t \to t_1} \frac{-16t^2 + 64t - (-16t_1^2 + 64t_1)}{t - t_1}$$

$$= \lim_{t \to t_1} \frac{-16(t^2 - t_1^2) + 64(t - t_1)}{t - t_1}$$

Dividing the numerator and the denominator by $t - t_1$ (since $t \neq t_1$), we obtain

$$v(t_1) = \lim_{t \to t_1} [-16(t + t_1) + 64] = -32t_1 + 64$$

(a) $v(1) = 32$; so that at the end of 1 sec the ball is rising with an instantaneous velocity of 32 ft/sec.

(b) $v(3) = -32$; so at the end of 3 sec the ball is falling with an instantaneous velocity of -32 ft/sec.

(c) The ball reaches its highest point when the direction of motion changes; that is, when $v(t_1) = 0$. Setting $v(t_1) = 0$, we obtain

$$-32\,t_1 + 64 = 0 \qquad \text{or} \qquad t_1 = 2$$

(d) When $t = 2$, $s = 64$; therefore the ball reaches a highest point of 64 ft above the starting point.

(e) $|v(t_1)| = $ the number of feet per second in the speed of the ball at t_1 sec.

$$|v(1)| = 32 \qquad \text{and} \qquad |v(3)| = 32$$

(f) The ball will reach the ground when $s = 0$. Setting $s = 0$, we have $-16t^2 + 64t = 0$, from which we obtain $t = 0$ and $t = 4$. Therefore, the ball will reach the ground in 4 sec.

(g) $v(4) = -64$; when the ball reaches the ground, its instantaneous velocity is -64 ft/sec.

Table 6.2.3

t	s	v
0	0	64
$\frac{1}{2}$	28	48
1	48	32
2	64	0
3	48	-32
$\frac{7}{2}$	28	-48
4	0	-64

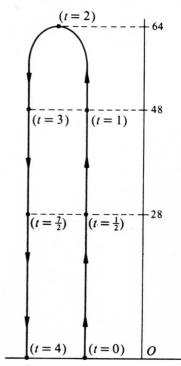

Figure 6.2.3

Table 6.2.3 gives values of s and v for some specific values of t. The motion of the ball is indicated in Fig. 6.2.3. The motion is assumed to be in a straight vertical line, and the behavior of the motion is indicated to the left of the line.

Exercises 6.2

1. Apply formula (5) to find $v(t_1)$ for the rectilinear motion in Example 1.

2. Apply formula (5) to find $v(t_1)$ for the rectilinear motion in Example 2.

In Exercises 3 through 8, a particle is moving along a horizontal line according to the given equation of motion, where s is the number of feet in the distance of the particle from a point O at t sec. Find the instantaneous velocity $v(t_1)$ ft/sec at t_1 sec; and then find $v(t_1)$ for the particular value of t_1 given.

3. $s = 3t^2 + 1$; $t_1 = 3$

6. $s = \dfrac{1}{4t}$; $t_1 = \dfrac{1}{2}$

4. $s = 8 - t^2$; $t_1 = 5$

7. $s = \dfrac{2}{\sqrt{5t + 6}}$; $t_1 = 2$

5. $s = \sqrt{t + 1}$; $t_1 = 3$

8. $s = \sqrt[3]{t + 2}$; $t_1 = 6$

In Exercises 9 through 12, the motion of a particle is along a horizontal line according to the given equation of motion, where s is the number of feet in the distance of the particle from a point O at t sec. The positive direction is to the right. Determine the intervals of time when the particle is moving to the right and when it is moving to the left. Also determine when the particle reverses its direction. Show the behavior of the motion by a figure similar to Fig. 6.2.2, choosing values of t at random but including the values of t when the particle reverses its direction.

9. $s = t^3 + 3t^2 - 9t + 4$

11. $s = \dfrac{1 + t}{4 + t^2}$

10. $s = 2t^3 - 3t^2 - 12t + 8$

12. $s = \dfrac{t}{1 + t^2}$

13. If an object falls from rest, its equation of motion is $s = -16t^2$, where t is the number of seconds in the time that has elapsed since the object left the starting point, and s is the number of feet in the distance of the object from the starting point at t sec. If a stone is dropped from a building 256 ft high, find: (*a*) the instantaneous velocity of the stone 1 sec after it is dropped; (*b*) the instantaneous velocity of the stone 2 sec after it is dropped; (*c*) how long it takes the stone to reach the ground; (*d*) the instantaneous velocity of the stone when it reaches the ground.

14. If a stone is thrown vertically upward from the ground with an initial velocity of 32 ft/sec, the equation of motion is $s = -16t^2 + 32t$, where t is the number of seconds in the time that has elapsed since the stone was

thrown, and s is the number of feet in the distance of the stone from the starting point at t sec. Find: (a) the average velocity of the stone during the time interval: $3/4 \leq t \leq 5/4$; (b) the instantaneous velocity of the stone at $3/4$ sec and at $5/4$ sec; (c) the speed of the stone at $3/4$ sec and at $5/4$ sec; (d) the average velocity of the stone during the time interval: $1/2 \leq t \leq 3/4$; (e) how many seconds it will take the stone to reach its highest point; (f) how high the stone will go; (g) how many seconds it will take the stone to reach the ground; (h) the instantaneous velocity of the stone when it reaches the ground. Show the behavior of the motion by a figure similar to Fig. 6.2.3.

(6.3) The derivative of a function

In Sec. 6.1 the slope of the tangent line to the graph of $y = f(x)$ at the point $(x_1, f(x_1))$ is defined by

$$(1) \qquad m(x_1) = \lim_{\Delta x \to 0} \frac{f(x_1 + \Delta x) - f(x_1)}{\Delta x}$$

In Sec. 6.2 we learned that if a particle is moving along a straight line so that its directed distance s from a fixed point at t units of time is given by $s = f(t)$, then the instantaneous velocity of the particle at t_1 is given by

$$(2) \qquad v(t_1) = \lim_{\Delta t \to 0} \frac{f(t_1 + \Delta t) - f(t_1)}{\Delta t}$$

The limits in formulas (1) and (2) are of the same form. This type of limit occurs in other problems too, and we give it a specific name.

6.3.1 DEFINITION The *derivative* of the function f is that function, denoted by f', such that its function value at any number x in the domain of f is given by

$$\text{((} (3) \qquad f'(x) = \lim_{\Delta x \to 0} \frac{f(x + \Delta x) - f(x)}{\Delta x}$$

if this limit exists. (f' is read "f prime," and $f'(x)$ is read "f prime of x.")

Another symbol that is used instead of $f'(x)$ is $D_x f(x)$, which is read "the derivative of f of x with respect to x."

If $y = f(x)$, then $f'(x)$ is the derivative of y with respect to x, and we use the notation $D_x y$. We also use the notation y' for the derivative of y with respect to an independent variable, if the independent variable is understood.

If x_1 is a particular number in the domain of f, then

$$\text{((} (4) \qquad f'(x_1) = \lim_{\Delta x \to 0} \frac{f(x_1 + \Delta x) - f(x_1)}{\Delta x}$$

if this limit exists.

Comparing formulas (1) and (4), you will note that the slope of the tangent line to the graph of $y = f(x)$ at the point $(x_1, f(x_1))$ is precisely the derivative of f evaluated at x_1.

If a particle is moving along a straight line according to the equation of motion $s = f(t)$, then upon comparing formulas (2) and (4), we see that the instantaneous velocity of the particle at t_1 is the derivative of f evaluated at t_1 or, equivalently, the derivative of s with respect to t evaluated at t_1.

EXAMPLE 1: Given $f(x) = 3x^2 + 5$, find the derivative of f.

Solution: If x is any number in the domain of f, from equation (3) we obtain

$$f'(x) = \lim_{\Delta x \to 0} \frac{f(x + \Delta x) - f(x)}{\Delta x}$$

$$= \lim_{\Delta x \to 0} \frac{[3(x + \Delta x)^2 + 5] - (3x^2 + 5)}{\Delta x}$$

$$= \lim_{\Delta x \to 0} \frac{3x^2 + 6x\,\Delta x + 3\,(\Delta x)^2 + 5 - 3x^2 - 5}{\Delta x}$$

$$= \lim_{\Delta x \to 0} \frac{6x\,\Delta x + 3\,(\Delta x)^2}{\Delta x} = \lim_{\Delta x \to 0} (6x + 3\Delta x)$$

$$= 6x$$

Therefore the derivative of f is the function f' defined by $f'(x) = 6x$. The domain of f' is the set of all real numbers, which is the same as the domain of f.

In Sec. 6.2 we showed that the limit

$$\lim_{\Delta t \to 0} \frac{f(t_1 + \Delta t) - f(t_1)}{\Delta t}$$

is equivalent to

$$\lim_{t \to t_1} \frac{f(t) - f(t_1)}{t - t_1}$$

Therefore an alternative formula to (4) for $f'(x_1)$ is given by

(5) $$f'(x_1) = \lim_{x \to x_1} \frac{f(x) - f(x_1)}{x - x_1}$$

EXAMPLE 2: For the function f of Example 1, find the derivative of f at 2 in three ways: (*a*) apply formula (4); (*b*) apply formula (5); (*c*) substitute 2 for x in the expression for $f'(x)$ found in Example 1.

Solution: (*a*) Applying formula (4), we have

$$f'(2) = \lim_{\Delta x \to 0} \frac{f(2 + \Delta x) - f(2)}{\Delta x}$$

$$= \lim_{\Delta x \to 0} \frac{[3(2 + \Delta x)^2 + 5] - [3(2)^2 + 5]}{\Delta x}$$

$$= \lim_{\Delta x \to 0} \frac{12 + 12\,\Delta x + 3\,(\Delta x)^2 + 5 - 12 - 5}{\Delta x}$$

$$= \lim_{\Delta x \to 0} \frac{12\,\Delta x + 3\,(\Delta x)^2}{\Delta x} = \lim_{\Delta x \to 0} (12 + 3\,\Delta x)$$

$$= 12$$

(b) From formula (5) we obtain

$$f'(2) = \lim_{x \to 2} \frac{f(x) - f(2)}{x - 2}$$

$$= \lim_{x \to 2} \frac{(3x^2 + 5) - 17}{x - 2} = \lim_{x \to 2} \frac{3x^2 - 12}{x - 2}$$

$$= 3 \lim_{x \to 2} \frac{(x - 2)(x + 2)}{x - 2} = 3 \lim_{x \to 2} (x + 2)$$

$$= 12$$

(c) Since, from Example 1, $f'(x) = 6x$, we obtain $f'(2) = 12$.

If the function f is given by the equation $y = f(x)$, we may let

$$\Delta y = f(x + \Delta x) - f(x)$$

and write $D_x y$ in place of $f'(x)$, so that from formula (3) we have

(6) $$D_x y = \lim_{\Delta x \to 0} \frac{\Delta y}{\Delta x}$$

A derivative is sometimes indicated by the notation dy/dx. But we shall avoid this symbolism for the present, until we have defined what is meant by dy and dx.

EXAMPLE 3: Given $y = (2 + x)/(3 - x)$, find $D_x y$.
Solution:

$$D_x y = \lim_{\Delta x \to 0} \frac{\Delta y}{\Delta x}$$

$$= \lim_{\Delta x \to 0} \frac{f(x + \Delta x) - f(x)}{\Delta x}$$

$$= \lim_{\Delta x \to 0} \frac{(2 + x + \Delta x)/(3 - x - \Delta x) - (2 + x)/(3 - x)}{\Delta x}$$

$$= \lim_{\Delta x \to 0} \frac{(3 - x)(2 + x + \Delta x) - (2 + x)(3 - x - \Delta x)}{\Delta x \, (3 - x - \Delta x)(3 - x)}$$

$$= \lim_{\Delta x \to 0} \frac{(6 + x - x^2 + 3 \, \Delta x - x \, \Delta x) - (6 + x - x^2 - 2 \, \Delta x - x \, \Delta x)}{\Delta x \, (3 - x - \Delta x)(3 - x)}$$

$$= \lim_{\Delta x \to 0} \frac{5 \, \Delta x}{\Delta x \, (3 - x - \Delta x)(3 - x)}$$

$$= \lim_{\Delta x \to 0} \frac{5}{(3 - x - \Delta x)(3 - x)}$$

$$= \frac{5}{(3 - x)^2}$$

EXAMPLE 4: Given $f(x) = x^{2/3}$, find $f'(x)$.
Solution:

$$f'(x) = \lim_{\Delta x \to 0} \frac{f(x + \Delta x) - f(x)}{\Delta x} = \lim_{\Delta x \to 0} \frac{(x + \Delta x)^{2/3} - x^{2/3}}{\Delta x}$$

We rationalize the numerator in order to obtain a common factor of Δx in the numerator and the denominator; this gives us

$$f'(x) = \lim_{\Delta x \to 0} \frac{[(x + \Delta x)^{2/3} - x^{2/3}][(x + \Delta x)^{4/3} + (x + \Delta x)^{2/3}x^{2/3} + x^{4/3}]}{\Delta x\,[(x + \Delta x)^{4/3} + (x + \Delta x)^{2/3}x^{2/3} + x^{4/3}]}$$

$$= \lim_{\Delta x \to 0} \frac{(x + \Delta x)^2 - x^2}{\Delta x\,[(x + \Delta x)^{4/3} + (x + \Delta x)^{2/3}x^{2/3} + x^{4/3}]}$$

$$= \lim_{\Delta x \to 0} \frac{x^2 + 2x\,(\Delta x) + (\Delta x)^2 - x^2}{\Delta x\,[(x + \Delta x)^{4/3} + (x + \Delta x)^{2/3}x^{2/3} + x^{4/3}]}$$

$$= \lim_{\Delta x \to 0} \frac{2x\,(\Delta x) + (\Delta x)^2}{\Delta x\,[(x + \Delta x)^{4/3} + (x + \Delta x)^{2/3}x^{2/3} + x^{4/3}]}$$

$$= \lim_{\Delta x \to 0} \frac{2x + \Delta x}{(x + \Delta x)^{4/3} + (x + \Delta x)^{2/3}x^{2/3} + x^{4/3}}$$

$$= \frac{2x}{x^{4/3} + x^{2/3}x^{2/3} + x^{4/3}}$$

$$= \frac{2x}{3x^{4/3}}$$

$$= \frac{2}{3x^{1/3}}$$

It should be noted that $f'(0)$ does not exist even though f is continuous at 0. A sketch of the graph of f is shown in Fig. 6.3.1.

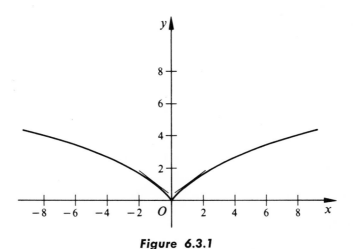

Figure 6.3.1

If for the function of Example 4 we evaluate

$$\lim_{\Delta x \to 0} \frac{f(x_1 + \Delta x) - f(x_1)}{\Delta x} \qquad \text{at } x_1 = 0$$

we have

$$\lim_{\Delta x \to 0} \frac{f(0 + \Delta x) - f(0)}{\Delta x} = \lim_{\Delta x \to 0} \frac{(\Delta x)^{2/3} - 0}{\Delta x}$$

$$= \lim_{\Delta x \to 0} \frac{1}{(\Delta x)^{1/3}}$$

$$= \infty$$

Therefore we conclude that the tangent line to the graph of f at the origin is the y axis, having an inclination of $\pi/2$.

As shown by the above example $f'(x)$ may exist for some values of x in the domain of f and fail to exist for other values of x in the domain of f. We have the following definition.

6.3.2 DEFINITION   The function f is said to be *differentiable* at x_1 if $f'(x_1)$ exists.

Exercises 6.3

In Exercises 1 through 10, find $f'(x)$ for the given function by applying formula (3) of this section.

1. $f(x) = 4x^2 + 5x + 3$ 6. $f(x) = \sqrt{3x}$

2. $f(x) = x^3$ 7. $f(x) = \dfrac{1}{x^2} - x$

3. $f(x) = \sqrt{x}$ 8. $f(x) = \dfrac{3}{1 + x^2}$

4. $f(x) = \sqrt{3x + 5}$ 9. $f(x) = \dfrac{1}{\sqrt{x + 1}}$

5. $f(x) = \dfrac{1}{x + 1}$ 10. $f(x) = \sqrt[3]{2x + 3}$

In Exercises 11 through 16, find $f'(a)$ for the given value of a by applying formula (4) of this section.

11. $f(x) = -x^2 + 1; \ a = 3$ 14. $f(x) = \dfrac{2}{\sqrt{x}} - 1; \ a = 4$

12. $f(x) = \dfrac{4}{5x}; \ a = 2$ 15. $f(x) = \sqrt{x^2 - 9}; \ a = 5$

13. $f(x) = \dfrac{2}{x^3}; \ a = 6$ 16. $f(x) = \dfrac{1}{x} + x + x^2; \ a = -3$

In Exercises 17 through 22, find $f'(a)$ for the given value of a by applying formula (5) of this section.

17. $f(x) = 3x + 2; \ a = -3$ 19. $f(x) = 2 - x^3; \ a = -2$

18. $f(x) = x^2 - x + 4; \ a = 4$ 20. $f(x) = \sqrt{1 + 9x}; \ a = 7$

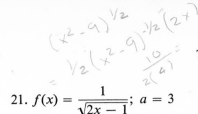

21. $f(x) = \dfrac{1}{\sqrt{2x-1}}$; $a = 3$

22. $f(x) = \dfrac{1}{\sqrt[3]{x}} - x$; $a = -8$

23. Given $f(x) = \sqrt[3]{x-1}$, find $f'(x)$. Is f differentiable at 1? Draw a sketch of the graph of the function f.

24. Given $f(x) = \sqrt[3]{(4x-3)^2}$, find $f'(x)$. Is f differentiable at 3/4? Draw a sketch of the graph of the function f.

(6.4) The derivative as a rate of change

If a particle is moving along a straight line according to the equation of motion $s = f(t)$, we have seen that the velocity of the particle at time t is the derivative of s with respect to t. Since velocity may be interpreted as a rate of change of distance with respect to time, we see that the derivative of s with respect to t is the rate of change of s with respect to t.

In a similar way, if a quantity y is a function of a quantity x, we may express the rate of change of y with respect to x. The discussion is analogous to the discussions of the slope of a tangent line to a graph and the instantaneous velocity of a particle moving along a straight line.

If the functional relationship between y and x is given by

$$y = f(x)$$

and if x changes from the value x_1 to $x_1 + \Delta x$, then y changes from $f(x_1)$ to $f(x_1 + \Delta x)$. So the change in y is $f(x_1 + \Delta x) - f(x_1)$ when the change in x is Δx. The average rate of change of y, with respect to x, as x changes from x_1 to $(x_1 + \Delta x)$ is then

(1)
$$\frac{f(x_1 + \Delta x) - f(x_1)}{\Delta x}$$

If the limit of fraction (1) exists as $\Delta x \to 0$, this limit is what we intuitively think of as the instantaneous rate of change of y with respect to x at x_1. Accordingly, we have the following definition.

6.4.1 DEFINITION   If $y = f(x)$, the *instantaneous rate of change of y with respect to x at x_1* is the derivative of y with respect to x at x_1, if it exists there.

EXAMPLE 1: Let $V =$ the number of cubic inches in the volume of a cube, and let $e =$ the number of inches in the length of an edge of the cube. Find the average rate of change of V with respect to e as e changes from (*a*) 3 to 3.2; (*b*) 3 to 3.1; (*c*) 3 to 3.01. (*d*) What is the instantaneous rate of change of V with respect to e when $e = 3$?

Solution: Since the formula for finding the volume of a cube is $V = e^3$, let f be the function defined by $f(e) = e^3$. Then the average rate of change of V with respect to e at e_1 is

$$\frac{f(e_1 + \Delta e) - f(e)}{\Delta e}$$

(a) $e_1 = 3$, $\Delta e = 0.2$, and $\dfrac{f(3.2) - f(3)}{0.2} = \dfrac{(3.2)^3 - 3^3}{0.2} = \dfrac{5.768}{0.2} = 28.84$

(b) $e_1 = 3$, $\Delta e = 0.1$, and $\dfrac{f(3.1) - f(3)}{0.1} = \dfrac{(3.1)^3 - 3^3}{0.1} = \dfrac{2.791}{0.1} = 27.91$

(c) $e_1 = 3$, $\Delta e = 0.01$, and $\dfrac{f(3.01) - f(3)}{0.01} = \dfrac{(3.01)^3 - 3^3}{0.01} = \dfrac{0.2709}{0.01} = 27.09$

(d)   The instantaneous rate of change of V with respect to e at 3 is $f'(3)$.

$$f'(3) = \lim_{\Delta e \to 0} \frac{f(3 + \Delta e) - f(3)}{\Delta e} = \lim_{\Delta e \to 0} \frac{(3 + \Delta e)^3 - 3^3}{\Delta e}$$

$$= \lim_{\Delta e \to 0} \frac{27 + 27\,\Delta e + 9\,(\Delta e)^2 + (\Delta e)^3 - 27}{\Delta e}$$

$$= \lim_{\Delta e \to 0} \frac{27\,\Delta e + 9\,(\Delta e)^2 + (\Delta e)^3}{\Delta e}$$

$$= \lim_{\Delta e \to 0} [27 + 9\,\Delta e + (\Delta e)^2] = 27$$

Exercises 6.4

1. If A is the number of square inches in the area of a square, and s is the number of inches in the length of a side of the square, find the average rate of change of A with respect to s as s changes from   (a) 4 to 4.6; (b) 4 to 4.3;   (c) 4 to 4.1.   (d) What is the instantaneous rate of change of A with respect to s when s is 4?

2. Suppose a right-circular cylinder has a constant height of 10 in. If V is the number of cubic inches in the volume of the right-circular cylinder, and r is the number of inches in the radius of its base, find the average rate of change of V with respect to r as r changes from   (a) 5 to 5.4;   (b) 5 to 5.1;   (c) 5 to 5.01.   (d) Find the instantaneous rate of change of V with respect to r when r is 5.

3. Find the instantaneous rate of change of the reciprocal of a number with respect to the number when the number is 4.

4. Find the rate of change of the area of a circle with respect to its radius, and show that it is equal to the circumference of the circle.

5. Find the rate of change of the volume of a sphere with respect to its radius, and show that it is equal to the surface area of the sphere.

Sphere: $V = \frac{4}{3}\pi R^3$

Rt circ. Cone $V = \frac{1}{3}\pi R^2$

SECTION 6.5 DIFFERENTIABILITY AND CONTINUITY *157*

6. A solid is composed of a right-circular cylinder with a hemisphere on each end, and the length of the cylinder is twice the radius of an end. Find the rate of change of the volume of the solid with respect to the radius of an end.

7. Find the instantaneous rate of change of the surface area of a sphere with respect to its radius when the radius is 8 in.

8. Find the instantaneous rate of change of the principal square root of a number with respect to the number when the number is 9.

9. If the altitude of a right-circular cone is always twice its radius, find the instantaneous rate of change of the volume with respect to the radius when the radius is 4 in.

10. A bomber is flying parallel to the ground at an altitude of 2 miles and at a speed of 4½ miles per minute. If the bomber flies directly over a target, at what rate is the distance between the bomber and the target changing 20 sec later?

11. At 8 A.M. a ship sailing due north at 24 knots is at a point P. At 10 A.M. a second ship sailing due east at 32 knots is at P. At what rate is the distance between the two ships changing at 9 A.M.?

12. At what rate is the distance between the two ships in Exercise 11 changing at 11 A.M.?

(6.5) Differentiability and continuity

We recall that a function is defined to be differentiable at a number if its derivative exists there. In Example 4 of Sec. 6.3, we saw that the function f defined by $f(x) = x^{2/3}$ is continuous at zero but that its derivative, given by $f'(x) = 2/3x^{1/3}$, does not exist at zero; hence f is not differentiable there. We may conclude, then, that continuity of a function at a number does not imply differentiability of the function at that number; however, differentiability *does* imply continuity. We shall now state this as a theorem and prove it.

6.5.1 THEOREM If a function f is differentiable at x_1, then f is continuous at x_1.

Proof: In order to prove that f is continuous at x_1, we must show that the three conditions of Definition 5.1.1 hold there. That is, we must show that (i) $f(x_1)$ exists; (ii) $\lim\limits_{x \to x_1} f(x)$ exists and is finite; and (iii) $\lim\limits_{x \to x_1} f(x) = f(x_1)$. By hypothesis, f is differentiable at x_1. Therefore $f'(x_1)$ exists. Since, by formula (5) of Sec. 6.3,

(1)
$$f'(x_1) = \lim_{x \to x_1} \frac{f(x) - f(x_1)}{x - x_1}$$

we may conclude that $f(x_1)$ must exist; otherwise the above limit has no meaning. Therefore condition (i) holds at x_1. Now let us consider

$$\lim_{x \to x_1} [f(x) - f(x_1)].$$

We may write

(2) $$\lim_{x \to x_1} [f(x) - f(x_1)] = \lim_{x \to x_1} \left[(x - x_1) \cdot \frac{f(x) - f(x_1)}{x - x_1} \right]$$

Since $$\lim_{x \to x_1} (x - x_1) = 0 \quad \text{and} \quad \lim_{x \to x_1} \frac{f(x) - f(x_1)}{x - x_1} = f'(x_1)$$

we may apply the theorem on the limit of a product (Theorem 4.2.6) to the right-hand side of equation (2), and we have

$$\lim_{x \to x_1} [f(x) - f(x_1)] = \lim_{x \to x_1} (x - x_1) \cdot \lim_{x \to x_1} \frac{f(x) - f(x_1)}{x - x_1} = 0 \cdot f'(x_1)$$

so that

(3) $$\lim_{x \to x_1} [f(x) - f(x_1)] = 0$$

Since $f(x_1)$ is a constant, $\lim_{x \to x_1} f(x_1) = f(x_1)$; and so, using this, Limit Theorem 4, and equation (3), we have

$$\lim_{x \to x_1} f(x) = \lim_{x \to x_1} [f(x) - f(x_1)] + \lim_{x \to x_1} f(x_1) = 0 + f(x_1)$$

which gives us

(4) $$\lim_{x \to x_1} f(x) = f(x_1)$$

From equation (4) we may conclude that conditions (ii) and (iii) for continuity of f at x_1 hold. Therefore, the theorem is proved.

Example 4 of Sec. 6.3 shows that the converse of the above theorem is not true. Before giving some additional examples of functions which are continuous at a number but which are not differentiable there, we shall introduce the concept of a *one-sided derivative*.

6.5.2 DEFINITION   If the function f is defined at x_1, then the *derivative from the right* of f at x_1, denoted by $f'_+(x_1)$, is defined by

(5) $$f'_+(x_1) = \lim_{\Delta x \to 0^+} \frac{f(x_1 + \Delta x) - f(x_1)}{\Delta x}$$

or, equivalently,

(6) $$f'_+(x_1) = \lim_{x \to x_1^+} \frac{f(x) - f(x_1)}{x - x_1}$$

if the limits exist.

6.5.3 DEFINITION   If the function f is defined at x_1, then the *derivative from the left* of f at x_1, denoted by $f'_-(x_1)$, is defined by

(7)
$$f'_-(x_1) = \lim_{\Delta x \to 0^-} \frac{f(x_1 + \Delta x) - f(x_1)}{\Delta x}$$

or, equivalently,

(8)
$$f'_-(x_1) = \lim_{x \to x_1^-} \frac{f(x) - f(x_1)}{x - x_1}$$

if the limits exist.

EXAMPLE 1: Let f be the function defined by

$$f(x) = \begin{cases} 2x - 1 & \text{if } x < 3 \\ 8 - x & \text{if } 3 \le x \end{cases}$$

(*a*) Draw a sketch of the graph of f. (*b*) Prove that f is continuous at 3. (*c*) Find $f'_-(3)$ and $f'_+(3)$. (*d*) Is f differentiable at 3?

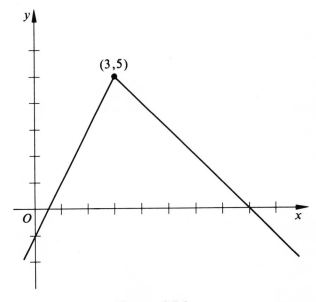

Figure 6.5.1

Solution: (*a*) A sketch of the graph is shown in Fig. 6.5.1. (*b*) To prove that f is continuous at 3, we verify the three conditions for continuity at a number:

(i) $f(3) = 5$

(ii) $\displaystyle \lim_{x \to 3^-} f(x) = \lim_{x \to 3^-} (2x - 1) = 5$

$\displaystyle \lim_{x \to 3^+} f(x) = \lim_{x \to 3^+} (8 - x) = 5$

Therefore,

$$\lim_{x \to 3} f(x) = 5$$

(iii) $\lim_{x \to 3} f(x) = f(3)$

Since conditions (i), (ii), and (iii) all hold at 3, f is continuous at 3.

(c) $f'_-(3) = \lim_{\Delta x \to 0^-} \frac{f(3 + \Delta x) - f(3)}{\Delta x} = \lim_{\Delta x \to 0^-} \frac{[2(3 + \Delta x) - 1] - 5}{\Delta x}$

$$= \lim_{\Delta x \to 0^-} \frac{6 + 2\,\Delta x - 6}{\Delta x} = \lim_{\Delta x \to 0^-} \frac{2\,\Delta x}{\Delta x} = \lim_{\Delta x \to 0^-} 2 = 2$$

$f'_+(3) = \lim_{\Delta x \to 0^+} \frac{f(3 + \Delta x) - f(3)}{\Delta x} = \lim_{\Delta x \to 0^+} \frac{[8 - (3 + \Delta x)] - 5}{\Delta x}$

$$= \lim_{\Delta x \to 0^+} \frac{8 - 3 - \Delta x - 5}{\Delta x} = \lim_{\Delta x \to 0^+} \frac{-\Delta x}{\Delta x} = \lim_{\Delta x \to 0^+} (-1) = -1$$

(d) Since $\lim_{\Delta x \to 0^-} \frac{f(3 + \Delta x) - f(3)}{\Delta x} \neq \lim_{\Delta x \to 0^+} \frac{f(3 + \Delta x) - f(3)}{\Delta x}$, we conclude

that $\lim_{\Delta x \to 0} \frac{f(3 + \Delta x) - f(3)}{\Delta x}$ does not exist. Hence f is not differentiable at 3.

However, the derivative from the left and the derivative from the right both exist at 3.

The function in the above example gives us another illustration of a function which is continuous at a number but not differentiable there.

Exercises 6.5

In Exercises 1 through 14, do each of the following: (a) draw a sketch of the graph of the function; (b) determine if f is continuous at x_1; (c) find $f'_-(x_1)$ and $f'_+(x_1)$ if they exist; (d) determine if f is differentiable at x_1.

1. $f(x) = \begin{cases} x + 2 & \text{if } x \leq -4 \\ -x - 6 & \text{if } -4 < x \end{cases}$
$x_1 = -4$

5. $f(x) = \begin{cases} -1 & \text{if } x < 0 \\ x - 1 & \text{if } 0 \leq x \end{cases}$
$x_1 = 0$

2. $f(x) = \begin{cases} 3 - 2x & \text{if } x < 2 \\ 3x - 7 & \text{if } 2 \leq x \end{cases}$
$x_1 = 2$

6. $f(x) = \begin{cases} x & \text{if } x \leq 0 \\ x^2 & \text{if } 0 < x \end{cases}$
$x_1 = 0$

3. $f(x) = |x - 3|$; $x_1 = 3$

7. $f(x) = \begin{cases} x^2 & \text{if } x \leq 0 \\ -x^2 & \text{if } 0 < x \end{cases}$
$x_1 = 0$

4. $f(x) = 1 + |x + 2|$; $x_1 = -2$

8. $f(x) = \begin{cases} x^2 - 4 & \text{if } x < 2 \\ \sqrt{x - 2} & \text{if } 2 \leq x \end{cases}$
$x_1 = 2$

9. $f(x) = \begin{cases} \sqrt{1-x} & \text{if } x < 1 \\ (1-x)^2 & \text{if } 1 \le x \end{cases}$
$\qquad x_1 = 1$

12. $f(x) = \dfrac{1}{(x-2)^2}; \; x_1 = 2$

10. $f(x) = \begin{cases} x^2 & \text{if } x < -1 \\ -1-2x & \text{if } -1 \le x \end{cases}$
$\qquad x_1 = -1$

13. $f(x) = \begin{cases} 5-6x & \text{if } x \le 3 \\ -4-x^2 & \text{if } 3 < x \end{cases}$
$\qquad x_1 = 3$

11. $f(x) = \sqrt[3]{x+1}; \; x_1 = -1$

14. $f(x) = \begin{cases} -x^{2/3} & \text{if } x \le 0 \\ x^{2/3} & \text{if } 0 < x \end{cases}$
$\qquad x_1 = 0$

15. Given $f(x) = |x|$, draw a sketch of the graph of f. Prove that f is continuous at 0. Prove that f is not differentiable at 0, but that $f'(x) = |x|/x$ for all $x \ne 0$.   HINT: Let $|x| = \sqrt{x^2}$.

16. Given $f(x) = \sqrt{9-x^2}$, prove that f is continuous on the closed interval $[-3,3]$. Prove that neither the derivative from the right at -3 nor the derivative from the left at 3 exist. Draw a sketch of the graph.

17. Given $f(x) = x^{3/2}$, prove that $f'_+(0)$ exists and find its value. Prove that f is continuous from the right at 0. Draw a sketch of the graph.

18. Given $f(x) = (1-x^2)^{3/2}$, prove that f is continuous on the closed interval $[-1,1]$. Prove that $f'(x)$ exists for all values of x in the open interval $(-1,1)$, and that both $f'_+(-1)$ and $f'_-(+1)$ exist. Draw a sketch of the graph of f on $[-1,1]$.

19. Given $f(x) = [\![x]\!]$, find $f'(x_1)$ if x_1 is not an integer. Prove by applying Theorem 6.5.1 that $f'(x_1)$ does not exist if x_1 is an integer. If x_1 is an integer, what can you say about $f'_-(x_1)$ and $f'_+(x_1)$?

20. Let f be the function defined by

$$f(x) = \begin{cases} \dfrac{g(x)-g(a)}{x-a} & \text{if } x \ne a \\ g'(a) & \text{if } x = a \end{cases}$$

Prove that if $g'(a)$ exists, f is continuous at a.

7 Differentiation of algebraic functions

(7.1)   Some theorems on differentiation of algebraic functions

The process of finding the derivative of a function is called *differentiation*. We may perform this differentiation by applying Definition 6.3.1. However, since this process is usually rather lengthy, we shall state and prove some theorems that enable us to find the derivative of certain functions more easily. These theorems are proved by applying Definition 6.3.1.

Following the proof of each theorem, we shall state the corresponding formula of differentiation.

7.1.1 THEOREM   If c is a constant and if $f(x) = c$ for all x, then

$$f'(x) = 0$$

Proof: $f'(x) = \lim\limits_{\Delta x \to 0} \dfrac{f(x + \Delta x) - f(x)}{\Delta x} = \lim\limits_{\Delta x \to 0} \dfrac{c - c}{\Delta x} = \lim\limits_{\Delta x \to 0} 0 = 0$

(((1) $D_x(c) = 0$

The derivative of a constant is zero.

EXAMPLE 1: Given $y = 5$, find $D_x y$.

Solution: $D_x y = 0$

7.1.2 THEOREM   If n is a positive integer and if $f(x) = x^n$, then

$$f'(x) = nx^{n-1}$$

Proof: $f'(x) = \lim\limits_{\Delta x \to 0} \dfrac{f(x + \Delta x) - f(x)}{\Delta x}$

$$= \lim\limits_{\Delta x \to 0} \dfrac{(x + \Delta x)^n - x^n}{\Delta x}$$

Applying the binomial theorem to $(x + \Delta x)^n$, we have

$$f'(x) = \lim_{\Delta x \to 0} \frac{[x^n + nx^{n-1}\,\Delta x + \dfrac{n(n-1)}{2!}x^{n-2}\,(\Delta x)^2 + \cdots + nx\,(\Delta x)^{n-1} + (\Delta x)^n] - x^n}{\Delta x}$$

$$= \lim_{\Delta x \to 0} \frac{nx^{n-1}\,\Delta x + \dfrac{n(n-1)}{2!}x^{n-2}\,(\Delta x)^2 + \cdots + nx\,(\Delta x)^{n-1} + (\Delta x)^n}{\Delta x}$$

Dividing the numerator and the denominator by Δx, we have

$$f'(x) = \lim_{\Delta x \to 0} \left[nx^{n-1} + \frac{n(n-1)}{2!}x^{n-2}\,(\Delta x) + \cdots + nx\,(\Delta x)^{n-2} + (\Delta x)^{n-1} \right]$$

Every term, except the first, has a factor of Δx; therefore every term, except the first, approaches zero as Δx approaches zero. So, we obtain

$$f'(x) = nx^{n-1}$$

(((2) $$D_x(x^n) = nx^{n-1}$$

EXAMPLE 2: Given $f(x) = x^8$, find $f'(x)$.
Solution: $f'(x) = 8x^7$

EXAMPLE 3: Given $f(x) = x$, find $f'(x)$.
Solution: $f'(x) = 1 \cdot x^0 = 1 \cdot 1 = 1$

7.1.3 THEOREM   If f is a function, c is a constant, and g is the function defined by

$$g(x) = c \cdot f(x)$$

then, if $f'(x)$ exists,

$$g'(x) = c \cdot f'(x)$$

Proof:

$$g'(x) = \lim_{\Delta x \to 0} \frac{g(x + \Delta x) - g(x)}{\Delta x} = \lim_{\Delta x \to 0} \frac{cf(x + \Delta x) - cf(x)}{\Delta x}$$

$$= \lim_{\Delta x \to 0} c \cdot \left[\frac{f(x + \Delta x) - f(x)}{\Delta x} \right] = c \cdot \lim_{\Delta x \to 0} \frac{f(x + \Delta x) - f(x)}{\Delta x}$$

$$= cf'(x)$$

(((3) $$D_x[c \cdot f(x)] = c \cdot D_x f(x)$$

The derivative of a constant times a function is the constant times the derivative of the function, if this derivative exists.

Combining Theorems 7.1.2 and 7.1.3, we have the following result: if $f(x) = cx^n$, where n is a positive integer and c is a constant,

$$f'(x) = cnx^{n-1}$$

(((4) $$D_x(cx^n) = cnx^{n-1}$$

EXAMPLE 4: Given $f(x) = 5x^7$, find $f'(x)$.
Solution: $f'(x) = 5 \cdot 7x^6 = 35x^6$

7.1.4 THEOREM If f and g are functions and if h is the function defined by

$$h(x) = f(x) + g(x)$$

then, if $f'(x)$ and $g'(x)$ exist,

$$h'(x) = f'(x) + g'(x)$$

Proof: $h'(x) = \lim\limits_{\Delta x \to 0} \dfrac{h(x + \Delta x) - h(x)}{\Delta x}$

$$= \lim\limits_{\Delta x \to 0} \frac{[f(x + \Delta x) + g(x + \Delta x)] - [f(x) + g(x)]}{\Delta x}$$

$$= \lim\limits_{\Delta x \to 0} \frac{[f(x + \Delta x) - f(x)] + [g(x + \Delta x) - g(x)]}{\Delta x}$$

$$= \lim\limits_{\Delta x \to 0} \frac{f(x + \Delta x) - f(x)}{\Delta x} + \lim\limits_{\Delta x \to 0} \frac{g(x + \Delta x) - g(x)}{\Delta x}$$

$$= f'(x) + g'(x)$$

❰❰ (5) $$D_x\,[f(x) + g(x)] = D_x\,f(x) + D_x\,g(x)$$

The derivative of the sum of two functions is the sum of their derivatives, if these derivatives exist.

The result of the preceding theorem may be extended to any finite number of functions, by mathematical induction. We shall state this as another theorem.

7.1.5 THEOREM The derivative of the sum of a finite number of functions is equal to the sum of their derivatives, if these derivatives exist.

The preceding theorems enable us to find easily the derivative of any polynomial function.

EXAMPLE 5: Given $f(x) = 7x^4 - 2x^3 + 8x + 5$, find $f'(x)$.

Solution: $f'(x) = D_x\,(7x^4 - 2x^3 + 8x + 5)$

$$= D_x\,(7x^4) + D_x\,(-2x^3) + D_x\,(8x) + D_x\,(5)$$

$$= 28x^3 - 6x^2 + 8$$

7.1.6 THEOREM If f and g are functions and if h is the function defined by

$$h(x) = f(x)g(x)$$

then, if $f'(x)$ and $g'(x)$ exist,

$$h'(x) = f(x)g'(x) + g(x)f'(x)$$

Proof: $h'(x) = \lim\limits_{\Delta x \to 0} \dfrac{h(x + \Delta x) - h(x)}{\Delta x}$

$$= \lim\limits_{\Delta x \to 0} \frac{f(x + \Delta x) \cdot g(x + \Delta x) - f(x) \cdot g(x)}{\Delta x}$$

We subtract and add $f(x + \Delta x) \cdot g(x)$ in the numerator, giving us

$$h'(x) = \lim_{\Delta x \to 0} \frac{f(x + \Delta x) \cdot g(x + \Delta x) - f(x + \Delta x) \cdot g(x) + f(x + \Delta x) \cdot g(x) - f(x) \cdot g(x)}{\Delta x}$$

$$= \lim_{\Delta x \to 0} \left[f(x + \Delta x) \cdot \frac{g(x + \Delta x) - g(x)}{\Delta x} + g(x) \cdot \frac{f(x + \Delta x) - f(x)}{\Delta x} \right]$$

$$= \lim_{\Delta x \to 0} \left[f(x + \Delta x) \cdot \frac{g(x + \Delta x) - g(x)}{\Delta x} \right] + \lim_{\Delta x \to 0} \left[g(x) \cdot \frac{f(x + \Delta x) - f(x)}{\Delta x} \right]$$

$$= \lim_{\Delta x \to 0} f(x + \Delta x) \cdot \lim_{\Delta x \to 0} \frac{g(x + \Delta x) - g(x)}{\Delta x} + \lim_{\Delta x \to 0} g(x) \cdot \lim_{\Delta x \to 0} \frac{f(x + \Delta x) - f(x)}{\Delta x}$$

Since f is differentiable at x, by Theorem 6.5.1, f is continuous at x, and therefore $\lim_{\Delta x \to 0} f(x + \Delta x) = f(x)$. Also, $\lim_{\Delta x \to 0} ([g(x + \Delta x) - g(x)]/\Delta x) = g'(x)$, $\lim_{\Delta x \to 0} ([f(x + \Delta x) - f(x)]/\Delta x) = f'(x)$, and $\lim_{\Delta x \to 0} g(x) = g(x)$, giving us

$$h'(x) = f(x)g'(x) + g(x)f'(x)$$

(((6) $$D_x [f(x)g(x)] = f(x) \cdot D_x \, g(x) + g(x) \cdot D_x f(x)$$

The derivative of the product of two functions is the first function times the derivative of the second function plus the second function times the derivative of the first function, if these derivatives exist.

EXAMPLE 6: Given $h(x) = (2x^3 - 4x^2)(3x^5 + x^2)$, find $h'(x)$.

Solution:
$$\begin{aligned} h'(x) &= (2x^3 - 4x^2)(15x^4 + 2x) + (3x^5 + x^2)(6x^2 - 8x) \\ &= (30x^7 - 60x^6 + 4x^4 - 8x^3) + (18x^7 - 24x^6 + 6x^4 - 8x^3) \\ &= 48x^7 - 84x^6 + 10x^4 - 16x^3 \end{aligned}$$

In this example, note that if we multiply first and then perform the differentiation, the same result is obtained. Doing this, we have

$$h(x) = 6x^8 - 12x^7 + 2x^5 - 4x^4$$

Thus

$$h'(x) = 48x^7 - 84x^6 + 10x^4 - 16x^3$$

7.1.7 THEOREM   If f and g are functions and if h is the function defined by

$$h(x) = \frac{f(x)}{g(x)} \qquad \text{where} \qquad g(x) \neq 0$$

then, if $f'(x)$ and $g'(x)$ exist,

$$h'(x) = \frac{g(x)f'(x) - f(x)g'(x)}{[g(x)]^2}$$

Proof:
$$\begin{aligned} h'(x) &= \lim_{\Delta x \to 0} \frac{h(x + \Delta x) - h(x)}{\Delta x} \\ &= \lim_{\Delta x \to 0} \frac{f(x + \Delta x)/g(x + \Delta x) - f(x)/g(x)}{\Delta x} \\ &= \lim_{\Delta x \to 0} \frac{f(x + \Delta x) \cdot g(x) - f(x) \cdot g(x + \Delta x)}{\Delta x \cdot g(x) \cdot g(x + \Delta x)} \end{aligned}$$

Subtracting and adding $f(x) \cdot g(x)$ in the numerator, we obtain

$$h'(x) = \lim_{\Delta x \to 0} \frac{f(x + \Delta x) \cdot g(x) - f(x) \cdot g(x) - f(x) \cdot g(x + \Delta x) + f(x) \cdot g(x)}{\Delta x \cdot g(x) \cdot g(x + \Delta x)}$$

$$= \lim_{\Delta x \to 0} \frac{\left[g(x) \cdot \dfrac{f(x + \Delta x) - f(x)}{\Delta x} \right] - \left[f(x) \cdot \dfrac{g(x + \Delta x) - g(x)}{\Delta x} \right]}{g(x) \cdot g(x + \Delta x)}$$

$$= \frac{\lim\limits_{\Delta x \to 0} g(x) \cdot \lim\limits_{\Delta x \to 0} \dfrac{f(x + \Delta x) - f(x)}{\Delta x} - \lim\limits_{\Delta x \to 0} f(x) \cdot \lim\limits_{\Delta x \to 0} \dfrac{g(x + \Delta x) - g(x)}{\Delta x}}{\lim\limits_{\Delta x \to 0} g(x) \cdot \lim\limits_{\Delta x \to 0} g(x + \Delta x)}$$

$$= \frac{g(x) \cdot f'(x) - f(x) \cdot g'(x)}{g(x) \cdot g(x)}$$

$$= \frac{g(x) f'(x) - f(x) g'(x)}{[g(x)]^2}$$

$$(7) \qquad D_x \left[\frac{f(x)}{g(x)} \right] = \frac{g(x) D_x f(x) - f(x) D_x g(x)}{[g(x)]^2}$$

The derivative of the quotient of two functions is the fraction having as its denominator the square of the original denominator, and as its numerator the denominator times the derivative of the numerator minus the numerator times the derivative of the denominator, if these derivatives exist.

EXAMPLE 7: Given $h(x) = (2x^3 + 4)/(x^2 - 4x + 1)$, find $h'(x)$.

Solution: $h'(x) = \dfrac{(x^2 - 4x + 1)(6x^2) - (2x^3 + 4)(2x - 4)}{(x^2 - 4x + 1)^2}$

$$= \frac{6x^4 - 24x^3 + 6x^2 - 4x^4 + 8x^3 - 8x + 16}{(x^2 - 4x + 1)^2}$$

$$= \frac{2x^4 - 16x^3 + 6x^2 - 8x + 16}{(x^2 - 4x + 1)^2}$$

7.1.8 THEOREM   If $f(x) = x^{-n}$, where $-n$ is a negative integer and $x \neq 0$, then

$$f'(x) = -nx^{-n-1}$$

Proof: If $-n$ is a negative integer, then n is a positive integer. We write

$$f(x) = \frac{1}{x^n}$$

Applying Theorem 7.1.7, we have

$$f'(x) = \frac{x^n \cdot 0 - 1 \cdot nx^{n-1}}{(x^n)^2} = \frac{-nx^{n-1}}{x^{2n}} = -nx^{n-1-2n}$$

$$= -nx^{-n-1}$$

EXAMPLE 8: Given $f(x) = 3/x^5$, find $f'(x)$.

Solution: $f(x) = 3x^{-5}$ Hence, $f'(x) = 3(-5x^{-6}) = -15x^{-6} = -15/x^6$.

We see that if r is any positive or negative integer, we obtain from Theorems 7.1.2 and 7.1.8

$$D_x(x^r) = rx^{r-1} \tag{8}$$

and from Theorems 7.1.2, 7.1.3, and 7.1.8 we get

$$D_x(cx^r) = crx^{r-1} \tag{9}$$

Exercises 7.1

In Exercises 1 through 26, differentiate the functions by applying the theorems of this section.

1. $f(x) = x^3 - 3x^2 + 5x - 2$

2. $f(x) = 3x^4 - 5x^2 + 1$

3. $f(x) = \dfrac{x^8}{8} - x^4$

4. $g(x) = x^7 - 2x^5 + 5x^3 - 7x$

5. $F(t) = \dfrac{t^4}{4} - \dfrac{t^2}{2}$

6. $H(x) = \dfrac{x^3 - 3x + 6}{3}$

7. $v(r) = \dfrac{4}{3} \pi r^3$

8. $G(y) = y^{10} + 7y^5 - y^3 + 1$

9. $F(x) = x^2 + 3x + \dfrac{1}{x^2}$

10. $f(x) = x^4 - 5 + x^{-2} + 4x^{-4}$

11. $g(x) = \dfrac{3}{x^2} + \dfrac{5}{x^4}$

12. $H(x) = \dfrac{5}{6x^5}$

13. $f(s) = \sqrt{3}(s^3 - s^2)$

14. $g(x) = (2x^2 + 5)(4x - 1)$

15. $f(x) = (2x^4 - 1)(5x^3 + 6x)$

16. $g(x) = (4x^2 + 3)^2$

17. $H(x) = \dfrac{x^2 + 2x + 1}{x^2 - 2x + 1}$

18. $F(y) = \dfrac{2y + 1}{3y + 4}$

19. $f(x) = \dfrac{x}{x - 1}$

20. $f(x) = (x^2 - 3x + 2)(2x^3 + 1)$

21. $h(x) = \dfrac{5x}{1 + 2x^2}$

22. $g(x) = \dfrac{x^4 - 2x^2 + 5x + 1}{x^4}$

23. $f(x) = \dfrac{x^3 - 8}{x^3 + 8}$

24. $f(x) = \dfrac{x^2 - a^2}{x^2 + a^2}$

25. $f(x) = \dfrac{2x + 1}{x + 5}(3x - 1)$

26. $g(x) = \dfrac{x^3 + 1}{x^2 + 3}(x^2 - 2x^{-1} + 1)$

27. If f, g, and h are functions and if $\phi(x) = f(x) \cdot g(x) \cdot h(x)$, prove that if $f'(x)$, $g'(x)$, and $h'(x)$ exist, $\phi'(x) = f(x) \cdot g(x) \cdot h'(x) + f(x) \cdot h(x) \cdot g'(x) + g(x) \cdot h(x) \cdot f'(x)$. HINT: Apply Theorem 7.1.6 twice.

Use the result of Exercise 27 to differentiate the functions in Exercises 28 through 31.

28. $f(x) = (x^2 + 3)(2x - 5)(3x + 2)$

29. $h(x) = (3x + 2)^2 (x^2 - 1)$

30. $g(x) = (3x^3 + x^{-3})(x + 3)(x^2 - 5)$

31. $\phi(x) = (2x^2 + x + 1)^3$

32. Find an equation of the tangent line to the curve $y = 8/(x^2 + 4)$ at the point $(2,1)$.

33. Find an equation of each of the lines through the point $(-1,2)$ which is a tangent line to the curve $y = (x - 1)/(x + 3)$.

34. Find an equation of each of the tangent lines to the curve $3y = x^3 - 3x^2 + 6x + 4$, which is parallel to the line $2x - y + 3 = 0$.

35. Find the angle between the curves $y = 2x^2 - 11$ and $y = x^2 - 2$ at their points of intersection.

36. Find an equation of each of the normal lines to the curve $y = x^3 - 4x$ which is parallel to the line $x + 8y - 8 = 0$.

37. An object is moving along a straight line according to the equation of motion $s = 3t/(t^2 + 9)$, with $t \geq 0$, where s is the number of feet in the distance of the object from the starting point at t seconds of time. What is the instantaneous velocity of the object at t_1 sec? What is the instantaneous velocity at 1 sec? At what time is the instantaneous velocity zero?

(7.2)   The derivative of a composite function

Suppose that y is a function of u and that u, in turn, is a function of x. For example, let

(1) $$y = u^5$$

and

(2) $$u = 2x^3 - 5x^2 + 4$$

Equations (1) and (2) together define y as a function of x, since, if we replace u in (1) by the right-hand side of (2), we have

(3) $$y = (2x^3 - 5x^2 + 4)^5$$

This is an example of a composite function. A composite function was defined previously. (Refer to Definition 3.2.2.)

In general, if y is a function of u, defined by $y = f(u)$, and if u is a function of x, defined by $u = g(x)$, then y is a function of x, defined by $y = h(x)$ where

$$h(x) = f(g(x))$$

and h is a composite function.

We shall now state and prove a theorem for finding the derivative of a composite function. This theorem is known as the *chain rule*.

7.2.1 THEOREM (*The Chain Rule*)   If y is a function of u, defined by $y = f(u)$, and $D_u y$ exists, and if u is a function of x, defined by $u = g(x)$, and $D_x u$ exists, then y is a function of x and $D_x y$ exists and is given by

$$D_x y = D_u y \, D_x u$$

Proof: From equation (6) of Sec. 6.3, we have

(4) $$D_u y = \lim_{\Delta u \to 0} \frac{\Delta y}{\Delta u}$$

Therefore, if Δu is close to zero, $\Delta y / \Delta u$ is close to $D_u y$; or for a small Δu, with $\Delta u \neq 0$, we have

$$\frac{\Delta y}{\Delta u} = D_u y + \epsilon$$

If $\Delta u = 0$, we define $\epsilon = 0$. So, ϵ is a function of Δu, and we have

(5) $$\epsilon = \begin{cases} \dfrac{\Delta y}{\Delta u} - D_u y & \text{if} \quad \Delta u \neq 0 \\ 0 & \text{if} \quad \Delta u = 0 \end{cases}$$

So,

$$\lim_{\Delta u \to 0} \epsilon = \lim_{\Delta u \to 0} \left(\frac{\Delta y}{\Delta u} - D_u y \right) = D_u y - D_u y = 0$$

From (5) if $\Delta u \neq 0$, we may write

(6) $$\Delta y = D_u y \cdot \Delta u + (\Delta u) \cdot \epsilon$$

Note that equation (6) also holds if $\Delta u = 0$. Dividing both sides of (6) by Δx, where $\Delta x \neq 0$, we obtain

(7) $$\frac{\Delta y}{\Delta x} = D_u y \frac{\Delta u}{\Delta x} + \left(\frac{\Delta u}{\Delta x} \right) \cdot \epsilon$$

Taking the limit of both sides of equation (7) as Δx approaches zero and applying limit theorems, we have

$$\lim_{\Delta x \to 0} \frac{\Delta y}{\Delta x} = \lim_{\Delta x \to 0} D_u y \cdot \lim_{\Delta x \to 0} \frac{\Delta u}{\Delta x} + \lim_{\Delta x \to 0} \frac{\Delta u}{\Delta x} \cdot \lim_{\Delta x \to 0} \epsilon$$

or

(8) $$D_x y = D_u y \cdot D_x u + D_x u \cdot \lim_{\Delta x \to 0} \epsilon$$

Since $D_x u$ exists, it follows from Theorem 6.5.1 that u is a continuous function of x, and so as $\Delta x \to 0$, $\Delta u \to 0$. Therefore,

(9) $$\lim_{\Delta x \to 0} \epsilon = \lim_{\Delta u \to 0} \epsilon = 0$$

Substituting the value from (9) into (8), we obtain

$$D_x y = D_u y \cdot D_x u + D_x u \cdot (0)$$

or

$$D_x y = D_u y \cdot D_x u \quad .$$

which is what we wanted to prove.

Now, let us apply the chain rule to our previous example.

EXAMPLE 1: Given $y = (2x^3 - 5x^2 + 4)^5$, find $D_x y$.

Solution: Considering y as a function of u, where u is a function of x, we have

$$y = u^5 \qquad \text{where} \qquad u = 2x^3 - 5x^2 + 4$$

Therefore, from the chain rule,

$$D_x y = D_u y \cdot D_x u = 5u^4 (6x^2 - 10x)$$
$$= 5(2x^3 - 5x^2 + 4)^4 (6x^2 - 10x)$$

EXAMPLE 2: Given $f(x) = 1/(4x^3 + 5x^2 - 7x + 8)$, find $f'(x)$.

Solution: Write $f(x) = (4x^3 + 5x^2 - 7x + 8)^{-1}$, and apply the chain rule in order to get

$$f'(x) = -1(4x^3 + 5x^2 - 7x + 8)^{-2}(12x^2 + 10x - 7)$$
$$= \frac{-12x^2 - 10x + 7}{(4x^3 + 5x^2 - 7x + 8)^2}$$

EXAMPLE 3: Given $f(x) = [(2x + 1)/(3x - 1)]^4$, find $f'(x)$.

Solution: Applying the chain rule, we have

$$f'(x) = 4\left(\frac{2x + 1}{3x - 1}\right)^3 \cdot \frac{(3x - 1)(2) - (2x + 1)(3)}{(3x - 1)^2} = \frac{4(2x + 1)^3(-5)}{(3x - 1)^5}$$
$$= -\frac{20(2x + 1)^3}{(3x - 1)^5}$$

EXAMPLE 4: Given $f(x) = (3x^2 + 2)^2(x^2 - 5x)^3$, find $f'(x)$.

Solution: Consider f as the product of the two functions g and h, where

$$g(x) = (3x^2 + 2)^2 \qquad \text{and} \qquad h(x) = (x^2 - 5x)^3$$

Using Theorem 7.1.6 for the derivative of the product of two functions, we have

$$f'(x) = g(x)h'(x) + h(x)g'(x).$$

We find $h'(x)$ and $g'(x)$ by the chain rule, giving us

$$f'(x) = (3x^2 + 2)^2[3(x^2 - 5x)^2(2x - 5)] + (x^2 - 5x)^3[2(3x^2 + 2)(6x)]$$
$$= 3(3x^2 + 2)(x^2 - 5x)^2[(3x^2 + 2)(2x - 5) + 4x(x^2 - 5x)]$$
$$= 3(3x^2 + 2)(x^2 - 5x)^2[6x^3 - 15x^2 + 4x - 10 + 4x^3 - 20x^2]$$
$$= 3(3x^2 + 2)(x^2 - 5x)^2(10x^3 - 35x^2 + 4x - 10)$$

Exercises 7.2

In Exercises 1 through 20, find the derivative of the given function.

1. $F(x) = (x^2 + 4x - 5)^3$

2. $f(x) = (10 - 5x)^4$

3. $f(t) = (2t^4 - 7t^3 + 2t - 1)^2$

4. $g(r) = (2r^4 + 8r^2 + 1)^5$

5. $f(x) = (x + 4)^{-2}$

13. $f(x) = \dfrac{2}{7x^2 + 3x - 1}$

6. $H(z) = (z^3 - 3z^2 + 1)^{-3}$

14. $h(x) = \left(\dfrac{x + 4}{2x^2 - 5x + 6}\right)^3$

7. $h(u) = (3u^2 + 5)^3(3u - 1)^2$

15. $f(r) = (r^2 + 1)^3(2r + 5)^2$

8. $f(x) = (4x^2 + 7)^2(2x^3 + 1)^4$

16. $f(y) = (y + 3)^3(5y + 1)^2(3y^2 - 4)$

9. $g(x) = (2x - 5)^{-1}(4x + 3)^{-2}$

17. $f(z) = \dfrac{(z^2 - 5)^3}{(z^2 + 4)^2}$

10. $f(x) = (x^2 - 4x^{-2})^2(x^2 + 1)^{-1}$

18. $g(x) = (2x - 9)^2(x^3 + 4x - 5)^3$

11. $f(y) = \left(\dfrac{y - 7}{y + 2}\right)^2$

19. $G(x) = \dfrac{(4x - 1)^3(x^2 + 2)^4}{(3x^2 + 5)^2}$

12. $g(t) = \left(\dfrac{2t^2 + 1}{3t^3 + 1}\right)^2$

20. $F(x) = \dfrac{(5x - 8)^{-2}}{(x^2 + 3)^{-3}}$

21. Find an equation of the tangent line to the curve $y = (x^2 - 4)^2/(3x - 5)^2$ at the point $(1,2\tfrac{1}{4})$.

22. Find an equation of the tangent line to the curve $y = 2/(4 - x)^2$ at each of the following points: $(0,1/8)$, $(1,2/9)$, $(2,1/2)$, $(3,2)$, $(5,2)$, $(6,1/2)$. Draw a sketch of the graph and segments of the tangent lines at the given points.

23. Find an equation of the normal line to the curve $y = 2/(x^2 - 2x - 4)^2$ at the point $(3,2)$.

24. A particle is moving along a straight line according to the equation of motion $s = [(t^2 - 1)/(t^2 + 1)]^2$, with $t \geq 0$, where s is the number of feet in the distance of the particle from the origin at t seconds of time. What is the instantaneous velocity of the particle at t_1 sec? What is the instantaneous velocity at 1 sec? What is the instantaneous velocity at $1\tfrac{1}{2}$ sec?

25. Use the chain rule to prove that the derivative of an even function is an odd function, and that the derivative of an odd function is an even function, provided that these derivatives exist.

26. If the two functions f and g are differentiable at the number x_1, is the composite function $f \circ g$ necessarily differentiable at x_1? If your answer is yes, prove it. If your answer is no, give an example.

27. Suppose that y is a function of v, v is a function of u, and u is a function of x, and that the derivatives $D_v y$, $D_u v$, $D_x u$, all exist. Prove the chain rule for three functions:

$$D_x y = (D_v y)(D_u v)(D_x u)$$

(7.3)   The derivative of the power function for rational exponents

The function f defined by

(1) $$f(x) = x^r$$

is called the *power function*. In Sec. 7.1 we considered the derivative of this function when r is a positive or negative integer, and we obtained the following formula for the derivative of f:

$$(2) \qquad f'(x) = rx^{r-1}$$

We shall now show that this formula holds when r is any rational number, provided that x^{r-1} is a real number.

We shall first consider the case when $x = 0$. Then r must be a positive number since $f(0)$ is not defined if $r \leq 0$. If $r > 0$, then $f'(0) = \lim_{x \to 0} [(x^r - 0^r)/(x - 0)] = \lim_{x \to 0} x^{r-1}$. If $r > 1$, $\lim_{x \to 0} x^{r-1} = 0$. So if $r > 1$, $f'(0) = 0$, which may be written as $r \cdot 0^{r-1}$. Thus formula (2) holds if $x = 0$, and $r > 1$. We shall now show that if $x \neq 0$, formula (2) holds when r is any rational number for which x^{r-1} is a real number. The following proof assumes $f'(x)$ exists.

Let $r = p/q$, where p and q are nonzero integers; that is, r is any rational number except zero. Then, equation (1) may be written as

$$f(x) = x^{p/q}$$

or, equivalently, $\qquad [f(x)]^q = x^p$

We now find the derivative with respect to x of both sides of this equation, by applying the chain rule to the left-hand side and formula (2) to the right-hand side, thus obtaining, if $f'(x)$ exists,

$$q[f(x)]^{q-1} \cdot [f'(x)] = px^{p-1}$$

Replacing $f(x)$ by $x^{p/q}$ gives us

$$q[x^{(p/q)(q-1)}] \cdot f'(x) = px^{p-1}$$
$$q[x^{p-p/q}] \cdot f'(x) = px^{p-1}$$

Since $x \neq 0$, we divide both sides of the above equation by $q \cdot x^{p-p/q}$ and obtain

$$f'(x) = \frac{px^{p-1}}{qx^{p-p/q}}$$

or, equivalently,

$$(3) \qquad f'(x) = \frac{p}{q} \cdot x^{p/q-1}$$

Equation (3) is the same as (2) with $r = p/q$.

If $r = 0$ and $x \neq 0$, equation (1) becomes $f(x) = x^0 = 1$. In this case $f'(x) = 0$, which may be written as $f'(x) = 0 \cdot x^{0-1}$. Therefore formula (2) holds if $r = 0$ and with $x \neq 0$. Thus, we have proved the following theorem.

7.3.1 THEOREM   If f is the power function, where r is any rational number — that is, $f(x) = x^r$ — then

$$f'(x) = rx^{r-1}$$

provided that x^{r-1} is a·real number.

An immediate consequence of Theorem 7.3.1 and the chain rule is the following theorem.

7.3.2 THEOREM   If f and g are functions such that $f(x) = [g(x)]^r$ where r is any rational number, and if $g'(x)$ exists, then

$$f'(x) = r[g(x)]^{r-1}g'(x)$$

for all x for which $[g(x)]^{r-1}$ is a real number.

EXAMPLE 1: Given $f(x) = 4\sqrt[3]{x^2}$, find $f'(x)$.
  Solution: $f(x) = 4x^{2/3}$
Applying Theorem 7.3.1, we get

$$f'(x) = 4 \cdot \frac{2}{3}[x^{2/3-1}] = \frac{8}{3}x^{-1/3} = \frac{8}{3x^{1/3}}$$

$$= \frac{8}{3\sqrt[3]{x}}$$

EXAMPLE 2: Given $h(x) = \sqrt{2x^3 - 4x + 5}$, find $h'(x)$.
  Solution: $h(x) = (2x^3 - 4x + 5)^{1/2}$
Applying Theorem 7.3.2, we have

$$h'(x) = \tfrac{1}{2}(2x^3 - 4x + 5)^{-1/2}(6x^2 - 4)$$

$$= \frac{3x^2 - 2}{\sqrt{2x^3 - 4x + 5}}$$

Exercises 7.3

In Exercises 1 through 18, find the derivative of the given function.

1. $f(x) = (3x + 5)^{2/3}$

2. $f(s) = \sqrt{2 - 3s^2}$

3. $g(x) = \sqrt{\dfrac{2x - 5}{3x + 1}}$

4. $h(t) = \dfrac{\sqrt{t - 1}}{\sqrt{t + 1}}$

5. $f(x) = 4x^{1/2} + 5x^{-1/2}$

6. $g(y) = (y^2 + 3)^{1/3}(y^3 - 1)^{1/2}$

7. $F(x) = \sqrt[3]{2x^3 - 5x^2 + x}$

8. $g(x) = \sqrt[3]{(3x^2 + 5x - 1)^2}$

9. $g(t) = \sqrt{2t} + \sqrt{2/t}$

10. $f(x) = 3x^{2/3} - 6x^{1/3} + x^{-1/3}$

11. $F(x) = \dfrac{\sqrt{x^2 - 1}}{x}$

12. $G(x) = \dfrac{4x + 6}{\sqrt{x^2 + 3x + 4}}$

13. $h(x) = \dfrac{\sqrt{x - 1}}{\sqrt[3]{x + 1}}$

14. $f(s) = (s^4 + 3s^2 + 1)^{-2/3}$

15. $f(x) = \sqrt{x^2 - 5} \cdot \sqrt[3]{x^2 + 3}$

16. $G(t) = \sqrt[3]{\dfrac{5t + 6}{5t - 4}}$

17. $f(x) = \sqrt{9 + \sqrt{9 - x}}$

18. $g(x) = \sqrt[4]{\dfrac{y^3 + 1}{y^3 - 1}}$

19. Find an equation of the tangent line to the curve $y = \sqrt{x^2 + 9}$ at the point $(4,5)$.

20. Find an equation of the tangent line to the curve $y = (6 - 2x)^{1/3}$ at each of the following points: $(-1,2)$, $(1,\sqrt[3]{4})$, $(3,0)$, $(5,-\sqrt[3]{4})$, $(7,-2)$. Draw a sketch of the graph and segments of the tangent lines at the given points.

21. Find an equation of the normal line to the curve $y = x\sqrt{16 + x^2}$ at the origin.

22. Find an equation of the tangent line to the curve $y = 1/\sqrt[3]{7x - 6}$ which is perpendicular to the line $12x - 7y + 2 = 0$.

23. An object is moving along a straight line according to the equation of motion $s = \sqrt{4t^2 + 3}$, with $t \geq 0$. Find the values of t for which the instantaneous velocity is (a) 0; (b) 1; (c) 2.

24. Given $f(x) = |x^2 - 4|$, find $f'(x)$. HINT: Let $|x^2 - 4| = \sqrt{(x^2 - 4)^2}$.

25. If $y = |f(x)|$, derive a formula for $D_x y$. HINT: Let $|f(x)| = \sqrt{[f(x)]^2}$.

26. If g and h are functions and if f is the function defined by

$$f(x) = [g(x)]^r[h(x)]^s$$

where r and s are rational numbers, prove that if $g'(x)$ and $h'(x)$ exist

$$f'(x) = [g(x)]^{r-1}[h(x)]^{s-1}[r \cdot h(x)g'(x) + s \cdot g(x)h'(x)]$$

In Exercises 27 through 30, use the result of Exercise 26 to find the derivative of the given function.

27. $f(x) = (3x + 2)^4(x^2 - 1)^{2/3}$

28. $g(x) = (4x + 3)^{1/2}(4 - x^2)^{1/3}$

29. $F(t) = (t^3 - 2t + 1)^{3/2}(t^2 + t + 5)^{1/3}$

30. $f(r) = \left(\dfrac{r + 1}{r^2 + 1}\right)^3(r^3 + 4)^{1/3}$

(7.4)   Derivatives of higher order

If f' is the derivative of the function f, then f' is also a function, and it is the *first derivative* of f. It is sometimes referred to as the *first derived function*. If the derivative of f' exists, it is called the *second derivative* of f, or the second derived function, and may be denoted by f'' (read "f double prime"). Similarly, we define the *third derivative* of f, or the third derived function, as the first derivative of f'' if it exists. We denote the third derivative of f by f''' (read "f triple prime").

The *nth derivative* of the function f, where n is a positive integer greater than 1, is the first derivative of the $(n - 1)$st derivative of f. We may denote the nth derivative of f by $f^{(n)}$. Thus, if $f^{(n)}$ denotes the nth derived function, we may denote the function f itself by $f^{(0)}$. Other symbols for the nth derivative of f are $D_x^n f$. If the function f is defined by the equation $y = f(x)$, we may denote the nth derivative of f by $D_x^n y$.

EXAMPLE 1: Find all the derivatives of the function f defined by
$$f(x) = 8x^4 + 5x^3 - x^2 + 7$$

Solution:

$$f'(x) = 32x^3 + 15x^2 - 2x$$
$$f''(x) = 96x^2 + 30x - 2$$
$$f'''(x) = 192x + 30$$
$$f^{(4)}(x) = 192$$
$$f^{(5)}(x) = 0$$
$$f^{(n)}(x) = 0 \qquad n \geq 5$$

If $P(x,y)$ is any point on the graph of $y = f(x)$, then $D_x y$ gives the slope of the tangent line to the graph at P. Then, $D_x^2 y$ is the *rate of change of the slope of the tangent line* with respect to x at P. *Acceleration*

EXAMPLE 2: Let $m(x)$ be the slope of the tangent line to the curve $y = x^3 - 2x^2 + x$ at x. Find the rate of change of m with respect to x at the point $(2,2)$.

Solution: $m(x) = D_x y = 3x^2 - 4x + 1$

The rate of change of m with respect to x is given by $D_x m$ or, equivalently, by $D_x^2 y$.

$$D_x^2 y = 6x - 4$$

At $(2,2)$, $D_x^2 y = 8$. Therefore at the point $(2,2)$, the change in m is 8 times the change in x.

If a particle is moving along a straight line according to the equation of motion $s = f(t)$, then the instantaneous velocity of the particle at t_1 is $f'(t_1)$. That is, the instantaneous velocity of the particle is the derivative of s with respect to t. In physics, the *instantaneous acceleration* of a particle in straight-line motion is defined to be the rate of change of the instantaneous velocity with respect to time. Therefore, if v is the instantaneous velocity at t and if a is the instantaneous acceleration at t, then v is the first derivative of s with respect to t, and a is the first derivative of v with respect to t or, equivalently, the second derivative of s with respect to t. That is, if $s = f(t)$, then

$$v = D_t s \qquad \text{and} \qquad a = D_t v = D_t^2 s$$

EXAMPLE 3: A particle is moving along a straight line according to the equation of motion

$$s = \frac{1}{2} t^2 + \frac{4t}{t + 1} \qquad t \geq 0$$

where s is the number of feet in the distance of the particle from the origin at t sec. If v is the number of feet per second in the instantaneous velocity at t sec and if a is the number of feet per second per second in the instantaneous acceleration at t sec, find t, s, and v when a is zero.

176 DIFFERENTIATION OF ALGEBRAIC FUNCTIONS

Solution:

$$v = D_t s = t + \frac{4}{(t+1)^2}$$

$$a = D_t v = D_t{}^2 s = 1 - \frac{8}{(t+1)^3}$$

Setting $a = 0$, we have

$$\frac{(t+1)^3 - 8}{t+1} = 0$$

$$\text{or} \quad (t+1)^3 = 8$$

from which the only real value of t is obtained from the principal cube root of 8, so that

$$t + 1 = 2$$

$$\text{or} \quad t = 1$$

When $t = 1$, $s = 2\frac{1}{2}$ and $v = 2$.

Exercises 7.4

In Exercises 1 through 10, find the first and second derivatives of the given function.

1. $f(x) = x^5 - 2x^3 + x$

2. $F(x) = 7x^3 - 8x^2$

3. $g(s) = 2s^4 - 4s^3 + 7s - 1$

4. $G(t) = t^3 - t^2 + t$

5. $f(x) = \sqrt{x^2 + 1}$

6. $h(y) = \sqrt[3]{2y^3 + 5}$

7. $F(x) = x^2\sqrt{x} - 5x$

8. $g(r) = \sqrt{r} + \dfrac{1}{\sqrt{r}}$

9. $G(x) = \dfrac{1}{\sqrt{3 + 2x^2}}$

10. $f(x) = \dfrac{2 - \sqrt{x}}{2 + \sqrt{x}}$

11. Find $D_x{}^3 y$ if $y = x^4 - 2x^2 + x - 5$.

12. Find $D_t{}^3 s$ if $s = \sqrt{4t + 1}$.

13. Find $D_x{}^3 f(x)$ if $f(x) = x/(1-x)^2$.

14. Find $f^{(4)}(x)$ if $f(x) = 2/(x - 1)$.

15. Find $D_x{}^4 y$ if $y = x^{7/2} - 2x^{5/2} + x^{1/2}$.

16. Find $D_v{}^3 u$ if $u = v\sqrt{v - 2}$.

17. Find the slope of the tangent line at each point of the graph of

$$y = x^4 + x^3 - 3x^2$$

where the rate of change of the slope is zero.

In Exercises 18 through 21, a particle is moving along a straight line according to the given equation of motion, where s is the number of feet in the distance of the particle from the origin at t sec. Find the time when the instantaneous acceleration is zero, and then find the directed distance of the particle from the origin and the instantaneous velocity at this instant.

18. $s = 2t^3 - 6t^2 + 3t - 4$, $t \geq 0$ 20. $s = 9t^2 + 2\sqrt{2t + 1}$, $t \geq 0$

19. $s = \dfrac{125}{16t + 32} - \dfrac{2}{5}t^5$, $t \geq 0$ 21. $s = \dfrac{4}{9}t^{3/2} + 2t^{1/2}$, $t \geq 0$

22. If f and g are two functions such that their first and second derivatives exist and if h is the function defined by

$$h(x) = [f(x)][g(x)]$$

prove that

$$h''(x) = [f(x)][g''(x)] + 2[f'(x)][g'(x)] + [f''(x)][g(x)]$$

23. If f is the function defined by

$$f(x) = \begin{cases} -x^2 & \text{if } x < 0 \\ x^2 & \text{if } 0 \leq x \end{cases}$$

prove that the domain of f' is the set of all real numbers, and that the domain of f'' is the set of all real numbers except zero.

24. If $y = x^n$, where n is any positive integer, prove by mathematical induction that $D_x^n y = n!$

25. If $y = 1/(1 - 2x)$, by mathematical induction prove that

$$D_x^n y = \frac{(2^n)(n!)}{(1 - 2x)^{n+1}}$$

(7.5)   Implicit Differentiation

If y is a function of x defined by the equation

(1) $y = 3x^2 + 5x + 1$

then y is defined *explicitly* in terms of x, and we may write

$$y = f(x) \quad \text{where} \quad f(x) = 3x^2 + 5x + 1$$

However, not all functions are defined explicitly. For example, if we have the equation

(2) $x^6 - 2x = 3y^6 + y^5 - y^2$

we cannot solve for y explicitly as a function of x; however, the value of y depends upon the value of x, and there may exist one or more functions f such that, if $y = f(x)$, equation (2) is satisfied. In this case we say that y is defined implicitly as a function of x.

Even though we cannot solve equation (2) for y in terms of x, we can find the derivative of y with respect to x by the process called *implicit differentiation*, which we shall now do.

The left-hand side of equation (2) is a function of x, and the right-hand side is a function of y. Let F be the function defined by the left-hand side of (2), and let G be the function defined by the right-hand side of (2). Thus,

(3) $$F(x) = x^6 - 2x$$

and

(4) $$G(y) = 3y^6 + y^5 - y^2$$

where y is a function of x, say,

$$y = f(x)$$

So, write equation (2) as

(5) $$F(x) = G(f(x))$$

Equation (5) is satisfied by all values of x in the domain of f for which $G[f(x)]$ exists.

Then for all values of x for which f is differentiable, we have

(6) $$D_x [x^6 - 2x] = D_x [3y^6 + y^5 - y^2]$$

The derivative on the left-hand side of equation (6) is easily found to be

(7) $$D_x [x^6 - 2x] = 6x^5 - 2$$

We find the derivative on the right-hand side of equation (6) by the chain rule, giving us

(8) $$D_x [3y^6 + y^5 - y^2] = 18y^5 \cdot D_x y + 5y^4 \cdot D_x y - 2y \cdot D_x y$$

Substituting the values from (7) and (8) into (6), we obtain

$$6x^5 - 2 = [18y^5 + 5y^4 - 2y] \cdot D_x y$$

Solving for $D_x y$, we get

$$D_x y = \frac{6x^5 - 2}{18y^5 + 5y^4 - 2y}$$

for all values of y for which $18y^5 + 5y^4 - 2y \neq 0$.

The reader must bear in mind that we assumed that equation (2) defines y as one or more differentiable functions of x. A discussion of the truth of this assumption is beyond the scope of this book. In the pages that follow, whenever we differentiate implicitly from an equation that defines one variable as an implicit function of another variable, we shall assume that the function is differentiable.

EXAMPLE 1: Given $x^3 y^2 - 5x^2 y^2 = 24xy - 5x + y$, find $D_x y$.

Solution: We differentiate both sides of the equation with respect to x, bearing in mind that y is a function of x. We apply the theorems for the derivative of a product, the derivative of a power, and the chain rule.

$$3x^2 y^2 + x^3 [2y \cdot D_x y] - 10xy^2 - 5x^2 [2y \cdot D_x y] = 24y + 24x \cdot D_x y - 5 + D_x y$$

Solving for D_xy, we have

$$D_xy \, (2x^3y - 10x^2y - 24x - 1) = -3x^2y^2 + 10xy^2 + 24y - 5$$

$$D_xy = \frac{-3x^2y^2 + 10xy^2 + 24y - 5}{2x^3y - 10x^2y - 24x - 1}$$

EXAMPLE 2: Find an equation of the tangent line to the curve $x^3 + y^3 = 9$ at the point (1,2).

Solution: Differentiating implicitly with respect to x, we obtain

$$3x^2 + 3y^2 \cdot D_xy = 0$$

Hence, $$D_xy = -\frac{x^2}{y^2}$$

Therefore, at the point (1,2), $D_xy = -1/4$. An equation of the tangent line is then

$$y - 2 = -\frac{1}{4}(x - 1)$$

EXAMPLE 3: Given $4x^2 + 9y^2 = 36$, find $D_x{}^2y$ by implicit differentiation.

Solution: Differentiating implicitly with respect to x, we have

$$8x + 18y \cdot D_xy = 0$$

so that

(9) $$D_xy = -\frac{4x}{9y}$$

To find $D_x{}^2y$, we find the derivative of a quotient and keep in mind that y is a function of x. So we have

(10) $$D_x{}^2y = \frac{9y(-4) - (-4x)(9D_xy)}{81y^2}$$

Substituting the value of D_xy from equation (9) into (10), we get

$$D_x{}^2y = \frac{-36y + 36x(-4x/9y)}{81y^2} = \frac{-36y^2 - 16x^2}{81y^3}$$

or

(11) $$D_x{}^2y = \frac{-4(9y^2 + 4x^2)}{81y^3}$$

Since any values of x and y satisfying equation (11) must also satisfy our original equation, we may replace $(9y^2 + 4x^2)$ by 36, and so we obtain

$$D_x{}^2y = \frac{-4(36)}{81y^3} = \frac{-16}{9y^3}$$

In Exercises 1 through 16, find $D_x y$ by implicit differentiation.

1. $x^2 + y^2 = 16$

9. $x^2 y^2 = x^2 + y^2$

2. $2x^3 y + 3xy^3 = 5$

10. $y\sqrt{2 + 3x} + x\sqrt{1 + y} = x$

3. $x^3 + y^3 = 8xy$

11. $(x + y)^2 - (x - y)^2 = x^3 + y^3$

4. $x^2 = \dfrac{x + 2y}{x - 2y}$

12. $(2x + 3)^4 = 3y^4$

5. $\dfrac{1}{x} + \dfrac{1}{y} = 1$

13. $\dfrac{y}{x - y} = 2 + x^2$

6. $\dfrac{x}{y} - 4y = x$

14. $\sqrt{y} + \sqrt[3]{y} + \sqrt[4]{y} = x$

7. $\sqrt{x} + \sqrt{y} = 4$

15. $\sqrt{xy} + 2x = \sqrt{y}$

8. $y + \sqrt{xy} = 3x^3$

16. $x^2 y^3 = x^4 - y^4$

17. Given $x^3 + y^3 = 1$, show that $D_x{}^2 y = -2x/y^5$.

18. Given $x^{1/2} + y^{1/2} = 2$, show that $D_x{}^2 y = 1/x^{3/2}$.

19. Given $x^4 + y^4 = a^4$ (a is a constant), find $D_x{}^2 y$ in simplest form.

20. Given $b^2 x^2 - a^2 y^2 = a^2 b^2$ (a and b are constants), find $D_x{}^2 y$ in simplest form.

21. Find an equation of the tangent line to the curve $16x^4 + y^4 = 32$ at the point $(1,2)$.

22. Find an equation of each tangent line to the curve
$$x^2 + 4y^2 - 4x - 8y + 3 = 0$$
containing the point $(-1,3)$.

23. Prove that the sum of the x and y intercepts of any tangent line to the curve $x^{1/2} + y^{1/2} = k^{1/2}$ is constant and equal to k.

24. Find the angles between the tangent lines at the points of intersection of the curves $2x^2 - y^2 = 41$ and $x^2 + 4y^2 = 61$.

In Exercises 25 through 28, an equation is given. Do the following in each of these problems: (*a*) Find two functions defined by the equation, and state their domains. (*b*) Draw a sketch of the graph of each of the functions obtained in part (*a*). (*c*) Draw a sketch of the graph of the equation. (*d*) Find the derivative of each of the functions obtained in part (*a*), and state the domains of the derivatives. (*e*) Find $D_x y$ by implicit differentiation from the given equation, and verify that the result so obtained agrees with the results in part (*d*). (*f*) Find an equation of each tangent line at the given value of x_1.

25. $y^2 = 4x - 8$; $x_1 = 3$

27. $x^2 - y^2 = 9$; $x_1 = -5$

26. $x^2 + y^2 = 25$; $x_1 = 4$

28. $y^2 - x^2 = 16$; $x_1 = -3$

(7.6)   Differentials

Suppose that the function f is differentiable on its domain, and let

$$y = f(x)$$

Then,

(1) $$f'(x) = \lim_{\Delta x \to 0} \frac{\Delta y}{\Delta x}$$

where $$\Delta y = f(x + \Delta x) - f(x)$$

From equation (1) we may conclude that when Δx is close to zero, $\Delta y / \Delta x$ is close to $f'(x)$. Or, if we let ϵ denote the difference between $\Delta y / \Delta x$ and $f'(x)$, that is,

(2) $$\frac{\Delta y}{\Delta x} = f'(x) + \epsilon \qquad \Delta x \neq 0$$

then $\epsilon \to 0$ as $\Delta x \to 0$. Multiplying both sides of equation (2) by Δx, we have

(3) $$\Delta y = f'(x)\,\Delta x + \epsilon \cdot \Delta x$$

So, if Δx is close to zero, ϵ is close to zero, and then $\epsilon \cdot \Delta x$ is also close to zero. Using the symbol $\approx$, meaning "approximately equal to," we say that if Δx is close to zero,

$$\Delta y \approx f'(x)\,\Delta x$$

The right-hand side of the above is defined to be the *differential* of y.

7.6.1 DEFINITION   If the function f is differentiable on its domain and if $y = f(x)$, then the *differential of y*, denoted by dy, is given by

(4) $$dy = f'(x)\,\Delta x$$

dy is a function of two independent variables x and Δx, where x may be any number in the domain of f' and Δx may be any number whatsoever. For example, if $y = 4x^2 - x$, then $f(x) = 4x^2 - x$, and so $f'(x) = 8x - 1$. Therefore, from Definition 7.6.1, $dy = (8x - 1)\Delta x$. In particular if $x = 2$, $dy = 15\Delta x$.

Definition 7.6.1 tells us what is meant by the differential of the dependent variable. We also wish to define the differential of the independent variable, or dx. To arrive at a suitable definition for dx that is consistent with the definition of dy, we consider the function f defined by $f(x) = x$. Then $f'(x) = 1$, and $y = x$; so, $dy = 1 \cdot \Delta x = \Delta x$. Since $y = x$, we have $dy = dx$ for this particular function. Hence, for this function, $dx = \Delta x$. It is this reasoning that leads us to define the differential of the independent variable by writing

(5) $$dx = \Delta x$$

From equations (5) and (4), we obtain

(6) $$dy = f'(x)\,dx$$

Dividing both sides of the above by dx, we have

(7) $$\frac{dy}{dx} = f'(x) \qquad \text{if } dx \neq 0$$

Equation (7) expresses the derivative as the quotient of two differentials. Often the notation dy/dx is used to denote the derivative of y with respect to x — a symbolism that we have avoided until now. However, the derivative shall be considered as the quotient of two differentials whenever it is convenient to do so.

Since $\Delta y \approx f'(x)\,\Delta x$ when Δx is close to zero, we may conclude that the differential of y, which is dy, and the increment of y, which is Δy, are approximately equal when dx is close to zero.

We shall now interpret the differential geometrically (refer to Fig. 7.6.1).

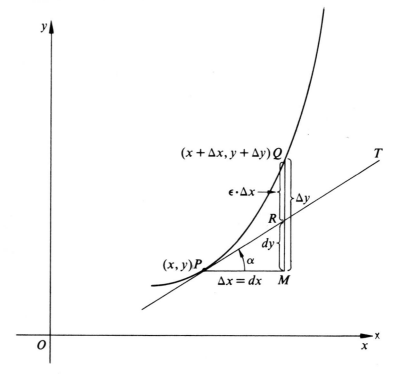

Figure 7.6.1

In Fig. 7.6.1, the equation of the curve is $y = f(x)$. The line PT is tangent to the curve at P; Δx and dx are equal and are represented by the directed distance $\overline{PM}$; $\overline{MQ}$ is Δy. α is the inclination of PT, and since $\tan \alpha = f'(x)$, and $f'(x) = dy/dx$, we have $\tan \alpha = dy/dx$. Also, $\tan \alpha = \overline{MR}/\overline{PM}$, and since $\overline{PM} = dx$, we have $dy = \overline{MR}$. If we replace $f'(x)\,\Delta x$ in equation (3) by dy, we have

$$\Delta y = dy + \epsilon\,\Delta x$$

So, we see from Fig. 7.6.1 that $\overline{RQ} = \epsilon\cdot\Delta x$.

It should be noted from Fig. 7.6.1 that the closer dx is to zero, the closer dy will be to Δy; that is, the smaller will be $\epsilon\cdot\Delta x$.

EXAMPLE 1: Given $y = x^2 - 3x + 1$, find Δy and dy for (a) any x and Δx; (b) $x = 2, \Delta x = 0.1$; (c) $x = 2, \Delta x = 0.01$; (d) $x = 2, \Delta x = 0.001$.

Solution: (a) Since $y = x^2 - 3x + 1$, we have

$$y + \Delta y = (x + \Delta x)^2 - 3(x + \Delta x) + 1$$

$$(x^2 - 3x + 1) + \Delta y = x^2 + 2x \Delta x + (\Delta x)^2 - 3x - 3 \Delta x + 1$$

$$\Delta y = (2x - 3) \Delta x + (\Delta x)^2$$

Also, $dy = f'(x)\, dx$

or $dy = (2x - 3)\, dx = (2x - 3) \Delta x$

The results for parts (b), (c), and (d) are given in Table 7.6.1, where $\Delta y = (2x - 3) \Delta x + (\Delta x)^2$, $dy = (2x - 3) \Delta x$, and $\epsilon \Delta x = \Delta y - dy$.

Table 7.6.1

x	Δx	Δy	dy	$\epsilon \Delta x$
2	0.1	0.11	0.1	0.01
2	0.01	0.0101	0.01	0.0001
2	0.001	0.001001	0.001	0.000001

We see from Table 7.6.1 that the closer Δx is to zero, the smaller is the difference between Δy and dy. Therefore, dy is an approximation of Δy, when Δx is small. Or, if x is changed by a small amount Δx, the corresponding change in y is approximately dy.

EXAMPLE 2: Find an approximate value for $\sqrt[3]{28}$ without using tables.

Solution: The nearest perfect cube to 28 is 27. We consider the function f, defined by

$$f(x) = \sqrt[3]{x}$$

Hence $y = \sqrt[3]{x}$ and $y + \Delta y = \sqrt[3]{x + \Delta x}$

Take $x = 27, \Delta x = 1$; then, $y = \sqrt[3]{27} = 3$, and

$$\sqrt[3]{28} = \sqrt[3]{x + \Delta x}$$

or $\sqrt[3]{28} = y + \Delta y$

We get an approximation for Δy by finding dy:

$$dy = f'(x)\, dx = \frac{1}{3x^{2/3}}\, dx$$

Since $dx = \Delta x$, and $\Delta x = 1$, we have $dx = 1$. Thus,

$$dy = \frac{1}{3(27)^{2/3}}\,(1) = \frac{1}{27}$$

Since $\Delta y \approx dy$, we have

$$\Delta y \approx \frac{1}{27}$$

Therefore, $\qquad y + \Delta y \approx 3 + \frac{1}{27}$

or $\qquad\qquad y + \Delta y \approx 3.037$

so that $\qquad\qquad \sqrt[3]{28} \approx 3.037$

EXAMPLE 3: Find the approximate volume of a spherical shell whose outer radius is 4 in. and whose thickness is 1/16 in.

Solution: We consider the volume of the spherical shell as an increment of the volume of a sphere.

Let $\quad r =$ the number of inches in the radius of a sphere
$\qquad V =$ the number of cubic inches in the volume of a sphere
$\quad - \Delta V =$ the number of cubic inches in the volume of a spherical shell

$$V = \frac{4}{3}\pi r^3 \qquad \text{so that} \qquad dV = 4\pi r^2 dr$$

Substituting $r = 4$ and $dr = -1/16$ into the above, we obtain

$$dV = 4\pi(4)^2\left(-\frac{1}{16}\right) = -4\pi$$

Therefore, $\qquad \Delta V \approx -4\pi$

We conclude that the volume of the spherical shell is approximately 4π in.[3]

Exercises 7.6

In Exercises 1 through 6, find (*a*) Δy; (*b*) dy; (*c*) $\Delta y - dy$.

1. $y = x^3$

2. $y = 4x^2 - 3x + 1$

3. $y = \sqrt{x}$

4. $y = \dfrac{1}{x^2 + 1}$

5. $y = 2x^3 + 3x^2$

6. $y = \dfrac{1}{\sqrt[3]{x}}$

In Exercises 7 through 12, find dy, Δy, and $\Delta y - dy$ for the given values.

7. $y = x^2 - 3x$; $x = 2$, $\Delta x = 0.03$

8. $y = x^2 - 3x$; $x = -1$; $\Delta x = 0.02$

9. $y = x^3 + 1$; $x = 1$; $\Delta x = -0.5$

10. $y = x^3 + 1$; $x = -1$; $\Delta x = 0.1$

11. $y = \dfrac{1}{x^2}$; $x = 2$; $\Delta x = 0.01$

12. $y = \dfrac{1}{x^2}$; $x = -3$; $\Delta x = -0.1$

In Exercises 13 through 18 use differentials to find an approximate value for the given quantity. Express each answer to three significant figures.

13. $\sqrt{37.5}$ 16. $\sqrt[4]{82}$

14. $\sqrt[3]{7.5}$ 17. $\sqrt{0.042}$

15. $\sqrt{82}$ 18. $\sqrt[3]{0.00098}$

19. Find the approximate error in the surface area of a cube having an edge of length 3 ft if an error of ¼ in. is made in measuring an edge.

20. The altitude of a right-circular cone is twice the radius of the base. The altitude is measured as 12 in., with a possible error of 0.005 in. Find the approximate error in the calculated volume of the cone.

21. Find the approximate volume of a right-circular cylindrical shell, having an altitude of three times the inner radius of the base, if the inner radius of the base is measured as 4 in. and the outer radius is measured as 4.02 in.

$$V = \pi R^2 h$$

(7.7)   Differential formulas

Suppose that y is a function of x and that x, in turn, is a function of a third variable t. That is,

(1) $y = f(x)$ and $x = g(t)$

The two equations in (1) together define y as a function of t. For example, suppose that $y = x^3$ and $x = 2t - 1$. Combining these two equations, we get $y = (2t - 1)^3$. In general, if we combine the two equations in (1), we obtain

(2) $y = f(g(t))$

We may obtain the derivative of y with respect to t by the chain rule, and we get

(3) $D_t y = D_x y \, D_t x$

Equation (3) expresses $D_t y$ as a function of x and t, since $D_x y$ is a function of x, and $D_t x$ is a function of t.

Since equation (2) defines y as a function of the independent variable t, we obtain the differential of y from Definition 7.6.1, giving us

(4) $dy = D_t y \, dt$

Equation (4) expresses dy as a function of t and dt. Substituting (3) into (4), we get

(5) $dy = D_x y \, D_t x \, dt$

Now, since x is a function of the independent variable t, we may apply Definition 7.6.1 to obtain the differential of x, and we have

(6) $dx = D_t x \, dt$

Equation (6) expresses dx as a function of t and dt. From (5) and (6), we get

(7) $$dy = D_x y \, dx$$

The reader should bear in mind that in equation (7) dy is a function of t and dt, and that dx is a function of t and dt. If we replace $D_x y$ in equation (7) by $f'(x)$, we have

(8) $$dy = f'(x) \, dx$$

Equation (8) resembles equation (6) of Sec. 7.6. However, in that equation x is the independent variable, and dy is expressed in terms of x and dx; whereas in equation (8), t is the independent variable, and both dy and dx are expressed in terms of t and dt. We have then the following theorem.

7.7.1 THEOREM   If $y = f(x)$ and if f is differentiable for all values of x in its domain, then

$$dy = f'(x) \, dx$$

whether or not x is an independent variable.

If we divide both sides of equation (8) by dx (if $dx \neq 0$), we get

(9) $$f'(x) = \frac{dy}{dx} \qquad dx \neq 0$$

Equation (9) tells us that if $y = f(x)$, then $f'(x)$ is the quotient of the two differentials dy and dx, even though x may not be an independent variable.

We shall now proceed to write the chain rule for differentiation by expressing the derivatives as quotients of differentials. If $y = f(u)$ and $D_u y$ exists, and if $u = f(x)$ and $D_x u$ exists, then the chain rule gives us

(10) $$D_x y = D_u y \, D_x u$$

But $D_x y = dy/dx$ if $dx \neq 0$; $D_u y = dy/du$ if $du \neq 0$; and $D_x u = du/dx$ if $dx \neq 0$. From (10), therefore, we have

$$\frac{dy}{dx} = \left(\frac{dy}{du}\right) \cdot \left(\frac{du}{dx}\right) \qquad \text{if} \qquad du \neq 0 \text{ and } dx \neq 0$$

The German mathematician Gottfried Leibnitz (1646–1719) was the first to use the notation dy/dx for the derivative of y with respect to x. The concept of a derivative was introduced, in the seventeenth century, almost simultaneously by Leibnitz and Sir Isaac Newton (1642–1727), who were working independently. Leibnitz probably thought of dx and dy as small changes in the variables x and y and of the derivative of y with respect to x as the ratio of dy to dx as dy and dx become small. The concept of a limit as we know it today was not known to Leibnitz.

Corresponding to the Leibnitz notation dy/dx for the first derivative of y with respect to x, we have the symbol d^2y/dx^2 for the second derivative of y with respect to x. However, d^2y/dx^2 must not be thought of as a quotient, since in this text we shall not consider the differential of a differential. Similarly,

$d^n y/dx^n$ is a notation for the nth derivative of y with respect to x. The symbolism f', f'', f''', etc., for the successive derivatives of a function f was introduced by the French mathematician Lagrange in the eighteenth century.

Earlier in this chapter, we derived formulas for finding derivatives. We shall now state these formulas using the Leibnitz notation. Along with the formula for the derivative, we shall give a corresponding formula for the differential, which is obtained by multiplying both sides of the first formula by dx. In these formulas, u and v are functions of x, and it is understood that the formulas hold if $D_x u$ and $D_x v$ exist. When c appears, it is a constant.

I $\quad \dfrac{d(c)}{dx} = 0$ $\qquad\qquad\qquad$ I' $\quad d(c) = 0$

II $\quad \dfrac{d(x^n)}{dx} = nx^{n-1}$ $\qquad\qquad$ II' $\quad d(x^n) = nx^{n-1}\, dx$

III $\quad \dfrac{d(cu)}{dx} = c\,\dfrac{du}{dx}$ $\qquad\qquad$ III' $\quad d(cu) = c\, du$

IV $\quad \dfrac{d(u + v)}{dx} = \dfrac{du}{dx} + \dfrac{dv}{dx}$ $\qquad$ IV' $\quad d(u + v) = du + dv$

V $\quad \dfrac{d(uv)}{dx} = u\,\dfrac{dv}{dx} + v\,\dfrac{du}{dx}$ $\qquad$ V' $\quad d(uv) = u\, dv + v\, du$

VI $\quad \dfrac{d(u/v)}{dx} = \dfrac{v(du/dx) - u(dv/dx)}{v^2}$ $\quad$ VI' $\quad d(u/v) = \dfrac{v\, du - u\, dv}{v^2}$

VII $\quad \dfrac{d(u^n)}{dx} = nu^{n-1}\,\dfrac{du}{dx}$ $\qquad$ VII' $\quad d(u^n) = nu^{n-1}\, du$

The operation of differentiation is extended to include the process of finding the differential as well as finding the derivative. If $y = f(x)$, we may find dy either by applying formulas I'–VII' or by finding $f'(x)$ and multiplying it by dx.

EXAMPLE 1: Given $y = \dfrac{\sqrt{x^2 + 1}}{2x + 1}$, find dy.

Solution: Applying formula VI', we obtain

(11) $\qquad dy = \dfrac{(2x + 1)\, d(\sqrt{x^2 + 1}) - \sqrt{x^2 + 1}\, d(2x + 1)}{(2x + 2)^2}$

From formula VII',

(12) $\qquad d(\sqrt{x^2 + 1}) = \tfrac{1}{2}(x^2 + 1)^{-1/2}\, 2x\, dx = x(x^2 + 1)^{-1/2}\, dx$

and

(13) $\qquad d(2x + 1) = 2\, dx$

Substituting values from (12) and (13) into (11), we get

$$dy = \frac{x(2x + 1)(x^2 + 1)^{-1/2}\, dx - 2(x^2 + 1)^{1/2}\, dx}{(2x + 1)^2}$$

or

$$dy = \frac{(2x^2 + x)\, dx - 2(x^2 + 1)dx}{(2x + 1)^2(x^2 + 1)^{1/2}}$$

or

$$dy = \frac{x - 2}{(2x + 1)^2\sqrt{x^2 + 1}}\, dx$$

EXAMPLE 2: Given $2x^2y^2 - 3x^3 + 5y^3 + 6xy^2 = 5$, where x and y are functions of a third variable t, find dy/dx by finding the differential of each term.

Solution: This is a problem in implicit differentiation. Taking the differential of each term, we get

$$4xy^2\, dx + 4x^2\, dy - 9x^2\, dx + 15y^2\, dy + 6y^2\, dx + 12xy\, dy = 0$$

Dividing by dx, if $dx \neq 0$, we have

$$(4x^2y + 15y^2 + 12xy)\frac{dy}{dx} = -4xy^2 + 9x^2 - 6y^2$$

$$\frac{dy}{dx} = \frac{9x^2 - 6y^2 - 4xy^2}{4x^2y + 15y^2 + 12xy}$$

Exercises 7.7

In Exercises 1 through 8, find dy.

1. $y = (3x^2 - 2x + 1)^3$

2. $y = \sqrt{4 - x^2}$

3. $y = x^2\sqrt[3]{2x + 3}$

4. $y = \dfrac{3x}{x^2 + 2}$

5. $y = \sqrt{\dfrac{x - 1}{x + 1}}$

6. $y = (x + 2)^{1/3}(x - 2)^{2/3}$

7. $y = \dfrac{2x}{\sqrt{x^2 + 1}}$

8. $y = \sqrt{3x + 4}\sqrt[3]{x^2 - 1}$

In Exercises 9 through 16, x and y are functions of a third variable t. Find dy/dx by finding the differential of each term (see Example 2).

9. $3x^3 + 4y^2 = 48$

10. $8x^2 - y^2 = 32$

11. $\sqrt{x} + \sqrt{y} = 4$

12. $2x^2y - 3xy^3 + 6y^2 = 1$

13. $x^4 - 3x^3y + 4xy^3 + y^4 = 2$

14. $x^{2/3} + y^{2/3} = a^{2/3}$

15. $3x^3 - x^2y + 2xy^2 - y^3 - 3x^2 + y^2 = 1$

16. $x^2 + y^2 = \sqrt[3]{x + y}$

In Exercises 17 through 24, find dy/dt.

17. $y = 3x^3 - 5x^2 + 1$; $x = t^2 - 1$

18. $y = \dfrac{5x - 2}{x^2 + 1}$; $x = (2t - 1)^2$

19. $y = x^2 - 3x + 1$; $x = \sqrt{t^2 - t + 4}$

20. $y = \sqrt[3]{5x - 1}$; $x = \sqrt{2t + 3}$

21. $y = x^2 - 5x + 1$; $x = s^3 - 2s + 1$; $s = \sqrt{t^2 + 1}$

22. $y = \dfrac{x^2 - 1}{x^2 + 1}$; $x = \dfrac{2s + 2}{\sqrt{s^2 + 2}}$; $s = t^2 - 4t + 5$

23. $x^3 - 3x^2y + y^3 = 5$; $x = 4t^2 + 1$

24. $3x^2y - 4xy^2 + 7y^3 = 0$; $2x^3 - 3xt^2 + t^3 = 1$

⓼ Applications of the derivative

Related rates

There are many problems in which we are concerned with the rate of change of two or more related variables with respect to time, in which it is not necessary to express each of these variables directly as functions of time. For example, suppose that we are given an equation involving the variables x and y, and that both x and y are functions of a third variable t, where t denotes time. Then since the rate of change of x with respect to t and the rate of change of y with respect to t are given by $D_t x$ and $D_t y$, respectively, we differentiate both sides of the given equation with respect to t by applying the chain rule and proceed as illustrated in the following examples.

EXAMPLE 1: A ladder 25 ft long is leaning against a vertical wall. If the bottom of the ladder is pulled horizontally away from the wall at 3 ft/sec, how fast is the top of the ladder sliding down the wall, when the bottom is 15 ft from the wall?
  Solution:

Let t = the number of seconds in the time that has elapsed since the ladder started to slide down the wall

   y = the number of feet in the distance from the ground to the top of the ladder at t sec

   x = the number of feet in the distance from the bottom of the ladder to the wall at t sec

See Fig. 8.1.1. Since the bottom of the ladder is pulled horizontally away from the wall at 3 ft/sec, $D_t x = 3$. We wish to find $D_t y$, when $x = 15$. From the pythagorean theorem, we have

(1) $$y^2 = 625 - x^2$$

Since x and y are functions of t, we differentiate both sides of equation (1) with respect to t and obtain

$$2y\, D_t y = -2x\, D_t x$$

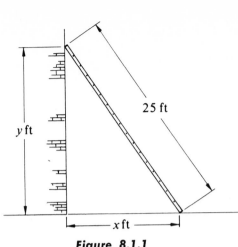

Figure 8.1.1   Figure 8.1.2

giving us

(2) $$D_t y = -\frac{x}{y} D_t x$$

When $x = 15$, it follows from equation (1) that $y = 20$. Since $D_t x = 3$, we get from (2)

$$D_t y\Big|_{y=20} = -\frac{15}{20}\cdot 3 = -\frac{9}{4}$$

Therefore the top of the ladder is sliding down the wall at the rate of $2\frac{1}{4}$ ft/sec when the bottom is 15 ft from the wall.

(The significance of the minus sign is that y is decreasing as t is increasing.)

EXAMPLE 2: A tank is in the form of an inverted cone, having an altitude of 16 ft and a base radius of 4 ft. Water is flowing into the tank at the rate of 2 ft³/min. How fast is the water level rising when the water is 5 ft deep?
Solution:

Let t = the number of minutes in the time that has elapsed since water started to flow into the tank.

h = the number of feet in the water level at t min.

r = the number of feet in the radius of the surface of the water at t min.

V = the number of cubic feet in the volume of water in the tank at t min.

At any time, the volume of water in the tank may be expressed in terms of the volume of a cone (see Fig. 8.1.2).

(3) $$V = \frac{1}{3}\pi r^2 h$$

V, r, and h are all functions of t. Since water is flowing into the tank at the rate of 2 ft³/min, $D_t V = 2$. We wish to find $D_t h$, when $h = 5$. To express r in terms of h, we have from similar triangles

$$\frac{r}{h} = \frac{4}{16}$$

$$r = \frac{1}{4} h$$

Substituting this value of r into formula (3), we obtain

$$V = \frac{1}{3} \pi \left(\frac{1}{4}h\right)^2 (h)$$

or

(4)
$$V = \frac{1}{48} \pi h^3$$

Differentiating both sides of equation (4) with respect to t, we get

$$D_t V = \frac{1}{16} \pi h^2 \, D_t h$$

Substituting 2 for $D_t V$ and solving for $D_t h$, we obtain

$$D_t h = \frac{32}{\pi h^2}$$

Therefore,
$$D_t h \Big|_{h=5} = \frac{32}{25 \pi}$$

We conclude that the water level is rising at the rate of $32/25\pi$ ft/min when the water is 5 ft deep.

Exercises 8.1

1. A kite is flying at a height of 40 ft. The boy who is flying it is carrying it horizontally at the rate of 3 ft/sec. At what rate is the string being paid out when the length of the string released is 50 ft?

2. A spherical balloon is being inflated so that its volume is increasing at the rate of 5 ft³/min. At what rate is the diameter increasing when the diameter is 12 ft?

3. A spherical snowball is being made so that its volume is increasing at the rate of 8 ft³/min. Find the rate at which the radius is increasing when the snowball is 4 ft in diameter.

4. Suppose that when the diameter is 6 ft the snowball in Exercise 3 started to melt at the rate of ¼ ft³/min. Find the rate at which the radius is changing when the radius is 2 ft.

$$\frac{6}{y-x} = \frac{15}{y}$$

$$6y = 15y - 15x$$

$$y = 5/3x$$

5. Sand is being dropped at the rate of 10 ft³/min into a conical pile. If the height of the pile is always twice the base radius, at what rate is the height increasing when the pile is 8 ft high?

6. A light is hung 15 ft above a straight horizontal path. If a man 6 ft tall is walking away from the light at the rate of 5 ft/sec, how fast is his shadow lengthening?

7. In Exercise 6 at what rate is the tip of the man's shadow moving?

8. A man 6 ft tall is walking toward a building at the rate of 5 ft/sec. If there is a light on the ground 50 ft from the building, how fast is the man's shadow on the building growing shorter when he is 30 ft from the building?

9. A water tank in the form of an inverted cone is being emptied at the rate of 6 ft³/min. The altitude of the cone is 24 ft, and the base radius is 12 ft. Find how fast the water level is lowering when the water is 10 ft deep.

10. Water is flowing at the rate of 8 ft³/min into a tank in the form of a right-circular cylinder of base radius 2 ft. How fast is the water level rising?

11. A trough is 12 ft long and its ends are in the form of inverted isosceles triangles having an altitude of 3 ft and a base of 3 ft. Water is flowing into the trough at the rate of 2 ft³/min. How fast is the water level rising when the water is 1 ft deep?

12. A man on a dock is pulling in a boat at the rate of 50 ft/min by means of a rope attached to the boat at water level. If the man's hands are 16 ft above the water level, how fast is the boat approaching the dock when the amount of rope out is 20 ft?

13. An automobile traveling at a rate of 30 ft/sec is approaching an intersection. When the automobile is 120 ft from the intersection, a truck traveling at the rate of 40 ft/sec crosses the intersection. The automobile and the truck are on roads that are at right angles to each other. How fast are the automobile and the truck separating 2 sec after the truck leaves the intersection?

14. A ship leaves a port at 12 noon and travels due west at 20 knots. At 12 noon the next day, a second ship leaves the same port and travels northwest at 15 knots. How fast are the two ships separating when the second ship has traveled 90 nautical miles?

15. A ladder 20 ft long is leaning against an embankment inclined 60° to the horizontal. If the bottom of the ladder is being moved horizontally toward the embankment at 1 ft/sec, how fast is the top of the ladder moving when the bottom is 4 ft from the embankment?

16. If the length of a side of an equilateral triangle is increasing at the rate of 3 in./min, how fast is the area of the triangle increasing when the length of the side is 8 in.?

17. The radius of a right-circular cylinder is increasing at the rate of ½ in./min. At a specific instant the radius and altitude of the cylinder are 5 in.

and 20 in., respectively. What should be the rate of change in the altitude of the cylinder in order for the volume to remain constant?

18. A funnel in the form of a cone is 10 in. across the top and 8 in. deep. Water is flowing into the funnel at the rate of 12 in.^{3}/sec, and out at the rate of 4 in.^{3}/sec. How fast is the surface of the water rising when it is 5 in. deep?

19. Water is being poured at the rate of 8 ft^3/min into a tank in the form of an inverted cone. The cone is 20 ft deep and 10 ft in diameter. If there is a leak in the bottom, and the water level is rising at the rate of 1 in./min, when the water is 16 ft deep, how fast is the water leaking?

20. A horizontal trough is 16 ft long, and its ends are isosceles trapezoids with an altitude of 4 ft, a lower base of 4 ft, and an upper base of 6 ft. Water is being poured into the trough at the rate of 10 ft^3/min. How fast is the water level rising when the water is 2 ft deep?

21. In Exercise 20 if the water level is decreasing at the rate of $\frac{1}{4}$ ft/min when the water is 3 ft deep, at what rate is water being drawn from the trough?

(8.2)   Maximum and minimum values of a function

We have seen that the geometrical interpretation of the derivative of a function is the slope of the tangent line to the graph of a function at a point. This fact enables us to apply derivatives as an aid in sketching graphs. For example, we may use the derivative to determine at what points the tangent line is horizontal; these will be the points where the derivative is zero. Also, the derivative may be used to find the intervals for which the graph of a function lies above the tangent line and the intervals for which the graph lies below the tangent line. Before we apply the derivative to draw sketches of graphs, we need some definitions and theorems.

8.2.1 DEFINITION   The function f is said to have a *relative maximum value* at c if there exists an open interval containing c, on which f is defined, such that $f(c) \geq f(x)$ for all x in this interval.

In Figs. 8.2.1 and 8.2.2, we have a sketch of a portion of the graph of a function having a relative maximum value at c

8.2.2 DEFINITION   The function f is said to have a *relative minimum value* at c if there exists an open interval containing c, on which f is defined, such that $f(c) \leq f(x)$ for all x in this interval.

In Figs. 8.2.3 and 8.2.4, we have a sketch of a portion of the graph of a function having a relative minimum value at c.

If the function f has either a relative maximum or a relative minimum value at c, then f is said to have a *relative extremum* at c. (The plurals of maximum and minimum are maxima and minima; the plural of extremum is extrema.)

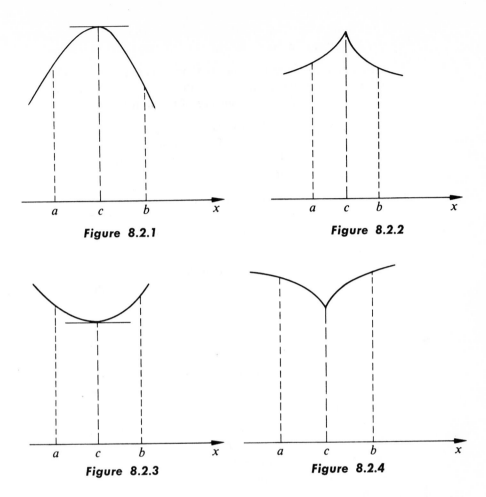

Figure 8.2.1 Figure 8.2.2

Figure 8.2.3 Figure 8.2.4

The following theorem enables us to locate the possible values of c for which we have a relative extremum.

8.2.3 THEOREM   If $f(x)$ exists for all values of x in the open interval (a,b) and if f has a relative extremum at c, where $a < c < b$, then if $f'(c)$ exists, $f'(c) = 0$.

Proof: The proof will be given for the case when f has a relative minimum value at c.

If $f'(c)$ exists, from formula (5) of Sec. 6.3 we have

(1) $$f'(c) = \lim_{x \to c} \frac{f(x) - f(c)}{x - c}$$

Since f has a relative minimum value at c, by Definition 8.2.2, if x is sufficiently close to c, we have

$$f(x) - f(c) \geq 0$$

If x is approaching c from the right, $x - c > 0$, and therefore

$$\frac{f(x) - f(c)}{x - c} \geq 0$$

By Theorem 4.6.4, if the limit exists,

(2)
$$\lim_{x \to c^+} \frac{f(x) - f(c)}{x - c} \geq 0$$

Similarly, if x is approaching c from the left, $x - c < 0$, and therefore

$$\frac{f(x) - f(c)}{x - c} \leq 0$$

so that by Theorem 4.6.3, if the limit exists,

(3)
$$\lim_{x \to c^-} \frac{f(x) - f(c)}{x - c} \leq 0$$

Since $f'(c)$ exists, the limits in inequalities (2) and (3) must be equal, and both must be equal to $f'(c)$. So, from (2) we have

(4)
$$f'(c) \geq 0$$

and from (3),

(5)
$$f'(c) \leq 0$$

Since both (4) and (5) are taken to be true, we conclude that

$$f'(c) = 0$$

which was to be proved.

The proof for the case when f has a relative maximum value at c is similar and is left for the reader (see Exercise 37 below).

The geometrical interpretation of Theorem 8.2.3 is that, if f has a relative extremum at c and if $f'(c)$ exists, then the graph of $y = f(x)$ must have a horizontal tangent line at the point where $x = c$.

If f is a differentiable function, then the only possible values of x for which f may have a relative extremum are those for which $f'(x) = 0$. However, $f'(x)$ may be equal to zero for a specific value of x, and yet f may not have a relative extremum there. For example consider the function f defined by

$$f(x) = (x - 1)^3$$

A sketch of the graph of this function is shown in Fig. 8.2.5. $f'(x) = 3(x - 1)^2$, and so $f'(1) = 0$. However, $f(x) < 0$, if $x < 1$, and $f(x) > 0$, if $x > 1$. So, f does not have a relative extremum at 1.

Furthermore, f may have a relative extremum at a number, and f' may fail to exist there. This is illustrated by the function f defined as follows:

$$f(x) = \begin{cases} 2x - 1 & \text{if } x \leq 3 \\ 8 - x & \text{if } 3 < x \end{cases}$$

A sketch of the graph of this function is shown in Fig. 8.2.6. f has a relative maximum at 3. The derivative from the left at 3 is given by $f'_-(3) = 2$, and the derivative from the right at 3 is given by $f'_+(3) = -1$. Therefore, we conclude that $f'(3)$ does not exist. This example demonstrates why the condition "$f'(x)$ exists" must be included in the hypothesis of Theorem 8.2.3.

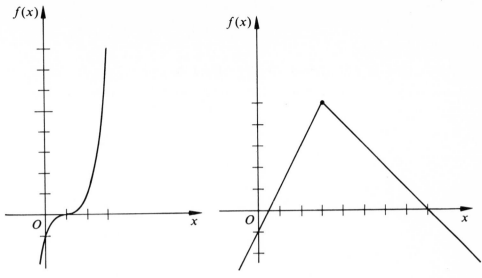

Figure 8.2.5   **Figure 8.2.6**

In summary, then, if a function f is defined at a number c, a necessary condition for f to have a relative extremum there is that either $f'(c) = 0$ or $f'(c)$ does not exist. But we have noted that this condition is not sufficient.

8.2.4 DEFINITION   If c is a number in the domain of the function f and if either $f'(c) = 0$ or $f'(c)$ does not exist, then c is called a *critical number* of f.

In view of this definition and the previous discussion, we may conclude that a necessary condition for a function to have a relative extremum at a number c is that c be a critical number.

EXAMPLE 1: Find the critical numbers of the function f defined by $f(x) = x^{4/3} + 4x^{1/3}$.

Solution: $f'(x) = \dfrac{4}{3}x^{1/3} + \dfrac{4}{3}x^{-2/3} = \dfrac{4}{3}x^{-2/3}(x + 1) = \dfrac{4(x + 1)}{3x^{2/3}}$

$f'(x) = 0$ when $x = -1$, and $f'(x)$ does not exist when $x = 0$. Both -1 and 0 are in the domain of f; therefore the critical numbers of f are -1 and 0.

Frequently we are concerned with a function which is defined on a given interval, and we wish to find the largest or smallest function value on the interval. These intervals may be either closed, open, or closed at one end and open at the other. The greatest function value on an interval is called the *absolute maximum value*, and the smallest function value on an interval is called the *absolute minimum value*. Following are the precise definitions.

8.2.5 DEFINITION   The function f is said to have an *absolute maximum value on an interval* if there is some number c in the interval such that $f(c) \geq f(x)$ for all x

in the interval. In such a case, $f(c)$ is the absolute maximum value of f on the interval.

8.2.6 DEFINITION   The function f is said to have an *absolute minimum value on an interval*, if there is some number c in the interval such that $f(c) \leq f(x)$ for all x in the interval. In such a case, $f(c)$ is the absolute minimum value of f on the interval.

An *absolute extremum* of a function on an interval is either an absolute maximum value or an absolute minimum value of the function on the interval. A function may or may not have an absolute extremum on a given interval. In each of the following examples we are given a function and an interval, and we shall determine the absolute extrema of the function on the interval if there are any.

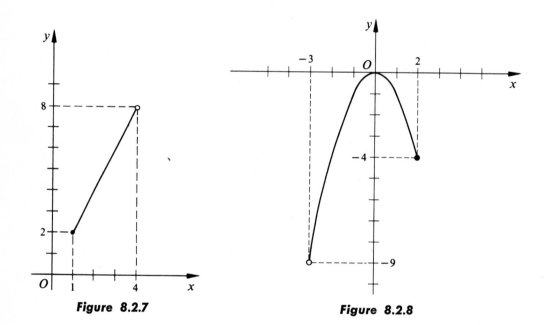

Figure 8.2.7   **Figure 8.2.8**

EXAMPLE 2: Given $f(x) = 2x$, find the absolute extrema of f on the interval $[1,4)$ if there are any.

Solution: A sketch of the graph of f on $[1,4)$ is shown in Fig. 8.2.7. f has an absolute minimum value of 2 on $[1,4)$. There is no absolute maximum value of f on $[1,4)$, since $\lim_{x \to 4^-} f(x) = 8$, but $f(x)$ is always less than 8 on the given interval.

EXAMPLE 3: Given $f(x) = -x^2$, find the absolute extrema of f on $(-3,2]$ if there are any.

Solution: A sketch of the graph of f on $(-3,2]$ is shown in Fig. 8.2.8. f has an absolute maximum value of 0 on $(-3,2]$. There is no absolute minimum value of f on $(-3,2]$ since $\lim\limits_{x \to -3^{+}} f(x) = -9$, but $f(x)$ is always greater than -9 on the given interval.

EXAMPLE 4: Given $f(x) = x/(1 - x^2)$, find the absolute extrema of f on $(-1,1)$ if there are any.

    Solution: A sketch of the graph of f on $(-1,1)$ is shown in Fig. 8.2.9. f has neither an absolute maximum value nor an absolute minimum value on $(-1,1)$.

$$\lim_{x \to -1^{+}} f(x) = -\infty \qquad \text{and} \qquad \lim_{x \to 1^{-}} f(x) = +\infty$$

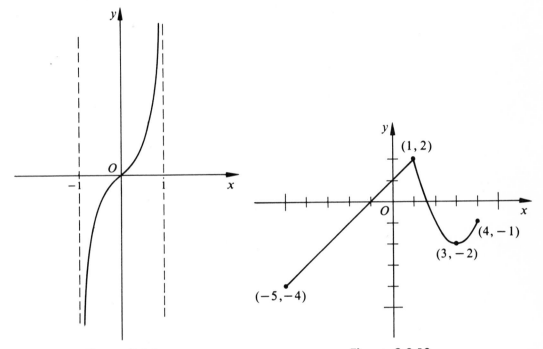

Figure 8.2.9   **Figure 8.2.10**

EXAMPLE 5: Given $f(x) = \begin{cases} x + 1 & \text{if } x < 1 \\ x^2 - 6x + 7 & \text{if } 1 \le x \end{cases}$

find the absolute extrema of f on $[-5,4]$ if there are any.

    Solution: A sketch of the graph of f on $[-5,4]$ is shown in Fig. 8.2.10. The absolute maximum value of f on $[-5,4]$ occurs at 1, and $f(1) = 2$; the absolute minimum value of f on $[-5,4]$ occurs at -5, and $f(-5) = -4$. You will note that f has a relative maximum value at 1, and a relative minimum value at 3. Also, note that 1 is a critical number of f since f' does not exist at 1, and 3 is a critical number of f because $f'(3) = 0$.

EXAMPLE 6: Given $f(x) = 1/(x - 3)$, find the absolute extrema of f on the interval $[1,5]$ if there are any.

Solution: A sketch of the graph is shown in Fig. 8.2.11. f has neither an absolute maximum value nor an absolute minimum value on $[1,5]$. $\lim_{x \to 3^-} f(x) = -\infty$; so $f(x)$ can be made less than any negative number by taking $(3 - x) > 0$ and less than a suitable positive δ. Also $\lim_{x \to 3^+} f(x) = +\infty$; so $f(x)$ can be made greater than any positive number by taking $(x - 3) > 0$ and less than a suitable positive δ.

We may speak of an absolute extremum of a function when no interval is specified. In such a case we are referring to an absolute extremum of the function on the entire domain of the function.

8.2.7 DEFINITION $f(c)$ is said to be the *absolute maximum value* of the function f if c is in the domain of f and if $f(c) \geq f(x)$ for all values of x in the domain of f.

8.2.8 DEFINITION $f(c)$ is said to be the *absolute minimum value* of the function f if c is in the domain of f and if $f(c) \leq f(x)$ for all values of x in the domain of f.

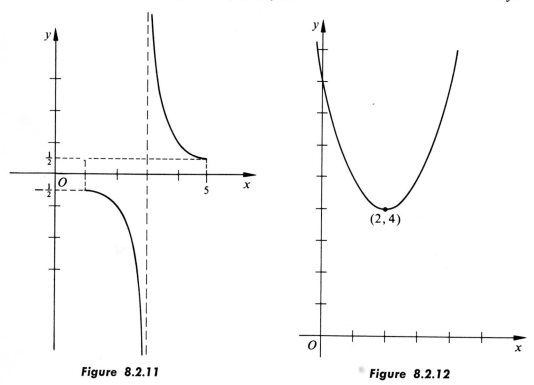

Figure 8.2.11

Figure 8.2.12

EXAMPLE 7: Given $f(x) = x^2 - 4x + 8$, determine the absolute extrema of f if there are any.

Solution: The graph of f is a parabola, and a sketch is shown in Fig. 8.2.12. The vertex of the parabola is at the point $(2,4)$, and the parabola opens upward. The function has an absolute minimum value of 4 at 2. There is no absolute maximum value of f.

Referring back to Examples 2 through 7, the only case in which there is both an absolute maximum function value and an absolute minimum function value is in Example 5, where the function is continuous on the closed interval $[-5,4]$. In the other examples, either we do not have a closed interval or we do not have a continuous function. If a function is continuous on a closed interval, there is a theorem, called the *extreme-value theorem*, which assures us that the function has both an absolute maximum value and an absolute minimum value on the interval. The proof of this theorem is beyond the scope of this book, but we shall state it without proof. The reader is referred to an advanced calculus text for the proof.

8.2.9 THEOREM (*Extreme-value Theorem*)   If the function f is continuous on the closed interval $[a,b]$, then f has an absolute maximum value and an absolute minimum value on $[a,b]$.

An absolute extremum of a function on a closed interval must be either a relative extremum or a function value at an end point of the interval. Since a necessary condition for a function to have a relative extremum at a number c is that c be a critical number, we may determine the absolute maximum value and the absolute minimum value of a continuous function f on a closed interval $[a,b]$ by the following procedure:
   (1) Find the critical numbers of f on $[a,b]$.
   (2) Find the values of $f(a)$ and $f(b)$.
   (3) The largest of the values from steps (1) and (2) is the absolute maximum value, and the smallest of the values from (1) and (2) is the absolute minimum value.

EXAMPLE 8: Given $f(x) = x^3 + x^2 - x + 1$, find the absolute extrema of f on $[-2,\frac{1}{2}]$.
   Solution: Since f is continuous on $[-2,\frac{1}{2}]$, the extreme-value theorem applies. To find the critical numbers of f we first find f':

$$f'(x) = 3x^2 + 2x - 1$$

$f'(x)$ exists for all real numbers, and so the only critical numbers of f will be the values of x for which $f'(x) = 0$. Setting $f'(x) = 0$, we have

$$(3x - 1)(x + 1) = 0$$

from which we obtain

$$x = \frac{1}{3} \quad \text{and} \quad x = -1$$

The critical numbers of f are -1 and $\frac{1}{3}$, and each of these numbers is in the given closed interval $[-2,\frac{1}{2}]$. We find the function values at the critical numbers and at the end points of the interval, which are given in Table 8.2.1.

Table 8.2.1

x	-2	-1	$\frac{1}{3}$	$\frac{1}{2}$
$f(x)$	-1	2	$\frac{22}{27}$	$\frac{7}{8}$

The absolute maximum value of f on $[-2,\frac{1}{2}]$ is therefore 2, which occurs at -1, and the absolute minimum value of f on $[-2,\frac{1}{2}]$ is -1, which occurs at the left end point -2. A sketch of the graph of this function on $[-2,\frac{1}{2}]$ is shown in Fig. 8.2.13.

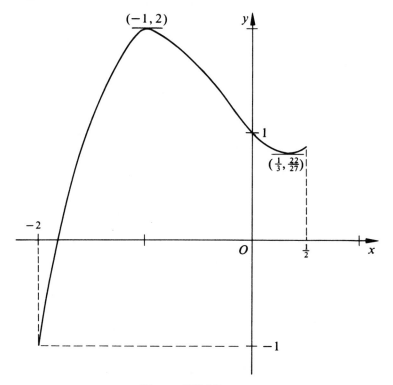

Figure 8.2.13

EXAMPLE 9: Given $f(x) = (x - 2)^{2/3}$, find the absolute extrema of f on $[1,5]$.

Solution: Since f is continuous on $[1,5]$, the extreme-value theorem applies.

$$f'(x) = \frac{2}{3(x - 2)^{1/3}}$$

There is no value of x for which $f'(x) = 0$. However, since $f'(x)$ does not exist at 2, we conclude that 2 is a critical number of f, so that the absolute extrema occur either at 2 or at one of the end points of the interval. The function values at these numbers are given in Table 8.2.2.

Table 8.2.2

x	1	2	5
$f(x)$	1	0	$\sqrt[3]{9}$

From the table we conclude that the absolute minimum value of f on $[1,5]$ is 0, occurring at 2, and the absolute maximum value of f on $[1,5]$ is $\sqrt[3]{9}$, occurring at 5. A sketch of the graph of this function on $[1,5]$ is shown in Fig. 8.2.14.

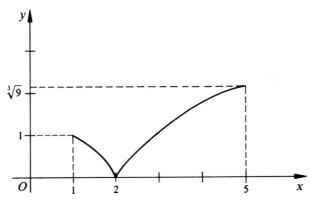

Figure 8.2.14

Exercises 8.2

In Exercises 1 through 10, find the critical numbers of the given function.

1. $f(x) = x^3 + 7x^2 - 5x$

2. $f(x) = 2x^3 - 2x^2 - 16x + 1$

3. $f(x) = x^4 + 4x^3 - 2x^2 - 12x$

4. $f(x) = x^{7/3} + x^{4/3} - 3x^{1/3}$

5. $f(x) = x^{6/5} - 12x^{1/5}$

6. $f(x) = x^4 + 11x^3 + 34x^2 + 15x - 2$

7. $f(x) = (x^2 - 4)^{2/3}$

8. $f(x) = (x^3 - 3x^2 + 4)^{1/3}$

9. $f(x) = \dfrac{x}{x^2 - 9}$

10. $f(x) = \dfrac{x + 1}{x^2 - 5x + 4}$

In Exericses 11 through 24, find the absolute extrema of the given function on the given interval, if there are any, and find the values of x at which the absolute extrema occur. Draw a sketch of the graph of the function on the interval.

11. $f(x) = 4 - 3x; \; (-1,2]$

12. $f(x) = x^2 - 2x + 4; \; (-\infty,+\infty)$

13. $f(x) = \dfrac{1}{x}; \; [-2,3]$

14. $f(x) = \dfrac{1}{x}; \; [2,3)$

15. $f(x) = \sqrt{3 + x}; [-3, +\infty)$ 18. $f(x) = \sqrt{4 - x^2}; (-2, 2)$

16. $f(x) = \dfrac{3x}{9 - x^2}; (-3, 2)$ 19. $f(x) = |x - 4| + 1; (0, 6)$

17. $f(x) = \dfrac{4}{(x - 3)^2}; [2, 5]$ 20. $f(x) = |4 - x^2|; (-\infty, +\infty)$

21. $f(x) = \begin{cases} \dfrac{2}{x - 5}, & \text{if } x \neq 5 \\ 2, & \text{if } x = 5 \end{cases}; [3, 5]$

22. $f(x) = \begin{cases} |x + 1|, & \text{if } x \neq -1 \\ 3, & \text{if } x = -1 \end{cases}; [-2; 1]$

23. $f(x) = x - [\![x]\!]; (1, 3)$ 24. $f(x) = U(x) - U(x - 1); (-1, 1)$

In Exercises 25 through 36, find the absolute maximum value and the absolute minimum value of the given function on the indicated interval, by the method used in Examples 8 and 9 of this section. Draw a sketch of the graph of the function on the interval.

25. $f(x) = x^3 + 5x - 4; [-3, -1]$ 30. $f(x) = x^4 - 8x^2 + 16; [-3, 2]$

26. $f(x) = x^3 + 3x^2 - 9x; [-4, 4]$ 31. $f(x) = \dfrac{x}{x + 2}; [-1, 2]$

27. $f(x) = x^4 - 8x^2 + 16; [-4, 0]$ 32. $f(x) = \dfrac{x + 5}{x - 3}; [-5, 2]$

28. $f(x) = x^4 - 8x^2 + 16; [-1, 4]$ 33. $f(x) = (x + 1)^{2/3}; [-2, 1]$

29. $f(x) = x^4 - 8x^2 + 16; [0, 3]$ 34. $f(x) = 1 - (x - 3)^{2/3}; [-5, 4]$

35. $f(x) = \begin{cases} 3x - 4, & \text{if } -3 \leq x < 1 \\ x^2 - 2, & \text{if } 1 \leq x \leq 3 \end{cases}; [-3, 3]$

36. $f(x) = \begin{cases} 4 - (x + 5)^2, & \text{if } -6 \leq x \leq -4 \\ 12 - (x + 1)^2, & \text{if } -4 < x \leq 0 \end{cases}; [-6, 0]$

37. Prove Theorem 8.2.3 for the case when f has a relative maximum value at c.

(8.3)   **Applications involving an absolute extremum on a closed interval**

We shall consider some problems in which the solution is an absolute extremum of a function on a closed interval. We shall make use of the extreme-value theorem, which assures us that both an absolute maximum value and an absolute minimum value of a function exist on a closed interval if the function is continuous on that closed interval. The procedure is illustrated by some examples.

EXAMPLE 1: A box is to be made from a sheet of tin 12 in. square by cutting equal squares from the four corners and turning up the sides. Find the length of the side of the square to be cut out in order to obtain a box of the largest possible volume.

Solution:

Let x = the number of inches in the length of the side of the square to be cut out.

V = the number of cubic inches in the volume of the box.

The number of inches in the dimensions of the box are then $x, (12 - 2x)$, and $(12 - 2x)$. Figure 8.3.1 represents the given piece of tin, and Fig. 8.3.2 represents the box.

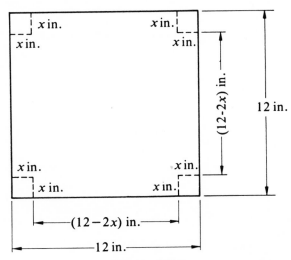

Figure 8.3.1

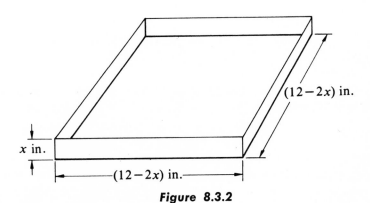

Figure 8.3.2

The volume of the box is the product of the three dimensions, and so we have V as a function of x and write

(1) $$V(x) = x(12 - 2x)(12 - 2x)$$

If $x = 0$, $V = 0$, and if $x = 6$, $V = 0$. The value of x that we wish to find is in the closed interval [0,6]. Since V is continuous on the closed interval [0,6], we conclude from the extreme-value theorem that V has an absolute maximum value on this interval. We also know that this absolute maximum value of V must occur either at a critical number or at an end point of the interval. To find the critical numbers of V, we find $V'(x)$, and then find the values of x for which either $V'(x) = 0$ or $V'(x)$ does not exist.

From equation (1), we obtain

$$V(x) = 144x - 48x^2 + 4x^3$$

Thus, $$V'(x) = 144 - 96x + 12x^2$$

$V'(x)$ exists for all values of x. Setting $V'(x) = 0$, we have

$$12(x^2 - 8x + 12) = 0$$

from which we obtain

$$x = 6 \quad \text{and} \quad x = 2$$

The critical numbers of V are 2 and 6, both of which are in the closed interval [0,6]. The absolute maximum value of V on [0,6] must occur at either a critical number or at an end point of the interval. Since $V(0) = 0$ and $V(6) = 0$, while $V(2) = 128$, we conclude that the absolute maximum value of V on [0,6] is 128, occurring at 2.

Therefore, the largest possible volume is 128 in.³, and this is obtained when the length of the side of the square cut out is 2 in.

It should be emphasized that in the preceding example the existence of an absolute maximum value of V is guaranteed by the extreme-value theorem. In the following example, the existence of an absolute minimum value is guaranteed by the same theorem.

EXAMPLE 2: An island is at point A, 6 miles off shore from the nearest point B on a straight beach. A store is at point C, 7 miles down the beach from B. If a man can row at the rate of 4 miles per hour and walk at the rate of 5 miles per hour, where should he land in order to get from the island to the store in the least possible time?

Solution: Refer to Fig. 8.3.3. Let P be the point on the beach where the man lands. Therefore, the man rows from A to P and walks from P to C.

Let x = the number of miles in the distance from B to P.

T = the number of hours in the time it takes the man to make the trip from A to C.

Then, let T = the number of hours in the time to go from A to P + the number of hours in the time to go from P to C. Since time equals distance divided by rate, we have

(2) $$T = \frac{|\overline{AP}|}{4} + \frac{|\overline{PC}|}{5}$$

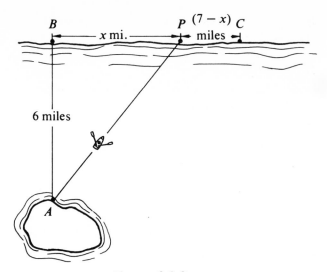

Figure 8.3.3

From Fig. 8.3.3, we see that $|\overline{AP}|$ is the length of the hypotenuse of right triangle ABP. Therefore,

$$|\overline{AP}| = \sqrt{x^2 + 36}$$

We also see from the figure that $|\overline{PC}| = 7 - x$.

So, from equation (2) we may express T as a function of x, and we have

$$T(x) = \frac{\sqrt{x^2 + 36}}{4} + \frac{7 - x}{5}$$

Since the distance from B to C is 7 miles and since P may be any point on the line segment BC, we know that x is in the closed interval [0,7].

We wish to find the value of x for which T has an absolute minimum value on [0,7]. Since T is a continuous function of x on [0,7], we know that such a value exists. We find the critical numbers of T by first finding $T'(x)$:

$$T'(x) = \frac{x}{4\sqrt{x^2 + 36}} - \frac{1}{5}$$

$T'(x)$ exists for all values of x. Setting $T'(x) = 0$ and solving for x, we have

$$\frac{x}{4\sqrt{x^2 + 36}} - \frac{1}{5} = 0$$

$$5x = 4\sqrt{x^2 + 36}$$

$$25x^2 = 16(x^2 + 36)$$

$$9x^2 = 16 \cdot 36$$

$$x^2 = 64$$

$$x = \pm 8$$

Since -8 is an extraneous root and 8 is not in $[0,7]$, there are no critical numbers of T in $[0,7]$. The absolute minimum value of T on $[0,7]$ must therefore occur at an end point of the interval. We compute $T(0)$ and $T(7)$, giving us

$$T(0) = \frac{29}{10} \quad \text{and} \quad T(7) = \frac{\sqrt{85}}{4}$$

Since $\sqrt{85}/4 < 29/10$, the absolute minimum value of T on $[0,7]$ is $\sqrt{85}/4$, occurring when $x = 7$. Therefore, in order for the man to get from the island to the store in the least possible time, he should row directly there and do no walking.

EXAMPLE 3: Find the dimensions of the right-circular cylinder of greatest volume that can be inscribed in a right-circular cone with a radius of 5 in. and a height of 12 in.

Solution: Let r = the number of inches in the radius of the cylinder.

h = the number of inches in the height of the cylinder.

V = the number of cubic inches in the volume of the cylinder.

Figure 8.3.4 illustrates the cylinder inscribed in the cone, and Fig. 8.3.5 illustrates a plane section through the axis of the cone.

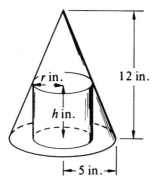

Figure 8.3.4

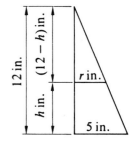

Figure 8.3.5

If $r = 0$ and $h = 12$, we have a degenerate cylinder, which is the axis of the cone. If $r = 5$ and $h = 0$, we also have a degenerate cylinder, which is a diameter of the base of the cone. We conclude that r is in the closed interval $[0,5]$ and h is in the closed interval $[0,12]$.

The following formula expresses V in terms of r and h:

(3) $$V = \pi r^2 h$$

We wish to express V in terms of a single variable; hence we need another equation involving r and h. From Fig. 8.3.5, and using similar triangles, we have

$$\frac{12 - h}{r} = \frac{12}{5}$$

or

(4) $$h = \frac{60 - 12r}{5}$$

Substituting from (4) into formula (3), we obtain V as a function of r and write

(5) $$V(r) = \frac{12\pi}{5}(5r^2 - r^3) \qquad \text{with } r \text{ in } [0,5]$$

Since V is continuous on the closed interval $[0,5]$, we know from the extreme-value theorem that V has an absolute maximum value on this interval. The values of r and h that give this absolute maximum value for V are the numbers we wish to find.

$$V'(r) = \frac{12\pi}{5}(10r - 3r^2)$$

To find the critical numbers of V, we set $V'(r) = 0$ and solve for r:

$$r(10 - 3r) = 0$$

from which we obtain

$$r = 0 \qquad \text{and} \qquad r = \frac{10}{3}$$

Since $V'(r)$ exists for all values of r, the only critical numbers of V are 0 and 10/3, both of which are in the closed interval $[0,5]$. The absolute maximum value of V on $[0,5]$ must occur at either 0, 10/3, or 5. From equation (5) we obtain $V(0) = 0$, $V(10/3) = 400\pi/9$, and $V(5) = 0$. We therefore conclude that the absolute maximum value of V is $400\pi/9$, and this occurs when $r = 10/3$. When $r = 10/3$, we find from equation (4) that $h = 4$.

Thus, the greatest volume of an inscribed cylinder in the given cone is $400\pi/9$ in.³, which occurs when the radius is 10/3 in. and the height is 4 in.

Exercises 8.3

1. Find the area of the largest rectangle having a perimeter of 200 ft.

2. Find the area of the largest isosceles triangle having a perimeter of 18 in.

3. A rectangular field is to be fenced off along the bank of a river, and no fence is required along the river. If the amount of fencing available is 100 yd, find the dimensions of the field having the largest possible area.

4. Find the area of the largest isosceles triangle that can be inscribed in a circle with a radius of 8 in.

5. Suppose a weight is to be held 10 ft below a horizontal line AB by a wire in the shape of a Y. If the points A and B are 8 ft apart, what is the shortest total length of wire that can be used?

6. The length of each of three sides of a trapezoid is to be 3 in. Find the length of the fourth side if the area is to be as large as possible.

7. Solve Example 2 of this section if the store is 9 miles down the beach from point *B*.

8. Two points *A* and *B* are diametrically opposite each other on the shores of a circular lake. A man desires to go from point *A* to point *B*. He can row at the rate of 1½ miles per hour and walk at the rate of 5 miles per hour. Find the least amount of time it can take for him to get from point *A* to point *B*.

9. Given the circle having the equation $x^2 + y^2 = 9$, find the shortest distance from the point (4,5) to a point on the circle. Also find the longest distance from the point (4,5) to a point on the circle.

10. Find the dimensions of the right-circular cylinder of greatest volume that can be inscribed in a sphere with a radius of 6 in.

11. Find the dimensions of the right-circular cylinder of greatest lateral surface area that can be inscribed in a sphere with a radius of 6 in.

12. Find the dimensions of the right-circular cone of largest possible volume that can be inscribed in a sphere with a radius of 4 in.

13. A piece of wire 10 ft long is cut into two pieces. One piece is bent into the shape of a circle and the other into the shape of a square. How should the wire be cut so that the combined area of the two figures is as small as possible?

14. In Exercise 13, how should the wire be cut so that the combined area of the two figures is as large as possible?

15. If, in Exercise 13, one piece of wire is bent into the shape of an equilateral triangle and the other piece is bent into the shape of a square, how should the wire be cut so that the combined area of the two figures is as small as possible?

16. In Exercise 15, how should the wire be cut so that the combined area of the two figures is as large as possible?

(8.4)   Rolle's theorem

Let *f* be a function that is continuous on the closed interval [*a*,*b*], differentiable on the open interval (*a*,*b*), and let $f(a) = 0$ and $f(b) = 0$. The French mathematician Michel Rolle (1652–1719) proved that if a function *f* satisfies these conditions, there is at least one number *c* between *a* and *b* for which $f'(c) = 0$.

Let us see what this means geometrically. Figure 8.4.1 shows a sketch of the graph of a function *f* that satisfies the conditions in the previous paragraph.

Intuitively, we see that there is at least one point on the curve between the points (*a*,0) and (*b*,0) where the tangent line is parallel to the *x* axis; that is, the slope of the tangent line is zero. This is illustrated in Fig. 8.4.1 at the point *P*. So the abscissa of *P* would be the *c* such that $f'(c) = 0$.

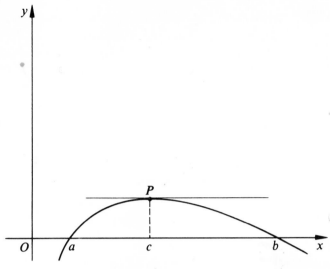

Figure 8.4.1

The function, whose graph is sketched in Figure 8.4.1, not only is differentiable on the open interval (a,b) but is also differentiable at the end points of the interval. However, the condition that *f* be differentiable at the end points is not necessary for the graph to have a horizontal tangent line at some point in the interval; Fig. 8.4.2 illustrates this.

We see in Fig. 8.4.2 that the function is not differentiable at *a* and *b*; there is, however, a horizontal tangent line at the point where $x = c$, and *c* is between *a* and *b*.

It is necessary, however, that the function be continuous at the end points of the interval in order to guarantee a horizontal tangent line at an interior point.

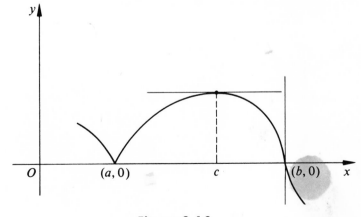

Figure 8.4.2

Figure 8.4.3 shows a sketch of the graph of a function that is continuous on the interval [a,b] but discontinuous at b; the function is differentiable on the open interval (a,b), and the function values are zero at both a and b. However, there is no point at which the graph has a horizontal tangent line.

We shall now state and prove Rolle's theorem.

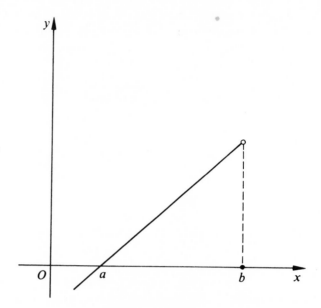

Figure 8.4.3

8.4.1 THEOREM (*Rolle's Theorem*)   Let f be a function such that

(i)   it is continuous on the closed interval [a,b]

(ii)   it is differentiable on the open interval (a,b)

(iii) $f(a) = f(b) = 0$

Then there is a number c in the open interval (a,b) such that

$$f'(c) = 0$$

Proof: We shall consider two cases.

Case 1: $f(x) = 0$ for all x in [a,b].

Then $f'(x) = 0$ for all x in [a,b]; therefore any number between a and b may be taken for c.

Case 2: $f(x)$ is not zero for some value of x in the open interval (a,b).

Since f is continuous on the closed interval [a,b], we know by Theorem 8.2.9 that f has an absolute maximum value on [a,b] and an absolute minimum value on [a,b]. Since $f(a) = 0$ and $f(b) = 0$ by hypothesis, and for this case $f(x)$ is not zero for some x in (a,b), we may conclude that f will have either a positive absolute maximum value at some c_1 in (a,b) or a negative absolute minimum value at some c_2 in (a,b), or both. Thus for $c = c_1$, or $c = c_2$ as the case may be, we have an absolute extremum at an interior point of the interval $[a,b]$. Therefore, the absolute extremum $f(c)$ is also a relative extremum, and since $f'(c)$ exists by hypothesis, it follows from Theorem 8.2.3 that $f'(c) = 0$. This proves the theorem.

It should be noted that there may be more than one number in the open interval (a,b) for which the derivative of f is zero. This is illustrated geometrically in Fig. 8.4.4, where there is a horizontal tangent line at the point where $x = c_1$ and also at the point where $x = c_2$, so that both $f'(c_1) = 0$ and $f'(c_2) = 0$.

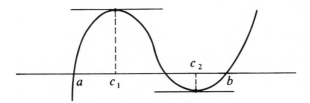

Figure 8.4.4

The converse of Rolle's theorem is not true. That is, we cannot conclude that, if a function f is such that $f'(c) = 0$, with $a < c < b$, then the conditions (i), (ii), and (iii) must hold. (See Exercise 20 below.)

EXAMPLE 1: Given $f(x) = 4x^3 - 9x$, verify that conditions (i), (ii), and (iii) of the hypothesis of Rolle's theorem are satisfied for each of the following intervals: $[-3/2,0]$, $[0,3/2]$, and $[-3/2,3/2]$. Then find a suitable value for c in each of these intervals for which $f'(c) = 0$.

Solution: $f'(x) = 12x^2 - 9$; $f'(x)$ exists for all values of x, and so f is differentiable on $(-\infty,+\infty)$ and therefore continuous on $(-\infty,+\infty)$. Conditions (i) and (ii) of Rolle's theorem thus hold on any interval. To determine on which intervals condition (iii) holds, we find the values of x for which $f(x) = 0$. Setting $f(x) = 0$, we have

$$4x\left(x^2 - \frac{9}{4}\right) = 0$$

which gives us

$$x = -\frac{3}{2} \qquad x = 0 \qquad \text{and} \qquad x = \frac{3}{2}$$

Taking $a = -3/2$ and $b = 0$, Rolle's theorem holds on $[-3/2,0]$. Similarly, Rolle's theorem holds on $[0,3/2]$ and $[-3/2,3/2]$.

To find the suitable values for c, we set $f'(x) = 0$ and get

$$12x^2 - 9 = 0$$

which gives us

$$x = -\frac{\sqrt{3}}{2} \qquad \text{and} \qquad x = \frac{\sqrt{3}}{2}$$

Therefore in the interval $[-3/2,0]$ a suitable choice for c is $-\sqrt{3}/2$. In the interval $[0,3/2]$, we take $c = \sqrt{3}/2$. In the interval $[-3/2,3/2]$, there are two possibilities for c: either $-\sqrt{3}/2$ or $\sqrt{3}/2$.

Exercises 8.4

In Exercises 1 through 4, verify that conditions (i), (ii), and (iii) of the hypothesis of Rolle's theorem are satisfied by the given function on the indicated interval. Then find a suitable value for c that satisfies the conclusion of Rolle's theorem.

1. $f(x) = x^2 - 4x + 3$; $[1,3]$
3. $f(x) = x^3 - 2x^2 - x + 2$; $[-1,2]$

2. $f(x) = x^3 - 2x^2 - x + 2$; $[1,2]$
4. $f(x) = x^3 - 16x$; $[-4,0]$

5. For the function f defined by $f(x) = 4x^3 + 12x^2 - x - 3$, determine three sets of values for a and b so that conditions (i), (ii), and (iii) of the hypothesis of Rolle's theorem are satisfied. Then find a suitable value for c in each of the three open intervals (a,b) for which $f'(c) = 0$.

In Exercises 6 through 17, (a) draw a sketch of the graph of the given function on the indicated interval; (b) test the three conditions (i), (ii), and (iii) of the hypothesis of Rolle's theorem and determine which conditions are satisfied, and which, if any, are not satisfied; (c) if the three conditions in part (b) are satisfied, determine a point at which there is a horizontal tangent line.

6. $f(x) = 4x^2 - 8x - 5$; $[-1/2, 5/2]$
9. $f(x) = \dfrac{-x^2 + 4x - 3}{(x-2)^2}$; $[1,3]$

7. $f(x) = x^{4/3} - 3x^{1/3}$; $[0,3]$
10. $f(x) = \dfrac{2x^2 - 5x - 3}{x - 1}$; $[-\frac{1}{2},3]$

8. $f(x) = x^{3/4} - 2x^{1/4}$; $[0,4]$
11. $f(x) = \begin{cases} x + 3, & \text{if } x \le 2 \\ 7 - x, & \text{if } 2 < x \end{cases}$; $[-3,7]$

12. $f(x) = \begin{cases} 3x + 6, & \text{if } x < 1 \\ x - 4, & \text{if } 1 \le x \end{cases}$; $[-2,4]$

13. $f(x) = \dfrac{x^2 - x - 12}{x - 3}$; $[-3,4]$

14. $f(x) = \begin{cases} \dfrac{x^2 - 5x + 4}{x - 1}, & \text{if } x \ne 1 \\ 0, & \text{if } x = 1 \end{cases}$; $[1,4]$

15. $f(x) = \begin{cases} x^2 - 4, & \text{if } x < 1 \\ 5x - 8, & \text{if } 1 \le x \end{cases}$; $[-2, 8/5]$

16. $f(x) = 1 - |x|$; $[-1,1]$
17. $f(x) = |9 - 4x^2|$; $[-3/2, 3/2]$

18. If $f(x) = x^4 - 2x^3 + 2x^2 - x$, then $f'(x) = 4x^3 - 6x^2 + 4x - 1$. Prove by Rolle's theorem that the equation $4x^3 - 6x^2 + 4x - 1 = 0$ has at least one real root in the open interval $(0,1)$.

19. Prove by Rolle's theorem that the equation $x^3 + 2x + c = 0$, where c is any constant, cannot have more than one real root.

20. The converse of Rolle's theorem is not true. Make up an example of a function for which the conclusion of Rolle's theorem is true and for which (a) condition (i) is not satisfied, but conditions (ii) and (iii) are satisfied; (b) condition (ii) is not satisfied, but conditions (i) and (iii) are satisfied; (c) condition (iii) is not satisfied, but conditions (i) and (ii) are satisfied. Draw a sketch of the graph showing the horizontal tangent line for each case.

(8.5)   The mean-value theorem

We shall now apply Rolle's theorem to prove one of the most important theorems in calculus — that known as the *mean-value theorem* (or law of the mean). The mean-value theorem is used to prove many theorems of both differential and integral calculus. The reader should become thoroughly familiar with the content of this theorem.

8.5.1 THEOREM (*Mean-value Theorem*)   Let f be a function such that

(i)   it is continuous on the closed interval $[a,b]$

(ii)   it is differentiable on the open interval (a,b)

Then there is a number c in the open interval (a,b) such that

$$f'(c) = \frac{f(b) - f(a)}{b - a}$$

Before proving this theorem, we shall interpret it geometrically. If we draw a sketch of the graph of the function f, then $[f(b) - f(a)]/(b - a)$ is the slope of the line segment joining the points $A(a,f(a))$ and $B(b,f(b))$. The mean-value theorem states that there is some point on the curve between A and B where the tangent line is parallel to the secant line through A and B; that is, there is some number c in (a,b), such that $f'(c) = [f(b) - f(a)]/(b - a)$. This is illustrated in Fig. 8.5.1.

The reader should notice that if the x axis were along the line segment AB, then the mean-value theorem resembles Rolle's theorem. Actually, the mean-value theorem is a generalization of Rolle's theorem, which is used in its proof.

Proof: An equation of the line through A and B in Fig. 8.5.1 is

$$y - f(a) = \frac{f(b) - f(a)}{b - a}(x - a)$$

Letting $y = f(x)$, we get

(1) $$f(x) - \frac{f(b) - f(a)}{b - a}(x - a) - f(a) = 0$$

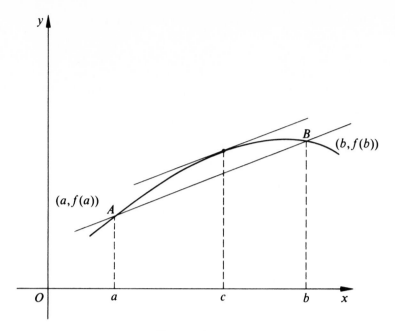

Figure 8.5.1

Now, we let F be the function such that $F(x)$ is the left-hand side of equation (1); that is,

$$(2) \qquad F(x) = f(x) - \frac{f(b) - f(a)}{b - a}(x - a) - f(a)$$

Geometrically, $F(x)$ measures the vertical distance between a point $(x, f(x))$ on the curve and the corresponding point on the secant line through A and B.

We shall show that this function F satisfies the three conditions of the hypothesis of Rolle's theorem.

F is continuous on the closed interval $[a,b]$, since f and the function h, defined by $h(x) = x - a$, are continuous there. Therefore condition (i) is satisfied by F. Condition (ii) is satisfied by F since f is differentiable on (a,b). From equation (2) we see that $F(a) = 0$ and $F(b) = 0$. Therefore condition (iii) of Rolle's theorem is satisfied by F.

The conclusion of Rolle's theorem states that there is a c in the open interval (a,b) such that $F'(c) = 0$. But,

$$F'(x) = f'(x) - \frac{f(b) - f(a)}{b - a}$$

Thus $\qquad F'(c) = f'(c) - \frac{f(b) - f(a)}{b - a}$

Therefore there is a number c in (a,b) such that

$$0 = f'(c) - \frac{f(b) - f(a)}{b - a}$$

or equivalently,

$$f'(c) = \frac{f(b) - f(a)}{b - a}$$

which was to be proved.

EXAMPLE 1: Given $f(x) = x^3 - 5x^2 - 3x$, verify that the hypothesis of the mean-value theorem is satisfied for $a = 1$ and $b = 3$. Then find all numbers c in the open interval $(1,3)$ such that $f'(c) = [f(3) - f(1)]/(3 - 1)$.

Solution: Since f is a polynomial function, f is continuous and differentiable for all values of x. Therefore, the hypothesis of the mean-value theorem is satisfied for any a and b.

$$f'(x) = 3x^2 - 10x - 3$$

$$f(1) = -7 \quad \text{and} \quad f(3) = -27$$

$$\text{Hence} \quad \frac{f(3) - f(1)}{3 - 1} = \frac{-27 - (-7)}{2} = -10$$

Setting $f'(c) = -10$, we obtain

$$3c^2 - 10c - 3 = -10$$

$$\text{or} \quad 3c^2 - 10c + 7 = 0$$

$$\text{or} \quad (3c - 7)(c - 1) = 0$$

which gives us

$$c = \frac{7}{3} \quad \text{and} \quad c = 1$$

Since 1 is not in the open interval $(1,3)$, the only possible value for c is 7/3.

EXAMPLE 2: Given $f(x) = x^{2/3}$, draw a sketch of the graph of f. Show that there is no number c in the open interval $(-2,2)$ such that

$$f'(c) = \frac{f(2) - f(-2)}{2 - (-2)}$$

Which condition of the hypothesis of the mean-value theorem fails to hold for f when $a = -2$ and $b = 2$?

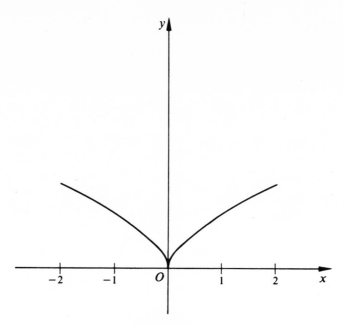

Figure 8.5.2

Solution: A sketch of the graph of f is shown in Fig. 8.5.2.

$$f'(x) = \frac{2}{3}x^{-1/3}$$

So,

$$f'(c) = \frac{2}{3c^{1/3}}$$

$$\frac{f(2) - f(-2)}{2 - (-2)} = \frac{4^{1/3} - 4^{1/3}}{4} = 0$$

There is no number c for which $2/3c^{1/3} = 0$.

f is continuous on the closed interval $[-2,2]$; however, f is not differentiable on the open interval $(-2,2)$, since $f'(0)$ does not exist. Therefore condition (ii) of the hypothesis of the mean-value theorem fails to hold for f when $a = -2$ and $b = 2$.

Exercises 8.5

In Exercises 1 through 8, verify that the hypothesis of the mean-value theorem is satisfied for the given function on the indicated interval. Then find a suitable value for c that satisfies the conclusion of the mean-value theorem.

1. $f(x) = x^2 + 2x - 1$; $[0,1]$

2. $f(x) = x^3 + x^2 - x$; $[-2,1]$

3. $f(x) = x^{2/3}$; $[0,1]$

5. $f(x) = \sqrt{x + 2}$; $[4,6]$

6. $f(x) = \sqrt{100 - x^2}$; $[-6,8]$

7. $f(x) = \dfrac{x^2 - 3x - 4}{x + 5}$; $[-1,4]$

4. $f(x) = x - 1 + \dfrac{1}{x - 1}$; [3/2,3]   8. $f(x) = \dfrac{x^2 + 4x}{x - 7}$; [2,6]

9. If $f(x) = (2x - 1)/(2x - 4)$, and if $a = 1$ and $b = 2$, show that there is no number c in the open interval (a,b) that satisfies the conclusion of the mean-value theorem. Which part of the hypothesis of the mean-value theorem fails to hold? Draw a sketch of the graph of f on [1,2].

The geometric interpretation of the mean-value theorem is that for a suitable c in the open interval (a,b), the tangent line to the curve $y = f(x)$ at the point $(c,f(c))$ is parallel to the secant line through the points $(a,f(a))$ and $(b,f(b))$. In Exercises 10 through 15, find a value of c satisfying the conclusion of the mean-value theorem, draw a sketch of the graph on the closed interval $[a,b]$, and show the tangent line and the secant line.

10. $f(x) = x^2$; $a = 2$, $b = 4$ 12. $f(x) = x - 1$; $a = 10$, $b = 26$

11. $f(x) = x^2$; $a = 3$, $b = 5$ 13. $f(x) = \dfrac{2}{x - 3}$; $a = 3.1$, $b = 3.2$

14. $f(x) = \dfrac{2}{x - 3}$; $a = 3.01$, $b = 3.02$

15. $f(x) = x^3 - 9x + 1$; $a = -3$, $b = 4$

For each of the functions in Exercises 16 through 19, there is no number c in the open interval (a,b) that satisfies the conclusion of the mean-value theorem. In each problem, determine which part of the hypothesis of the mean-value theorem fails to hold. Draw a sketch of the graph of $y = f(x)$ and the line through the points $(a,f(a))$ and $(b,f(b))$.

16. $f(x) = \dfrac{2x - 1}{3x - 4}$; $a = 1$, $b = 2$ 17. $f(x) = \dfrac{4}{(x - 3)^2}$; $a = 1$, $b = 6$

18. $f(x) = \begin{cases} 2x + 3, & \text{if } x < 3 \\ 15 - 2x, & \text{if } 3 \le x \end{cases}$; $a = -1$, $b = 5$

19. $f(x) = 3(x - 4)^{2/3}$; $a = -4$, $b = 5$.

(8.6)   Increasing and decreasing functions and the first-derivative test

Suppose that Fig. 8.6.1 represents a sketch of the graph of a function f for all x in the closed interval $[x_1,x_7]$. In drawing this sketch, we have assumed that, for all values of x in this interval, f is defined and that the first and second derivatives of f exist. Then, since f is differentiable for all x in the interval, it follows that f is continuous on the interval. Since the second derivative of f exists for all values of x in the interval, f' is differentiable for all x in the interval, and so f' is continuous on the interval. Therefore, the slope of the tangent line to the curve is a continuous function of x; thus, as a point P moves along

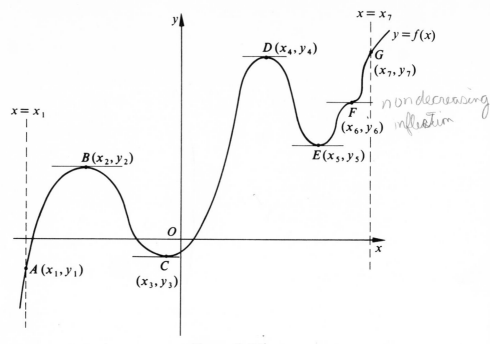

Figure 8.6.1

the curve so that its abscissa x increases, the tangent line to the curve at P turns continuously.

It can be seen from Fig. 8.6.1 that as a point moves along the curve from A to B, the function values increase as the abscissa increases, and that as a point moves along the curve from B to C, the function values decrease as the abscissa increases. We say, then, that f is *increasing* on the closed interval $[x_1,x_2]$ and that f is *decreasing* on the closed interval $[x_2,x_3]$. Following are the precise definitions of a function increasing or decreasing on an interval.

8.6.1 DEFINITION   A function f defined on an interval is said to be *increasing* on that interval if

$$f(x_1) < f(x_2) \qquad \text{whenever} \qquad x_1 < x_2$$

where x_1 and x_2 are any numbers in the interval.

The function of Fig. 8.6.1 is increasing on the following closed intervals:

$$[x_1,x_2]; \; [x_3,x_4]; \; [x_5,x_6]; \; [x_6,x_7]; \; [x_5,x_7]$$

8.6.2 DEFINITION   A function f defined on an interval is said to be *decreasing* on that interval if

$$f(x_1) > f(x_2) \qquad \text{whenever} \qquad x_1 < x_2$$

where x_1 and x_2 are any numbers in the interval.

The function of Fig. 8.6.1 is decreasing on the following closed intervals:

$$[x_2,x_3]; \; [x_4,x_5]$$

If a function f is either increasing on an interval or decreasing on the interval, then f is said to be *monotonic* on the interval.

Before stating a theorem that gives a test for determining if a given function is monotonic on an interval, let us see what is happening geometrically. Referring to Fig. 8.6.1, we observe that when the slope of the tangent line is positive the function is increasing, and when the slope of the tangent line is negative the function is decreasing. Since $f'(x)$ is the slope of the tangent line to the curve $y = f(x)$, f is increasing when $f'(x) > 0$, and f is decreasing when $f'(x) < 0$. Also, since $f'(x)$ is the rate of change of the function values $f(x)$ with respect to x, when $f'(x) > 0$ the function values are increasing as x increases; and when $f'(x) < 0$, the function values are decreasing as x increases. We have the following theorem.

8.6.3 THEOREM   Let the function f be continuous on the closed interval $[a,b]$ and differentiable on the open interval (a,b).

(i)   If $f'(x) > 0$ for all x in (a,b), then f is increasing on $[a,b]$.

(ii)   If $f'(x) < 0$ for all x in (a,b), then f is decreasing on $[a,b]$.

Proof of (i): Let x_1 and x_2 be any two numbers in $[a,b]$ such that $x_1 < x_2$. Then f is continuous on $[x_1,x_2]$ and differentiable on (x_1,x_2). Applying the mean-value theorem, there is some number c in (x_1,x_2) such that

$$f'(c) = \frac{f(x_2) - f(x_1)}{x_2 - x_1}$$

Since $x_1 < x_2$, then $x_2 - x_1 > 0$. Also, $f'(c) > 0$ by hypothesis. Therefore $f(x_2) - f(x_1) > 0$, and so $f(x_2) > f(x_1)$. We have shown then that $f(x_1) < f(x_2)$ whenever $x_1 < x_2$, where x_1 and x_2 are any numbers in the interval $[a,b]$. Therefore, by Definition 8.6.1, it follows that f is increasing on $[a,b]$.

The proof of part (ii) is similar and is left for the reader (see Exercise 33 below).

An immediate application of the preceding theorem is in the proof of what is known as the *first-derivative test for relative extrema* of a function, which we shall now state and prove.

8.6.4 THEOREM (*First-derivative Test for Relative Extrema*)   Let the function f be continuous at all points of the open interval (a,b) containing the critical number c, and suppose f' exists at all points of (a,b) except possibly at c.

(i)   If $f'(x) > 0$ for values of x close to c and $x < c$, and if $f'(x) < 0$ for values of x close to c and $x > c$, f has a relative maximum value at c.

(ii)   If $f'(x) < 0$ for values of x close to c and $x < c$, and if $f'(x) > 0$ for values of x close to c and $x > c$, f has a relative minimum value at c.

(iii)   If neither (i) nor (ii) holds, f does not have a relative extremum at c.

Proof of (i): If $f'(x) > 0$ for values of x close to c and $x < c$, then there is an interval I', having c as its right end point, on which f is increasing. This follows from Theorem 8.6.3(i). Similarly, from Theorem 8.6.3(ii), if $f'(x) < 0$ for values of x close to c and $x > c$, there is an interval I'', having c as its left end point, on which f is decreasing. Since f is increasing on I', it follows from Definition 8.6.1 that if x_1 is in I' and $x_1 \neq c$, then $f(x_1) < f(c)$. Also, since f is decreasing on I'', it follows from Definition 8.6.2 that if x_2 is in I'' and $x_2 \neq c$, then $f(c) > f(x_2)$. Therefore, from Definition 8.2.1, f has a relative maximum value at c.

The proof of part (ii) is similar to the proof of (i), and it is left for the reader. The proof of part (iii) is also left for the reader. (See Exercises 34 and 35 below).

The first-derivative test for relative extrema essentially says that if $f'(x)$ changes algebraic sign from positive to negative as x increases through the critical number c, then f has a relative maximum value at c, and if $f'(x)$ changes algebraic sign from negative to positive as x increases through c, then f has a relative minimum value at c. Furthermore, if $f'(x)$ does not change its algebraic sign as x increases through c, then f does not have a relative extremum at c.

Figures 8.6.2 and 8.6.3 illustrate parts (i) and (ii), respectively, of Theorem 8.6.4, when $f'(c)$ exists.

Figure 8.6.4 shows a sketch of the graph of a function f that has a relative maximum value at a number c, but $f'(c)$ does not exist; however, $f'(x) > 0$

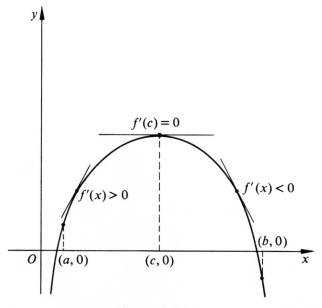

Figure 8.6.2

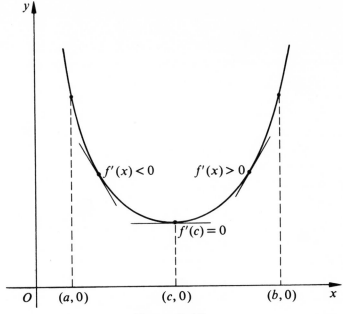

Figure 8.6.3

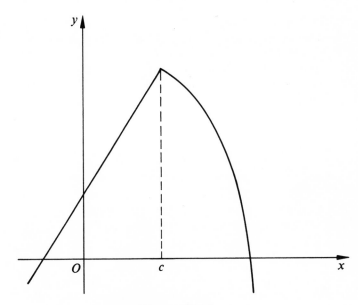

Figure 8.6.4

when $x < c$, and $f'(x) < 0$ when $x > c$. In Fig. 8.6.5 we illustrate Theorem 8.6.4(iii) by showing a sketch of the graph of a function f for which c is a critical number, and $f'(x) < 0$ when $x < c$, and $f'(x) < 0$ when $x > c$; f does not have a relative extremum at c.

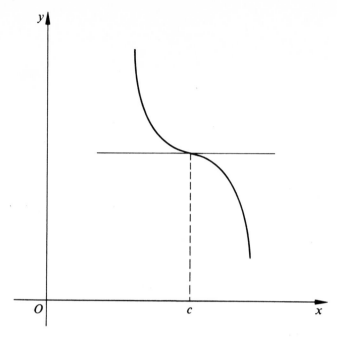

Figure 8.6.5

Further illustrations of Theorem 8.6.4 occur in Fig. 8.6.1. At x_2 and x_4 the function has a relative maximum value, and at x_3 and x_5 the function has a relative minimum value; while even though x_6 is a critical number for the function, there is no relative extremum at x_6.

In summary, to determine the relative extrema of a function f:

(1) Find $f'(x)$.
(2) Find the critical numbers of f — that is, the values of x for which $f'(x) = 0$ or for which $f'(x)$ does not exist.
(3) Apply the first-derivative test (Theorem 8.6.4).

The following examples illustrate this procedure.

EXAMPLE 1: Given $f(x) = x^3 - 6x^2 + 9x + 1$, find the relative extrema of f by applying the first-derivative test. Determine the values of x at which the relative extrema occur, as well as the intervals on which f is increasing and the intervals on which f is decreasing. Draw a sketch of the graph.

Solution: $f'(x) = 3x^2 - 12x + 9$.

$f'(x)$ exists for all values of x. Setting $f'(x) = 0$, we have

$$3x^2 - 12x + 9 = 0$$

$$\text{or} \quad 3(x - 3)(x - 1) = 0$$

which gives us

$$x = 3 \quad \text{and} \quad x = 1$$

Thus, the critical numbers of f are 1 and 3. To determine whether f has a rela-tive extremum at either of these numbers, we apply the first-derivative test. The results are summarized in Table 8.6.1.

Table 8.6.1

	$f(x)$	$f'(x)$	Conclusion
$x < 1$		$+$	f is increasing
$x = 1$	5	0	f has a relative maximum value
$1 < x < 3$		$-$	f is decreasing
$x = 3$	1	0	f has a relative minimum value
$3 < x$		$+$	f is increasing

We see from the table that 5 is a relative maximum value of f, occurring at 1, and 1 is a relative minimum value of f, occurring at 3. A sketch of the graph is shown in Fig. 8.6.6.

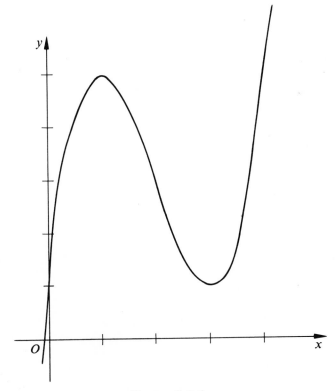

Figure 8.6.6

EXAMPLE 2: Given $f(x) = \begin{cases} x^2 - 4 & \text{if } x < 3 \\ 8 - x & \text{if } 3 \leq x \end{cases}$

find the relative extrema of f by applying the first-derivative test. Determine the values of x at which the relative extrema occur, as well as the intervals on which f is increasing and the intervals on which f is decreasing. Draw a sketch of the graph.

Solution: If $x < 3$, $f'(x) = 2x$.

If $x > 3$, $f'(x) = -1$.

Since $f'_-(3) = 6$ and $f'_+(3) = -1$, we conclude that $f'(3)$ does not exist. Therefore, 3 is a critical number of f.

$f'(x) = 0$, when $2x = 0$ or $x = 0$. Therefore, 0 is a critical number of f. Applying the first-derivative test, we summarize the results in Table 8.6.2. A sketch of the graph is shown in Fig. 8.6.7.

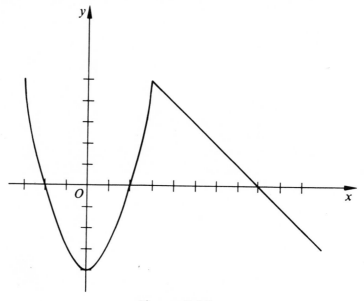

Figure 8.6.7

Table 8.6.2

	$f(x)$	$f'(x)$	Conclusion
$x < 0$		$-$	f is decreasing
$x = 0$	-4	0	f has a relative minimum value
$0 < x < 3$		$+$	f is increasing
$x = 3$	5	does not exist	f has a relative maximum value
$3 < x$		$-$	f is decreasing

EXAMPLE 3: Given $f(x) = x^{4/3} + 4x^{1/3}$, find the relative extrema of f, determine the values of x at which the relative extrema occur, and determine the intervals on which f is increasing and the intervals on which f is decreasing. Draw a sketch of the graph.

Solution: $f'(x) = \frac{4}{3}x^{1/3} + \frac{4}{3}x^{-2/3} = \frac{4}{3}x^{-2/3}(x + 1)$

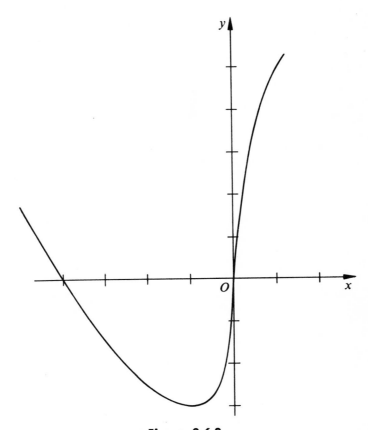

Figure 8.6.8

Table 8.6.3

	$f(x)$	$f'(x)$	Conclusion
$x < -1$		$-$	f is decreasing
$x = -1$	-3	0	f has a relative minimum value
$-1 < x < 0$		$+$	f is increasing
$x = 0$	0	does not exist	f does not have a relative extremum at $x = 0$
$0 < x$		$+$	f is increasing

Since $f'(x)$ does not exist when $x = 0$, and $f'(x) = 0$ when $x = -1$, the critical numbers of f are -1 and 0. We apply the first-derivative test and summarize the results in Table 8.6.3. A sketch of the graph is shown in Fig. 8.6.8.

Exercises 8.6

In Exercises 1 through 29, do each of the following: (a) find the relative extrema of f by applying the first-derivative test; (b) determine the values of x at which the relative extrema occur; (c) determine the intervals on which f is increasing; (d) determine the intervals on which f is decreasing; (e) draw a sketch of the graph.

1. $f(x) = x^2 - 4x - 1$

2. $f(x) = x^3 - 9x^2 + 15x - 5$

3. $f(x) = 2x^3 - x^2 + 3x - 1$

4. $f(x) = x^4 + 4x$

5. $f(x) = x^5 - 5x^3 - 20x - 2$

6. $f(x) = 2x + \dfrac{1}{2x}$

7. $f(x) = \sqrt{x} - \dfrac{1}{\sqrt{x}}$

8. $f(x) = \dfrac{x - 2}{x + 2}$

9. $f(x) = 2x\sqrt{3 - x}$

10. $f(x) = x\sqrt{5 - x^2}$

11. $f(x) = (1 - x)^2(1 + x)^3$

12. $f(x) = (x + 2)^2(x - 1)^2$

13. $f(x) = 2 - 3(x - 4)^{2/3}$

14. $f(x) = 2 - (x - 1)^{1/3}$

15. $f(x) = \begin{cases} 2x + 1, \text{ if } x \le 4 \\ 13 - x, \text{ if } 4 < x \end{cases}$

16. $f(x) = \begin{cases} 5 - 2x, \text{ if } x < 3 \\ 3x - 10, \text{ if } 3 \le x \end{cases}$

17. $f(x) = \begin{cases} 2x + 9, \text{ if } x \le -2 \\ x^2 + 1, \text{ if } -2 < x \end{cases}$

18. $f(x) = \begin{cases} 4 - (x + 5)^2, \text{ if } x < -4 \\ 12 - (x + 1)^2, \text{ if } -4 \le x \end{cases}$

19. $f(x) = \begin{cases} (x - 2)^2 - 3, \text{ if } x \le 5 \\ \dfrac{x + 7}{2}, \qquad \text{ if } 5 < x \end{cases}$

20. $f(x) = \begin{cases} \sqrt{25 - (x + 7)^2}, \text{ if } x \le -3 \\ 12 - x^2, \qquad \text{ if } -3 < x \end{cases}$

21. $f(x) = \begin{cases} 3x + 5, \text{ if } x < -1 \\ x^2 + 1, \text{ if } -1 \le x < 2 \\ 7 - x, \text{ if } 2 \le x \end{cases}$

22. $f(x) = \begin{cases} x - 6, \qquad\qquad \text{ if } x \le 6 \\ -\sqrt{4 - (x - 8)^2}, \text{ if } 6 < x \le 10 \\ 20 - 2x, \qquad\quad \text{ if } 10 < x \end{cases}$

23. $f(x) = \begin{cases} (x + 9)^2 - 8, \qquad \text{ if } x < -7 \\ -\sqrt{25 - (x + 4)^2}, \text{ if } -7 \le x \le 0 \\ (x - 2)^2 - 7, \qquad \text{ if } 0 < x \end{cases}$

24. $f(x) = \begin{cases} 12 - (x + 5)^2, \qquad \text{ if } x \le -3 \\ 5 - x, \qquad\qquad\quad \text{ if } -3 < x \le -1 \\ \sqrt{100 - (x - 7)^2}, \text{ if } -1 < x \end{cases}$

25. $f(x) = x^{5/4} + 10x^{1/4}$ 28. $f(x) = (4x - a)^{1/3}(2x - a)^{2/3}$

26. $f(x) = x^{5/3} - 10x^{2/3}$ 29. $f(x) = x^{1/3}(x + 4)^{-2/3}$

27. $f(x) = (x + 1)^{2/3}(x - 2)^{1/3}$

30. Find a and b such that the function defined by $f(x) = x^3 + ax^2 + b$ will have a relative extremum at $(2,3)$.

31. Find a, b, and c such that the function defined by $f(x) = ax^2 + bx + c$ will have a relative maximum value of 7 at 1 and the graph of $y = f(x)$ will go through the point $(2, -2)$.

32. Find a, b, c, and d such that the function f defined by

$$f(x) = ax^3 + bx^2 + cx + d$$

will have relative extrema at $(1,2)$ and $(2,3)$.

33. Prove Theorem 8.6.3(ii).

34. Prove Theorem 8.6.4(ii).

35. Prove Theorem 8.6.4 (iii).

36. Given that the function f is continuous for all values of x, $f(3) = 2$, $f'(x) < 0$ if $x < 3$, and $f'(x) > 0$ if $x > 3$, draw a sketch of a possible graph of f in each of the following cases, where the additional condition is satisfied: (a) f' is continuous at 3; (b) $f'(x) = -1$ if $x < 3$, and $f'(x) = 1$ if $x > 3$; (c) $\lim\limits_{x \to 3^-} f'(x) = -1$, $\lim\limits_{x \to 3^+} f'(x) = 1$, and $f'(a) \neq f'(b)$ if $a \neq b$.

37. Given $f(x) = x^p(1 - x)^q$, where p and q are positive integers greater than 1, prove each of the following: (a) if p is even, f has a relative minimum value at 0; (b) if q is odd, f has a relative minimum value at 1; (c) f has a relative maximum value at $p/(p + q)$ whether p and q are odd or even.

(8.7) The second-derivative test for relative extrema

In the previous section we learned how to determine whether a function f has a relative maximum value or a relative minimum value at a critical number c by checking the algebraic sign of f' at numbers close to c. Another test for relative extrema is one that involves only the critical number c, and often it is the easier test to apply. It is called the *second-derivative test for relative extrema*, and we shall state it as a theorem.

8.7.1 THEOREM (*Second-derivative Test for Relative Extrema*).   Let c be a critical number of a function f at which $f'(c) = 0$, and let f' and f'' exist for all values of x in some open interval containing c.

   (i) If $f''(c) < 0$, then f has a relative maximum value at c.

  (ii) If $f''(c) > 0$, then f has a relative minimum value at c.

Proof of (i): By hypothesis, $f''(c)$ exists and is negative, so that we have

$$f''(c) = \lim_{x \to c} \frac{f'(x) - f'(c)}{x - c} < 0$$

Therefore by Theorem 4.6.2, there is an open interval I containing c such that

(1)
$$\frac{f'(x) - f'(c)}{x - c} < 0$$

for every $x \ne c$ in the interval.

Let I' be the open interval containing all values of x in I for which $x < c$; therefore c is the right end point of the open interval I'. Let I'' be the open interval containing all values of x in I for which $x > c$; so c is the left end point of the open interval I''.

Then if x is in I', $(x - c) < 0$, and it follows from inequality (1) that we have $[f'(x) - f'(c)] > 0$ or, equivalently, $f'(x) > f'(c)$. If x is in I'', $(x - c) > 0$, and it follows from (1) that $[f'(x) - f'(c)] < 0$ or, equivalently, $f'(x) < f'(c)$.

But since $f'(c) = 0$, we conclude that if x is in I', $f'(x) > 0$, and if x is in

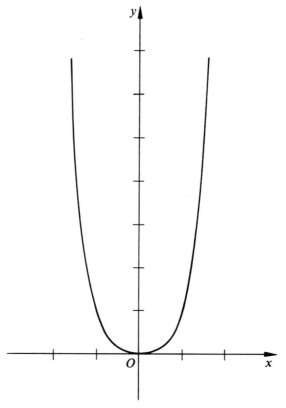

Figure 8.7.1

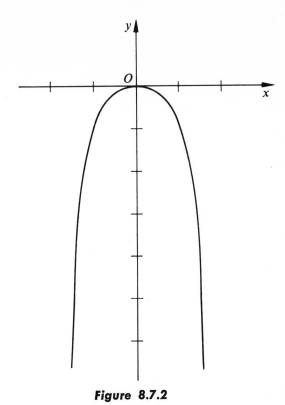

Figure 8.7.2

I'', $f'(x) < 0$. Therefore, $f'(x)$ changes algebraic sign from positive to negative as x increases through c, and so by Theorem 8.6.4 f has a relative maximum value at c.

The proof of part (ii) is similar and is left for the reader. (See Exercise 15 below.)

It should be noted that if $f''(c) = 0$, as well as $f'(c) = 0$, nothing can be concluded regarding a relative extremum of f at c. For example, if $f(x) = x^4$, then $f'(x) = 4x^3$ and $f''(x) = 12x^2$; hence $f(0)$, $f'(0)$, and $f''(0)$ all have the value zero. In this case, f has a relative minimum value at 0, as can be seen by applying the first-derivative test. If $g(x) = -x^4$, then $g'(x) = -4x^3$ and $g''(x) = -12x^2$; thus $g(0) = g'(0) = g''(0) = 0$. By applying the first-derivative test, we see that g has a relative maximum value at 0. If $h(x) = x^3$, then $h'(x) = 3x^2$ and $h''(x) = 6x$; so $h(0) = h'(0) = h''(0) = 0$. Applying the first-derivative test, we see that h does not have a relative extremum at 0. Here we have examples of three functions, each of which has zero for its second derivative at a number for which its first derivative is zero; yet one function has a relative minimum at that number, another function has a relative maximum at that number, and the third function has neither a relative maximum nor a relative minimum at that number. Sketches of the graphs of these functions f, g, and h are shown in Figs. 8.7.1, 8.7.2, and 8.7.3, respectively.

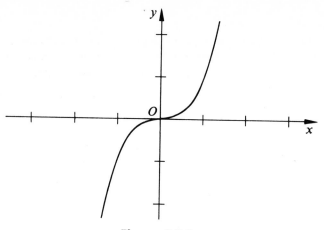

Figure 8.7.3

EXAMPLE 1: Given $f(x) = x^4 + (4/3)x^3 - 4x^2$, find the relative maxima and the relative minima of f by applying the second-derivative test.

Solution: $f'(x) = 4x^3 + 4x^2 - 8x$

$$f''(x) = 12x^2 + 8x - 8$$

Setting $f'(x) = 0$, we have

$$4x(x + 2)(x - 1) = 0$$

which gives us

$$x = 0 \qquad x = -2 \qquad \text{and} \qquad x = 1$$

Thus, the critical numbers of f are -2, 0, and 1. We determine whether or not we have a relative extremum at any of these critical numbers by finding the sign of the second derivative there. The results are summarized in Table 8.7.1.

Table 8.7.1

	$f(x)$	$f'(x)$	$f''(x)$	Conclusion
$x = -2$	$-\dfrac{32}{3}$	0	$+$	f has a relative minimum value
$x = 0$	0	0	$-$	f has a relative maximum value
$x = 1$	$-\dfrac{5}{3}$	0	$+$	f has a relative minimum value

Exercises 8.7

In Exercises 1 through 14, find the relative extrema of the given function by using the second-derivative test, if it can be applied. If the second-derivative test cannot be applied, use the first-derivative test.

1. $f(x) = 3x^2 - 2x + 1$

2. $g(x) = x^3 - 5x + 6$

3. $f(x) = -4x^3 + 3x^2 + 18x$

4. $h(x) = 2x^3 - 9x^2 + 27$

5. $f(x) = (x - 4)^2$

6. $G(x) = (x + 2)^3$

7. $G(x) = (x - 3)^4$

8. $f(x) = x(x - 1)^3$

9. $h(x) = x\sqrt{x + 3}$

10. $f(x) = x\sqrt{8 - x^2}$

11. $f(x) = 4x^{1/2} + 4x^{-1/2}$

12. $g(x) = \dfrac{9}{x} + \dfrac{x^2}{9}$

13. $F(x) = 6x^{1/3} - x^{2/3}$

14. $G(x) = x^{2/3}(x - 4)^2$

15. Prove Theorem 8.7.1(ii).

16. Given $f(x) = x^3 + 3rx + 5$, prove that (*a*) if $r > 0$, f has no relative extrema; (*b*) if $r < 0$, f has both a relative maximum value and a relative minimum value.

17. Given $f(x) = x^r - rx + k$, where $r > 0$ and $r \neq 1$, prove that (*a*) if $0 < r < 1$, f has a relative maximum value at 1; (*b*) if $r > 1$, f has a relative minimum value at 1.

(8.8)   Additional problems involving absolute extrema

The extreme-value theorem (Theorem 8.2.9) guarantees an absolute maximum value and an absolute minimum value for a function that is continuous on a closed interval. We shall now consider some functions defined on intervals for which the extreme-value theorem does not apply and which may or may not have absolute extrema.

EXAMPLE 1: Given $f(x) = (x^2 - 27)/(x - 6)$, find the absolute extrema of f on the interval [0,6) if there are any.

Solution: f is continuous on the interval [0,6) since the only discontinuity of f is at 6, which is not in the interval.

$$f'(x) = \frac{2x(x - 6) - (x^2 - 27)}{(x - 6)^2} = \frac{x^2 - 12x + 27}{(x - 6)^2} = \frac{(x - 3)(x - 9)}{(x - 6)^2}$$

$f'(x)$ exists for all values of x in [0,6), and $f'(x) = 0$ when $x = 3$ or 9, so that the only critical number of f in the interval [0,6) is 3. We apply the first-derivative test to determine if f has a relative extremum at 3, and the results are summarized in Table 8.8.1.

Table 8.8.1

	$f(x)$	$f'(x)$	Conclusion
$0 \leq x < 3$		$+$	f is increasing
$x = 3$	6	0	f has a relative maximum value
$3 < x < 6$		$-$	f is decreasing

Since f has a relative maximum value at 3, and f is increasing on the interval $[0,3)$ and decreasing on the interval $(3,6)$, we conclude that on $[0,6)$ f has an absolute maximum value at 3, and it is $f(3)$ which is 6. There is no absolute minimum value of f on $[0,6)$.

EXAMPLE 2: Given $f(x) = -x/(x^2 + 6)^2$, find the absolute extrema of f on $[0,+\infty)$ if there are any.

Solution: f is continuous for all values of x.

$$f'(x) = \frac{-1(x^2 + 6)^2 + 4x^2(x^2 + 6)}{(x^2 + 6)^4} = \frac{-(x^2 + 6) + 4x^2}{(x^2 + 6)^3} = \frac{3x^2 - 6}{(x^2 + 6)^3}$$

$f'(x)$ exists for all values of x. Setting $f'(x) = 0$, we obtain $x = \pm\sqrt{2}$, so that $\sqrt{2}$ is the only critical number of f in $[0,+\infty)$. Applying the first-derivative test at $\sqrt{2}$, we summarize the results in Table 8.8.2.

Table 8.8.2

	$f(x)$	$f'(x)$	Conclusion
$0 \leq x < \sqrt{2}$		$-$	f is decreasing
$x = \sqrt{2}$	$-\sqrt{2}/64$	0	f has a relative minimum value
$\sqrt{2} < x < +\infty$		$+$	f is increasing

Since f has a relative minimum value at $\sqrt{2}$ and since f is decreasing on $[0,\sqrt{2})$ and increasing on $(\sqrt{2},+\infty)$, we conclude that f has an absolute minimum value at $\sqrt{2}$ on $[0,+\infty)$. The absolute minimum value is $-\sqrt{2}/64$. There is no absolute maximum value of f on $[0,+\infty)$.

EXAMPLE 3: Find the shortest distance from the point $A(2,\frac{1}{2})$ to a point on the parabola $y = x^2$, and find the point on the parabola that is closest to A.

Solution: Let $z =$ the number of units in the distance from the point $A(2,\frac{1}{2})$ to a point $P(x,y)$ on the parabola. Refer to Fig. 8.8.1.

(1) $$z = \sqrt{(x - 2)^2 + (y - \frac{1}{2})^2}$$

Since $P(x,y)$ is on the parabola, its coordinates satisfy the equation $y = x^2$.

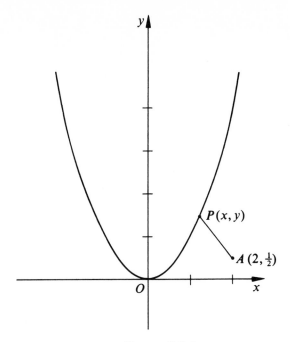

Figure 8.8.1

Substituting this value of y into equation (1), we obtain z as a function of x and write

$$z(x) = \sqrt{(x - 2)^2 + (x^2 - \tfrac{1}{2})^2}$$

or

(2) $$z(x) = \sqrt{x^4 - 4x + 17/4}$$

Since P may be any point on the parabola, x is any real number. We wish to find the absolute minimum value of z on $(-\infty, +\infty)$.

$$z'(x) = \tfrac{1}{2}(4x^3 - 4)\left(x^4 - 4x + \frac{17}{4}\right)^{-1/2} = \frac{2(x - 1)(x^2 + x + 1)}{\sqrt{x^4 - 4x + 17/4}}$$

$z'(x)$ exists for all values of x since the denominator is $z(x)$, which is never zero. Consequently, the critical numbers are obtained by setting $z'(x) = 0$. The only real solution is 1; thus 1 is the only critical number of z. Applying the first-derivative test, we summarize the results in Table 8.8.3.

Table 8.8.3

	$z(x)$	$z'(x)$	Conclusion
$-\infty < x < 1$		$-$	z is decreasing
$x = 1$	$\sqrt{5}/2$	0	z has a relative minimum value
$1 < x < +\infty$		$+$	z is increasing

We conclude that z has an absolute minimum value of $\sqrt{5}/2$ at 1, so that the point on the parabola closest to A is $(1,1)$.

It can be shown that the point $A(2,\frac{1}{2})$ lies on the normal line at $(1,1)$ of the graph of the parabola. Since the slope of the tangent line at any point (x,y) of the parabola is $2x$, the slope of the tangent line at $(1,1)$ is 2. Therefore, the slope of the normal line at $(1,1)$ is $-\frac{1}{2}$, which is the same as the slope of the line through $A(2,\frac{1}{2})$ and $(1,1)$.

In the preceding example and in the Exercises of Sec. 8.3, we expressed the variable for which we wished to find an absolute extremum as a function of only one variable. Sometimes this procedure is either too difficult or too laborious, or occasionally even impossible. Often the given information enables us to obtain two equations involving three variables. Instead of eliminating one of the variables, it may be more advantageous to differentiate implicitly. The following example illustrates this method.

EXAMPLE 4: If a closed tin can of specific volume is to be in the form of a right-circular cylinder, find the ratio of the height to the base radius if the least amount of material is to be used in its manufacture.

Solution: We wish to find a relationship between the height and the base radius of the right-circular cylinder in order for the total surface area to be an absolute minimum for a fixed volume. Therefore, we consider the volume of the cylinder as a constant, and introduce a letter to stand for it.

Let V = number of cubic units in the volume of the cylinder (a constant).

We now define the variables:

r = number of units in the base radius of the cylinder; $0 < r < +\infty$

h = number of units in the height of the cylinder; $0 < h < +\infty$

S = number of square units in the total surface area of the cylinder

We have the following equations:

(3) $$S = 2\pi r^2 + 2\pi rh$$

(4) $$V = \pi r^2 h$$

Since V is a constant, we could solve equation (4) for either r or h in terms of the other and substitute into equation (3), which will give us S as a function of one variable. The alternative method of solution is to consider S as a function of two variables r and h; however, r and h are not independent of each other. That is, if we choose r as the independent variable, then S depends upon r; also, h depends upon r.

Differentiating S and V with respect to r and bearing in mind that h is a function of r, we have

(5) $$D_r S = 4\pi r + 2\pi h + 2\pi r\, D_r h$$

and

(6) $$D_r V = 2\pi rh + \pi r^2\, D_r h$$

Since V is a constant, $D_r V = 0$; therefore from equation (6) we have

$$2\pi rh + \pi r^2\, D_r h = 0$$

with $r \neq 0$, and we may divide by r and solve for $D_r h$, obtaining

$$(7) \qquad\qquad\qquad D_r h = -\frac{2h}{r}$$

Substituting from equation (7) into (5), we obtain

$$D_r S = 2\pi\left[2r + h + r\left(-\frac{2h}{r}\right)\right]$$

or

$$(8) \qquad\qquad\qquad D_r S = 2\pi(2r - h)$$

In order to find when S has a relative minimum value, we set $D_r S = 0$ and obtain $2r - h = 0$, which gives us

$$r = \frac{h}{2}$$

To determine if this relationship between r and h makes S a relative minimum, we shall apply the second-derivative test. From equation (8), we find that

$$(9) \qquad\qquad\qquad D_r{}^2 S = 2\pi(2 - D_r h)$$

Substituting from equation (7) into (9), we get

$$D_r{}^2 S = 2\pi\left[2 - \left(\frac{-2h}{r}\right)\right] = 2\pi\left(2 + \frac{2h}{r}\right)$$

The results of the second-derivative test are summarized in Table 8.8.4.

Table 8.8.4

	$D_r S$	$D_r{}^2 S$	Conclusion
$r = \dfrac{h}{2}$	0	+	S has a relative minimum value

Since r is in the interval $(0, +\infty)$ and S is continuous on $(0, +\infty)$, we conclude that the relative minimum value of S is the absolute minimum value of S. Therefore the total surface area of the tin can will be least for a specific volume when the ratio of the height to the base radius is 2.

Exercises 8.8

In Exercises 1 through 8 find the absolute extrema of the given function on the given interval if there are any.

1. $f(x) = x^2$; $(-3, 2]$
2. $g(x) = x^3 + 2x^2 - 4x + 1$; $(-3, 2)$

3. $F(x) = \dfrac{x+2}{x-2}; [-4,4]$

6. $G(x) = (x-5)^{2/3}; (-\infty,+\infty)$

4. $f(x) = \dfrac{x^2}{x+3}; [-4,-1]$

7. $f(x) = \dfrac{x}{(x^2+4)^{3/2}}; [0,+\infty)$

5. $g(x) = 4x^2 - 2x + 1; (-\infty,+\infty)$

8. $f(x) = \dfrac{x^2-30}{x-4}; (-\infty,4)$

9. A box with a rectangular base, whose length is twice its width, is to have a closed top. The area of the material in the box is to be 192 in.^{2} What should the dimensions of the box be in order to have the largest possible volume?

10. Find the most economical dimensions for a closed box of specific volume whose base is a rectangle having a length that is three times its width.

11. Solve Exercise 10 if the box is to have an open top.

12. A rectangular field is fenced off along the bank of a river, and no fence is required along the river. If the field is to have an area of 1800 yd^2, what should the dimensions of the field be in order to require the least amount of fencing?

13. A rectangular open tank is to have a square base, and its volume is to be 125 yd^3. The cost per square yard for the bottom is \$8 and for the sides is \$4. Find the dimensions of the tank in order for the cost of the material to be the least.

14. A page of print is to contain 24 in.^{2} of printed area, a margin of 1½ in. at the top and bottom, and a margin of 1 in. at the sides. What are the dimensions of the smallest page that would fill these requirements?

15. A funnel of specific volume is to be in the shape of a right-circular cone. Find the ratio of the height to the base radius if the least amount of material is to be used in its manufacture.

16. A right-circular cone is to be inscribed in a sphere of given radius. Find the ratio of the altitude to the base radius of the cone of largest possible volume.

17. A right-circular cone is to be circumscribed about a sphere of given radius. Find the ratio of the altitude to the base radius of the cone of least possible volume.

18. A Norman window consists of a rectangle surmounted by a semicircle. Find the shape of such a window that will admit the most light for a given perimeter.

19. Solve Exercise 18 if the window is such that the semicircle transmits only half as much light per square unit of area as the rectangle.

20. Find the shortest distance from the point $A(4½,0)$ to the curve $y = \sqrt{x}$, and then find the point on the curve closest to A.

21. Find the point on the curve $y^2 - x^2 = 1$ that is closest to the point $(0,2)$.

22. A ladder is to reach over a fence h feet high to a wall w feet behind the fence. Find the length of the shortest ladder that may be used.

23. A manufacturer offers to deliver to a dealer 300 tables at $90 per table and to reduce the price per table on the entire order by 25 cents for each additional table over 300. Find the dollar total involved in the largest possible transaction between the manufacturer and the dealer under these circumstances.

24. A manufacturer can make a profit of $20 on each item if not more than 800 items are produced each week. The profit decreases 2 cents per item over 800. How many items should the manufacturer produce per week in order to have the greatest profit?

25. A school-sponsored trip will cost $15 per student if not more than 150 students make the trip; however, the cost per student will be reduced 5 cents for each student in excess of 150. How many students should take the trip in order for the school to receive the largest gross income?

26. Solve Exercise 25 if the reduction per student in excess of 150 is 7 cents.

27. Prove by the method of this section that the shortest distance from the point $P_1(x_1,y_1)$ to the line l, having the equation $Ax + By + C = 0$, is $|Ax_1 + By_1 + C|/\sqrt{A^2 + B^2}$. HINT: If s is the number of units in the distance from P_1 to a point $P(x,y)$ on l, then s will be an absolute maximum when s^2 is an absolute maximum.

(8.9)   Concavity and points of inflection

Figure 8.9.1 shows a sketch of the graph of a function f whose first and second derivatives exist on the closed interval $[x_1,x_7]$. Since both f and f' are differentiable there, f and f' are continuous on $[x_1,x_7]$.

If we consider a point P moving along the graph of Figure 8.9.1 from A to G,

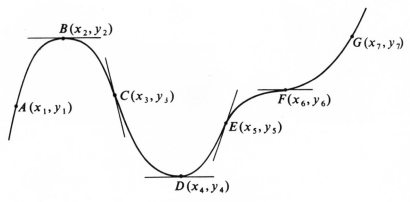

Figure 8.9.1

then the position of P varies as we increase x from x_1 to x_7. As P moves along the graph from A to B, the slope of the tangent line to the graph is positive and is decreasing; that is, the tangent line is turning clockwise, and the graph lies below its tangent line. When the point P is at B, the slope of the tangent line is zero and is still decreasing. As P moves along the graph from B to C, the slope of the tangent line is negative and is still decreasing; the tangent line is still turning clockwise, and the graph is below its tangent line. We say that the graph is *concave downward* from A to C. As P moves along the graph from C to D, the slope of the tangent line is negative and is increasing; that is, the tangent line is turning counterclockwise, and the graph is above its tangent line. At D, the slope of the tangent line is zero and is still increasing. From D to E, the slope of the tangent line is positive and increasing; the tangent line is still turning counterclockwise, and the graph is above its tangent line. We say that the graph is *concave upward* from C to E. At the point C, the graph changes from concave downward to concave upward. Point C is called a *point of inflection*. We have the following definitions.

8.9.1 DEFINITION   The graph of a function f is said to be *concave upward* at the point $(c, f(c))$ if $f'(c)$ exists and if there is an open interval I containing c such that for all values of $x \neq c$ in I the point $(x, f(x))$ on the graph is above the tangent line to the graph at $(c, f(c))$.

8.9.2 DEFINITION   The graph of a function f is said to be *concave downward* at the point $(c, f(c))$ if $f'(c)$ exists and if there is an open interval I containing c such that for all values of $x \neq c$ in I the point $(x, f(x))$ on the graph is below the tangent line to the graph at $(c, f(c))$.

Figure 8.9.2 shows a sketch of a portion of the graph of a function f that is concave upward at the point $(c, f(c))$, and Fig. 8.9.3 shows a sketch of a portion of the graph of a function f that is concave downward at the point $(c, f(c))$.

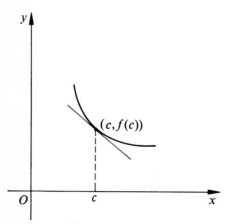

Figure 8.9.2

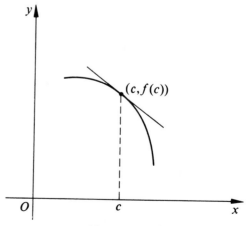

Figure 8.9.3

The graph of the function f of Fig. 8.9.1 is concave downward at all points $(x, f(x))$ for which x is in either of the following open intervals: (x_1, x_3) or (x_5, x_6). Similarly the graph of the function f in Fig. 8.9.1 is concave upward at all points $(x, f(x))$ for which x is in either (x_3, x_5) or (x_6, x_7). The following theorem gives us a test for concavity.

8.9.3 THEOREM   Let f be a function which is differentiable on some open interval containing c. Then,

    (i)   the graph of f is concave upward at $(c, f(c))$ if $f''(c) > 0$

    (ii) the graph of f is concave downward at $(c, f(c))$ if $f''(c) < 0$

Proof of (i):

$$f''(c) = \lim_{x \to c} \frac{f'(x) - f'(c)}{x - c}$$

Since $f''(c) > 0$,

$$\lim_{x \to c} \frac{f'(x) - f'(c)}{x - c} > 0$$

Then, by Theorem 4.6.1, there is an open interval I containing c such that

(1) $$\frac{f'(x) - f'(c)}{x - c} > 0$$

for every $x \neq c$ in I.

Now consider the tangent line to the graph of f at the point $(c, f(c))$. An equation of this tangent line is

$$y - f(c) = f'(c)(x - c)$$

    or

(2) $$y = f(c) + f'(c)(x - c)$$

Let x be a number in the interval I such that $x \neq c$, and let Q be the point on the graph of f whose abscissa is x. Through Q draw a line parallel to the y axis, and let T be the point of intersection of this line with the tangent line (see Fig. 8.9.4).

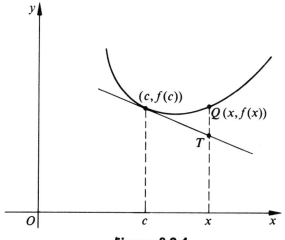

Figure 8.9.4

In order to prove that the graph of f is concave upward at $(c, f(c))$, we must show that the point Q is above the point T or, equivalently, that the directed distance $\overline{TQ} > 0$ for all values of $x \neq c$ in I. $\overline{TQ} =$ the ordinate of Q minus the ordinate of T. The ordinate of Q is $f(x)$, and the ordinate of T is obtained from equation (2), so that we have

$$\overline{TQ} = f(x) - [f(c) + f'(c)(x - c)]$$

or

(3) $$\overline{TQ} = [f(x) - f(c)] - f'(c)(x - c)$$

From the mean-value theorem, there exists some number d between x and c such that

$$f'(d) = \frac{f(x) - f(c)}{x - c}$$

or

(4) $$f(x) - f(c) = f'(d)(x - c) \qquad \text{for some } d \text{ between } x \text{ and } c$$

Substituting from equation (4) into (3), we have

$$\overline{TQ} = f'(d)(x - c) - f'(c)(x - c)$$

or

(5) $$\overline{TQ} = (x - c)[f'(d) - f'(c)]$$

Since d is between x and c, d is in the interval I, and so by taking $x = d$ in inequality (1), we obtain

(6) $$\frac{f'(d) - f'(c)}{d - c} > 0$$

In order to show that $\overline{TQ} > 0$, we shall show that both of the factors on the right-hand side of equation (5) have the same sign. If $(x - c) > 0$, then $x > c$, and since d is between x and c, then $d > c$; therefore, from inequality (6), $[f'(d) - f'(c)] > 0$. If $(x - c) < 0$, then $x < c$, and so $d < c$; therefore, from (6), $[f'(d) - f'(c)] < 0$. We may conclude that $(x - c)$ and $[f'(d) - f'(c)]$ have the same sign; therefore $\overline{TQ}$ is a positive number. Thus the graph of f is concave upward at $(c, f(c))$, which is what we wished to prove.

The proof of part (ii) is similar and is left for the reader. (See Exercise 18 below.)

The converse of Theorem 8.9.3 is not true. For example, if f is the function defined by $f(x) = x^4$, the graph of f is concave upward at the point $(0,0)$ but $f''(0) = 0$ (see Fig. 8.7.1). Accordingly, a sufficient condition for the graph of a function f to be concave upward at the point $(c, f(c))$ is that $f''(c) > 0$, but this is not a necessary condition. Similarly, a sufficient — but not a necessary — condition that the graph of a function f be concave downward at the point $(c, f(c))$ is that $f''(c) < 0$.

If there is a point on the graph of a function at which the sense of concavity changes, then the graph crosses its tangent line at this point, as shown in Figs. 8.9.5, 8.9.6, and 8.9.7. Such a point is called a *point of inflection*.

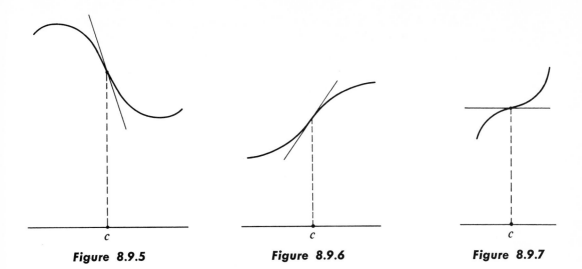

Figure 8.9.5   Figure 8.9.6   Figure 8.9.7

8.9.4 DEFINITION   The point $(c, f(c))$ is a *point of inflection* of the graph of the function f if there exists an open interval I containing c such that if x is in I, then either

(i) $f''(x) < 0$ if $x < c$ and $f''(x) > 0$ if $x > c$

or

(ii) $f''(x) > 0$ if $x < c$ and $f''(x) < 0$ if $x > c$

Figure 8.9.5 illustrates a point of inflection where condition (i) of the above definition holds; in this case, the graph is concave downward at points immediately to the left of the point of inflection, and the graph is concave upward at points immediately to the right of the point of inflection. Condition (ii) is illustrated in Fig. 8.9.6, where the sense of concavity changes from upward to downward at the point of inflection. Figure 8.9.7 is another illustration of condition (i), where the sense of concavity changes from downward to upward at the point of inflection. It should be noted that in Fig. 8.9.7 there is a horizontal tangent line at the point of inflection. For the graph in Fig. 8.9.1, there are points of inflection at C, E, and F.

Definition 8.9.4 says nothing about the value of the second derivative of f at a point of inflection. The following theorem states that if the second derivative exists at a point of inflection it must be zero there.

8.9.5 THEOREM   If the function f is differentiable on some open interval containing c, then if $(c, f(c))$ is a point of inflection of the graph of f and if $f''(c)$ exists, $f''(c) = 0$.

Proof: Let g be the function such that $g(x) = f'(x)$; then $g'(x) = f''(x)$. Since $(c, f(c))$ is a point of inflection of the graph of f, then $f''(x)$ changes sign at c and so $g'(x)$ changes sign at c. Therefore, by the first-derivative test (Theorem 8.6.4), g has a relative extremum at c, and c is a critical number of g. Since $g'(c) = f''(c)$ and since by hypothesis $f''(c)$ exists, it follows that $g'(c)$ exists. Therefore, $g'(c) = 0$ and $f''(c) = 0$, which is what we wanted to prove.

The converse of Theorem 8.9.5 is not true. That is, if the second derivative of a function is zero at a number c, it is not necessarily true that the graph of the function has a point of inflection at the point where $x = c$. This may be shown by again considering the function f defined by $f(x) = x^4$. $f'(x) = 4x^3$ and $f''(x) = 12x^2$. Further, $f''(0) = 0$; but since $f''(x) > 0$ if $x < 0$ and $f''(x) > 0$ if $x > 0$, the graph is concave upward at points on the graph immediately to the left of $(0,0)$ and at points immediately to the right of $(0,0)$. Consequently, $(0,0)$ is not a point of inflection. Previously we showed that this function f has a relative minimum value at zero and that the graph is concave upward at the point $(0,0)$ (see Fig. 8.7.1).

The graph of a function may have a point of inflection at a point, and the second derivative may fail to exist there. For example, if f is the function defined by $f(x) = x^{1/3}$, then

$$f'(x) = \frac{1}{3} x^{-2/3} \quad \text{and} \quad f''(x) = -\frac{2}{9} x^{-5/3}$$

$f''(0)$ does not exist; but if $x < 0$, $f''(x) > 0$, and if $x > 0$, $f''(x) < 0$. Hence f has a point of inflection at $(0,0)$. A sketch of the graph of this function is shown in Fig. 8.9.8. Note that for this function $f'(0)$ also fails to exist. The tangent line to the graph at $(0,0)$ is the y axis.

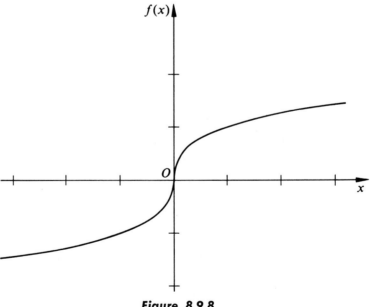

Figure 8.9.8

In drawing a sketch of a graph having points of inflection, it is helpful to draw a segment of the tangent line at a point of inflection. Such a tangent line is called an *inflectional tangent*.

EXAMPLE 1: For the function in Example 1 of Sec. 8.6, find the points of inflection of the graph of the function, and determine where the graph is concave upward and where it is concave downward.

Solution: $f(x) = x^3 - 6x^2 + 9x + 1$

$f'(x) = 3x^2 - 12x + 9$

$f''(x) = 6x - 12$

$f''(x)$ exists for all values of x, so that the only possible point of inflection is where $x = 2$. To determine whether there is a point of inflection at $x = 2$, we must check to see if $f''(x)$ changes sign; at the same time, we determine the concavity of the graph for the respective intervals. The results are summarized in Table 8.9.1.

Table 8.9.1

	$f(x)$	$f'(x)$	$f''(x)$	Conclusion
$-\infty < x < 2$			$-$	graph is concave downward
$x = 2$	3	-3	0	graph has a point of inflection
$2 < x < +\infty$			$+$	graph is concave upward

In Sec. 8.6 we showed that f has a relative maximum value at 1 and a relative minimum value at 3. A sketch of the graph showing a segment of the inflectional tangent is shown in Fig. 8.9.9.

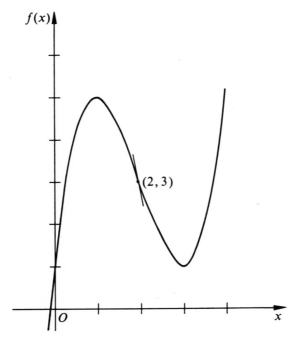

Figure 8.9.9

Exercises 8.9

In Exercises 1 through 8, determine where the graphs of the given functions are concave upward and where they are concave downward, and find the points of inflection if there are any.

1. $f(x) = x^3 + 9x$

2. $g(x) = x^3 + 3x^2 - 3x - 3$

3. $F(x) = x^4 - 8x^3 + 24x^2$

4. $f(x) = 16x^4 + 32x^3 + 24x^2 - 5x - 20$

5. $g(x) = \dfrac{x}{x^2 - 1}$ ⁣   7. $f(x) = (x - 2)^{1/5}$

6. $G(x) = \dfrac{2x}{(x^2 + 4)^{3/2}}$ ⁣   8. $F(x) = (2x - 6)^{3/2} + 1$

9. If $f(x) = ax^3 + bx^2$, determine a and b so that the graph of f will have a point of inflection at (1,2).

10. If $f(x) = ax^3 + bx^2 + cx$, determine a, b, and c so that the graph of f will have a point of inflection at (1,2) and so that the slope of the inflectional tangent there will be -2.

11. If $f(x) = ax^3 + bx^2 + cx + d$, determine a, b, c, and d so that f will have a relative extremum at (0,3) and so that the graph of f will have a point of inflection at $(1, -1)$.

In Exercises 12 through 17, draw a sketch of a portion of the graph of the function f through the point where $x = c$ if the given conditions are satisfied. If the conditions are incomplete or inconsistent, explain. It is assumed that f is continuous on some open interval containing c.

12. $f'(x) > 0$ if $x < c$; $f'(x) < 0$ if $x > c$; $f''(x) > 0$ if $x < c$; $f''(x) > 0$ if $x > c$.

13. $f'(x) > 0$ if $x < c$; $f'(x) > 0$ if $x > c$; $f''(x) > 0$ if $x < c$; $f''(x) < 0$ if $x > c$.

14. $f''(c) = 0$; $f'(c) = 0$; $f''(x) > 0$ if $x < c$; $f''(x) > 0$ if $x > c$.

15. $f'(c) = 0$; $f'(x) > 0$ if $x < c$; $f''(x) > 0$ if $x > c$.

16. $f'(c) = 0$; $f'(x) < 0$ if $x < c$; $f''(x) > 0$ if $x > c$.

17. $f''(c) = 0$; $f'(c) = \frac{1}{2}$; $f''(x) > 0$ if $x < c$; $f''(x) < 0$ if $x > c$.

18. Prove Theorem 8.9.3(ii).

(8.10) **Applications to drawing the sketch of a graph of a function**

We shall now apply the discussions in Secs. 8.6, 8.7, and 8.9 to drawing a sketch of the graph of a function. If we are given $f(x)$ and wish to draw a sketch of the graph of f, we proceed as follows. First, find $f'(x)$ and $f''(x)$. Then the critical numbers of f are the values of x in the domain of f for which either $f'(x)$ does not exist or $f'(x) = 0$. Next, apply the first-derivative test (Theorem 8.6.4) or the second-derivative test (Theorem 8.7.1), to determine whether we have at a critical number a relative maximum value, a relative minimum value, or neither. To determine the intervals on which f is increasing, we find the values of x for which $f'(x)$ is positive; to determine the intervals on which f is decreasing, we find the values of x for which $f'(x)$ is negative. In determining the intervals on which f is monotonic, we also check the critical numbers at which f does not have a relative extremum. The values of x for which $f''(x) = 0$ or $f''(x)$ does not exist give us the possible points of inflection, and we check to see if $f''(x)$ changes sign at each of these values of x to determine whether we actually have a point of inflection. The values of x for which $f''(x)$ is positive and those for which $f''(x)$ is negative will give us points at which the graph is concave upward and points at which the graph is concave downward. It is also helpful to find the slope of each inflectional tangent. It is suggested that all the information so obtained be incorporated into a table, as illustrated in the following examples.

EXAMPLE 1: Given $f(x) = x^3 - 3x^2 + 3$, find: the relative extrema of f; the points of inflection of the graph of f; the intervals on which f is increasing; the intervals on which f is decreasing; where the graph is concave upward; where the graph is concave downward; the slope of any inflectional tangent. Draw a sketch of the graph.

  Solution: $f'(x) = 3x^2 - 6x$; $f''(x) = 6x - 6$. Setting $f'(x) = 0$, we obtain $x = 0$ and $x = 2$. Setting $f''(x) = 0$, we obtain $x = 1$. In making the table, we shall consider the points at which $x = 0$, $x = 1$, and $x = 2$, and the intervals excluding these values of x:

$$-\infty < x < 0 \quad 0 < x < 1 \quad 1 < x < 2 \quad 2 < x < +\infty$$

Table 8.10.1

	$f(x)$	$f'(x)$	$f''(x)$	Conclusion
$-\infty < x < 0$		$+$	$-$	f is increasing; graph is concave downward
$x = 0$	3	0	$-$	f has a relative maximum value; graph is concave downward
$0 < x < 1$		$-$	$-$	f is decreasing; graph is concave downward
$x = 1$	1	-3	0	f is decreasing; graph has a point of inflection
$1 < x < 2$		$-$	$+$	f is decreasing; graph is concave upward
$x = 2$	-1	0	$+$	f has a relative minimum value; graph is concave upward
$2 < x < +\infty$		$+$	$+$	f is increasing; graph is concave upward

Using the information in Table 8.10.1 and plotting a few points, we obtain the sketch of the graph shown in Fig. 8.10.1.

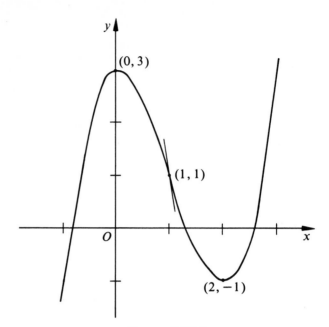

Figure 8.10.1

EXAMPLE 2: Given $f(x) = 5x^{2/3} - x^{5/3}$, find: the relative extrema of f; the points of inflection of the graph of f; the intervals on which f is increasing; the intervals on which f is decreasing; where the graph is concave upward; where the graph is concave downward; the slope of any inflectional tangent. Draw a sketch of the graph.

Solution:

$$f'(x) = \frac{10}{3}x^{-1/3} - \frac{5}{3}x^{2/3} \qquad f''(x) = -\frac{10}{9}x^{-4/3} - \frac{10}{9}x^{-1/3}$$

$f'(x)$ does not exist when $x = 0$. Setting $f'(x) = 0$, we obtain $x = 2$. Therefore, the critical numbers of f are 0 and 2. $f''(x)$ does not exist when $x = 0$. Setting $f''(x) = 0$, we obtain $x = -1$. In making the table, we consider the points at which $x = -1$, $x = 0$, and $x = 2$, and the following intervals:

$$-\infty < x < -1 \qquad -1 < x < 0 \qquad 0 < x < 2 \qquad 2 < x < +\infty$$

A sketch of the graph, drawn from the information in Table 8.10.2 and by plotting a few points, is shown in Fig. 8.10.2.

Table 8.10.2

	$f(x)$	$f'(x)$	$f''(x)$	Conclusion
$-\infty < x < -1$		$-$	$+$	f is decreasing; graph is concave upward
$x = -1$	6	-5	0	f is decreasing; graph has a point of inflection
$-1 < x < 0$		$-$	$-$	f is decreasing; graph is concave downward
$x = 0$	0	does not exist	does not exist	f has a relative minimum value
$0 < x < 2$		$+$	$-$	f is increasing; graph is concave downward
$x = 2$	$3\sqrt[3]{4} \approx 4.8$	0	$-$	f has a relative maximum value; graph is concave downward
$2 < x < +\infty$		$-$	$-$	f is decreasing; graph is concave downward

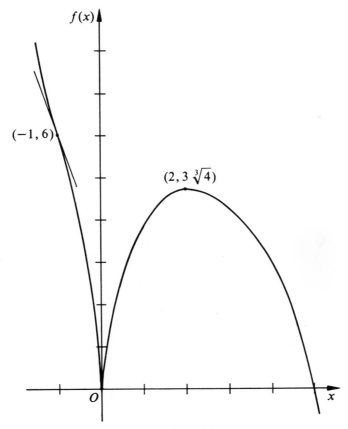

Figure **8.10.2**

For each of the following functions find: the relative extrema of f; the points of inflection of the graph of f; the intervals on which f is increasing; the intervals on which f is decreasing; where the graph is concave upward; where the graph is concave downward; the slope of any inflectional tangent. Draw a sketch of the graph.

1. $f(x) = 2x^3 - 6x + 1$

2. $f(x) = x^3 + x^2 - 5x$

3. $f(x) = x^4 - 2x^3$

4. $f(x) = 3x^4 + 2x^3$

5. $f(x) = x^3 + 5x^2 + 3x - 4$

6. $f(x) = 2x^3 - \frac{1}{2}x^2 - 12x + 1$

7. $f(x) = x^4 - 3x^3 + 3x^2 + 1$

8. $f(x) = x^4 - 4x^3 + 16x$

9. $f(x) = \frac{1}{4}x^4 - \frac{1}{3}x^3 - x^2 + 1$

10. $f(x) = 3x^4 + 4x^3 + 6x^2 - 4$

11. $f(x) = (x + 1)^3(x - 2)^2$

12. $f(x) = x^2(x + 4)^3$

13. $f(x) = 3x^5 + 5x^4$

14. $f(x) = 3x^5 + 5x^3$

15. $f(x) = 3x^{2/3} - 2x$

16. $f(x) = 3x^{1/3} - x$

17. $f(x) = x^{1/3} + 2x^{4/3}$

18. $f(x) = 3x^{4/3} - 4x$

19. $f(x) = 2 + (x - 3)^{1/3}$

20. $f(x) = 2 + (x - 3)^{4/3}$

21. $f(x) = 2 + (x - 3)^{5/3}$

22. $f(x) = 2 + (x - 3)^{2/3}$

23. $f(x) = 3 + (x + 1)^{6/5}$

24. $f(x) = 3 + (x + 1)^{7/5}$

25. $f(x) = x^2\sqrt{4 - x}$

26. $f(x) = x\sqrt{9 - x^2}$

27. $f(x) = \dfrac{(x + 1)^2}{x^2 + 1}$

28. $f(x) = \dfrac{9x}{x^2 + 9}$

29. $f(x) = (x + 2)\sqrt{-x}$

30. $f(x) = \dfrac{x - 1}{x^2 - 2x + 2}$

⑨ Antidifferentiation

(9.1) The inverse of differentiation

The reader is already familiar with *inverse operations*. Addition and subtraction are inverse operations; multiplication and division are also inverse operations, as well as raising to powers and extracting roots. The inverse operation of differentiation is called *antidifferentiation*.

9.1.1 DEFINITION A function F is called an *antiderivative* of a function f on an interval I if $F'(x) = f(x)$ for every value of x in I.

For example, if F is defined by $F(x) = 4x^3 + x^2 + 5$, then $F'(x) = 12x^2 + 2x$. Thus, if f is the function defined by $f(x) = 12x^2 + 2x$, we say that f is the derivative of F and that F is an antiderivative of f. If G is the function defined by $G(x) = 4x^3 + x^2 - 17$, then G is also an antiderivative of f, since $G'(x) = 12x^2 + 2x$. Actually any function whose function value is given by $4x^3 + x^2 + C$, where C is any constant, will be an antiderivative of f.

In general, if a function F is an antiderivative of a function f on an interval I and if G is defined by

$$G(x) = F(x) + C$$

where C is an arbitrary constant, then

$$G'(x) = F'(x) = f(x)$$

and G is also an antiderivative of f on the interval I.

In the next chapter, we shall state that if f is a continuous function on an interval I, then an antiderivative of f exists on I. We shall now proceed to prove that if F is any particular antiderivative of f on an interval I, then all possible antiderivatives of f on I are defined by $F(x) + C$, where C is an arbitrary constant. First we need two preliminary theorems.

9.1.2 THEOREM If f is a function such that $f'(x) = 0$ for all values of x in the closed interval $[a,b]$, then f is constant on $[a,b]$.

Proof: Let d be any number such that $a < d \leq b$. Since $f'(x) = 0$ for all values of x in the closed interval $[a,b]$, f is differentiable on the closed interval $[a,d]$ and, therefore, continuous on the closed interval $[a,d]$. Therefore, the hypothesis of the mean-value theorem is satisfied, and we may conclude that there is a number c, with $a < c < d$, such that

(1) $$f'(c) = \frac{f(d) - f(a)}{d - a}$$

But since $f'(x) = 0$ for all x in the interval $[a,d]$, we have $f'(c) = 0$, and from equation (1) it follows that

(2) $$f(d) = f(a)$$

Since d is any number such that $a < d \leq b$, equation (2) says that f has the same value at any point of the interval $[a,b]$ that it has at the left end point of the interval. Hence f is constant on $[a,b]$, which is what we wished to prove.

9.1.3 THEOREM If f and g are two functions such that $f'(x) = g'(x)$ for all values of x in the closed interval $[a,b]$, then there is a constant K such that

$$f(x) = g(x) + K \qquad \text{for all } x \text{ in } [a,b]$$

Proof: Let h be the function defined on $[a,b]$ by

$$h(x) = f(x) - g(x)$$

so that for all values of x in $[a,b]$ we have

$$h'(x) = f'(x) - g'(x)$$

But, by hypothesis, $f'(x) = g'(x)$ for all values of x in $[a,b]$. Therefore,

$$h'(x) = 0 \qquad \text{for all values of } x \text{ in } [a,b]$$

Thus, Theorem 9.1.2 applies to the function h, and there is a constant K such that

$$h(x) = K \qquad \text{for all values of } x \text{ in } [a,b]$$

Replacing $h(x)$ by $[f(x) - g(x)]$, we have

$$f(x) = g(x) + K \qquad \text{for all values of } x \text{ in } [a,b]$$

and the theorem is proved.

We have, then, the next theorem, which follows immediately from Theorem 9.1.3.

9.1.4 THEOREM If F is any particular antiderivative of f on an interval I, then the most general antiderivative of f on I is given by

(3) $$F(x) + C$$

where C is an arbitrary constant, and all antiderivatives of f on I may be obtained from (3) by assigning particular values to C.

Proof: Let G be any antiderivative of f on I; then,

(4) $$G'(x) = f(x) \qquad \text{on } I$$

Since F is a particular antiderivative of f on I, we have

(5) $$F'(x) = f(x) \qquad \text{on } I$$

From equations (4) and (5), it follows that

$$G'(x) = F'(x) \qquad \text{on } I$$

Therefore, from Theorem 9.1.3, there is a constant K such that

$$G(x) = F(x) + K \qquad \text{for all } x \text{ in } I$$

Since G is any antiderivative of f on I, it follows that all antiderivatives of f on I may be obtained from $F(x) + C$, where C is an arbitrary constant. Hence, the theorem is proved.

If F is an antiderivative of f, then $F'(x) = f(x)$, and so

$$d(F(x)) = f(x)\,dx$$

Hence, we may call $F(x)$ an *antidifferential* of $f(x)\ dx$. *Antidifferentiation*, then, is the process of finding the most general antiderivative or antidifferential of a given function. The symbol

$$\int f$$

is used to denote any antiderivative of the function f, and we write

(6) $$\int f(x)\,dx = F(x) + C$$

where

(7) $$d(F(x)) = f(x)\,dx$$

From equations (6) and (7), we may write

(8) $$\int d(F(x)) = F(x) + C$$

Equation (8) says that when we antidifferentiate the differential of a function we obtain that function plus an arbitrary constant. So, we think of the $\int$ symbol for antidifferentiation as meaning that operation which is the inverse of the operation denoted by d for finding the differential.

Since antidifferentiation is the inverse operation of differentiation, we may obtain antidifferentiation formulas from differentiation formulas. We shall make use of the following formulas that may be proved from the corresponding formulas for differentials.

9.1.5 FORMULA 1 $\int dx = x + C.$

9.1.6 FORMULA 2 $\int af(x)\,dx = a \int f(x)\,dx$, where a is a constant.

Formula 2 states that to find an antiderivative of a constant times a function, first find an antiderivative of the function, and then multiply it by the constant.

9.1.7 FORMULA 3 $\int [f_1(x) + f_2(x)]\,dx = \int f_1(x)\,dx + \int f_2(x)\,dx.$

Formula 3 states that to find an antiderivative of the sum of two functions, find an antiderivative of each of the functions separately, and then add the results. It is understood that both functions must be defined on the same interval. Formula 3 may be extended to any finite number of functions. Combining this with Formula 2, we have Formula 4.

9.1.8 FORMULA 4 $\int [c_1 f_1(x) + c_2 f_2(x) + \cdots + c_n f_n(x)] \, dx =$
$$c_1 \int f_1(x) \, dx + c_2 \int f_2(x) \, dx + \cdots + c_n \int f_n(x) \, dx.$$

9.1.9 FORMULA 5 $\int x^n \, dx = x^{n+1}/(n + 1) + C$, if $n \neq -1$.

As stated above, these formulas follow from the corresponding formulas for finding the differential. Following is the proof of Formula 5:

$$d\left(\frac{x^{n+1}}{n + 1} + C\right) = \frac{(n + 1)x^n}{n + 1} \, dx$$
$$= x^n \, dx$$

Application of the above formulas is illustrated in the following examples.

EXAMPLE 1: Evaluate $\int (3x + 5) \, dx$.
 Solution:

$$\int (3x + 5) \, dx = 3 \int x \, dx + 5 \int dx \qquad \text{by Formula 4}$$
$$= 3\left(\frac{x^2}{2} + C_1\right) + 5(x + C_2) \qquad \text{by Formulas 5 and 1}$$
$$= \frac{3}{2}x^2 + 5x + 3C_1 + 5C_2$$

Since $3C_1 + 5C_2$ is an arbitrary constant, we may call it C, and we have for our answer

$$\frac{3}{2}x^2 + 5x + C$$

EXAMPLE 2: Evaluate $\int \sqrt[3]{x^2} \, dx$.
 Solution:

$$\int \sqrt[3]{x^2} \, dx = \int x^{2/3} \, dx$$
$$= \frac{x^{2/3+1}}{\frac{2}{3} + 1} + C \qquad \text{from Formula 5}$$
$$= \frac{3}{5}x^{5/3} + C$$

Many antiderivatives cannot be found directly by applying formulas. However, sometimes it is possible to find an antiderivative by the formulas after changing the variable. For example, suppose that we wished to find

(9) $$\int 2x\sqrt{1 + x^2} \, dx$$

If we make the substitution $u = 1 + x^2$, then $du = 2x\,dx$, and (9) becomes

$$\int u^{1/2}\,du$$

which by Formula 5 gives us

$$\frac{2}{3}u^{3/2} + C$$

Then, replacing u by $(1 + x^2)$, we have as our result

$$\frac{2}{3}(1 + x^2)^{3/2} + C$$

Justification of this procedure is provided by the following theorem, which is analogous to the chain rule for differentiation, and hence may be called the *chain rule for antidifferentiation*.

9.1.10 THEOREM (*Chain Rule for Antidifferentiation*)   Let g be a differentiable function of x, and let the range of g be an interval I. Suppose that f is a function defined on I and that F is an antiderivative of f on I. Then if $u = g(x)$,

$$\int f(g(x))g'(x)\,dx = \int f(u)\,du = F(u) + C = F(g(x)) + C$$

Proof: Since $u = g(x)$, then u is in I, and since F is an antiderivative of f on I, we have

(10)
$$\frac{dF(u)}{du} = f(u)$$

and

(11)
$$\int f(u)\,du = F(u) + C$$

We also have

(12)
$$\frac{dF(g(x))}{dx} = \frac{dF(u)}{dx}$$

Applying the chain rule for differentiation to the right-hand side of equation (12), we obtain

(13)
$$\frac{dF(g(x))}{dx} = \frac{dF(u)}{du} \cdot \frac{du}{dx}$$

Substituting from equation (10) into (13) gives us

(14)
$$\frac{dF(g(x))}{dx} = f(u) \cdot \frac{du}{dx}$$

Since $u = g(x)$, from equation (14) we have

$$\frac{dF(g(x))}{dx} = f(g(x)) \cdot g'(x)$$

from which we conclude that

(15)
$$\int f(g(x)) \cdot g'(x)\,dx = F(g(x)) + C$$

Since $u = g(x)$, we have

(16) $$F(g(x)) + C = F(u) + C$$

Therefore, from (11), (15), and (16), we have

$$\int f(g(x))g'(x)\, dx = \int f(u)\, du = F(u) + C = F(g(x)) + C$$

which is what we wished to prove.

As a particular case of Theorem 9.1.10, from Formula 5 we have the generalized power formula for antiderivatives, which we state as Formula 6.

9.1.11 FORMULA 6   If g is a differentiable function, then if $u = g(x)$,

$$\int [g(x)]^n g'(x)\, dx = \int u^n\, du = \frac{u^{n+1}}{n+1} + C = \frac{[g(x)]^{n+1}}{n+1} + C \qquad \text{where } n \neq -1$$

Examples 3, 4, and 5 illustrate the application of Formula 6.

EXAMPLE 3: Evaluate $\int \sqrt{3x+4}\, dx$.

Solution: To apply Formula 6, we make the substitution $u = 3x + 4$; then, $du = 3\, dx$, or $du/3 = dx$. So, we have

$$\int \sqrt{3x+4}\, dx = \int u^{1/2} \cdot \frac{du}{3} = \frac{1}{3}\int u^{1/2}\, du = \frac{1}{3} \cdot \frac{u^{3/2}}{3/2} + C$$

$$= \frac{2}{9}u^{3/2} + C = \frac{2}{9}(3x+4)^{3/2} + C$$

EXAMPLE 4: Evaluate $\int t(5 + 3t^2)^8\, dt$.

Solution: Let $u = 5 + 3t^2$; then $du = 6t\, dt$, or $du/6 = t\, dt$. Therefore,

$$\int t(5t + 3t^2)^8\, dt = \int u^8 \cdot \frac{du}{6} = \frac{1}{6} \cdot \frac{u^9}{9} + C = \frac{1}{54}(5 + 3t^2)^9 + C$$

EXAMPLE 5: Evaluate $\int x^2 \sqrt{1+x}\, dx$.

Solution: Let $v = \sqrt{1+x}$; then $v^2 = 1 + x$. Hence $x = v^2 - 1$, and $dx = 2v\, dv$. Making these substitutions, we have

$$\int x^2\sqrt{1+x}\, dx = \int (v^2 - 1)^2 \cdot v \cdot (2v\, dv)$$

$$= 2\int v^6\, dv - 4\int v^4\, dv + 2\int v^2\, dv$$

$$= \frac{2}{7}v^7 - \frac{4}{5}v^5 + \frac{2}{3}v^3 + C$$

$$= \frac{2}{7}(1+x)^{7/2} - \frac{4}{5}(1+x)^{5/2} + \frac{2}{3}(1+x)^{3/2} + C$$

The answers to each of the above examples may be checked by finding the derivative (or the differential) of the answer. In particular, in Example 4, we have

$$\int t(5 + 3t^2)^8\, dt = \frac{1}{54}(5 + 3t^2)^9 + C$$

Checking by differentiation gives us

$$D_t \left[\frac{1}{54}(5 + 3t^2)^9 \right] = \frac{1}{54} \cdot 9(5 + 3t^2)^8 \cdot 6t$$
$$= t(5 + 3t^2)^8$$

In Example 5, we have

$$\int x^2 \sqrt{1 + x} \, dx = \frac{2}{7}(1 + x)^{7/2} - \frac{4}{5}(1 + x)^{5/2} + \frac{2}{3}(1 + x)^{3/2} + C$$

Checking by differentiation gives us

$$D_x \left[\frac{2}{7}(1 + x)^{7/2} - \frac{4}{5}(1 + x)^{5/2} + \frac{2}{3}(1 + x)^{3/2} \right] = (1 + x)^{5/2} - 2(1 + x)^{3/2} + (1 + x)^{1/2}$$
$$= (1 + x)^{1/2}[(1 + x)^2 - 2(1 + x) + 1]$$
$$= (1 + x)^{1/2}[1 + 2x + x^2 - 2 - 2x + 1]$$
$$= x^2\sqrt{1 + x}$$

Exercises 9.1

In Exercises 1 through 26 find the most general antiderivative. In Exercises 1 through 10, check by finding the derivative of your answer.

1. $\int 3x^4 \, dx$

2. $\int (4x^3 - 3x^2 + 6x - 1) \, dx$

3. $\int (3 - 2t + t^2) \, dt$

4. $\int (ax^2 + bx + c) \, dx$

5. $\int \left(\frac{2}{x^3} + \frac{3}{x^2} + 5 \right) dx$

6. $\int \frac{y^4 + 2y^2 - 1}{\sqrt{y}} \, dy$

7. $\int \left(\sqrt{2x} - \frac{1}{\sqrt{2x}} \right) dx$

8. $\int \frac{27t^3 - 1}{\sqrt[3]{t}} \, dt$

9. $\int x^2\sqrt{x^3 - 1} \, dx$

10. $\int \sqrt[3]{(4 - x^2)^2} \, x \, dx$

11. $\int \frac{s \, ds}{\sqrt{3s^2 + 1}}$

12. $\int \sqrt{5r + 1} \, dr$

13. $\int \sqrt{1 + \frac{1}{2x}} \frac{dx}{x^2}$

14. $\int x^4\sqrt{3x^5 - 5} \, dx$

15. $\int x^2(4 - x^2)^3 \, dx$

16. $\int (x^2 - 4x + 4)^{4/3} \, dx$

17. $\int \frac{t \, dt}{\sqrt{t + 3}}$

18. $\int \frac{2r \, dr}{(1 - r)^{2/3}}$

19. $\int \sqrt{3 - x} \, x^2 \, dx$

20. $\int (x^3 + 3)^{1/4} x^5 \, dx$

21. $\int \frac{(x^2 + 2x) \, dx}{\sqrt{x^3 + 3x^2 + 1}}$

22. $\int \sqrt{3 + s} \, (s + 1)^2 \, ds$

23. $\int \frac{y + 3}{(3 - 2y)^{2/3}} \, dy$

24. $\int (2t^2 + 1)^{1/3} t^3 \, dt$

25. $\int \frac{(r^{1/3} + 2)^4}{\sqrt[3]{r^2}} \, dr$

26. $\int \left(t + \frac{1}{t} \right)^{3/2} \left(\frac{t^2 - 1}{t^2} \right) dt$

27. Evaluate $\int (2x + 1)^3 \, dx$ by two methods: (*a*) expand $(2x + 1)^3$ by the binomial theorem, and apply Formulas 1, 4, and 5; (*b*) make the substitution $u = 2x + 1$. Explain the difference in appearance of the answers obtained in (*a*) and (*b*).

28. Evaluate $\int \sqrt{x - 1} \, x^2 \, dx$ by two methods: (*a*) make the substitution $u = x - 1$; (*b*) make the substitution $v = \sqrt{x - 1}$. Compare the answers obtained in (*a*) and (*b*).

(9.2) Differential equations with variables separable

If F is a function defined by the equation

(1) $$y = F(x)$$

and f is the derivative of F, then

(2) $$\frac{dy}{dx} = f(x)$$

and F is an antiderivative of f.

If we multiply both sides of equation (2) by dx, we obtain

(3) $$dy = f(x) \, dx$$

Equations (2) and (3) are very simple types of *differential equations*. They are differential equations of the *first order*, in which the variables are separable. In order to solve equation (3), we must find all functions G for which $y = G(x)$, so that the equation will be satisfied. So, if F is an antiderivative of f, all functions G will be defined by $G(x) = F(x) + C$, where C is an arbitrary constant. That is, if $dF(x) = f(x) \, dx$, then the complete solution of equation (3) is given by

(4) $$y = F(x) + C$$

Equation (4) represents a family of functions depending upon an arbitrary constant C. This is called a *one-parameter family*. The graphs of these functions form a one-parameter family of curves in the plane. Through any particular point (x_1, y_1), there passes just one curve of the family. The value of C corresponding to the curve through (x_1, y_1) is found by substituting x_1 and y_1 for x and y in equation (4) and solving for C, as is illustrated in the following example.

EXAMPLE 1: Find all solutions of the differential equation

$$dy = 2x \, dx$$

and then find the particular solution for which $y = 6$ when $x = 2$.

Solution: We antidifferentiate both sides of the equation, giving us

$$\int dy = \int 2x \, dx$$

The most general antidifferential of dy is $(y + C_1)$, and the most general anti-differential of $2x\,dx$ is $(x^2 + C_2)$. So, we have

$$y + C_1 = x^2 + C_2$$

Since $(C_2 - C_1)$ is an arbitrary constant if C_2 and C_1 are, we may replace $(C_2 - C_1)$ by C, thereby obtaining

(5) $$y = x^2 + C$$

which is the complete solution of the given differential equation.

Equation (5) represents a one-parameter family of functions. In Fig. 9.2.1, we have sketches of the graphs of the functions corresponding to $C = -4$, $C = -1$, $C = 0$, $C = 1$, and $C = 2$.

To find the particular solution for which $y = 6$ when $x = 2$, we substitute

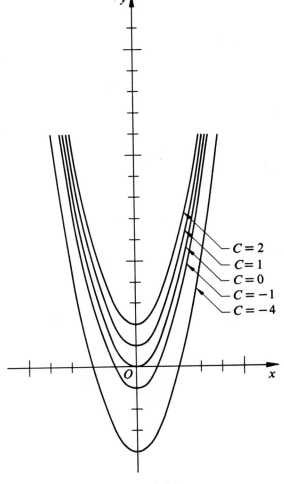

Figure 9.2.1

these values in equation (5) and solve for C, giving us $6 = 4 + C$, or $C = 2$. Substituting this value of C in (5), we get

$$y = x^2 + 2$$

which is the particular solution desired.

Another type of differential equation is

(6)
$$\frac{d^2y}{dx^2} = f(x)$$

Equation (6) is a differential equation of the *second order*. Two successive antidifferentiations are necessary to solve equation (6), and two arbitrary constants will occur in the complete solution. The complete solution of equation (6) therefore represents a *two-parameter family* of functions, and the graphs of these functions form a two-parameter family of curves in the plane.

EXAMPLE 2: Find the complete solution of the differential equation

$$\frac{d^2y}{dx^2} = 4x + 3$$

Solution: Since $d^2y/dx^2 = dy'/dx$, we may write the given equation as

$$\frac{dy'}{dx} = 4x + 3$$

Multiplying both sides of the above equation by dx, we obtain

$$dy' = (4x + 3)\,dx$$

Antidifferentiating both sides, we have

$$\int dy' = \int (4x + 3)\,dx$$

from which we get

$$y' = 2x^2 + 3x + C_1$$

Since $y' = dy/dx$, we make this substitution in the above equation and get

$$\frac{dy}{dx} = 2x^2 + 3x + C_1$$

Multiplying both sides by dx, we get

$$dy = (2x^2 + 3x + C_1)\,dx$$

Antidifferentiating both sides, we obtain

$$\int dy = \int (2x^2 + 3x + C_1)\,dx$$

which gives us

$$y = \frac{2}{3}x^3 + \frac{3}{2}x^2 + C_1x + C_2$$

which is the complete solution.

EXAMPLE 3: Find the particular solution of the differential equation in Example 2 for which $y = 2$ and $y' = -3$ when $x = 1$.

Solution: Since $y' = 2x^2 + 3x + C_1$, we substitute -3 for y' and 1 for x, giving us $-3 = 2 + 3 + C_1$, or $C_1 = -8$. Substituting this value of C_1 into the complete solution, we have

$$y = \frac{2}{3}x^3 + \frac{3}{2}x^2 - 8x + C_2$$

Since $y = 2$ when $x = 1$, we substitute these values in the above equation and get $2 = 2/3 + 3/2 - 8 + C_2$, from which we obtain $C_2 = 47/6$. The particular solution desired, then, is

$$y = \frac{2}{3}x^3 + \frac{3}{2}x^2 - 8x + \frac{47}{6}$$

A more general type of differential equation of the first order is of the form

(7) $$\frac{dy}{dx} = \frac{f(x)}{g(y)}$$

For such equations, we may separate the variables by multiplying both sides of the equation by $g(y)\, dx$, and thus equation (7) may be written as

$$g(y)\, dy = f(x)\, dx$$

The following example gives us an equation of this type.

EXAMPLE 4: The slope of the tangent line to a curve at any point (x,y) on the curve is equal to $3x^2y^2$. Find an equation of the curve if it contains the point (2,1).

Solution: Since the slope of the tangent line to a curve at any point (x,y) is the value of the derivative at that point, we have

$$\frac{dy}{dx} = 3x^2y^2$$

This is a first-order differential equation, in which the variables may be separated, and we have

$$\frac{dy}{y^2} = 3x^2\, dx$$

Antidifferentiating both sides, we have

$$\int y^{-2}\, dy = \int 3x^2\, dx$$

from which we obtain

$$-\frac{1}{y} = x^3 + C$$

This is an equation of a one-parameter family of curves. To find the particular curve of this family which contains the point (2,1), we substitute 2 for x and 1 for y, which gives us $-1 = 8 + C$, from which we obtain $C = -9$. Therefore, the required curve has the equation

$$-\frac{1}{y} = x^3 - 9$$

EXAMPLE 5: A projectile is thrown vertically upward from the ground with an intitial velocity of 128 ft/sec. If the only force considered is that due to the acceleration of gravity, which is 32 ft/sec² and which is directed downward, find how high the projectile will rise and the speed with which it will strike the ground. Also, find how long it will take for the projectile to strike the ground.

Solution: The motion of the particle is illustrated in Fig. 9.2.2.

Let t = the number of seconds in the time that has elapsed since the projectile was fired

s = the number of feet in the distance of the projectile from the ground at t sec of time

v = the number of feet per second in the velocity of the projectile at t sec of time

Then $|v|$ = the number of feet per second in the speed of the projectile at t sec of time.

The projectile will be at its highest point when the velocity is zero. Let $\bar{s}$ be the particular value of s when $v = 0$. When the projectile strikes the ground, $s = 0$. Let $\bar{t}$ and $\bar{v}$ be the particular values of t and v when $s = 0$, and $t \neq 0$. Table 9.2.1 is a table of *boundary conditions* for this problem.

Table 9.2.1

t	0		$\bar{t}$
s	0	$\bar{s}$	0
v	128	0	$\bar{v}$

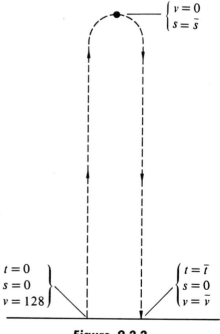

Figure 9.2.2

The positive direction of the projectile from the starting point will be taken as upward. Since the only acceleration is that due to gravity, which is in the downward direction, the acceleration has a constant value of -32. Since the acceleration is the derivative of the velocity with respect to time, we have

$$\frac{dv}{dt} = -32$$

Multiplying both sides of the above differential equation by dt, we obtain

$$dv = -32\, dt$$

Antidifferentiating both sides of the above, we have

$$\int dv = \int -32\, dt$$

from which we obtain

$$v = -32t + C_1$$

Since $v = 128$ when $t = 0$, we substitute these values in the above and get $C_1 = 128$. Therefore, we have

(8) $$v = -32t + 128$$

Since the velocity is the derivative of the distance s with respect to the time t, then $v = ds/dt$, and so we have

$$\frac{ds}{dt} = -32t + 128$$

Multiplying both sides of the above differential equation by dt, we get

$$ds = (-32t + 128)\, dt$$

Antidifferentiating both sides gives us

$$\int ds = \int (-32t + 128)\, dt$$

from which we obtain

$$s = -16t^2 + 128t + C_2$$

Since $s = 0$ when $t = 0$, we get $C_2 = 0$. So, we have

$$s = -16t^2 + 128t$$

Substituting $\bar{t}$ for t and 0 for s, we get

$$0 = -16\bar{t}(\bar{t} - 8)$$

from which we obtain $\bar{t} = 0$ and $\bar{t} = 8$. However, the value 0 occurs when the projectile is fired, so that we conclude that it takes 8 sec for the projectile to strike the ground.

To obtain $\bar{v}$, we substitute 8 for t and $\bar{v}$ for v in equation (8) which gives us $\bar{v} = (-32)(8) + 128$, from which we obtain $\bar{v} = -128$. So, $|\bar{v}| = 128$. Therefore, the projectile strikes the ground with a speed of 128 ft/sec.

In Exercises 1 through 8, find the complete solution of the given differential equation.

1. $\dfrac{dy}{dx} = 3x^2 + 2x - 7$

2. $\dfrac{dy}{dx} = (3x + 1)^3$

3. $\dfrac{dy}{dx} = 3xy^2$

4. $\dfrac{ds}{dt} = 5\sqrt{s}$

5. $\dfrac{dy}{dx} = \dfrac{3x\sqrt{1 + y^2}}{y}$

6. $\dfrac{dy}{dx} = \dfrac{\sqrt{x} + x}{\sqrt{y} - y}$

7. $\dfrac{d^2y}{dx^2} = 5x^2 + 1$

8. $\dfrac{d^2y}{dx^2} = \sqrt{x + 1}$

In Exercises 9 through 14, for each of the differential equations find the particular solution determined by the given values of the variables.

9. $\dfrac{dy}{dx} = x^2 - 2x - 4$; $y = -6$ when $x = 3$

10. $\dfrac{dy}{dx} = (x + 1)(x + 2)$; $y = -\dfrac{3}{2}$ when $x = -3$

11. $\dfrac{dx}{y} = \dfrac{4\,dy}{x}$; $y = -2$ when $x = 4$

12. $\dfrac{dy}{dx} = \dfrac{x}{4\sqrt{(1 + x^2)^3}}$; $y = 0$ when $x = 1$

13. $\dfrac{d^2y}{dx^2} = 1 - x^2$; $y = 1$ and $y' = -1$ when $x = 1$

14. $\dfrac{d^2y}{dx^2} = 2 - 4x$; $y = 2$ when $x = 0$; $y = 1$ when $x = -1$

15. The point (3,2) is on a curve, and at any point (x,y) on the curve the tangent line has a slope equal to $(2x - 3)$. Find an equation of the curve.

16. The slope of the tangent line at any point (x,y) on a curve is $3\sqrt{x}$. If the point (9,4) is on the curve, find an equation of the curve.

17. The points $(-1,3)$ and $(0,2)$ are on a curve, and at any point (x,y) on the curve $D_x^2y = 2 - 4x$. Find an equation of the curve.

18. An equation of the tangent line to a curve at the point (1,3) is $y = x + 2$. If at any point (x,y) on the curve, $D_x^2y = 6x$, find an equation of the curve.

19. At any point (x,y) on a curve, $d^2y/dx^2 = 1 - x^2$, and an equation of the tangent line to the curve at the point (1,1) is $y = 2 - x$. Find an equation of the curve.

20. At any point (x,y) on a curve, $D_x^3y = 2$, and (1,3) is a point of inflection at which the slope of the inflectional tangent is -2. Find an equation of the curve.

In Exercises 21 through 23, a particle is moving on a straight line; s is the number of feet in the directed distance of the particle from the origin at t sec of time, v is the number of feet per second in the velocity of the particle at t sec, and a is the number of feet per second per second in the acceleration of the particle at t sec.

21. $a = 5 - 2t$; $v = 2$ and $s = 0$ when $t = 0$. Express v and s in terms of t.

22. $a = 3t - t^2$; $v = 7/6$ and $s = 1$ when $t = 1$. Express v and s in terms of t.

23. $a = 800$; $v = 20$ when $s = 1$. Find an equation involving v and s. HINT:
$$a = \frac{dv}{dt} = \frac{dv}{ds}\frac{ds}{dt} = v\frac{dv}{ds}.$$

In Exercises 24 through 28, the only force considered is that due to the acceleration of gravity, which we take as 32 ft/sec^2 in the downward direction.

24. A stone is thrown vertically upward from the ground with an initial velocity of 20 ft/sec. How long will it take the stone to strike the ground, and with what speed will it strike? How long will the stone be going upward, and how high will it go?

25. A ball is dropped from the top of the Washington monument, which is 555 ft high. How long will it take the ball to reach the ground, and with what speed will it strike the ground?

26. A stone is thrown vertically upward from the top of a house 60 ft above the ground with an initial velocity of 40 ft/sec. At what time will the stone reach its greatest height, and what is its greatest height? How long will it take the stone to pass the top of the house on its way down, and what is its velocity at that instant? How long will it take the stone to strike the ground, and with what velocity does it strike the ground?

27. A stone is dropped from a balloon when it is 150 ft above the ground and rising at the rate of 10 ft/sec. How long will it take the stone to strike the ground, and with what speed does it strike?

28. A stone is thrown vertically upward with an initial velocity of 40 ft/sec from a point 20 ft above the ground. Express the velocity of the stone in terms of its distance from the starting point. What is the velocity of the stone when it is 36 ft from the ground and rising? HINT: See hint for Exercise 23 above.

29. If the driver of an automobile wishes to increase his speed from 20 miles/hr to 50 miles/hr while traveling a distance of 528 ft, what constant acceleration should he maintain?

30. If a ball is rolled across level ground with an initial velocity of 20 ft/sec and if the speed of the ball is decreasing at the rate of 6 ft/sec^2 due to friction, how far will the ball roll?

31. A ball is started upward from the bottom of an inclined plane with an initial velocity of 6 ft/sec. If there is a downward acceleration of 4 ft/sec^2, how far up the plane will the ball go before rolling down?

32. Suppose a bullet strikes the side of a house and comes to rest at a depth of 8 in. in a time of 1/100 sec after impact. Assuming that the acceleration of the bullet is constant, find the velocity of the bullet at impact.

10 The definite integral

(10.1)   The sigma notation

In this chapter we shall be concerned with the sums of many terms, and so we introduce a notation called the *sigma notation* to facilitate writing these sums. This notation involves the use of the symbol $\sum$, the capital sigma of the Greek alphabet, which corresponds to our letter S. Here are some examples of the sigma notation:

$$\sum_{i=1}^{5} i^2 = 1^2 + 2^2 + 3^2 + 4^2 + 5^2$$

$$\sum_{i=-2}^{2} (3i + 2) = [3(-2) + 2] + [3(-1) + 2] + [3 \cdot 0 + 2] + [3 \cdot 1 + 2] + [3 \cdot 2 + 2]$$

$$= (-4) + (-1) + 2 + 5 + 8$$

$$\sum_{j=1}^{n} j^3 = 1^3 + 2^3 + 3^3 + \cdots + n^3$$

$$\sum_{k=3}^{8} \frac{1}{k} = \frac{1}{3} + \frac{1}{4} + \frac{1}{5} + \frac{1}{6} + \frac{1}{7} + \frac{1}{8}$$

We have, in general,

(1) $$\sum_{i=m}^{n} F(i) = F(m) + F(m + 1) + F(m + 2) + \cdots + F(n)$$

where m and n are integers, and $m \leq n$.

The right-hand side of formula (1) consists of the sum of $(n - m + 1)$ terms, the first of which is obtained by replacing i by m in $F(i)$, the second by replacing i by $(m + 1)$ in $F(i)$, and so on, until the last term is obtained by replacing i by n in $F(i)$.

m is called the *lower limit* of the sum, and n is called the *upper limit*.

i is called the *index of summation*. It is a "dummy" symbol since any other letter can be used. For example,

$$\sum_{i=3}^{5} i^2 = 3^2 + 4^2 + 5^2$$

is the same as

$$\sum_{k=3}^{5} k^2 = 3^2 + 4^2 + 5^2$$

The following is an example of formula (1):

$$\sum_{i=3}^{6} \frac{i^2}{i+1} = \frac{3^2}{3+1} + \frac{4^2}{4+1} + \frac{5^2}{5+1} + \frac{6^2}{6+1}$$

Sometimes the terms of the sum involve subscripts, as illustrated in the following:

$$\sum_{i=1}^{n} A_i = A_1 + A_2 + \cdots + A_n$$

$$\sum_{k=4}^{9} k b_k = 4b_4 + 5b_5 + 6b_6 + 7b_7 + 8b_8 + 9b_9$$

$$\sum_{i=1}^{5} f(x_i)\,\Delta x = f(x_1)\,\Delta x + f(x_2)\,\Delta x + f(x_3)\,\Delta x + f(x_4)\,\Delta x + f(x_5)\,\Delta x$$

The following properties of the sigma notation will be useful, and they are easily proved.

10.1.1 PROPERTY 1 $\quad \sum_{i=1}^{n} c = cn$ where c is any constant.

The proof is left for the reader (see Exercise 9 below).

10.1.2 PROPERTY 2 $\quad \sum_{i=1}^{n} c \cdot F(i) = c \sum_{i=1}^{n} F(i)$ where c is any constant.

Proof:

$$\sum_{i=1}^{n} c \cdot F(i) = c \cdot F(1) + c \cdot F(2) + c \cdot F(3) + \cdots + c \cdot F(n)$$

$$= c[F(1) + F(2) + F(3) + \cdots + F(n)]$$

$$= c \sum_{i=1}^{n} F(i) \qquad\qquad\qquad \text{Q.E.D.}$$

10.1.3 PROPERTY 3 $\quad \sum_{i=1}^{n} [F(i) + G(i)] = \sum_{i=1}^{n} F(i) + \sum_{i=1}^{n} G(i).$

The proof is left for the reader (see Exercise 10 below). Property 3 may be extended to the sum of any number of functions.

10.1.4 PROPERTY 4 $\displaystyle\sum_{i=1}^{n} [F(i) - F(i-1)] = F(n) - F(0).$

Proof:

$$\sum_{i=1}^{n} [F(i) - F(i-1)] = [F(1) - F(0)] + [F(2) - F(1)] + [F(3) - F(2)] + \cdots$$
$$+ [F(n-1) - F(n-2)] + [F(n) - F(n-1)]$$
$$= -F(0) + [F(1) - F(1)] + [F(2) - F(2)] + \cdots$$
$$+ [F(n-1) - F(n-1)] + F(n)$$
$$= -F(0) + 0 + 0 + \cdots + 0 + F(n)$$
$$= F(n) - F(0) \qquad\qquad \text{Q.E.D.}$$

We shall also find useful the following formulas, which are numbered for future reference.

10.1.5 FORMULA 1 $\displaystyle\sum_{i=1}^{n} i = \frac{n(n+1)}{2}.$

10.1.6 FORMULA 2 $\displaystyle\sum_{i=1}^{n} i^2 = \frac{n(n+1)(2n+1)}{6}.$

10.1.7 FORMULA 3 $\displaystyle\sum_{i=1}^{n} i^3 = \frac{n^2(n+1)^2}{4}.$

10.1.8 FORMULA 4 $\displaystyle\sum_{i=1}^{n} i^4 = \frac{n(n+1)(6n^3 + 9n^2 + n - 1)}{30}.$

These formulas may be proved with or without using mathematical induction.

EXAMPLE 1: Prove Formula 1 without using mathematical induction.
Solution:

$$\sum_{i=1}^{n} i = 1 + 2 + 3 + \cdots + (n-1) + n$$

and

$$\sum_{i=1}^{n} i = n + (n-1) + (n-2) + \cdots + 2 + 1$$

We add these two equations term by term. The left side is

$$2 \sum_{i=1}^{n} i$$

(k+1)(k+2)(2k+3)

and on the right side we have n terms, each having the value $(n + 1)$. So, we have

$$2 \sum_{i=1}^{n} i = (n + 1) + (n + 1) + (n + 1) + \cdots + (n + 1) \qquad n \text{ terms}$$

$$= n(n + 1)$$

Therefore,

$$\sum_{i=1}^{n} i = \frac{n(n + 1)}{2} \qquad\qquad \text{Q.E.D.}$$

The proof of Formula 1 by mathematical induction is left for the reader. (See Exercise 11 below.)

EXAMPLE 2: Prove Formula 2 by mathematical induction.

Solution: We wish to prove that

$$\sum_{i=1}^{n} i^2 = \frac{n(n + 1)(2n + 1)}{6}$$

First, we verify the formula for $n = 1$. The left-hand side is then $\sum_{i=1}^{1} i^2 = 1$.

When $n = 1$, the right-hand side is $[1(1 + 1)(2 + 1)]/6 = (1 \cdot 2 \cdot 3)/6 = 1$. Therefore, the formula is true when $n = 1$. Now we assume the formula is true for $n = k$, where k is any positive integer; and with this assumption we wish to prove that the formula is also true for $n = k + 1$. If the formula is true for $n = k$, we have

$$(2) \qquad\qquad \sum_{i=1}^{k} i^2 = \frac{k(k + 1)(2k + 1)}{6}$$

When $n = k + 1$, we have

$$\sum_{i=1}^{k+1} i^2 = 1^2 + 2^2 + 3^2 + \cdots + k^2 + (k + 1)^2$$

$$= \sum_{i=1}^{k} i^2 + (k + 1)^2$$

$$= \frac{k(k + 1)(2k + 1)}{6} + (k + 1)^2 \qquad \text{by applying equation (2)}$$

$$= \frac{k(k + 1)(2k + 1) + 6(k + 1)^2}{6}$$

$$= \frac{(k + 1)[k(2k + 1) + 6(k + 1)]}{6}$$

$$= \frac{(k + 1)(2k^2 + 7k + 6)}{6}$$

$$= \frac{(k + 1)(k + 2)(2k + 3)}{6}$$

$$= \frac{(k + 1)[(k + 1) + 1][2(k + 1) + 1]}{6}$$

Therefore, the formula is true for $n = k + 1$. We have proved that the formula holds for $n = 1$, and we have also proved that when the formula holds for $n = k$, the formula also holds for $n = k + 1$. Therefore, we have proved that the formula holds when n is any positive integer.

A proof of Formula 2, analogous to the proof of Formula 1, without using mathematical induction is left for the reader. The proofs of Formulas 3 and 4 are also left to the reader (see Exercises 12 through 16 below).

EXAMPLE 3: Evaluate $\displaystyle\sum_{i=1}^{n} (4^i - 4^{i-1})$.

Solution: From Property 4, where $F(i) = 4^i$, we have

$$\sum_{i=1}^{n} (4^i - 4^{i-1}) = 4^n - 4^0$$

$$= 4^n - 1$$

EXAMPLE 4: Evaluate $\displaystyle\sum_{i=1}^{n} i(3i - 2)$ by using Properties 1 through 4 and Formulas 1 through 4.

Solution:

$$\sum_{i=1}^{n} i(3i - 2) = \sum_{i=1}^{n} (3i^2 - 2i)$$

$$= \sum_{i=1}^{n} (3i^2) + \sum_{i=1}^{n} (-2i) \qquad \text{by Property 3}$$

$$= 3 \sum_{i=1}^{n} i^2 - 2 \sum_{i=1}^{n} i \qquad \text{by Property 2}$$

$$= 3 \cdot \frac{n(n + 1)(2n + 1)}{6} - 2 \cdot \frac{n(n + 1)}{2} \qquad \text{by Formulas 2 and 1}$$

$$= \frac{2n^3 + 3n^2 + n - 2n^2 - 2n}{2}$$

$$= \frac{2n^3 + n^2 - n}{2}$$

Exercises 10.1

In Exercises 1 through 8, find the given sum.

1. $\displaystyle\sum_{i=1}^{6} (3i - 2)$

2. $\displaystyle\sum_{i=1}^{7} (i + 1)^2$

3. $\displaystyle\sum_{i=2}^{5} \frac{i}{i-1}$

6. $\displaystyle\sum_{i=0}^{3} \frac{1}{1+i^2}$

4. $\displaystyle\sum_{j=3}^{6} \frac{2}{j(j-2)}$

7. $\displaystyle\sum_{k=1}^{4} \frac{(-1)^{k+1}}{k}$

5. $\displaystyle\sum_{i=-2}^{3} 2^i$

8. $\displaystyle\sum_{k=-2}^{3} \frac{k}{k+3}$

9. Prove Property 1 (10.1.1).   10. Prove Property 3 (10.1.3).

11. Prove Formula 1 (10.1.5) by mathematical induction.

12. Prove Formula 2 (10.1.6) without using mathematical induction. HINT: $i^3 - (i-1)^3 = 3i^2 - 3i + 1$, so that

$$\sum_{i=1}^{n} [i^3 - (i-1)^3] = \sum_{i=1}^{n} (3i^2 - 3i + 1)$$

On the left side of the above equation, use Property 4; on the right side, use Properties 1, 2, and 3 and Formula 1.

13. Prove Formula 3 (10.1.7) without using mathematical induction. HINT: $i^4 - (i-1)^4 = 4i^3 - 6i^2 + 4i - 1$, and use a method similar to the one for Exercise 12.

14. Prove Formula 4 (10.1.8) without using mathematical induction (see hints for Exercises 12 and 13 above).

15. Prove Formula 3 (10.1.7) by mathematical induction.

16. Prove Formula 4 (10.1.8) by mathematical induction.

In Exercises 17 through 25, evaluate the indicated sum by using Properties 1 through 4 and Formulas 1 through 4.

17. $\displaystyle\sum_{i=1}^{25} 2i(i-1)$ *10,400*

21. $\displaystyle\sum_{k=1}^{100} \left[\frac{1}{k} - \frac{1}{k+1}\right]$

18. $\displaystyle\sum_{i=1}^{20} 3i(i^2+2)$

22. $\displaystyle\sum_{i=1}^{40} [\sqrt{2i+1} - \sqrt{2i-1}]$

19. $\displaystyle\sum_{i=1}^{n} (10^{i+1} - 10^i)$

23. $\displaystyle\sum_{i=1}^{n} 4i^2(i-2)$

20. $\displaystyle\sum_{k=1}^{n} (2^{k-1} - 2^k)$

24. $\displaystyle\sum_{i=1}^{n} 2i(1+i^2)$

25. $\displaystyle\sum_{k=1}^{n} [(3^{-k} - 3^k)^2 - (3^{k-1} + 3^{-k-1})^2]$

(10.2)   Area

The reader has an intuitive idea of what is meant by the area of certain geometrical figures; it is a number that in some way measures the size of the region enclosed by the figure. The area of a rectangle is the product of its length and width, and the area of a triangle is half the product of the lengths of the base and the altitude.

The area of a polygon may be defined as the sum of the areas of triangles into which it is decomposed, and it can be proved that the area thus obtained is independent of how the polygon is decomposed into triangles (see Fig. 10.2.1).

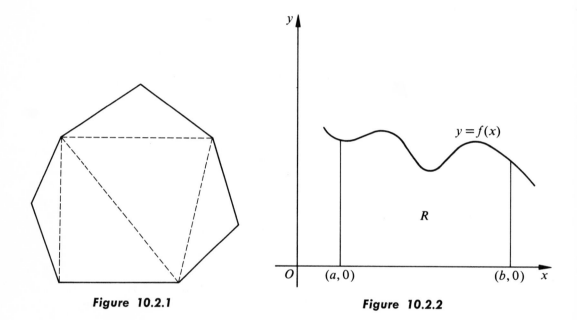

Figure 10.2.1   **Figure 10.2.2**

However, how do we define the area of a region in a plane if the region is bounded by a curve? Are we even certain that such a region has an area?

Let us consider a region R in the plane as shown in Fig. 10.2.2. R is the region bounded by the x axis, the lines $x = a$ and $x = b$, and the curve having the equation $y = f(x)$, where f is a function continuous on the closed interval $[a,b]$. For simplicity, we take $f(x) \geq 0$ for all x in $[a,b]$. We wish to assign a number A to be the measure of the area of R. We use a limiting process similar to the one used in defining the area of a circle: the area of a circle is defined as the limit of the areas of inscribed regular polygons as the number of sides increases without bound. Intuitively, we realize that, whatever number is chosen to represent the area A of region R, that number must be at least as great as the area of any polygonal region contained in R, and must be no greater than the area of any polygonal region containing R.

We shall first define a polygonal region contained in R. Divide the closed interval $[a,b]$ into n subintervals. For simplicity, we shall now take each of these subintervals as being of equal length, say, Δx. Therefore $\Delta x = (b - a)/n$. Denote the end points of these subintervals by $x_0, x_1, x_2, \ldots, x_{n-1}, x_n$, where $x_0 = a$, $x_1 = a + \Delta x, \ldots, x_i = a + i\,\Delta x, \ldots, x_{n-1} = a + (n-1)\,\Delta x, x_n = b$. Let the ith subinterval be denoted by $[x_{i-1}, x_i]$. Since f is continuous on the closed interval $[a,b]$, it is continuous on each closed subinterval. By the extreme-value theorem (8.2.9), there is a number in each subinterval for which f has an absolute minimum value. In the ith subinterval, let this number be c_i, so that $f(c_i)$ is the absolute minimum value of f on the subinterval $[x_{i-1}, x_i]$. Consider n

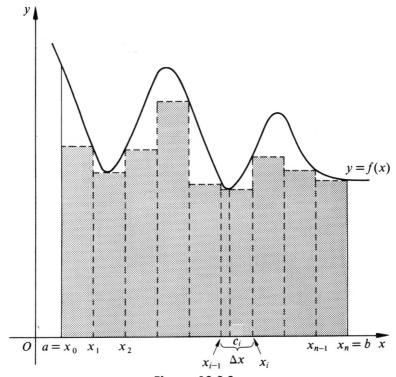

Figure 10.2.3

rectangles each having a width Δx and an altitude $f(c_i)$ (see Fig. 10.2.3). Let S_n be the sum of the areas of these n rectangles; then,

$$S_n = f(c_1)\,\Delta x + f(c_2)\,\Delta x + \cdots + f(c_i)\,\Delta x + \cdots + f(c_n)\,\Delta x$$

or, using the sigma notation,

(1)
$$S_n = \sum_{i=1}^{n} f(c_i)\,\Delta x$$

The summation on the right-hand side of equation (1) is the sum of the areas of n inscribed rectangles. Thus, however we define A, it must be such that

$$A \geq S_n$$

In Fig. 10.2.3 the shaded region has an area of S_n. Now, let n increase. Specifically, multiply n by 2, then the number of rectangles is doubled, and the width of each rectangle is halved. This is illustrated in Fig. 10.2.4, showing

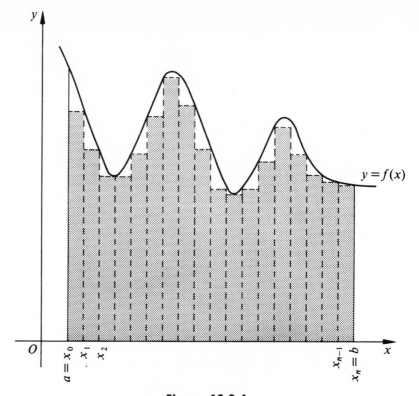

Figure 10.2.4

twice as many rectangles as Fig. 10.2.3. By comparing the two figures, the reader should notice that the shaded region in Fig. 10.2.4 appears to more nearly approximate the region R than that of Fig. 10.2.3. So the sum of the areas of the rectangles in Fig. 10.2.4 is closer to the number we wish to represent the area of R.

As n increases, it turns out that the values of S_n found from equation (1) will increase, and successive values of S_n will differ from each other by amounts that become arbitrarily small. This is proved in advanced calculus by a theorem which states that if f is continuous on $[a,b]$, then as n increases without bound, the value of S_n given by (1) approaches a limit. It is this limit that we shall take as the definition of the area of region R.

10.2.1 DEFINITION   Suppose that the function f is continuous on the closed interval $[a,b]$, with $f(x) \geq 0$ for all x in $[a,b]$, and that R is the region bounded by the curve $y = f(x)$, the x axis, and the lines $x = a$ and $x = b$. Divide the interval $[a,b]$ into n subintervals, each of width $\Delta x = (b - a)/n$, and denote the ith subinterval by $[x_{i-1}, x_i]$. Then, if $f(c_i)$ is the absolute minimum function value on the ith subinterval, the area A of region R is given by

$$(2) \qquad\qquad A = \lim_{n \to +\infty} \sum_{i=1}^{n} f(c_i)\, \Delta x$$

Equation (2) means that, for any $\epsilon > 0$, there is a number $N > 0$ such that

$$\left| \sum_{i=1}^{n} f(c_i)\, \Delta x - A \right| < \epsilon \qquad \text{whenever} \qquad n > N$$

and n is a positive integer.

We could take circumscribed rectangles instead of inscribed rectangles. In this case, we take as the altitudes of the rectangles the absolute maximum value of f on each subinterval. The existence of an absolute maximum value of f on each subinterval is guaranteed by the extreme-value theorem (8.2.9). The corresponding sums of the areas of the circumscribed rectangles will be at least as great as the area of the region R, and it can be shown that the limit of these sums as n increases without bound is exactly the same as the limit of the sum of the areas of the inscribed rectangles. This is also proved in advanced calculus. Thus, we could define the area A of the region R by

$$(3) \qquad\qquad A = \lim_{n \to +\infty} \sum_{i=1}^{n} f(d_i)\, \Delta x$$

where $f(d_i)$ is the absolute maximum value of f on $[x_{i-1}, x_i]$.

Actually, the altitude of the rectangle in the ith subinterval may be taken as the function value of any number in that subinterval, and the limit of the sum of the areas of the rectangles is the same no matter what numbers are selected. This is also proved in advanced calculus, and later in this chapter we shall extend our definition of the area of a region to be the limit of such a sum.

EXAMPLE 1: Find the area of the region bounded by the curve $y = x^2$, the x axis, and the line $x = 3$ by taking inscribed rectangles.

Solution: Figure 10.2.5 shows the region and the ith inscribed rectangle. We apply Definition 10.2.1. Divide the closed interval $[0,3]$ into n subintervals, each of width Δx: $x_0 = 0$, $x_1 = \Delta x$, $x_2 = 2\,\Delta x, \ldots, x_i = i\,\Delta x, \ldots, x_{n-1} = (n-1)\,\Delta x$, $x_n = 3$.

$$\Delta x = \frac{3 - 0}{n} = \frac{3}{n}$$

Since f is increasing on $[0,3]$, the absolute minimum value of f on the ith subinterval $[x_{i-1}, x_i]$ is $f(x_{i-1})$. Therefore, from equation (2),

$$(4) \qquad\qquad A = \lim_{n \to +\infty} \sum_{i=1}^{n} f(x_{i-1})\, \Delta x$$

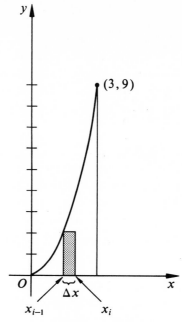

Figure 10.2.5

Since $x_{i-1} = (i - 1)\, \Delta x$ and $f(x) = x^2$, we have

$$f(x_{i-1}) = [(i - 1)\, \Delta x]^2$$

Therefore,

$$\sum_{i=1}^{n} f(x_{i-1})\, \Delta x = \sum_{i=1}^{n} (i - 1)^2 (\Delta x)^3$$

But $\Delta x = 3/n$, so that

$$\sum_{i=1}^{n} f(x_{i-1})\, \Delta x = \sum_{i=1}^{n} (i - 1)^2 \frac{27}{n^3} = \frac{27}{n^3} \sum_{i=1}^{n} (i - 1)^2$$

$$= \frac{27}{n^3} [0^2 + 1^2 + 2^2 + \cdots + (n - 1)^2]$$

Hence, we have

(5)
$$\sum_{i=1}^{n} f(x_{i-1})\, \Delta x = \frac{27}{n^3} \sum_{i=1}^{n-1} i^2$$

From Formula 2 (10.1.6), we have

$$\sum_{i=1}^{n} i^2 = \frac{n(n + 1)(2n + 1)}{6}$$

so that

(6)
$$\sum_{i=1}^{n-1} i^2 = \frac{(n - 1) \cdot n \cdot (2n - 1)}{6}$$

Substituting from (6) into (5), we obtain

$$\sum_{i=1}^{n} f(x_{i-1})\,\Delta x = \frac{27}{n^3}\cdot\frac{n(2n^2 - 3n + 1)}{6} = \frac{9}{2}\cdot\frac{2n^2 - 3n + 1}{n^2}$$

Then, from equation (4), we have

$$A = \lim_{n\to+\infty} \left[\frac{9}{2}\cdot\frac{2n^2 - 3n + 1}{n^2}\right] = \frac{9}{2}\cdot\lim_{n\to+\infty}\left(2 - \frac{3}{n} + \frac{1}{n^2}\right)$$

$$= \frac{9}{2}(2 - 0 + 0) = 9$$

Therefore, the area of the region is 9 square units.

EXAMPLE 2: Find the area of the region in Example 1 by taking circumscribed rectangles.

Solution: We take as the altitude of the ith rectangle the absolute maximum value of f on the ith subinterval $[x_{i-1}, x_i]$, which is $f(x_i)$. From equation (3), we have

(7) $$A = \lim_{n\to+\infty} \sum_{i=1}^{n} f(x_i)\,\Delta x$$

Since $x_i = i\,\Delta x$, then $f(x_i) = (i\,\Delta x)^2$, and so

$$\sum_{i=1}^{n} f(x_i)\,\Delta x = \sum_{i=1}^{n} i^2\,(\Delta x)^3 = \frac{27}{n^3}\sum_{i=1}^{n} i^2$$

$$= \frac{27}{n^3}\left[\frac{n(n + 1)(2n + 1)}{6}\right]$$

$$= \frac{9}{2}\cdot\frac{2n^2 + 3n + 1}{n^2}$$

Therefore, from equation (7), we obtain

$$A = \lim_{n\to+\infty} \frac{9}{2}\cdot\left(2 + \frac{3}{n} + \frac{1}{n^2}\right)$$

$$= 9 \qquad \text{as in Example 1}$$

Exercises 10.2

In Exercises 1 through 10, use the method of this section to find the area of the given region; use inscribed or circumscribed rectangles as indicated. For each exercise, draw a figure showing the region and the ith rectangle.

1. The region bounded by $y = x^2$, the x axis, and the line $x = 2$; inscribed rectangles.
2. The region in Exercise 1; circumscribed rectangles.
3. The region bounded by $y = 2x$, the x axis, and the lines $x = 1$ and $x = 4$; inscribed rectangles.

4. The region in Exercise 3; circumscribed rectangles.

⑤ The region bounded by $y = 4 - x^2$, the x axis, and the line $x = 1$; inscribed rectangles.

6. The region in Exercise 5; circumscribed rectangles.

7. The region bounded by $y = 3x^4$, the x axis, and the line $x = 1$; inscribed rectangles.

8. The region in Exercise 7; circumscribed rectangles.

9. The region bounded by $y = mx$, with $m > 0$, the x axis, and the lines $x = a$ and $x = b$, with $b > a > 0$; inscribed rectangles.

10. The region in Exercise 9; circumscribed rectangles.

In Exercises 11 through 14, find the area of the region by taking as the altitude of the ith rectangle $f(m_i)$, where m_i is the midpoint of the ith subinterval. HINT: $m_i = (x_i + x_{i-1})/2$.

11. The region in Example 1 of this section.

12. The region in Exercise 1.

13. The region in Exercise 3.

14. The region in Exercise 5.

(10.3) The definite integral

In the preceding section, the area of a region was defined as the following limit

$$(1) \qquad \lim_{n \to +\infty} \sum_{i=1}^{n} f(c_i) \, \Delta x$$

To lead up to this definition, we divided the closed interval $[a,b]$ into subintervals of equal length and then took c_i as the point in the ith subinterval for which f has an absolute minimum value. We also restricted the function values $f(x)$ to be nonnegative on $[a,b]$ and further required f to be continuous on $[a,b]$.

In order to define the definite integral, we need to consider a new kind of limiting process, of which the limit given in (1) is a special case.

Let f be a function defined on the closed interval $[a,b]$. Divide this interval into n subintervals by choosing any $(n - 1)$ intermediate points between a and b. Let $x_0 = a$ and $x_n = b$, and $x_1, x_2, \ldots, x_{n-1}$ be the intermediate points, so that

$$x_0 < x_1 < x_2 < \cdots < x_{n-1} < x_n$$

The points $x_0, x_1, x_2, \ldots, x_{n-1}, x_n$ are not necessarily equidistant. Let $\Delta_1 x$ be the length of the first subinterval, so that $\Delta_1 x = x_1 - x_0$; let $\Delta_2 x$ be the length of the second subinterval, so that $\Delta_2 x = x_2 - x_1$; and so forth, so that the length of the ith subinterval is $\Delta_i x$, and

$$\Delta_i x = x_i - x_{i-1}$$

A set of all such subintervals of the interval $[a,b]$ is called a *partition* of the

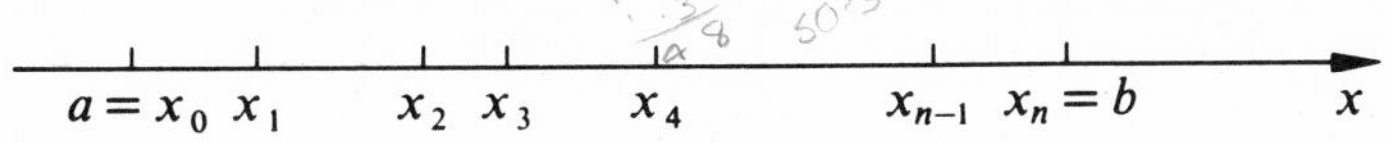

Figure 10.3.1

interval $[a,b]$. Let Δ be such a partition. Figure 10.3.1 illustrates one such partition Δ of $[a,b]$.

The partition Δ contains n subintervals. One of these subintervals is longest; however, there may be more than one such subinterval. The length of the longest subinterval of the partition Δ, called the *norm* of the partition, is denoted by $||\Delta||$.

Choose a point in each subinterval of the partition Δ:

Let ξ_1 be the point chosen in $[x_0,x_1]$, so that $x_0 \leq \xi_1 \leq x_1$

Let ξ_2 be the point chosen in $[x_1,x_2]$, so that $x_1 \leq \xi_2 \leq x_2$

and so forth, so that

ξ_i is the point chosen in $[x_{i-1},x_i]$, and $x_{i-1} \leq \xi_i \leq x_i$

Form the sum

$$f(\xi_1)\,\Delta_1 x + f(\xi_2)\,\Delta_2 x + \cdots + f(\xi_i)\,\Delta_i x + \cdots + f(\xi_n)\,\Delta_n x$$

$$\text{or} \qquad \sum_{i=1}^{n} f(\xi_i)\,\Delta_i x$$

Such a sum is called a *Riemann sum*.

EXAMPLE 1: Given $f(x) = 10 - x^2$, with $\frac{1}{4} \leq x \leq 3$, find the Riemann sum for the function f on $[\frac{1}{4},3]$ for the partition Δ: $x_0 = \frac{1}{4}$, $x_1 = 1$, $x_2 = 1\frac{1}{2}$, $x_3 = 1\frac{3}{4}$, $x_4 = 2\frac{1}{4}$, $x_5 = 3$, and $\xi_1 = \frac{1}{2}$, $\xi_2 = 1\frac{1}{4}$, $\xi_3 = 1\frac{3}{4}$, $\xi_4 = 2$, $\xi_5 = 2\frac{3}{4}$.

Draw a sketch of the graph of the function on $[\frac{1}{4},3]$, and show the rectangles whose areas are the terms of the Riemann sum.

Solution: Figure 10.3.2 shows a sketch of the graph and the five rectangles.

$$\sum_{i=1}^{5} f(\xi_i)\,\Delta_i x = f(\xi_1)\,\Delta_1 x + f(\xi_2)\,\Delta_2 x + f(\xi_3)\,\Delta_3 x + f(\xi_4)\,\Delta_4 x + f(\xi_5)\,\Delta_5 x$$

$$= f\left(\frac{1}{2}\right)\left(1 - \frac{1}{4}\right) + f\left(\frac{5}{4}\right)\left(1\frac{1}{2} - 1\right) + f\left(\frac{7}{4}\right)\left(1\frac{3}{4} - 1\frac{1}{2}\right)$$

$$+ f(2)\left(2\frac{1}{4} - 1\frac{3}{4}\right) + f\left(\frac{11}{4}\right)\left(3 - 2\frac{1}{4}\right)$$

$$= \left(9\frac{3}{4}\right)\left(\frac{3}{4}\right) + \left(8\frac{7}{16}\right)\left(\frac{1}{2}\right) + \left(6\frac{15}{16}\right)\left(\frac{1}{4}\right) + (6)\left(\frac{1}{2}\right) + \left(2\frac{7}{16}\right)\left(\frac{3}{4}\right)$$

$$= 18\frac{3}{32}$$

Since the function values $f(x)$ are not restricted to nonnegative values, some of the $f(\xi_i)$ could be negative. In such a case, the geometrical interpretation of the Riemann sum would be the sum of the areas of the rectangles lying above

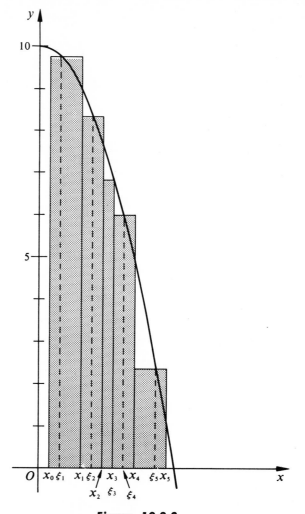

Figure 10.3.2

the x axis plus the negatives of the areas of the rectangles lying below the x axis. This situation is illustrated in Fig. 10.3.3. Here,

$$\sum_{i=1}^{10} f(\xi_i)\,\Delta_i x = A_1 + A_2 - A_3 - A_4 - A_5 + A_6 + A_7 - A_8 - A_9 - A_{10}$$

since $f(\xi_3)$, $f(\xi_4)$, $f(\xi_5)$, $f(\xi_8)$, $f(\xi_9)$, and $f(\xi_{10})$ are negative numbers.

We are now in a position to define what is meant by a function f being *integrable* on the closed interval $[a,b]$.

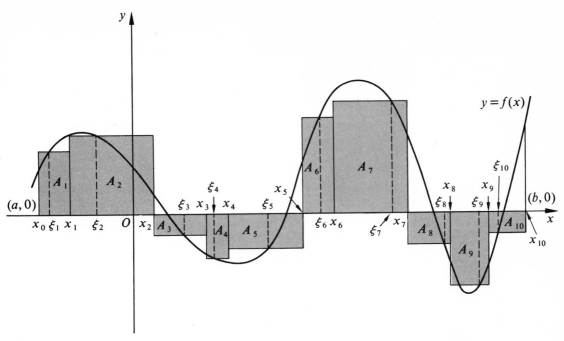

Figure 10.3.3

10.3.1 DEFINITION   A function f is said to be *integrable* on the closed interval $[a,b]$ if there is a number L satisfying the condition that, for every $\epsilon > 0$, there exists a $\delta > 0$ such that

$$\left| \sum_{i=1}^{n} f(\xi_i)\, \Delta_i x - L \right| < \epsilon$$

for every partition Δ for which $||\Delta|| < \delta$, and for any ξ_i in the closed interval $[x_{i-1}, x_i]$, $i = 1, 2, \ldots, n$.

In words, Definition 10.3.1 states that, for a given function f defined on the closed interval $[a,b]$, we can make the values of the Riemann sums as close as we please to L by taking the norms $||\Delta||$ of all partitions Δ of $[a,b]$ sufficiently small. If Definition 10.3.1 holds, we write

$$\lim_{||\Delta|| \to 0} \sum_{i=1}^{n} f(\xi_i)\, \Delta_i x = L$$

A question that now arises is: Under what conditions does a number L satisfying Definition 10.3.1 exist? An answer is given by the following theorem.

10.3.2 THEOREM   If a function f is continuous on a closed interval $[a,b]$, then there exists

$$\lim_{||\Delta|| \to 0} \sum_{i=1}^{n} f(\xi_i)\, \Delta_i x$$

The proof of this theorem is beyond the scope of this book and is given in advanced calculus texts.

We are now in a position to define the *definite integral*.

10.3.3 DEFINITION   If f is a function defined on a closed interval $[a,b]$, then the *definite integral* of f from a to b, denoted by $\int_a^b f(x)\,dx$, is given by

$$(2) \qquad \int_a^b f(x)\,dx = \lim_{||\Delta|| \to 0} \sum_{i=1}^{n} f(\xi_i)\,\Delta_i x$$

if the limit exists.

From Theorem 10.3.2 we know that if the function f is continuous on the closed interval $[a,b]$, then the limit in (2) exists. But, Theorem 10.3.2 is not a necessary condition for the existence of this limit. In Chapter 20 we shall consider some functions f which are not continuous on a closed interval $[a,b]$ but for which $\int_a^b f(x)\,dx$ exists.

In the notation for the definite integral, $\int_a^b f(x)\,dx$, $f(x)$ is called the *integrand*, a is called the *lower limit*, and b is called the *upper limit*. The symbol

$$\int$$

is called an *integral sign*. The integral sign resembles a capital S, which is appropriate since the definite integral is the limit of a sum.

In Definition 10.3.3 it is assumed that $a < b$, since we are considering the closed interval $[a,b]$. In order to consider the definite integral from a to b when $a > b$, or when $a = b$, we have the following definitions.

10.3.4 DEFINITION   If $a > b$, then

$$\int_a^b f(x)\,dx = -\int_b^a f(x)\,dx$$

if $\int_b^a f(x)\,dx$ exists.

10.3.5 DEFINITION $\int_a^a f(x)\,dx = 0$ if $f(a)$ exists.

At the beginning of this section, we stated that the limit used in Definition 10.2.1 to define the area of a region is a special case of the limit used in Definition 10.3.3 to define the definite integral. In the discussion of area, we divided the interval $[a,b]$ into n subintervals of equal length. Such a partition of the interval $[a,b]$ is called a *regular partition*. If Δx is the length of each subinterval in a regular partition, then each $\Delta_i x = \Delta x$, and the norm of the partition is Δx. Making these substitutions in equation (2), we have

$$(3) \qquad \int_a^b f(x)\,dx = \lim_{\Delta x \to 0} \sum_{i=1}^{n} f(\xi_i)\,\Delta x$$

Furthermore,

(4)
$$\Delta x = \frac{b - a}{n}$$

and

(5)
$$n = \frac{b - a}{\Delta x}$$

So, from equation (4),

(6)
$$\lim_{n \to +\infty} \Delta x = 0$$

and from (5), since $b > a$ and Δx approaches zero through positive values (since $\Delta x > 0$),

(7)
$$\lim_{\Delta x \to 0} n = +\infty$$

From limits (6) and (7), we conclude that

(8) $\Delta x \to 0$ is equivalent to $n \to +\infty$

Thus we have from equation (3) and statement (8),

(9)
$$\int_a^b f(x)\, dx = \lim_{n \to +\infty} \sum_{i=1}^{n} f(\xi_i)\, \Delta x$$

It should be remembered that ξ_i may be any point in the ith subinterval $[x_{i-1}, x_i]$.

In applications of the definite integral to mechanics and geometry, we often use regular partitions, and therefore formulas (3) and (9) are especially important.

Comparing the limit used in Definition 10.2.1, which gives the area of a region, with the limit on the right-hand side of equation (9), we have in the first case:

(10)
$$\lim_{n \to +\infty} \sum_{i=1}^{n} f(c_i)\, \Delta x$$

where $f(c_i)$ is the absolute minimum function value on $[x_{i-1}, x_i]$. In the second case, we have

(11)
$$\lim_{n \to +\infty} \sum_{i=1}^{n} f(\xi_i)\, \Delta x$$

where ξ_i is any number in $[x_{i-1}, x_i]$.

A theorem of advanced calculus guarantees the equality of limits (10) and (11). Because of this, we shall redefine the area of a region in a more general way by using (11) instead of (10).

10.3.6 DEFINITION   Let the function f be continuous on $[a,b]$, and $f(x) \geq 0$ for all x in $[a,b]$. Let R be the region bounded by the curve $y = f(x)$, the x axis, and the lines $x = a$ and $x = b$. Divide the interval $[a,b]$ into n subintervals, each of width $\Delta x = (b - a)/n$. The ith subinterval is $[x_{i-1}, x_i]$, where $x_i = a + i\,\Delta x$. ξ_i is any point in $[x_{i-1}, x_i]$, so that $x_{i-1} \le \xi_i \le x_i$.

The area A of region R is given by

(12)
$$A = \lim_{n \to +\infty} \sum_{i=1}^{n} f(\xi_i)\,\Delta x$$

Comparing equations (9) and (12), we see that the right-hand sides are identical, so that if $f(x) \ge 0$ for all x in $[a,b]$, the definite integral $\int_a^b f(x)\,dx$ may be interpreted geometrically as the area of the region R given in Definition 10.3.6. The region R is shown in Fig. 10.3.4.

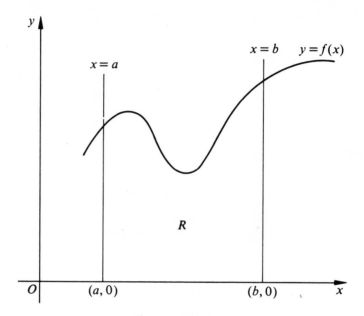

Figure 10.3.4

Following is an example of evaluating a definite integral by equation (9).

EXAMPLE 2: Find the exact value of the definite integral

$$\int_1^3 x^2\,dx$$

Solution: Consider a regular partition of the closed interval $[1,3]$ into n subintervals. Then the length of each subinterval is $\Delta x = 2/n$.

If we choose ξ_i as the right end point of each subinterval, we have

$$\xi_1 = 1 + \frac{2}{n},\ \xi_2 = 1 + 2\left(\frac{2}{n}\right),\ \xi_3 = 1 + 3\left(\frac{2}{n}\right), \cdots ,$$

$$\xi_i = 1 + i\left(\frac{2}{n}\right), \cdots ,\ \xi_n = 1 + n\left(\frac{2}{n}\right)$$

Since $f(x) = x^2$,

$$f(\xi_i) = \left(1 + \frac{2i}{n}\right)^2 = \left(\frac{n + 2i}{n}\right)^2$$

Therefore, by using equation (9) and applying properties and formulas from Sec. 10.1, we get

$$\int_1^3 x^2\,dx = \lim_{n\to+\infty} \sum_{i=1}^{n} \left(\frac{n+2i}{n}\right)^2 \frac{2}{n}$$

$$= \lim_{n\to+\infty} \frac{2}{n^3} \sum_{i=1}^{n} (n^2 + 4ni + 4i^2)$$

$$= \lim_{n\to+\infty} \frac{2}{n^3}\left[n^2 \sum_{i=1}^{n} 1 + 4n \sum_{i=1}^{n} i + 4 \sum_{i=1}^{n} i^2 \right]$$

$$= \lim_{n\to+\infty} \frac{2}{n^3}\left[n^2 n + 4n\cdot\frac{n(n+1)}{2} + \frac{4n(n+1)(2n+1)}{6} \right]$$

$$= \lim_{n\to+\infty} \frac{2}{n^3}\left[n^3 + 2n^3 + 2n^2 + \frac{2n(2n^2 + 3n + 1)}{3} \right]$$

$$= \lim_{n\to+\infty} \left[6 + \frac{4}{n} + \frac{8n^2 + 12n + 4}{3n^2} \right]$$

$$= \lim_{n\to+\infty} \left[6 + \frac{4}{n} + \frac{8}{3} + \frac{4}{n} + \frac{4}{3n^2} \right]$$

$$= 6 + 0 + \frac{8}{3} + 0 + 0 = 8\frac{2}{3}$$

Let us interpret the result of Example 2 geometrically. Since $x^2 \geq 0$ for all x in [1,3], the region bounded by the curve $y = x^2$, the x axis, and the lines $x = 1$ and $x = 3$ has an area of 8⅔ square units. The region is shown in Fig. 10.3.5.

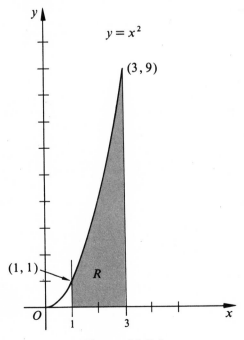

Figure 10.3.5

Exercises 10.3

In Exercises 1 through 6, find the Riemann sum for the function on the interval, using the given partition Δ and the given values of ξ_i. Draw a sketch of the graph of the function on the given interval, and show the rectangles whose areas are the terms of the Riemann sum. (See Example 1 and Fig. 10.3.2.)

1. $f(x) = x^2, 0 \le x \le 3$; for Δ: $x_0 = 0$, $x_1 = \frac{1}{2}$, $x_2 = 1\frac{1}{4}$, $x_3 = 2\frac{1}{4}$, $x_4 = 3$; $\xi_1 = \frac{1}{4}$, $\xi_2 = 1$, $\xi_3 = 1\frac{1}{2}$, $\xi_4 = 2\frac{1}{2}$

2. $f(x) = x^2, 0 \le x \le 3$; for Δ: $x_0 = 0$, $x_1 = \frac{3}{4}$, $x_2 = 1\frac{1}{4}$, $x_3 = 2$, $x_4 = 2\frac{3}{4}$, $x_5 = 3$; $\xi_i = \frac{1}{2}$, $\xi_2 = 1$, $\xi_3 = 1\frac{3}{4}$, $\xi_4 = 2\frac{1}{4}$, $\xi_5 = 2\frac{3}{4}$

3. $f(x) = \dfrac{1}{x}$, $1 \le x \le 3$; for Δ: $x_0 = 1$, $x_1 = 1\frac{2}{3}$, $x_2 = 2\frac{1}{4}$, $x_3 = 2\frac{2}{3}$, $x_4 = 3$; $\xi_1 = 1\frac{1}{4}$, $\xi_2 = 2$, $\xi_3 = 2\frac{1}{2}$, $\xi_4 = 2\frac{3}{4}$

4. $f(x) = x^3$, $-1 \le x \le 2$; for Δ: $x_0 = -1$, $x_1 = -\frac{1}{3}$, $x_2 = \frac{1}{2}$, $x_3 = 1$, $x_4 = 1\frac{1}{4}$, $x_5 = 2$; $\xi_1 = -\frac{1}{2}$, $\xi_2 = 0$, $\xi_3 = \frac{2}{3}$, $\xi_4 = 1$, $\xi_5 = 1\frac{1}{2}$

5. $f(x) = x^2 - x + 1, 0 \le x \le 1$; for Δ: $x_0 = 0$, $x_1 = 0.2$, $x_2 = 0.5$, $x_3 = 0.7$, $x_4 = 1$; $\xi_1 = 0.1$, $\xi_2 = 0.4$, $\xi_3 = 0.6$, $\xi_4 = 0.9$

6. $f(x) = \dfrac{1}{x+2}$, $-1 \le x \le 3$; for Δ: $x_0 = -1$, $x_1 = -\frac{1}{4}$, $x_2 = 0$, $x_3 = \frac{1}{2}$, $x_4 = 1\frac{1}{4}$, $x_5 = 2$, $x_6 = 2\frac{1}{4}$, $x_7 = 2\frac{3}{4}$, $x_8 = 3$; $\xi_1 = -\frac{3}{4}$, $\xi_2 = 0$, $\xi_3 = \frac{1}{4}$, $\xi_4 = 1$, $\xi_5 = 1\frac{1}{2}$, $\xi_6 = 2$, $\xi_7 = 2\frac{1}{2}$, $\xi_8 = 3$

In Exercises 7 through 14, find the exact value of the definite integral. Use the method of Example 2 in this section.

7. $\int_0^2 x^2 \, dx$

8. $\int_2^4 x^2 \, dx$

9. $\int_1^2 x^3 \, dx$

10. $\int_{-2}^1 x^4 \, dx$

11. $\int_1^4 (x^2 + 4x + 5) \, dx$

12. $\int_0^4 (x^2 + x - 6) \, dx$

13. $\int_{-2}^2 (x^3 + 1) \, dx$

14. $\int_{-1}^2 (4x^3 - 3x^2) \, dx$

In Exercises 15 through 20, find the exact area of the region in the following way: (a) express the area as the limit of a Riemann sum with regular partitions; (b) express this limit as a definite integral; (c) evaluate the definite integral by the method of this section and a suitable choice of ξ_i. Draw a figure showing the region.

15. Bounded by the line $y = 2x - 1$, the x axis, and lines $x = 1$, $x = 5$.
16. Bounded by the line $y = 2x - 6$, the x axis, and lines $x = 4$, $x = 7$.
17. Bounded by the curve $y = 4 - x^2$, the x axis, and lines $x = 1$, $x = 2$.
18. Bounded by the curve $y = (x + 3)^2$, the x axis, and lines $x = -3$, $x = 0$.
19. Bounded by the curve $y = 12 - x - x^2$, the x axis, and lines $x = -3$, $x = 2$.
20. Bounded by the curve $y = 6x + x^2 - x^3$, the x axis, and lines $x = -1$, $x = 3$.

(10.4)   Properties of the definite integral

From Definitions 10.3.3 and 10.3.1, the function f is integrable on the closed interval $[a,b]$ if the definite integral $\int_a^b f(x)\,dx$ exists or, equivalently, if

$$\lim_{\|\Delta\|\to 0} \sum_{i=1}^{n} f(\xi_i)\,\Delta_i x$$

exists. In considering the above limit, we have a different kind of limiting process than that discussed in Chapter 4. From Definition 10.3.1,

(1) $$\lim_{\|\Delta\|\to 0} \sum_{i=1}^{n} f(\xi_i)\,\Delta_i x = L$$

if for every $\epsilon > 0$, there exists a $\delta > 0$ such that

$$\left| \sum_{i=1}^{n} f(\xi_i)\,\Delta_i x - L \right| < \epsilon$$

$\Delta_i x = \|\Delta\|$ in a regular partition

for every partition Δ for which $\|\Delta\| < \delta$, and for any ξ_i in the closed interval $[x_{i-1}, x_i]$, $i = 1, 2, \ldots, n$.

In Definition 4.1.1 we had the following:

(2) $$\lim_{x\to a} f(x) = L$$

if for every $\epsilon > 0$, there exists a $\delta > 0$ such that

$$|f(x) - L| < \epsilon \qquad \text{whenever} \qquad 0 < |x - a| < \delta$$

In limiting process (1), for a particular $\delta > 0$ there are infinitely many partitions Δ having norm $\|\Delta\| < \delta$. This is analogous to the fact that in limiting process (2), for a given $\delta > 0$ there are infinitely many values of x for which $0 < |x - a| < \delta$. However, in limiting process (1), for each partition Δ there are infinitely many choices of ξ_i. It is in this respect that the two limiting processes differ.

As a consequence of the above discussion, we cannot assume any of the limit theorems that were proved in Chapter 4 for limits of functions of the form (2). We shall need to make use of the following two theorems regarding the limit of a Riemann sum.

10.4.1 THEOREM   If Δ is any partition of the closed interval $[a,b]$, then

$$\lim_{\|\Delta\|\to 0} \sum_{i=1}^{n} \Delta_i x = b - a$$

The proof of this theorem follows immediately from Definition 10.3.1 and is left for the reader (see Exercise 1 below).

10.4.2 THEOREM   If f is defined on the closed interval $[a,b]$ and if $\displaystyle\lim_{||\Delta||\to 0} \sum_{i=1}^{n} f(\xi_i)\,\Delta_i x$ exists, where Δ is any partition of $[a,b]$, then if k is any constant

$$\lim_{||\Delta||\to 0} \sum_{i=1}^{n} kf(\xi_i)\,\Delta_i x = k \lim_{||\Delta||\to 0} \sum_{i=1}^{n} f(\xi_i)\,\Delta_i x$$

The proof of this theorem is also left for the reader. (See Exercise 2 below.)

We shall now prove some important properties of the definite integral. We shall need these properties in order to arrive at a method of evaluating a definite integral by a process simpler than applying the definition. These properties are given as theorems.

10.4.3 THEOREM   If the function f is integrable on the closed interval $[a,b]$ and if c is any constant, then

$$\int_a^b cf(x)\,dx = c\int_a^b f(x)\,dx$$

Proof: From Definition 10.3.3, we have

$$\int_a^b cf(x)\,dx = \lim_{||\Delta||\to 0} \sum_{i=1}^{n} cf(\xi_i)\,\Delta_i x$$

$$= c \lim_{||\Delta||\to 0} \sum_{i=1}^{n} f(\xi_i)\,\Delta_i x \qquad \text{by Theorem 10.4.2}$$

$$= c\int_a^b f(x)\,dx \qquad \text{by hypothesis that } f \text{ is integrable on } [a,b]$$

10.4.4 THEOREM   If the functions f and g are integrable on the closed interval $[a,b]$, then

$$\int_a^b [f(x) + g(x)]\,dx = \int_a^b f(x)\,dx + \int_a^b g(x)\,dx$$

Proof: Since f and g are integrable on $[a,b]$, $\int_a^b f(x)\,dx$ and $\int_a^b g(x)\,dx$ both exist.

Let $\displaystyle\int_a^b f(x)\,dx = M$ and $\displaystyle\int_a^b g(x)\,dx = N$

Let $\displaystyle\sum_{i=1}^{n} f(\xi_i)\,\Delta_i x$ and $\displaystyle\sum_{i=1}^{n} g(\xi_i)\,\Delta_i x$

be Riemann sums having the same partition Δ and the same set of ξ_i.

Since $\displaystyle M = \int_a^b f(x)\,dx = \lim_{||\Delta||\to 0} \sum_{i=1}^{n} f(\xi_i)\,\Delta_i x$

and $\displaystyle N = \int_a^b g(x)\,dx = \lim_{||\Delta||\to 0} \sum_{i=1}^{n} g(\xi_i)\,\Delta_i x$

for any $\epsilon/2 > 0$, there exists a $\delta_1 > 0$ such that

$$(3) \qquad \left| M - \sum_{i=1}^{n} f(\xi_i)\, \Delta_i x \right| < \frac{\epsilon}{2} \qquad \text{whenever} \qquad ||\Delta|| < \delta_1$$

and there exists a $\delta_2 > 0$ such that

$$(4) \qquad \left| N - \sum_{i=1}^{n} g(\xi_i)\, \Delta_i x \right| < \frac{\epsilon}{2} \qquad \text{whenever} \qquad ||\Delta|| < \delta_2$$

Let δ be the smaller of δ_1 and δ_2; then both inequalities in (3) and (4) hold whenever $||\Delta|| < \delta$, and we have

$$(5) \quad \left| M - \sum_{i=1}^{n} f(\xi_i)\, \Delta_i x \right| + \left| N - \sum_{i=1}^{n} g(\xi_i)\, \Delta_i x \right| < \frac{\epsilon}{2} + \frac{\epsilon}{2} \qquad \text{whenever} \qquad ||\Delta|| < \delta$$

Applying the triangle inequality to the left-hand side of the inequality in (5) and replacing $\epsilon/2 + \epsilon/2$ by ϵ, we obtain

$$\left| \left(M - \sum_{i=1}^{n} f(\xi_i)\, \Delta_i x \right) + \left(N - \sum_{i=1}^{n} g(\xi_i)\, \Delta_i x \right) \right| < \epsilon \qquad \text{whenever} \qquad ||\Delta|| < \delta$$

or

$$(6) \quad \left| (M + N) - \left(\sum_{i=1}^{n} f(\xi_i)\, \Delta_i x + \sum_{i=1}^{n} g(\xi_i)\, \Delta_i x \right) \right| < \epsilon \qquad \text{whenever} \qquad ||\Delta|| < \delta$$

From Property (10.1.3) of the sigma notation, we have

$$(7) \qquad \sum_{i=1}^{n} f(\xi_i)\, \Delta_i x + \sum_{i=1}^{n} g(\xi_i)\, \Delta_i x = \sum_{i=1}^{n} [f(\xi_i) + g(\xi_i)]\, \Delta_i x$$

Substituting from (7) into (6), we get

$$\left| (M + N) - \sum_{i=1}^{n} [f(\xi_i) + g(\xi_i)]\, \Delta_i x \right| < \epsilon \qquad \text{whenever} \qquad ||\Delta|| < \delta$$

Therefore

$$(8) \qquad \lim_{||\Delta|| \to 0} \sum_{i=1}^{n} [f(\xi_i) + g(\xi_i)]\, \Delta_i x = M + N$$

But, the left side of equation (8) is $\int_a^b [f(x) + g(x)]\, dx$ by Definition 10.3.3. So, from (8) we obtain

$$\int_a^b [f(x) + g(x)]\, dx = \int_a^b f(x)\, dx + \int_a^b g(x)\, dx \qquad \text{Q.E.D.}$$

Theorem 10.4.4 may be extended to any number of functions. That is, if the functions $f_1, f_2, \ldots, f_n$ are all integrable on $[a,b]$, then

$$\int_a^b [f_1(x) + f_2(x) + \cdots + f_n(x)]\, dx = \int_a^b f_1(x)\, dx + \int_a^b f_2(x)\, dx + \cdots + \int_a^b f_n(x)\, dx$$

10.4.5 THEOREM   If the function f is integrable on the closed interval $[a,b]$,

$$\int_a^b f(x)\, dx = \int_a^c f(x)\, dx + \int_c^b f(x)\, dx$$

where $a < c < b$.

Proof: Let Δ be a partition of $[a,b]$. Form the partition Δ' of $[a,b]$ in the following way. If c is one of the partitioning points of Δ — that is, $c = x_i$ for some i — then Δ' is exactly the same as Δ. If c is not one of the partitioning points of Δ but is contained in the subinterval $[x_{i-1}, x_i]$, then the partition Δ' has as its partitioning points all the partitioning points of Δ and, in addition, the point c. Therefore, the subintervals of the partition Δ' are the same as the subintervals of Δ, with the exception that the subinterval $[x_{i-1}, x_i]$ of Δ is divided into the two subintervals $[x_{i-1}, c]$ and $[c, x_i]$.

If $||\Delta'||$ is the norm of Δ' and if $||\Delta||$ is the norm of Δ, then

$$||\Delta'|| \leq ||\Delta||$$

If in the partition Δ', the interval $[a,c]$ is divided into r subintervals and the interval $[c,b]$ is divided into $(n - r)$ subintervals, then the part of the partition Δ' from a to c gives a Riemann sum of the form

$$\sum_{i=1}^{r} f(\xi_i)\, \Delta_i x$$

and the other part of the partition Δ', from c to b, gives a Riemann sum of the form

$$\sum_{i=r+1}^{n} f(\xi_i)\, \Delta_i x$$

Using the definition of the definite integral and properties of the sigma notation, we have

$$\int_a^b f(x)\, dx = \lim_{||\Delta|| \to 0} \sum_{i=1}^{n} f(\xi_i)\, \Delta_i x$$

$$= \lim_{||\Delta|| \to 0} \left[\sum_{i=1}^{r} f(\xi_i)\, \Delta_i x + \sum_{i=r+1}^{n} f(\xi_i)\, \Delta_i x \right]$$

$$= \lim_{||\Delta|| \to 0} \sum_{i=1}^{r} f(\xi_i)\, \Delta_i x + \lim_{||\Delta|| \to 0} \sum_{i=r+1}^{n} f(\xi_i)\, \Delta_i x$$

Since $0 < ||\Delta'|| \leq ||\Delta||$, we may replace $||\Delta|| \to 0$ by $||\Delta'|| \to 0$, giving us

$$\int_a^b f(x)\, dx = \lim_{||\Delta'|| \to 0} \sum_{i=1}^{r} f(\xi_i)\, \Delta_i x + \lim_{||\Delta'|| \to 0} \sum_{i=r+1}^{n} f(\xi_i)\, \Delta_i x$$

Applying the definition of the definite integral to the right-hand side of the above, we have

$$\int_a^b f(x)\, dx = \int_a^c f(x)\, dx + \int_c^b f(x)\, dx \qquad \text{Q.E.D.}$$

We shall now interpret Theorem 10.4.5 geometrically. If $f(x) \geq 0$ for all x in $[a,b]$, then Theorem 10.4.5 states that the area of the region bounded by the curve $y = f(x)$ and the x axis from a to b is equal to the sum of the areas of the regions from a to c and from c to b (see Fig. 10.4.1).

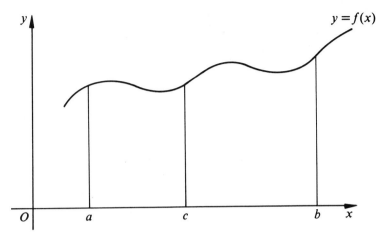

Figure 10.4.1

The result of Theorem 10.4.5 is true for any ordering of the numbers a, b, and c. We state this as another theorem.

10.4.6 THEOREM   If f is integrable on a closed interval containing the three numbers a, b, and c, then

(9) $$\int_a^b f(x)\, dx = \int_a^c f(x)\, dx + \int_c^b f(x)\, dx$$

regardless of the order of a, b, and c.

Proof: If a, b, and c are distinct, we have six possible orderings of these three numbers: $a < b < c$, $a < c < b$, $b < a < c$, $b < c < a$, $c < a < b$, and $c < b < a$.

The second ordering, $a < c < b$, is Theorem 10.4.5. We make use of Theorem 10.4.5 in proving that equation (9) holds for the other orderings.

Suppose that $a < b < c$; then from Theorem 10.4.5 we have

(10) $$\int_a^b f(x)\, dx + \int_b^c f(x)\, dx = \int_a^c f(x)\, dx$$

From Definition 10.3.4,

(11) $$\int_b^c f(x)\, dx = -\int_c^b f(x)\, dx$$

Substituting from (11) into (10), we obtain

$$\int_a^b f(x)\, dx - \int_c^b f(x)\, dx = \int_a^c f(x)\, dx$$

or $$\int_a^b f(x)\, dx = \int_a^c f(x)\, dx + \int_c^b f(x)\, dx$$

which is the desired result.

The proofs for the other four orderings are similar and are left for the reader (see Exercises 3 through 6 below).

There is also the possibility that two of the three numbers are equal, say, $a = c < b$. Then,

$$\int_a^c f(x)\,dx = \int_a^a f(x)\,dx = 0 \qquad \text{by Definition 10.3.5}$$

Also, since $a = c$,

$$\int_c^b f(x)\,dx = \int_a^b f(x)\,dx$$

Therefore,

$$\int_a^c f(x)\,dx + \int_c^b f(x)\,dx = 0 + \int_a^b f(x)\,dx$$

which is the desired result.

10.4.7 THEOREM   If k is any constant and if f is a function such that $f(x) = k$ for all x in $[a,b]$, then

$$\int_a^b f(x)\,dx = k(b - a)$$

Proof: From Definition 10.3.3,

$$\int_a^b f(x)\,dx = \lim_{\|\Delta\| \to 0} \sum_{i=1}^n f(\xi_i)\,\Delta_i x$$

$$= \lim_{\|\Delta\| \to 0} \sum_{i=1}^n k\,\Delta_i x$$

$$= k \lim_{\|\Delta\| \to 0} \sum_{i=1}^n \Delta_i x \qquad \text{by Theorem 10.4.2}$$

$$= k(b - a) \qquad \text{by Theorem 10.4.1}$$

which is the desired result.

10.4.8 THEOREM   If the functions f and g are integrable on the closed interval $[a,b]$ and if $f(x) \geq g(x)$ for all x in $[a,b]$, then

$$\int_a^b f(x)\,dx \geq \int_a^b g(x)\,dx$$

Proof: Since f and g are integrable on $[a,b]$, $\int_a^b f(x)\,dx$ and $\int_a^b g(x)\,dx$ both exist. Therefore,

$$\int_a^b f(x)\,dx - \int_a^b g(x)\,dx = \int_a^b f(x)\,dx + \int_a^b [-g(x)]\,dx \qquad \text{by Theorem 10.4.3}$$

$$= \int_a^b [f(x) - g(x)]\,dx \qquad \text{by Theorem 10.4.4}$$

Let h be the function defined by

$$h(x) = f(x) - g(x)$$

Then, $h(x) \geq 0$ for all x in $[a,b]$, since $f(x) \geq g(x)$ for all x in $[a,b]$.

We wish to prove $\int_a^b [f(x) - g(x)]\, dx \geq 0$:

(12) $$\int_a^b [f(x) - g(x)]\, dx = \int_a^b h(x)\, dx = \lim_{\|\Delta\| \to 0} \sum_{i=1}^n h(\xi_i)\, \Delta_i x$$

Assume that

(13) $$\lim_{\|\Delta\| \to 0} \sum_{i=1}^n h(\xi_i)\, \Delta_i x = L < 0$$

Then by Definition 10.3.1, taking $\epsilon = -L$, there exists a $\delta > 0$ such that

(14) $$\left| \sum_{i=1}^n h(\xi_i)\, \Delta_i x - L \right| < -L \qquad \text{whenever} \qquad \|\Delta\| < \delta$$

But since

$$\sum_{i=1}^n h(\xi_i)\, \Delta_i x - L \leq \left| \sum_{i=1}^n h(\xi_i)\, \Delta_i x - L \right|$$

from inequality (14) we have

$$\sum_{i=1}^n h(\xi_i)\, \Delta_i x - L < -L \qquad \text{whenever} \qquad \|\Delta\| < \delta$$

or

(15) $$\sum_{i=1}^n h(\xi_i)\, \Delta_i x < 0 \qquad \text{whenever} \qquad \|\Delta\| < \delta$$

But statement (15) is impossible since every $h(\xi_i)$ is nonnegative and every $\Delta_i x > 0$; thus we have a contradiction to our assumption (13). Therefore, (13) is false, and

(16) $$\lim_{\|\Delta\| \to 0} \sum_{i=1}^n h(\xi_i)\, \Delta_i x \geq 0$$

From (12) and (16), we have

$$\int_a^b [f(x) - g(x)]\, dx \geq 0$$

Hence, from Theorem 10.4.4,

$$\int_a^b f(x)\, dx - \int_a^b g(x)\, dx \geq 0$$

and so

$$\int_a^b f(x)\, dx \geq \int_a^b g(x)\, dx$$

which is what we wished to prove.

Exercises 10.4

1. Prove Theorem 10.4.1.   2. Prove Theorem 10.4.2.

In Exercises 3 through 8 prove that Theorem 10.4.6 is valid in each case, using the result of Theorem 10.4.5.

3. $b < a < c$ 6. $c < b < a$
4. $b < c < a$ 7. $a < c = b$
5. $c < a < b$ 8. $a = b < c$

(10.5)   The mean-value theorem for integrals

Before stating and proving the mean-value theorem for integrals, we shall discuss an important theorem about a function that is continuous on a closed interval. It is called the *intermediate-value theorem*, and we shall need to make use of it in order to prove the mean-value theorem for integrals.

10.5.1 THEOREM   (*Intermediate-value Theorem*)   If the function f is continuous on the closed interval $[a,b]$ and if $f(a) \neq f(b)$, then for any number k between $f(a)$ and $f(b)$ there exists a number c between a and b such that $f(c) = k$.

The proof of this theorem is beyond the scope of this book; it may be found in an advanced calculus text. However, we shall discuss the geometrical interpretation of the theorem. In Fig. 10.5.1, $(0, k)$ is any point on the y axis be-

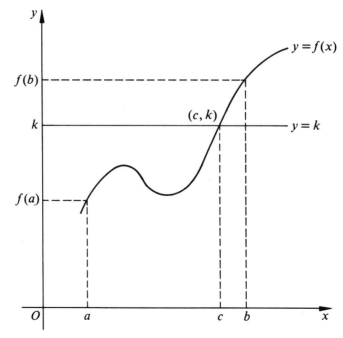

Figure 10.5.1

tween the points $(0, f(a))$ and $(0, f(b))$. Theorem 10.5.1 states that the line $y = k$ must intersect the curve whose equation is $y = f(x)$ at the point (c,k), where c lies between a and b. Figure 10.5.1 shows this intersection.

It should be noted that for some values of k there may be more than one possible value for c. The theorem states that there is always at least one value of c, but that it is not necessarily unique. Figure 10.5.2 shows three possible values of $c — c_1$, c_2, and c_3 — for a particular k.

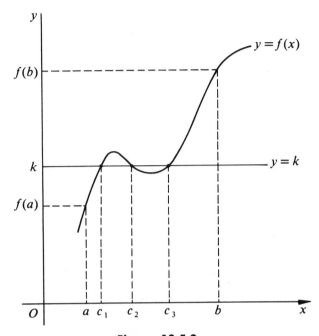

Figure 10.5.2

Intuitively, Theorem 10.5.1 states that if the function f is continuous on a closed interval $[a,b]$ then f assumes every value between $f(a)$ and $f(b)$ as x assumes all values between a and b. The importance of the continuity of f on $[a,b]$ should be pointed out. For example, consider the function f, defined by

$$f(x) = \begin{cases} x - 1 & \text{if} \quad 0 \leq x \leq 2 \\ x^2 & \text{if} \quad 2 < x \leq 3 \end{cases}$$

A sketch of the graph of this function is shown in Fig. 10.5.3.

f is discontinuous at 2, which is in the closed interval $[0,3]$; $f(0) = -1$ and $f(3) = 9$. If k is any number between 1 and 4, there is no value of c such that $f(c) = k$, since there are no function values between 1 and 4.

Let us consider an example of another function for which Theorem 10.5.1 does not hold. Let g be defined by

$$g(x) = \frac{2}{x - 4}$$

A sketch of the graph of this function is shown in Fig. 10.5.4.

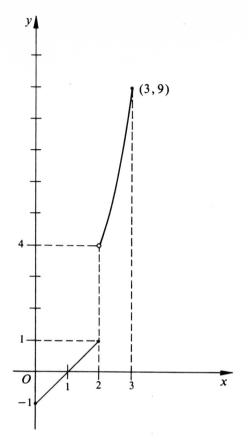

Figure 10.5.3

g is discontinuous at 4, which is in the closed interval [2,5]; $g(2) = -1$ and $g(5) = 2$. If k is any number between -1 and 2, there is no value of c between 2 and 5 such that $g(c) = k$. In particular if $k = 1$, then $g(6) = 1$, but 6 is not in the interval [2,5].

EXAMPLE 1: Given the function f defined by

$$f(x) = 4 + 3x - x^2 \qquad 2 \leq x \leq 5$$

verify the intermediate-value theorem if $k = 1$.

Solution: $f(2) = 6, f(5) = -6$.

To find c, set $f(c) = k$, or

$$4 + 3c - c^2 = 1$$

$$c^2 - 3c - 3 = 0$$

This gives us

$$c = \frac{3 \pm \sqrt{21}}{2}$$

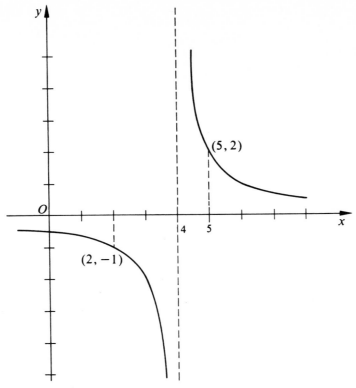

Figure 10.5.4

We reject $(3 - \sqrt{21})/2$ since this number is outside the interval [2,5]. The number $(3 + \sqrt{21})/2$ is in the interval [2,5], and

$$f\left(\frac{3 + \sqrt{21}}{2}\right) = 1$$

We are now ready to state and prove the mean-value theorem for integrals.

10.5.2 THEOREM   *(Mean-value Theorem for Integrals)*   If the function f is continuous on the closed interval [a,b], then there exists a number X such that $a \leq X \leq b$, and

$$\int_a^b f(x)\,dx = f(X)(b - a)$$

Proof: Since f is continuous on [a,b], from the extreme-value theorem (8.2.9), f has an absolute maximum value and an absolute minimum value on [a,b].

Let m be the absolute minimum value occurring at $x = x_m$. Thus,

(1) $f(x_m) = m \qquad a \leq x_m \leq b$

Let M be the absolute maximum value, occurring at $x = x_M$. Thus

(2) $f(x_M) = M \qquad a \leq x_M \leq b$

We have, then,

$$m \le f(x) \le M \qquad \text{for all } x \text{ in } [a,b]$$

Therefore, by Theorem 10.4.8, we have

(3) $$\int_a^b m\, dx \le \int_a^b f(x)\, dx \le \int_a^b M\, dx$$

But, from Theorem 10.4.7, we have

(4) $$\int_a^b m\, dx = m(b - a)$$

and

(5) $$\int_a^b M\, dx = M(b - a)$$

Substituting from equations (4) and (5) into (3), we obtain

$$m(b - a) \le \int_a^b f(x)\, dx \le M(b - a)$$

Dividing by $(b - a)$ and noting that $(b - a)$ is positive since $b > a$, we get

$$m \le \frac{\int_a^b f(x)\, dx}{b - a} \le M$$

But from equations (1) and (2), $m = f(x_m)$ and $M = f(x_M)$, and so we have

(6) $$f(x_m) \le \frac{\int_a^b f(x)\, dx}{b - a} \le f(x_M)$$

From inequalities (6) and the intermediate-value theorem (10.5.1), there is some number X in a closed interval containing x_m and x_M such that

$$f(\text{X}) = \frac{\int_a^b f(x)\, dx}{b - a}$$

or $$\int_a^b f(x)\, dx = f(\text{X})(b - a) \qquad a \le \text{X} \le b \qquad \text{Q.E.D.}$$

To interpret Theorem 10.5.2 geometrically, we consider $f(x) \ge 0$ for all values of x in $[a,b]$. Then, $\int_a^b f(x)\, dx$ is the area of the region bounded by the curve whose equation is $y = f(x)$, the x axis, and the lines $x = a$ and $x = b$ (see Fig. 10.5.5).

Theorem 10.5.2 states that there is a number X in $[a,b]$ such that the area of the rectangle *AEFB* of height $f(\text{X})$ and width $(b - a)$ is equal to the area of the region *ADCB*.

The value of X is not necessarily unique. The theorem does not provide a method for finding X, but it states that a value of X exists, and this will be used to prove other theorems. In some particular cases we can find the value of X, as is illustrated in the following example.

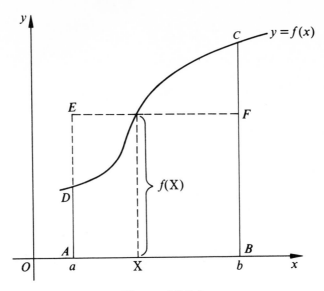

Figure 10.5.5

EXAMPLE 2: Find the value of X such that

$$\int_1^3 f(x)\, dx = f(X)(3 - 1)$$

if $f(x) = x^2$. Use the result of Example 2 in Sec. 10.3.

Solution: In Example 2 of Sec. 10.3, we obtained

$$\int_1^3 x^2\, dx = 8\frac{2}{3}$$

Therefore, we wish to find X such that

$$f(X)\cdot(2) = \frac{26}{3}$$

or $\qquad$ $$X^2 = \frac{13}{3}$$

Therefore, $\qquad$ $$X = \pm\frac{\sqrt{39}}{3}$$

We reject $-\sqrt{39}/3$ since it is not in the interval [1,3], so that we have

$$\int_1^3 f(x)\, dx = f\left(\frac{\sqrt{39}}{3}\right)(3 - 1)$$

The value $f(X)$ given by Theorem 10.5.2 is called the *mean value* (or *average value*) of f on the interval $[a,b]$. It is a generalization of the arithmetic mean of a finite set of numbers. That is, if $f(x_1), f(x_2), \ldots, f(x_n)$ is a set of n numbers, then the arithmetic mean is given by

$$\frac{\sum_{i=1}^{n} f(x_i)}{n}$$

To generalize this definition, consider a regular partition of the closed interval $[a,b]$, which is divided into n subintervals of equal length $\Delta x = (b - a)/n$. Let ξ_i be any point in the ith subinterval. Form the sum:

(7)
$$\frac{\sum\limits_{i=1}^{n} f(\xi_i)}{n}$$

The quotient (7) corresponds to the arithmetic mean of n numbers. Since $\Delta x = (b - a)/n$, we have

(8)
$$n = \frac{b - a}{\Delta x}$$

Substituting from (8) into (7), we obtain

$$\frac{\sum\limits_{i=1}^{n} f(\xi_i)}{(b - a)/\Delta x}$$

$$\text{or} \qquad \frac{\sum\limits_{i=1}^{n} f(\xi_i) \cdot \Delta x}{b - a}$$

Taking the limit as $n \to +\infty$ (or $\Delta x \to 0$), we have

$$\lim_{n \to +\infty} \frac{\sum\limits_{i=1}^{n} f(\xi_i) \, \Delta x}{b - a} = \frac{\int_a^b f(x) \, dx}{b - a}$$

So, $\dfrac{\int_a^b f(x) \, dx}{b - a}$ may be interpreted as the average function value of f on the interval $[a,b]$.

EXAMPLE 3: Find the average value of the function f defined by $f(x) = x^2$ on the interval $[1,3]$.

Solution: In Example 2 of Sec. 10.3, we obtained

$$\int_1^3 x^2 \, dx = \frac{26}{3}$$

So if A.V. = the average value of f on $[1,3]$, we have

$$\text{A.V.} = \frac{26/3}{3 - 1} = \frac{13}{3}$$

Exercises 10.5

In Exercises 1 through 8, a function f and a closed interval $[a,b]$ are given. Determine if the intermediate-value theorem holds for the given value of k. If the theorem holds, find a number c such that $f(c) = k$. If the theorem does not hold, give the reason. Draw a sketch of the curve and the line $y = k$.

1. $f(x) = 2 + x - x^2$; $[a,b] = [0,3]$; $k = 1$

2. $f(x) = x^2 + 5x - 6$; $[a,b] = [-1,2]$; $k = 4$

3. $f(x) = \sqrt{25 - x^2}$; $[a,b] = [-4.5,3]$; $k = 3$

4. $f(x) = -\sqrt{100 - x^2}$; $[a,b] = [0,8]$; $k = -8$

5. $f(x) = \dfrac{4}{x + 2}$; $[a,b] = [-3,1]$; $k = \frac{1}{2}$

6. $f(x) = \begin{cases} 1 + x & \text{if } -4 \le x \le -2 \\ 2 - x & \text{if } -2 < x \le 1 \end{cases}$; $[a,b] = [-4,1]$; $k = \frac{1}{2}$

7. $f(x) = \begin{cases} x^2 - 4 & \text{if } -2 \le x < 1 \\ x^2 - 1 & \text{if } 1 \le x \le 3 \end{cases}$; $[a,b] = [-2,3]$; $k = -1$

8. $f(x) = \dfrac{5}{2x - 1}$; $[a,b] = [0,1]$; $k = 2$

In Exercises 9 through 13, find the value of X satisfying the mean-value theorem for integrals. For the value of the definite integral, use the results of corresponding Exercises 9 through 13 in Sec. 10.3. Draw a figure illustrating the application of the theorem.

9. $\int_1^2 f(x)\, dx$ with $f(x) = x^3$

10. $\int_{-2}^1 f(x)\, dx$ with $f(x) = x^4$

11. $\int_1^4 f(x)\, dx$ with $f(x) = x^2 + 4x + 5$

12. $\int_0^4 f(x)\, dx$ with $f(x) = x^2 + x - 6$

13. $\int_{-2}^2 f(x)\, dx$ with $f(x) = x^3 + 1$

In Exercises 14 and 15, find the average value of the function f defined by $f(x) = x^2$ on the given interval $[a,b]$, and find the value of x at which it occurs. Make a sketch. Use the results of Exercises 7 and 8 of Sec. 10.3 for the value of the definite integral.

14. $[a,b] = [0,2]$ \qquad\qquad 15. $[a,b] = [2,4]$

16. Find the average value of the function f defined by $f(x) = \sqrt{16 - x^2}$ on the interval $[-4,4]$. Draw a figure. HINT: Find the value of the definite integral by interpreting it as the area of a semicircle.

17. Find the average value of the function f defined by $f(x) = \sqrt{49 - x^2}$ on the interval $[0,7]$. Draw a figure. HINT: Find the value of the definite integral by interpreting it as the area of a quarter-circle.

(10.6)   The fundamental theorem of integral calculus

Evaluating a definite integral from the definition, by actually finding the limit of a sum, as we did in Sec. 10.3, is usually quite tedious. In this section we shall learn a much simpler method. In order to establish this method, we shall learn a relationship between the derivative and the definite integral.

Historically the basic concepts of the definite integral were used by the ancient Greeks many years before the differential calculus was discovered. In the seventeenth century, almost simultaneously but working independently, Newton and Leibnitz showed how the calculus could be used to find the area of a region bounded by a curve or a set of curves, by evaluating a definite integral by antidifferentiation. The procedure involves what is known as the *fundamental theorem of integral calculus*.

Before we state and prove this theorem, we shall discuss definite integrals having a variable upper limit, and a preliminary theorem.

Let f be a function continuous on the closed interval $[a,b]$. Then the value of the definite integral $\int_a^b f(x)\, dx$ depends only upon the function f and the numbers a and b, and not upon the letter x, which is used here as the independent variable. In Example 2 of Sec. 10.3, we found the value of $\int_1^3 x^2\, dx$ to be $8\frac{2}{3}$. We could have used any other letter instead of x; for example,

$$\int_1^3 t^2\, dt = \int_1^3 u^2\, du = \int_1^3 r^2\, dr = 8\frac{2}{3}$$

If f is continuous on the closed interval $[a,b]$, then by Theorem 10.3.2 and the definition of the definite integral, $\int_a^b f(t)\, dt$ exists. It is also proved in advanced calculus that if $\int_a^b f(t)\, dt$ exists, its value is a unique number. If x is a number in $[a,b]$, then f is continuous on $[a,x]$ since it is continuous on $[a,b]$. Consequently,

$$\int_a^x f(t)\, dt$$

exists and is a unique number whose value depends upon x. Therefore, $\int_a^x f(t)dt$ defines a function F having as its domain all numbers in the closed interval $[a,b]$, and whose function value at any point x in $[a,b]$ is given by

(1)
$$F(x) = \int_a^x f(t)\, dt$$

As a notational observation, if the limits of the definite integral are variables, we use different letters for these limits and for the independent variable in the integrand. Hence, in equation (1), since x is the upper limit, we use the letter t as the independent variable in the integrand.

If, in equation (1), $f(t) \geq 0$ for all values of t in $[a,b]$, then the function value $F(x)$ may be interpreted geometrically as the area of the region bounded by the curve whose equation is $y = f(t)$, the t axis, and the lines $t = a$ and $t = x$. (See Fig. 10.6.1.)

Note that $F(a) = \int_a^a f(t)\, dt$, which by Definition 10.3.5 equals 0.

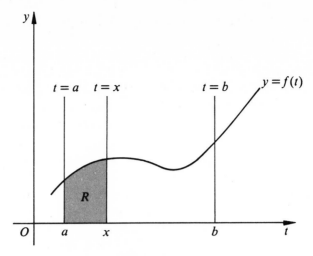

Figure 10.6.1

We shall now state and prove an important theorem giving the derivative of a function F defined as a definite integral having a variable upper limit.

10.6.1 THEOREM   If the function f is continuous on the closed interval $[a,b]$ and if x is any number in $[a,b]$, then the function F defined by

$$F(x) = \int_a^x f(t)\, dt$$

is differentiable on $[a,b]$, and its derivative is given by

$$(2) \qquad\qquad\qquad F'(x) = f(x)$$

Proof: Consider two numbers x_1 and $(x_1 + \Delta x)$ in $[a,b]$. Then,

$$F(x_1) = \int_a^{x_1} f(t)\, dt$$

$$\text{and} \qquad F(x_1 + \Delta x) = \int_a^{x_1+\Delta x} f(t)\, dt$$

so that

$$(3) \qquad F(x_1 + \Delta x) - F(x_1) = \int_a^{x_1+\Delta x} f(t)\, dt - \int_a^{x_1} f(t)\, dt$$

By Theorem 10.4.6,

$$\int_a^{x_1} f(t)\, dt + \int_{x_1}^{x_1+\Delta x} f(t)\, dt = \int_a^{x_1+\Delta x} f(t)\, dt$$

or equivalently,

$$(4) \qquad \int_a^{x_1+\Delta x} f(t)\, dt - \int_a^{x_1} f(t)\, dt = \int_{x_1}^{x_1+\Delta x} f(t)\, dt$$

Substituting from equation (4) into (3), we get

$$(5) \qquad\qquad F(x_1 + \Delta x) - F(x_1) = \int_{x_1}^{x_1+\Delta x} f(t)\, dt$$

By the mean-value theorem for integrals (10.5.2), there is some number X in the closed interval bounded by x_1 and $(x_1 + \Delta x)$ such that

$$\text{(6)} \qquad \int_{x_1}^{x_1+\Delta x} f(t)\, dt = f(X)\, \Delta x$$

From equations (5) and (6), we get

$$F(x_1 + \Delta x) - F(x_1) = f(X)\, \Delta x$$

or, dividing by Δx,

$$\text{(7)} \qquad \frac{F(x_1 + \Delta x) - F(x_1)}{\Delta x} = f(X)$$

Now consider x_1 as a fixed number, and let Δx approach zero. Then, since X is in the closed interval bounded by x_1 and $(x_1 + \Delta x)$, we can make X as close as we please to x_1 by taking Δx close enough (but not equal) to zero; since f is continuous at x_1, then $f(X)$ can be made as close as we please to $f(x_1)$ by taking Δx close enough to zero. Therefore,

$$\text{(8)} \qquad \lim_{\Delta x \to 0} f(X) = f(x_1)$$

If in equation (7) we take the limit of both sides, as Δx approaches zero, we have

$$\text{(9)} \qquad \lim_{\Delta x \to 0} \frac{F(x_1 + \Delta x) - F(x_1)}{\Delta x} = \lim_{\Delta x \to 0} f(X)$$

The left side of equation (9) is $F'(x_1)$, and the right side is $f(x_1)$ by equation (8), so that we have

$$F'(x_1) = f(x_1)$$

Since x_1 is any number in $[a,b]$, we have proved the theorem.

Theorem 10.6.1 states that the definite integral $\int_a^x f(t)\, dt$, with variable upper limit x, is an antiderivative of f.

10.6.2 THEOREM (*Fundamental Theorem of Integral Calculus*)   If the function f is continuous on the closed interval $[a,b]$ and if F is any antiderivative of f on $[a,b]$, then

$$\int_a^b f(x)\, dx = F(b) - F(a)$$

Proof: From Theorem 10.6.1 we know that the definite integral $\int_a^x f(t)\, dt$, with variable upper limit x, defines a function F whose derivative is f. Thus, if F is any antiderivative of f,

$$\text{(10)} \qquad F(x) = \int_a^x f(t)\, dt + C$$

where C is some constant. This is true since, by Theorem 9.1.3, any two anti-derivatives of a function differ by a constant.

Letting $x = b$ and $x = a$, successively, in equation (10), we get

(11) $$F(b) = \int_a^b f(t)\, dt + C$$

and

(12) $$F(a) = \int_a^a f(t)\, dt + C$$

From equations (12) and (11), we obtain

$$F(b) - F(a) = \int_a^b f(t)\, dt - \int_a^a f(t)\, dt$$

But, by Definition 10.3.5, $\int_a^a f(t)\, dt = 0$, so that we have

$$F(b) - F(a) = \int_a^b f(t)\, dt$$

or, since t is a dummy variable,

$$F(b) - F(a) = \int_a^b f(x)\, dx \qquad\qquad \text{Q.E.D.}$$

We are now in a position to find the exact value of a definite integral by applying the fundamental theorem. In applying the theorem, we shall denote

$$[F(b) - F(a)] \qquad \text{by} \qquad F(x)\Big]_a^b$$

EXAMPLE 1: Evaluate $\int_1^3 x^2\, dx$ by the fundamental theorem of integral calculus.

Solution: In this example, $f(x) = x^2$.

An antiderivative of x^2 is $x^3/3$. From this we choose

$$F(x) = \frac{x^3}{3}$$

Therefore, from Theorem 10.6.2, we get

$$\int_1^3 x^2\, dx = \frac{x^3}{3}\Big]_1^3 = 9 - \frac{1}{3} = 8\frac{2}{3}$$

Compare this result with that of Example 2 in Sec. 10.3.

Because of the connection between definite integrals and antiderivatives, we used the integral sign $\int$ for the notation $\int f(x)\, dx$ for an antiderivative. We shall now dispense with the terminology of antiderivatives and antidifferentiation and shall begin to call $\int f(x)\, dx$ the *indefinite integral* of "f of x, dx." The process of evaluating an indefinite integral or a definite integral is called *integration*.

The difference between an indefinite integral and a definite integral should be emphasized. The indefinite integral $\int f(x)\, dx$ is defined as a function F such that its differential $d[F(x)] = f(x)\, dx$. However, the definite integral $\int_a^b f(x)\, dx$ is a number whose value depends upon the function f and the numbers a and b, and it is defined as the limit of a Riemann sum. The definition of the definite integral makes no reference to differentiation.

The general indefinite integral involves an arbitrary constant; that is,

$$\int x^2 \, dx = \frac{x^3}{3} + C$$

This arbitrary constant C is called a *constant of integration*.

In applying the fundamental theorem to evaluate a definite integral, we do not need to include the arbitrary constant C in the expression for $F(x)$, since the fundamental theorem permits us to select *any* antiderivative, including the one for which $C = 0$.

EXAMPLE 2: Evaluate $\int_0^2 2x^2 \sqrt{x^3 + 1} \, dx$.

Solution: To evaluate the indefinite integral $\int 2 x^2 \sqrt{x^3 + 1} \, dx$, we let

$$u = x^3 + 1 \quad \text{and} \quad du = 3x^2 \, dx \quad \text{or} \quad \frac{du}{3} = x^2 \, dx$$

Substituting, we have

$$\int 2x^2 \sqrt{x^3 + 1} \, dx = \frac{2}{3} \int u^{1/2} \, du$$

$$= \frac{4}{9} u^{3/2} + C$$

$$= \frac{4}{9}(x^3 + 1)^{3/2} + C$$

Therefore the definite integral

$$\int_0^2 2x^2 \sqrt{x^3 + 1} \, dx = \frac{4}{9}(x^3 + 1)^{3/2} \Big]_0^2$$

$$= \frac{4}{9}(8 + 1)^{3/2} - \frac{4}{9}(0 + 1)^{3/2}$$

$$= \frac{4}{9}(27 - 1) = \frac{104}{9}$$

Another method for evaluating the definite integral in Example 2 involves changing the limits of the definite integral to values of u. Since $u = x^3 + 1$, we see that when $x = 0$, $u = 1$, and when $x = 2$, $u = 9$. Thus, we have

$$\int_0^2 2x^2 \sqrt{x^3 + 1} \, dx = \frac{2}{3} \int_1^9 u^{1/2} \, du$$

$$= \frac{4}{9} u^{3/2} \Big]_1^9$$

$$= \frac{4}{9} \cdot (27 - 1) = \frac{104}{9}$$

Often this second method is shorter, and its justification follows immediately from Theorems 9.1.10 and 10.6.2.

EXAMPLE 3: Find the area of the region in the first quadrant bounded by the curve whose equation is $y = x\sqrt{x^2 + 16}$, the x axis, and the line $x = 3$. Make a sketch.

Solution: See Fig. 10.6.2: the region is shown together with one of the rectangular elements of area.

We take a regular partition of the interval $[0,3]$. The width of each rectangle is Δx, and the altitude of the ith rectangle is $f(\xi_i)$, where ξ_i is any point in the ith subinterval. Therefore, the area of the rectangular element is $f(\xi_i)\,\Delta x$. The sum of the areas of n such rectangles is

$$\sum_{i=1}^{n} f(\xi_i)\,\Delta x$$

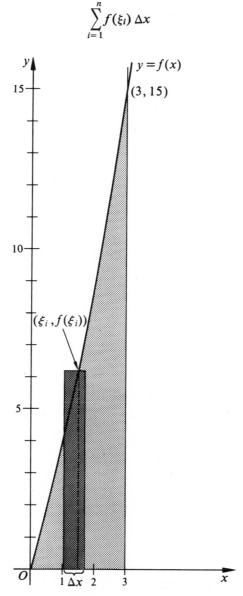

Figure 10.6.2

The limit of this sum as Δx approaches zero (or $n \to +\infty$) is the area desired. The limit of the Riemann sum is a definite integral, which we evaluate by the fundamental theorem of integral calculus.

Let A = the number of square units in the area of the region; then,

$$A = \lim_{\Delta x \to 0} \sum_{i=1}^{n} f(\xi_i)\, \Delta x$$

$$= \int_0^3 x\sqrt{x^2 + 16}\, dx$$

To integrate, we let $u = x^2 + 16$; then $du = 2x\, dx$, or $du/2 = x\, dx$. When $x = 0$, $u = 16$; when $x = 3$, $u = 25$. Then,

$$A = \frac{1}{2} \int_{16}^{25} u^{1/2}\, du = \frac{1}{2} \cdot \frac{2}{3} u^{3/2} \Big]_{16}^{25}$$

$$= \frac{1}{3}[(25)^{3/2} - (16)^{3/2}]$$

$$= \frac{1}{3}[125 - 64] = 20\frac{1}{3}$$

EXAMPLE 4: Given $f(x) = x\sqrt{x - 4}$, find the average value of f on the interval $[5, 8]$.

Solution: Let A.V. = the average value of f on $[5,8]$. We have, from Sec. 10.5,

$$\text{A.V.} = \frac{1}{8 - 5} \int_5^8 x\sqrt{x - 4}\, dx$$

Let $u = \sqrt{x - 4}$; then $u^2 = x - 4$; $x = u^2 + 4$; $dx = 2u\, du$; when $x = 5$, $u = 1$; when $x = 8$, $u = 2$. Therefore,

$$\text{A.V.} = \frac{1}{3} \int_1^2 (u^2 + 4)\, u\, (2u\, du)$$

$$= \frac{2}{3} \int_1^2 (u^4 + 4u^2)\, du$$

$$= \frac{2}{3}\left[\frac{1}{5}u^5 + \frac{4}{3}u^3\right]_1^2$$

$$= \frac{2}{3}\left[\frac{32}{5} + \frac{32}{3} - \frac{1}{5} - \frac{4}{3}\right] = 10\frac{16}{45}$$

Exercises 10.6

In Exercises 1 through 18, evaluate the definite integral by using the fundamental theorem of integral calculus.

1. $\displaystyle\int_{2}^{7} (x^2 - 2x)\, dx$

2. $\displaystyle\int_{-1}^{3} (3x^2 + 5x - 1)\, dx$

3. $\displaystyle\int_{0}^{4} (y^3 - y^2 + 1)\, dy$

4. $\displaystyle\int_{-3}^{3} (t^6 - 3t)\, dt$

5. $\displaystyle\int_{2}^{4} \frac{4dx}{5x^4}$

6. $\displaystyle\int_{-1}^{3} \frac{dy}{(y + 2)^2}$

7. $\displaystyle\int_{-2}^{0} 3w\sqrt{4 - w^2}\, dw$

8. $\displaystyle\int_{1}^{3} \frac{x\, dx}{(3x^2 - 1)^2}$

9. $\displaystyle\int_{-5}^{5} 2x\sqrt[3]{x^2 + 2}\, dx$

10. $\displaystyle\int_{1}^{5} \frac{dx}{\sqrt{3x - 1}}$

11. $\displaystyle\int_{0}^{1} \frac{(y^2 + 2y)\, dy}{\sqrt[3]{y^3 + 3y^2 + 4}}$

12. $\displaystyle\int_{4}^{5} x^2\sqrt{x - 4}\, dx$

13. $\displaystyle\int_{0}^{15} \frac{w\, dw}{(1 + w)^{3/4}}$

14. $\displaystyle\int_{-2}^{1} (x + 1)\sqrt{x + 3}\, dx$

15. $\displaystyle\int_{1}^{4} \frac{x^5 - x}{3x^3}\, dx$

16. $\displaystyle\int_{1}^{64} \left(\sqrt{t} - \frac{1}{\sqrt{t}} + \sqrt[3]{t}\right) dt$

17. $\displaystyle\int_{1}^{2} \frac{x^3 + 2x^2 + x + 2}{(x + 1)^2}\, dx$

HINT: Divide numerator by denominator.

18. $\displaystyle\int_{-3}^{2} \frac{3x^3 - 24x^2 + 48x + 5}{x^2 - 8x + 16}\, dx$

In Exercises 19 through 28, find the area of the region bounded by the given curve and lines. Draw a figure showing the region and a rectangular element of area. Express the area as the limit of a Riemann sum and then as a definite integral. Evaluate the definite integral by the fundamental theorem of integral calculus.

19. $y = 4x - x^2$; x axis; $x = 1$, $x = 3$

20. $y = 9 - x^2$; x axis, y axis; $x = 3$

21. $y = x^2 - 2x + 3$; x axis; $x = -2$, $x = 1$

22. $y = 16 - x^2$; x axis; $x = -4$, $x = 4$

23. $y = \sqrt{x + 1}$; x axis, y axis; $x = 8$

24. $y = 2\sqrt{x - 1}$; x axis; $x = 5$, $x = 17$

25. $y = x\sqrt{x^2 + 9}$; x axis, y axis; $x = 4$

26. $y = x\sqrt{x + 5}$; x axis; $x = -1$, $x = 4$

27. $y = \dfrac{1}{x^2} - x$; x axis; $x = 2$, $x = 3$

28. $y = \dfrac{4}{x^2}$; x axis; $x = -2$, $x = -1$

In Exercises 29 through 33, find the average value of the function f on the given interval $[a,b]$. In Exercises 29, 30, and 31, find the value of x at which the average value of f occurs, and make a sketch.

29. $f(x) = 8x - x^2$; $[a,b] = [0,4]$

30. $f(x) = 9 - x^2$; $[a,b] = [0,3]$

31. $f(x) = \sqrt{x}$; $[a,b] = [1,4]$

32. $f(x) = 3x\sqrt{x^2 - 16}$; $[a,b] = [4,5]$

33. $f(x) = x^2\sqrt{x - 3}$; $[a,b] = [7,12]$

34. (*a*) Find the average value of the function f defined by $f(x) = 1/x^2$ on the interval $[1,r]$. (*b*) If A is the average value found in part (*a*), find $\lim\limits_{r \to +\infty} A$.

11 Applications of the definite integral

(11.1) Area of a region in a plane

If f is a function continuous on the closed interval $[a,b]$ and if $f(x) \geq 0$ for all x in $[a,b]$, then the area of the region bounded by the curve $y = f(x)$, the x axis, and the lines $x = a$ and $x = b$ was defined in Chapter 10 to be

$$\lim_{n \to +\infty} \sum_{i=1}^{n} f(\xi_i)\, \Delta x$$

which is equal to the definite integral $\int_a^b f(x)\, dx$.

Suppose that $f(x) < 0$ for all x in $[a,b]$. Then each $f(\xi_i)$ is a negative number, and so we define the area of the region bounded by $y = f(x)$, the x axis, and the lines $x = a$ and $x = b$, to be $\lim_{n \to +\infty} \sum_{i=1}^{n} [-f(\xi_i)]\, \Delta x$, which equals $-\int_a^b f(x)\, dx$.

EXAMPLE 1: Find the area of the region bounded by the curve $y = x^2 - 4x$, the x axis, and the lines $x = 1$ and $x = 3$.

Solution: The region, together with a rectangular element of area, is shown in Fig. 11.1.1.

If one takes a regular partition of the interval $[1,3]$, the width of each rectangle is Δx. Since $f(x) < 0$ on $[1,3]$, the altitude of the ith rectangle is $-f(\xi_i)$, so that the sum of the areas of n rectangles is

$$\sum_{i=1}^{n} [-f(\xi_i)]\, \Delta x$$

The desired area is the limit of this sum as n approaches $+\infty$, so if A is the number of square units in the area of the region, we have

$$A = \lim_{n \to +\infty} \sum_{i=1}^{n} [-f(\xi_i)]\, \Delta x = -\int_1^3 f(x)\, dx$$

$$= -\int_1^3 (x^2 - 4x)\, dx = -\left[\frac{1}{3}x^3 - 2x^2 \right]_1^3 = 7\frac{1}{3}$$

Thus, the area of the region is $7\frac{1}{3}$ square units.

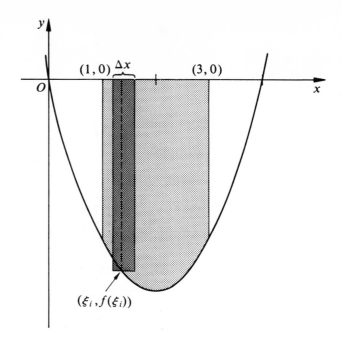

Figure 11.1.1

EXAMPLE 2: Find the area of the region bounded by the curve

$$y = x^3 - 2x^2 - 5x + 6$$

the x axis, and the lines $x = -1$ and $x = 2$.

Solution: The region is shown in Fig. 11.1.2.

Since $f(x) \geq 0$ when x is in the closed interval $[-1,1]$ and $f(x) \leq 0$ when x is in the closed interval $[1,2]$, we separate the region into two parts. Let A_1 be the area of the region when x is in $[-1,1]$, and let A_2 be the area of the region when x is in $[1,2]$. Then,

$$A_1 = \lim_{n \to +\infty} \sum_{i=1}^{n} f(\xi_i) \, \Delta x = \int_{-1}^{1} f(x) \, dx$$

$$= \int_{-1}^{1} (x^3 - 2x^2 - 5x + 6) \, dx$$

and $\quad A_2 = \lim_{n \to +\infty} \sum_{i=1}^{n} [-f(\xi_i)] \, \Delta x = \int_{1}^{2} - (x^3 - 2x^2 - 5x + 6) \, dx$

If A is the number of square units in the area of the entire region, then

$$A = A_1 + A_2$$

$$= \int_{-1}^{1} (x^3 - 2x^2 - 5x + 6) \, dx - \int_{1}^{2} (x^3 - 2x^2 - 5x + 6) \, dx$$

$$= \left[\frac{x^4}{4} - \frac{2}{3}x^3 - \frac{5}{2}x^2 + 6x \right]_{-1}^{1} - \left[\frac{x^4}{4} - \frac{2}{3}x^3 - \frac{5}{2}x^2 + 6x \right]_{1}^{2}$$

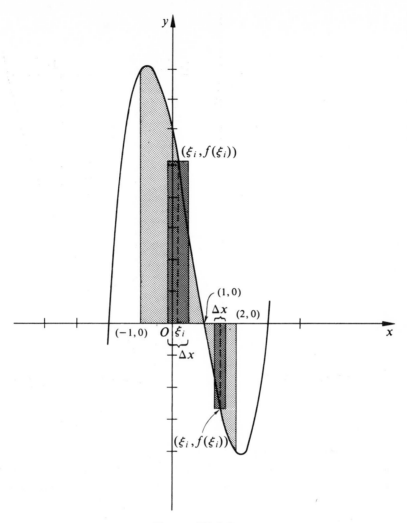

Figure 11.1.2

$$= \left[\left(\frac{1}{4} - \frac{2}{3} - \frac{5}{2} + 6 \right) - \left(\frac{1}{4} + \frac{2}{3} - \frac{5}{2} - 6 \right) \right]$$

$$- \left[\left(4 - \frac{16}{3} - 10 + 12 \right) - \left(\frac{1}{4} - \frac{2}{3} - \frac{5}{2} + 6 \right) \right]$$

$$= \frac{32}{3} - \left(-\frac{29}{12} \right) = 13\frac{1}{12}$$

The area of the region is thus 13 1/12 square units.

Now consider two functions f and g continuous on the closed interval $[a,b]$ and such that $f(x) \geq g(x)$ for all x in $[a,b]$. We wish to find the area of the region bounded by the two curves $y = f(x)$ and $y = g(x)$ and the two lines $x = a$ and $x = b$. Such a situation is shown in Fig. 11.1.3.

Take a regular partition of the interval $[a,b]$, each subinterval having a width of Δx. In each subinterval choose a point ξ_i. Consider the rectangle having altitude $[f(\xi_i) - g(\xi_i)]$ and width Δx. Such a rectangle is shown in Fig. 11.1.3. There are n such rectangles, one associated with each subinterval. The sum of the areas of these n rectangles is given by the following Riemann sum:

$$\sum_{i=1}^{n} [f(\xi_i) - g(\xi_i)] \, \Delta x$$

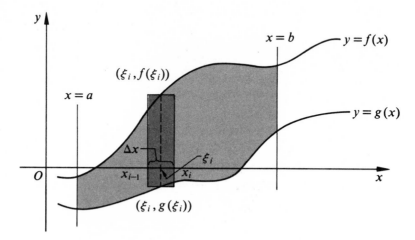

Figure 11.1.3

This Riemann sum is an approximation to what we intuitively think of as the number representing the "area" of the region. The larger the value of n — or equivalently, the smaller the value of Δx — the closer is this approximation. If A is the area of the region, we define

(1)
$$A = \lim_{n \to +\infty} \sum_{i=1}^{n} [f(\xi_i) - g(\xi_i)] \, \Delta x$$

Because f and g are continuous on $[a,b]$, so also is $(f - g)$, and therefore the limit in equation (1) exists and is equal to the definite integral

$$\int_a^b [f(x) - g(x)] \, dx$$

EXAMPLE 3: Find the area of the region bounded by the curves $y = x^2$ and $y = -x^2 + 4x$.

Solution: To find the points of intersection of the two curves, we solve the equations simultaneously and obtain the points $(0,0)$ and $(2,4)$. The region is shown in Fig. 11.1.4.

Let $f(x) = -x^2 + 4x$, and $g(x) = x^2$. Therefore, in the interval $[0,2]$ the curve $y = f(x)$ is above the curve $y = g(x)$. We draw a vertical rectangular element of area, having altitude $[f(\xi_i) - g(\xi_i)]$ and width Δx. The area of this

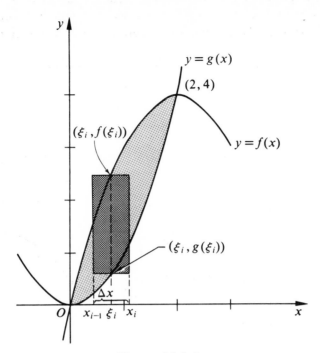

Figure 11.1.4

rectangle is then $[f(\xi_i) - g(\xi_i)]\,\Delta x$. The sum of the areas of n such rectangles is given by the Riemann sum

$$\sum_{i=1}^{n} [f(\xi_i) - g(\xi_i)]\,\Delta x$$

If A is the number of square units in the area of the region, then

$$A = \lim_{n\to+\infty} \sum_{i=1}^{n} [f(\xi_i) - g(\xi_i)]\,\Delta x$$

and the limit of the Riemann sum is a definite integral. Hence we have

$$A = \int_0^2 [f(x) - g(x)]\,dx = \int_0^2 [(-x^2 + 4x) - x^2]\,dx$$

$$= \int_0^2 (-2x^2 + 4x)\,dx = \left[-\frac{2}{3}x^3 + 2x^2 \right]_0^2$$

$$= -\frac{16}{3} + 8 - 0 = \frac{8}{3} = 2\frac{2}{3}$$

The area of the region is $2\frac{2}{3}$ square units.

EXAMPLE 4: Find the area of the region bounded by the parabola $y^2 = 2x - 2$ and the straight line $y = x - 5$.

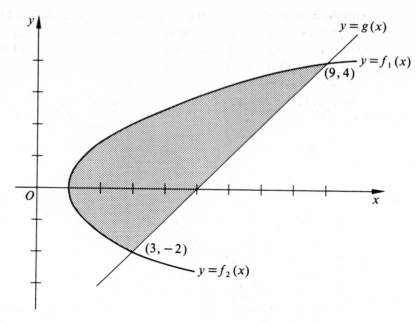

Figure 11.1.5

Solution: The two curves intersect at the points $(3, -2)$ and $(9,4)$. The region is shown in Fig. 11.1.5.

The equation $y^2 = 2x - 2$ is equivalent to the two equations

$$y = \sqrt{2x - 2} \qquad \text{and} \qquad y = -\sqrt{2x - 2}$$

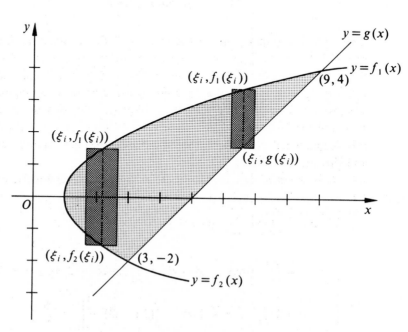

Figure 11.1.6

with the first equation giving the upper half of the parabola and the second equation giving the bottom half. If we let $f_1(x) = \sqrt{2x - 2}$ and $f_2(x) = -\sqrt{2x - 2}$, the equation of the top half of the parabola is $y = f_1(x)$, and the equation of the bottom half of the parabola is $y = f_2(x)$. If we let $g(x) = x - 5$, the equation of the line is $y = g(x)$.

In Fig. 11.1.6 we see two vertical rectangular elements of area. Each rec-

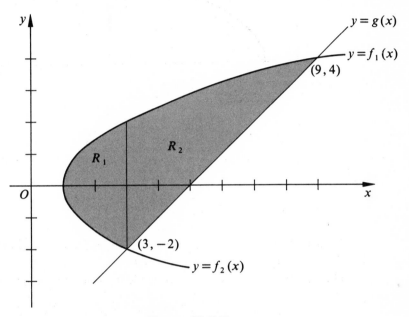

Figure 11.1.7

tangle has the upper base on the curve $y = f_1(x)$. Since the base of the first rectangle is on the curve $y = f_2(x)$, the altitude is $[f_1(\xi_i) - f_2(\xi_i)]$. Since the base of the second rectangle is on the curve $y = g(x)$, its altitude is $[f_1(\xi_i) - g(\xi_i)]$. If we wish to solve this problem by using vertical rectangular elements of area, we must divide the region into two separate regions, say R_1 and R_2, where R_1 is the region bounded by the curves $y = f_1(x)$ and $y = f_2(x)$ and the line $x = 3$, and where R_2 is the region bounded by the curves $y = f_1(x)$ and $y = g(x)$ and the line $x = 3$ (see Fig. 11.1.7).

If A_1 is the number of square units in the area of region R_1, we have

$$A_1 = \lim_{n \to +\infty} \sum_{i=1}^{n} [f_1(\xi_i) - f_2(\xi_i)]\, \Delta x$$

$$= \int_1^3 [f_1(x) - f_2(x)]\, dx = \int_1^3 [\sqrt{2x - 2} + \sqrt{2x - 2}]\, dx$$

$$= 2 \int_1^3 \sqrt{2x - 2}\, dx = \tfrac{2}{3}(2x - 2)^{3/2} \Big]_1^3 = \frac{16}{3}$$

If A_2 is the number of square units in the area of region R_2, we have

$$A_2 = \lim_{n \to +\infty} \sum_{i=1}^{n} [f_1(\xi_i) - g(\xi_i)] \, \Delta x$$

$$= \int_3^9 [f_1(x) - g(x)] \, dx = \int_3^9 [\sqrt{2x-2} - (x-5)] \, dx$$

$$= \left[\frac{1}{3}(2x-2)^{3/2} - \frac{1}{2}x^2 + 5x \right]_3^9$$

$$= \left[\frac{64}{3} - \frac{81}{2} + 45 \right] - \left[\frac{8}{3} - \frac{9}{2} + 15 \right] = \frac{38}{3}$$

Hence $A_1 + A_2 = \dfrac{16}{3} + \dfrac{38}{3} = 18$

Therefore, the area of the entire region is 18 square units.

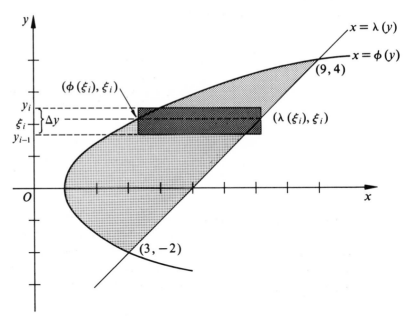

Figure 11.1.8

EXAMPLE 5: Find the area of the region in Example 4 by taking horizontal rectangular elements of area.

Solution: Figure 11.1.8 illustrates the region with a horizontal rectangular element of area.

If in the equations of the parabola and the line we solve for x, we have

$$x = \frac{y^2 + 2}{2} \qquad \text{and} \qquad x = y + 5$$

If we let $\phi(y) = (y^2 + 2)/2$ and $\lambda(y) = y + 5$, the equation of the parabola may be written as $x = \phi(y)$, and the equation of the line as $x = \lambda(y)$. If we consider the closed interval $[-2,4]$ on the y axis and take a regular partition of this interval, each subinterval will have a width of Δy. In the ith subinterval $[y_{i-1}, y_i]$, choose a point ξ_i. Then the length of the ith rectangular element is $[\lambda(\xi_i) - \phi(\xi_i)]$ and the width is Δy. We approximate the area of the region by the Riemann sum:

$$\sum_{i=1}^{n} [\lambda(\xi_i) - \phi(\xi_i)] \, \Delta y$$

If A is the number of square units in the area of the region, then

$$A = \lim_{n \to +\infty} \sum_{i=1}^{n} [\lambda(\xi_i) - \phi(\xi_i)] \, \Delta y$$

Since λ and ϕ are continuous on $[-2,4]$, so also is $(\lambda - \phi)$, and the limit of the Riemann sum is a definite integral:

$$A = \int_{-2}^{4} [\lambda(y) - \phi(y)] \, dy$$

$$= \int_{-2}^{4} \left[(y + 5) - \frac{y^2 + 2}{2} \right] dy = \frac{1}{2} \int_{-2}^{4} (-y^2 + 2y + 8) \, dy$$

$$= \frac{1}{2} \left[-\frac{1}{3} y^3 + y^2 + 8y \right]_{-2}^{4}$$

$$= \frac{1}{2} \left[\left(-\frac{64}{3} + 16 + 32 \right) - \left(\frac{8}{3} + 4 - 16 \right) \right] = 18$$

Comparing the solutions in Examples 4 and 5, we see that in the first case we have two definite integrals to evaluate, whereas in the second case we have only one. In general, if possible, the rectangular elements of area should be constructed so that a single definite integral is obtained for the area. The following example illustrates a situation where two definite integrals are necessary.

EXAMPLE 6: Find the area of the region bounded by the two curves $y = x^3 - 6x^2 + 8x$ and $y = x^2 - 4x$.

Solution: The points of intersection of the two curves are $(0,0)$, $(3,-3)$, and $(4,0)$. The region is shown in Fig. 11.1.9.

Let $f(x) = x^3 - 6x^2 + 8x$ and $g(x) = x^2 - 4x$. In the interval $[0,3]$ the curve $y = f(x)$ is above the curve $y = g(x)$, and in the interval $[3,4]$ the curve $y = g(x)$ is above the curve $y = f(x)$. So, we must divide the region into two separate regions R_1 and R_2, where R_1 is the region bounded by the two curves in the interval $[0,3]$ and R_2 is the region bounded by the two curves in the interval [3,4]. Letting A_1 be the number of square units in the area of R_1 and A_2 be the number of square units in the area of R_2, we have

$$A_1 = \lim_{n \to +\infty} \sum_{i=1}^{n} [f(\xi_i) - g(\xi_i)] \, \Delta x$$

and $$A_2 = \lim_{n \to +\infty} \sum_{i=1}^{n} [g(\xi_i) - f(\xi_i)] \, \Delta x$$

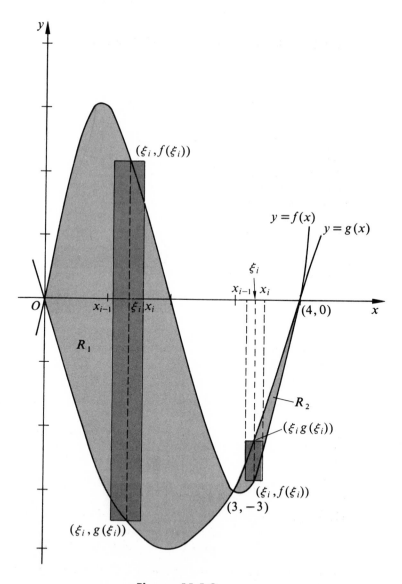

Figure 11.1.9

so that

$$A_1 + A_2 = \int_0^3 [(x^3 - 6x^2 + 8x) - (x^2 - 4x)]\, dx$$

$$+ \int_3^4 [(x^2 - 4x) - (x^3 - 6x^2 + 8x)]\, dx$$

$$= \int_0^3 (x^3 - 7x^2 + 12x)\, dx + \int_3^4 (-x^3 + 7x^2 - 12x)\, dx$$

$$= \left[\frac{1}{4}x^4 - \frac{7}{3}x^3 + 6x^2\right]_0^3 + \left[-\frac{1}{4}x^4 + \frac{7}{3}x^3 - 6x^2\right]_3^4$$

$$= \frac{45}{4} + \frac{7}{12} = \frac{71}{6} = 11\frac{5}{6}$$

Therefore, the required area is 11 5/6 square units.

Exercises 11.1

In Exercises 1 through 18, find the area of the region bounded by the given curves. In each problem do the following: (*a*) draw a figure showing the region and a rectangular element of area; (*b*) express the area of the region as the limit of a Riemann sum; (*c*) find the limit in part (*b*) by evaluating a definite integral by the fundamental theorem of integral calculus.

1. $x^2 = -y;\ y = -4$ 2. $y^2 = -x;\ x = -2;\ x = -4$

3. $x^2 + y + 4 = 0;\ y = -8$. Take the elements of area perpendicular to the y axis.

4. The same region as in Exercise 3. Take the elements of area parallel to the y axis.

5. $x^3 = 2y^2;\ x = 0;\ y = -2$ 11. $y = \sqrt{x};\ y = x^3$

6. $y^3 = 4x;\ x = 0;\ y = -2$ 12. $x = 4 - y^2;\ x = 4 - 4y$

7. $y = 2 - x^2;\ y = -x$ 13. $y^3 = x^2;\ x - 3y + 4 = 0$

8. $y = x^2;\ y = x^4$ 14. $xy^2 = y^2 - 1;\ x = 1;\ y = 1;\ y = 4$

9. $y^2 = x - 1;\ x = 3$ 15. $x = y^2 - 2;\ x = 6 - y^2$

10. $y = x^2;\ x^2 = 18 - y$ 16. $x = y^2 - y;\ x = y - y^2$

17. $y = 2x^3 - 3x^2 - 9x;\ y = x^3 - 2x^2 - 3x$

18. $3y = x^3 - 2x^2 - 15x;\ y = x^3 - 4x^2 - 11x + 30$

19. Find by integration the area of the triangle having vertices (5,1), (1,3), and (−1,−2).

20. Find by integration the area of the triangle having vertices (3,4), (2,0), and (0,1).

21. Find the area of the region bounded by the curve $x^3 - x^2 + 2xy - y^2 = 0$, and the line $x = 4$. HINT: Solve the cubic equation for y in terms of x, and express y as two functions of x.

(11.2) Volume of a solid of revolution: circular-disk and circular-ring methods

We earlier developed a method for finding the area of a plane region. Now we extend this process to find the volume of a solid of revolution. A *solid of revolution* is obtained by revolving a region in a plane about a line in the plane, called the *axis of revolution*, which either touches the boundary of the region or does not intersect the region at all. For example, if the region bounded by a semi-circle and its diameter is revolved about the diameter, a sphere is generated. A right-circular cone is generated if the region bounded by a right triangle is revolved about one of its legs.

As we did when we considered the area of a plane region, we must first define what we mean by the "volume" of a solid of revolution. That is, we wish to as-sign a number, say V, to what we intuitively think of as the volume of such a solid. We shall assume that the volume of a right-circular cylinder of base radius r and altitude h is given by $\pi r^2 h$.

First we shall consider the case where the axis of revolution is a boundary of the region that is revolved. Let the function f be continuous on the closed in-terval $[a,b]$, and assume that $f(x) \geq 0$ for all x in $[a,b]$. Let R be the region bounded by the curve $y = f(x)$, the x axis, and the lines $x = a$ and $x = b$. Let S be the solid of revolution obtained by revolving the region R about the x axis, and let V be the volume of S. We shall proceed to find a suitable definition for V.

Let Δ be a partition of the closed interval $[a,b]$ given by

$$a = x_0 < x_1 < x_2 < \cdots < x_{n-1} < x_n = b$$

We have then n subintervals of the form $[x_{i-1}, x_i]$, where $i = 1, 2, \ldots, n$; the length of the ith subinterval being $\Delta_i x = x_i - x_{i-1}$. Choose any point ξ_i, with $x_{i-1} \leq \xi_i \leq x_i$, in each subinterval and draw the rectangles having widths $\Delta_i x$ and altitudes $f(\xi_i)$. In Fig. 11.2.1 the region R is shown together with the ith rectangle.

When the ith rectangle is revolved about the x axis, we obtain a circular disk in the form of a right-circular cylinder of base radius $f(\xi_i)$ and altitude $\Delta_i x$, as shown in Fig. 11.2.2. The volume of this circular disk, which we shall denote by $\Delta_i V$, is given by

(1) $$\Delta_i V = \pi [f(\xi_i)]^2 \, \Delta_i x$$

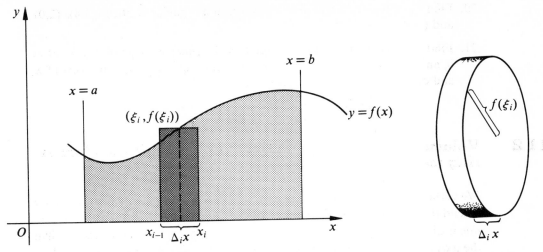

Figure 11.2.1   **Figure 11.2.2**

Since we have n rectangles, we obtain n circular disks in this way, and the sum of the volume of these n circular disks is given by

$$(2) \qquad \sum_{i=1}^{n} \Delta_i V = \sum_{i=1}^{n} \pi [f(\xi_i)]^2 \, \Delta_i x$$

which is a Riemann sum.

The Riemann sum given in equation (2) is an approximation to what we intuitively think of as the volume of the solid of revolution. The smaller we take the norm $\|\Delta\|$ of the partition, then the larger will be n, and the closer this approximation will be to the number we wish to assign to the volume. We therefore define the volume to be the limit of the Riemann sum in equation (2) as $\|\Delta\|$ approaches zero. This limit exists since f^2 is continuous on $[a,b]$, which is true because f is continuous there. We have then the following definition.

11.2.1 DEFINITION   Let the function f be continuous on the closed interval $[a,b]$, and assume $f(x) \geq 0$ for all x in $[a,b]$. If S is the solid of revolution obtained by revolving about the x axis the region bounded by the curve $y = f(x)$, the x axis, and the lines $x = a$ and $x = b$, and if V is the volume of S, then

$$(3) \qquad V = \lim_{\|\Delta\| \to 0} \sum_{i=1}^{n} \pi [f(\xi_i)]^2 \, \Delta_i x$$

The limit of the Riemann sum in formula (3) is evaluated by the definite integral

$$\pi \int_a^b [f(x)]^2 \, dx$$

EXAMPLE 1: The region bounded by the curve $y = x^2$, the x axis, and the lines $x = 1$ and $x = 2$ is revolved about the x axis. Find the volume of the solid generated.

Solution: Refer to Fig. 11.2.3, showing the region and a rectangular element of area. Figure 11.2.4 shows an element of volume.

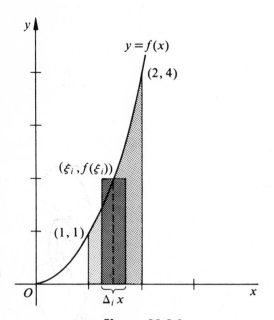

Figure 11.2.3

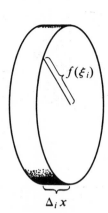

Figure 11.2.4

The volume of the circular disk is given by

$$\Delta_i V = \pi [f(\xi_i)]^2 \, \Delta_i x$$

Then, $\qquad V = \lim_{||\Delta|| \to 0} \sum_{i=1}^{n} \pi [f(\xi_i)]^2 \, \Delta_i x = \pi \int_1^2 [f(x)]^2 \, dx$

so that $\qquad V = \pi \int_1^2 x^4 \, dx = \pi \dfrac{x^5}{5} \Big]_1^2 = \dfrac{31}{5} \pi$

Therefore, the volume of the solid of revolution is $31\pi/5$ cubic units.

Now, suppose that the axis of revolution is not a boundary of the region being revolved. Let f and g be two continuous functions on the closed interval $[a,b]$, and assume $f(x) \geq g(x) \geq 0$ for all x in $[a,b]$. Let R be the region bounded by the curves $y = f(x)$ and $y = g(x)$ and the lines $x = a$ and $x = b$. Let S be the solid of revolution generated by revolving the region R about the x axis. If V is the volume of S, we wish to find a value for V.

Let Δ be a partition of the interval $[a,b]$, given by

$$a_0 = x_1 < x_2 < \cdots < x_{n-1} < x_n = b,$$

and the ith subinterval $[x_{i-1}, x_i]$ has length $\Delta_i x = x_i - x_{i-1}$. In the ith sub-interval, choose any ξ_i, with $x_{i-1} \leq \xi_i \leq x_i$. Draw the n rectangular elements of area for the region R. See Fig. 11.2.5 illustrating the region and the ith rectangle.

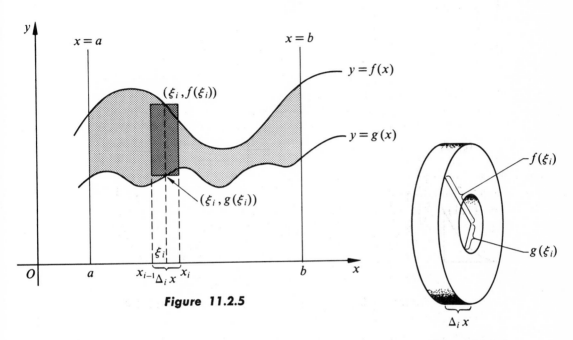

Figure 11.2.5

Figure 11.2.6

When the ith rectangle is revolved about the x axis, a circular ring (or "washer"), as shown in Fig. 11.2.6, is obtained. The volume of this circular ring is given by

$$\Delta_i V = \pi([f(\xi_i)]^2 - [g(\xi_i)]^2)\, \Delta_i x$$

The sum of the volumes of the n circular rings formed by revolving the n rectangular elements of area about the x axis is

(4) $$\sum_{i=1}^{n} \Delta_i V = \sum_{i=1}^{n} \pi([f(\xi_i)]^2 - [g(\xi_i)]^2)\, \Delta_i x$$

The volume then is defined to be the limit of the Riemann sum in equation (4) as $\|\Delta\|$ approaches zero. The limit exists since f^2 and g^2 are continuous on $[a,b]$, because f and g are continuous there.

11.2.2 DEFINITION   Let the functions f and g be continuous on the closed interval $[a,b]$, and assume $f(x) \geq g(x) \geq 0$ for all x in $[a,b]$. Then the volume V of the solid of revolution generated by revolving about the x axis the region bounded by the curves $y = f(x)$ and $y = g(x)$ and the lines $x = a$ and $x = b$ is given by

$$(5) \qquad V = \lim_{\|\Delta\| \to 0} \sum_{i=1}^{n} \pi([f(\xi_i)]^2 - [g(\xi_i)]^2) \, \Delta_i x$$

We evaluate the limit of the Riemann sum in formula (5) by the definite integral

$$\pi \int_a^b ([f(x)]^2 - [g(x)]^2) \, dx$$

EXAMPLE 2: Find the volume of the solid generated by revolving about the x axis the region bounded by the parabola $y = x^2 + 1$ and the line $y = x + 3$.

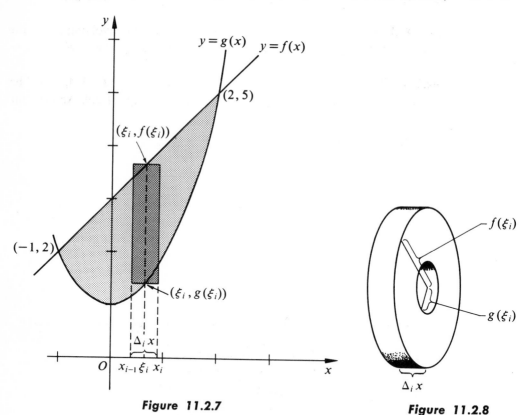

Figure 11.2.7   **Figure 11.2.8**

Solution: The points of intersection are $(-1,2)$ and $(2,5)$. Figure 11.2.7 shows the region and a rectangular element of area. In Fig. 11.2.8 an element of volume is shown.

We take $f(x) = x + 3$ and $g(x) = x^2 + 1$. The volume of the circular ring is given by

$$\Delta_i V = \pi([f(\xi_i)]^2 - [g(\xi_i)]^2) \, \Delta_i x$$

Then if V is the number of cubic units in the volume of the solid,

$$V = \lim_{\|\Delta\| \to 0} \sum_{i=1}^{n} \pi([f(\xi_i)]^2 - [g(\xi_i)]^2)\, \Delta_i x$$

$$= \pi \int_{-1}^{2} ([f(x)]^2 - [g(x)]^2)\, dx$$

$$= \pi \int_{-1}^{2} [(x+3)^2 - (x^2+1)^2]\, dx = \pi \int_{-1}^{2} [-x^4 - x^2 + 6x + 8]\, dx$$

$$= \pi \left[-\frac{1}{5}x^5 - \frac{1}{3}x^3 + 3x^2 + 8x \right]_{-1}^{2}$$

$$= \pi \left[\left(-\frac{32}{5} - \frac{8}{3} + 12 + 16 \right) - \left(\frac{1}{5} + \frac{1}{3} + 3 - 8 \right) \right] = \frac{117}{5}\pi$$

Therefore the volume of the solid of revolution is $117\pi/5$ cubic units.

EXAMPLE 3: Find the volume of the solid generated by revolving about the line $x = -4$ the region bounded by the two parabolas $x = y - y^2$ and $x = y^2 - 3$.

Solution: The curves intersect at the points $(-2, -1)$ and $(-3/4, 3/2)$. The region and a rectangular element of area are shown in Fig. 11.2.9. An element

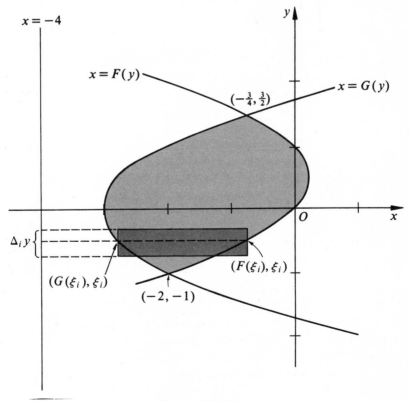

Figure 11.2.9

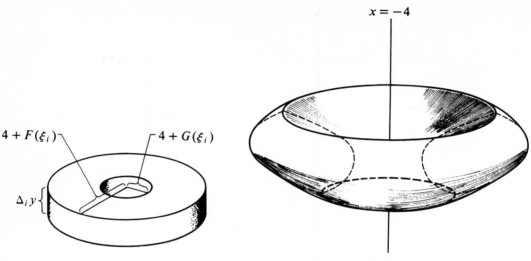

Figure 11.2.10

Figure 11.2.11

of volume, which is a circular ring, is shown in Fig. 11.2.10. Figure 11.2.11 shows the solid of revolution.

Let $F(y) = y - y^2$ and $G(y) = y^2 - 3$. The volume of the circular ring is given by

$$\Delta_i V = \pi([4 + F(\xi_i)]^2 - [4 + G(\xi_i)]^2)\, \Delta_i y$$

Thus, $$V = \lim_{||\Delta|| \to 0} \sum_{i=1}^{n} \pi([4 + F(\xi_i)]^2 - [4 + G(\xi_i)]^2)\, \Delta_i y$$

$$= \pi \int_{-1}^{3/2} [(4 + y - y^2)^2 - (4 + y^2 - 3)^2]\, dy$$

$$= \pi \int_{-1}^{3/2} (-2y^3 - 9y^2 + 8y + 15)\, dy$$

$$= \pi[-\tfrac{1}{2}y^4 - 3y^3 + 4y^2 + 15y]_{-1}^{3/2} = \frac{875}{32}\pi$$

The volume of the solid of revolution is then $875\pi/32$ cubic units.

Exercises 11.2

In Exercises 1 through 8, the equation of the curve in Fig. 11.2.12 is $y^2 = x^3$. Find the volume of the solid of revolution generated when the given region is revolved about the indicated line.

1. *OAC* is revolved about the *x* axis.
2. *OAC* is revolved about the line *AC*.
3. *OAC* is revolved about the line *BC*.
4. *OAC* is revolved about the *y* axis.

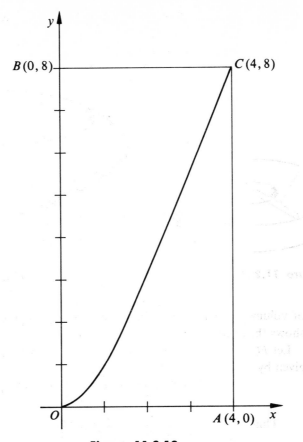

Figure 11.2.12

5. *OBC* is revolved about the *y* axis.
6. *OBC* is revolved about the line *BC*.
7. *OBC* is revolved about the line *AC*.
8. *OBC* is revolved about the *x* axis.

9. Find the volume of the sphere generated by revolving the circle whose equation is $x^2 + y^2 = r^2$ about a diameter.

10. Find the volume of the solid generated by revolving about the *x* axis the region bounded by the curve $y = x^3$ and the lines $y = 0$ and $x = 2$.

11. Find the volume generated by revolving the region in Exercise 10 about the *y* axis.

12. Find the volume generated by revolving about the line $x = -4$, the region bounded by $x = 4 + 6y - 2y^2$.

13. Find the volume of a right-circular cone of altitude *h* and base radius *a* by integration.

14. Find the volume of a segment of a sphere if the sphere is of radius *r* and the altitude of the segment is *h*.

15. A paraboloid of revolution is obtained by revolving a parabola about its axis. Find the volume bounded by a paraboloid of revolution and a plane perpendicular to its axis if the plane is 10 in. from the vertex, and if the plane section of intersection is a circle having a radius of 6 in.

16. Find the volume of the solid generated by revolving about the x axis the region bounded by the loop of the curve whose equation is

$$2y^2 = x(x^2 - 4).$$

17. Find the volume of the solid generated when one loop of the curve whose equation is $x^2y^2 = (x^2 - 9)(1 - x^2)$ is revolved about the x axis.

(11.3) Volume of a solid of revolution: cylindrical-shell method

In the preceding section we found the volume of a solid of revolution by taking the rectangular elements of area perpendicular to the axis of revolution, and the element of volume was either a circular disk or a circular ring. If a rectangular element of area is parallel to the axis of revolution, then when this element of area is revolved about the axis of revolution, a *cylindrical shell* is obtained. A cylindrical shell is a solid contained between two cylinders having the same center and axis. Such a cylindrical shell is shown in Fig. 11.3.1.

If the cylindrical shell has an inner radius r_1, outer radius r_2, and altitude h, then its volume V is given by

(1) $$V = \pi r_2^2 h - \pi r_1^2 h$$

Let R be the region bounded by the curve $y = f(x)$, the x axis, and the lines $x = a$ and $x = b$, where f is continuous on the closed interval $[a,b]$ and $f(x) \geq 0$

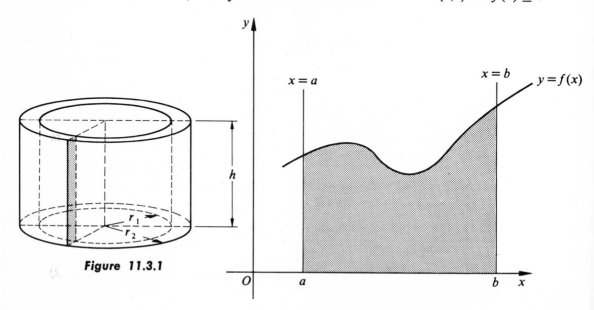

Figure 11.3.1

Figure 11.3.2

for all x in $[a,b]$; furthermore, assume $a \geq 0$. Such a region is shown in Fig. 11.3.2. If R is revolved about the y axis, a solid of revolution S is generated. To find the volume of S when the rectangular elements of area are taken parallel to the y axis, we proceed in the following manner.

Let Δ be a partition of the closed interval $[a,b]$ given by

$$a = x_0 < x_1 < x_2 < \cdots < x_{n-1} < x_n = b.$$

Let m_i be the midpoint of the ith subinterval $[x_{i-1}, x_i]$. Then $m_i = (x_{i-1} + x_i)/2$. Consider the rectangle having altitude $f(m_i)$ and width $\Delta_i x$. If this rectangle is revolved about the y axis, a cylindrical shell is obtained. Figure 11.3.3 shows the rectangular element of area, and Fig. 11.3.4 shows the cylindrical shell.

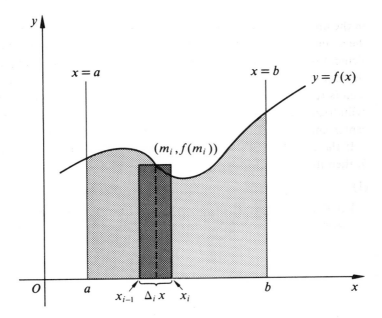

Figure 11.3.3

If $\Delta_i V$ is the volume of this cylindrical shell, we have from formula (1), where $r_1 = x_{i-1}$, $r_2 = x_i$, and $h = f(m_i)$,

$$\Delta_i V = \pi x_i^2 f(m_i) - \pi x_{i-1}^2 f(m_i)$$

$$= \pi(x_i^2 - x_{i-1}^2) f(m_i)$$

(2) $$\Delta_i V = \pi(x_i - x_{i-1})(x_i + x_{i-1}) f(m_i)$$

Since $x_i - x_{i-1} = \Delta_i x$ and since $x_i + x_{i-1} = 2m_i$, we have from equation (2) that

(3) $$\Delta_i V = 2\pi m_i f(m_i) \Delta_i x$$

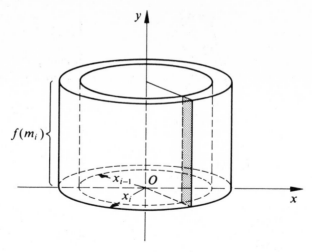

Figure 11.3.4

If we revolve n rectangular elements of area about the y axis, we obtain n cylindrical shells, and the sum of their volumes is given by

$$(4) \qquad \sum_{i=1}^{n} \Delta_i V = \sum_{i=1}^{n} 2\pi m_i f(m_i)\, \Delta_i x$$

which is a Riemann sum.

We then define the volume of the solid of revolution to be the limit of the Riemann sum in equation (4) as $\|\Delta\|$ approaches zero. The limit exists since f is continuous on $[a,b]$.

11.3.1 DEFINITION Let the function f be continuous on the closed interval $[a,b]$ where $a \geq 0$. Assume $f(x) \geq 0$ for all x in $[a,b]$. If R is the region bounded by the curve $y = f(x)$, the x axis, and the lines $x = a$ and $x = b$, and S is the solid of revolution obtained by revolving R about the y axis, then the volume V of S is defined by

$$(5) \qquad V = \lim_{\|\Delta\| \to 0} \sum_{i=1}^{n} 2\pi m_i f(m_i)\, \Delta_i x$$

Definition 11.3.1 is consistent with Definitions 11.2.1 and 11.2.2 for the volume of a solid of revolution for which the definitions apply.

Since f is continuous on $[a,b]$, the limit in equation (5) exists and may be evaluated by the definite integral

$$2\pi \int_a^b x f(x)\, dx$$

The volume of the shell is easily remembered by noticing that $2\pi m_i$ is the circumference of the circle having as radius the mean of the inner and outer radii of the shell, $f(m_i)$ is the altitude of the shell, and $\Delta_i x$ is the thickness.

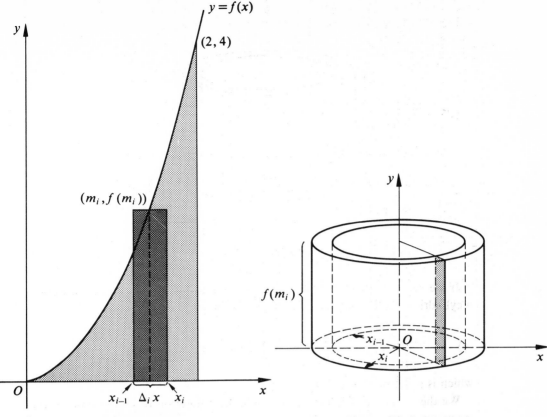

Figure 11.3.5   **Figure 11.3.6**

EXAMPLE 1: The region bounded by the curve $y = x^2$, the x axis, and the line $x = 2$ is revolved about the y axis. Find the volume of the solid generated. Take the elements of area parallel to the axis of revolution.

Solution: Figure 11.3.5 shows the region and a rectangular element of area. Figure 11.3.6 shows the cylindrical shell obtained by revolving the rectangular element of area about the y axis. The solid of revolution obtained is shown in Fig. 11.3.7.

The element of volume is a cylindrical shell whose volume is given by

$$\Delta_i V = 2\pi m_i f(m_i) \, \Delta_i x$$

Thus, $$V = \lim_{\|\Delta\| \to 0} \sum_{i=1}^{n} 2\pi m_i f(m_i) \, \Delta_i x$$

$$= 2\pi \int_0^2 x f(x) \, dx = 2\pi \int_0^2 x(x^2) \, dx$$

$$= 2\pi \int_0^2 x^3 \, dx = 2\pi \left[\frac{x^4}{4}\right]_0^2 = 8\pi$$

Therefore, the volume of the solid of revolution is 8π cubic units.

EXAMPLE 2: The region bounded by the curve $y = x^2$ and the lines $y =$

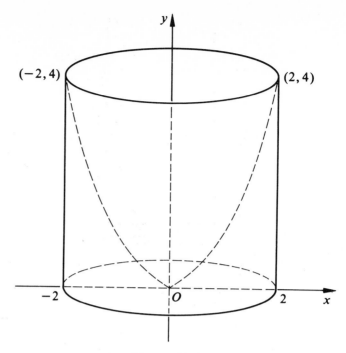

Figure 11.3.7

1 and $x = 2$ is revolved about the line $y = -3$. Find the volume of the solid generated by taking the rectangular elements of area parallel to the axis of revolution.

Solution: The region and a rectangular element of area are shown in Fig. 11.3.8.

The equation of the curve is $y = x^2$. Solving for x, we obtain $x = \pm\sqrt{y}$. Since $x > 0$ for the given region, we have $x = \sqrt{y}$. If we let $g(y) = \sqrt{y}$, the equation of the curve for the given region is $x = g(y)$.

The element of volume is a cylindrical shell that has an outer radius $y_i + 3$, inner radius $y_{i-1} + 3$, altitude $2 - g(m_i)$, and thickness $\Delta_i y$. Therefore, the mean of the inner and outer radii is $m_i + 3$, and the volume of the cylindrical shell is

$$2\pi(m_i + 3)[2 - g(m_i)] \, \Delta_i y$$

The volume of the solid of revolution is then given by

$$
\begin{aligned}
V &= \lim_{||\Delta|| \to 0} \sum_{i=1}^{n} 2\pi(m_i + 3)[2 - g(m_i)] \, \Delta_i y \\
&= \int_{1}^{4} 2\pi(y + 3)[2 - g(y)] \, dy = 2\pi \int_{1}^{4} (y + 3)(2 - \sqrt{y}) \, dy \\
&= 2\pi \int_{1}^{4} (-y^{3/2} + 2y - 3y^{1/2} + 6) \, dy \\
&= 2\pi \left[-\frac{2}{5}y^{5/2} + y^2 - 2y^{3/2} + 6y \right]_{1}^{4} = \frac{66}{5}\pi
\end{aligned}
$$

Hence the volume is $66\pi/5$ cubic units.

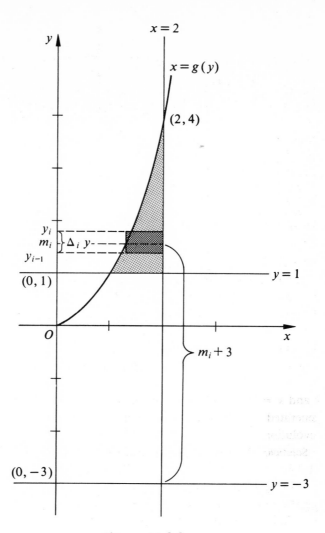

Figure 11.3.8

1–8. Solve Exercises 1 through 8 in Sec. 11.2 by taking the rectangular elements parallel to the axis of revolution.

In Fig. 11.3.9 the region bounded by the x axis, the line $x = 1$, and the curve $y = x^2$ is denoted by R_1; the region bounded by the two curves $y = x^2$ and $y^2 = x$ is denoted by R_2; the region bounded by the y axis, the line $y = 1$, and the curve $y^2 = x$ is denoted by R_3. In Exercises 9 through 16, find the volume of the solid generated when the indicated region is revolved about the given line.

9. R_1 revolved about y axis; rectangular elements parallel to axis of revolution.
10. Same as Exercise 9; but rectangular elements perpendicular to axis of revolution.

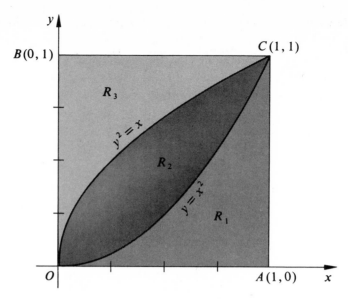

Figure 11.3.9

11. R_2 revolved about x axis; rectangular elements parallel to axis of revolution.

12. Same as Exercise 11; but rectangular elements perpendicular to axis of revolution.

13. R_3 revolved about line $y = 2$; rectangular elements parallel to axis of revolution.

14. Same as Exercise 13; but rectangular elements perpendicular to axis of revolution.

15. R_2 is revolved about line $x = -2$; rectangular elements parallel to axis of revolution.

16. Same as Exercise 15; but rectangular elements perpendicular to axis of revolution.

17. Find the volume of the solid generated if the region bounded by the parabola $y^2 = 4ax$ (with $a > 0$) and the line $x = a$ is revolved about $x = a$.

18. Find the volume of the solid generated by revolving the region bounded by the curve $x^{2/3} + y^{2/3} = a^{2/3}$ about the y axis.

19. Find the volume of the solid generated by revolving about the y axis the region outside the curve $y = x^2$ and between the lines $y = 2x - 1$ and $y = x + 2$.

20. Find the volume of the solid generated by revolving about the line $y = -1$ the region bounded by the line $2y = x + 3$ and outside the curves $y^2 + x = 0$ and $y^2 - 4x = 0$.

21. If a hole of radius a is drilled through the center of a sphere of radius r, find the volume of the solid remaining.

22. Find the volume of the solid generated if the region bounded by a parabola and its latus rectum is revolved about a line through its vertex and perpendicular to its axis.

(11.4)   Work

The "work" done by a force acting on an object is defined in physics as "force times displacement." For example, suppose that an object is moving to the right along the x axis from a point a to a point b, and let F be the number of pounds in the force acting upon the object in the direction of motion. Then if the distance is measured in feet, $(b - a)$ is the number of feet in the distance that the object moves, and if W is the number of foot-pounds of work done by the force, W is defined by

(1) $$W = F(b - a)$$

EXAMPLE 1: Find the work necessary to lift a 70-lb weight to a height of 3 ft.
Solution: Let $W = $ the number of foot-pounds in the work done:
$$W = 70 \times 3 = 210$$

In this section we shall consider the work done by a variable force, which is a function of the position of the object upon which the force is acting. We wish to define what we mean by the term "work" in such a case.

Suppose that F is the force acting in the direction of motion upon an object as it moves to the right along the x axis from point a to point b, and also that F is a function of x. Let Δ be a partition of the closed interval $[a,b]$:

$$a = x_0 < x_1 < x_2 < \cdots < x_{n-1} < x_n = b$$

The ith subinterval is $[x_{i-1}, x_i]$, and let ξ_i be any point in this subinterval, with $x_{i-1} \le \xi_i \le x_i$. If x_{i-1} is close to x_i, the force is almost constant in the ith subinterval. If we assume that the force is constant in the ith subinterval, and if $\Delta_i W$ is the work done on the object as it moves from the point x_{i-1} to the point x_i, then from formula (1) we have

$$\Delta_i W = F(\xi_i)(x_i - x_{i-1})$$

Replacing $x_i - x_{i-1}$ by $\Delta_i x$, we have
$$\Delta_i W = F(\xi_i) \, \Delta_i x$$
and

(2) $$\sum_{i=1}^{n} \Delta_i W = \sum_{i=1}^{n} F(\xi_i) \, \Delta_i x$$

The smaller we take the norm of the partition Δ, then the larger n will be and the closer the Riemann sum in equation (2) will be to what we intuitively think of as the total work done. We therefore define the total work as the limit of the Riemann sum in equation (2).

11.4.1 DEFINITION Let the function F be continuous on the closed interval $[a,b]$. $F(x)$ is the number of units in the force acting upon an object at point x on the x axis. Then if W is the work done by the force as the object moves from a to b,

(3)
$$W = \lim_{\|\Delta\|\to 0} \sum_{i=1}^{n} F(\xi_i)\, \Delta_i x$$

Since F is continuous on $[a,b]$, the limit in equation (3) exists and is equal to the definite integral $\int_a^b F(x)\, dx$.

In the following example, we shall make use of *Hooke's law*, which states that if a spring is stretched x inches beyond its natural length, it is pulled back with a force equal to kx, where k is a constant depending upon the wire used.

EXAMPLE 2: A spring has a natural length of 14 in. If a force of 5 lb is required to keep the spring stretched 2 in., how much work is done in stretching the spring from its natural length to a length of 18 in.?

Solution: Place the spring along the x axis with the origin at the point where the stretching starts (see Fig. 11.4.1).

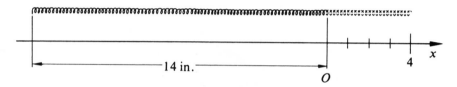

Figure 11.4.1

Let x = number of inches the spring is stretched

F = number of pounds in the force acting upon the spring x inches beyond its natural length

Then, by Hooke's law, $F = kx$. Since $F = 5$, when $x = 2$, we have

$$5 = k\cdot 2$$

$$k = \frac{5}{2}$$

Therefore, $$F = \frac{5}{2}x$$

If W = the number of inch-pounds of work done in stretching the spring from its natural length of 14 in. to a length of 18 in., we have

$$W = \lim_{\|\Delta\|\to 0} \sum_{i=1}^{n} F(\xi_i)\, \Delta_i x = \int_0^4 F(x)\, dx$$

$$= \int_0^4 \frac{5}{2}x\, dx = \frac{5}{4}x^2 \Big]_0^4 = 20$$

Therefore, the work done in stretching the spring is 20 in.-lb.

EXAMPLE 3: A water tank in the form of an inverted right-circular cone is

20 ft across the top and 15 ft deep. If the surface of the water is 5 ft below the top of the tank, find the work done in pumping the water to the top of the tank.

Solution: Refer to Fig. 11.4.2.

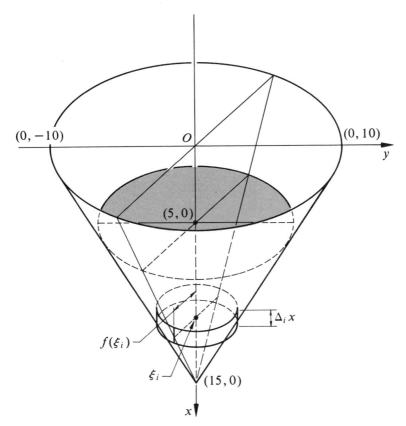

Figure 11.4.2

We choose the positive x axis in the downward direction since the motion is vertical. Take the origin at the top of the tank. Take a partition of the closed interval [5,15] on the x axis. Let ξ_i be any point in the ith subinterval $[x_{i-1}, x_i]$. An element of volume is a circular disk having thickness $\Delta_i x$ and radius $f(\xi_i)$, where the function f is determined by the equation of the line through the points (0,10) and (15,0). The volume of this element is given by $\Delta_i V = \pi[f(\xi_i)]^2 \Delta_i x$, where $\Delta_i x = x_i - x_{i-1}$. If w is the number of pounds in the weight of 1 ft^3 of water, then the number of pounds in the weight of this element is $w\pi[f(\xi_i)]^2 \Delta_i x$, which is the force required to pump the element to the top of the tank. If x_{i-1} is close to x_i, then the distance through which this element moves is approximately ξ_i. Thus if $\Delta_i W$ is the work done in pumping the element to the top of the tank, $\Delta_i W$ is approximately $(w\pi[f(\xi_i)]^2 \Delta_i x) \cdot \xi_i$, so that

$$W = \lim_{\|\Delta\| \to 0} \sum_{i=1}^{n} w\pi[f(\xi_i)]^2 \cdot \xi_i \, \Delta_i x$$
$$= w\pi \int_5^{15} [f(x)]^2 x \, dx$$

To find $f(x)$, we find an equation of the line through the points $(15,0)$ and $(0,10)$, using the intercept form:

$$\frac{x}{15} + \frac{y}{10} = 1 \quad \text{or} \quad y = -\frac{2}{3}x + 10$$

Therefore, $f(x) = -\frac{2}{3}x + 10$, and

$$W = w\pi \int_5^{15} \left(-\frac{2}{3}x + 10\right)^2 x \, dx$$

$$= w\pi \int_5^{15} \left(\frac{4}{9}x^3 - \frac{40}{3}x^2 + 100x\right) dx$$

$$= w\pi \left[\frac{1}{9}x^4 - \frac{40}{9}x^3 + 50x^2\right]_5^{15}$$

$$= \frac{10,000}{9}\pi w$$

The work done is $10,000\pi w/9$ ft-lb.

Exercises 11.4

1. A spring has a natural length of 8 in. If a force of 20 lb stretches the spring ½ in., find the work done in stretching the spring from 8 in. to 11 in.

2. A spring has a natural length of 10 in., and a 30-lb force stretches it to 11½ in. Find the work done in stretching the spring from 10 in. to 12 in. Then find the work done in stretching the spring from 12 in. to 14 in.

3. A spring has a natural length of 6 in. A 12,000-lb force compresses the spring to 5½ in. Find the work done in compressing it from 6 in. to 5 in. Hooke's law holds for compression as well as for extension.

4. A spring has a natural length of 6 in. A 1200-lb force compresses it to 5½ in. Find the work done in compressing it from 6 in. to 4½ in. Then find the work required to bring the spring to 9 in. from its compressed state of 4½ in.

5. A swimming pool full of water is in the form of a rectangular parallelepiped 5 ft deep, 15 ft wide, and 25 ft long. Find the work required to pump the water in the pool up to a level 1 ft above the surface of the pool.

6. A trough full of water is 10 ft long, and its cross section is in the shape of an isosceles triangle 2 ft wide across the top and 2 ft high. How much work is done in pumping all the water out of the trough over the top?

7. A trough full of water is 6 ft long, and its cross section is in the shape of a semicircle with a diameter of 2 ft at the top. How much work is required to pump the water out over the top?

8. A right-circular cylindrical tank with a depth of 12 ft and a radius of 4 ft is half full of oil weighing 60 lb per cubic foot. Find the work done in pumping the oil to a height 6 ft above the tank.

9. A hemispherical tank with a radius of 6 ft is filled with water to a depth of 4 ft. Find the work done in pumping the water to the top of the tank.

10. A meteorite is a miles from the center of the earth and falls to the surface of the earth. The force of gravity is inversely proportional to the square of the distance of a body from the center of the earth. Find the work done by gravity if the weight of the meteorite is w lb at the surface of the earth. Let R be the number of miles in the radius of the earth.

(11.5)   Liquid pressure

Suppose a flat plate is inserted horizontally into a liquid in a container. The weight of the liquid exerts a force on the plate. The force per square unit of area exerted by the liquid on the plate is called the *pressure* of the liquid.

Let w be the number of pounds in the weight of one cubic foot of the liquid and h be the number of feet in the depth of a point below the surface of the liquid. If p is the number of pounds per square foot of pressure exerted by the liquid at the point, then

(1) $$p = wh$$

If A is the number of square feet in the area of a flat plate that is submerged horizontally in the liquid, and F is the number of pounds in the force, due to liquid pressure, acting on the upper face of the plate, then

(2) $$F = pA$$

Substituting from formula (1) into (2) gives us

(3) $$F = whA$$

Note that formula (1) states that the size of the container is immaterial as far as liquid pressure is concerned. For example, at a depth of 5 ft in a swimming pool filled with salt water the pressure is the same as at a depth of 5 ft in the Pacific Ocean, assuming the density of the water is the same.

Now, suppose that the plate is submerged vertically in the liquid. Then at points on the plate at different depths, the pressure p, computed from formula (1), will be different and will be greater at the bottom of the plate than at the top. We now proceed to define the force F in the case when the plate is submerged vertically in the liquid. We shall make use of Pascal's principle: at any point in a liquid, the pressure is the same in all directions.

In Fig. 11.5.1 let $ABCD$ be the region bounded by the x axis, the lines $x = a$ and $x = b$, and the curve $y = f(x)$, where the function f is continuous and $f(x) \geq 0$ on the closed interval $[a,b]$. We choose the coordinate axes so that the y axis lies along the line of the surface of the liquid and take the x axis vertical with the positive direction downward. The length of the plate at a depth x is given by $f(x)$.

Let Δ be a partition of the closed interval $[a,b]$ which divides the interval into n subintervals. Choose a point ξ_i in the ith subinterval, with $x_{i-1} \leq \xi_i \leq x_i$. Draw n horizontal rectangles. The ith rectangle has a length of $f(\xi_i)$ and a width of $\Delta_i x$ (see Figure 11.5.1).

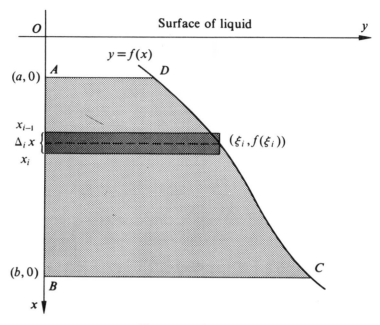

Figure 11.5.1

If we rotate each rectangular element through an angle of 90°, each element becomes a plate submerged in the liquid at a depth of ξ_i ft below the surface of the liquid and perpendicular to the region $ABCD$. Then the force on the ith rectangular element is $w\xi_i f(\xi_i)\, \Delta_i x$. An approximation to the total force on the vertical plate is given by

(4)
$$\sum_{i=1}^{n} w\xi_i f(\xi_i)\, \Delta_i x$$

which is a Riemann sum.

The smaller we take $\|\Delta\|$, the larger n will be and the closer the approximation given by (4) will be to what we wish to be the total force F. Therefore, we define F by

(5)
$$F = \lim_{\|\Delta\| \to 0} \sum_{i=1}^{n} w\xi_i f(\xi_i)\, \Delta_i x$$

Since f is continuous on $[a,b]$, the limit in equation (5) exists and is equal to the definite integral $\int_a^b wxf(x)\, dx$.

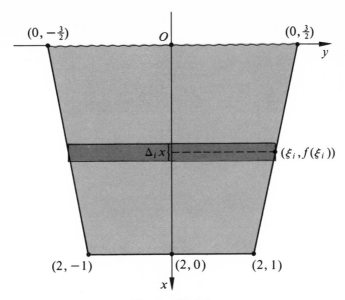

Figure 11.5.2

EXAMPLE 1: A trough having a trapezoidal cross section is full of water. If the trapezoid is 3 ft wide at the top, 2 ft wide at the bottom, and 2 ft deep, find the total force due to liquid pressure on one end of the trough.

Solution: Figure 11.5.2 illustrates one end of the trough together with a rectangular element of area.

If we rotate the rectangular element through 90°, the force on the element is $2w\xi_i f(\xi_i)\,\Delta_i x$. If F is the number of pounds in the total force on the side of the trough.

$$F = \lim_{\|\Delta\| \to 0} \sum_{i=1}^{n} 2w\xi_i f(\xi_i)\,\Delta_i x$$

$$= 2w \int_0^2 xf(x)\,dx$$

To find $f(x)$, we get an equation of line AB, which is $y = 3/2 - x/4$; therefore, $f(x) = 3/2 - x/4$, and

$$F = 2w \int_0^2 x\left(\frac{3}{2} - \frac{1}{4}x\right) dx = 2w\left[\frac{3}{4}x^2 - \frac{1}{12}x^3\right]_0^2 = \frac{14}{3}w$$

If we take $w = 62.5$, then the total force is 291.2 lb.

EXAMPLE 2: The ends of a trough are semicircles, each with a radius of 2 ft. Find the force due to liquid pressure on one end if the trough is full of water.

Solution: Figure 11.5.3 shows one end of the trough, together with a rectangular element of area. The force on the element is $2w\xi_i f(\xi_i)\,\Delta_i x$.

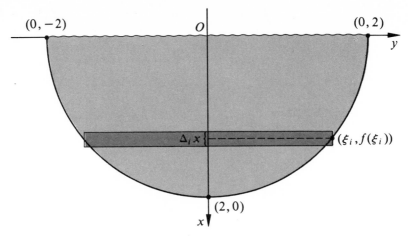

Figure 11.5.3

If F is the number of pounds in the total force on the side of the trough,

$$F = \lim_{\|\Delta\|\to 0} \sum_{i=1}^{n} 2w\xi_i f(\xi_i)\,\Delta_i x$$

$$= 2w \int_0^2 x f(x)\,dx$$

An equation of the semicircle is $x^2 + y^2 = 4$. Solving for y gives us $y = \sqrt{4 - x^2}$, so that $f(x) = \sqrt{4 - x^2}$. Therefore,

$$F = 2w \int_0^2 x\sqrt{4 - x^2}\,dx = -\frac{2}{3}w(4 - x^2)^{3/2}\Big]_0^2 = \frac{16}{3}w$$

Therefore, the total force is $16w/3$ lb.

Exercises 11.5

1. A plate in the shape of a rectangle is submerged vertically in a tank of water, with the upper edge lying in the surface. If the width of the plate is 10 ft and the depth is 8 ft, find the force due to liquid pressure on one side of the plate.

2. A plate in the shape of an isosceles right triangle is submerged vertically in a tank of water, with one leg lying in the surface. The legs are each 6 ft long. Find the force due to liquid pressure on one side of the plate.

3. A rectangular tank full of water is 2 ft wide and 18 in. deep. Find the force due to liquid pressure on one end of the tank.

4. The ends of a trough are equilateral triangles having sides with lengths of 2 ft. If the water in the trough is 1 ft deep, find the force due to liquid pressure on one end.

5. The face of a dam adjacent to the water is vertical, and its shape is in the form of an isosceles triangle 250 ft wide across the top and 100 ft high in the center. If the water is 10 ft deep in the center, find the total force on the dam due to liquid pressure.

6. An oil tank is in the shape of a right-circular cylinder 4 ft in diameter, and its axis is horizontal. If the tank is half full of oil weighing 50 lb per cubic foot, find the total force on one end.

7. The face of the gate of a dam is in the shape of an isosceles triangle 4 ft wide at the top and 3 ft high. If the upper edge of the face of the gate is 15 ft below the surface of the water, find the total force due to liquid pressure on the gate.

8. The face of a gate of a dam is vertical and in the shape of an isosceles trapezoid 3 ft wide at the top, 4 ft wide at the bottom, and 3 ft high. If the upper base is 20 ft below the surface of the water, find the total force due to liquid pressure on the gate.

9. The bottom of a swimming pool is an inclined plane. The pool is 2 ft deep at one end and 8 ft deep at the other. If the width of the pool is 25 ft and the length is 40 ft, find the total force due to liquid pressure on the bottom.

10. The face of a dam adjacent to the water is inclined at an angle of 30° from the vertical. The shape of the face is an isosceles trapezoid 120 ft wide at the top, 80 ft wide at the bottom, and with a slant height of 40 ft. If the dam is full of water, find the total force due to liquid pressure on the face.

(11.6) Center of mass of a rod

In Sec. 10.5 we saw that if the function f is continuous on the closed interval $[a,b]$ the average value of f on $[a,b]$ is given by

$$\frac{\int_a^b f(x)\, dx}{b - a}$$

An important application of the average value of a function occurs in physics in connection with the concept of *center of mass*.

Suppose, for example, that a rigid horizontal rod has P as its point of support, and a particle having a weight of n pounds is suspended on the rod at a distance of d feet from P. From observation, the greater the value of d, the greater, will be the tendency of the rod to turn about the point P. The turning effect of the particle is called the *moment* of the particle about the point P. In general, if a force of F pounds is applied at a distance d feet from a reference point P, and if M is the number of foot-pounds in the moment with respect to P, due to the force, then

(1) $$M = Fd$$

Suppose that two children are on a seesaw. Let the first child, having a weight of w_1 lb, be at a distance of d_1 ft to the left of the fulcrum (point of support), and let the second child, having a weight of w_2 lb, be at a point d_2 ft to the right of the fulcrum. Then the seesaw will balance if and only if

$$(2) \qquad\qquad w_1d_1 = w_2d_2$$

Consider the seesaw as a horizontal line; call it the x axis with origin at the fulcrum. Let the unit of length be 1 ft. If the first child is at the point having coordinate x_1, and the second child is at the point having coordinate x_2, then $x_1 = -d_1$ and $x_2 = d_2$, so that equation (2) becomes

$$(3) \qquad\qquad w_1x_1 + w_2x_2 = 0$$

Equation (3) is a simple example of the following principle of mechanics:

Principle 1: A plane system of parallel forces acting on a rigid body is in equilibrium if and only if the algebraic sum of the moments of these forces, with respect to an arbitrary reference point in the plane, is zero.

In the following discussion we shall also make use of another principle of mechanics.

Principle 2: A plane system of parallel forces acting on a rigid body is in equilibrium if and only if the vector sum of those forces is zero.

Suppose now that we have a rod and neglect the weight of the rod. Place the rod on the x axis. On the rod is a system of a finite number n of particles having masses $m_1, m_2, \ldots, m_n$, located at points $(x_1,0), (x_2,0), \ldots, (x_n,0)$ (see Fig. 11.6.1).

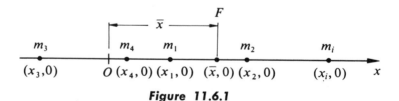

Figure 11.6.1

From physics, the weight of a particle of mass m is equal to mg, where g is the constant of acceleration due to gravity. So the weight of the ith particle having mass m_i is m_ig. If we denote this weight by F_i, we have

$$(4) \qquad\qquad F_i = m_ig$$

If F is the magnitude of the force that must be applied on the rod at a distance $\bar{x}$ from O in order to keep the system in equilibrium (that is, to keep the rod from turning owing to the weight of the particles), then from Principle 1 we have

$$F\bar{x} - \sum_{i=1}^{n} m_igx_i = 0$$

or, equivalently,

(5)
$$\bar{x} = \frac{\sum\limits_{i=1}^{n} m_i g x_i}{F}$$

From Principle 2, we have

$$F - \sum_{i=1}^{n} m_i g = 0$$

or, equivalently,

(6)
$$F = \sum_{i=1}^{n} m_i g$$

Substituting from equation (6) into (5), we get

$$\bar{x} = \frac{\sum\limits_{i=1}^{n} m_i g x_i}{\sum\limits_{i=1}^{n} m_i g}$$

Since g is a constant, we divide both numerator and denominator by it and get

(7)
$$\bar{x} = \frac{\sum\limits_{i=1}^{n} m_i x_i}{\sum\limits_{i=1}^{n} m_i}$$

The point that is at a distance $\bar{x}$ from the origin is called the *center of mass* of the system. So, the center of mass of a system of particles on a line is the point where the system will balance if the line is considered weightless and if each particle is assumed to have its position at exactly one point. The position of the center of mass is independent of the position of the origin; that is, the location of the center of mass relative to the positions of the particles does not change when the origin is changed.

EXAMPLE 1: Given four particles of masses 2, 3, 1, and 5 units located on the x axis at the points (5,0), (2,0), (−3,0), and (−4,0), respectively, find the center of mass of this system.

Solution: If $\bar{x}$ is the abscissa of the center of mass, we have from formula (7)

$$\bar{x} = \frac{2(5) + 3(2) + 1(-3) + 5(-4)}{2 + 3 + 1 + 5} = -\frac{7}{11}$$

Therefore, the center of mass is at the point (−7/11,0).

We now extend the previous discussion to a rigid horizontal rod having a continuously distributed mass. The rod is said to be *homogeneous* if the mass of a segment of it is directly proportional to the length of the segment. That is, if the segment of length $\Delta_i x$ has mass $\Delta_i m$, then

$$\Delta_i m = k\,\Delta_i x$$

The constant k is called the *density*.

If the rod is nonhomogeneous, we proceed as follows to define the density. Let L be the number of units in the length of the rod. Place the rod on the x axis so that the left end point of the rod is at the origin and the right end point is at the point $(L,0)$ (see Fig. 11.6.2).

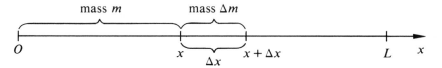

Figure 11.6.2

Choose a point $(x,0)$ on the rod, with $0 < x < L$. Let m be the mass of the portion of the rod from the origin to the point $(x,0)$ where m is a continuous function of x on the closed interval $[0,L]$. Say, $m = g(x)$ on $[0,L]$. Then Δm is the mass of the portion of the rod from $(x,0)$ to $(x + \Delta x, 0)$.

The average density of the segment of the rod from $(x,0)$ to $(x + \Delta x, 0)$ is defined as

$$\frac{\Delta m}{\Delta x} = \frac{g(x + \Delta x) - g(x)}{\Delta x}$$

Then, the density ρ at the point $(x,0)$ is defined by

$$\rho = \lim_{\Delta x \to 0} \frac{g(x + \Delta x) - g(x)}{\Delta x}$$

or equivalently,

(8) $$\rho = g'(x)$$

From equation (8),

$$g(x) = \int_0^x \rho\,dx$$

or equivalently, if m is the mass of the rod from the origin to the point $(x,0)$, then

(9) $$m = \int_0^x \rho\,dx$$

Then if M is the total mass of the rod,

(10) $$M = \int_0^L \rho\,dx$$

EXAMPLE 2: The density at any point of a rod 4 ft long varies directly as the distance from the point to an external point in the line of the rod and 2 ft from an end, where the density is 5 units per foot. Find the total mass of the rod.

Solution: The rod placed on the x axis is shown in Fig. 11.6.3.

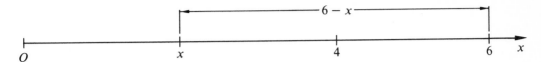

Figure 11.6.3

$\rho = c(6 - x)$, where c is the constant of proportionality. When $x = 4$, $\rho = 5$, so that we have

$$5 = 2c \qquad \text{or} \qquad c = \frac{5}{2}$$

Therefore, $\rho = \frac{5}{2}(6 - x)$

And from equation (10), if M is the number of units in the total mass of the rod,

$$M = \int_0^4 \frac{5}{2}(6 - x)\,dx$$

$$= \frac{5}{2}\left[6x - \frac{x^2}{2} \right]_0^4 = 40$$

We now find the center of mass of a nonhomogeneous rod L ft long, where the density at a point x ft from the left end point is given by $\rho = f(x)$, where f is continuous and $f(x) \geq 0$ on $[a,b]$. As above, place the rod on the x axis with the left end point at the origin and the right end point at $(L,0)$ (see Fig.11.6.4).

Figure 11.6.4

Let Δ be a partition of the closed interval $[0,L]$ into n subintervals. The ith subinterval is $[x_{i-1},x_i]$, having length $\Delta_i x$. Let η_i be the midpoint of this interval. Assume that the mass of the element of length $\Delta_i x$ is concentrated at η_i. If m_i is the mass of the ith element, we have

(11) $m_i = f(\eta_i)\,\Delta_i x$

In formula (7), then, we let $x_i = \eta_i$ and m_i equal its value from (11), and taking the limit of the quotient of Riemann sums as $\|\Delta\|$ approaches zero, we define $\bar{x}$ as follows:

(12) $$\bar{x} = \lim_{\|\Delta\| \to 0} \frac{\displaystyle\sum_{i=1}^{n} \eta_i f(\eta_i)\,\Delta_i x}{\displaystyle\sum_{i=1}^{n} f(\eta_i)\,\Delta_i x}$$

Since f is continuous on $[0, L]$, the limit of each Riemann sum in equation (12) may be evaluated by a definite integral:

$$(13) \qquad \bar{x} = \frac{\int_0^L xf(x)\, dx}{\int_0^L f(x)\, dx}$$

Since $\rho = f(x)$, the denominator in formula (13) is M from (10), and we may rewrite (13) as

$$(14) \qquad \bar{x} = \frac{\int_0^L x\rho\, dx}{\int_0^L \rho\, dx}$$

or

$$(15) \qquad \bar{x} = \frac{\int_0^L x\rho\, dx}{M}$$

EXAMPLE 3: Find the center of mass for the rod in Example 2.

Solution: We found $M = 40$, and $\rho = 5(6-x)/2$ so that

$$\bar{x} = \frac{\int_0^4 \frac{5}{2}x(6 - x)\, dx}{40} = \frac{1}{16}\left[3x^2 - \frac{x^3}{3}\right]_0^4 = \frac{5}{3}$$

Therefore, the center of mass is at $(5/3, 0)$.

Note that if a rod is of uniform density k, where k is a constant, then from formula (14) we have

$$\bar{x} = \frac{\int_0^L xk\, dx}{\int_0^L k\, dx} = \frac{\dfrac{kx^2}{2}\Big]_0^L}{kx\Big]_0^L} = \frac{kL^2/2}{kL} = \frac{L}{2}$$

Thus, the center of mass is at the center of the rod, which is to be expected.

Exercises 11.6

In Exercises 1 through 4, find the center of mass of the system of particles having the given masses and located on the x axis at the indicated points.

1. $m_1 = 5$ at $(2,0)$; $m_2 = 6$ at $(3,0)$; $m_3 = 4$ at $(5,0)$; $m_4 = 3$ at $(8,0)$
2. $m_1 = 2$ at $(-4,0)$; $m_2 = 8$ at $(-1,0)$; $m_3 = 4$ at $(2,0)$; $m_4 = 2$ at $(3,0)$
3. $m_1 = 2$ at $(-3,0)$; $m_2 = 4$ at $(-2,0)$; $m_3 = 20$ at $(4,0)$; $m_4 = 10$ at $(6,0)$; $m_5 = 30$ at $(9,0)$
4. $m_1 = 5$ at $(-7,0)$; $m_2 = 3$ at $(-2,0)$; $m_3 = 5$ at $(0,0)$; $m_4 = 1$ at $(2,0)$; $m_5 = 8$ at $(10,0)$
5. Find the center of mass of a rod 9 in. long if the number of pounds per inch in the density of the rod at a distance x in. from the one end of the rod is given by $\rho = 4x + 1$.

6. The length of a rod is 3 ft, and the number of pounds per foot in the density of the rod at a point x ft from one end is given by $\rho = 5 + 2x$. Find the center of mass of the rod.

7. The density of a rod at a point is a linear function of the distance of the point from the left end of the rod. The density at the left end is 2 lb/ft and at the right end is 3 lb/ft. If the length of the rod is 10 ft, find the center of mass.

8. A rod is 10 ft long, and its density is a linear function of the distance from the center of the rod. If the density is 5 lb/ft at each end and 3½ lb/ft at the center, find the center of mass of the rod.

9. The density of a rod varies directly as the third power of the distance from one end of the rod. If the length of the rod is 4 ft and the density is 2 lb/ft at the center, find the total mass of the rod.

10. Find the center of mass of the rod in Exercise 9.

(11.7)   Center of mass of a plane region

Let $m_1, m_2, \ldots, m_n$ be the masses of n particles located at points $(x_1,y_1), (x_2,y_2), \ldots, (x_n,y_n)$ in the xy plane, and consider the problem of finding the center of mass of this system. We may imagine the particles being supported by a sheet of negligible weight, negligible thickness, and may assume that each particle has its position at exactly one point. The center of mass is the point where the sheet will balance. In order to find the center of mass, we must find two averages: $\bar{x}$, which is the average value for the abscissas of the n points, and $\bar{y}$, the average value of the ordinates of the n points. We first define the moment of mass with respect to an axis.

If a particle of mass m is at a distance d from an axis, then the moment M of mass, with respect to the axis, is given by

(1) $$M = md$$

If the ith particle of mass m_i is located at the point (x_i,y_i), its distance from the y axis is x_i; and thus from formula (1), the moment of mass with respect to the y axis is $m_i x_i$. Similarly, the moment of mass with respect to the x axis is $m_i y_i$.

The moment of the system of n particles with respect to the y axis, then, denoted by M_y, is given by

(2) $$M_y = \sum_{i=1}^{n} m_i x_i$$

and the moment of this system with respect to the x axis, denoted by M_x, is given by

(3) $$M_x = \sum_{i=1}^{n} m_i y_i$$

If we denote the total mass of the system by M, then

(4)
$$M = \sum_{i=1}^{n} m_i$$

The average abscissa $\bar{x}$ is then given by

(5)
$$\bar{x} = \frac{M_y}{M}$$

and the average ordinate $\bar{y}$ is given by

(6)
$$\bar{y} = \frac{M_x}{M}$$

The center of mass of the system is at the point $(\bar{x}, \bar{y})$. It may be interpreted as the point such that, if the total mass M of the system were concentrated there, its moment of mass with respect to the y axis would be $M\bar{x} = M_y$, and its moment of mass with respect to the x axis would be $M\bar{y} = M_x$.

EXAMPLE 1: Find the center of mass of the four particles having masses 2, 6, 4, and 1, located at the points $(5, -2)$, $(-2, 1)$, $(0, 3)$, and $(4, -1)$, respectively.

Solution:

$$M_y = \sum_{i=1}^{4} m_i x_i = 2(5) + 6(-2) + 4(0) + 1(4) = 2$$

$$M_x = \sum_{i=1}^{4} m_i y_i = 2(-2) + 6(1) + 4(3) + 1(-1) = 13$$

$$M = \sum_{i=1}^{4} m_i = 2 + 6 + 4 + 1 = 13$$

Therefore, $\quad \bar{x} = \dfrac{M_y}{M} = \dfrac{2}{13} \quad$ and $\quad \bar{y} = \dfrac{M_x}{M} = \dfrac{13}{13} = 1$

The center of mass is at $(2/13, 1)$.

Consider now a thin sheet of continuously distributed mass: for example, a piece of paper or a flat strip of tin. We regard such sheets as being two-dimensional. Such a plane region is called a *lamina*. In this section we shall confine ourselves to homogeneous laminae, that is, laminae having constant density. Laminae of variable density will be considered later in connection with applications of multiple integrals.

Let M be the mass of a homogeneous lamina of area A, and let k be the density; then, since density is mass per unit area,

$$M = kA$$

We wish to define what we mean by the center of mass of a homogeneous lamina. First we define the center of mass of a rectangular homogeneous lamina to be at the center of the rectangle. Then if a rectangular homogeneous lamina has mass M, density k, and center of mass at (α,β), its moment of mass with respect to the x axis M_x is given by

$$M_x = \beta k A$$

and its moment of mass with respect to the y axis M_y is given by

$$M_y = \alpha k A$$

Let f be a function continuous on the closed interval $[a,b]$, such that $f(x) \geq 0$ for all x in $[a,b]$. Let L be the homogeneous lamina of density k bounded by the curve $y = f(x)$, the x axis, and the lines $x = a$ and $x = b$ (see Fig. 11.7.1).

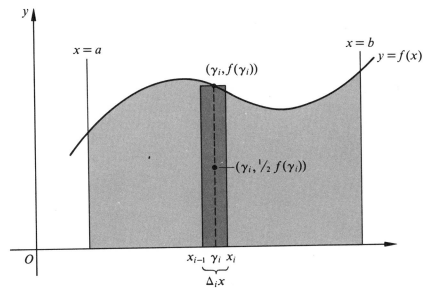

Figure 11.7.1

Let Δ: $a = x_0 < x_1 < \ldots < x_{n-1} < x_n = b$ be a partition of the interval $[a,b]$ into n subintervals. The ith subinterval $[x_{i-1},x_i]$ has a width of $\Delta_i x$, and let γ_i be the midpoint of this interval. Associated with each subinterval is a rectangular lamina having a width $\Delta_i x$, an altitude $f(\gamma_i)$, a density k, and a center of mass at $(\gamma_i,\frac{1}{2}f(\gamma_i))$. The area of this lamina is $f(\gamma_i)\,\Delta_i x$, and so its mass is $kf(\gamma_i)\,\Delta_i x$. Consequently, the moment of mass of this element with respect to the y axis is

$$\gamma_i k f(\gamma_i)\,\Delta_i x$$

The sum of the moments of mass of n such rectangular laminae with respect to the y axis is given by the Riemann sum

$$\sum_{i=1}^{n} k\gamma_i f(\gamma_i)\,\Delta_i x$$

We define the moment of mass of the entire lamina L as the limit of this Riemann sum as $||\Delta||$ approaches zero; that is,

$$(7) \qquad M_y = \lim_{||\Delta|| \to 0} \sum_{i=1}^{n} k\gamma_i f(\gamma_i) \, \Delta_i x$$

Since f is continuous on $[a,b]$ the limit in equation (7) may be evaluated by a definite integral, and we have

$$(8) \qquad M_y = k \int_a^b x f(x) \, dx$$

Similarly, the moment of mass of the ith rectangular lamina with respect to the x axis is

$$\tfrac{1}{2} f(\gamma_i) k f(\gamma_i) \, \Delta_i x$$

and the sum of the moments of mass of n such rectangular laminae with respect to the x axis is given by the Riemann sum

$$(9) \qquad \sum_{i=1}^{n} \tfrac{1}{2} k f(\gamma_i) f(\gamma_i) \, \Delta_i x$$

Thus, the moment of mass of the lamina L about the x axis is M_x, defined by

$$M_x = \lim_{||\Delta|| \to 0} \sum_{i=1}^{n} \tfrac{1}{2} k [f(\gamma_i)]^2 \, \Delta_i x$$

Since f is continuous on $[a,b]$, so also is f^2, and we have

$$(10) \qquad M_x = \tfrac{1}{2} k \int_a^b [f(x)]^2 \, dx$$

The mass of the ith rectangular lamina is $k f(\gamma_i) \, \Delta_i x$ (density times area), so that the sum of the masses of n rectangular laminae is

$$\sum_{i=1}^{n} k f(\gamma_i) \, \Delta_i x$$

and we define the total mass M of the lamina L by

$$M = \lim_{||\Delta|| \to 0} \sum_{i=1}^{n} k f(\gamma_i) \, \Delta_i x$$

Since f is continuous on $[a,b]$,

$$(11) \qquad M = k \int_a^b f(x) \, dx$$

If $(\bar{x}, \bar{y})$ denotes the center of mass of the lamina L, we define

$$\bar{x} = \frac{M_y}{M} \qquad \text{and} \qquad \bar{y} = \frac{M_x}{M}$$

which, by using formulas (8), (10), and (11), gives us

$$\bar{x} = \frac{k \int_a^b xf(x) \, dx}{k \int_a^b f(x) \, dx}$$

If we divide both numerator and denominator by k, we get

(12)
$$\bar{x} = \frac{\int_a^b xf(x) \, dx}{\int_a^b f(x) \, dx}$$

and, similarly,

(13)
$$\bar{y} = \frac{\frac{1}{2} \int_a^b [f(x)]^2 \, dx}{\int_a^b f(x) \, dx}$$

In formulas (12) and (13) the denominator is the area of the region, and so we have expressed a physical problem in terms of a geometrical problem; that is, $\bar{x}$ and $\bar{y}$ may be considered as the average abscissa and the average ordinate, respectively, of a geometric region. In such a case, $\bar{x}$ and $\bar{y}$ depend only upon the region, not upon the mass of the lamina. So we refer to the center of mass of a plane region instead of to the center of mass of a homogeneous lamina. In such a case, we call the center of mass the *centroid* of the region. Instead of moments of mass, we shall consider moments of the region. We define the moments of the plane region in the above discussion with respect to the x axis and the y axis as follows:

$$M_x = \lim_{||\Delta|| \to 0} \sum_{i=1}^{n} \frac{1}{2} [f(\gamma_i)]^2 \, \Delta_i x = \frac{1}{2} \int_a^b [f(x)]^2 \, dx$$

$$M_y = \lim_{||\Delta|| \to 0} \sum_{i=1}^{n} \gamma_i f(\gamma_i) \, \Delta_i x = \int_a^b xf(x) \, dx$$

If $(\bar{x}, \bar{y})$ is the centroid of the plane region and if M_x and M_y are defined as above,

$$\bar{x} = \frac{M_y}{A} \quad \text{and} \quad \bar{y} = \frac{M_x}{A}$$

EXAMPLE 2: Find the centroid of the region bounded by the curve $y^2 = 4x$, the x axis, and the lines $x = 1$ and $x = 4$.

Solution: Let $f(x) = 2x^{1/2}$. The equation of the curve is then $y = f(x)$. In Fig. 11.7.2, the region is shown together with the ith rectangular element. The centroid of the rectangle is at $(\gamma_i, \frac{1}{2} f(\gamma_i))$. The area of the region is given by

$$A = \lim_{||\Delta|| \to 0} \sum_{i=1}^{n} f(\gamma_i) \, \Delta_i x = \int_1^4 f(x) \, dx$$

$$= \int_1^4 2x^{1/2} \, dx = \frac{4}{3} x^{3/2} \Big]_1^4 = \frac{28}{3}$$

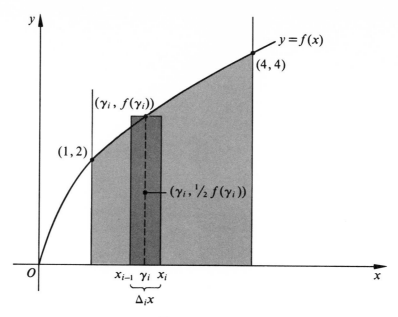

Figure 11.7.2

$$M_y = \lim_{||\Delta||\to 0} \sum_{i=1}^{n} \gamma_i f(\gamma_i) \, \Delta_i x = \int_1^4 x f(x) \, dx$$

$$= \int_1^4 x(2x^{1/2}) \, dx = 2 \int_1^4 x^{3/2} \, dx$$

$$= \frac{4}{5}x^{5/2} \Big]_1^4 = \frac{124}{5}$$

$$M_x = \lim_{||\Delta||\to 0} \sum_{i=1}^{n} \tfrac{1}{2}f(\gamma_i) \cdot f(\gamma_i) \, \Delta_i x = \tfrac{1}{2} \int_1^4 [f(x)]^2 \, dx$$

$$= \tfrac{1}{2} \int_1^4 4x \, dx = x^2 \Big]_1^4 = 15$$

Hence $\quad \bar{x} = \dfrac{M_y}{A} = \dfrac{124/5}{28/3} = \dfrac{93}{35}$

and $\quad \bar{y} = \dfrac{M_x}{A} = \dfrac{15}{28/3} = \dfrac{45}{28}$

Therefore, the centroid is at the point $(93/35, 45/28)$.

EXAMPLE 3: Find the centroid of the region bounded by the curves $y = x^2$ and $y = 2x + 3$.

Solution: The points of intersection of the two curves are $(-1,1)$ and $(3,9)$. The region is shown in Fig. 11.7.3, together with the ith rectangular element.

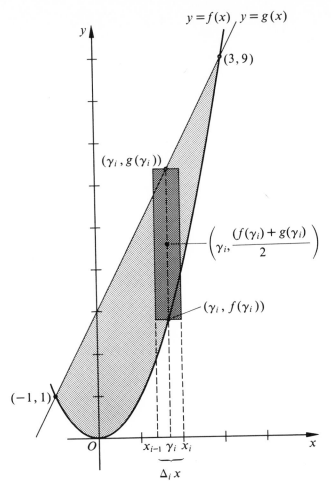

Figure 11.7.3

Let $f(x) = x^2$ and $g(x) = 2x + 3$. The centroid of the ith rectangular element is at the point $\left(\gamma_i, \dfrac{f(\gamma_i) + g(\gamma_i)}{2}\right)$, where γ_i is the midpoint of the ith sub-interval $[x_{i-1}, x_i]$. The area of the region is given by

$$A = \lim_{\|\Delta\| \to 0} \sum_{i=1}^{n} [g(\gamma_i) - f(\gamma_i)]\, \Delta_i x = \int_{-1}^{3} [g(x) - f(x)]\, dx$$

$$= \int_{-1}^{3} [2x + 3 - x^2]\, dx = \frac{32}{3}$$

$$M_y = \lim_{\|\Delta\| \to 0} \sum_{i=1}^{n} \gamma_i [g(\gamma_i) - f(\gamma_i)]\, \Delta_i x$$

$$= \int_{-1}^{3} x[g(x) - f(x)]\, dx = \int_{-1}^{3} x[2x + 3 - x^2]\, dx = \frac{32}{3}$$

$$M_x = \lim_{\|\Delta\| \to 0} \sum_{i=1}^{n} \tfrac{1}{2}[g(\gamma_i) + f(\gamma_i)][g(\gamma_i) - f(\gamma_i)] \, \Delta_i x$$

$$= \tfrac{1}{2} \int_{-1}^{3} [g(x) + f(x)][g(x) - f(x)] \, dx$$

$$= \tfrac{1}{2} \int_{-1}^{3} [2x + 3 + x^2][2x + 3 - x^2] \, dx$$

$$= \tfrac{1}{2} \int_{-1}^{3} [4x^2 + 12x + 9 - x^4] \, dx = \frac{544}{15}$$

Therefore, $\bar{x} = \dfrac{M_y}{A} = \dfrac{32/3}{32/3} = 1$ and $\bar{y} = \dfrac{M_x}{A} = \dfrac{544/15}{32/3} = \dfrac{17}{5}$

Hence, the centroid is at the point $(1, 17/5)$.

If a plane region has an axis of symmetry, then the centroid of the region lies on the axis of symmetry. We next state and prove this as a theorem.

11.7.1 THEOREM   If the plane region R has the line L as an axis of symmetry, then the centroid of R lies on L.

Proof: Choose the coordinate axes so that L is on the y axis and the origin is in the region R. Figure 11.7.4 illustrates an example of this situation. In the figure, R is the region CDE, C is the point $(-a, 0)$, E is the point $(a, 0)$, and the equation of the curve CDE is $y = f(x)$.

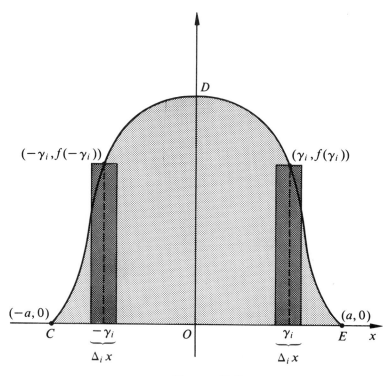

Figure 11.7.4

Consider a partition of the interval $[0,a]$. Let γ_i be the midpoint of the ith subinterval $[x_{i-1}, x_i]$. The moment with respect to the y axis of the rectangular element having an altitude $f(\gamma_i)$ and a width $\Delta_i x$ is $\gamma_i[f(\gamma_i)\,\Delta_i x]$. Because of symmetry, for a similar partition of the interval $[-a, 0]$ there is a corresponding element having as its moment with respect to the y axis: $-\gamma_i f(\gamma_i)\,\Delta_i x$. The sum of these two moments is zero; therefore, $M_y = 0$. Since $\bar{x} = M_y/A$, we conclude that $\bar{x} = 0$. Therefore, the centroid of the region R lies on the y axis, which is what was to be proved.

By applying the preceding theorem, we may simplify the problem of finding the centroid of a plane region that can be divided into regions having axes of symmetry.

EXAMPLE 4: Find the centroid of the region bounded by the semicircle $y = \sqrt{4 - x^2}$ and the x axis.

Solution: The region is shown in Fig. 11.7.5.

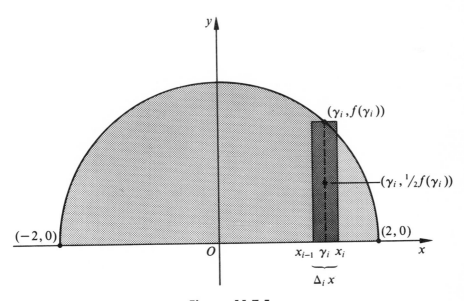

Figure 11.7.5

Let $f(x) = \sqrt{4 - x^2}$. Since the y axis is an axis of symmetry, we may conclude that the centroid lies on the y axis, so that $\bar{x} = 0$.

The moment of the region with respect to the x axis is given by

$$M_x = \lim_{\|\Delta\|\to 0} \sum_{i=1}^{n} \tfrac{1}{2}[f(\gamma_i)]^2 \,\Delta_i x$$

$$= 2 \cdot \tfrac{1}{2} \int_0^2 [f(x)]^2 \, dx = \int_0^2 (4 - x^2)\, dx$$

$$= 4x - \frac{x^3}{3} \Big]_0^2 = 8 - \frac{8}{3} = \frac{16}{3}$$

The area of the region is 2π, so that

$$\bar{y} = \frac{16/3}{2\pi} = \frac{8}{3\pi}$$

There is a useful relation between the force due to liquid pressure on a plane region and the location of the centroid of the region. As in Sec. 11.5, let $ABCD$ be the region bounded by the x axis, the lines $x = a$ and $x = b$, and the curve $y = f(x)$, where f is continuous and $f(x) \geq 0$ on the closed interval $[a,b]$. The region $ABCD$ may be considered as a vertical plate immersed in a liquid having weight w per cubic unit of the liquid (see Fig. 11.7.6).

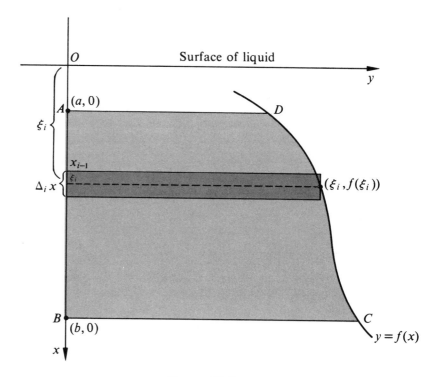

Figure 11.7.6

The force, due to liquid pressure, on the vertical plate is defined by

$$F = \lim_{||\Delta|| \to 0} \sum_{i=1}^{n} w\xi_i f(\xi_i)\, \Delta_i x$$

or equivalently,

(14) $$F = w \int_a^b xf(x)\, dx$$

If $\bar{x}$ is the abscissa of the centroid of the region $ABCD$, then $\bar{x} = M_y/A$. Since

$M_y = \int_a^b xf(x)\,dx$, we have

$$\bar{x} = \frac{\int_a^b xf(x)\,dx}{A}$$

and so

(15) $$\int_a^b xf(x)\,dx = \bar{x}A$$

Substituting from equation (15) into (14), we obtain

(16) $$F = w\bar{x}A$$

Formula (16) states that the total force, due to liquid pressure, against a plane region is the same as it would be if the entire area of the region were concentrated at a depth $\bar{x}$ units below the surface of a liquid.

For example, consider a trough full of water having as ends semicircles each with a radius of 2 ft. Using the result of Example 3 of this section, the centroid of the region is at a depth of $8/3\pi$ ft. Therefore, using formula (16), if F is the number of pounds in the force on one end of the trough,

$$F = w \cdot \frac{8}{3\pi} \cdot 2\pi = \frac{16}{3}w$$

This agrees with the result found in Example 2 of Sec. 11.5.

For various simple plane regions, the centroid may be found in a table. When both the area of the region and the centroid of the region may be obtained directly, formula (16) is easy to apply and is used in such cases by engineers to find the force due to liquid pressure.

Exercises 11.7

1. Find the center of mass of the three particles having masses of 1, 2, and 3 units and located at the points $(-1,3)$, $(2,1)$, and $(3,-1)$, respectively.

2. Find the center of mass of the four particles having masses of 2, 3, 3, and 4 units and located at the points $(-1,-2)$, $(1,3)$, $(0,5)$, and $(2,1)$, respectively.

3. Prove that the centroid of three equal masses in a plane lies at the point of intersection of the medians of the triangle having as vertices the points at which the masses are located.

4. Find the center of mass of four particles having equal masses, located at the points $(3,0)$, $(2,2)$, $(2,4)$, and $(-1,2)$.

In Exercises 5 through 13, find the centroid of the region with boundaries as noted.

5. The parabola $y = 4 - x^2$ and the x axis.
6. The curve $x = 2y - y^2$ and the y axis.
7. The curve $y = x^2$ and the line $y = 4$.
8. The curve $y^2 = 4x$, the y axis, and the line $y = 4$.

9. The lines $y = 2x + 1$, $x + y = 7$, and $x = 8$.
10. The parabola $y^2 = x$ and the line $y = x - 2$.
11. The curves $y = x^3$ and $y = 4x$ in the first quadrant.
12. The curves $y = x^2$ and $y = x^3$.
13. The curves $y = x^2 - 4$ and $y = 2x - x^2$.

14. Prove that the distance from the centroid of a triangle to any side of the triangle is equal to one-third the length of the altitude to that side.

15. If the centroid of the region bounded by the parabola $y^2 = 4px$ and the line $x = a$ is to be the focus of the parabola, find the value of a.

16. Solve Exercise 2 of Sec. 11.5 by using formula (16) of this section.

17. Solve Exercise 3 of Sec. 11.5 by using formula (16) of this section.

18. The face of a dam adjacent to the water is vertical and is in the shape of an isosceles trapezoid 90 ft wide at the top, 60 ft wide at the bottom, and 20 ft high. Use formula (16) of this section to find the total force due to liquid pressure on the face of the dam.

19. Find the moment about the lower base of the trapezoid of the force in Exercise 18.

20. A semicircular plate with a radius of 3 ft is submerged vertically in a tank of water, with its diameter lying in the surface. Use formula (16) of this section to find the force due to liquid pressure on one side of the plate.

21. Let R be the region bounded by the curves $y = f_1(x)$ and $y = f_2(x)$ (see Fig. 11.7.7). If A is the area of R and if $\bar{y}$ is the centroid of R, prove that the volume V of the solid of revolution obtained by revolving R about the x axis is given by

$$V = 2\pi\bar{y}A$$

Stating this formula in words we have:

If a plane region is revolved about a line in its plane that does not cut the region, then the volume of the solid of revolution generated is equal to the product of the area of the region and the distance traveled by the centroid of the region.

The above statement is known as the *theorem of Pappus* for volumes of solids of revolution.

22. Use the theorem of Pappus to find the volume of the torus (doughnut-shaped) generated by revolving a circle with a radius of r about a line in its plane at a distance of b units from its center, where $b > r$.

23. Use the theorem of Pappus to find the centroid of the region bounded by a semicircle and its diameter.

24. Use the theorem of Pappus to find the volume of a right-circular cone with a base radius of r and an altitude of h.

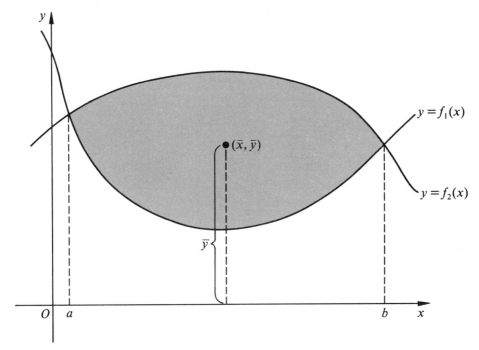

Figure 11.7.7

25. Use the theorem of Pappus to find the volume of a sphere with a radius of r.

26. Let R be the region bounded by the semicircle $y = \sqrt{r^2 - x^2}$ and the x axis. Use the theorem of Pappus to find the moment of R with respect to the line $y = -r$.

27. If R is the region of Exercise 26, use the theorem of Pappus to find the volume of the solid of revolution generated by revolving R about the line $x - y = r$. HINT: Use the result of Exercise 27 in Sec. 8.8.

(11.8)   Center of mass of a solid of revolution

In order to find the center of mass of a solid, in general we must make use of multiple integration. This procedure will be taken up later as an application of multiple integrals. However, if the shape of the solid is that of a solid of revolution, and its density is constant, we may find the center of mass by a method similar to the one used to obtain the center of mass of a homogeneous lamina. Following is the procedure for finding the center of mass of a homogeneous solid of revolution, with the assumption that the center of mass is on the axis of revolution.

We first set up a three-dimensional coordinate system. The x and y axes are taken as in two dimensions, and the third axis, the z axis, is taken perpendicular to them at the origin O. A point in three dimensions is then given by

(x,y,z). The plane containing the x and y axes is called the xy plane, and the xz plane and the yz plane are defined similarly.

Suppose that the x axis is the axis of revolution. Then under the assumption that the center of mass lies on the axis of revolution, the y and z coordinates of the center of mass are each zero, and so it is only necessary to find the x coordinate, which we call $\bar{x}$. In order to find $\bar{x}$, we make use of the moment of the solid of revolution with respect to the yz plane.

Let f be a function that is continuous on the closed interval $[a,b]$, and assume $f(x) \geq 0$ for all x in $[a,b]$. R is the region bounded by the curve $y = f(x)$, the x axis, and the lines $x = a$ and $x = b$; S is the homogeneous solid of revolution, of constant density k, generated by revolving the region R about the x axis. Take a partition Δ of the closed interval $[a,b]$, and denote the ith subinterval by $[x_{i-1},x_i]$ (with $i = 1, 2, \ldots, n$), having length $\Delta_i x = x_i - x_{i-1}$. Let γ_i be the midpoint of $[x_{i-1},x_i]$. Form n rectangles having altitudes of length $f(\gamma_i)$ and bases of a width $\Delta_i x = x_i - x_{i-1}$. Refer to Fig. 11.8.1, showing the

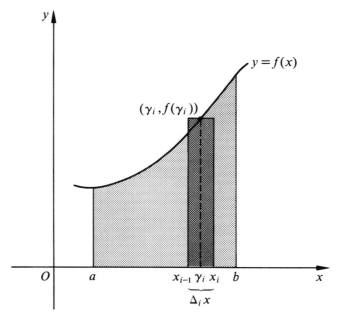

Figure 11.8.1

region R and the ith rectangle. If each of the n rectangles is revolved about the x axis, n circular disks are generated. The ith rectangle generates a circular disk having a radius of $f(\gamma_i)$ and a thickness of $\Delta_i x$; its volume is $\pi[f(\gamma_i)]^2 \Delta_i x$, and its mass is $k\pi[f(\gamma_i)]^2 \Delta_i x$. Figure 11.8.2 shows the solid of revolution S and the ith circular disk.

The center of mass of the circular disk lies on the axis of revolution at the center of the disk: $(\gamma_i,0,0)$. The moment of mass of the disk with respect to the yz plane is then

$$\gamma_i(k\pi[f(\gamma_i)]^2 \Delta_i x)$$

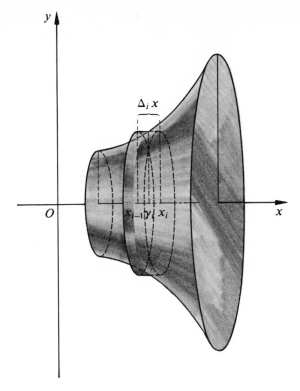

Figure 11.8.2

The sum of the moments of mass of the n circular disks with respect to the yz plane is

(1)
$$\sum_{i=1}^{n} \gamma_i k\pi [f(\gamma_i)]^2 \, \Delta_i x$$

The moment of mass of S with respect to the yz plane, denoted by M_{yz}, is then defined to be the limit of the Riemann sum in (1) as $||\Delta||$ approaches zero; so that we have

(2)
$$M_{yz} = \lim_{||\Delta|| \to 0} \sum_{i=1}^{n} \gamma_i k\pi [f(\gamma_i)]^2 \, \Delta_i x$$

or equivalently,

(3)
$$M_{yz} = k\pi \int_a^b x[f(x)]^2 \, dx$$

The volume of S was defined in Sec. 11.2 as

$$V = \lim_{||\Delta|| \to 0} \sum_{i=1}^{n} \pi [f(\gamma_i)]^2 \, \Delta_i x$$

or equivalently,

(4)
$$V = \pi \int_a^b [f(x)]^2 \, dx$$

We define the mass of solid S as

$$M = \lim_{||\Delta|| \to 0} \sum_{i=1}^{n} k\pi [f(\gamma_i)]^2 \, \Delta_i x$$

or equivalently,

(5) $$M = k\pi \int_a^b [f(x)]^2 \, dx$$

We define the center of mass of S as the point $(\bar{x},0,0)$ such that

(6) $$\bar{x} = \frac{M_{yz}}{M}$$

Substituting from equations (3) and (5) into (6), we get

$$\bar{x} = \frac{k\pi \int_a^b x[f(x)]^2 \, dx}{k\pi \int_a^b [f(x)]^2 \, dx}$$

or equivalently,

(7) $$\bar{x} = \frac{\int_a^b x[f(x)]^2 \, dx}{\int_a^b [f(x)]^2 \, dx}$$

From equation (7), we see that the center of mass of a homogeneous solid of revolution depends only upon the shape of the solid, not on its substance. Therefore, as in the case of a homogeneous lamina, we refer to the center of mass as the *centroid* of the solid of revolution. When we have a homogeneous solid of revolution, instead of the moment of mass we shall consider the moment of the solid. If M_{yz} is the moment of the solid S with respect to the yz plane,

$$M_{yz} = \lim_{||\Delta|| \to 0} \sum_{i=1}^{n} \gamma_i \pi [f(\gamma_i)]^2 \, \Delta_i x$$

or equivalently,

(8) $$M_{yz} = \pi \int_a^b x[f(x)]^2 \, dx$$

Thus, if $(\bar{x},0,0)$ is the centroid of S, from equations (4), (7), and (8) we have

$$\bar{x} = \frac{M_{yz}}{V}$$

EXAMPLE 1: Find the centroid of the solid of revolution generated by revolving about the x axis the region bounded by the curve $y = x^2$, the x axis, and the line $x = 3$.

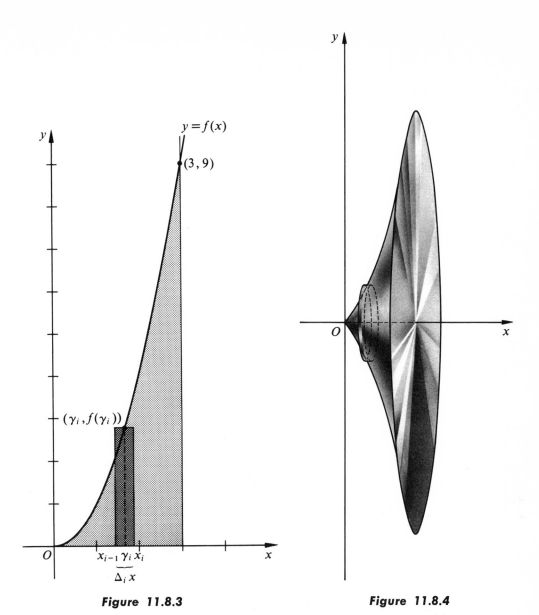

Figure 11.8.3   **Figure 11.8.4**

Solution: The region and a rectangular element are shown in Fig. 11.8.3. The solid of revolution and an element of volume are shown in Fig. 11.8.4.

$$f(x) = x^2$$

$$M_{yz} = \lim_{\|\Delta\| \to 0} \sum_{i=1}^{n} \gamma_i \pi [f(\gamma_i)]^2 \, \Delta_i x$$

$$= \pi \int_0^3 x[f(x)]^2 \, dx = \pi \int_0^3 x^5 \, dx = \frac{243}{2}\pi$$

$$V = \lim_{||\Delta||\to 0} \sum_{i=1}^{n} \pi[f(\gamma_i)]^2 \, \Delta_i x$$

$$= \int_0^3 [f(x)]^2 \, dx = \pi \int_0^3 x^4 \, dx = \frac{243}{5} \pi$$

Therefore, $\bar{x} = \dfrac{M_{yz}}{V} = \dfrac{(243/2)\pi}{(243/5)\pi} = \dfrac{5}{2}$

Therefore, the centroid is at the point (5/2,0,0).

The centroid of a solid of revolution may also be found by the cylindrical-shell method. Let R be the region bounded by the curve $y = f(x)$, where f is continuous and $f(x) \geq 0$ on $[a,b]$, the x axis and the lines $x = a$ and $x = b$. Let S be the solid of revolution generated by revolving R about the y axis. The centroid of S is then at the point $(0,\bar{y},0)$. If the rectangular elements are taken parallel to the y axis, then the element of volume is a cylindrical shell. Let the ith rectangle have a width of $\Delta_i x = x_i - x_{i-1}$, and let γ_i be the midpoint of the interval $[x_{i-1},x_i]$. The centroid of the cylindrical shell obtained by revolving this rectangle about the y axis is at the center of the cylindrical shell, which is the point $(0,\tfrac{1}{2}f(\gamma_i),0)$. Figure 11.8.5 shows the region R and a rectangular element

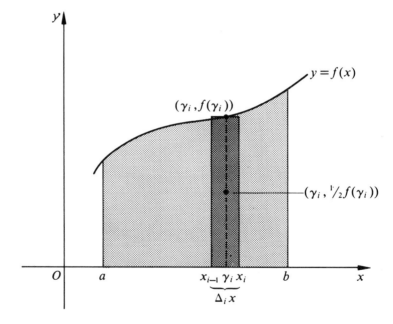

Figure 11.8.5

of area, and Fig. 11.8.6 shows the cylindrical shell. The moment of S with respect to the xz plane is given by

$$M_{xz} = \lim_{||\Delta||\to 0} \sum_{i=1}^{n} \tfrac{1}{2} f(\gamma_i) 2\pi \gamma_i f(\gamma_i) \, \Delta_i x$$

$$= \pi \int_a^b x[f(x)]^2 \, dx$$

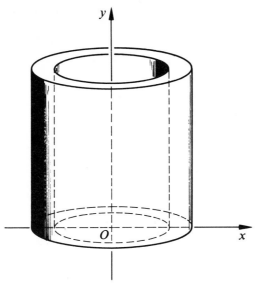

Figure 11.8.6

The volume V of S is given by

$$V = \lim_{\|\Delta\|\to 0} \sum_{i=1}^{n} 2\pi\gamma_i f(\gamma_i)\,\Delta_i x$$

$$= 2\pi \int_a^b xf(x)\,dx$$

Then, $\bar{y} = \dfrac{M_{xz}}{V}$

EXAMPLE 2: Use the cylindrical-shell method to find the centroid of the solid of revolution generated by revolving the region in Example 1 about the y axis.

Solution: Figure 11.8.7 shows the region and a rectangular element of area. The solid of revolution and a cylindrical-shell element of volume are shown in Fig. 11.8.8.

$$M_{xz} = \lim_{\|\Delta\|\to 0} \sum_{i=1}^{n} \tfrac{1}{2} f(\gamma_i) 2\pi\gamma_i f(\gamma_i)\,\Delta_i x$$

$$= \pi \int_0^3 x[f(x)]^2\,dx = \pi \int_0^3 x^5\,dx = \frac{243}{2}\pi$$

$$V = \lim_{\|\Delta\|\to 0} \sum_{i=1}^{n} 2\pi\gamma_i f(\gamma_i)\,\Delta_i x$$

$$= 2\pi \int_0^3 xf(x)\,dx = 2\pi \int_0^3 x^3\,dx = \frac{81}{2}\pi$$

Therefore, $\bar{y} = \dfrac{M_{xz}}{V} = \dfrac{(243/2)\pi}{(81/2)\pi} = 3$

Hence, the centroid is at the point $(0,3,0)$.

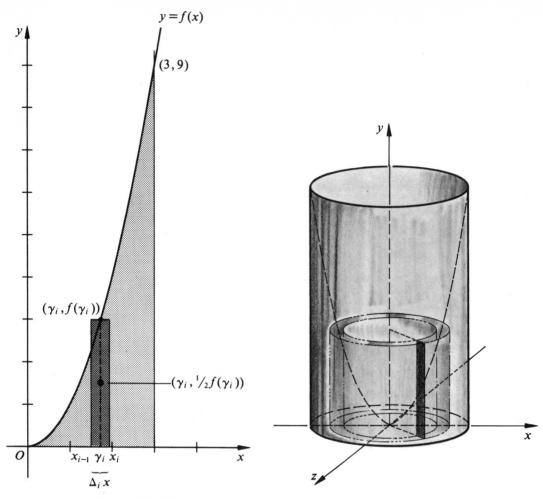

Figure 11.8.7　　　　　　　　　　**Figure 11.8.8**

EXAMPLE 3: Solve Example 1 by the cylindrical-shell method.

Solution: The equation of the curve is $y = x^2$, so that $x = \sqrt{y}$. Let $g(y) = \sqrt{y}$. Figure 11.8.9 shows the region and a rectangular element of area, and Fig. 11.8.10 shows the cylindrical-shell element of volume obtained by revolving the rectangle about the x axis. The centroid of the cylindrical shell is at its center, which is the point $(\frac{1}{2}(3 + g(\gamma_i)), 0, 0)$. The centroid of the solid of revolution is at the point $(\bar{x}, 0, 0)$.

$$M_{yz} = \lim_{\|\Delta\| \to 0} \sum_{i=1}^{n} \frac{3 + g(\gamma_i)}{2} 2\pi\gamma_i[3 - g(\gamma_i)] \, \Delta_i y$$

$$= \pi \int_0^9 y[3 + g(y)][3 - g(y)] \, dy$$

$$= \pi \int_0^9 (9y - y^2) \, dy = \frac{243}{2}\pi$$

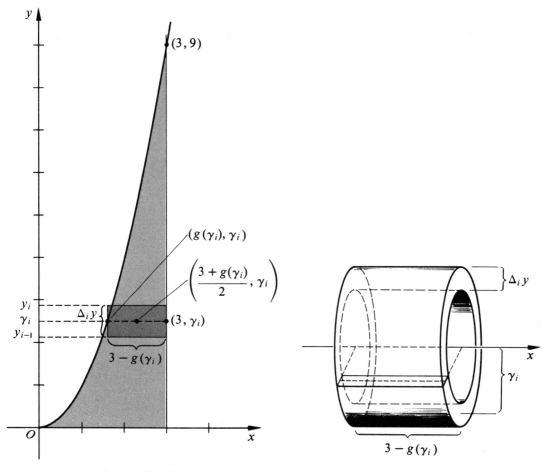

Figure 11.8.9   **Figure 11.8.10**

Finding the volume V by the cylindrical-shell method, we have

$$V = \lim_{||\Delta|| \to 0} \sum_{i=1}^{n} 2\pi\gamma_i[3 - g(\gamma_i)] \, \Delta_i y$$

$$= 2\pi \int_0^9 y(3 - y^{1/2}) \, dy = \frac{243}{5}\pi$$

Thus, $\bar{x} = \dfrac{M_{yz}}{V} = \dfrac{5}{2}$

and the centroid is at $(5/2, 0, 0)$.

Our results agree with those of Example 1.

Exercises 11.8

In Exercises 1 through 16 find the centroid of the solid of revolution generated by revolving the given region about the indicated line.

1. The region bounded by $y = 4x - x^2$ and the x axis, about the y axis. Take the rectangular elements perpendicular to the axis of revolution.
2. Same as Exercise 1, but take the rectangular elements parallel to the axis of revolution.
3. The region bounded by $x + 2y = 2$, the x axis, and the y axis, about the x axis. Take the rectangular elements perpendicular to the axis of revolution.
4. Same as Exercise 3, but take the rectangular elements parallel to the axis of revolution.
5. The region bounded by $y^2 = x^3$ and $x = 4$, about the x axis. Take the rectangular elements perpendicular to the axis of revolution.
6. Same as Exercise 5, but take the rectangular elements parallel to the axis of revolution.
7. The region bounded by $y = x^3$, $x = 2$, and the x axis, about the line $x = 2$. Take the rectangular elements perpendicular to the axis of revolution.
8. Same as Exercise 7, but take the rectangular elements parallel to the axis of revolution.
9. The region bounded by $x^4 y = 1$, $y = 1$, and $y = 4$, about the y axis.
10. The region in Exercise 9, about the x axis.
11. The region bounded by the lines $y = x$, $y = 2x$, and $x + y = 6$, about the y axis.
12. The region bounded by the portion of the circle $x^2 + y^2 = 4$ in the first quadrant, the portion of the line $2x - y = 4$ in the fourth quadrant, and the y axis, about the y axis.
13. The region bounded by $y = x^2$ and $y = x + 2$, about the line $y = 4$.
14. The region bounded by $y^2 = 4x$ and $y^2 = 16 - 4x$, about the x axis.
15. The region bounded by $y = \sqrt{4px}$, the x axis, and the line $x = p$, about the line $x = p$.
16. The region of Exercise 15, about the line $y = 2p$.

17. Find the centroid of the right-circular cone of altitude h and radius r.

18. Find the center of mass of the solid of revolution in Exercise 3 if the density of the solid at any point is equal to a constant k times the distance of the point from the yz plane.

19. Find the center of mass of the solid of revolution of Exercise 5 if the density of the solid at any point is equal to a constant k times the distance of the point from the xz plane.

20. Suppose that a cylindrical hole with a radius of r is bored through a wooden hemisphere of radius $2r$, so that the axis of the cylinder is the same as the axis of the hemisphere. Find the centroid of the solid remaining.

(11.9)   Volume of a solid having known parallel plane sections

Let S be a solid. By a *plane section* of S, we mean a plane region formed by the intersection of a plane with S. In Sec. 11.2 we learned how to find the volume of a solid of revolution for which all plane sections perpendicular to the axis of revolution are circles. In this section we shall consider the volume of a solid for which it is possible to express the area of any plane section perpendicular to a fixed line, in terms of the distance of the plane section from a fixed point. We first define what is meant by a *cylinder*.

11.9.1 DEFINITION   A *cylinder* is a solid bounded by two congruent plane regions R_1 and R_2 lying in parallel planes and by a lateral surface generated by a line segment, having its end points on the boundaries of R_1 and R_2, which moves so that it is always perpendicular to the planes of R_1 and R_2.

Figure 11.9.1 illustrates a cylinder.

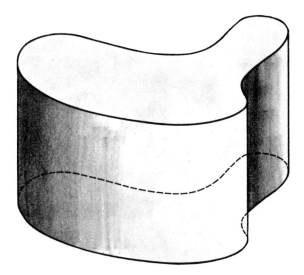

Figure 11.9.1

The *height* of the cylinder is the distance between the planes of R_1 and R_2, and the base is either R_1 or R_2. If the base of the cylinder is a circle, we have a *right-circular cylinder*. If the base of the cylinder is a rectangle, we have a *rectangular parallelepiped*.

If the area of the base of a cylinder is A and the height is h, we shall define the volume of the cylinder to be the product of A and h.

As stated above, we are considering solids for which the area of any plane section that is perpendicular to a fixed line is a function of the distance of the plane section from a fixed point. Let us choose the coordinate axes so that the x axis is along the fixed line, and the origin is at the fixed point. Let the solid S lie between the planes perpendicular to the x axis at the points $(a,0)$ and $(b,0)$.

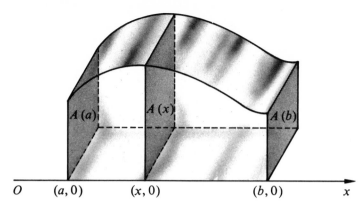

Figure 11.9.2

We represent the area of the plane section of S in the plane perpendicular to the x axis at $(x,0)$ by $A(x)$, where A is continuous on $[a,b]$ (refer to Fig. 11.9.2).

Let Δ be a partition of the closed interval $[a,b]$ given by

$$a = x_0 < x_1 < x_2 < \cdots < x_n = b$$

We have then n subintervals of the form $[x_{i-1},x_i]$, where $i = 1, 2, \ldots, n$, with the length of the ith subinterval being $\Delta_i x = x_i - x_{i-1}$. Choose any value ξ_i, with $x_{i-1} \leq \xi_i \leq x_i$, in each subinterval and construct the cylinders of heights $\Delta_i x$ and plane section areas $A(\xi_i)$. The volume of the ith cylinder is $A(\xi_i)\,\Delta_i x$. We obtain n cylinders, and the sum of the volumes of these n cylinders is given by the Riemann sum

(1)
$$\sum_{i=1}^{n} A(\xi_i)\,\Delta_i x$$

This Riemann sum is an approximation of what we intuitively think of as the volume of S, and the smaller we take the norm $||\Delta||$ of the partition Δ, the larger will be n, and the closer this approximation will be to the number we wish to assign to the volume. We have then the following definition.

11.9.2 DEFINITION   Let S be a solid such that S lies between planes drawn perpendicular to the x axis at $(a,0)$ and $(b,0)$. Denote the area of the plane section of S drawn perpendicular to the x axis at $(x,0)$ by $A(x)$, where A is continuous on $[a,b]$. Then the volume of S is given by

(2)
$$V = \lim_{||\Delta|| \to 0} \sum_{i=1}^{n} A(\xi_i)\,\Delta_i x$$

Since A is continuous on $[a,b]$, the limit in equation (2) is evaluated by the definite integral

$$\int_a^b A(x)\,dx$$

EXAMPLE 1: If the base of a solid is a circle with a radius of r and if all plane sections perpendicular to a fixed diameter of the base are squares, find the volume of the solid.

Solution: Take the circle in the xy plane, the center at the origin, and the fixed diameter along the x axis. Therefore, the equation of the circle is $x^2 + y^2 = r^2$. Figure 11.9.3 shows the solid and an element of volume, which is a cylinder of

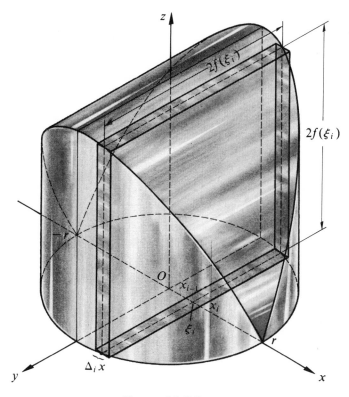

Figure 11.9.3

altitude $\Delta_i x$ and with an area of base $[2f(\xi_i)]^2$. $f(x)$ is obtained by solving the equation of the circle for y, giving $f(x) = \sqrt{r^2 - x^2}$. Therefore, we have

$$V = \lim_{\|\Delta\| \to 0} \sum_{i=1}^{n} [2f(\xi_i)]^2 \, \Delta_i x$$

$$= 4 \int_{-r}^{r} (r^2 - x^2) \, dx = \frac{16}{3} r^3$$

EXAMPLE 2: Find the volume of the tetrahedron having three mutually perpendicular faces and three mutually perpendicular edges of lengths a, b, and c.

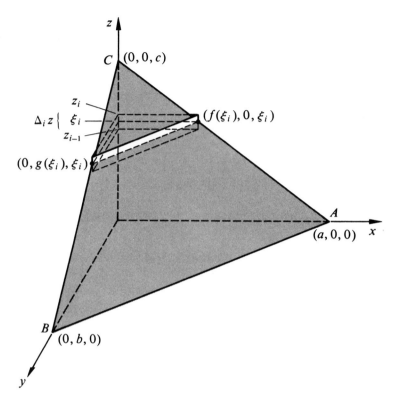

Figure 11.9.4

Solution: The tetrahedron is shown in Fig. 11.9.4. The three mutually perpendicular faces are taken in the xy plane, the xz plane, and the yz plane. The mutually perpendicular edges are OA along the x axis of length a, OB along the y axis of length b, and OC along the z axis of length c. Every plane section of the tetrahedron perpendicular to the z axis is a right triangle. Hence, an element of volume parallel to the xy plane is a cylinder with altitude $\Delta_i z$ and with an area of base $\frac{1}{2} f(\xi_i) g(\xi_i)$, where an equation of line AC in the xz plane is $x = f(z)$ and an equation of line BC in the yz plane is $y = g(z)$. The volume then is given by

$$V = \lim_{\|\Delta\| \to 0} \sum_{i=1}^{n} \tfrac{1}{2} f(\xi_i) g(\xi_i)\, \Delta_i z$$

or

(3) $$V = \tfrac{1}{2} \int_{0}^{c} f(z) g(z)\, dz$$

To find $f(z)$, we find an equation of line AC in the xz plane, which from the intercept form is

$$\frac{x}{a} + \frac{z}{c} = 1$$

Solving for x, we obtain

$$x = \frac{a}{c}(c - z) \qquad \text{so that} \qquad f(z) = \frac{a}{c}(c - z)$$

Similarly, we find $g(z)$ by finding an equation of BC in the yz plane and solving for y:

$$g(z) = \frac{b}{c}(c - z)$$

So, from equation (3) we have

$$V = \frac{1}{2} \int_0^c \frac{a}{c}(c - z)\frac{b}{c}(c - z)\, dz$$

$$= \frac{ab}{2c^2} \int_0^c (c^2 - 2cz + z^2)\, dz$$

$$= \frac{ab}{2c^2}\left[c^2z - cz^2 + \frac{1}{3}z^3 \right]_0^c = \frac{1}{6}abc$$

Exercises 11.9

1. The base of a solid is a circle with a radius of r. Find the volume of the solid if all plane sections perpendicular to a fixed diameter of the base are equilateral triangles.

2. The base of a solid is a circle with a radius of r, and all plane sections perpendicular to a fixed diameter of the base are isosceles right triangles having the hypotenuse in the plane of the base. Find the volume of the solid.

3. Solve Exercise 2 if the isosceles right triangles have one leg in the plane of the base.

4. Find the volume of a right pyramid having a height of h units and a square base of side a units.

5. The base of a tetrahedron is an isosceles triangle whose altitude and base have the same length a. If the fourth vertex is h units above the vertex of the base, find the volume of the tetrahedron.

6. The base of a solid is a region bounded by a parabola and a line perpendicular to the axis of the parabola. If the segment of the line between its points of intersection with the parabola has a length of 16 in. and is 8 in. from the vertex of the parabola, find the volume of the solid if every plane section perpendicular to the axis of the base is a square.

7. A wedge is cut from a right-circular cylinder with a radius of r in. by a plane through a diameter of the base and inclined to the plane of the base at an angle of 45°. Find the volume of the wedge.

8. The base of a solid is a circle with a radius of 4 in., and each plane section perpendicular to a fixed diameter of the base is an isosceles triangle having

an altitude of 10 in. and a chord of the circle as a base. Find the volume of the solid.

9. The base of a solid is a circle with a radius of 9 in., and each plane section perpendicular to a fixed diameter of the base is a square having a chord of the circle as a diagonal. Find the volume of the solid.

10. Two right-circular cylinders with an equal radius of r have axes that intersect at right angles. Find the volume of the solid common to the two cylinders.

(11.10) Length of arc of a plane curve

Let the function f be continuous on the closed interval $[a,b]$, and consider the graph of the equation $y = f(x)$. A sketch of the graph is shown in Fig. 11.10.1.

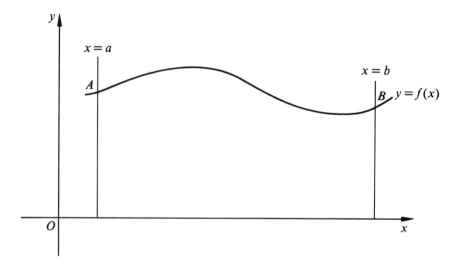

Figure 11.10.1

The portion of the curve from the point $A(a,f(a))$ to the point $B(b,f(b))$ is called an *arc*. We wish to assign a number to what we intuitively think of as the length of such an arc. If the arc is a line segment from the point (x_1,y_1) to the point (x_2,y_2), we know from the formula for the distance between two points that its length is given by $\sqrt{(x_1 - x_2)^2 + (y_1 - y_2)^2}$. We shall make use of this in defining the length of an arc, in general. The reader will recall that the circumference of a circle is defined as the limit of the perimeters of regular polygons inscribed in the circle. For other curves we proceed in a similar way.

Let Δ be a partition of the closed interval $[a,b]$ formed by dividing the interval into n subintervals by choosing any $(n - 1)$ intermediate numbers between a and b. Let $x_0 = a$, and $x_n = b$, and let $x_1, x_2, x_3, \ldots, x_{n-1}$ be the intermediate numbers so that $x_0 < x_1 < x_2 < \cdots < x_{n-1} < x_n$. Then the ith subinterval is $[x_{i-1}, x_i]$; and its length, denoted by $\Delta_i x$, is $x_i - x_{i-1}$, where $i = 1, 2, 3, \ldots, n$. Then if $\|\Delta\|$ is the norm of the partition Δ, each $\Delta_i x \leq \|\Delta\|$.

Associated with each point $(x_i, 0)$ on the x axis is a point $P_i(x_i, f(x_i))$ on the curve. Draw a line segment from each point P_{i-1} to the next point P_i as shown in Fig. 11.10.2. The length of the line segment from P_{i-1} to P_i is denoted by $|\overline{P_{i-1}P_i}|$ and is given by the distance formula,

$$(1) \qquad |\overline{P_{i-1}P_i}| = \sqrt{(x_i - x_{i-1})^2 + (y_i - y_{i-1})^2}$$

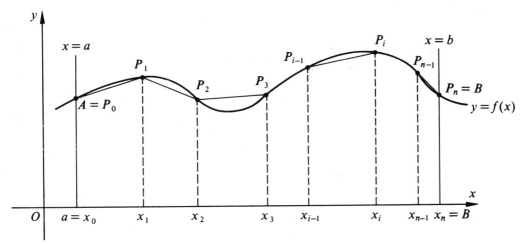

Figure 11.10.2

The sum of the lengths of the line segments is

$$|\overline{P_0P_1}| + |\overline{P_1P_2}| + |\overline{P_2P_3}| + \cdots + |\overline{P_{i-1}P_i}| + \cdots + |\overline{P_{n-1}P_n}|$$

which may be written in sigma notation as

$$(2) \qquad \sum_{i=1}^{n} |\overline{P_{i-1}P_i}|$$

It seems plausible that if n is sufficiently large, the sum in formula (2) will be "close to" what we would intuitively think of as the length of the arc AB. So we shall define the length of the arc as the limit of the sum in (2) as the norm of Δ approaches zero, in which case n approaches positive infinity. We have then the following definition.

11.10.1 DEFINITION   If the function f is continuous on the closed interval $[a,b]$ and if there exists a number L having the following property: for any $\epsilon > 0$, there is a $\delta > 0$ such that

$$\left| \sum_{i=1}^{n} |\overline{P_{i-1}P_i}| - L \right| < \epsilon$$

for every partition Δ of the interval $[a,b]$ for which $||\Delta|| < \delta$, then we write

$$(3) \qquad L = \lim_{||\Delta|| \to 0} \sum_{i=1}^{n} |\overline{P_{i-1}P_i}|$$

and L is called the length of the arc of the curve $y = f(x)$ from the point $A(a, f(a))$ to the point $B(b, f(b))$.

If the limit in equation (3) exists, the arc is said to be *rectifiable*.

We shall now derive a formula for finding the length L of an arc that is rectifiable. The derivation requires that the derivative of f be continuous on $[a,b]$. See Fig. 11.10.3.

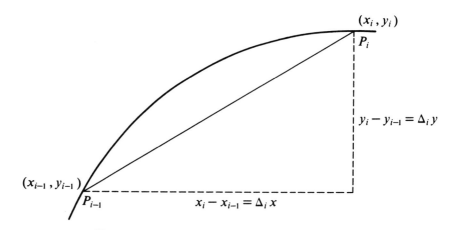

Figure 11.10.3

If P_{i-1} has coordinates (x_{i-1}, y_{i-1}) and P_i has coordinates (x_i, y_i), then the length of the chord $P_{i-1}P_i$ is given by formula (1).

Letting $x_i - x_{i-1} = \Delta_i x$ and $y_i - y_{i-1} = \Delta_i y$, we have

$$(4) \qquad |\overline{P_{i-1}P_i}| = \sqrt{(\Delta_i x)^2 + (\Delta_i y)^2}$$

or equivalently, since $\Delta_i x \neq 0$,

$$(5) \qquad |\overline{P_{i-1}P_i}| = \sqrt{1 + \left(\frac{\Delta_i y}{\Delta_i x}\right)^2} \; (\Delta_i x)$$

Since we required that f' be continuous on $[a,b]$, the hypothesis of the mean-value theorem (8.5.1) is satisfied by f, and so there is a number z_i in the open interval (x_{i-1}, x_i) such that

$$(6) \qquad f(x_i) - f(x_{i-1}) = f'(z_i)(x_i - x_{i-1})$$

Since $\Delta_i y = f(x_i) - f(x_{i-1})$ and $\Delta_i x = x_i - x_{i-1}$, from equation (6) we have

$$(7) \qquad \frac{\Delta_i y}{\Delta_i x} = f'(z_i)$$

Substituting from equation (7) into (5), we get

(8) $$|\overline{P_{i-1}P_i}| = \sqrt{1 + [f'(z_i)]^2}\, \Delta_i x$$

where $x_{i-1} < z_i < x_i$.

We have an equation of the form (8) for each i from 1 to n:

(9) $$\sum_{i=1}^{n} |\overline{P_{i-1}P_i}| = \sum_{i=1}^{n} \sqrt{1 + [f'(z_i)]^2}\, \Delta_i x$$

Taking the limit of both sides of equation (9) as $||\Delta||$ approaches zero, we obtain

(10) $$\lim_{||\Delta|| \to 0} \sum_{i=1}^{n} |\overline{P_{i-1}P_i}| = \lim_{||\Delta|| \to 0} \sum_{i=1}^{n} \sqrt{1 + [f'(z_i)]^2}\, \Delta_i x$$

if this limit exists.

To show that the limit on the right side of equation (10) exists, let g be the function defined by

$$g(x) = \sqrt{1 + [f'(x)]^2}$$

Since f' is continuous on $[a,b]$, g is continuous on $[a,b]$. Therefore, since $x_{i-1} < z_i < x_i$, for $i = 1, 2, \ldots, n$,

$$\lim_{||\Delta|| \to 0} \sum_{i=1}^{n} \sqrt{1 + [f'(z_i)]^2}\, \Delta_i x = \lim_{||\Delta|| \to 0} \sum_{i=1}^{n} g(x_i)\, \Delta_i x$$

or equivalently,

(11) $$\lim_{||\Delta|| \to 0} \sum_{i=1}^{n} \sqrt{1 + [f'(z_i)]^2}\, \Delta_i x = \int_a^b g(x)\, dx$$

Since $g(x) = \sqrt{1 + [f'(x)]^2}$, from equation (11) we have

(12) $$\lim_{||\Delta|| \to 0} \sum_{i=1}^{n} \sqrt{1 + [f'(z_i)]^2}\, \Delta_i x = \int_a^b \sqrt{1 + [f'(x)]^2}\, dx$$

Substituting from equation (12) into (10), we get

(13) $$\lim_{||\Delta|| \to 0} \sum_{i=1}^{n} |\overline{P_{i-1}P_i}| = \int_a^b \sqrt{1 + [f'(x)]^2}\, dx$$

From equations (3) and (13), then, we obtain

(14) $$L = \int_a^b \sqrt{1 + [f'(x)]^2}\, dx$$

In this way, we have proved the following theorem.

11.10.2 THEOREM   If the function f and its derivative f' are continuous on the closed interval $[a,b]$, then the length of arc of the curve $y = f(x)$ from the point $(a, f(a))$ to the point $(b, f(b))$ is given by

$$L = \int_a^b \sqrt{1 + [f'(x)]^2}\, dx$$

We also have the following theorem, which gives the length of the arc of a curve when x is expressed as a function of y.

11.10.3 THEOREM   If the function F and its derivative F' are continuous on the closed interval $[c,d]$, then the length of arc of the curve $x = F(y)$ from the point $(F(c),c)$ to the point $(F(d),d)$ is given by

$$L = \int_c^d \sqrt{1 + [F'(y)]^2}\, dy$$

The proof of Theorem 11.10.3 is identical with the proof of Theorem 11.10.2, interchanging x and y as well as the function f and the function F.

The definite integral obtained when applying Theorem 11.10.2 or Theorem 11.10.3 is often difficult to evaluate. Since our techniques of integration have so far been limited to integration of powers, we are further restricted in finding equations of curves for which we can evaluate the resulting definite integrals to find the length of an arc.

EXAMPLE 1: Find the length of the arc of the curve $y = x^{2/3}$ from the point $(1,1)$ to $(8,4)$ by using Theorem 11.10.2.

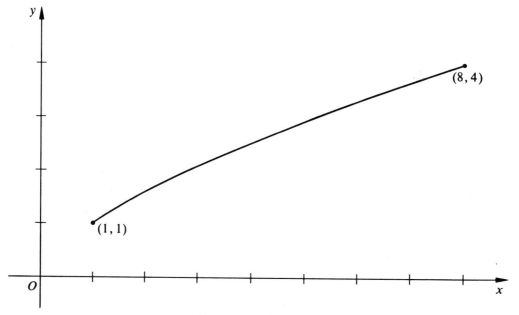

Figure 11.10.4

Solution: See Fig. 11.10.4. Since $f(x) = x^{2/3}$, $f'(x) = \frac{2}{3}x^{-1/3}$. From Theorem 11.10.2 we have

$$L = \int_1^8 \sqrt{1 + 4/9x^{2/3}}\, dx$$

$$= \frac{1}{3} \int_1^8 \frac{\sqrt{9x^{2/3} + 4}}{x^{1/3}}\, dx$$

To evaluate this definite integral, let $u = 9x^{2/3} + 4$; then $du = 6x^{-1/3}\, dx$; when $x = 1$, $u = 13$; when $x = 8$, $u = 40$. Therefore,

$$L = \frac{1}{18} \int_{13}^{40} u^{1/2}\, du = \frac{1}{18}\left[\frac{2}{3}u^{3/2}\right]_{13}^{40}$$

$$= \frac{1}{27}[40^{3/2} - 13^{3/2}] \approx 7.6$$

EXAMPLE 2: Find the length of the arc in Example 1 by using Theorem 11.10.3.

Solution: Since $y = x^{2/3}$, we solve for x and obtain $x = y^{3/2}$. Letting $F(y) = y^{3/2}$,

$$F'(y) = \frac{3}{2}y^{1/2}$$

Then, from Theorem 11.10.3, we have

$$L = \int_1^4 \sqrt{1 + \frac{9}{4}y}\, dy$$

$$= \frac{1}{2} \int_1^4 \sqrt{4 + 9y}\, dy$$

$$= \frac{1}{18}\left[\frac{2}{3}(4 + 9y)^{3/2}\right]_1^4$$

$$= \frac{1}{27}[40^{3/2} - 13^{3/2}] \approx 7.6$$

If f' is continuous on $[a,b]$, then the definite integral $\int_a^x \sqrt{1 + [f'(t)]^2}\, dt$ is a function of x; and it gives the length of the arc of the curve $y = f(x)$ from the point $(a, f(a))$ to the point $(x, f(x))$, where x is any number in the closed interval $[a,b]$. Let s denote the length of this arc; thus s is a function of x, and we have

$$s(x) = \int_a^x \sqrt{1 + [f'(t)]^2}\, dt$$

From Theorem 10.6.1, we have

$$s'(x) = \sqrt{1 + [f'(x)]^2}$$

or since $s'(x) = ds/dx$ and $f'(x) = dy/dx$,

$$\frac{ds}{dx} = \sqrt{1 + \left(\frac{dy}{dx}\right)^2}$$

Multiplying by dx, we obtain

(15)
$$ds = \sqrt{1 + \left(\frac{dy}{dx}\right)^2}\ dx$$

Similarly, if we are talking about the length of arc of the curve $x = g(y)$ from $(g(c),c)$ to $(g(y),y)$, we have

(16)
$$ds = \sqrt{\left(\frac{dx}{dy}\right)^2 + 1}\ dy$$

Squaring both sides of equation (15) gives

(17)
$$(ds)^2 = (dx)^2 + (dy)^2$$

From equation (17) we get the geometrical interpretation of ds, which is shown in Fig. 11.10.5.

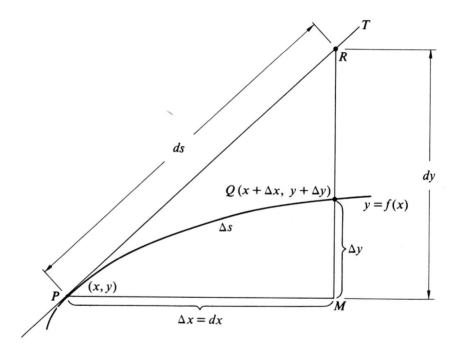

Figure 11.10.5

In Fig. 11.10.5, line T is tangent to the curve $y = f(x)$ at the point P. $|\overline{PM}| = \Delta x = dx$; $|\overline{MQ}| = \Delta y$; $|\overline{MR}| = dy$; $|\overline{PR}| = ds$; the length of arc $PQ = \Delta s$.

Exercises 11.10

1. Find the length of the arc of the curve $9y^2 = 4x^3$ from the origin to the point $(3, 2\sqrt{3})$.

2. Find the length of the arc of the curve $y = \frac{1}{3}(x^2 + 2)^{3/2}$ from the point where $x = 0$ to the point where $x = 3$.

3. Find the length of the arc of the curve $8y = x^4 + 2x^{-2}$ from the point where $x = 1$ to the point where $x = 2$.

4. Use Theorem 11.10.2 to find the length of the arc of the curve $y^3 = 8x^2$ from the point $(1,2)$ to the point $(27,18)$.

5. Solve Exercise 4 by using Theorem 11.10.3.

6. Find the entire length of the curve $x^{2/3} + y^{2/3} = 1$.

7. Find the length of the loop of the curve $9y^2 = x(x - 3)^2$.

8. Find the length of the loop of the curve $9y^2 = x^2(2x + 3)$.

9. Find the length of the curve $(x/a)^{2/3} + (y/b)^{2/3} = 1$ in the first quadrant from $x = a/8$ to $x = a$.

12 Logarithmic and exponential functions

(12.1) Introduction

The definition of the logarithmic function that the reader has encountered in algebra is based on exponents. The laws of logarithms are then proved from corresponding laws of exponents. One such law of exponents is

(1) $$a^x \cdot a^y = a^{x+y}$$

If the exponents, x and y, are positive integers and a is any real number, (1) follows from the definition of a positive integer exponent and mathematical induction. If the exponents are allowed to be any integers, either positive, negative, or zero, and $a \neq 0$, then (1) will hold if a zero exponent and a negative integer exponent are defined by

$$a^0 = 1$$

and $$a^{-n} = \frac{1}{a^n} \qquad n > 0$$

If the exponents are rational numbers and $a \geq 0$, then equation (1) holds when $a^{m/n}$ is defined by

$$a^{m/n} = \left(\sqrt[n]{a}\right)^m$$

It is not quite so simple to define a^x when x is an irrational number. For example, what is meant by $4^{\sqrt{3}}$? The definition of the logarithmic function, as given in elementary algebra, is based upon the assumption that a^x exists if a is any positive number and x is any real number.

This definition states that the equation

$$a^x = N$$

where a is any positive number except 1 and N is any real number, may be solved for x, and x is uniquely determined by

$$x = \log_a N$$

In elementary algebra, logarithms are used mainly as an aid to computation, and for such purposes the number a (called the base) is taken as 10. The following laws of logarithms are proved from the laws of exponents:

Law 1 $\log_a MN = \log_a M + \log_a N$

Law 2 $\log_a \dfrac{M}{N} = \log_a M - \log_a N$

Law 3 $\log_a 1 = 0$

Law 4 $\log_a M^n = n \log_a M$

Law 5 $\log_a a = 1$

In this chapter we shall define the logarithmic function by using calculus and prove the laws of logarithms by means of this definition. The exponential function will then be defined in terms of the logarithmic function. This definition will enable us to define a^x when x is any real number and $a \neq 0$. The laws of exponents will then be proved if the exponent is any real number.

(12.2)   The natural logarithmic function

Let us recall the formula

$$\int t^n \, dt = \frac{t^{n+1}}{n+1} + C \qquad n \neq -1$$

This formula does not hold when $n = -1$. Consider the function defined by the equation $y = t^n$ when $n = -1$ and t is positive. A sketch of the graph of the equation $y = 1/t$ for $t > 0$ is shown in Fig. 12.2.1.

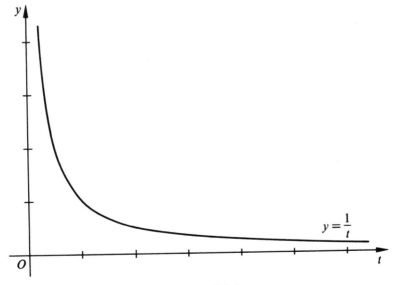

Figure 12.2.1

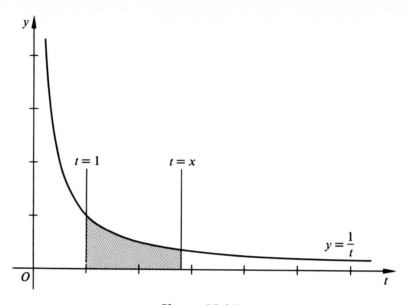

Figure 12.2.2

Let R be the region bounded above by the curve $y = 1/t$, below by the t axis, on the left by the line $t = 1$, and on the right by the line $t = x$, where x is greater than 1. This region R is shown in Fig. 12.2.2. The area of R is a function of x; call it $A(x)$ and define it as a definite integral by

(1) $$A(x) = \int_1^x \frac{1}{t}\, dt$$

Now, consider the integral in (1) if $0 < x < 1$. From Definition 10.3.4, we have

$$\int_1^x \frac{1}{t}\, dt = -\int_x^1 \frac{1}{t}\, dt$$

Then the integral $\int_x^1 1/t\, dt$ represents the area of the region bounded above by the curve $y = 1/t$, below by the t axis, on the left by the line $t = x$, and on the right by the line $t = 1$. So the integral $\int_1^x 1/t\, dt$ is then the negative of the area of the region shown in Fig. 12.2.3.

If $x = 1$, the integral $\int_1^x 1/t\, dt$ becomes $\int_1^1 1/t\, dt$, which equals 0 by Definition 10.3.5. In this case the left and right boundaries of the region are the same and so the area is 0.

So, we see that the integral $\int_1^x 1/t\, dt$ for $x > 0$ may be interpreted in terms of the area of a region. Its value depends upon x and is therefore a function of x.

We define this integral as the *natural logarithmic function*.

12.2.1 DEFINITION   The *natural logarithmic function* is the function defined by

$$\ln x = \int_1^x \frac{1}{t}\, dt \qquad x > 0$$

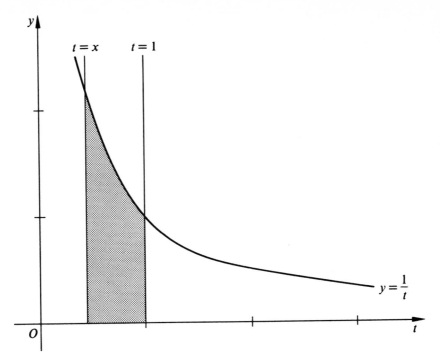

t = x   *t = 1*

$y = \dfrac{1}{t}$

O

Figure 12.2.3

The domain of this function is the set of all positive numbers.

We read ln *x* as "the natural logarithm of *x*."

We shall show that this function obeys the laws of logarithms as stated in Sec. 12.1. However, first we need a preliminary theorem, which we state and prove.

12.2.2 THEOREM   If *a* and *b* are any positive numbers, then

$$\int_a^{ab} \frac{1}{t}\, dt = \int_1^b \frac{1}{t}\, dt$$

Proof: In the integral $\int_a^{ab} 1/t\, dt$, make the substitution $t = au$; then $dt = a\, du$. When $t = a$, $u = 1$, and when $t = ab$, $u = b$. So, we have

$$\int_a^{ab} \frac{1}{t}\, dt = \int_1^b \frac{1}{au}(a\, du) = \int_1^b \frac{1}{u}\, du$$

$$= \int_1^b \frac{1}{t}\, dt \qquad\qquad \text{Q.E.D.}$$

Geometrically, Theorem 12.2.2 states that the area of the region shown in Fig. 12.2.4 is the same as the area of the region shown in Fig. 12.2.5.

If we take $x = 1$ in Definition 12.2.1, we have

$$\ln 1 = \int_1^1 \frac{1}{t}\, dt$$

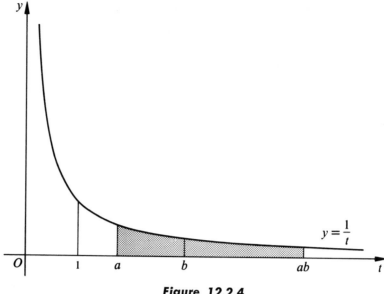

Figure 12.2.4

The right-hand side of the above is zero by Definition 10.3.5. So, we have

(2) $$\ln 1 = 0$$

Equation (2) corresponds to law 3 of logarithms, given in Sec. 12.1.

The following three theorems give some properties of the natural logarithmic function.

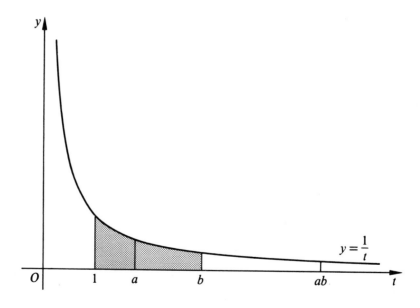

Figure 12.2.5

12.2.3 THEOREM   If a and b are any positive numbers, then

$$\ln (ab) = \ln a + \ln b$$

Proof: From Definition 12.2.1,

$$\ln (ab) = \int_1^{ab} \frac{1}{t}\, dt$$

which, from Theorem 10.4.6, gives us

$$\ln (ab) = \int_1^a \frac{1}{t}\, dt + \int_a^{ab} \frac{1}{t}\, dt$$

Applying Theorem 12.2.2 to the second integral on the right-hand side of the above, we obtain

$$\ln (ab) = \int_1^a \frac{1}{t}\, dt + \int_1^b \frac{1}{t}\, dt$$

and so from Definition 12.2.1 we have

$$\ln (ab) = \ln a + \ln b \qquad\qquad \text{Q.E.D.}$$

12.2.4 THEOREM   If a and b are any positive numbers, then

$$\ln \frac{a}{b} = \ln a - \ln b$$

Proof: Since $a = (a/b)\cdot b$, we have

$$\ln a = \ln \left(\frac{a}{b}\cdot b\right)$$

Applying Theorem 12.2.3 to the right-hand side of the above, we get

$$\ln a = \ln \frac{a}{b} + \ln b$$

Subtracting $\ln b$ from both sides of the above equation, we obtain

$$\ln \frac{a}{b} = \ln a - \ln b \qquad\qquad \text{Q.E.D.}$$

12.2.5 THEOREM   If a is any positive number and r is any rational number, then

(3) $$\ln a^r = r \ln a$$

Proof: We shall consider three cases.
Case 1: r is a positive integer n.
We shall use mathematical induction. If $r = 1$, then (3) becomes

$$\ln a^1 = 1 \cdot \ln a$$

which is obviously true. So, (3) holds when $r = 1$. We now assume that (3) holds when $r = k$, any positive integer, and we wish to prove that (3) holds when $r = k + 1$. So, we are assuming

(4) $$\ln a^k = k \cdot \ln a$$

Then, $\ln a^{k+1} = \ln (a^k \cdot a)$
$\phantom{Then, \ln a^{k+1}} = \ln a^k + \ln a$ by Theorem 12.2.3
$\phantom{Then, \ln a^{k+1}} = k \cdot \ln a + \ln a$ by (4)
$\phantom{Then, \ln a^{k+1}} = (k + 1) \ln a$

So, we have shown that if (3) holds when r is any positive integer k, then (3) also holds when $r = k + 1$. Since we have shown that (3) holds when $r = 1$, this proves that (3) holds when $r \geq 1$ and r is an integer.

Case 2: r is a negative integer $-n$.

From Theorem 12.2.4, we have

$$\ln a^{-n} = \ln \frac{1}{a^n} = \ln 1 - \ln a^n$$

Since $\ln 1 = 0$, from (2), and $\ln a^n = n \cdot \ln a$, from Case 1, we have

$$\ln a^{-n} = -n \cdot \ln a$$

which is (3) when $r = -n$.

Case 3: r is a rational number of the form p/q, where p and q are integers, $q \neq 0$.

Using the law of exponents from algebra, $(a^m)^n = a^{mn}$ when $a > 0$ and m and n are rational numbers, we have

$$(a^{p/q})^q = a^p$$

Then, $$\ln [(a^{p/q})^q] = \ln a^p$$

Since p and q are integers, we have from Cases 1 and 2,

$$q \cdot \ln a^{p/q} = p \cdot \ln a$$

and since $q \neq 0$, dividing both sides by q, we obtain

$$\ln a^{p/q} = \frac{p}{q} \cdot \ln a$$

which is (3) when $r = p/q$.

The reader should note that Theorems 12.2.3, 12.2.4, and 12.2.5 are the same properties as the laws of logarithms 1, 2, and 4, respectively, given in Sec. 12.1.

The natural logarithm function is differentiable, since by applying Theorem 10.6.1 we have

$$D_x(\ln x) = D_x\left(\int_1^x \frac{1}{t}\, dt \right) = \frac{1}{x}$$

Therefore,

(5) $$D_x(\ln x) = \frac{1}{x}$$

From (5) and the chain rule, if u is a differentiable function of x and $u(x) > 0$, then

(6) $$D_x(\ln u) = \frac{1}{u} \cdot D_x u$$

EXAMPLE 1: *Given:* $y = \ln (2x - 1)^3$. *Find:* $D_x y$.
Solution: From Theorem 12.2.5 we have

$$y = \ln (2x - 1)^3 = 3 \ln (2x - 1)$$

Applying (6), we get

$$D_x y = 3 \cdot \frac{1}{2x - 1} \cdot 2 = \frac{6}{2x - 1}$$

EXAMPLE 2: *Given:* $y = \ln [x/(x + 1)]$. *Find:* $D_x y$.
Solution:

$$D_x y = \frac{1}{x/(x + 1)} \cdot \frac{(x + 1) - x}{(x + 1)^2} = \frac{x + 1}{x} \cdot \frac{1}{(x + 1)^2}$$

$$= \frac{1}{x(x + 1)}$$

Following is an alternate solution to Example 2.
By applying Theorem 12.2.4, we may write

$$y = \ln x - \ln (x + 1)$$

Then

$$D_x y = \frac{1}{x} - \frac{1}{x + 1} = \frac{1}{x(x + 1)}$$

The following example illustrates how the properties of the natural logarithmic function, given in Theorems 12.2.3, 12.2.4, and 12.2.5, may be used to simplify the work involved in differentiating complicated expressions involving products, quotients, and powers.

EXAMPLE 3: *Given:* $y = \sqrt{x + 1}/(x + 2)\sqrt{x + 3}$. *Find:* $D_x y$.
Solution: We take the natural logarithm of both sides of the given equation and then apply the properties of logarithms to obtain

$$\ln y = \tfrac{1}{2} \ln (x + 1) - \ln (x + 2) - \tfrac{1}{2} \ln (x + 3)$$

Differentiating both sides implicitly with respect to x, we get

$$\frac{1}{y} D_x y = \frac{1}{2(x + 1)} - \frac{1}{x + 2} - \frac{1}{2(x + 3)}$$

Multiplying both sides by y, we obtain

$$D_x y = y \cdot \frac{(x + 2)(x + 3) - 2(x + 1)(x + 3) - (x + 1)(x + 2)}{2(x + 1)(x + 2)(x + 3)}$$

Replacing y by its given value, we obtain

$$D_x y = \frac{(x + 1)^{1/2}}{(x + 2)(x + 3)^{1/2}} \cdot \frac{x^2 + 5x + 6 - 2x^2 - 8x - 6 - x^2 - 3x - 2}{2(x + 1)(x + 2)(x + 3)}$$

$$= \frac{-2x^2 - 6x - 2}{2(x + 1)^{1/2}(x + 2)^2(x + 3)^{3/2}}$$

$$= \frac{-x^2 - 3x - 1}{(x + 1)^{1/2}(x + 2)^2(x + 3)^{3/2}}$$

The process illustrated in Example 3 is called *logarithmic differentiation*. From (5), we have

$$D_u(\ln u) = \frac{1}{u}$$

Since the domain of the natural logarithmic function is the set of positive numbers, it is understood that $u > 0$. We have then the following formula for indefinite integration.

(7) $$\int \frac{1}{u} du = \ln u + C \qquad \text{if} \qquad u > 0$$

If $u < 0$, then $-u > 0$, and we have

$$\int \frac{1}{u} du = \int \frac{1}{-u} d(-u) \qquad \text{where} \qquad -u > 0$$

So, from (7) we obtain

(8) $$\int \frac{1}{u} du = \ln(-u) + C \qquad \text{if} \qquad u < 0$$

Combining (7) and (8), we have

(9) $$\int \frac{1}{u} du = \begin{cases} \ln u + C & \text{if} \quad u > 0 \\ \ln(-u) + C & \text{if} \quad u < 0 \end{cases}$$

We may write (9) in the following form.

(((10) $$\int \frac{1}{u} du = \ln|u| + C \qquad \text{if} \qquad u \neq 0$$

Combining (10) with formula 9.1.9 we have, for n any real number,

(((11) $$\int u^n du = \begin{cases} \dfrac{u^{n+1}}{n+1} + C & \text{if} \quad n \neq -1 \\ \ln|u| + C & \text{if} \quad n = -1 \end{cases}$$

EXAMPLE 4: *Evaluate:* $\int [(x^2)/(x^3 + 1)]\, dx.$
Solution: Let $u = x^3 + 1$; then $du/3 = x^2\, dx$, and we have

$$\int \frac{x^2\, dx}{x^3 + 1} = \frac{1}{3} \int \frac{1}{u} du = \frac{1}{3} \ln|u| + C$$

$$= \frac{1}{3} \ln|x^3 + 1| + C$$

EXAMPLE 5: *Evaluate:* $\int_0^2 [(x^2 + 2)/(x + 1)]\, dx.$
Solution: Since $(x^2 + 2)/(x + 1)$ is an improper fraction, we divide numerator by denominator and obtain

$$\frac{x^2 + 2}{x + 1} = x - 1 + \frac{3}{x + 1}$$

Therefore,

$$\int_0^2 \frac{x^2 + 2}{x + 1}\, dx = \int_0^2 \left(x - 1 + \frac{3}{x + 1}\right) dx$$

$$= \frac{x^2}{2} - x + 3 \ln |x + 1|\,\Big]_0^2$$

$$= 2 - 2 + 3 \ln 3 - 3 \ln 1 = 3 \ln 3 - 3 \cdot 0$$

$$= 3 \ln 3$$

The answer in the above example may also be written as ln 27, since by Theorem 12.2.5, 3 ln 3 = ln 3^3.

EXAMPLE 6: *Evaluate:* $\int [(\ln x)/x]\, dx.$
   Solution: Let $u = \ln x$; then $du = dx/x$; so, we have

$$\int \frac{\ln x}{x}\, dx = \int u\, du = \frac{1}{2}u^2 + C = \frac{1}{2}(\ln x)^2 + C$$

Exercises 12.2

In Exercises 1 through 10, differentiate the given function and simplify the result.

1. $f(x) = \ln (1 + x^2)$

2. $f(x) = \ln \sqrt{1 + x^2}$

3. $f(x) = \ln \sqrt{4 - x^2}$

4. $g(x) = \ln (\ln x)$

5. $h(x) = \ln (x^2 \ln x)$

6. $f(x) = \ln \sqrt[4]{\dfrac{x^2 - 1}{x^2 + 1}}$

7. $H(x) = (\ln x^2)^2$

8. $f(x) = \sqrt[3]{\ln x^3}$

9. $F(x) = \sqrt{x + 1} - \ln (1 + \sqrt{x + 1})$

10. $G(x) = x \ln (x + \sqrt{1 + x^2}) - \sqrt{1 + x^2}$

In Exercises 11 through 16, find $D_x y$ by logarithmic differentiation.

11. $y = \dfrac{\sqrt{x^3 + 2x}}{\sqrt[5]{x^7 + 1}}$

12. $y = \dfrac{x\sqrt{x + 1}}{\sqrt[3]{x - 1}}$

13. $y = \dfrac{3x}{\sqrt{(x + 1)(x + 2)}}$

14. $y = \dfrac{\sqrt{1 - x^2}}{(x + 1)^{2/3}}$

15. $y = \sqrt{x^2 + 1} \ln (x^2 - 1)$

16. $y = (5x - 4)(x^2 + 3)(3x^3 - 5)$

In Exercises 17 and 18, find $D_x y$ by implicit differentiation.

17. $\ln xy + x + y = 2$

18. $\ln \dfrac{y}{x} + xy = 1$

In Exercises 19 through 26, evaluate the indefinite integrals.

19. $\int \dfrac{dx}{3 - 2x}$

23. $\int \dfrac{\ln^2 3x}{x} \, dx$

20. $\int \dfrac{3x \, dx}{5x^2 - 1}$

24. $\int \dfrac{5 - 4x^2}{3 + 2x} \, dx$

21. $\int \dfrac{dx}{x \ln x}$

25. $\int \dfrac{2x^3}{x^2 - 4} \, dx$

22. $\int \dfrac{dx}{\sqrt{x}(1 + \sqrt{x})}$

26. $\int \dfrac{(2 + \ln^2 x)}{x(1 - \ln x)} \, dx$

In Exercises 27 through 30, evaluate the definite integrals.

27. $\int_3^5 \dfrac{2x \, dx}{x^2 - 5}$

29. $\int_4^5 \dfrac{x \, dx}{4 - x^2}$

28. $\int_1^3 \dfrac{2x + 3}{x + 1} \, dx$

30. $\int_1^5 \dfrac{4x^3 - 1}{2x - 1} \, dx$

31. *Prove:* $\ln x^n = n \cdot \ln x$ by first showing that $\ln x^n$ and $n \cdot \ln x$ differ by a constant, and then find the constant by taking $x = 1$.

32. *Prove:* $D_x{}^n(\ln x) = (-1)^{n-1} \cdot (n - 1)!/x^n$. HINT: Use mathematical induction.

(12.3) The graph of the natural logarithmic function

In order to draw a sketch of the graph of the natural logarithmic function, we must first consider some properties of this function.

Let f be the function defined by

$$f(x) = \ln x = \int_1^x \frac{1}{t} \, dt \qquad x > 0$$

The domain of f is the set of all positive numbers. f is differentiable for all x in its domain, and

(1) $$f'(x) = \frac{1}{x}$$

Since f is differentiable for all $x > 0$, f is continuous for all $x > 0$.

From (1) we conclude that $f'(x) > 0$ for all $x > 0$, and therefore f is an increasing function.

(2) $$f''(x) = -\frac{1}{x^2}$$

From (2) we see that $f''(x) < 0$ when $x > 0$. Therefore the graph of $y = f(x)$ is concave downward at every point. Since $f(1) = \ln 1 = 0$, the x intercept of the graph is 1.

$$f(2) = \ln 2 = \int_1^2 \frac{1}{t} \, dt$$

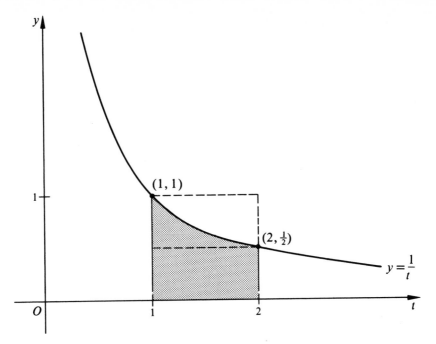

Figure 12.3.1

To determine an approximate numerical value for ln 2, we shall interpret the definite integral $\int_1^2 1/t \, dt$ as the area of the region shown in Fig. 12.3.1.

From Fig. 12.3.1 we see that ln 2 is between the areas of the rectangles each having a base of length 1 and altitudes of lengths 1/2 and 1. That is,

(3) $$0.5 < \ln 2 < 1$$

We may obtain an inequality analytically by using Theorem 10.4.8. We proceed as follows.

Let $f(t) = 1/t$ and $g(t) = 1/2$. Then $f(t) \geq g(t)$ for all t in [1,2]. Since f and g are continuous on [1,2], they are integrable on [1,2], and we have from Theorem 10.4.8

$$\int_1^2 \frac{1}{t} \, dt \geq \int_1^2 \frac{1}{2} \, dt$$

or, equivalently,

(4) $$\ln 2 \geq \frac{1}{2}$$

Similarly, if $f(t) = 1/t$ and $h(t) = 1$, then $h(t) \geq f(t)$ for all t in [1,2]. Since h and f are continuous on [1,2], they are integrable there, and again using Theorem 10.4.8, we obtain

$$\int_1^2 1 \, dt \geq \int_1^2 \frac{1}{t} \, dt$$

or, equivalently,

(5) $$1 \geq \ln 2$$

Combining (4) and (5), we get

(6) $$0.5 \leq \ln 2 \leq 1$$

0.5 is a lower bound of ln 2 and 1 is an upper bound of ln 2. In a similar manner we may obtain a lower and upper bound for the natural logarithm of any positive real number. Later we shall learn how to compute the natural logarithm of any positive real number to any desired number of decimal places. This will be done by applying infinite series. The value of ln 2 to 5 decimal places is given by

$$\ln 2 \approx 0.69315$$

Using this value of ln 2 and applying Theorem 12.2.5, we may obtain an approximate value for the natural logarithm of any power of 2. In particular, we have

$$\ln 4 = \ln 2^2 \;=\; 2 \ln 2 \approx \;\;1.38630$$
$$\ln 8 = \ln 2^3 \;=\; 3 \ln 2 \approx \;\;2.07945$$
$$\ln \frac{1}{2} = \ln 2^{-1} = -1 \ln 2 \approx -0.69315$$
$$\ln \frac{1}{4} = \ln 2^{-2} = -2 \ln 2 \approx -1.38630$$

In the Appendix there is a table of natural logarithms, giving the values to four decimal places.

We shall now determine the behavior of the natural logarithmic function for large values of x by considering $\lim\limits_{x \to +\infty} \ln x$.

Since the natural logarithmic function is an increasing function, if we take p any positive number,

(7) $$\ln x > \ln 2^p \qquad \text{whenever} \qquad x > 2^p$$

From Theorem 12.2.5 we have

(8) $$\ln 2^p = p \ln 2$$

Substituting (8) into (7), we get

$$\ln x > p \ln 2 \qquad \text{whenever} \qquad x > 2^p$$

Since from (6), $\ln 2 \geq \frac{1}{2}$, we have from the above

$$\ln x > \tfrac{1}{2}p \qquad \text{whenever} \qquad x > 2^p$$

Letting $p = 2n$ where $n > 0$, we have

(9) $$\ln x > n \qquad \text{whenever} \qquad x > 2^{2n}$$

It follows from (9) that for any $n > 0$, by taking $N = 2^{2n}$, we have

$$\ln x > n \qquad \text{whenever} \qquad x > N$$

So, we may conclude,

(10) $$\lim_{x \to +\infty} \ln x = +\infty$$

To determine the behavior of the natural logarithmic function for positive values of x close to zero, we investigate $\lim\limits_{x \to 0^+} \ln x$.

Since $\ln x = \ln (x^{-1})^{-1}$, we have

(11)
$$\ln x = -\ln \frac{1}{x}$$

"$x \to 0^+$" is equivalent to "$1/x \to +\infty$," and so from (11) we may write

(12)
$$\lim_{x \to 0^+} \ln x = - \lim_{1/x \to +\infty} \ln \frac{1}{x}$$

From (10), we have

(13)
$$\lim_{1/x \to +\infty} \ln \frac{1}{x} = +\infty$$

Therefore, from (12) and (13) we get

(14)
$$\lim_{x \to 0^+} \ln x = -\infty$$

From (14) and (10) and the intermediate-value theorem (10.5.1), we may conclude that the range of the natural logarithmic function is the set of all real numbers. From (14), we may conclude that the graph of the natural logarithmic function is asymptotic to the negative side of the y axis through the fourth quadrant. We summarize the properties of the natural logarithmic function as follows.

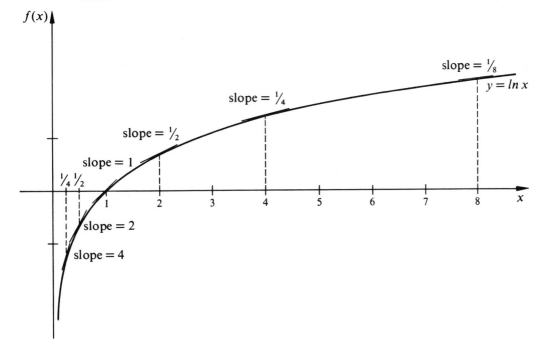

Figure 12.3.2

(i)   The domain is the set of all positive numbers.

(ii) The range is the set of all real numbers.

(iii) The function is increasing on its entire domain.

(iv) The function is continuous at all numbers in its domain.

(v)   The graph of the function is concave downward at all points.

(vi) The graph of the function is asymptotic to the negative side of the
      y axis through the fourth quadrant.

By using these properties and plotting a few points with a piece of the tangent line at the points, we may draw a sketch of the graph of the natural logarithmic function. In Fig. 12.3.2, we have plotted the points having abscissas of $\frac{1}{4}$, $\frac{1}{2}$, 1, 2, 4, and 8. The slope of the tangent line is found from $D_x(\ln x) = 1/x$.

Exercises 12.3

1. Draw a sketch of the graph of $y = \ln x$ by plotting the points having abscissas $1/9$, $1/3$, 1, 3, and 9, and use $\ln 3 \approx 1.09861$. At each of the five points, find the slope of the tangent line and draw a piece of the tangent line.

In Exercises 2 through 9, draw a sketch of the graph of the curve having the given equation.

2. $x = \ln y$

3. $y = \ln(-x)$

4. $y = \ln|x|$

5. $y = \ln(x + 1)$

6. $y = \ln(x - 1)$

7. $y = x - \ln x$

8. $y = x \ln x$

9. $y = \ln \dfrac{1}{x}$

10. Find an equation of the tangent line to the curve $y = \ln x$ at the point whose abscissa is 2.

11. Find an equation of the normal line to the curve $y = \ln x$ that is parallel to the line $x + 2y - 1 = 0$.

12. Find an equation of the tangent line to the curve $y = \ln 1/x$, having a slope of $\frac{1}{2}$.

In Exercises 13 through 17, find the exact value of the number to be found and then give an approximation of this number to three decimal places by using the table of natural logarithms in the Appendix.

13. Find the area of the region bounded by the curve $y = 2/(x - 3)$, the x axis, and the lines $x = 4$ and $x = 5$.

14. Find the area of the region bounded by the curves $y = (x^2 + 1)/(x + 1)$ and $x + 3y = 7$.

15. Find the volume of the solid of revolution generated when the region bounded by the curve $y = 1 - 3/x$, the x axis, and the line $x = 1$, is revolved about the x axis.

16. If $f(x) = 1/x$, find the average value of f on the interval $[1,5]$.

17. In a telegraph cable, the speed of the signal is proportional to $x^2 \ln (1/x)$, where x is the ratio of the radius of the core of the cable to the thickness of the cable's winding. Find the value of x for which the speed of the signal is greatest.

18. By comparing areas, show that if r is any positive number,

$$\frac{r}{r+1} < \ln (r+1) < r$$

19. Prove that if $x < 1$, $\ln x < x$. HINT: Let $f(x) = x - \ln x$. Show f is decreasing on the open interval $(0,1)$ and find $f(1)$.

20. *Prove:* $\lim\limits_{x \to +\infty} \ln x/x = 0$. HINT: First prove: $\int_1^x (1/\sqrt{t})\, dt \geq \int_1^x (1/t)\, dt$ by using Theorem 10.4.8.

(12.4)   The inverse of a function

Let us consider the equation

(1) $$x^2 - y^2 = 4$$

If we solve this equation for y in terms of x we obtain

$$y = \pm\sqrt{x^2 - 4}$$

Therefore, equation (1) does not define y as a function of x, since for each value of x greater than 2 or less than -2, there are two values of y, and in order to have a functional relationship, there must be a unique value of the dependent variable for a value of the independent variable. If we solve equation (1) for x in terms of y, we obtain

$$x = \pm \sqrt{y^2 + 4}$$

and so x is not a function of y. Therefore, equation (1) neither defines y as a function of x nor x as a function of y. The equation

(2) $$y = x^2 - 1$$

expresses y as a function of x, because for each value of x, a unique value of y is determined. As stated in Sec. 3.1, no vertical line can intersect the graph of a function in more than one point. In Fig. 12.4.1, we have a sketch of the graph of equation (1) and we see that if $a > 2$ or $a < -2$, the straight line $x = a$ intersects the graph in two points. In Fig. 12.4.2 we have a sketch of the graph of equation (2), and here we see that any vertical line intersects the graph in only one point.

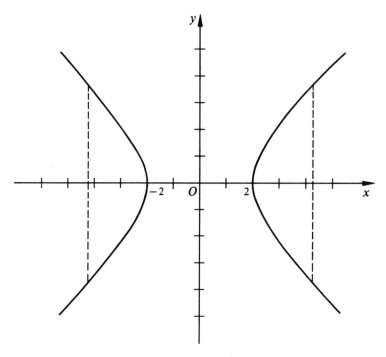

Figure 12.4.1

Equation (2) does not define x as a function of y because for each value of y greater than -1, two values of x are determined.

In some cases, an equation involving x and y will define both y as a function of x and x as a function of y. For example, consider the equation

(3)
$$y = x^3 + 1$$

If we let f be the function defined by

(4)
$$f(x) = x^3 + 1$$

then equation (3) may be written as $y = f(x)$ and y is a function of x. If we solve equation (3) for x, we obtain

(5)
$$x = \sqrt[3]{y - 1}$$

and letting g be the function defined by

(6)
$$g(y) = \sqrt[3]{y - 1}$$

we may write (5) as $x = g(y)$, and x is a function of y.

The functions f and g defined by (4) and (6) are called *inverse functions*. We also say that the function g is the *inverse* of the function f and that f is the *inverse* of g. We use the notation f^{-1} to denote the inverse of function f. The reader should note that in using -1 to denote the inverse of a function, it should not be confused with the exponent -1. We have the following formal definition of the inverse of a function.

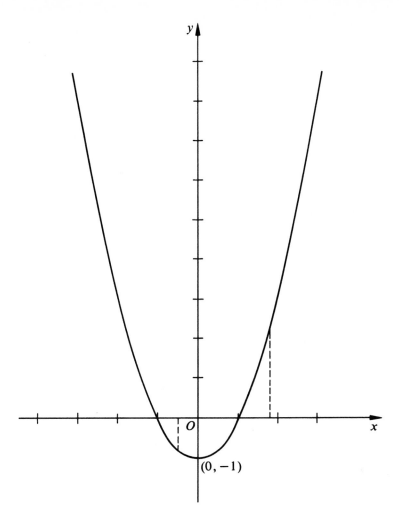

Figure 12.4.2

12.4.1 DEFINITION   If the function f is the set of ordered pairs (x,y), then the function f^{-1} defined by

(7) $x = f^{-1}(y)$ if and only if $y = f(x)$

is called the *inverse of the function f*. The domain of f^{-1} is the range of f and the range of f^{-1} is the domain of f.

Eliminating y between the equations in (7), we obtain

(8) $x = f^{-1}(f(x))$,

and eliminating x between the same pair of equations, we get

(9) $y = f(f^{-1}(y))$

So, we see from (8) and (9) that if the inverse of the function f is the function f^{-1}, then the inverse of the function f^{-1} is the function f.

Since the functions f and g defined by (4) and (6) are inverse functions, we may write f^{-1} in place of g and we have from (4) and (6)

(10) $\qquad f(x) = x^3 + 1 \qquad$ and $\qquad f^{-1}(x) = \sqrt[3]{x - 1}$

Sketches of the graphs of functions f and f^{-1} defined in (10) are shown in Figs. 12.4.3 and 12.4.4, respectively.

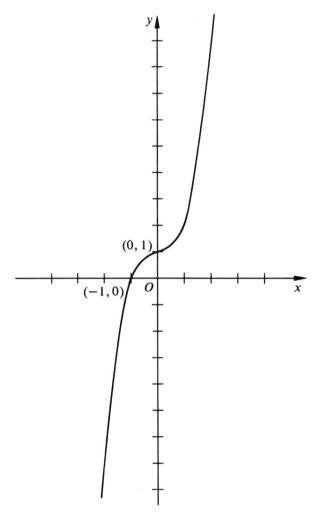

Figure 12.4.3

We observe that in Fig. 12.4.3, the function f is continuous and increasing on its entire domain. The definition of an increasing function (Definition 8.6.1) is satisfied by f for all values of x in its domain. We also observe in Fig. 12.4.3 that a horizontal line intersects the graph of f in only one point. Intuitively we suspect that if a function is continuous and increasing, then a horizontal line will intersect the graph of the function in only one point, and so the function will have an inverse. The following theorem verifies this fact.

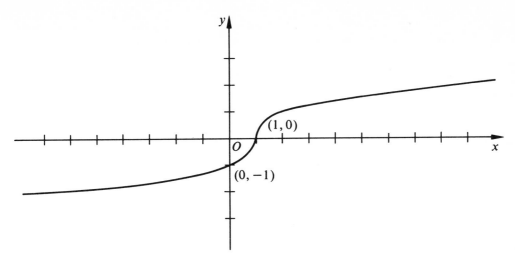

Figure 12.4.4

12.4.2 THEOREM   Suppose the function f is continuous and increasing on the closed interval $[a,b]$. Then,

   (i) f has an inverse f^{-1}, which is defined on $[f(a),f(b)]$.

   (ii) f^{-1} is increasing on $[f(a),f(b)]$.

   (iii) f^{-1} is continuous on $[f(a),f(b)]$.

Proof of (i): Since f is continuous on $[a,b]$, then if k is any number such that $f(a) < k < f(b)$, by the intermediate-value theorem (10.5.1), there exists a number c in $[a,b]$ such that $f(c) = k$. So, if y is any number in the closed interval $[f(a),f(b)]$, there is at least one number x in $[a,b]$ such that $y = f(x)$. We wish to show that for each such number y there corresponds only one number x. Suppose to a number y_1 in $[f(a),f(b)]$ there correspond two numbers x_1 and x_2, $x_1 \neq x_2$, in $[a,b]$ such that $y_1 = f(x_1)$ and $y_1 = f(x_2)$. Then, we must have

(11) $$f(x_1) = f(x_2)$$

Since we have assumed $x_1 \neq x_2$, either $x_1 < x_2$ or $x_2 < x_1$. If $x_1 < x_2$, since f is increasing on $[a,b]$, it follows that $f(x_1) < f(x_2)$; this contradicts (11). If $x_2 < x_1$, then $f(x_2) < f(x_1)$, and this also contradicts (11). Therefore, our assumption that $x_1 \neq x_2$ is false, and so to each value of y in $[f(a), f(b)]$ there corresponds exactly one number x in $[a,b]$ such that $y = f(x)$. Therefore, f has an inverse f^{-1}, which is defined for all numbers in $[f(a),f(b)]$.

Proof of (ii): To show that f^{-1} is increasing on $[f(a),f(b)]$, we must show that if y_1 and y_2 are two numbers in $[f(a),f(b)]$ such that $y_1 < y_2$, then $f^{-1}(y_1) < f^{-1}(y_2)$. Since f^{-1} is defined on $[f(a),f(b)]$, there exist numbers x_1 and x_2 in $[a,b]$ such that $y_1 = f(x_1)$ and $y_2 = f(x_2)$. Therefore,

(12) $$f^{-1}(y_1) = f^{-1}(f(x_1)) = x_1$$
           and

(13) $$f^{-1}(y_2) = f^{-1}(f(x_2)) = x_2$$

If $x_2 < x_1$, then since f is increasing on $[a,b]$, $f(x_2) < f(x_1)$, or, equivalently, $y_2 < y_1$. But $y_1 < y_2$. Therefore x_2 cannot be less than x_1.

If $x_2 = x_1$, then since f is a function, $f(x_1) = f(x_2)$, or, equivalently, $y_1 = y_2$, but this also contradicts the fact that $y_1 < y_2$. Therefore $x_2 \neq x_1$.

So, if x_2 is not less than x_1 and $x_2 \neq x_1$, it follows that $x_1 < x_2$, and so from (12) and (13), $f^{-1}(y_1) < f^{-1}(y_2)$. So, we have proved that f^{-1} is increasing on $[f(a),f(b)]$.

Proof of (iii): To prove that f^{-1} is continuous on the closed interval $[f(a),f(b)]$ we must show that if r is any number in the open interval $(f(a),f(b))$, then f^{-1} is continuous at r, and f^{-1} is continuous from the right at $f(a)$, and f^{-1} is continuous from the left at $f(b)$.

We shall show that f^{-1} is continuous at any r in the open interval $(f(a),f(b))$ by showing that Definition 5.2.4 holds at r. We wish to show that for any $\epsilon > 0$, small enough so that $f^{-1}(r) - \epsilon$ and $f^{-1}(r) + \epsilon$ are both in $[a,b]$ there exists a $\delta > 0$ such that

$$|f^{-1}(y) - f^{-1}(r)| < \epsilon \qquad \text{whenever} \qquad |y - r| < \delta$$

Let $f^{-1}(r) = s$. Since from (ii), f^{-1} is increasing on $[f(a),f(b)]$, we may conclude that $a < s < b$. Therefore,

$$a \leq s - \epsilon < s < s + \epsilon \leq b$$

Since f is increasing on $[a,b]$,

(14) $$f(a) \leq f(s - \epsilon) < r < f(s + \epsilon) \leq f(b)$$

Let δ be the smaller of the two numbers $r - f(s - \epsilon)$ and $f(s + \epsilon) - r$, so that $\delta \leq r - f(s - \epsilon)$ and $\delta \leq f(s + \epsilon) - r$, or, equivalently,

(15) $$f(s - \epsilon) \leq r - \delta$$
$$\text{and}$$
(16) $$r + \delta \leq f(s + \epsilon)$$

Whenever $|y - r| < \delta$, we have $-\delta < y - r < \delta$, or, equivalently,

(17) $$r - \delta < y < r + \delta$$

From (14), (15), (16), and (17), we have, whenever $|y - r| < \delta$,

$$f(a) \leq f(s - \epsilon) < y < f(s + \epsilon) \leq f(b)$$

Since f^{-1} is increasing on $[f(a),f(b)]$, it follows from the above that

$$f^{-1}(f(s - \epsilon)) < f^{-1}(y) < f^{-1}(f(s + \epsilon)) \qquad \text{whenever} \qquad |y - r| < \delta$$

or, equivalently,

$$s - \epsilon < f^{-1}(y) < s + \epsilon \qquad \text{whenever} \qquad |y - r| < \delta$$

or, equivalently,

$$-\epsilon < f^{-1}(y) - s < \epsilon \qquad \text{whenever} \qquad |y - r| < \delta$$

or, equivalently,

$$|f^{-1}(y) - f^{-1}(r)| < \epsilon \qquad \text{whenever} \qquad |y - r| < \delta$$

So f^{-1} is continuous on the open interval $(f(a),f(b))$.

The proofs that f^{-1} is continuous from the right at $f(a)$ and continuous from the left at $f(b)$ are left for the reader (see Exercise 25 at the end of the section).

A theorem analogous to the above theorem is obtained if the function f is continuous and *decreasing* (instead of increasing) on the closed interval $[a,b]$.

12.4.3 THEOREM   Suppose the function f is continuous and decreasing on the closed interval $[a,b]$. Then,

   (i) f has an inverse f^{-1}, which is defined on $[f(b), f(a)]$.

   (ii) f^{-1} is decreasing on $[f(b), f(a)]$.

   (iii) f^{-1} is continuous on $[f(b), f(a)]$.

The proof is similar to the proof of Theorem 12.4.2 and is left for the reader (see Exercises 26 through 28 at the end of the section).

Let us now reconsider equation (2):

$$y = x^2 - 1$$

As stated earlier in this section, this equation does not define x as a function of y, because if we solve for x we obtain

(18) $$x = \sqrt{y + 1} \quad \text{and} \quad x = -\sqrt{y + 1}$$

So actually equation (2) defines x as two distinct functions of y. If in equation (2) we restrict x to the closed interval $[0,c]$ and let $y = f_1(x)$ if x is in $[0,c]$, we have

(19) $$f_1(x) = x^2 - 1 \quad \text{and } x \text{ in } [0,c]$$

If in equation (2) we restrict x to the closed interval $[-c,0]$ and let $y = f_2(x)$ if x is in $[-c,0]$, we have

(20) $$f_2(x) = x^2 - 1 \quad \text{and } x \text{ in } [-c,0]$$

The functions f_1 and f_2 defined by (19) and (20) are distinct functions, since their domains are different. If we find the derivatives of f_1 and f_2, we obtain

$$f_1'(x) = 2x \quad \text{and } x \text{ in } [0,c]$$

and

$$f_2'(x) = 2x \quad \text{and } x \text{ in } [-c,0]$$

Since f_1 is continuous on $[0,c]$ and $f_1'(x) > 0$ for all x in $(0,c)$, by Theorem 8.6.3(i), f is increasing on $[0,c]$ and so by Theorem 12.4.2, f_1 has an inverse on $[-1, c^2 - 1]$. The inverse function is given by

(21) $$f_1^{-1}(y) = \sqrt{y + 1}$$

Similarly since f_2 is continuous on $[-c,0]$ and since $f_2'(x) < 0$ for all x in $(-c,0)$, by Theorem 8.6.3(ii), f_2 is decreasing on $[-c,0]$ and so by Theorem 12.4.3, f_2 has an inverse on $[-1, c^2 - 1]$, and the inverse function is given by

(22) $$f_2^{-1}(y) = -\sqrt{y + 1}$$

Since the letter used to represent the independent variable is irrelevant as far as the function is concerned, we could use x instead of y in (21) and (22), and we write

$$(23) \qquad f_1^{-1}(x) = \sqrt{x+1} \qquad \text{and } x \text{ in } [-1, c^2 - 1]$$

and

$$(24) \qquad f_2^{-1}(x) = -\sqrt{x+1} \qquad \text{and } x \text{ in } [-1, c^2 - 1]$$

In Fig. 12.4.5, we have sketches of the graphs of f_1 and its inverse f_1^{-1} as defined in (19) and (23), plotted on the same set of axes. In Fig. 12.4.6, we have sketches of the graphs of f_2 and its inverse f_2^{-1} as defined in (20) and (24), plotted on the same set of axes. It appears intuitively true from Fig. 12.4.5 that if the point $Q(u,v)$ is on the graph of f_1, then the point $R(v,u)$ is on the graph of f_1^{-1}. From Fig. 12.4.6, it appears to be true that if the point $Q(u,v)$ is on the graph of f_2, then the point $R(v,u)$ is on the graph of f_2^{-1}.

In general, if Q is the point (u,v) and R is the point (v,u), the line segment QR is perpendicular to the line $y = x$ and is bisected by it. We say that the point Q is a *reflection* of the point R with respect to the line $y = x$, and the point R is a *reflection* of the point Q with respect to the line $y = x$. If x and y are interchanged in the equation $y = f(x)$, we obtain the equation $x = f(y)$, and the graph of the equation $x = f(y)$ is said to be a *reflection of the graph* of the equation $y = f(x)$ with respect to the line $y = x$. Since the equation $x = f(y)$ is equivalent to the equation $y = f^{-1}(x)$, we may conclude that the graph of the

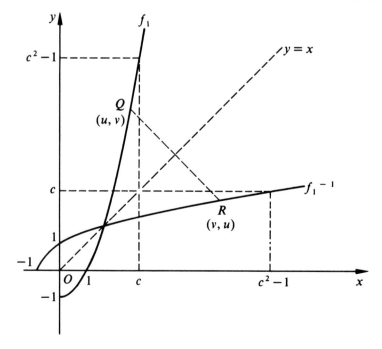

Figure 12.4.5

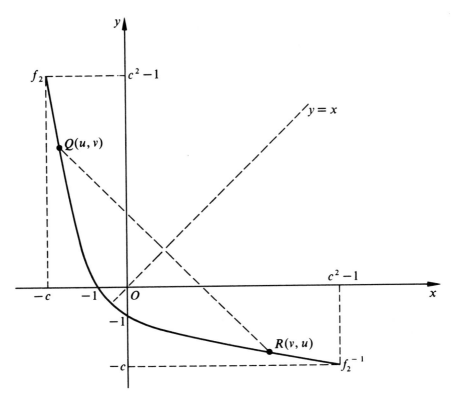

Figure 12.4.6

equation $y = f^{-1}(x)$ is a reflection of the graph of the equation $y = f(x)$ with respect to the line $y = x$. Therefore, if a function f has an inverse f^{-1}, their graphs are reflections of each other with respect to the line $y = x$.

EXAMPLE 1: *Given:* the function f is defined by $f(x) = (2x + 3)/(x - 1)$. *Find:* The inverse f^{-1} if it exists. Draw a sketch of the graph of f, and if f^{-1} exists, draw a sketch of the graph of f^{-1} on the same set of axes as the graph of f.

Solution: $f'(x) = -5/(x - 1)^2$. Since f is continuous for all values of x except 1, and $f'(x) < 0$ if $x \neq 1$, it follows from Theorem 12.4.3 that f has an inverse if x is any real number except 1. To find f^{-1}, let $y = f(x)$, and solve for x, giving $x = f^{-1}(y)$. So, we have

$$y = \frac{2x + 3}{x - 1}$$

$$xy - y = 2x + 3$$

$$x(y - 2) = y + 3$$

$$x = \frac{y + 3}{y - 2}$$

So, $f^{-1}(y) = \dfrac{y + 3}{y - 2}$

or, equivalently, $f^{-1}(x) = \dfrac{x + 3}{x - 2}$

The domain of f^{-1} is the set of all real numbers except 2.

Sketches of the graphs of f and f^{-1} are shown in Fig. 12.4.7.

The following theorem expresses a relationship between the derivative of a function and the derivative of the inverse of the function if the function has an inverse.

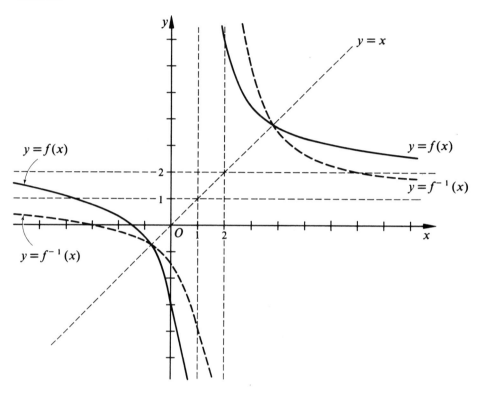

Figure 12.4.7

12.4.4 THEOREM   Suppose the function f is continuous and monotonic on the closed interval $[a,b]$, and let $y = f(x)$. If f is differentiable on $[a,b]$ and $f'(x) \neq 0$ for all x in $[a,b]$, then the derivative of the inverse function f^{-1}, defined by $x = f^{-1}(y)$, is given by

$$D_y x = \frac{1}{D_x y}$$

Proof: Since f is continuous and monotonic on $[a,b]$, then by Theorems 12.4.2 and 12.4.3, f has an inverse which is continuous and monotonic on $[f(a),f(b)]$.

If x is a number in $[a,b]$, let Δx be an increment of x, $\Delta x \neq 0$, such that $x + \Delta x$ is also in $[a,b]$. Then, the corresponding increment of y is given by

(25) $\Delta y = f(x + \Delta x) - f(x)$

$\Delta y \neq 0$, since $\Delta x \neq 0$ and f is monotonic on $[a,b]$; that is, either

$$f(x + \Delta x) < f(x) \quad \text{or} \quad f(x + \Delta x) > f(x) \quad \text{on } [a,b].$$

If x is in $[a,b]$ and $y = f(x)$, then y is in $[f(a),f(b)]$. Also if $x + \Delta x$ is in $[a,b]$ then $y + \Delta y$ is in $[f(a), f(b)]$ because $y + \Delta y = f(x + \Delta x)$ by (25). So,

(26) $$x = f^{-1}(y)$$

and

(27) $$x + \Delta x = f^{-1}(y + \Delta y)$$

It follows from (26) and (27) that

(28) $$\Delta x = f^{-1}(y + \Delta y) - f^{-1}(y)$$

From the definition of a derivative,

$$D_y x = \lim_{\Delta y \to 0} \frac{f^{-1}(y + \Delta y) - f^{-1}(y)}{\Delta y}$$

Substituting (25) and (28) into the above, we get

$$D_y x = \lim_{\Delta y \to 0} \frac{\Delta x}{f(x + \Delta x) - f(x)}$$

and since $\Delta x \neq 0$,

(29) $$D_y x = \lim_{\Delta y \to 0} \frac{1}{[f(x + \Delta x) - f(x)]/\Delta x}$$

Before we find the limit in (29) we shall show that under the hypothesis of this theorem, "$\Delta x \to 0$" is equivalent to "$\Delta y \to 0$." From (28) we have

$$\lim_{\Delta y \to 0} \Delta x = \lim_{\Delta y \to 0} [f^{-1}(y + \Delta y) - f^{-1}(y)]$$

Since f^{-1} is continuous on $[f(a), f(b)]$, the limit on the right-hand side of the above is zero. So,

(30) $$\lim_{\Delta y \to 0} \Delta x = 0$$

From (25) we have

$$\lim_{\Delta x \to 0} \Delta y = \lim_{\Delta x \to 0} [f(x + \Delta x) - f(x)]$$

Since f is continuous on $[a,b]$, the limit on the right-hand side of the above is zero, and therefore we have

(31) $$\lim_{\Delta x \to 0} \Delta y = 0$$

From (30) and (31) it follows that

(32) $$\Delta x \to 0 \quad \text{if and only if} \quad \Delta y \to 0$$

So, applying the limit theorem, regarding the limit of a quotient, to (29) and using (32), we have

$$D_y x = \frac{1}{\displaystyle\lim_{\Delta x \to 0} \frac{f(x + \Delta x) - f(x)}{\Delta x}}$$

Since f is differentiable on $[a,b]$, the limit in the denominator of the above is $f'(x)$, or, equivalently, D_xy, and so we have

$$D_yx = \frac{1}{D_xy}$$ Q.E.D.

EXAMPLE 2: *Given:* f is the function defined by $f(x) = x^3 + x$. Determine if f has an inverse, and if it does, find the derivative of the inverse function.

Solution: Since $f(x) = x^3 + x$, $f'(x) = 3x^2 + 1$. Therefore $f'(x) > 0$ for all real numbers, and so f is increasing on its entire domain. Since f is also continuous on its entire domain, it follows from Theorem 12.4.2 that f has an inverse f^{-1}.

Let $y = f(x)$, and then $x = f^{-1}(y)$. So, by Theorem 12.4.4,

$$D_yx = \frac{1}{D_xy} = \frac{1}{3x^2 + 1}$$

Exercises 12.4

In Exercises 1 through 10, find the inverse of the given function, if there is one, and determine its domain. Draw a sketch of the graph of the given function and if the given function does not have an inverse, show that a horizontal line intersects the graph in more than one point. If the given function has an inverse, draw a sketch of the graph of the inverse function on the same set of axes as the graph of the given function.

1. $f(x) = x^3$

2. $f(x) = x^2 + 5$

3. $f(x) = \dfrac{1}{x^2}$

4. $f(x) = (x + 2)^3$

5. $f(x) = \dfrac{2x - 1}{x}$

6. $f(x) = \dfrac{x + 4}{2x - 3}$

7. $f(x) = \dfrac{8}{x^3 + 1}$

8. $f(x) = \dfrac{2}{8x^3 - 1}$

9. $f(x) = 2|x| + x$

10. $f(x) = \dfrac{3}{1 + |x|}$

In Exercises 11 through 16, perform each of the following steps: (*a*) solve the equation for y in terms of x and express y as one or more functions of x; (*b*) for each of the functions obtained in (*a*), determine if the function has an inverse, and if it does, determine the domain of the inverse function; (*c*) use implicit differentiation to find D_xy and D_yx and determine the values of x and y for which D_xy and D_yx are reciprocals.

11. $x^2 + y^2 = 9$

12. $x^2 - y^2 = 16$

13. $xy = 4$

14. $y^2 - x^3 = 0$

15. $2x^2 - 3xy + 1 = 0$

16. $2x^2 + 2y + 1 = 0$

In Exercises 17 through 22, determine if the given function has an inverse, and if it does, determine the domain and range of the inverse function.

17. $f(x) = \sqrt{x - 4}$

18. $f(x) = (x + 3)^3$

19. $f(x) = x^2 - \dfrac{1}{x}$, $x > 0$

20. $f(x) = \dfrac{1}{x^2 + 4}$, $x \leq 0$

21. $f(x) = x^5 + x^3$

22. $f(x) = x^3 + x$

23. Let the function f be defined by $f(x) = \int_0^x \sqrt{1 - t^4}\, dt$. Determine if f has an inverse, and if it does, find the derivative of the inverse function.

24. Determine the value of the constant k so that the function defined by $f(x) = (x + 5)/(x + k)$ will be its own inverse.

25. *Given:* the function f is continuous and increasing on the closed interval $[a,b]$. Assuming Theorem 12.4.2(i) and (ii), prove f^{-1} is continuous from the right at $f(a)$ and continuous from the left at $f(b)$.

26. Prove Theorem 12.4.3(i).

27. Prove Theorem 12.4.3(ii).

28. Prove Theorem 12.4.3(iii).

(12.5)   The exponential function

Since the natural logarithmic function is increasing on its entire domain, then by Theorem 12.4.2 it has an inverse which is also an increasing function. The inverse of the natural logarithmic function is called the *exponential function,* which we now define.

12.5.1 DEFINITION   The *exponential function* is the inverse of the natural logarithmic function, and it is defined by

(1) $\qquad\qquad \exp(x) = y \quad$ if and only if $\quad x = \ln y$

"exp (x)" is read as "the value of the exponential function at x."

Since the range of the natural logarithmic function is the set of all real numbers, the domain of the exponential function is the set of all real numbers. The range of the exponential function is the set of positive numbers, since this is the domain of the natural logarithmic function.

Since the natural logarithmic function and the exponential function are inverses of each other, we may write

(2) $\qquad\qquad\qquad \ln(\exp(x)) = x$

and

(3) $\qquad\qquad\qquad \exp(\ln x) = x$

Since $0 = \ln 1$, we have

$$\exp 0 = \exp (\ln 1)$$

which from (3) gives us

(4) $$\exp 0 = 1$$

We now state some properties of the exponential function as theorems.

12.5.2 THEOREM If a and b are any real numbers,

$$\exp (a + b) = \exp (a) \cdot \exp (b)$$

Proof: Let $A = \exp (a)$, and so from Definition 12.5.1 we have

(5) $$a = \ln A$$

Let $B = \exp (b)$, and from Definition 12.5.1 it follows that

(6) $$b = \ln B$$

From Theorem 12.2.3, we have

(7) $$\ln A + \ln B = \ln AB$$

Substituting (5) and (6) into (7), we obtain

$$a + b = \ln AB$$

So,

(8) $$\exp (a + b) = \exp (\ln AB)$$

From (3), it follows that the right-hand side of (8) is AB. So, we have

$$\exp (a + b) = AB$$

and replacing A and B by their values, we get

$$\exp (a + b) = \exp (a) \cdot \exp (b) \qquad \text{Q.E.D.}$$

12.5.3 THEOREM If a and b are any real numbers,

$$\exp (a - b) = \exp (a) \div \exp (b)$$

The proof is analogous to the proof of Theorem 12.5.2, where Theorem 12.2.3 is replaced by Theorem 12.2.4. It is left for the reader (see Exercise 1 at the end of this section).

12.5.4 THEOREM If a is any real number and r is any rational number, then

$$\exp (ra) = [\exp (a)]^r$$

Proof: If in (3) we take $x = [\exp (a)]^r$, we have

$$[\exp (a)]^r = \exp\{\ln [\exp (a)]^r\}$$

Applying Theorem 12.2.5 to the right-hand side of the above, we obtain

$$[\exp (a)]^r = \exp \{r \ln [\exp (a)]\}$$

But from (2), $\ln [\exp (a)] = a$, and so we have

$$[\exp (a)]^r = \exp (ra) \qquad \text{Q.E.D.}$$

We now wish to define what is meant by a^x where a is a positive number and x is an irrational number. To arrive at a reasonable definition, consider the case a^r, where $a > 0$ and r is a rational number. We have from (3)

(9) $$a^r = \exp [\ln (a^r)]$$

But by Theorem 12.2.5, $\ln a^r = r \ln a$; so from (9)

(10) $$a^r = \exp (r \ln a)$$

Since the right-hand side of (10) has a meaning if r is any real number, we use it for our definition.

12.5.5 DEFINITION   If a is any positive number and x is any real number, we define

$$a^x = \exp (x \ln a)$$

Following is the definition of one of the most important numbers in mathematics.

12.5.6 DEFINITION   The number e is defined by the formula

$$e = \exp 1$$

The letter "e" was chosen because of the mathematician Leonard Euler (1707–1783).

The number e is a *transcendental* number; that is, it cannot be expressed as the root of any polynomial with integer coefficients. The number π is another example of a transcendental number. The proof that e is transcendental was first given in 1873, by Charles Hermite. The value of e may be expressed to any required degree of accuracy. In the chapter on infinite series, we shall learn an easy method for doing this. The value of e to seven decimal places is 2.7182818.

12.5.7 THEOREM $\ln e = 1$.
    Proof: By Definition 12.5.6,

$$e = \exp 1$$

So

(11) $$\ln e = \ln (\exp 1)$$

Since the natural logarithmic function and the exponential function are inverse functions, we have

(12) $$\ln (\exp 1) = 1$$

Substituting (12) into (11), we have

$$\ln e = 1 \qquad \text{Q.E.D.}$$

12.5.8 THEOREM $\exp(x) = e^x$, for all values of x.

Proof: By Definition 12.5.5,

(13)
$$e^x = \exp(x \ln e)$$

But by Theorem 12.5.7, $\ln e = 1$. Substituting this in (13), we obtain

$$e^x = \exp(x) \qquad\qquad \text{Q.E.D.}$$

From now on, we shall write e^x in place of $\exp(x)$, and so from Definition 12.5.1 we have

(14)
$$e^x = y \quad \text{if and only if} \quad x = \ln y$$

We shall now derive the formula for the derivative of the exponential function.

$$\text{Let} \quad y = e^x$$

Then, from (14) we have

(15)
$$x = \ln y$$

Differentiating both sides of (15) implicitly with respect to x, we get

$$1 = \frac{1}{y} \cdot D_x y$$

$$\text{So,} \quad D_x y = y$$

Replacing y by e^x, we obtain,

(16)
$$D_x(e^x) = e^x$$

If u is a differentiable function of x, it follows from (16) and the chain rule that

(17)
$$D_x(e^u) = e^u \, D_x u$$

It follows that the derivative of the function defined by $f(x) = ke^x$, where k is a constant, is itself. The only other function we have previously encountered that has this property is the constant function zero; actually this is the special case of $f(x) = ke^x$ when $k = 0$. It can be proved that the most general function which is its own derivative is given by $f(x) = ke^x$ (see Exercise 40 at the end of this section).

EXAMPLE 1: *Given:* $y = e^{1/x^2}$. *Find:* $D_x y$.

Solution: From (17),

$$D_x y = e^{1/x^2}\left(-\frac{2}{x^3}\right) = -\frac{2e^{1/x^2}}{x^3}$$

From (17) we obtain the following indefinite integration formula:

(18)
$$\int e^u \, du = e^u + C$$

EXAMPLE 2: *Find:* $\int (e^{\sqrt{x}}/\sqrt{x})\,dx$.

Solution: Let $u = \sqrt{x}$; then $du = (1/2\sqrt{x})\,dx$; so

$$\int \frac{e^{\sqrt{x}}}{\sqrt{x}}\,dx = 2 \int e^u\,du = 2e^u + C$$

$$= 2e^{\sqrt{x}} + C$$

Since from (14), $e^x = y$ if and only if $x = \ln y$, the graph of $y = e^x$ is identical with the graph of $x = \ln y$. So we may obtain the graph of $y = e^x$ by interchanging the x and y axes in Fig. 12.3.2 (see Fig. 12.5.1).

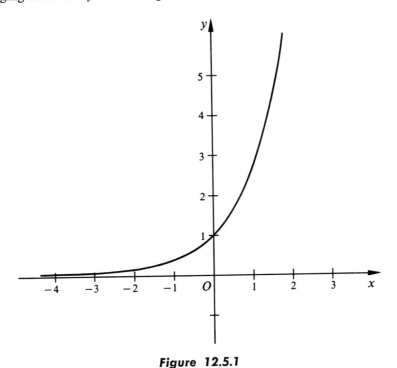

Figure 12.5.1

The graph of $y = e^x$ may be obtained without referring to the graph of the natural logarithmic function. Since the range of the exponential function is the set of all positive numbers, it follows that $e^x > 0$ for all values of x. So the graph lies entirely above the x axis.

$D_x y = e^x > 0$ for all x; so the function is increasing for all x.

$D_x^2 y = e^x > 0$ for all x; so the graph is concave upward at all points.

We have the following two limits:

(19)
$$\lim_{x \to +\infty} e^x = +\infty$$

and

(20)
$$\lim_{x \to -\infty} e^x = 0$$

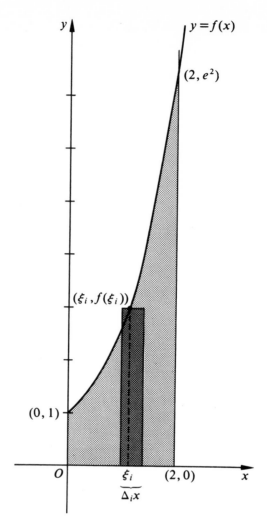

Figure 12.5.2

The proofs of (19) and (20) are left for the reader (see Exercises 44 and 45). To plot some specific points, use the table in the Appendix giving powers of e.

EXAMPLE 3: Find the area of the region bounded by the curve $y = e^x$, the coordinate axes, and the line $x = 2$.

Solution: The region is shown in Fig. 12.5.2.

$$A = \lim_{||\Delta|| \to 0} \sum_{i=1}^{n} f(\xi_i)\, \Delta_i x = \int_0^2 f(x)\, dx$$

$$= \int_0^2 e^x\, dx = e^x \Big]_0^2 = e^2 - e^0 = e^2 - 1$$

From a table of powers of e, we see that the value of e^2 to two decimal places is 7.39. Therefore, the area of the region is approximately 6.39 square units.

We now restate the conclusions of Theorems 12.5.2, 12.5.3, and 12.5.4, using e^x in place of exp (x). If a and b are any real numbers, then

$$e^{a+b} = e^a \cdot e^b$$

$$e^{a-b} = e^a \div e^b$$

$$e^{ra} = (e^a)^r \qquad \text{where } r \text{ is any rational number}$$

Writing (2), (3), and (4) using e^x in place of exp (x), we have

$$\ln (e^x) = x$$

$$e^{\ln x} = x$$

$$\text{and} \qquad e^0 = 1$$

EXAMPLE 4: *Given:* $y = e^{2x + \ln x}$. *Find:* $D_x y$.
Solution: $e^{2x + \ln x} = e^{2x} e^{\ln x} = e^{2x}(x)$.

So, $\qquad\qquad y = xe^{2x}$

Therefore, $\qquad D_x y = e^{2x} + 2xe^{2x}$

Exercises 12.5

1. Prove Theorem 12.5.3.

2. Draw a sketch of the graph of $y = e^{-x}$.

3. Draw a sketch of the graph of $y = e^{|x|}$.

In Exercises 4 through 15, find $D_x y$.

4. $y = e^{5x}$

5. $y = e^{-3x^2}$

6. $y = \dfrac{e^x}{x}$

7. $y = \dfrac{e^{2x}}{x^2}$

8. $y = e^{e^x}$

9. $y = \dfrac{e^x - e^{-x}}{e^x + e^{-x}}$

10. $y = \ln \dfrac{e^x - 1}{e^x + 1}$

11. $y = x^5 e^{-3 \ln x}$

12. $y = \ln (e^x + e^{-x})$

13. $y = \dfrac{e^x}{(e^x + e^{-x})^2}$

14. $y = e^{x/\sqrt{4+x^2}}$

15. $y = e^{x \ln x}$

In Exercises 16 through 19, find $D_x y$ by implicit differentiation.

16. $ye^{2x} + xe^{2y} = 1$

17. $e^x + e^y = e^{x+y}$

18. $e^y = \ln (x + y)$

19. $y^2 e^{2x} + xy^3 = 1$

In Exercises 20 through 29, evaluate the indefinite integrals.

20. $\int e^{2x}\, dx$

21. $\int e^{2-5x}\, dx$

22. $\int e^{3x}e^{2x}\, dx$

23. $\int \dfrac{1+e^{2x}}{e^x}\, dx$

24. $\int \dfrac{3e^{2x}}{1+e^{2x}}\, dx$

25. $\int \dfrac{e^{3x}}{(1-2e^{3x})^2}\, dx$

26. $\int x^2 e^{2x^3}\, dx$

27. $\int e^{2x^2-4x}(x-1)\, dx$

28. $\int \dfrac{dx}{1+e^x}$

29. $\int \dfrac{e^{2x}}{e^x+3}\, dx$

In Exercises 30 through 35, evaluate the definite integral.

30. $\int_0^2 x^2 e^{x^3}\, dx$

31. $\int_0^1 e^2\, dx$

32. $\int_1^2 \dfrac{e^x}{e^x+e}\, dx$

33. $\int_0^2 xe^{4-x^2}\, dx$

34. $\int_0^3 (e^x + e^{-x})\, dx$

35. $\int_0^1 (e^{2x}+1)^2\, dx$

In Exercises 36 and 37, find the relative extrema of f, the points of inflection of the graph of f, the intervals on which f is increasing, the intervals on which f is decreasing, where the graph is concave upward, where the graph is concave downward, and the slope of any inflectional tangent. Draw a sketch of the graph of f.

36. $f(x) = e^{-x^2}$

37. $f(x) = xe^{-x}$

38. Find an equation of the tangent line to the curve $y = e^{-x}$ which is perpendicular to the line $2x + y = 5$.

39. Find the area of the region bounded by the curve $y = e^x$ and the line through the points $(0,1)$ and $(1,e)$.

40. Prove that the most general function which is equal to its derivative is given by $y = ke^x$. HINT: Let $y = f(x)$ and solve the differential equation $dy/dx = y$.

41. Prove that if a rectangle is to have its base on the x axis and two of its vertices on the curve $y = e^{-x^2}$, then the rectangle will have the largest possible area if the two vertices are at the points of inflection of the graph.

42. The area of the region, bounded by the curve $y = e^{-x}$, the coordinate axes, and the line $x = b(b > 0)$, is a function of b. If f is this function, find $f(b)$. Find $\lim\limits_{b \to +\infty} f(b)$.

43. The volume of the solid of revolution obtained by revolving the region in

Exercise 42 about the x axis is a function of b. If g is this function, find $g(b)$. Find $\lim\limits_{b \to +\infty} g(b)$.

44. *Prove:* $\lim\limits_{x \to +\infty} e^x = +\infty$, by showing that for any $N > 0$, there exists an $M > 0$ such that $e^x > N$ whenever $x > M$.

45. *Prove:* $\lim\limits_{x \to -\infty} e^x = 0$, by showing that for any $\epsilon > 0$ there exists an $N < 0$ such that $e^x < \epsilon$ whenever $x < N$.

(12.6)   Other exponential and logarithmic functions

12.6.1 DEFINITION   If a is any positive number and x is any real number, then the function f defined by

$$f(x) = a^x$$

is called the *exponential function to the base a.*

From Definition 12.5.5, we have

(1) $$a^x = e^{x \ln a}$$

The exponential function to the base a satisfies the same properties as the exponential function to the base e. For example, if x and y are any real numbers and a is positive, then

(2) $$a^x a^y = a^{x+y}$$

The proof of (2) follows. From (1) we have

$$
\begin{aligned}
a^x a^y &= e^{x \ln a} e^{y \ln a} \\
&= e^{x \ln a + y \ln a} \\
&= e^{(x+y) \ln a} \\
&= a^{x+y} \qquad\qquad \text{Q.E.D.}
\end{aligned}
$$

We also have the following properties:

(3) $$a^x \div a^y = a^{x-y}$$

(4) $$(a^x)^y = a^{xy}$$

(5) $$(ab)^x = a^x b^x$$

(6) $$a^0 = 1$$

The proofs of (3) through (6) are left for the reader (see Exercises 1 through 4 at the end of this section).

To find the derivative of a^x, we set $a^x = e^{x \ln a}$ and apply the chain rule. We have

$$a^x = e^{x \ln a}$$

$$
\begin{aligned}
D_x(a^x) &= e^{x \ln a} D_x(x \ln a) \\
&= e^{x \ln a}(\ln a) \\
&= a^x \ln a
\end{aligned}
$$

If u is a differentiable function of x, we have

(((7)
$$D_x(a^u) = a^u \ln a\ D_xu$$

EXAMPLE 1: *Given*: $y = 3^{x^2}$. *Find*: D_xy.
Solution: Applying (7), we have

$$D_xy = 3^{x^2} \ln 3(2x) = 2(\ln 3)x3^{x^2}$$

From (7) we obtain the following indefinite integration formula:

(((8)
$$\int a^u\ du = \frac{a^u}{\ln a} + C$$

EXAMPLE 2: *Find*: $\int \sqrt{10^{3x}}\ dx$.
Solution: $\int \sqrt{10^{3x}}\ dx = \int 10^{3x/2}\ dx$. Let $u = 3x/2$; then $du = 3\ dx/2$; so $\frac{2}{3}\ du = dx$. We have then

$$\int 10^{3x/2}\ dx = \int 10^u \frac{2}{3}\ du = \frac{2}{3}\ \frac{10^u}{\ln 10} + C$$

$$= \frac{2 \cdot 10^{3x/2}}{3 \ln 10} + C$$

We are now in a position to define the *logarithmic function to the base a* if a is any positive number other than 1.

12.6.2 DEFINITION   If a is any positive number except 1, the *logarithmic function to the base a* is the inverse of the exponential function to the base a; and we write

(9)
$$y = \log_a x \quad \text{if and only if} \quad a^y = x$$

The above is the definition of the logarithmic function to the base a usually given in elementary algebra; however (9) has meaning for y any real number since a^y has been precisely defined. It should be noted that if $a = e$, we have the logarithmic function to the base e, which is the natural logarithmic function.

We read $\log_a x$ as "the logarithm of x to the base a."

The logarithmic function to the base a obeys the same laws as the natural logarithmic function. We list them.

(10)
$$\log_a (xy) = \log_a x + \log_a y$$

(11)
$$\log_a (x \div y) = \log_a x - \log_a y$$

(12)
$$\log_a 1 = 0$$

(13)
$$\log_a x^y = y \log_a x$$

The proofs of (10) through (13) are left for the reader (see Exercises 5 through 8).

A relationship between logarithms to the base a and natural logarithms follows easily. Let

$$y = \log_a x$$

$$\text{Then} \qquad a^y = x$$
$$\ln a^y = \ln x$$
$$y \ln a = \ln x$$
$$y = \frac{\ln x}{\ln a}$$

Replacing y by $\log_a x$, we obtain

(14) $$\log_a x = \frac{\ln x}{\ln a}$$

Equation (14) is sometimes used as the definition of the logarithmic function to the base a. Since the natural logarithmic function is continuous at all $x > 0$, it follows from (14) that the logarithmic function to the base a is continuous at all $x > 0$.

If in (14) we take $x = e$, we have

$$\log_a e = \frac{\ln e}{\ln a}$$

or, equivalently,

(15) $$\log_a e = \frac{1}{\ln a}$$

We shall now find the derivative of the logarithmic function to the base a. We differentiate both sides of (14) with respect to x, and we obtain

$$D_x(\log_a x) = \frac{1}{\ln a} D_x(\ln x)$$

or

(16) $$D_x(\log_a x) = \frac{1}{\ln a} \cdot \frac{1}{x}$$

Substituting (15) into (16), we get

(((17) $$D_x(\log_a x) = \frac{\log_a e}{x}$$

If u is a differentiable function of x, we have

(((18) $$D_x(\log_a u) = \frac{\log_a e}{u} D_x u$$

Note that if in (18) we take $a = e$, we get

$$D_x(\log_e u) = \frac{\log_e e}{u} D_x u$$

or, equivalently,

$$D_x(\ln u) = \frac{1}{u} D_x u$$

which is the formula we had previously for the derivative of the natural logarithmic function.

EXAMPLE 3: *Given:* $y = \log_{10} [(x + 1)/(x^2 + 1)]$. *Find:* $D_x y$.

Solution: Using (11), we write

$$y = \log_{10} (x + 1) - \log_{10} (x^2 + 1)$$

From (18) we have

$$D_x y = \frac{\log_{10} e}{x + 1} - \frac{\log_{10} e}{x^2 + 1} \cdot 2x$$

$$= \log_{10} e \left(\frac{1}{x + 1} - \frac{2x}{x^2 + 1} \right)$$

$$= \frac{\log_{10} e(1 - 2x - x^2)}{(x + 1)(x^2 + 1)}$$

Since x^n has now been defined for n any real number, we may now prove the formula for finding the derivative of the power function if the exponent is any real number.

12.6.3 THEOREM   If n is any real number and the function f is defined by

$$f(x) = x^n \qquad \text{where} \qquad x > 0$$
$$\text{then} \qquad f'(x) = nx^{n-1}$$

Proof: Let $y = x^n$. Then, from (1),

$$y = e^{n \ln x}$$

So, $$D_x y = e^{n \ln x} D_x(n \ln x)$$

$$= e^{n \ln x} \frac{n}{x}$$

$$= x^n \cdot \frac{n}{x}$$

$$= nx^{n-1} \qquad\qquad \text{Q.E.D.}$$

Theorem 12.6.3 enables us to find the derivative of a variable to a constant power. Previously in this section, we learned how to differentiate a constant to a variable power. We shall now consider the derivative of a function whose function value is a variable to a variable power. We use the method of *logarithmic differentiation*, which is illustrated in the following example.

EXAMPLE 4: *Given:* $y = x^x$. *Find:* $D_x y$.

Solution: We take the natural logarithm of both sides of the given equation, and we have

$$\ln y = \ln x^x$$

or, equivalently,

$$\ln y = x \ln x$$

Differentiating both sides of the above with respect to x, we obtain

$$\frac{1}{y} D_x y = \ln x + x \frac{1}{x}$$

So, $$D_x y = y(\ln x + 1)$$

$$= x^x(\ln x + 1)$$

In Exercises 1 through 4, prove the given property if a is any positive number and x and y are any real numbers.

1. $a^x \div a^y = a^{x-y}$

3. $(ab)^x = a^x b^x$

2. $(a^x)^y = a^{xy}$

4. $a^0 = 1$

In Exercises 5 through 8, prove the given property if a is any positive number and x and y are any positive numbers.

5. $\log_a (xy) = \log_a x + \log_a y$

7. $\log_a x^y = y \log_a x$

6. $\log_a (x \div y) = \log_a x - \log_a y$

8. $\log_a 1 = 0$

In Exercises 9 through 26, find $f'(x)$.

9. $f(x) = 3^{5x}$

18. $f(x) = \log_a [\log_a (\log_a x)]$

10. $f(x) = 6^{-3x}$

19. $f(x) = x^{\sqrt{x}}$

11. $f(x) = 2^{5x} 3^{4x^2}$

20. $f(x) = x^{\ln x}$

12. $f(x) = (x^3 + 3)2^{-7x}$

21. $f(x) = x^{e^x}$

13. $f(x) = \dfrac{\log_{10} x}{x}$

22. $f(x) = x^{x^2}$

14. $f(x) = \log_{10} \dfrac{x}{x+1}$

23. $f(x) = x^{1/\ln x}$

15. $f(x) = \sqrt{\log_a x}$

24. $f(x) = (x)^{x^z}$

16. $f(x) = \sqrt{\log_{10} \dfrac{1+x}{1-x}}$

25. $f(x) = (e^x)^x$

17. $f(x) = \log_{10} [\log_{10} (x + 1)]$

26. $f(x) = (\ln x)^{\ln x}$

In Exercises 27 through 36, evaluate the indefinite integral.

27. $\displaystyle\int 3^{2x}\, dx$

32. $\displaystyle\int 5^{x^4+2x}(2x^3 + 1)\, dx$

28. $\displaystyle\int a^{nx}\, dx$

33. $\displaystyle\int \dfrac{10^{\ln x^2}}{x}\, dx$

29. $\displaystyle\int a^x e^x\, dx$

34. $\displaystyle\int a^{x \ln x} (\ln x + 1)\, dx$

30. $\displaystyle\int (e^{3x} + a^{3x})\, dx$

35. $\displaystyle\int e^x 2^{e^x} 3^{e^x}\, dx$

31. $\displaystyle\int x^2 10^{x^3}\, dx$

36. $\displaystyle\int \dfrac{4^{\ln (1/x)}}{x}\, dx$

37. Draw sketches of the graphs of $y = \log_{10} x$ and $y = \ln x$ on the same set of coordinate axes.

38. Find an equation of the tangent line to the curve $y = x^{x-1}$ at the point $(2,2)$.

39. Find an equation of the tangent line to the curve $y^24^y = x2^x$ at (4,2).

40. Use differentials to find an approximate value of $\log_{10} 1.015$ and express the answer correct to three decimal places.

(12.7) Laws of growth and decay

The laws of growth and decay which occur in chemistry, biology, and business provide an application of the exponential function. Such a situation would arise when the rate of change of the amount of a substance with respect to time is proportional to the amount of the substance present at a given instant. This would occur in chemistry when the rate of decay of radium is proportional to the amount of radium present at a given instant. In biology, under certain circumstances the rate of growth of a culture of bacteria is proportional to the amount of bacteria present at any given instant. An application in business occurs when interest on a loan is compounded continuously.

In such cases, if the time is represented by t and A is the amount of the substance present at any time t, then

$$\frac{dA}{dt} = kA$$

If A increases as t increases, then $k > 0$, and we have the *law of natural growth*. If A decreases as t increases, then $k < 0$, and we have the *law of natural decay*. In problems involving the law of natural decay, the *half-life* of a substance is the time required for half of it to decay.

EXAMPLE 1: The rate of decay of radium is proportional to the amount present at any time. If 60 milligrams of radium are present now, and its half-life is 1,690 years, how much radium will be present 100 years from now?
Solution:

Let t = the number of years in the time from now

Let A = the number of milligrams of radium present at t years

We have the table of initial conditions given in Table 12.7.1.

Table 12.7.1

t	0	1,690	100
A	60	30	A_{100}

The differential equation is

$$\frac{dA}{dt} = kA$$

Separating the variables, we obtain

$$\frac{dA}{A} = k\, dt$$

Taking the indefinite integral of both sides of this equation, we have

$$\int \frac{dA}{A} = k \int dt$$

$$\ln |A| = kt + \bar{c}$$

$$A = e^{kt+\bar{c}} = e^{\bar{c}} \cdot e^{kt}$$

Letting $e^{\bar{c}} = C$, we have

$$A = Ce^{kt}$$

Since $A = 60$ when $t = 0$, we get $60 = C$. So,

(1) $A = 60e^{kt}$

Since $A = 30$ when $t = 1,690$, we get $30 = 60e^{1,690k}$, or

$$0.5 = e^{1,690k}$$

So, $\ln 0.5 = 1,690k$

and $k = \dfrac{\ln 0.5}{1,690} = \dfrac{-0.6931}{1,690} = -0.000411$

Substituting this value of k into equation (1), we obtain

$$A = 60e^{-0.000411t}$$

When $t = 100$, $A = A_{100}$, and we have

$$A_{100} = 60e^{-0.0411} \approx 58$$

Therefore, there will be 58 milligrams of radium present 100 years from now.

EXAMPLE 2: Newton's law of cooling states that the rate at which a body changes temperature is proportional to the difference between its temperature and that of the surrounding medium. If a body is in air of temperature 35° and the body cools from 120° to 60° in 40 minutes, find the temperature of the body after 100 minutes.

Solution:

Let t = the number of minutes in the time that has elapsed since the body started to cool

Let x = the number of degrees in the temperature of the body at t minutes

Table 12.7.2 gives the initial conditions.

Table 12.7.2

t	0	40	100
x	120	60	x_{100}

From Newton's law of cooling, we have

$$\frac{dx}{dt} = k(x - 35)$$

Separating the variables, we obtain

$$\frac{dx}{x - 35} = k \, dt$$

So, $\displaystyle\int \frac{dx}{x-35} = k\int dt$

$$\ln|x-35| = kt + \overline{C}$$

$$x - 35 = Ce^{kt}$$

$$x = Ce^{kt} + 35$$

When $t = 0$, $x = 120$; so $C = 85$. Therefore,

$$x = 85e^{kt} + 35$$

When $t = 40$, $x = 60$; and we obtain

$$60 = 85e^{40k} + 35$$

$$40k = \ln 5/17$$

$$k = \frac{1}{40}(\ln 5 - \ln 17) = \frac{1}{40}(1.6094 - 2.8332)$$

$$= -0.0306$$

So, $x = 85e^{-0.0306t} + 35$

Then, $x_{100} = 85e^{-3.06} + 35 \approx 39$

Therefore, the temperature of the body is $39°$ after 100 minutes.

Exercises 12.7

1. In a certain culture, the rate of growth of bacteria is proportional to the amount present. If there are 1,000 bacteria present initially and the amount doubles in 1 hour, how many bacteria will there be in $3\frac{1}{2}$ hours?

2. The rate of increase of the population of a certain city is proportional to the population. If the population increases from 40,000 to 60,000 in 40 years, what will be the population in 60 years?

3. When interest is *compounded continuously*, the amount of money invested increases at a rate proportional to its size. If $100 is invested at 5 per cent, compounded continuously, in how many years will the original investment double itself?

4. If an amount of money invested doubles itself in 10 years at interest compounded continuously, how long will it take for the original amount to triple itself?

5. What rate of interest compounded annually is equivalent to 5 per cent compounded continuously?

6. Under the conditions of Example 2, after how many minutes will the temperature of the body be $45°$?

7. Using Newton's law of cooling (see Example 2), if a body in air temperature $0°$ cools from $200°$ to $100°$ in 40 minutes, how many more minutes will it take for the body to cool to $50°$?

8. If a thermometer is taken from a room in which the temperature is 75° into the open, where the temperature is 35°, and the reading of the thermometer is 65° after 30 seconds, how long after the removal will the reading be 50°? Use Newton's law of cooling (see Example 2).

9. In Exercise 8, what is the thermometer reading 3 minutes after the removal?

10. The rate of natural increase of the population of a certain city is proportional to the population. If the population doubles in 60 years, and if the population in 1950 was 60,000, estimate the population in the year 2,000.

(12.8) The number e

In Definition 12.5.6, the number *e* was defined as the value of the exponential function at 1. To arrive at another way of defining the number *e*, we consider the function defined by

(1) $$f(x) = \log_e x$$

We know the derivative of *f* is given by

(2) $$f'(x) = \frac{1}{x}$$

However, let us apply the definition of a derivative and properties of logarithms to find $f'(x)$. We have

$$f'(x) = \lim_{\Delta x \to 0} \frac{f(x + \Delta x) - f(x)}{\Delta x}$$

$$= \lim_{\Delta x \to 0} \frac{\log_e (x + \Delta x) - \log_e x}{\Delta x}$$

$$= \lim_{\Delta x \to 0} \frac{\log_e [(x + \Delta x)/x]}{\Delta x}$$

$$= \lim_{\Delta x \to 0} \frac{x}{x} \cdot \frac{1}{\Delta x} \log_e \left(1 + \frac{\Delta x}{x}\right)$$

$$= \lim_{\Delta x \to 0} \frac{1}{x} \log_e \left(1 + \frac{\Delta x}{x}\right)^{x/\Delta x}$$

Since $f'(x) = 1/x$, we may conclude that

(3) $$\lim_{\Delta x \to 0} \log_e \left(1 + \frac{\Delta x}{x}\right)^{x/\Delta x} = 1$$

Since the natural logarithmic function is continuous, it follows from (3) and Theorem 5.2.5 that

$$\log_e \left[\lim_{\Delta x \to 0} \left(1 + \frac{\Delta x}{x}\right)^{x/\Delta x} \right] = 1$$

or, equivalently,

(4)
$$\lim_{\Delta x \to 0} \left(1 + \frac{\Delta x}{x}\right)^{x/\Delta x} = e$$

If we let $z = \Delta x/x$, then $x/\Delta x = 1/z$ and "$\Delta x \to 0$" is equivalent to "$z \to 0$." Making these substitutions in (4), we obtain

(5)
$$e = \lim_{z \to 0} (1 + z)^{1/z}$$

Equation (5) is often given as the definition of the number e.

Let us consider the function F defined by

(6)
$$F(z) = (1 + z)^{1/z}$$

and determine the function values for some values of z close to zero. These values are given in Table 12.8.1.

Table 12.8.1

z	1	0.5	0.05	0.01	0.001	-0.001	-0.01	-0.05	-0.5
$F(z) = (1+z)^{1/z}$	2	2.25	2.65	2.70	2.7169	2.7196	2.73	2.79	4

Table 12.8.1 leads us to suspect that $\lim_{z \to 0} (1 + z)^{1/z}$ is probably a number that lies between 2.7169 and 2.7196. As previously mentioned, in the chapter on infinite series we shall learn a method for finding the value of e to any desired number of decimal places. The value of e correct to four decimal places is 2.7183.

Exercises 12.8

1. *Given:* $F(z) = (1 + z)^{1/z}$. *Find:* $F(0.0001)$ and $F(-0.0001)$ correct to four decimal places.

2. Draw a sketch of the graph of F, if $F(z) = (1 + z)^{1/z}$.

3. *Prove:* If $x > 0$ and $\int_1^x t^{z-1} \, dt = 1$, then $\lim_{z \to 0} x = \lim_{z \to 0} (1 + z)^{1/z}$.

13 Trigonometric functions

(13.1)   A brief review of trigonometry

It is assumed that the reader has studied trigonometry. However, we shall review some of the basic definitions and formulas, since a knowledge of them is indispensable for what follows.

Two systems of units for measuring angles are generally used. In one system the unit of measure is the *degree* and in the other system the unit is the *radian*. Degree measure is used in computation. In calculus we use radian measure because we obtain simpler formulas when differentiating and integrating trigonometric functions.

13.1.1 DEFINITION   The number of *radians*, θ, in the measure of an angle having its vertex at the center of a circle of radius r units and which intercepts on the circumference of the circle an arc of length s units is given by

$$\theta = \frac{s}{r}$$

If $s = r$, then $\theta = 1$. An angle of 1 radian is shown in Fig. 13.1.1. An angle of θ radians is shown in Fig. 13.1.2.

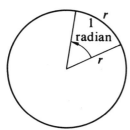

Figure 13.1.1

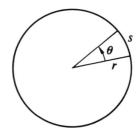

Figure 13.1.2

If C is the number of units in the circumference of a circle, then $C = 2\pi r$. Hence, if in Definition 13.1.1, $s = C$, we have $\theta = 2\pi r/r$, or $\theta = 2\pi$. So, we have the following relationship between degree measure and radian measure:

$$360° = 2\pi \text{ radians}$$

or, equivalently,

$$180° = \pi \text{ radians}$$

From this it follows that

$$1° = \frac{\pi}{180} \text{ radians}$$

and $1 \text{ radian} = \frac{180°}{\pi}$

or $1 \text{ radian} \approx 57°18'$

EXAMPLE 1: Express 162° in radians.
   Solution: $162° = 162 \times 1° = 162 \times \pi/180 \text{ radians} = 9\pi/10 \text{ radians}.$
Therefore an angle of 162° is equal to an angle of $9\pi/10$ radians.

EXAMPLE 2: Express $5\pi/12$ radians in degrees.
   Solution: $5\pi/12 \text{ radians} = 5\pi/12 \times 1 \text{ radian} = 5\pi/12 \times 180°/\pi = 75°.$
Therefore, an angle of $5\pi/12$ radians is equal to an angle of 75°.

We now define the trigonometric functions of any angle θ. Consider an angle θ in standard position on a rectangular cartesian coordinate system; that is, its vertex is at the origin and its initial side is along the positive side of the x axis. Choose point P on the terminal side of θ and also on the unit circle having its center at the origin. Let P be the point (x,y). Figure 13.1.3 shows angles having terminal sides in the first, second, third, and fourth quadrants.

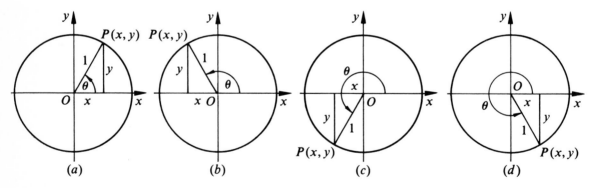

(a)   (b)   (c)   (d)

Figure 13.1.3

The six trigonometric functions of angle θ are defined as follows:

$$\sin \theta = y \quad \cos \theta = x \quad \tan \theta = \frac{y}{x} \quad \cot \theta = \frac{x}{y} \quad \sec \theta = \frac{1}{x} \quad \csc \theta = \frac{1}{y}$$

where (x,y) is the point where the terminal side of θ intersects the unit circle.

These definitions of the six trigonometric functions depend only upon the angle θ. The signs of these functions depend upon the quadrant of θ since the signs of x and y vary from quadrant to quadrant.

Positive angles are measured in the counterclockwise direction from the positive side of the x axis and negative angles are measured in the clockwise direction. Figure 13.1.4 shows a negative angle $(-\theta)$ and its corresponding positive angle θ.

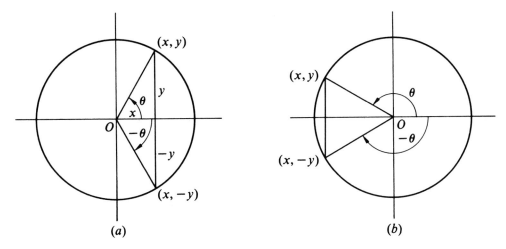

Figure 13.1.4

The following are easily shown to be true:

$$\sin (-\theta) = -\sin \theta \qquad \cos (-\theta) = \cos \theta \qquad \tan (-\theta) = -\tan \theta$$
$$\cot (-\theta) = -\cot \theta \qquad \sec (-\theta) = \sec \theta \qquad \csc (-\theta) = -\csc \theta$$

An equation of the unit circle with center at the origin is

(1) $$x^2 + y^2 = 1$$

Since $\cos \theta = x$ and $\sin \theta = y$, it follows that

(2) $$\cos^2 \theta + \sin^2 \theta = 1$$

for every angle θ.

If we divide both sides of (1) by x^2, we obtain

(3) $$1 + \tan^2 \theta = \sec^2 \theta$$

and if we divide both sides of (1) by y^2, we get

(4) $$\cot^2 \theta + 1 = \csc^2 \theta$$

Equations (2), (3), and (4) are called *identities*, since they are valid for any angle θ for which both sides of the equations are defined. Five other fundamental identities which follow immediately from the definitions are

(5) $$\sin \theta \; \csc \theta = 1$$

(6) $$\cos \theta \; \sec \theta = 1$$

(7) $$\tan \theta \; \cot \theta = 1$$

(8) $$\tan \theta = \frac{\sin \theta}{\cos \theta}$$

(9) $$\cot \theta = \frac{\cos \theta}{\sin \theta}$$

We list some other formulas from trigonometry.

(10) $$\sin(\alpha + \beta) = \sin\alpha\cos\beta + \cos\alpha\sin\beta$$

(11) $$\sin(\alpha - \beta) = \sin\alpha\cos\beta - \cos\alpha\sin\beta$$

(12) $$\cos(\alpha + \beta) = \cos\alpha\cos\beta - \sin\alpha\sin\beta$$

(13) $$\cos(\alpha - \beta) = \cos\alpha\cos\beta + \sin\alpha\sin\beta$$

(14) $$\tan(\alpha + \beta) = \frac{\tan\alpha + \tan\beta}{1 - \tan\alpha\tan\beta}$$

(15) $$\tan(\alpha - \beta) = \frac{\tan\alpha - \tan\beta}{1 + \tan\alpha\tan\beta}$$

(16) $$\sin 2\theta = 2\sin\theta\cos\theta$$

(17) $$\cos 2\theta = \cos^2\theta - \sin^2\theta$$

(18) $$\cos 2\theta = 2\cos^2\theta - 1$$

(19) $$\cos 2\theta = 1 - 2\sin^2\theta$$

(20) $$\tan 2\theta = \frac{2\tan\theta}{1 - \tan^2\theta}$$

(21) $$\sin^2\frac{\theta}{2} = \frac{1 - \cos\theta}{2}$$

(22) $$\cos^2\frac{\theta}{2} = \frac{1 + \cos\theta}{2}$$

(23) $$\tan\frac{\theta}{2} = \frac{1 - \cos\theta}{\sin\theta}$$

(24) $$\tan\frac{\theta}{2} = \frac{\sin\theta}{1 + \cos\theta}$$

(25) $$\sin\alpha\sin\beta = \tfrac{1}{2}[-\cos(\alpha + \beta) + \cos(\alpha - \beta)]$$

(26) $$\cos\alpha\cos\beta = \tfrac{1}{2}[\cos(\alpha + \beta) + \cos(\alpha - \beta)]$$

(27) $$\sin\alpha\cos\beta = \tfrac{1}{2}[\sin(\alpha + \beta) + \sin(\alpha - \beta)]$$

(28) $$\sin A + \sin B = 2\sin\frac{A + B}{2}\cos\frac{A - B}{2}$$

(29) $$\sin A - \sin B = 2\cos\frac{A + B}{2}\sin\frac{A - B}{2}$$

(30) $$\cos A + \cos B = 2\cos\frac{A + B}{2}\cos\frac{A - B}{2}$$

(31) $$\cos A - \cos B = -2\sin\frac{A + B}{2}\sin\frac{A - B}{2}$$

It would be beneficial for the reader to review the proofs of the above formulas.

Table 13.1.1 gives some special angles in degree measure, radian measure, and their sines, cosines, and tangents.

Table 13.1.1

θ, in degrees	0°	30°	45°	60°	90°	120°	135°	150°	180°	270°	360°
θ, in radians	0	$\pi/6$	$\pi/4$	$\pi/3$	$\pi/2$	$2\pi/3$	$3\pi/4$	$5\pi/6$	π	$3\pi/2$	2π
$\sin\theta$	0	$1/2$	$\sqrt{2}/2$	$\sqrt{3}/2$	1	$\sqrt{3}/2$	$\sqrt{2}/2$	$1/2$	0	-1	0
$\cos\theta$	1	$\sqrt{3}/2$	$\sqrt{2}/2$	$1/2$	0	$-1/2$	$-\sqrt{2}/2$	$-\sqrt{3}/2$	-1	0	1
$\tan\theta$	0	$\sqrt{3}/3$	1	$\sqrt{3}$	not de-fined	$-\sqrt{3}$	-1	$-\sqrt{3}/3$	0	not de-fined	0

In calculus we are concerned with functions of real variables. So, we wish to consider such functions as sin x, cos x, tan x, cot x, sec x, and csc x, where x is a real number. We make the following definition.

13.1.2 DEFINITION   If x is a real number and θ is the angle whose radian measure is the number x, then

$$\sin x = \sin\theta \qquad \cos x = \cos\theta \qquad \tan x = \tan\theta$$
$$\cot x = \cot\theta \qquad \sec x = \sec\theta \qquad \csc x = \csc\theta$$

whenever the function of θ is defined.

Because of this definition, all the formulas that are valid for trigonometric functions for angles also are valid for trigonometric functions of real numbers.

Exercises 13.1

1. Which of the six trigonometric functions are even functions and which are odd functions? NOTE: f is an even function if $f(-x) = f(x)$, and f is an odd function if $f(-x) = -f(x)$.

2. (a) Derive formula (17) from formula (12); (b) derive (18) from (17) and (2); (c) derive (19) from (17) and (2).

3. Derive formula (16).

4. Derive formula (20).

5. Derive formula (23) from (8), (21), and (22), and then rationalize the numerator and apply (2).

6. Derive formula (24). Use a method similar to that suggested in Exercise 5.

7. Derive formula (14).

8. Derive formula (15).

9. Derive a formula for sin 3θ in terms of sin θ by using formulas (10), (16), (17), and (2).

10. Derive a formula for cos 3θ in terms of cos θ. Use a method similar to that suggested in Exercise 9.

11. Without using tables, find the values of each of the following: (a) sin 15°; (b) cos 15°; (c) tan 15°.

12. Without using tables, find the values of each of the following: (a) sin 22½°; (b) cos 22½°; (c) tan 22½°.

13. Without using tables, find the values of each of the following: (a) sin 75°; (b) cos 75°; (c) tan 75°.

14. Express each of the following in terms of either sin θ or cos θ: (a) sin $(3\pi/2 - \theta)$; (b) cos $(3\pi/2 - \theta)$; (c) sin $(3\pi/2 + \theta)$; (d) cos $(3\pi/2 + \theta)$.

15. Express each of the following in terms of either sin θ or cos θ: (a) sin $(\pi - \theta)$; (b) cos $(\pi - \theta)$; (c) sin $(\pi + \theta)$; (d) cos $(\pi + \theta)$.

16. Derive formula (25) by subtracting (12) from (13).

17. Derive formula (26). Use a method similar to that suggested in Exercise 16.

18. Derive formula (27). Use a method similar to that suggested in Exercise 16.

19. Derive formula (28) by letting $A = \alpha + \beta$ and $B = \alpha - \beta$ in formula (27).

20. Derive formula (31). Use a method similar to that suggested in Exercise 19.

(13.2)   Some trigonometric limits

Before we can derive the formula for the derivative of the sine function we shall need to find the value of

$$\lim_{\theta \to 0} \frac{\sin \theta}{\theta}$$

If θ is measured in radians and $f(\theta) = \sin \theta / \theta$, we see that $f(0)$ does not exist, since if we replace θ by 0 in the expression for $f(\theta)$, we get sin 0/0, which is not defined. However, we shall prove that $\lim_{\theta \to 0} (\sin \theta / \theta)$ exists and is equal to 1.

13.2.1 THEOREM   If θ is measured in radians, then

$$\lim_{\theta \to 0} \frac{\sin \theta}{\theta} = 1$$

Proof: Let us first assume $0 < \theta < \pi/2$. Let θ be the number of radians in the central angle of a unit circle — see Fig. 13.2.1. $|\overline{OP}|$ and $|\overline{OB}|$ are each equal to 1 since P and B are points on the unit circle. From Definition 13.1.1,

(1)   Length of arc $BP = \theta$

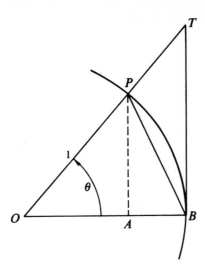

Figure 13.2.1

T is the point of intersection of the tangent line to the circle at B with the line through O and P. We see from Fig. 13.2.1,

(2)   Area $\triangle BOP$ < area sector BOP < area $\triangle BOT$ if $0 < \theta < \pi/2$

(3)   Area $\triangle BOP = \frac{1}{2}|\overline{AP}| \cdot |\overline{OB}| = \frac{1}{2}|\overline{AP}| \cdot 1 = \frac{1}{2}|\overline{AP}|$

Since $\sin\theta = |\overline{AP}|/|\overline{OP}| = |\overline{AP}|/1$, we have from (3)

(4)   Area $\triangle BOP = \frac{1}{2}\sin\theta$

The area of a circular sector of radius r and central angle θ is $\frac{1}{2}r^2\theta$, and so

(5)   Area sector $BOP = \frac{1}{2}\theta$

(6)   Area $\triangle BOT = \frac{1}{2}|\overline{BT}| \cdot |\overline{OB}| = \frac{1}{2}|\overline{BT}| \cdot 1 = \frac{1}{2}|\overline{BT}|$

Since $\tan\theta = |\overline{BT}|/|\overline{OB}| = |\overline{BT}|/1 = |\overline{BT}|$, we have from (6)

(7)   Area $\triangle BOT = \frac{1}{2}\tan\theta$

Substituting (4), (5), and (7) into (2), we get

$$\frac{1}{2}\sin\theta < \frac{1}{2}\theta < \frac{1}{2}\tan\theta \qquad \text{if } 0 < \theta < \frac{\pi}{2}$$

Multiplying each member of this inequality by $2/\sin\theta$, which is positive, since $0 < \theta < \pi/2$, we obtain

$$1 < \frac{\theta}{\sin\theta} < \frac{1}{\cos\theta} \qquad \text{if } 0 < \theta < \frac{\pi}{2}$$

Taking the reciprocal of each member of the above and reversing the direction of the inequality signs, we get

(8) $\cos\theta < \dfrac{\sin\theta}{\theta} < 1$ if $0 < \theta < \dfrac{\pi}{2}$

Now, since $|\overline{BP}| <$ length of arc BP, from (1) we have

(9) $$|\overline{BP}| < \theta$$

Also, from the law of cosines applied to $\triangle OPB$, we have

$$|\overline{BP}|^2 = 1^2 + 1^2 - 2 \cdot 1 \cdot 1 \cdot \cos \theta$$

or

(10) $$|\overline{BP}|^2 = 2 - 2 \cos \theta$$

So, from (9) and (10) it follows that

$$2 - 2 \cos \theta < \theta^2$$

$$\text{or} \quad 1 - \cos \theta < \tfrac{1}{2}\theta^2$$

$$\text{or}$$

(11) $$1 - \tfrac{1}{2}\theta^2 < \cos \theta$$

From (8) and (11), we get

(12) $$1 - \frac{1}{2}\theta^2 < \frac{\sin \theta}{\theta} < 1 \qquad \text{if } 0 < \theta < \frac{\pi}{2}$$

If $-\pi/2 < \theta < 0$, then $0 < -\theta < \pi/2$, and so from (12),

$$1 - \frac{1}{2}(-\theta)^2 < \frac{\sin (-\theta)}{-\theta} < 1 \qquad \text{if } -\frac{\pi}{2} < \theta < 0$$

But $\sin (-\theta)/(-\theta) = -\sin \theta/(-\theta) = \sin \theta/\theta$, and so from the above we get

(13) $$1 - \frac{1}{2}\theta^2 < \frac{\sin \theta}{\theta} < 1 \qquad \text{if } -\frac{\pi}{2} < \theta < 0$$

From (12) and (13), we conclude

(14) $$1 - \frac{1}{2}\theta^2 < \frac{\sin \theta}{\theta} < 1 \qquad \text{if } -\frac{\pi}{2} < \theta < \frac{\pi}{2} \text{ and } \theta \neq 0$$

Since $\lim\limits_{\theta \to 0} (1 - \tfrac{1}{2}\theta^2) = 1$ and $\lim\limits_{\theta \to 0} 1 = 1$, it follows from (14) and the theorem of Exercise 2 in Sec 4.6 that

$$\lim_{\theta \to 0} \frac{\sin \theta}{\theta} = 1 \qquad \qquad \text{Q.E.D.}$$

From the above theorem, we can prove that the sine function and the cosine function are continuous at 0.

13.2.2 THEOREM   The sine function is continuous at 0.

   Proof: We show that the three conditions necessary for continuity at a number are satisfied.

   (i) $\sin 0 = 0$

   (ii) $\lim\limits_{\theta \to 0} \sin \theta = \lim\limits_{\theta \to 0} \dfrac{\sin \theta}{\theta} \cdot \theta = \lim\limits_{\theta \to 0} \dfrac{\sin \theta}{\theta} \cdot \lim\limits_{\theta \to 0} \theta = 1 \cdot 0 = 0$

   (iii) $\lim\limits_{\theta \to 0} \sin \theta = \sin 0$

   Therefore, the sine function is continuous at 0.   Q.E.D.

13.2.3 THEOREM   The cosine function is continuous at 0.
   Proof:

  (i) $\cos 0 = 1$

  (ii) $\lim\limits_{\theta \to 0} \cos \theta = \lim\limits_{\theta \to 0} \sqrt{1 - \sin^2\theta} = \sqrt{\lim\limits_{\theta \to 0} (1 - \sin^2\theta)} = \sqrt{1 - 0} = 1$

  NOTE: We may replace $\cos \theta$ by $\sqrt{1 - \sin^2 \theta}$ since $\cos \theta > 0$ when $0 < \theta < \pi/2$ and when $-\pi/2 < \theta < 0$.

  (iii) $\lim\limits_{\theta \to 0} \cos \theta = \cos 0$

Therefore, the cosine function is continuous at 0.   Q.E.D.

The limit in the following theorem is also important. It follows from the previous three theorems and limit theorems.

13.2.4 THEOREM   If θ is measured in radians, then

$$\lim_{\theta \to 0} \frac{1 - \cos \theta}{\theta} = 0$$

Proof: $\quad \lim\limits_{\theta \to 0} \dfrac{1 - \cos \theta}{\theta} = \lim\limits_{\theta \to 0} \dfrac{(1 - \cos \theta)(1 + \cos \theta)}{\theta(1 + \cos \theta)}$

$$= \lim_{\theta \to 0} \frac{(1 - \cos^2 \theta)}{\theta(1 + \cos \theta)}$$

$$= \lim_{\theta \to 0} \frac{\sin^2 \theta}{\theta(1 + \cos \theta)}$$

$$= \lim_{\theta \to 0} \frac{\sin \theta}{\theta} \cdot \lim_{\theta \to 0} \frac{\sin \theta}{1 + \cos \theta}$$

$$= 1 \cdot \frac{0}{1 + 1}$$

$$= 0 \qquad\qquad\qquad\qquad\text{Q.E.D.}$$

EXAMPLE 1: *Find:* $\lim\limits_{x \to 0} \dfrac{2 \tan^2 x}{x^2}$.

Solution: $\quad \lim\limits_{x \to 0} \dfrac{2 \tan^2 x}{x^2} = 2 \lim\limits_{x \to 0} \dfrac{\sin^2 x}{x^2 \cos^2 x}$

$$= 2 \lim_{x \to 0} \frac{\sin x}{x} \cdot \lim_{x \to 0} \frac{\sin x}{x} \cdot \lim_{x \to 0} \frac{1}{\cos^2 x}$$

$$= 2 \cdot 1 \cdot 1 \cdot 1 = 2$$

Exercises 13.2

In Exercises 1 through 10, evaluate the given limit, if it exists.

1. $\lim\limits_{x \to 0} \dfrac{\sin 4x}{x}$

2. $\lim\limits_{x \to 0} \dfrac{\tan x}{2x}$

3. $\displaystyle\lim_{x\to 0} \frac{x}{\cos x}$

7. $\displaystyle\lim_{x\to 0} \frac{1 - \cos x}{x^2}$

4. $\displaystyle\lim_{x\to\pi/2} \frac{\pi/2 - x}{\cos x}$

8. $\displaystyle\lim_{x\to 0} \frac{1 - \cos^2 x}{2x^2}$

5. $\displaystyle\lim_{x\to 0} \frac{\sin 3x}{\sin 5x}$

9. $\displaystyle\lim_{x\to 0} \frac{3x^2}{1 - \cos^2 \tfrac{1}{2}x}$

6. $\displaystyle\lim_{x\to 0} \frac{1 - \cos x}{\sin x}$

10. $\displaystyle\lim_{x\to 0} \frac{\tan^4 2x}{4x^4}$

11. Prove the tangent function is continuous at 0.

12. Prove the cotangent function is discontinuous at 0.

13. Prove the secant function is continuous at 0.

14. Prove the cosecant function is discontinuous at 0.

(13.3)   Differentiation of trigonometric functions

We shall now consider the problem of finding the derivative of the sine function. Let f be the function defined by

$$f(x) = \sin x$$

From the definition of a derivative, we have

$$f'(x) = \lim_{\Delta x\to 0} \frac{f(x + \Delta x) - f(x)}{\Delta x}$$

$$= \lim_{\Delta x\to 0} \frac{\sin (x + \Delta x) - \sin x}{\Delta x}$$

$$= \lim_{\Delta x\to 0} \frac{\sin x \cos (\Delta x) + \cos x \sin (\Delta x) - \sin x}{\Delta x}$$

$$= \lim_{\Delta x\to 0} \frac{\sin x[\cos (\Delta x) - 1]}{\Delta x} + \lim_{\Delta x\to 0} \frac{\cos x \sin (\Delta x)}{\Delta x}$$

$$= -\lim_{\Delta x\to 0} \frac{1 - \cos (\Delta x)}{\Delta x} (\lim_{\Delta x\to 0} \sin x) + (\lim_{\Delta x\to 0} \cos x) \lim_{\Delta x\to 0} \frac{\sin (\Delta x)}{\Delta x}$$

$$= -0\cdot \sin x + \cos x\cdot 1 \qquad \text{by Theorems 13.2.1 and 13.2.4}$$

$$= \cos x$$

Therefore, we have the formula

(((2) $D_x(\sin x) = \cos x$

If u is a differentiable function of x, we have from (2) and the chain rule,

(((3) $D_x(\sin u) = \cos u \, D_x u$

We obtain the derivative of the cosine function by making use of (2) and the following identities:

$$\cos x = \sin\left(\frac{\pi}{2} - x\right) \quad \text{and} \quad \sin x = \cos\left(\frac{\pi}{2} - x\right)$$

$$D_x(\cos x) = D_x\left[\sin\left(\frac{\pi}{2} - x\right)\right] = \cos\left(\frac{\pi}{2} - x\right) \cdot D_x\left(\frac{\pi}{2} - x\right) = \sin x(-1)$$

Therefore,

(((4) $$D_x(\cos x) = -\sin x$$

So, if u is a differentiable function of x, it follows from (4) and the chain rule that

(((5) $$D_x(\cos u) = -\sin u \ D_x u$$

To find the derivative of the tangent function, we make use of (2) and (4) and the following identities:

$$\tan x = \sin x/\cos x \qquad 1/\cos x = \sec x \qquad \sin^2 x + \cos^2 x = 1$$

$$D_x(\tan x) = D_x\left(\frac{\sin x}{\cos x}\right) = \frac{\cos x \cdot D_x(\sin x) - \sin x \cdot D_x(\cos x)}{\cos^2 x}$$

$$= \frac{(\cos x)(\cos x) - (\sin x)(-\sin x)}{\cos^2 x}$$

$$= \frac{\cos^2 x + \sin^2 x}{\cos^2 x} = \frac{1}{\cos^2 x} = \sec^2 x$$

So, we write,

(((6) $$D_x(\tan x) = \sec^2 x$$

If u is a differentiable function of x, then from (6) and the chain rule we obtain

(((7) $$D_x(\tan u) = \sec^2 u \ D_x u$$

The derivative of the cotangent function is derived in an analogous manner, by making use of (2) and (4) and the following identities: $\cot x = \cos x/\sin x$, $1/\sin x = \csc x$, $\sin^2 x + \cos^2 x = 1$. The result is the following formula:

(((8) $$D_x(\cot x) = -\csc^2 x$$

The derivation of (8) is left for the reader (see Exercise 1 at the end of this section).

From (8) and the chain rule, if u is a differentiable function of x, we have

(((9) $$D_x(\cot u) = -\csc^2 u \ D_x u$$

We obtain the formula for the derivative of the secant function by using (4) and the identities $\sec x = 1/\cos x$ and $\tan x = \sin x/\cos x$.

$$D_x(\sec x) = D_x[(\cos x)^{-1}] = -1(\cos x)^{-2}(-\sin x)$$

$$= \frac{1}{\cos^2 x} \cdot \sin x = \frac{1}{\cos x} \cdot \frac{\sin x}{\cos x} = \sec x \tan x$$

We have then, the following formula.

(((10) $$D_x(\sec x) = \sec x \tan x$$

If u is a differentiable function of x, then from (10) and the chain rule we get

(((11) $$D_x(\sec u) = \sec u \tan u \; D_x u$$

In a similar manner, we derive the formula for the derivative of the cosecant function, and we obtain

(((12) $$D_x(\csc x) = -\csc x \cot x$$

So, applying (12) and the chain rule, if u is a differentiable function of x, we have

(((13) $$D_x(\csc u) = -\csc u \cot u \; D_x u$$

The derivation of (12) is left for the reader (see Exercise 2 at the end of this section).

The following examples illustrate the use of the above formulas.

EXAMPLE 1: *Given:* $f(x) = \tan^4 3x$. *Find:* $f'(x)$.
Solution: $f'(x) = 4(\tan^3 3x) \, D_x(\tan 3x) = 4 \tan^3 3x (\sec^2 3x) \, D_x(3x)$
$$= 4 \tan^3 3x \sec^2 3x \, (3) = 12 \tan^3 3x \sec^2 3x$$

EXAMPLE 2: *Given:* $f(x) = \sin x / (1 - 2 \cos x)$. *Find:* $f'(x)$.

Solution: $f'(x) = \dfrac{(1 - 2 \cos x) \, D_x(\sin x) - \sin x \cdot D_x(1 - 2 \cos x)}{(1 - 2 \cos x)^2}$

$$= \frac{(1 - 2 \cos x)(\cos x) - \sin x(2 \sin x)}{(1 - 2 \cos x)^2}$$

$$= \frac{\cos x - 2(\cos^2 x + \sin^2 x)}{(1 - 2 \cos x)^2} = \frac{\cos x - 2}{(1 - 2 \cos x)^2}$$

EXAMPLE 3: *Given:* $y = \ln [\cos (e^x)]$. *Find:* $D_x y$.
Solution: $D_x y = [1/\cos (e^x)][-\sin (e^x)] \; e^x = -e^x \tan (e^x)$.

EXAMPLE 4: *Given:* $x \cos y + y \cos x = 1$. *Find:* $D_x y$.
Solution: Differentiating implicitly with respect to x, we get

$$1 \cdot \cos y + x(-\sin y) \, D_x y + D_x y \, (\cos x) + y(-\sin x) = 0$$

$$D_x y \, (\cos x - x \sin y) = y \sin x - \cos y$$

$$D_x y = \frac{y \sin x - \cos y}{\cos x - x \sin y}$$

Exercises 13.3

1. *Derive:* $D_x(\cot x) = -\csc^2 x.$

2. *Derive:* $D_x(\csc x) = -\csc x \cot x.$

In Exercises 3 through 28 find the derivative of the given function.

3. $f(x) = 3 \sin 2x$

4. $f(x) = \cos(3x^2 + 1)$

5. $g(x) = \sin x \cos x$

6. $h(t) = \sec t^2$

7. $F(x) = \sec^2 x - \tan^2 x$

8. $g(s) = 2 \tan \frac{1}{2}s - s$

9. $G(r) = \sqrt{\cot r}$

10. $h(x) = \sec x \tan x$

11. $f(x) = \sin x \tan x$

12. $g(t) = 2 \sec \sqrt{t}$

13. $g(x) = \ln \sin x$

14. $F(x) = \sin(\ln x)$

15. $G(t) = \csc(t^3 + 1)$

16. $f(x) = \frac{1}{3}\sec^3 2x - \sec 2x$

17. $h(x) = \dfrac{\sin x}{2 + \cos x}$

18. $g(x) = 2 \cos x \sin 2x - \sin x \cos 2x$

19. $h(y) = y^3 - y^2 \cos y + 2y \sin y + 2 \cos y$

20. $F(t) = \sin(\cos t)$

21. $G(x) = \dfrac{\cot^2 2x}{1 + x^2}$

22. $H(t) = \cot^4 t - \csc^4 t$

23. $f(x) = (\sin x)^x$

24. $g(x) = (\sin x)^{\cos x}$

25. $h(x) = x^{\sin x}$

26. $F(t) = (\sin t)^{\tan t}$

27. $G(x) = (\sin x)^{\sin x}$

28. $f(x) = (\ln \sin x)^{e^x}$

In Exercises 29 through 32, use logarithmic differentiation to find $D_x y$.

29. $y = \dfrac{\sin x \sqrt{1 + \cos^2 x}}{\tan^3 x}$

30. $y = \dfrac{x \sin x}{\sqrt{x^2 + 1}}$

31. $y = \dfrac{\sin^3 x}{\sqrt{1 - 3 \cos x}}$

32. $y = \dfrac{\tan^2 x}{\sqrt{1 + \sec^2 x}}$

In Exercises 33 through 38, find $D_x y$ by implicit differentiation.

33. $y = \cos(x - y)$

34. $\sin(x + y) + \sin(x - y) = 1$

35. $y = \tan(x + y)$

36. $\cos(x + y) = y \sin x$

37. $\cot xy + xy = 0$

38. $\csc(x - y) + \sec(x + y) = x$

39. Show that $\dfrac{d(\ln \sin x)}{d(\ln x)} = x \cot x.$

40. Find the absolute maximum value attained by the function f if $f(x) = a \sin kx + b \cos kx$, where a, b, and k are positive constants.

41. *Given:* $f(x) = x \sin(\pi/x)$. *Prove:* f has an infinite number of relative extrema.

42. If the domain of the function f in Exercise 41 is the interval $(0,1]$, how should $f(0)$ be defined so that f is continuous on the closed interval $[0,1]$?

(13.4) Graphs of the trigonometric functions

Since $D_x(\sin x) = \cos x$, and $\cos x$ exists for all values of x, the sine function is differentiable everywhere, and therefore continuous everywhere. Similarly the cosine function is differentiable everywhere, and therefore continuous everywhere. The other four trigonometric functions are ratios of the sine and cosine functions, and so are continuous wherever they exist. We shall now discuss the graphs of the trigonometric functions.

We first consider the graph of the sine function. Let

$$f(x) = \sin x$$

Then, $f'(x) = \cos x$ and $f''(x) = -\sin x$. To determine the relative extrema, we set $f'(x) = 0$, and we get $x = \pi/2 + n\pi$, where $n = 0, \pm 1, \pm 2, \ldots$. If n is an even integer, then $f''(\pi/2 + n\pi) = -\sin(\pi/2 + n\pi) = -\sin(\pi/2) = -1$; and if n is an odd integer, $f''(\pi/2 + n\pi) = -\sin(\pi/2 + n\pi) = -\sin(3\pi/2) = 1$. Therefore, f has relative extrema when $x = \pi/2 + n\pi$, and if n is an even integer, f has a relative maximum value, and if n is an odd integer, f has a relative minimum value.

To determine the points of inflection of the graph, we set $f''(x) = 0$, and we obtain $x = n\pi$, where $n = 0, \pm 1, \pm 2, \ldots$. Since $f''(x)$ changes sign at each of these values of x, the graph has a point of inflection at each point having these abscissas. At each point of inflection, $f'(x) = \cos n\pi = \pm 1$. Therefore, the slopes of the inflectional tangents are either $+1$ or -1. Furthermore, because $\sin(x + 2\pi) = \sin x$, the sine function is said to be *periodic* and has the period 2π. The absolute maximum value of the sine function is 1, and the absolute minimum value is -1. The graph intersects the x axis at those points where $\sin x = 0$; that is, at the points where $x = n\pi$, where n is any integer.

From the information obtained above, we draw a sketch of the graph of the sine function; it is shown in Fig. 13.4.1.

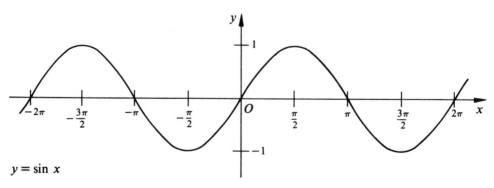

$y = \sin x$

Figure 13.4.1

To obtain the graph of the cosine function, we make use of the identity

$$\cos x = \sin\left(\frac{\pi}{2} + x\right)$$

So, the graph of the cosine function is obtained from the graph of the sine function by translating the y axis $\pi/2$ units to the right (see Fig. 13.4.2).

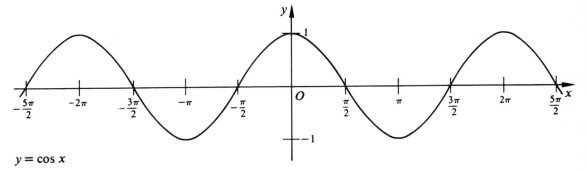

$y = \cos x$

Figure 13.4.2

Since $\tan x = \sin x / \cos x$, the tangent function is continuous at all values of x except those for which $\cos x = 0$; that is, for $x = \pi/2 + n\pi$, where n is any integer. When $\cos x = 0$, $\tan x$ does not exist. However, $\lim\limits_{x \to \pi/2 + n\pi} \tan x = \infty$, and so the lines having equations $x = \pi/2 + n\pi$ are vertical asymptotes of the graph of the tangent function.

If n is any integer, $\tan n\pi = 0$, and so the graph of the tangent function intersects the x axis at the points $(n\pi, 0)$. The period of the tangent function is π, since $\tan x = \tan(x + \pi)$.

To find the relative extrema of the tangent function and the points of inflection of its graph, we find the first and second derivatives. So, if $f(x) = \tan x$, we have $f'(x) = \sec^2 x$ and $f''(x) = 2 \sec^2 x \tan x$.

Setting $f'(x) = 0$, we get $\sec^2 x = 0$. Since $\sec^2 x \geq 1$ for all x, we conclude that there are no relative extrema. Setting $f''(x) = 0$, we obtain $2 \sec^2 x \tan x = 0$, from which we get $\tan x = 0$, since $\sec^2 x \neq 0$. Therefore, $f''(x) = 0$ if $x = n\pi$, where n is any integer. At these values of x, $f''(x)$ changes sign, and so the points of inflection are the points $(n\pi, 0)$, which are the points where the graph intersects the x axis. $f'(n\pi) = \sec^2(n\pi) = 1$; so the slopes of the inflectional tangents are 1.

A sketch of the graph of the tangent function may be drawn from the above information, and it is shown in Fig. 13.4.3.

We make use of the identity

$$\cot x = -\tan\left(\frac{\pi}{2} + x\right)$$

to obtain the graph of the cotangent function. A sketch of the graph of the cotangent function is shown in Fig. 13.4.4.

From the identity $\sec x = 1/\cos x$, we conclude that the secant function is continuous at all values of x except those for which $\cos x = 0$; that is, for $x = \pi/2 + n\pi$, where n is any integer. Since $\lim\limits_{x \to \pi/2 + n\pi} \sec x = \infty$, the graph of the secant function has the lines $x = \pi/2 + n\pi$ as vertical asymptotes.

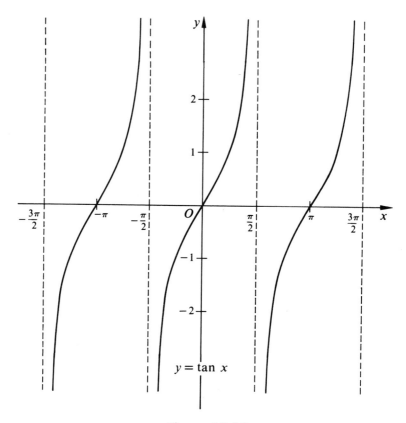

Figure 13.4.3

Since $\sec x = \sec(x + 2\pi)$, the period of the secant function is 2π. The graph of the secant function does not intersect the x axis, since $\sec x$ is never zero.

If $f(x) = \sec x$, it follows that $f'(x) = \sec x \tan x$ and $f''(x) = \sec x \,(2 \tan^2 x + 1)$. Setting $f'(x) = 0$, we have $\sec x \tan x = 0$. Since $\sec x \neq 0$, $f'(x) = 0$ when $\tan x = 0$; that is, when $x = n\pi$, where n is any integer. $f'(n\pi) = \sec n\pi \times [2 \tan^2 n\pi + 1]$. If n is an even integer, $f'(n\pi) = 1 \cdot (0 + 1) = 1$, and if n is an odd integer, $f'(n\pi) = (-1)(0 + 1) = -1$. Therefore, when $x = n\pi$ and n is an even integer, f has a relative minimum value, and when $x = n\pi$ and n is an odd integer, f has a relative maximum value. There are no points of inflection, since $f''(x) \neq 0$ for all x.

A sketch of the graph of the secant function is shown in Fig. 13.4.5.

The graph of the cosecant function is obtained from the graph of the secant function by the following identity:

$$\csc x = \sec \left(\frac{\pi}{2} + x \right)$$

A sketch of the graph of the cosecant function is shown in Fig. 13.4.6.

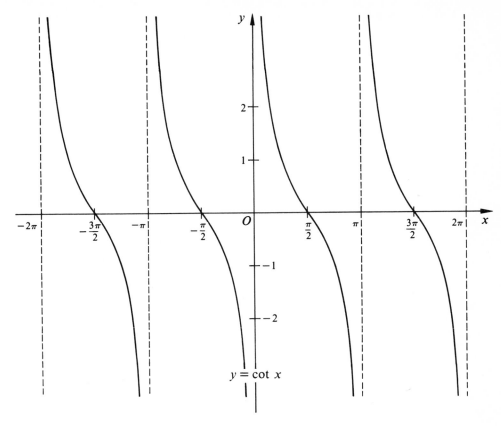

Figure 13.4.4

Exercises 13.4

In Exercises 1 through 6, (*a*) find the relative extrema of the given function, (*b*) find the points of inflection of the graph of the given function, (*c*) find the slopes of the inflectional tangents, (*d*) draw a sketch of the graph of the given function.

1. The cotangent function.
2. The cosecant function.
3. The haversine function. The haversine of x is defined by the equation hav $(x) = \frac{1}{2}(1 - \cos x)$.
4. The versed sine function. The versed sine of x is defined by the equation vers $(x) = 1 - \cos x$.
5. The coversed sine function. The coversed sine of x is defined by the equation covers $(x) = 1 - \sin x$.
6. The exsecant function. The exsecant of x is defined by the equation exsec $(x) = \sec x - 1$.

In Exercises 7 through 14, draw a sketch of the graph of the given function.

7. $f(x) = \sin 2x$

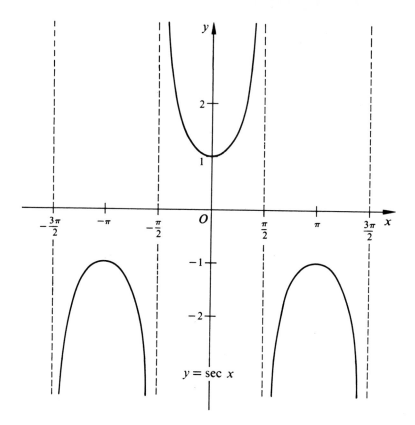

Figure 13.4.5

8. $f(x) = 2 \cos 3x$

9. $f(x) = \tan 2x$

10. $f(x) = \frac{1}{2} \sec 2x$

11. $f(x) = |\cos 2x|$

12. $f(x) = \frac{1}{2} |\cot x|$

13. $f(x) = \begin{cases} \sin x & \text{if } 0 \le x < \dfrac{\pi}{2} \\ \sin\left(x - \dfrac{\pi}{2}\right) & \text{if } \dfrac{\pi}{2} \le x \le \pi \end{cases}$

14. $f(x) = \begin{cases} \cos x & \text{if } -\pi \le x \le 0 \\ \cos(\pi - x) & \text{if } 0 < x \le \pi \end{cases}$

15. Find the points of intersection of the graphs of the sine and cosine functions, and find the angle between the tangent lines at their points of intersection.

16. Find an equation of the tangent line to the curve $y = \sin x$ at the point $(\pi/4, \sqrt{2}/2)$.

17. Find an equation of the normal line to the curve $y = \cos x$ at the point $(2\pi/3, -\frac{1}{2})$.

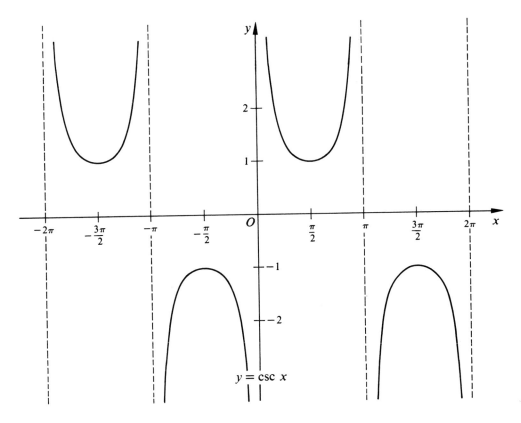

Figure 13.4.6

(13.5)   Applications of derivatives of trigonometric functions

The following two examples illustrate the solution of related rate problems involving trigonometric functions.

EXAMPLE 1: If a triangle has two sides of lengths 10 in. and 15 in., and the included angle between these two sides is increasing at the rate of 1°/hr, at what rate is the area of the triangle changing when the included angle is 45°?

Solution: Refer to Fig. 13.5.1.

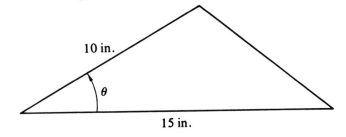

Figure 13.5.1

Let t = the number of hours in the time

Let θ = the number of radians in the included angle at time t hr

Let A = the number of square inches in the area of the triangle at time t hr

$$A = \tfrac{1}{2} \cdot 10 \cdot 15 \cdot \sin \theta$$

or

(1) $$A = 75 \sin \theta$$

Since the included angle is increasing at the rate of 1°/hr, or $\pi/180$ radians per hour, $D_t \theta = \pi/180$. We wish to find $D_t A$ when $\theta = \pi/4$.

Differentiating both sides of equation (1) with respect to t, we obtain

$$D_t A = 75 \cos \theta \; D_t \theta$$

Replacing $D_t \theta$ by $\pi/180$, we get

$$D_t A = \frac{5\pi}{12} \cos \theta$$

When $\theta = \pi/4$,

$$D_t A = \frac{5\pi}{12} \cdot \frac{\sqrt{2}}{2} \approx 0.926$$

Therefore, the area is increasing at the rate of 0.926 in.²/hr at the instant when the included angle is 45°.

EXAMPLE 2: An airplane is flying west at 500 ft/sec, at an elevation of 4,000 ft, in a vertical plane with a searchlight on the ground. If the light is to be kept on the plane, what is the rate of revolution of the searchlight when the airplane is due east of the searchlight at an airline distance of 2,000 ft?

Solution: Refer to Fig. 13.5.2. The searchlight is at point L, and at a particular instant of time, the airplane is at point P.

Let t = the number of seconds in the time

Let x = the number of feet due east in the airline distance of the airplane from the searchlight at time t sec

Let θ = the number of radians in the angle of elevation of the airplane at the searchlight at time t sec

We are given $D_t x = -500$. We wish to find $D_t \theta$ when $x = 2,000$.

(2) $$\tan \theta = \frac{4,000}{x}$$

Differentiating both sides of equation (2) with respect to t, we obtain

$$\sec^2 \theta \; D_t \theta = -\frac{4,000}{x^2} D_t x$$

Substituting $D_t x = -500$ in the above and dividing by $\sec^2 \theta$ gives us

(3) $$D_t \theta = \frac{2,000,000}{x^2 \sec^2 \theta}$$

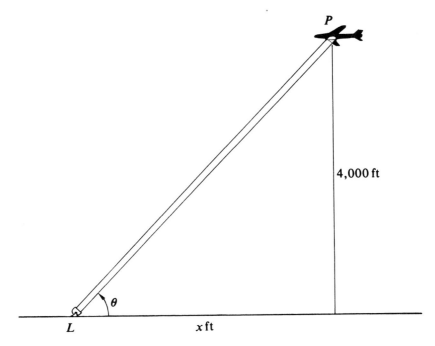

Figure 13.5.2

When $x = 2,000$, $\tan \theta = 2$; so $\sec^2 \theta = 1 + \tan^2 \theta = 5$.
Substituting these values into (3), we have, when $x = 2,000$,

$$D_t\theta = \frac{2,000,000}{4,000,000(5)} = \frac{1}{10}$$

Therefore, the angle is increasing at the rate of $1/10$ radians/sec at the given instant.

Occasionally geometrical problems involving absolute extrema are more easily solved by using trigonometric functions. The following example illustrates this.

EXAMPLE 3: A right-circular cylinder is to be inscribed in a sphere of given radius. Find the ratio of the altitude to the base radius of the cylinder having the largest lateral surface area.

Solution: Refer to Fig. 13.5.3. The constant radius of the sphere is taken as a.

Let θ = the number of radians in the angle at the center of the sphere subtended by the radius of the cylinder

Let r = the number of inches in the radius of the cylinder

Let h = the number of inches in the altitude of the cylinder

Let S = the number of square inches in the lateral surface area of the cylinder.

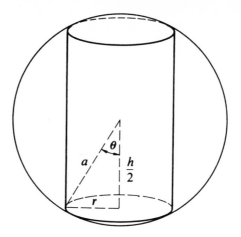

Figure 13.5.3

From Fig. 13.5.3, we see that

$$r = a \sin \theta \quad \text{and} \quad h = 2a \cos \theta$$

Since $S = 2\pi rh$, we have

$$S = 2\pi(a \sin \theta)(2a \cos \theta) = 2\pi a^2(2 \sin \theta \cos \theta) = 2\pi a^2 \sin 2\theta$$

So,

$$D_\theta S = 4\pi a^2 \cos 2\theta \quad \text{and} \quad D_\theta^2 S = -8\pi a^2 \sin 2\theta$$

Setting $D_\theta S = 0$, we get

$$\cos 2\theta = 0$$

Since $0 < \theta < \pi/2$,

$$\theta = \frac{\pi}{4}$$

We apply the second derivative test for relative extrema, and the results are summarized in Table 13.5.1.

Table 13.5.1

	$D_\theta S$	$D_\theta^2 S$	Conclusion
$\theta = \pi/4$	0	−	S has a relative maximum value

Since the domain of θ is the open interval $(0, \pi/2)$, the relative maximum value of S is the absolute maximum value of S.

When $\theta = \pi/4$, $r = \sqrt{2}a/2$, and $h = \sqrt{2}\,a$. So, for the cylinder having the largest lateral surface area, $h/r = 2$.

1. The length of the hypotenuse of a right triangle is 10 in., and one of the acute angles is decreasing at the rate of 5°/sec. How fast is the area of the triangle decreasing when this acute angle is 30°?

2. The length of one side of a triangle is increasing at the rate of 2 ft/min, the length of a second side of the triangle is increasing at the rate of 3 ft/min, and the included angle between these two sides is increasing at the rate of 1°/min. How fast is the area of the triangle changing at the instant when the first side has a length of 40 ft, the second side has a length of 75 ft, and the included angle is 30°?

3. If a ladder of length 30 ft , which is leaning against a wall, has its upper end sliding down the wall at the rate of ½ ft /sec, what is the rate of change of the acute angle made by the ladder with the ground when the upper end is 18 ft above the ground?

4. A fence 16 ft high is 2 ft from a building. Find the length of the shortest ladder that will rest with one end on the ground and the other end on the building.

5. Solve Exercise 4 if the fence is x ft from the building and y ft high.

6. The cross section of a trough has the shape of an inverted isosceles triangle. If the lengths of the equal sides are 15 in., find the size of the vertex angle that will give maximum capacity for the trough.

7. Find the altitude of the right-circular cone of largest possible volume which can be inscribed in a sphere of radius a. Use 2θ as the number of radians in the vertical angle of the cone.

8. A right-circular cylinder is to be inscribed in a hemisphere of given radius, and the base of the cylinder is on the plane face of the hemisphere. Find the ratio of the altitude to the base radius of the cylinder having the largest lateral surface area.

9. A steel girder 27 ft long is moved horizontally along a passageway 8 ft wide and into a corridor at right angles to the passageway. How wide must the corridor be in order for the girder to go around the corner? Neglect the horizontal width of the girder.

10. If two corridors at right angles to each other are 10 ft and 15 ft wide, respectively, what is the length of the longest steel girder that can be moved horizontally around the corner? Neglect the horizontal width of the girder.

11. If a body of weight W lb is dragged along a horizontal floor by means of a force of magnitude F lb and directed at an angle of θ radians with the plane of the floor, then F is given by the equation

$$F = \frac{kW}{k \sin \theta + \cos \theta},$$

where k is a constant and is called the coefficient of friction. Find $\tan \theta$ when F is least.

12. A radar antenna is located on a ship which is 4 miles from a straight shore and it is rotating at 32 rpm. How fast is the radar beam moving along the shore line when the beam makes an angle of 45° with the shore?

(13.6) Integration of the trigonometric functions

The formulas for the indefinite integral of the sine and cosine function follow immediately from the corresponding formulas for differentiation.

$$((\quad (1) \qquad \int \sin u \; du = -\cos u + C$$

Proof: $d(-\cos u + c) = \sin u \; du$.

$$((\quad (2) \qquad \int \cos u \; du = \sin u + C$$

Proof: $d(\sin u + c) = \cos u \; du$.

The indefinite integrals of the other four trigonometric functions involve more discussion.

We derive a formula for $\int \tan u \; du$ as follows.

Write $\tan u = \sin u / \cos u$, and so we have

$$\int \tan u \; du = \int \frac{\sin u}{\cos u} \; du$$

If we let $v = \cos u$, then $dv = -\sin u \; du$, and we obtain

$$\int \tan u \; du = -\int \frac{dv}{v}$$

$$= -\ln |v| + C$$

So,

$$(3) \qquad \int \tan u \; du = -\ln |\cos u| + C$$

Since $-\ln |\cos u| = \ln |(\cos u)^{-1}| = \ln |\sec u|$, we also may write

$$((\quad (4) \qquad \int \tan u \; du = \ln |\sec u| + C$$

The following formula is derived in a way similar to the derivation of (3).

$$((\quad (5) \qquad \int \cot u \; du = \ln |\sin u| + C$$

(See Exercise 21 at the end of this section.)

To integrate $\int \sec u \; du$, we multiply the integrand by $(\sec u + \tan u) \div (\sec u + \tan u)$, and we have

$$\int \sec u \; du = \int \frac{\sec u(\sec u + \tan u)}{\sec u + \tan u} \; du$$

$$= \int \frac{(\sec^2 u + \sec u \tan u)}{\sec u + \tan u} \; du$$

Let $v = \sec u + \tan u$; then $dv = (\sec u \tan u + \sec^2 u)\, du$; and so we have

$$\int \sec u \, du = \int \frac{dv}{v}$$

$$= \ln |v| + C$$

Therefore,

(((6) $$\int \sec u \, du = \ln |\sec u + \tan u| + C$$

The formula for $\int \csc u \, du$ is derived by multiplying the integrand by

$$(\csc u - \cot u)/(\csc u - \cot u)$$

and proceeding as above. This derivation is left for the reader (see Exercise 22 at the end of this section). The formula is

(((7) $$\int \csc u \, du = \ln |\csc u - \cot u| + C$$

The application of these formulas to the evaluation of other integrals is illustrated in the following examples.

EXAMPLE 1: *Find:* $\int \tan 3x \, dx$.
Solution: Let $u = 3x$; then $du = 3 \, dx$ and we have

$$\int \tan 3x \, dx = \tfrac{1}{3} \int \tan u \, du$$
$$= -\tfrac{1}{3} \ln |\cos u| + C$$
$$= -\tfrac{1}{3} \ln |\cos 3x| + C$$

EXAMPLE 2: *Find:* $\int du/\sin 2u$.
Solution: $\int du/\sin 2u = \int \csc 2u \, du$

$$= \tfrac{1}{2} \int \csc 2u(2 \, du)$$
$$= \tfrac{1}{2} \ln |\csc 2u - \cot 2u| + C.$$

EXAMPLE 3: *Find:* $\int \{[\cos (\ln x)]/x\} \, dx$.
Solution: Let $u = \ln x$; then $du = dx/x$; so we have

$$\int \frac{\cos (\ln x)}{x} \, dx = \int \cos u \, du$$
$$= \sin u + C$$
$$= \sin (\ln x) + C$$

EXAMPLE 4: *Find:* $\int [\sin x/(1 - \cos x)] \, dx$.
Solution: Let $u = 1 - \cos x$; then $du = \sin x \, dx$; so

$$\int \frac{\sin x \, dx}{1 - \cos x} = \int \frac{du}{u}$$
$$= \ln |u| + C$$
$$= \ln |1 - \cos x| + C$$

EXAMPLE 5: *Find:* $\int_0^\pi (1 + \sin x)\,dx$.

Solution: $\int_0^\pi (1 + \sin x)\,dx = [x - \cos x]_0^\pi$

$$= \pi - \cos \pi - (0 - \cos 0)$$
$$= \pi + 1 - (0 - 1)$$
$$= \pi + 2.$$

Exercises 13.6

In Exercises 1 through 12, evaluate the indefinite integral.

1. $\int \tan 2x\,dx$

2. $\int (3 \sin x + 2 \cos x)\,dx$

3. $\int (\sin 3x + \cos 2x)\,dx$

4. $\int \dfrac{\cos x}{2 + \sin x}\,dx$

5. $\int \cot (3x + 1)\,dx$

6. $\int \dfrac{dt}{\cos 3t}$

7. $\int \sin x\, e^{\cos x}\,dx$

8. $\int \dfrac{\cos 3\sqrt{x}}{\sqrt{x}}\,dx$

9. $\int x \csc 5x^2\,dx$

10. $\int 2x^2 \cos x^3\,dx$

11. $\int \sin x \cdot \sin (\cos x)\,dx$

12. $\int \sec x \cdot \tan x \cdot \tan (\sec x)\,dx$

In Exercises 13 through 20, evaluate the definite integral.

13. $\int_0^{\pi/4} \sin 2x\,dx$

14. $\int_{\pi/16}^{\pi/12} \tan 4x\,dx$

15. $\int_{\pi/12}^{\pi/4} \cot 2x\,dx$

16. $\int_0^{\sqrt[3]{\pi}} 2x^2 \sin x^3\,dx$

17. $\int_{\pi/3}^{5\pi/12} \tfrac{1}{3} \tan 2x\,dx$

18. $\int_{\pi/3}^{2\pi/3} \sec \dfrac{x}{2}\,dx$

19. $\int_{\pi/8}^{\pi/4} 3 \csc 2x\,dx$

20. $\int_{\ln \pi}^{2} e^x \sin e^x\,dx$

21. Derive the formula $\int \cot u\,du = \ln |\sin u| + C$.

22. Derive the formula $\int \csc u\,du = \ln |\csc u - \cot u| + C$.

23. Find the area of the region bounded by $y = \sin x$ and the x axis from $x = 0$ to $x = \pi$.

24. Find the area of the region bounded by $y = \cos 2x$ and the x axis from $x = -\pi/4$ to $x = \pi/4$.

25. Find the area of the region bounded by the two curves $y = \sin x$ and $y = \cos x$ between two consecutive points of intersection.

26. Find the area of the region bounded by $y = \tan x$, the x axis, and the line $x = \pi/4$.

27. Find the length of the arc of the curve $y = \ln \csc x$ from $x = \pi/6$ to $x = \pi/2$.

28. Find the average value of the function f defined by $f(x) = \sin x$ on the closed interval $[0, \pi]$.

29. Find the length of the arc of the curve $y = \ln \cos x$ from $(0,0)$ to $(\pi/3, -\ln 2)$.

30. Find the length of the arc of the curve $y = \ln \sec x$ from the point where $x = 0$ to the point where $x = \pi/3$.

(13.7)   Integrals involving powers of sine and cosine

We consider four cases and illustrate the method used in each case by some examples.

     Case 1: $\int \sin^n u \, du$ or $\int \cos^n u \, du$, where n is an odd integer.

EXAMPLE 1: *Find:* $\int \cos^3 x \, dx$.

     Solution:
$$\int \cos^3 x \, dx = \int \cos^2 x \, (\cos x \, dx)$$
$$= \int (1 - \sin^2 x)(\cos x \, dx)$$

So,

(1) $$\int \cos^3 x \, dx = \int \cos x \, dx - \int \sin^2 x \cos x \, dx$$

To evaluate the second integral on the right side of (1), we let $u = \sin x$; then $du = \cos x \, dx$. So, we have

$$\int \sin^2 x (\cos x \, dx) = \int u^2 \, du$$

$$= \frac{u^3}{3} + C_1$$

$$= \frac{\sin^3 x}{3} + C_1$$

Since the first integral on the right side of (1) is $\sin x + C_2$, we have

$$\int \cos^3 x \, dx = \sin x + \frac{\sin^3 x}{3} + C$$

EXAMPLE 2: *Find:* $\int \sin^5 x \, dx$.

     Solution:
$$\int \sin^5 x \, dx = \int (\sin^2 x)^2 \sin x \, dx$$
$$= \int (1 - \cos^2 x)^2 \sin x \, dx$$
$$= \int (1 - 2 \cos^2 x + \cos^4 x) \sin x \, dx$$

So,

(2) $$\int \sin^5 x \, dx = \int \sin x \, dx - 2 \int \cos^2 x \sin x \, dx + \int \cos^4 x (\sin x \, dx)$$

To evaluate the second and third integrals in (2), we let $u = \cos x$; $du = -\sin x \, dx$; and we obtain

$$\int \sin^5 x \, dx = -\cos x + 2 \int u^2 \, du - \int u^4 \, du$$

$$= -\cos x + \frac{2}{3}u^3 - \frac{u^5}{5} + C$$

$$= -\cos x + \frac{2}{3}\cos^3 x - \frac{1}{5}\cos^5 x + C$$

Case 2: $\int \sin^n u \, du$ and $\int \cos^n u \, du$, where n is an even integer.

The method used in Case 1 will not work in this case. We use the following formulas:

$$\sin^2 x = \frac{1 - \cos 2x}{2}$$

$$\cos^2 x = \frac{1 + \cos 2x}{2}$$

EXAMPLE 3: *Find:* $\int \sin^2 x \, dx$.

Solution: $\displaystyle\int \sin^2 x \, dx = \int \frac{1 - \cos 2x}{2} \, dx$

$$= \frac{x}{2} - \frac{\sin 2x}{4} + C$$

EXAMPLE 4: *Find:* $\int \cos^4 x \, dx$.

Solution: $\displaystyle\int \cos^4 x \, dx = \int (\cos^2 x)^2 \, dx$

$$= \int \left(\frac{1 + \cos 2x}{2}\right)^2 dx$$

$$= \frac{1}{4} \int dx + \frac{1}{2} \int \cos 2x \, dx + \frac{1}{4} \int \cos^2 2x \, dx$$

$$= \frac{x}{4} + \frac{1}{4} \sin 2x + \frac{1}{4} \int \frac{1 + \cos 4x}{2} \, dx$$

$$= \frac{x}{4} + \frac{1}{4} \sin 2x + \frac{x}{8} + \frac{1}{32} \sin 4x + C$$

$$= \frac{3}{8}x + \frac{1}{4} \sin 2x + \frac{1}{32} \sin 4x + C$$

Case 3: $\int \sin^n x \cos^m x \, dx$, where at least one of the exponents is odd. The solution of this case is similar to the method used for Case 1.

EXAMPLE 5: *Find:* $\int \sin^3 x \cos^4 x \, dx$.

Solution: $\displaystyle\int \sin^3 x \cos^4 x \, dx = \int \sin^2 x \cos^4 x (\sin x \, dx)$

$$= \int (1 - \cos^2 x) \cos^4 x (\sin x \, dx)$$

$$= \int \cos^4 x \sin x \, dx - \int \cos^6 x \sin x \, dx$$

$$= (-\cos^5 x)/5 + (\cos^7 x)/7 + C$$

Case 4: $\int \sin^n x \cos^m x \, dx$, where both m and n are even.
The solution of this case is similar to the method used for Case 2.

EXAMPLE 6: *Find:* $\int \sin^2 x \cos^4 x \, dx$.

Solution: $\int \sin^2 x \cos^4 x \, dx = \int \left(\dfrac{1 - \cos 2x}{2}\right)\left(\dfrac{1 + \cos 2x}{2}\right)^2 dx$

$$= \frac{1}{8} \int dx + \frac{1}{8} \int \cos 2x \, dx - \frac{1}{8} \int \cos^2 2x \, dx$$

$$- \frac{1}{8} \int \cos^3 2x \, dx$$

$$= \frac{x}{8} + \frac{1}{16} \sin 2x - \frac{1}{8} \int \frac{1 + \cos 4x}{2} dx$$

$$- \frac{1}{8} \int (1 - \sin^2 2x) \cos 2x \, dx$$

$$= \frac{x}{8} + \frac{\sin 2x}{16} - \frac{x}{16} - \frac{\sin 4x}{64} - \frac{1}{8} \int \cos 2x \, dx$$

$$+ \frac{1}{8} \int \sin^2 2x \cos 2x \, dx$$

$$= \frac{x}{16} + \frac{\sin 2x}{16} - \frac{\sin 4x}{64} - \frac{\sin 2x}{16} + \frac{\sin^3 2x}{48} + C$$

$$= \frac{x}{16} + \frac{\sin^3 2x}{48} - \frac{\sin 4x}{64} + C$$

EXAMPLE 7: *Find:* $\int \sin^4 x \cos^4 x \, dx$.
Solution: If we make use of the formula $\sin x \cos x = (\sin 2x)/2$ we have

$$\int \sin^4 x \cos^4 x \, dx = \frac{1}{16} \int \sin^4 2x \, dx$$

$$= \frac{1}{16} \int \left(\frac{1 - \cos 4x}{2}\right)^2 dx$$

$$= \frac{1}{64} \int dx - \frac{1}{32} \int \cos 4x \, dx + \frac{1}{64} \int \cos^2 4x \, dx$$

$$= \frac{x}{64} - \frac{\sin 4x}{128} + \frac{1}{64} \int \frac{1 + \cos 8x}{2} dx$$

$$= \frac{x}{64} - \frac{\sin 4x}{128} + \frac{x}{128} + \frac{\sin 8x}{1,024} + C$$

$$= \frac{3x}{128} - \frac{\sin 4x}{128} + \frac{\sin 8x}{1,024} + C$$

The following example illustrates another type of integral involving a product of a sine and a cosine.

EXAMPLE 8: *Find:* $\int \sin 3x \cos 2x \, dx$.

Solution: We use the following formula:

$$\sin A \cos B = \tfrac{1}{2} \sin (A - B) + \tfrac{1}{2} \sin (A + B)$$

So, $\int \sin 3x \cos 2x \, dx = \int \left[\frac{1}{2} \sin x + \frac{1}{2} \sin 5x \right] dx$

$$= \frac{1}{2} \int \sin x \, dx + \frac{1}{2} \int \sin 5x \, dx$$

$$= -\frac{1}{2} \cos x - \frac{1}{10} \cos 5x + C$$

Exercises 13.7

In Exercises 1 through 22, evaluate the indefinite integral.

1. $\int \sin^3 x \, dx$

2. $\int \cos^5 x \, dx$

3. $\int \sin^4 x \, dx$

4. $\int \cos^6 x \, dx$

5. $\int \cos^2 \tfrac{1}{2} x \, dx$

6. $\int \sin^3 x \cos^3 x \, dx$

7. $\int \sin^2 x \cos^5 x \, dx$

8. $\int \sin^2 2t \cos^4 2t \, dt$

9. $\int \sin^2 3t \cos^2 3t \, dt$

10. $\int \sqrt{\cos z} \, \sin^3 z \, dz$

11. $\int \sin^4 \frac{x}{2} \cos^2 \frac{x}{2} \, dx$

12. $\tfrac{1}{2} \int (1 + \cos 2x)^2 \, dx$

13. $\int (2 - \sin x)^2 \, dx$

14. $\int (\sin^2 t + \cos t)^2 \, dt$

15. $\int \dfrac{\cos^3 3x}{\sqrt[3]{\sin 3x}} \, dx$

16. $\int \sin 2x \cos 4x \, dx$

17. $\int \sin 3x \cos 5x \, dx$

18. $\int \sin 3x \sin 2x \, dx$

19. $\int \cos 4x \cos 3x \, dx$

20. $\int \cos 5x \cos 7x \, dx$

21. $\int (\sin 3x - \sin 2x)^2 \, dx$

22. $\int \sin x \sin 3x \sin 5x \, dx$

In Exercises 23 through 30, evaluate the definite integral.

23. $\int_0^{\pi/2} \cos^3 x \, dx$

24. $\int_0^{\pi/4} \sin^6 2x \, dx$

25. $\int_0^1 \sin^4 \frac{\pi x}{2} \, dx$

26. $\int_0^1 \sin^2 \pi x \cos^2 \pi x \, dx$

27. $\int_0^{\pi/6} (\sin 3x + \cos 3x)^2 \sin 3x \, dx$

28. $\int_0^{\pi/4} \cos x \cos 3x \, dx$

29. $\int_{\pi/4}^{\pi/2} (\sin^4 2x - 2 \sin 4x) \, dx$

30. $\int_0^{\pi/6} \sin 2x \cos 4x \, dx$

31. If n is any positive integer prove: $\int_0^\pi \sin^2 nx \, dx = \pi/2$.

32. If n is a positive odd integer prove: $\int_0^\pi \cos^n x \, dx = 0$.

In Exercises 33 through 35, m and n are any integers except zero; show that the given formula is true.

33. $\int_{-1}^1 \cos n\pi x \cos m\pi x \, dx = \begin{cases} 0 & \text{if } m \neq n \\ 1 & \text{if } m = n \end{cases}$

34. $\int_{-1}^1 \cos n\pi x \sin m\pi x \, dx = 0$

35. $\int_{-1}^1 \sin n\pi x \sin m\pi x \, dx = \begin{cases} 0 & \text{if } m \neq n \\ 1 & \text{if } m = n \end{cases}$

36. Find the volume of the solid generated if the region bounded by the curve $y = \sin x$ and the x axis in the interval $[0,\pi]$ is revolved about the x axis.

37. Find the area of the region bounded by the curve $y = \sin^2 x$ and the x axis in the interval $[0,\pi]$.

38. Find the volume of the solid generated if the region in Exercise 37 is revolved about the x axis.

39. Find the volume of the solid generated if the region in Exercise 37 is revolved about the line $y = 1$.

(13.8) Integrals involving powers of tangent and secant or cotangent and cosecant

The following two indefinite integral formulas follow immediately from the corresponding differentiation formulas.

(((1) $\int \sec^2 u \, du = \tan u + C$

(((2) $\int \sec u \tan u \, du = \sec u + C$

We can evaluate many integrals involving powers of tangent and secant by applying these two formulas and the trigonometric identity

(3) $1 + \tan^2 \theta = \sec^2 \theta$

We have similar formulas involving the cotangent and the cosecant.

(((4) $\int \csc^2 u \, du = -\cot u + C$

Proof: $d(-\cot u + C) = \csc^2 u \, du$.

(((5) $\int \csc u \cot u \, du = -\csc u + C$

Proof: $d(-\csc u + C) = \csc u \cot u \, du$.
We also have the identity

(6) $1 + \cot^2 u = \csc^2 u$

Formulas (1), (2), and (3) are used to evaluate integrals of the form

$$\int \tan^m u \, \sec^n u \, du$$

and formulas (4), (5), and (6) are used to evaluate integrals of the form

$$\int \cot^m u \, \sec^n u \, du$$

where m and n are positive integers.

We distinguish various cases.

Case 1: $\int \tan^n u \, du$ or $\int \cot^n u \, du$, where n is a positive integer.

We write

$$\tan^n u = \tan^{n-2} u \tan^2 u$$
$$= \tan^{n-2} u(\sec^2 u - 1)$$

and

$$\cot^n u = \cot^{n-2} u \cot^2 u$$
$$= \cot^{n-2} u(\csc^2 u - 1)$$

The following examples illustrate this method.

EXAMPLE 1: *Find:* $\int \tan^3 x \, dx$.

Solution:
$$\int \tan^3 x \, dx = \int \tan x(\sec^2 x - 1) \, dx$$
$$= \int \tan x \sec^2 x \, dx - \int \tan x \, dx$$
$$= \tfrac{1}{2} \tan^2 x + \ln |\cos x| + C$$

EXAMPLE 2: *Find:* $\int \cot^4 3x \, dx$.

Solution:
$$\int \cot^4 3x \, dx = \int \cot^2 3x(\csc^2 3x - 1) \, dx$$
$$= \int \cot^2 3x \csc^2 3x \, dx - \int \cot^2 3x \, dx$$
$$= (- \cot^3 3x)/9 - \int (\csc^2 3x - 1) \, dx$$
$$= (-\cot^3 3x)/9 + (\cot 3x)/3 + x + C$$

Case 2: $\int \sec^n u \, du$ or $\int \csc^n u \, du$, where n is a positive even integer.

We write

$$\sec^n u = \sec^{n-2} u \sec^2 u$$
$$= (\tan^2 u + 1)^{(n-2)/2} \sec^2 u$$

and

$$\csc^n u = \csc^{n-2} u \csc^2 u$$
$$= (\cot^2 u + 1)^{(n-2)/2} \csc^2 u$$

EXAMPLE 3: *Find:* $\int \csc^6 x \, dx$.

Solution:
$$\int \csc^6 x \, dx = \int (\cot^2 x + 1)^2 \csc^2 x \, dx$$
$$= \int \cot^4 x \csc^2 x \, dx + 2 \int \cot^2 x \csc^2 x \, dx + \int \csc^2 x \, dx$$
$$= (-\cot^5 x)/5 - 2(\cot x)/3 - \cot x + C$$

To integrate $\int \sec^n u \, du$ or $\int \csc^n u \, du$ in the case when n is a positive odd integer, we must use integration by parts, which will be taken up in the next chapter.

Case 3: $\int \tan^m u \sec^n u \, du$ or $\int \cot^m u \csc^n u \, du$, where n is a positive even integer.

This case is illustrated by the following example.

EXAMPLE 4: *Find:* $\int \tan^5 x \sec^4 x \, dx$.

Solution:
$$\int \tan^5 x \sec^4 x \, dx = \int \tan^5 x (\tan^2 x + 1) \sec^2 x \, dx$$
$$= \int \tan^7 x \sec^2 x \, dx + \int \tan^5 x \sec^2 x \, dx$$
$$= (\tan^8 x)/8 + (\tan^6 x)/6 + C.$$

Case 4: $\int \tan^m u \sec^n u \, du$ or $\int \cot^m u \csc^n u \, du$, where m is a positive odd integer.

We illustrate this case by an example.

EXAMPLE 5: *Find:* $\int \tan^5 x \sec^7 x \, dx$.

Solution:
$$\int \tan^5 x \sec^7 x \, dx = \int \tan^4 x \sec^6 x \sec x \tan x \, dx$$
$$= \int (\sec^2 x - 1)^2 \sec^6 x \, (\sec x \tan x \, dx)$$
$$= \int \sec^{10} x (\sec x \tan x \, dx)$$
$$-2 \int \sec^8 x (\sec x \tan x \, dx)$$
$$+ \int \sec^6 x (\sec x \tan x \, dx)$$
$$= (\sec^{11} x)/11 - 2(\sec^9 x)/9 + (\sec^7 x)/7 + C$$

Exercises 13.8

In Exercises 1 through 18, evaluate the indefinite integral.

1. $\int \cot^3 x \, dx$

2. $\int \csc^4 x \, dx$

3. $\int \csc^2 6x \, dx$

4. $\int x^2 \sec^2 x^3 \, dx$

5. $\int \tan^6 x \sec^4 x \, dx$

6. $\int \tan^5 x \sec^3 x \, dx$

7. $\int \cot^2 3x \csc^4 3x \, dx$

8. $\int (\sec 5x + \csc 5x)^2 \, dx$

9. $\int (\tan 3x + \cot 3x)^2 \, dx$

10. $\int \dfrac{dx}{1 + \cos x}$

11. $\int \tan^4 \tfrac{1}{2}x \, dx$

12. $\int \tan^5 3x \, dx$

13. $\int \cot^6 2t\ dt$

14. $\int \dfrac{du}{1 + \sec(u/2)}$

15. $\int \dfrac{\sec^3 x}{\tan^4 x}\ dx$

16. $\int \dfrac{\tan^4 x}{\sec^5 x}\ dx$

17. $\int \dfrac{\csc^4 x}{\cot^2 x}\ dx$

18. $\int \dfrac{\sin^2 \pi x}{\cos^6 \pi x}\ dx$

In Exercises 19 through 26, evaluate the definite integral.

19. $\int_0^{\pi/4} \tan^3 x\ dx$

20. $\int_0^{\pi/6} \tan^4 2x\ dx$

21. $\int_{-\pi/4}^{\pi/4} \sec^6 x\ dx$

22. $\int_{\pi/6}^{\pi/4} \cot^3 w\ dw$

23. $\int_0^{\pi/3} \sec^3 x \tan^5 x\ dx$

24. $\int_0^{\pi/3} \dfrac{\tan^3 x}{\sec x}\ dx$

25. $\int_{\pi/4}^{\pi/2} \dfrac{\cos^4 t}{\sin^6 t}\ dt$

26. $\int_0^{\pi/9} \tan^4 3x \sec^2 3x\ dx$

27. Find the volume of the solid generated by revolving about the x axis the region bounded by the curve $y = \sec x$, the x axis, the y axis, and the line $x = \pi/4$.

28. Find the volume of the solid generated by revolving about the x axis the region bounded by the curve $y = \tan x$, the x axis, and the line $x = \pi/3$.

29. Find the area of the region bounded by the curve $y = \tan^2 x$, the x axis, and the line $x = \pi/4$.

30. Find the area of the region bounded by the curve $y = \sec^4 x$, and the lines $x = \pi/3$ and $y = 4$.

31. Find the area of the region bounded by the y axis and the curves $y = \sec^2 x$ and $y = 2\tan^2 x$.

32. Find the volume of the solid generated if the region bounded by the curve $y = \sec^2 x$, the axes, and the line $x = \pi/4$ is revolved about the x axis.

33. *Prove:* $\int \tan^n x\ dx = (\tan^{n-1} x)/(n - 1) - \int \tan^{n-2} x\ dx$, if n is a positive integer greater than 1.

34. *Prove:* $\int \cot x \csc^n x\ dx = -\dfrac{\csc^n x}{n} + C$, if $n \neq 0$.

35. Derive a formula similar to that in Exercise 33 for $\int \cot^n x\ dx$, if n is a positive integer greater than 1.

36. Derive a formula similar to that in Exercise 34 for $\int \tan x \sec^n x\ dx$, if $n \neq 0$.

37. We may integrate $\int \sec^2 x \tan x\ dx$ in two ways as follows: $\int \sec^2 x \tan x\ dx = \int \tan x\ (\sec^2 x\ dx) = \frac{1}{2}\tan^2 x + C$ and $\int \sec^2 x \tan x\ dx = \int \sec x(\sec x \tan x\ dx) = \frac{1}{2}\sec^2 x + C$. Explain the difference in the two answers.

(13.9)   Inverse trigonometric functions

Let f be the sine function defined by $f(x) = \sin x$. f will have an inverse function only if to each number of its range there corresponds exactly one number
of its domain. The range of f consists of all numbers y such that $-1 \leq y \leq 1$,
and to each number in this range there correspond many numbers x such that
$y = \sin x$. For example, if $y = \frac{1}{2}$, then $x = \pi/6, 5\pi/6, 13\pi/6, 17\pi/6, -7\pi/6,$
$-13\pi/6$, etc. will all satisfy the equation $\frac{1}{2} = \sin x$. So, the function f does
not have an inverse function.

We define a new function so that to each number in its range there corresponds exactly one number in its domain. Let us call this function F and define
it as follows:

$$(1) \qquad\qquad F(x) = \sin x \qquad \text{for } -\frac{\pi}{2} \leq x \leq \frac{\pi}{2}$$

The range of this function F is the closed interval $[-1,1]$, and the domain of
F is the closed interval $[-\pi/2, \pi/2]$. A sketch of the graph of F is shown in Fig.
13.9.1.

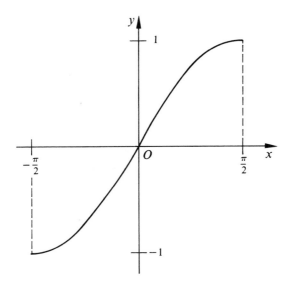

Figure 13.9.1

The function F defined by (1) is continuous and increasing on its domain.
Therefore, by Theorem 12.4.2, F has an inverse function. We call this function
the *inverse sine function* and we denote it by the symbol $\sin^{-1}$.

13.9.1 DEFINITION   The *inverse sine function*, denoted by $\sin^{-1}$, is defined as follows:

$$y = \sin^{-1} x \qquad \text{if and only if} \qquad x = \sin y \text{ and } -\frac{\pi}{2} \leq y \leq \frac{\pi}{2}$$

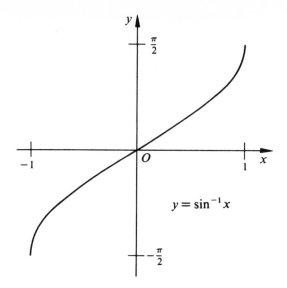

Figure 13.9.2

A sketch of the graph of the inverse sine function is shown in Fig. 13.9.2. The domain of the inverse sine function is the closed interval $[-1,1]$ and the range is the closed interval $[-\pi/2, \pi/2]$.

It follows from Definition 13.9.1 that

(2) $\sin(\sin^{-1} x) = x$ for x in $[-1,1]$

and

(3) $\sin^{-1}(\sin y) = y$ for y in $[-\pi/2, \pi/2]$.

It should be noted that in (1) the domain of F was restricted to the closed interval $[-\pi/2, \pi/2]$, so that F is monotonic on its domain and therefore has an inverse function. Referring to the graph of the sine function (Fig. 13.4.1), we observe that the sine function has period 2π and in particular is increasing on the closed intervals $[-5\pi/2, -3\pi/2]$ and $[3\pi/2, 5\pi/2]$ and decreasing on the closed intervals $[-3\pi/2, -\pi/2]$ and $[\pi/2, 3\pi/2]$, and so any one of these intervals could just as well have been chosen for the domain of F. The choice of the interval $[-\pi/2, \pi/2]$, however, is customary.

We now proceed in a similar manner to define the other inverse trigonometric functions. In order to define the inverse cosine function, we restrict the cosine to the interval $[0,\pi]$. We define the function G as follows:

(4) $G(x) = \cos x$ for $0 \le x \le \pi$

The range of this function G is the closed interval $[-1,1]$, and its domain is the closed interval $[0,\pi]$. A sketch of the graph of G is shown in Fig. 13.9.3.

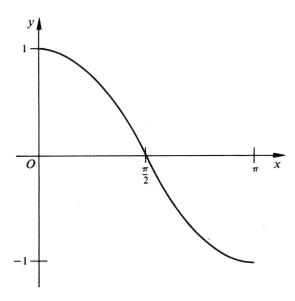

Figure 13.9.3

Since the function G defined by (4) is continuous and decreasing on its domain, G has an inverse function, which is called the *inverse cosine function* and is denoted by $\cos^{-1}$.

13.9.2 DEFINITION   The *inverse cosine function*, denoted by $\cos^{-1}$, is defined as follows:

$$y = \cos^{-1} x \quad \text{if and only if} \quad x = \cos y \text{ and } 0 \le y \le \pi$$

A sketch of the graph of the inverse cosine function is shown in Fig. 13.9.4. The domain of the inverse cosine function is the closed interval $[-1,1]$ and the range is the closed interval $[0,\pi]$.

From Definition 13.9.2 we have

(5)
$$\cos (\cos^{-1} x) = x \quad \text{for } x \text{ in } [-1,1]$$

and

(6)
$$\cos^{-1} (\cos y) = y \quad \text{for } y \text{ in } [0,\pi]$$

We shall restrict the tangent function to the interval $(-\pi/2,\pi/2)$ and let H be the function defined by

(7)
$$H(x) = \tan x \quad \text{for } -\frac{\pi}{2} < x < \frac{\pi}{2}$$

A sketch of the graph of H is shown in Fig. 13.9.5. The range of H is the set of all real numbers, and the domain of H is the interval $(-\pi/2,\pi/2)$. For each number in the range there is only one number in the domain, and so H has an inverse function, which is called the *inverse tangent function* and is denoted by $\tan^{-1}$.

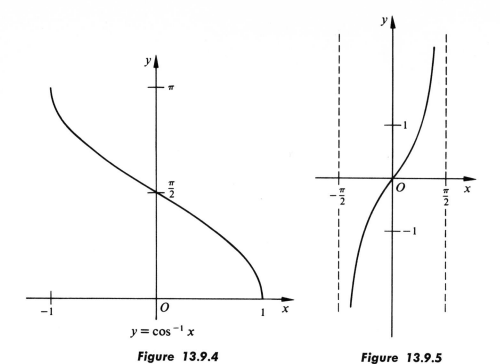

$y = \cos^{-1} x$

Figure 13.9.4   **Figure 13.9.5**

13.9.3 DEFINITION   The *inverse tangent function*, denoted by $\tan^{-1}$, is defined as follows:

$$y = \tan^{-1} x \qquad \text{if and only if} \qquad x = \tan y \text{ and } -\frac{\pi}{2} < y < \frac{\pi}{2}$$

The domain of the inverse tangent function is the set of all real numbers and the range is the interval $(-\pi/2, \pi/2)$. A sketch of the graph of the inverse tangent function is shown in Fig. 13.9.6.

From Definition 13.9.3 we have

(8) $\tan (\tan^{-1} x) = x \qquad$ for x in $(-\infty, +\infty)$

and

(9) $\tan^{-1} (\tan y) = y \qquad$ for y in $\left(-\frac{\pi}{2}, \frac{\pi}{2}\right)$

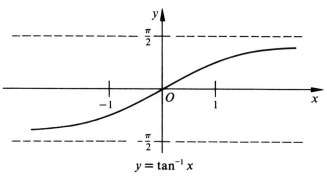

$y = \tan^{-1} x$

Figure 13.9.6

The inverse cotangent function, the inverse secant function, and the inverse cosecant function are defined in terms of the previous inverse trigonometric functions, and they are given in the following definitions.

13.9.4 DEFINITION   The *inverse cotangent function*, denoted by $\cot^{-1}$, is defined by

$$\cot^{-1} x = \frac{\pi}{2} - \tan^{-1} x \qquad \text{for } x \text{ any real number}$$

13.9.5 DEFINITION   The *inverse secant function*, denoted by $\sec^{-1}$, is defined by

$$\sec^{-1} x = \cos^{-1}\left(\frac{1}{x}\right) \qquad \text{for } |x| \geq 1$$

13.9.6 DEFINITION   The *inverse cosecant function*, denoted by $\csc^{-1}$, is defined by

$$\csc^{-1} x = \sin^{-1}\left(\frac{1}{x}\right) \qquad \text{for } |x| \geq 1$$

From Definition 13.9.4 it follows that the domain of the inverse cotangent function is the set of all real numbers. We obtain the range of the inverse cotangent function by noting that

(10) $$\tan^{-1} x = \frac{\pi}{2} - \cot^{-1} x$$

and since

(11) $$-\frac{\pi}{2} < \tan^{-1} x < \frac{\pi}{2}$$

By substituting (10) into (11), we obtain

$$-\frac{\pi}{2} < \frac{\pi}{2} - \cot^{-1} x < \frac{\pi}{2}$$

or, equivalently, $-\pi < -\cot^{-1} x < 0$

or, equivalently, $0 < \cot^{-1} x < \pi$

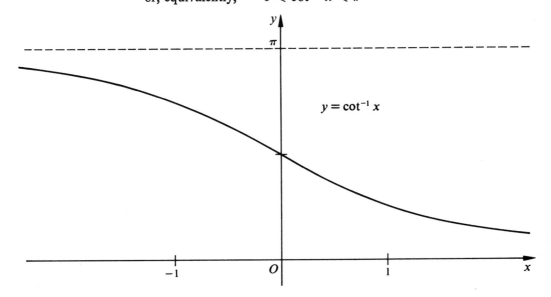

Figure 13.9.7

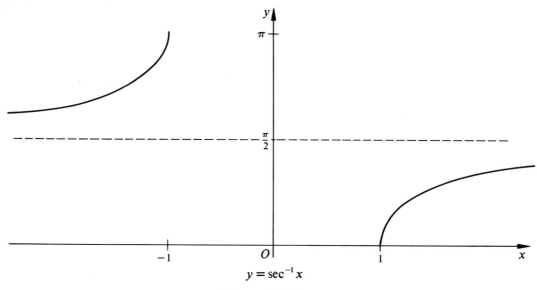

$$y = \sec^{-1} x$$

Figure 13.9.8

Therefore the range of the inverse cotangent function is $(0,\pi)$. A sketch of the graph of the inverse cotangent function is shown in Fig. 13.9.7.

From Definition 13.9.5, we see that the domain of the inverse secant function consists of the two intervals $(-\infty,-1]$ and $[1,+\infty)$, and the range consists of the two intervals $[0,\pi/2)$ and $(\pi/2,\pi]$. You will note that the number $\pi/2$ is not in the range, since $\sec \pi/2$ does not exist. A sketch of the graph of the inverse secant function is shown in Fig. 13.9.8.

It follows from Definition 13.9.6 that the domain of the inverse cosecant

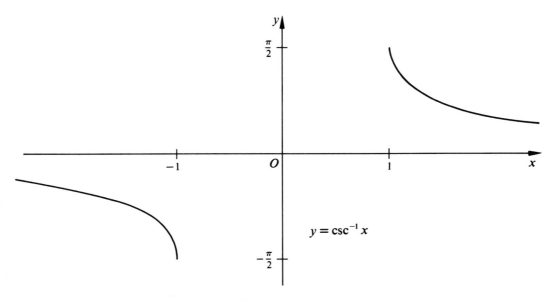

$$y = \csc^{-1} x$$

Figure 13.9.9

function consists of the two intervals $(-\infty,-1]$ and $[1,+\infty)$, and the range consists of the two intervals $[-\pi/2,0)$ and $(0,\pi/2]$. The number 0 is not in the range, since csc 0 does not exist. A sketch of the graph of the inverse cosecant function is shown in Fig. 13.9.9.

EXAMPLE 1: Find the exact value of $\sec[\sin^{-1}(-3/4)]$.

   Solution: Let $\theta = \sin^{-1}(-3/4)$. Then $\sin\theta = -3/4$. Since the range of the inverse sine function is $[-\pi/2,\pi/2]$, and since $\sin\theta$ is negative, it follows that $-\pi/2 < \theta < 0$. Figure 13.9.10 shows angle θ satisfying these requirements.

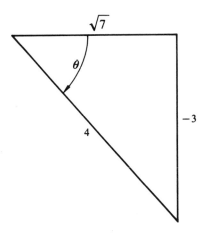

Figure 13.9.10

From the figure we see that $\sec\theta = 4/\sqrt{7}$, and so we conclude that $\sec[\sin^{-1}(-3/4)] = 4/\sqrt{7}$.

EXAMPLE 2: Find the exact value of $\sin[2\cos^{-1}(-3/5)]$.

   Solution: Let $\theta = \cos^{-1}(-3/5)$. So, we wish to find the exact value of $\sin 2\theta$. From formula (16), Sec. 13.1, we have

(12) $$\sin 2\theta = 2\sin\theta\cos\theta$$

Since $\theta = \cos^{-1}(-3/5)$, it follows that $\cos\theta = (-3/5)$ and $\pi/2 < \theta < \pi$. From the identity, $\sin^2\theta + \cos^2\theta = 1$, and since $\sin\theta > 0$, because θ is a second quadrant angle, we obtain

$$\sin\theta = \sqrt{1 - \cos^2\theta} = \sqrt{1 - (-3/5)^2} = 4/5$$

Therefore, from formula (12) we get

$$\sin 2\theta = 2(4/5)(-3/5) = -24/25$$

from which we conclude that

$$\sin[2\cos^{-1}(-3/5)] = -24/25$$

1. Find the value of each of the following: (a) $\sin^{-1}(-1)$; (b) $\cos^{-1}(-1)$; (c) $\tan^{-1}(-1)$; (d) $\cot^{-1}(-1)$; (e) $\sec^{-1}(-1)$; (f) $\csc^{-1}(-1)$.

2. Find the value of each of the following: (a) $\sin^{-1}(\frac{1}{2})$; (b) $\sin^{-1}(-\frac{1}{2})$; (c) $\cos^{-1}(\frac{1}{2})$; (d) $\cos^{-1}(-\frac{1}{2})$; (e) $\sec^{-1}(2)$; (f) $\csc^{-1}(-2)$.

3. *Given:* $y = \sin^{-1}(\frac{1}{3})$. Find the exact value of each of the following: (a) $\cos y$; (b) $\tan y$; (c) $\cot y$; (d) $\sec y$; (e) $\csc y$.

4. *Given:* $y = \cos^{-1}(-\frac{2}{3})$. Find the exact value of each of the following: (a) $\sin y$; (b) $\tan y$; (c) $\cot y$; (d) $\sec y$; (e) $\csc y$.

5. *Given:* $y = \tan^{-1}(-2)$. Find the exact value of each of the following: (a) $\sin y$; (b) $\cos y$; (c) $\cot y$; (d) $\sec y$; (e) $\csc y$.

6. *Given:* $y = \cot^{-1}(-\frac{1}{2})$. Find the exact value of each of the following: (a) $\sin y$; (b) $\cos y$; (c) $\tan y$; (d) $\sec y$; (e) $\csc y$.

7. Find the exact value of each of the following: (a) $\tan[\sin^{-1}(\sqrt{3}/2)]$; (b) $\sin[\tan^{-1}(\sqrt{3}/2)]$.

8. Find the exact value of each of the following: (a) $\cos[\tan^{-1}(-3)]$; (b) $\tan[\sec^{-1}(-3)]$.

9. Find the exact value of each of the following: (a) $\sin^{-1}[\tan(\pi/4)]$; (b) $\tan^{-1}[\sin(-\pi/2)]$; (c) $\sec^{-1}[\tan(-\pi/4)]$; (d) $\cot^{-1}[\csc(-\pi/2)]$.

10. Find the exact value of each of the following: (a) $\cos^{-1}[\sin(-\pi/6)]$; (b) $\sin^{-1}[\cos(-\pi/6)]$; (c) $\cos^{-1}[\sin(2\pi/3)]$; (d) $\sin^{-1}[\cos(2\pi/3)]$.

In Exercises 11 through 18, find the exact value of the given quantity.

11. $\cos[2\sin^{-1}(-5/13)]$

12. $\tan[2\sec^{-1}(-5/4)]$

13. $\sin[\sin^{-1}\frac{2}{3} + \cos^{-1}\frac{1}{3}]$

14. $\cos[\sin^{-1}(-\frac{1}{2}) + \sin^{-1}\frac{1}{4}]$

15. $\tan(\tan^{-1}\frac{3}{4} - \sin^{-1}\frac{1}{2})$

16. $\tan[\sec^{-1}5/3 + \csc^{-1}(-13/12)]$

17. $\cos(\sin^{-1}\frac{1}{3} - \tan^{-1}\frac{1}{2})$

18. $\sin[\cos^{-1}(-\frac{2}{3}) + 2\sin^{-1}(-\frac{1}{3})]$

19. *Prove:* $\cos^{-1}(3/\sqrt{10}) + \cos^{-1}(2/\sqrt{5}) = \pi/4$.

20. *Prove:* $2\tan^{-1}1/3 - \tan^{-1}(-1/7) = \pi/4$.

21. Draw a sketch of the graph of $y = \frac{1}{2}\sin^{-1}x$.

22. Draw a sketch of the graph of $y = \sin^{-1}(x/2)$.

23. Draw a sketch of the graph of $y = \tan^{-1}2x$.

24. Draw a sketch of the graph of $y = 2\tan^{-1}x$.

25. Draw a sketch of the graph of $y = \cos^{-1}3x$.

26. Draw a sketch of the graph of $y = \frac{1}{2} \sec^{-1} 2x$.

27. Draw a sketch of the graph of $y = 2 \cot^{-1} (x/2)$.

28. Draw a sketch of the graph of $y = \frac{1}{2} \csc^{-1} (x/2)$.

(13.10) Derivatives of inverse trigonometric functions

To derive the formula for the derivative of the inverse sine function, let

$$y = \sin^{-1} x$$

which is equivalent to

(1) $$x = \sin y \quad \text{and } y \text{ in } \left[-\frac{\pi}{2}, \frac{\pi}{2} \right]$$

Differentiating both sides of (1) with respect to y, we obtain

(2) $$D_y x = \cos y \quad \text{and } y \text{ in } \left[-\frac{\pi}{2}, \frac{\pi}{2} \right]$$

From the identity $\sin^2 y + \cos^2 y = 1$, and replacing $\sin y$ by x, we obtain

(3) $$\cos^2 y = 1 - x^2$$

If y is in $[-\pi/2, \pi/2]$, $\cos y$ is nonnegative, and so from (3) we have

(4) $$\cos y = \sqrt{1 - x^2} \quad \text{if } y \text{ is in } \left[-\frac{\pi}{2}, \frac{\pi}{2} \right]$$

Substituting (4) into (2), we get

$$D_y x = \sqrt{1 - x^2}$$

From Theorem 12.4.4 $D_x y = 1/D_y x$, and so we have

(5) $$D_x(\sin^{-1} x) = \frac{1}{\sqrt{1 - x^2}}$$

The domain of the derivative of the inverse sine function is the open interval $(-1,1)$.

If u is a differentiable function of x, we obtain from (5) and the chain rule

(6) $$D_x(\sin^{-1} u) = \frac{1}{\sqrt{1 - u^2}} D_x u$$

In a similar manner we derive the formula for the derivative of the inverse cosine function. If

$$y = \cos^{-1} x$$

then $\quad x = \cos y \quad$ and y is in $[0, \pi]$

Differentiating both sides of the above with respect to y, we obtain

(7) $$D_y x = -\sin y, \quad \text{and } y \text{ is in } [0, \pi]$$

From the identity $\sin^2 y + \cos^2 y = 1$, and replacing $\cos y$ by x, we have

(8) $$\sin y = \sqrt{1 - x^2} \quad \text{if } y \text{ is in } [0, \pi]$$

Substituting (8) into (7), we get

$$D_y x = -\sqrt{1 - x^2}$$

and since $D_x y = 1/D_y x$, from Theorem 12.4.4, we obtain

◖◖ (9)
$$D_x(\cos^{-1} x) = -\frac{1}{\sqrt{1 - x^2}}$$

where x is in $(-1,1)$.

If u is a differentiable function of x, we obtain from (9) and the chain rule

◖◖ (10)
$$D_x(\cos^{-1} u) = -\frac{1}{\sqrt{1 - u^2}} D_x u$$

We now derive the formula for the derivative of the inverse tangent function. If

$$y = \tan^{-1} x$$

then $\qquad x = \tan y \qquad$ and y is in $\left(-\frac{\pi}{2}, \frac{\pi}{2}\right)$

Differentiating both sides of the above with respect to y, we obtain

(11)
$$D_y x = \sec^2 y \qquad \text{and } y \text{ is in } \left(-\frac{\pi}{2}, \frac{\pi}{2}\right)$$

From the identity $\sec^2 y = 1 + \tan^2 y$, and replacing $\tan y$ by x, we have

(12)
$$\sec^2 y = 1 + x^2$$

Substituting (12) into (11), we have

$$D_y x = 1 + x^2$$

So, from Theorem 12.4.4, we have

◖◖ (13)
$$D_x(\tan^{-1} x) = \frac{1}{1 + x^2}$$

The domain of the derivative of the inverse tangent function is the set of all real numbers.

If u is a differentiable function of x, we obtain from (13) and the chain rule

◖◖ (14)
$$D_x(\tan^{-1} u) = \frac{1}{1 + u^2} D_x u$$

The formula for the derivative of the inverse cotangent function is

◖◖ (15)
$$D_x(\cot^{-1} x) = -\frac{1}{1 + x^2}$$

The proof of (15) is left for the reader (see Exercise 1 at the end of this section).

If u is a differentiable function of x, then from (15) and the chain rule, we have

◖◖ (16)
$$D_x(\cot^{-1} u) = -\frac{1}{1 + u^2} D_x u$$

We apply Definition 13.9.5 and formula (10) of this section to derive the formula for the derivative of the inverse secant function. From Definition 13.9.5,

$$\sec^{-1} x = \cos^{-1} \frac{1}{x}$$

So, $$D_x(\sec^{-1} x) = -\frac{1}{\sqrt{1 - (1/x)^2}}\left(-\frac{1}{x^2}\right)$$

$$= \frac{1}{(x^2\sqrt{x^2 - 1})/\sqrt{x^2}} = \frac{|x|}{x^2\sqrt{x^2 - 1}}$$

Therefore, we have

(((17) $$D_x(\sec^{-1} x) = \frac{1}{|x|\sqrt{x^2 - 1}}$$

If u is a differentiable function of x, it follows from (17) and the chain rule that

(((18) $$D_x(\sec^{-1} u) = \frac{1}{|u|\sqrt{u^2 - 1}} D_x u$$

Using Definition 13.9.6 and formula (6) of this section, we obtain the formula for the derivative of the inverse cosecant function.

(((19) $$D_x(\csc^{-1} x) = -\frac{1}{|x|\sqrt{x^2 - 1}}$$

The proof of (19) is left for the reader (see Exercise 2 at the end of this section).

If u is a differentiable function of x, then from (19) and the chain rule we have

(((20) $$D_x(\csc^{-1} u) = -\frac{1}{|u|\sqrt{u^2 - 1}} D_x u$$

Following are some examples applying the above formulas.

EXAMPLE 1: *Given:* $y = \sin^{-1} x^2$. *Find:* $D_x y$.
Solution: Applying formula (6), we get

$$D_x y = \frac{1}{\sqrt{1 - x^4}}(2x) = \frac{2x}{\sqrt{1 - x^4}}$$

EXAMPLE 2: *Given:* $y = x^3 \cot^{-1}(x/3)$. *Find:* $D_x y$.

Solution: $D_x y = 3x^2 \cot^{-1} \frac{x}{3} + x^3 \cdot \frac{-1}{1 + x^2/9} \cdot \frac{1}{3}$

$$= 3x^2 \cot^{-1} \frac{x}{3} + \frac{3x^3}{9 + x^2}$$

EXAMPLE 3: *Given:* $\ln(x + y) = \tan^{-1}(x/y)$. *Find:* D_xy.

Solution: We differentiate both sides of the original equation implicitly with respect to x, and we have

$$\frac{1}{x + y}(1 + D_xy) = \frac{1}{1 + x^2/y^2} \cdot \frac{y - x\,D_xy}{y^2}$$

or

$$\frac{1 + D_xy}{x + y} = \frac{y - x\,D_xy}{y^2 + x^2}$$

or

$$y^2 + x^2 + (y^2 + x^2)\,D_xy = xy + y^2 - (x^2 + xy)\,D_xy$$

or

$$D_xy = \frac{xy - x^2}{2x^2 + xy + y^2}$$

EXAMPLE 4: A ladder 25 ft long is leaning against a vertical wall. If the bottom of the ladder is pulled horizontally away from the wall so that the top is sliding down at 3 ft/sec, how fast is the angle between the ladder and the ground changing when the bottom of the ladder is 15 ft from the wall?

Solution:

Let $t =$ the number of seconds in the time that has elapsed since the ladder started to slide down the wall

Let $x =$ the number of feet in the distance from the bottom of the ladder to the wall at t sec.

Let $y =$ the number of feet in the distance from the ground to the top of the ladder at t sec.

Let $\theta =$ the number of radians in the angle between the ladder and the ground at t sec.

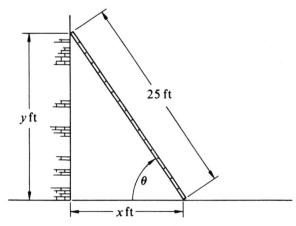

Figure 13.10.1

See Fig. 13.10.1. We are given $D_t y = -3$. We wish to find $D_t \theta$ when $x = 15$.

$$\theta = \sin^{-1} \frac{y}{25}$$

$$D_t \theta = \frac{1}{\sqrt{1 - y^2/625}} \cdot \frac{1}{25} \cdot D_t y = \frac{D_t y}{\sqrt{625 - y^2}}$$

When $x = 15$, we apply the pythagorean theorem to obtain $y = 20$. So,

$$D_t \theta]_{x=15} = \frac{-3}{\sqrt{625 - 400}} = -\frac{3}{15} = -\frac{1}{5}$$

Therefore, the angle is decreasing at the rate of 1/5 radians/sec at the given instant.

Exercises 13.10

1. Derive the formula $D_x(\cot^{-1} x) = -1/(1 + x^2)$.

2. Derive the formula $D_x(\csc^{-1} x) = -1/(|x|\sqrt{x^2 - 1})$.

In Exercises 3 through 22, find the derivative of the given function.

3. $f(x) = \sin^{-1} \frac{x}{2}$

4. $g(x) = \tan^{-1} 2x$

5. $g(t) = \sec^{-1} 5t$

6. $F(x) = \cos^{-1} \sqrt{x}$

7. $F(x) = \cot^{-1} \frac{2}{x} + \tan^{-1} \frac{x}{2}$

8. $f(x) = \csc^{-1} 2x$

9. $h(y) = y \sin^{-1} 2y$

10. $f(t) = t^2 \cos^{-1} t$

11. $g(x) = x \csc^{-1} \frac{1}{x}$

12. $h(x) = \tan^{-1} \frac{2x}{1 - x^2}$

13. $f(x) = 4 \sin^{-1} \frac{x}{2} + x\sqrt{4 - x^2}$

14. $g(s) = \cos^{-1} s + \frac{s}{1 - s^2}$

15. $f(t) = a \sin^{-1} \frac{t}{a} + \sqrt{a^2 - t^2}$

16. $F(x) = \ln (\tan^{-1} x)$

17. $g(x) = \cos^{-1} (\sin x)$

18. $f(x) = \sin^{-1} x + \cos^{-1} x$

19. $h(x) = \sec^{-1} x + \csc^{-1} x$

20. $F(x) = \sec^{-1} \sqrt{x^2 + 1}$

21. $G(x) = x \cot^{-1} x + \ln \sqrt{1 + x^2}$

22. $f(t) = \sin^{-1} \frac{t - 1}{t + 1}$

In Exercises 23 through 26, find $D_x y$.

23. $e^x + y = \cos^{-1} x$

24. $\ln (\sin^2 3x) = e^x + \cot^{-1} y$

25. $x \sin y + x^3 = \tan^{-1} y$

26. $\sin^{-1} (xy) = \cos^{-1} (x + y)$

27. A light is 3 miles from a straight beach. If the light revolves and makes 2 rpm, find the speed of the spot of light along the beach when the spot is 2 miles from the point on the beach nearest the light.

28. A picture 7 ft high is placed on a wall with its base 9 ft above the level of the

eye of an observer. How far from the wall should the observer stand in order for the angle subtended at his eye by the picture to be greatest?

29. A picture 4 ft high is placed on a wall with its base 3 ft above the level of the eye of an observer. If the observer is approaching the wall at the rate of 4 ft/sec, how fast is the angle subtended at his eye by the picture changing when the observer is 10 ft from the wall?

30. A man on a dock is pulling in at the rate of 2 ft/sec a rowboat by means of a rope. The man's hands are 20 ft above the level of the point where the rope is attached to the boat. How fast is the angle of depression of the rope changing when there are 52 ft of rope out?

31. A man is walking at the rate of 5 ft/sec along the diameter of a circular courtyard. A light at one end of a diameter perpendicular to his path casts a shadow on the circular wall. How fast is the shadow moving along the wall when the distance from the man to the center of the courtyard is $\frac{1}{2}r$, where r is the number of feet in the radius of the courtyard?

32. In Exercise 31, how far is the man from the center of the courtyard when the speed of his shadow along the wall is 9 ft/sec?

(13.11) Integrals yielding inverse trigonometric functions

From the formulas for the derivatives of the inverse trigonometric functions, we obtain the following indefinite integral formulas:

(((1)
$$\int \frac{du}{\sqrt{1 - u^2}} = \sin^{-1} u + C$$

(((2)
$$\int \frac{du}{1 + u^2} = \tan^{-1} u + C$$

(((3)
$$\int \frac{du}{u\sqrt{u^2 - 1}} = \sec^{-1} |u| + C$$

Formulas (1) and (2) follow directly from the formulas for the derivatives of $\sin^{-1} u$ and $\tan^{-1} u$. Formula (3) needs an explanation.

If $u > 0$, then $u = |u|$, and we have

$$\int \frac{du}{u\sqrt{u^2 - 1}} = \int \frac{du}{|u|\sqrt{u^2 - 1}} = \sec^{-1} u + C = \sec^{-1} |u| + C$$

If $u < 0$, then $u = -|u|$, and we have

$$\int \frac{du}{u\sqrt{u^2 - 1}} = \int \frac{du}{-|u|\sqrt{u^2 - 1}} = \int \frac{-du}{|u|\sqrt{u^2 - 1}} = \int \frac{d(-u)}{|-u|\sqrt{(-u)^2 - 1}}$$

$$= \sec^{-1} (-u) + C = \sec^{-1} |u| + C$$

Therefore, if $u > 0$ or $u < 0$, we obtain (3).

We also have the following formulas.

(((4) $$\int \frac{du}{\sqrt{a^2 - u^2}} = \sin^{-1} \frac{u}{a} + C \qquad \text{where } a > 0$$

(((5) $$\int \frac{du}{a^2 + u^2} = \frac{1}{a} \tan^{-1} \frac{u}{a} + C$$

(((6) $$\int \frac{du}{u\sqrt{u^2 - a^2}} = \frac{1}{a} \sec^{-1} \left|\frac{u}{a}\right| + C \qquad \text{where } a > 0$$

These formulas may be proved by finding the differential of the right-hand side and obtaining the integrand. We illustrate this by proving (4).

$$d\left(\sin^{-1} \frac{u}{a}\right) = \frac{1}{\sqrt{1 - (u/a)^2}} d\left(\frac{u}{a}\right) = \frac{\sqrt{a^2}}{\sqrt{a^2 - u^2}} \cdot \frac{du}{a} = \frac{a}{\sqrt{a^2 - u^2}} \cdot \frac{du}{a} \qquad \text{if } a > 0$$

$$= \frac{du}{\sqrt{a^2 - u^2}} \qquad \text{if } a > 0$$

The proofs of (5) and (6) are left for the reader (see Exercises 1 and 2 at the end of this section).

EXAMPLE 1: *Evaluate:* $\int dx/\sqrt{4 - 9x^2}$.
   Solution: If we let $u = 3x$, $du = 3\,dx$, or $\frac{1}{3}\,du = dx$. So, we have

$$\int \frac{dx}{\sqrt{4 - 9x^2}} = \frac{1}{3} \int \frac{du}{\sqrt{4 - u^2}} = \frac{1}{3} \sin^{-1} \frac{u}{2} + C = \frac{1}{3} \sin^{-1} \frac{3x}{2} + C$$

EXAMPLE 2: *Evaluate:* $\int dx/(3x^2 - 2x + 5)$.
   Solution: $\int dx/(3x^2 - 2x + 5) = \int dx/[3(x^2 - 2x/3) + 5]$.
   To complete the square of $x^2 - \frac{2}{3}x$, we add $1/9$, and since we are multiplying $1/9$ by 3, we actually add $\frac{1}{3}$ to the denominator, and so we also subtract $\frac{1}{3}$ from the denominator. Therefore, we have

$$\int \frac{dx}{3x^2 - 2x + 5} = \int \frac{dx}{3(x^2 - 2x/3 + 1/9) + 5 - 1/3}$$

$$= \int \frac{dx}{3(x - 1/3)^2 + 14/3} = \frac{1}{3} \int \frac{dx}{(x - 1/3)^2 + 14/9}$$

$$= \frac{1}{3} \cdot \frac{3}{\sqrt{14}} \tan^{-1} \frac{x - 1/3}{\sqrt{14/3}} + C = \frac{1}{\sqrt{14}} \tan^{-1} \frac{3x - 1}{\sqrt{14}} + C$$

EXAMPLE 3: *Evaluate:* $\int [(2x + 7)/(x^2 + 2x + 5)]\,dx$.
   Solution: Since $d(x^2 + 2x + 5) = (2x + 2)\,dx$, we write the numerator as $(2x + 2)\,dx + 5\,dx$, and express the original integral as the sum of two integrals.

$$\int \frac{(2x + 7)\,dx}{x^2 + 2x + 5} = \int \frac{(2x + 2)\,dx}{x^2 + 2x + 5} + 5 \int \frac{dx}{x^2 + 2x + 5}$$

$$= \ln |x^2 + 2x + 5| + 5 \int \frac{dx}{(x + 1)^2 + 4}$$

$$= \ln (x^2 + 2x + 5) + \frac{5}{2} \tan^{-1} \frac{x + 1}{2} + C$$

NOTE: Since $x^2 + 2x + 5 > 0$ for all x, $|x^2 + 2x + 5| = x^2 + 2x + 5$.

1. *Prove:*

$$\int \frac{du}{a^2 + u^2} = \frac{1}{a} \tan^{-1} \frac{u}{a} + C$$

by showing that the differential of the right-hand side is equal to the integrand.

2. *Prove:*

$$\int \frac{du}{u\sqrt{u^2 - a^2}} = \frac{1}{a} \sec^{-1} \left|\frac{u}{a}\right| + C$$

if $a > 0$, by showing that the differential of the right-hand side is equal to the integrand. Take two cases: $u > 0$ and $u < 0$.

3. *Prove:*

$$\int \frac{du}{\sqrt{1 - u^2}} = -\cos^{-1} u + C$$

by showing that the differential of the right-hand side is equal to the integrand. Is this formula equivalent to formula (1)? Why?

4. *Prove:*

$$\int \frac{du}{1 + u^2} = -\cot^{-1} u + C$$

by showing that the differential of the right-hand side is equal to the integrand. Is this formula equivalent to formula (2)? Why?

5. *Prove:*

$$\int \frac{du}{u\sqrt{u^2 - 1}} = -\csc^{-1} |u| + C$$

by showing that the differential of the right-hand side is equal to the integrand. Take two cases: $u > 0$ and $u < 0$. Is this formula equivalent to formula (3)? Why?

In Exercises 6 through 25, evaluate the indefinite integral.

6. $\int \dfrac{dx}{\sqrt{1 - 4x^2}}$

7. $\int \dfrac{dx}{x^2 + 25}$

8. $\int \dfrac{x\,dx}{x^4 + 16}$

9. $\int \dfrac{dx}{\sqrt{2 - 5x^2}}$

10. $\int \dfrac{3\,dx}{x\sqrt{x^2 - 9}}$

11. $\int \dfrac{r\,dr}{\sqrt{16 - 9r^4}}$

12. $\int \dfrac{du}{u\sqrt{16u^2 - 9}}$

13. $\int \dfrac{e^x\,dx}{7 + e^{2x}}$

14. $\int \dfrac{\sin x\,dx}{\sqrt{2 - \cos^2 x}}$

15. $\int \dfrac{dx}{(1 + x)\sqrt{x}}$

16. $\int \dfrac{ds}{\sqrt{2s - s^2}}$

17. $\int \dfrac{dx}{x^2 - x + 2}$

18. $\int \dfrac{dx}{\sqrt{3x - x^2 - 2}}$

19. $\int \dfrac{dx}{\sqrt{15 + 2x - x^2}}$

20. $\int \dfrac{dx}{2x^2 + 2x + 3}$

21. $\int \dfrac{x \, dx}{\sqrt{3 - 2x - x^2}}$

22. $\int \dfrac{x \, dx}{x^2 + x + 1}$

23. $\int \dfrac{(2 + x) \, dx}{\sqrt{4 - 2x - x^2}}$

24. $\int \dfrac{3 \, dx}{(x + 2)\sqrt{x^2 + 4x + 3}}$

25. $\int \dfrac{2x^3 \, dx}{2x^2 - 4x + 3}$

In Exercises 26 through 35, evaluate the definite integral.

26. $\int_0^{1/2} \dfrac{dx}{\sqrt{1 - x^2}}$

27. $\int_{-1/2}^{1/2} \dfrac{dx}{1 + 4x^2}$

28. $\int_0^{\sqrt{3}} \dfrac{x \, dx}{\sqrt{1 + x^2}}$

29. $\int_0^1 \dfrac{1 + x}{1 + x^2} \, dx$

30. $\int_2^5 \dfrac{dx}{x^2 - 4x + 13}$

31. $\int_{-4}^{-2} \dfrac{dt}{\sqrt{-t^2 - 6t - 5}}$

32. $\int_{1/\sqrt{2}}^1 \dfrac{dx}{x\sqrt{4x^2 - 1}}$

33. $\int_1^2 \dfrac{(x + 2) \, dx}{\sqrt{4x - x^2}}$

34. $\int_0^1 \dfrac{dx}{e^x + e^{-x}}$

35. $\int_1^e \dfrac{dx}{x[1 + (\ln x)^2]}$

36. Find the circumference of the circle $x^2 + y^2 = r^2$ by integration.

37. Find the area of the region bounded by the curve $y = 8/(x^2 + 4)$, the x axis, the y axis, and the line $x = 2$.

38. Find the area of the region bounded by the curve $y = 9/\sqrt{9 - x^2}$, the y axis, the x axis, and the line $x = 2\sqrt{2}$.

39. Find the abscissa of the centroid of the region of Exercise 37.

40. Find the area of the region bounded by the curves $x^2 = 4ay$ and $y = 8a^3/(x^2 + 4a^2)$.

14 Techniques of integration

Introduction

In Chap. 10, the definite integral of a function f from a to b was defined as the limit of a Riemann sum as follows:

(1)
$$\int_a^b f(x)\,dx = \lim_{||\Delta||\to 0} \sum_{i=1}^{n} f(\xi_i)\,\Delta_i x$$

if the limit exists. We stated a theorem, proved in advanced calculus, that the limit on the right-hand side of (1) exists if f is continuous on the closed interval $[a,b]$.

The exact value of a definite integral may be calculated by the fundamental theorem of integral calculus, provided we can find an antiderivative of the integrand. The process of finding the most general antiderivative of a given integrand is called *indefinite integration*. We use the term *indefinite integral* to mean the most general antiderivative of a given integrand. In practice, it is not always possible to find the indefinite integral. That is, we may have a definite integral that exists, but the integrand has no antiderivative that can be expressed in terms of elementary functions. However, most of the definite integrals that occur may be evaluated by the fundamental theorem.

The standard indefinite integration formulas, which we learned in previous chapters and which are used frequently, are listed below.

I_1 $\displaystyle \int du = u + C$

I_2 $\displaystyle \int a\,du = au + C$ where a is any constant

I_3 $\displaystyle \int [f(u) + g(u)]\,du = \int f(u)\,du + \int g(u)\,du$

I_4 $\displaystyle \int u^n\,du = \frac{u^{n+1}}{n+1} + C \qquad n \neq -1$

I_5 $\displaystyle \int \frac{du}{u} = \ln|u| + C$

I_6 $\displaystyle \int a^u\,du = \frac{a^u}{\ln a} + C$

I_7 $\displaystyle \int e^u\,du = e^u + C$

I_8 $\quad \int \sin u \; du = -\cos u + C$

I_9 $\quad \int \cos u \; du = \sin u + C$

I_{10} $\quad \int \sec^2 u \; du = \tan u + C$

I_{11} $\quad \int \csc^2 u \; du = -\cot u + C$

I_{12} $\quad \int \sec u \tan u \; du = \sec u + C$

I_{13} $\quad \int \csc u \cot u \; du = -\csc u + C$

I_{14} $\quad \int \tan u \; du = \ln |\sec u| + C$

I_{15} $\quad \int \cot u \; du = \ln |\sin u| + C$

I_{16} $\quad \int \sec u \; du = \ln |\sec u + \tan u| + C$

I_{17} $\quad \int \csc u \; du = \ln |\csc u - \cot u| + C$

I_{18} $\quad \int \dfrac{du}{\sqrt{a^2 - u^2}} = \sin^{-1} \dfrac{u}{a} + C \quad$ where $a > 0$

I_{19} $\quad \int \dfrac{du}{a^2 + u^2} = \dfrac{1}{a} \tan^{-1} \dfrac{u}{a} + C$

I_{20} $\quad \int \dfrac{du}{u\sqrt{u^2 - a^2}} = \dfrac{1}{a} \sec^{-1} \left| \dfrac{u}{a} \right| + C \quad$ where $a > 0$

(14.2) Integration by parts

A method of integration that is quite useful is *integration by parts*. It depends upon the formula for the differential of a product:

$$d(uv) = u \; dv + v \; du$$

or

(1) $$u \; dv = d(uv) - v \; du$$

Integrating both sides of (1) we have

(((2) $$\int u \; dv = uv - \int v \; du$$

Formula (2) is called the *formula for integration by parts*. This formula expresses the integral $\int u \; dv$ in terms of another integral, $\int v \; du$. By a suitable choice of u and dv, it may be easier to integrate the second integral than the first. This method is shown by the following examples.

EXAMPLE 1: *Find:* $\int \tan^{-1} x \, dx$.

Solution: Let $u = \tan^{-1} x$ and $dv = dx$.

$$\text{Then} \quad du = \frac{dx}{1 + x^2}$$

$$\text{and} \quad v = x + C_1$$

So from (2) we have

$$\int \tan^{-1} x \, dx = (\tan^{-1} x)(x + C_1) - \int (x + C_1) \frac{dx}{1 + x^2}$$

$$= x \tan^{-1} x + C_1 \tan^{-1} x - \int \frac{x \, dx}{1 + x^2} - C_1 \int \frac{dx}{1 + x^2}$$

$$= x \tan^{-1} x + C_1 \tan^{-1} x - \tfrac{1}{2} \ln |1 + x^2| - C_1 \tan^{-1} x + C_2$$

$$= x \tan^{-1} x - \tfrac{1}{2} \ln (1 + x^2) + C_2$$

It should be noted that the first constant of integration C_1 does not appear in the final result. This is true in general, and we prove it as follows: by writing $v + C_1$ in place of v, we have

$$\int u \, dv = u(v + C_1) - \int (v + C_1) \, du$$

$$= uv + C_1 u - \int v \, du - C_1 \int du$$

$$= uv + C_1 u - \int v \, du - C_1 u$$

$$= uv - \int v \, du$$

Therefore it is not necessary to write C_1 when finding v from dv.

EXAMPLE 2: *Find:* $\int x \ln x \, dx$.

Solution: Let $u = \ln x$ and $dv = x \, dx$.

$$\text{Then} \quad du = \frac{dx}{x} \quad v = \frac{x^2}{2}$$

$$\text{So,} \quad \int x \ln x \, dx = \frac{x^2}{2} \ln x - \int \frac{x^2}{2} \cdot \frac{dx}{x}$$

$$= \frac{x^2}{2} \ln x - \frac{1}{2} \int x \, dx$$

$$= \frac{x^2}{2} \ln x - \frac{x^2}{4} + C$$

EXAMPLE 3: *Find:* $\int x \sin x \, dx$.

Solution: Let $u = x$ and $dv = \sin x \, dx$.

$$\text{Then,} \quad du = dx \quad \text{and} \quad v = -\cos x$$

Therefore, we have

$$\int x \sin x \, dx = -x \cos x + \int \cos x \, dx$$

$$= -x \cos x + \sin x + C$$

NOTE: If instead of our choices of u and dv as above, we let

$$u = \sin x \qquad \text{and} \qquad dv = x \, dx$$

we get $\qquad du = \cos x \, dx \qquad$ and $\qquad v = \dfrac{x^2}{2}$

So, we have

$$\int x \sin x \, dx = \frac{x^2}{2} \sin x - \frac{1}{2} \int x^2 \cos x \, dx$$

The integral on the right is more complicated than the integral with which we started, indicating these are not desirable choices for u and dv.

It may happen that a particular integral may require repeated applications of integration by parts. This is illustrated in the following example.

EXAMPLE 4: *Find:* $\int x^2 e^x \, dx$.
  Solution: Let $u = x^2$ and $dv = e^x \, dx$.

$$\text{Then,} \qquad du = 2x \, dx \qquad \text{and} \qquad v = e^x$$

We have, then,

$$\int x^2 e^x \, dx = x^2 e^x - 2 \int x e^x \, dx$$

We now apply integration by parts to the integral on the right.

$$\text{Let} \qquad \bar{u} = x \qquad \text{and} \qquad d\bar{v} = e^x \, dx$$
$$\text{Then} \qquad d\bar{u} = dx \qquad \text{and} \qquad \bar{v} = e^x$$

So we have $\qquad \displaystyle\int x e^x \, dx = x e^x - \int e^x \, dx$

$$= x e^x - e^x + \overline{C}$$

Therefore, $\qquad \displaystyle\int x^2 e^x \, dx = x^2 e^x - 2[x e^x - e^x + \overline{C}]$

$$= x^2 e^x - 2x e^x + 2e^x + C$$

Another situation that sometimes occurs when using integration by parts is shown in the next example.

EXAMPLE 5: *Find:* $\int e^x \sin x \, dx$.
  Solution: Let $u = e^x$ and $dv = \sin x \, dx$.

$$\text{Then} \qquad du = e^x \, dx \qquad \text{and} \qquad v = -\cos x$$

Therefore, $\qquad \displaystyle\int e^x \sin x \, dx = -e^x \cos x + \int e^x \cos x \, dx$

The integral on the right is similar to the first integral, except it has $\cos x$ in place of $\sin x$. We apply integration by parts again by letting

$$\bar{u} = e^x \qquad \text{and} \qquad d\bar{v} = \cos x \, dx$$
$$\text{So,} \qquad d\bar{u} = e^x \, dx \qquad \text{and} \qquad \bar{v} = \sin x$$

So, we have

$$\int e^x \sin x \, dx = -e^x \cos x + [e^x \sin x - \int e^x \sin x \, dx]$$

Now, we have on the right the same integral that we have on the left. So we add $\int e^x \sin x \, dx$ to both sides of the equation, giving us

$$2 \int e^x \sin x \, dx = -e^x \cos x + e^x \sin x + \overline{C}$$

Dividing both sides by 2, we obtain

$$\int e^x \sin x \, dx = \tfrac{1}{2} e^x (\sin x - \cos x) + C$$

In Sec. 13.8 we noted that in order to integrate odd powers of the secant and cosecant we use integration by parts. We illustrate this in Example 6.

EXAMPLE 6: *Find:* $\int \sec^3 x \, dx$.
Solution: Let $u = \sec x$ and $dv = \sec^2 x \, dx$.

Then $\qquad du = \sec x \tan x \, dx \qquad$ and $\qquad v = \tan x$

Therefore

$$\int \sec^3 x \, dx = \sec x \tan x - \int \sec x \tan^2 x \, dx$$

or $\quad \int \sec^3 x \, dx = \sec x \tan x - \int \sec x \, (\sec^2 x - 1) \, dx$

or $\quad \int \sec^3 x \, dx = \sec x \tan x - \int \sec^3 x \, dx + \int \sec x \, dx$

Adding $\int \sec^3 x \, dx$ to both sides, we get

$$2 \int \sec^3 x \, dx = \sec x \tan x + \ln |\sec x + \tan x| + 2C$$

So, $\quad \int \sec^3 x \, dx = \tfrac{1}{2} \sec x \tan x + \tfrac{1}{2} \ln |\sec x + \tan x| + C$

In applying integration by parts to a specific integral, one pair of choices for u and dv may work while another pair may not. We saw this in the note after Example 3.

Furthermore, in Example 5, in the step where we have

$$\int e^x \sin x \, dx = -e^x \cos x + \int e^x \cos x \, dx$$

if we evaluate the integral on the right by letting

$$\bar{u} = \cos x \qquad \text{and} \qquad d\bar{v} = e^x \, dx$$
$$d\bar{u} = -\sin x \, dx \qquad \text{and} \qquad \bar{v} = e^x$$

we get

$$\int e^x \sin x \, dx = -e^x \cos x + (e^x \cos x + \int e^x \sin x \, dx)$$

or $\quad \int e^x \sin x \, dx = \int e^x \sin x \, dx$

Integration by parts is used often when the integrand involves logarithms, inverse trigonometric functions, and products.

Exercises 14.2

In Exercises 1 through 16, evaluate the indefinite integral.

1. $\int \ln x \, dx$

2. $\int x \cos 2x \, dx$

3. $\int x \sec^2 x \, dx$

4. $\int x \, 3^x \, dx$

5. $\int \sin^{-1} x \, dx$

6. $\int x^2 \ln x \, dx$

7. $\int x \tan^{-1} x \, dx$

8. $\int x^2 \sin 3x \, dx$

9. $\int e^x \cos x \, dx$

10. $\int \sin(\ln x) \, dx$

11. $\int \dfrac{x^3 \, dx}{\sqrt{1 - x^2}}$

12. $\int x^3 e^{x^2} \, dx$

13. $\int (\ln x)^2 \, dx$

14. $\int \csc^3 x \, dx$

15. $\int \sec^5 x \, dx$

16. $\int \dfrac{\cot^{-1} \sqrt{x}}{\sqrt{x}} \, dx$

In Exercises 17 through 24, evaluate the definite integral.

17. $\int_0^{\pi/3} \sin 3x \cos x \, dx$

18. $\int_{-\pi}^{\pi} x^2 \cos 2x \, dx$

19. $\int_0^2 x e^{2x} \, dx$

20. $\int_0^{\pi^2/2} \cos \sqrt{2x} \, dx$

21. $\int_0^{\pi/4} e^{3x} \sin 4x \, dx$

22. $\int_{\pi/4}^{3\pi/4} x \cot x \csc x \, dx$

23. $\int_1^4 \sec^{-1} \sqrt{x} \, dx$

24. $\int_0^1 x \sin^{-1} x \, dx$

25. Find the area of the region bounded by the curve $y = \ln x$, the x axis, and the line $x = e^2$.

26. Find the volume of the solid generated by revolving the region in Exercise 25 about the x axis.

27. Find the volume of the solid generated by revolving the region in Exercise 25 about the y axis.

28. Find the area of the region bounded by the curve $y = \sin^{-1} 2x$ and the line $x = \sqrt{3}/4$.

29. Find the centroid of the region bounded by the curve $y = \sin x$ and the x axis, from $x = 0$ to $x = \pi$.

30. Find the area of the region bounded by the curve $y = x \sin x$ and the x axis, from $x = 0$ to $x = \pi$.

31. Find the volume of the solid of revolution generated by revolving the region in Exercise 30 about the x axis.

(14.3) Integration by trigonometric substitution

If the integrand contains an expression of the form $\sqrt{a^2 - u^2}$, $\sqrt{a^2 + u^2}$, or $\sqrt{u^2 - a^2}$, where $a > 0$, it is often possible to perform the integration by making a trigonometric substitution which results in an integral involving trigonometric functions. We shall consider each form as a separate case.

Case 1: The integrand contains an expression of the form $\sqrt{a^2 - u^2}$, $a > 0$. We introduce a new variable θ by letting $\theta = \sin^{-1}(u/a)$. Then

$$u = a \sin \theta \qquad -\pi/2 \le \theta \le \pi/2 \qquad du = a \cos \theta \, d\theta$$

and

$$\sqrt{a^2 - u^2} = \sqrt{a^2 - a^2 \sin^2 \theta} = \sqrt{a^2(1 - \sin^2 \theta)} = a\sqrt{\cos^2 \theta}$$

Since $-\pi/2 \le \theta \le \pi/2$, $\cos \theta \ge 0$; so $\sqrt{\cos^2 \theta} = \cos \theta$, and we have

$$\sqrt{a^2 - u^2} = a \cos \theta$$

EXAMPLE 1: *Evaluate:* $\int (x^3 \, dx)/\sqrt{4 - x^2}$.

Solution: Let $x = 2 \sin \theta$, $-\pi/2 < \theta < \pi/2$. Note in this case that $\theta \ne -\pi/2$ or $\pi/2$, since then $\sqrt{4 - x^2} = 0$. $dx = 2 \cos \theta \, d\theta$.

$$\sqrt{4 - x^2} = \sqrt{4 - 4 \sin^2 \theta} = 2\sqrt{\cos^2 \theta} = 2 \cos \theta$$

Therefore,
$$\int \frac{x^3 \, dx}{\sqrt{4 - x^2}} = \int \frac{8 \sin^3 \theta \, (2 \cos \theta \, d\theta)}{2 \cos \theta}$$

$$= 8 \int \sin^3 \theta \, d\theta$$

$$= 8 \int (1 - \cos^2 \theta) \sin \theta \, d\theta$$

$$= 8 \int \sin \theta \, d\theta - 8 \int \cos^2 \theta \sin \theta \, d\theta$$

$$= -8 \cos \theta + \frac{8}{3} \cos^3 \theta + C$$

Since $\theta = \sin^{-1}(x/2)$,

$$\cos \theta \ge 0 \qquad \text{and} \qquad \cos \theta = \sqrt{1 - \sin^2 \theta} = \sqrt{1 - \frac{x^2}{4}} = \frac{\sqrt{4 - x^2}}{2}$$

We have then

$$\int \frac{x^3 \, dx}{\sqrt{4 - x^2}} = -8 \cdot \frac{\sqrt{4 - x^2}}{2} + \frac{8}{3} \cdot \frac{(4 - x^2)^{3/2}}{8} + C$$

$$= -4\sqrt{4 - x^2} + \tfrac{1}{3}(4 - x^2)^{3/2} + C$$

Case 2: The integrand contains an expression of the form $\sqrt{a^2 + u^2}$, $a > 0$. We introduce a new variable θ by letting $\theta = \tan^{-1}(u/a)$. Then $u = a \tan \theta$, $-\pi/2 < \theta < \pi/2$. $du = a \sec^2 \theta \, d\theta$

and
$$\sqrt{a^2 + u^2} = \sqrt{a^2 + a^2 \tan^2 \theta} = a\sqrt{1 + \tan^2 \theta} = a\sqrt{\sec^2 \theta}$$

INTEGRATION BY TRIGONOMETRIC SUBSTITUTION

Since $-\pi/2 < \theta < \pi/2$, $\sec \theta \geq 1$; so $\sqrt{\sec^2 \theta} = \sec \theta$.

EXAMPLE 2: *Evaluate:* $\int \sqrt{x^2 + 9}\, dx.$
Solution: Let $x = 3 \tan \theta$, $-\pi/2 < \theta < \pi/2$. $dx = 3 \sec^2 \theta\, d\theta.$

$$\sqrt{x^2 + 9} = \sqrt{9 \tan^2 \theta + 9} = 3\sqrt{\sec^2 \theta} = 3 \sec \theta$$

We have then

$$\int \sqrt{x^2 + 9}\, dx = \int 3 \sec \theta (3 \sec^2 \theta\, d\theta) = 9 \int \sec^3 \theta\, d\theta$$

Using the result of Example 6 of Sec. 14.2, we have

$$\int \sqrt{x^2 + 9}\, dx = \frac{9}{2} \sec \theta \tan \theta + \frac{9}{2} \ln |\sec \theta + \tan \theta| + C$$

Since $\theta = \tan^{-1}(x/3)$, $\tan \theta = x/3$; and since $\sec \theta \geq 1$, $\sec \theta = \sqrt{1 + \tan^2 \theta} = \sqrt{x^2 + 9}/3.$

So, $\int \sqrt{x^2 + 9}\, dx = \frac{9}{2} \cdot \frac{\sqrt{x^2 + 9}}{3} \cdot \frac{x}{3} + \frac{9}{2} \ln \left| \frac{\sqrt{x^2 + 9}}{3} + \frac{x}{3} \right| + C$

$$= \frac{1}{2} x \sqrt{x^2 + 9} + \frac{9}{2} \ln |\sqrt{x^2 + 9} + x| - \frac{9}{2} \ln 3 + C$$

$$= \frac{1}{2} x \sqrt{x^2 + 9} + \frac{9}{2} \ln (\sqrt{x^2 + 9} + x) + C_1$$

NOTE: Since $\sqrt{x^2 + 9} + x > 0$, we drop the absolute-value bars.

Case 3: The integrand contains an expression of the form $\sqrt{u^2 - a^2}$, $a > 0$.
We introduce a new variable θ by letting $\theta = \sec^{-1}(u/a)$. Then $u = a \sec \theta$, $0 \leq \theta < \pi/2$, or $\pi/2 < \theta \leq \pi$. $du = a \sec \theta \tan \theta\, d\theta.$
We have a problem that didn't arise in Cases 1 and 2. Since when $0 \leq \theta < \pi/2$, $\tan \theta \geq 0$, and when $\pi/2 < \theta \leq \pi$, $\tan \theta \leq 0$, we must consider two separate cases for $\sqrt{\tan^2 \theta}$. That is,

$$\text{if} \quad 0 \leq \theta < \frac{\pi}{2} \quad \tan \theta \geq 0$$

$$\text{so} \quad \sqrt{\tan^2 \theta} = \tan \theta$$

$$\text{and if} \quad \frac{\pi}{2} < \theta \leq \pi \quad \tan \theta \leq 0$$

$$\text{so} \quad \sqrt{\tan^2 \theta} = -\tan \theta$$

EXAMPLE 3: *Evaluate:* $\int dx/\sqrt{x^2 - 25}.$
Solution: Let $x = 5 \sec \theta$, $0 < \theta < \pi/2$ or $\pi/2 < \theta < \pi.$

$$dx = 5 \sec \theta \tan \theta\, d\theta$$

$$\sqrt{x^2 - 25} = \sqrt{25 \sec^2 \theta - 25} = 5\sqrt{\tan^2 \theta} = \begin{cases} 5 \tan \theta & \text{if } 0 < \theta < \frac{\pi}{2} \\ \\ -5 \tan \theta & \text{if } \frac{\pi}{2} < \theta < \pi \end{cases}$$

So,

$$\int \frac{dx}{\sqrt{x^2 - 25}} = \int \frac{5 \sec \theta \tan \theta \, d\theta}{5\sqrt{\tan^2 \theta}}$$

$$= \begin{cases} \int \sec \theta \, d\theta & \text{if } 0 < \theta < \dfrac{\pi}{2} \\[2mm] -\int \sec \theta \, d\theta & \text{if } \dfrac{\pi}{2} < \theta < \pi \end{cases}$$

$$= \begin{cases} \ln |\sec \theta + \tan \theta| + C & \text{if } 0 < \theta < \dfrac{\pi}{2} \\[2mm] -\ln |\sec \theta + \tan \theta| + C & \text{if } \dfrac{\pi}{2} < \theta < \pi \end{cases}$$

$$\sec \theta = \frac{x}{5} \qquad \tan \theta = \pm\sqrt{\sec^2 \theta - 1} = \pm\sqrt{\frac{x^2}{25} - 1}$$

$$\text{or} \qquad \tan \theta = \begin{cases} \dfrac{\sqrt{x^2 - 25}}{5} & \text{if } 0 < \theta < \dfrac{\pi}{2} \\[3mm] -\dfrac{\sqrt{x^2 - 25}}{5} & \text{if } \dfrac{\pi}{2} < \theta < \pi \end{cases}$$

If $0 < \theta < \pi/2$, the integral is $\ln|\sec \theta + \tan \theta| + C$, and $\tan \theta = \sqrt{x^2 - 25}/5$. So, we have

$$\int \frac{dx}{\sqrt{x^2 - 25}} = \ln \left| \frac{x}{5} + \frac{\sqrt{x^2 - 25}}{5} \right| + C$$

$$= \ln |x + \sqrt{x^2 - 25}| - \ln 5 + C$$

$$= \ln |x + \sqrt{x^2 - 25}| + C_1$$

If $\pi/2 < \theta < \pi$, the integral is $-\ln |\sec \theta + \tan \theta| + C$, and

$$\tan \theta = -\sqrt{x^2 - 25}/5$$

So, we have

$$\int \frac{dx}{\sqrt{x^2 - 25}} = -\ln \left| \frac{x}{5} - \frac{\sqrt{x^2 - 25}}{5} \right| + C$$

$$= -\ln \left| \frac{(x - \sqrt{x^2 - 25})(x + \sqrt{x^2 - 25})}{5(x + \sqrt{x^2 - 25})} \right| + C$$

$$= -\ln \left| \frac{25}{5(x + \sqrt{x^2 - 25})} \right| + C$$

$$= \ln |x + \sqrt{x^2 - 25}| - \ln 5 + C$$

$$= \ln |x + \sqrt{x^2 - 25}| + C_1$$

Therefore, we obtain the same result in both cases, and we conclude

$$\int \frac{dx}{\sqrt{x^2 - 25}} = \ln |x + \sqrt{x^2 - 25}| + C$$

EXAMPLE 4: *Evaluate:* $\int dx/(x^2 + a^2)^2$.

Solution: Let $x = a \tan \theta$, $-\pi/2 < \theta < \pi/2$. $dx = a \sec^2 \theta \, d\theta$.

$$x^2 + a^2 = a^2 \tan^2 \theta + a^2 = a^2 \sec^2 \theta$$

Therefore,

$$\int \frac{dx}{(x^2 + a^2)^2} = \int \frac{a \sec^2 \theta \, d\theta}{a^4 \sec^4 \theta} = \frac{1}{a^3} \int \frac{d\theta}{\sec^2 \theta} = \frac{1}{a^3} \int \cos^2 \theta \, d\theta$$

$$= \frac{1}{a^3} \int \frac{1 + \cos 2\theta}{2} \, d\theta = \frac{1}{2a^3}\theta + \frac{1}{4a^3} \sin 2\theta + C$$

(1) $$= \frac{1}{2a^3}\theta + \frac{1}{2a^3} \sin \theta \cos \theta + C$$

To obtain $\sin \theta$ and $\cos \theta$ from the knowledge that $\tan \theta = x/a$ and $-\pi/2 < \theta < \pi/2$ we must consider two separate cases. If $0 \le \theta < \pi/2$ and $\tan \theta = x/a$, then $x \ge 0$, and we obtain $\sin \theta$ and $\cos \theta$ from the triangle in Fig. 14.3.1. If

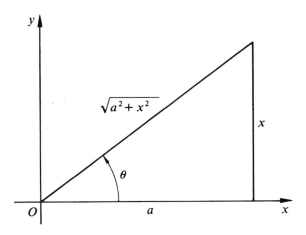

Figure 14.3.1

$-\pi/2 < \theta \le 0$ and $\tan \theta = x/a$ then $x \le 0$, and we obtain $\sin \theta$ and $\cos \theta$ from the triangle in Fig. 14.3.2. In both cases, $\sin \theta = x/\sqrt{a^2 + x^2}$ and $\cos \theta = a/\sqrt{a^2 + x^2}$. So, substituting these values and $\theta = \tan^{-1}(x/a)$ in (1), we obtain

$$\int \frac{dx}{(a^2 + x^2)^2} = \frac{1}{2a^3}\left(\tan^{-1} \frac{x}{a} + \frac{ax}{a^2 + x^2}\right) + C$$

EXAMPLE 5: *Evaluate:* $\int_1^2 dx/(5 - x^2)^{3/2}$.

Solution: To evaluate the indefinite integral $\int dx/(5 - x^2)^{3/2}$, we make the substitution $x = \sqrt{5} \sin \theta$. In this case we may restrict θ to the first quadrant

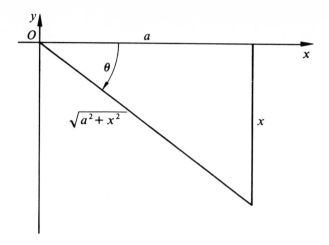

Figure 14.3.2

since we are evaluating a definite integral for which $x > 0$, since x is in $[1,2]$. So, we have

$$x = \sqrt{5}\ \sin\theta \qquad 0 < \theta < \frac{\pi}{2} \qquad dx = \sqrt{5}\ \cos\theta\ d\theta$$

$$(5 - x^2)^{3/2} = (5 - 5\ \sin^2\theta)^{3/2} = 5\sqrt{5}(1 - \sin^2\theta)^{3/2}$$

$$= 5\sqrt{5}\ (\cos^2\theta)^{3/2} = 5\sqrt{5}\ \cos^3\theta$$

So,

$$\int \frac{dx}{(5 - x^2)^{3/2}} = \int \frac{\sqrt{5}\ \cos\theta\ d\theta}{5\sqrt{5}\ \cos^3\theta} = \frac{1}{5}\int \frac{d\theta}{\cos^2\theta} = \frac{1}{5}\int \sec^2\theta\ d\theta$$

$$= \frac{1}{5}\ \tan\theta + C$$

Since $\theta = \sin^{-1}(x/\sqrt{5})$, $0 < \theta < \pi/2$, $\tan\theta = x/\sqrt{5 - x^2}$.

Therefore $\qquad \displaystyle\int \frac{dx}{(5 - x^2)^{3/2}} = \frac{x}{5\sqrt{5 - x^2}} + C$

So $\qquad \displaystyle\int_1^2 \frac{dx}{(5 - x^2)^{3/2}} = \frac{x}{5\sqrt{5 - x^2}}\Big]_1^2 = \frac{2}{5} - \frac{1}{10} = \frac{3}{10}$

Exercises 14.3

In Exercises 1 through 18, evaluate the indefinite integral.

1. $\displaystyle\int \frac{dx}{x^2\sqrt{4 - x^2}}$

2. $\displaystyle\int \frac{dx}{x\sqrt{x^2 + 4}}$

3. $\displaystyle\int \frac{\sqrt{9 - x^2}}{x^2}\ dx$

4. $\displaystyle\int \frac{x^2\ dx}{\sqrt{x^2 + 6}}$

5. $\int \dfrac{dx}{x\sqrt{25 - x^2}}$

6. $\int \dfrac{dx}{\sqrt{x^2 - a^2}}$

7. $\int \sqrt{1 - u^2}\; du$

8. $\int \dfrac{dw}{w^2\sqrt{w^2 - 7}}$

9. $\int x^2\sqrt{16 - x^2}\; dx$

10. $\int \dfrac{dx}{(4 + x^2)^{3/2}}$

11. $\int \dfrac{dx}{(4x^2 - 9)^{3/2}}$

12. $\int \dfrac{dx}{x^4\sqrt{16 + x^2}}$

13. $\int \dfrac{dx}{\sqrt{4x + x^2}}$

14. $\int \dfrac{dx}{\sqrt{4x - x^2}}$

15. $\int \dfrac{dx}{(5 - 4x - x^2)^{3/2}}$

16. $\int \dfrac{dx}{x\sqrt{x^4 - 4}}$

17. $\int \dfrac{\sec^2 x\; dx}{(4 - \tan^2 x)^{3/2}}$

18. $\int \dfrac{e^{-x}\; dx}{(9e^{-2x} + 1)^{3/2}}$

In Exercises 19 through 26, evaluate the definite integral.

19. $\int_0^2 \dfrac{x^3\; dx}{\sqrt{16 - x^2}}$

20. $\int_0^4 \dfrac{dx}{(16 + x^2)^{3/2}}$

21. $\int_{\sqrt 3}^{3\sqrt 3} \dfrac{dx}{x^2\sqrt{x^2 + 9}}$

22. $\int_0^1 \dfrac{x^2\; dx}{\sqrt{4 - x^2}}$

23. $\int_4^6 \dfrac{dx}{x\sqrt{x^2 - 4}}$

24. $\int_4^8 \dfrac{dw}{(w^2 - 4)^{3/2}}$

25. $\int_0^5 x^2\sqrt{25 - x^2}\; dx$

26. $\int_1^3 \dfrac{dx}{x^4\sqrt{x^2 + 3}}$

27. Find the area of the region enclosed by one loop of the curve $x^2 = y^4\,(1 - y^2)$.

28. Find the length of the arc of the curve $y = \ln x$ from $x = 1$ to $x = 3$.

29. Find the length of the arc of the parabola $y^2 = 6x$ from $x = 6$ to $x = 12$.

30. Find the area of the region bounded by the curve $y = \sqrt{x^2 - 9}/x^2$, the x axis, and the line $x = 5$.

31. Find the volume of the solid generated by revolving the region of Exercise 30 about the y axis.

32. Find the centroid of the region of Exercise 30.

33. Find the centroid of the solid of revolution of Exercise 31.

(14.4)   Integration of rational functions by partial fractions. Cases 1 and 2: the denominator has only linear factors

In Sec. 3.3 we defined a rational function as one which can be expressed as the quotient of two polynomial functions. That is, the function H is a rational function if $H(x) = P(x)/Q(x)$ where $P(x)$ and $Q(x)$ are polynomials. We saw previously that if the degree of the numerator is not less than the degree of the denominator we have an improper fraction, and in that case we divide numerator by denominator until we obtain a proper fraction, one in which the degree of the numerator is less than the degree of the denominator. For example,

$$\frac{x^4 - 10x^2 + 3x + 1}{x^2 - 4} = x^2 - 6 + \frac{3x - 23}{x^2 - 4}$$

So, if we wish to integrate

$$\int \frac{x^4 - 10x^2 + 3x + 1}{x^2 - 4}\, dx$$

the problem is reduced to integrating

$$\int \frac{3x - 23}{x^2 - 4}\, dx$$

In general, then, we shall be concerned with the integration of expressions of the form

$$\int \frac{P(x)}{Q(x)}\, dx$$

where the degree of $P(x)$ is less than the degree of $Q(x)$.

In order to do this it is often necessary to write $P(x)/Q(x)$ as the sum of *partial fractions*. The denominators of the partial fractions are obtained by factoring $Q(x)$ into a product of linear and quadratic factors. It may be difficult to find these factors of $Q(x)$ in some cases; however, a theorem from advanced algebra states that theoretically this may always be done. We state this theorem without proof.

14.4.1 THEOREM   Any polynomial with real coefficients may be expressed as a product of linear and quadratic factors in such a way that each of the factors has real coefficients.

After $Q(x)$ has been factored into products of linear and quadratic factors, the method of determining the partial fractions depends upon the nature of these factors. We shall consider various cases separately. The results of advanced algebra, which we shall not prove here, provide us with the form of the partial fractions in each case.

We may assume, without loss of generality, that if $Q(x)$ is a polynomial of the nth degree, then the coefficient of x^n is 1, since if

$$Q(x) = C_0 x^n + C_1 x^{n-1} + \cdots + C_{n-1} x + C_n$$

then if $C_0 \neq 1$, we divide numerator and denominator of the fraction $P(x)/Q(x)$ by C_0.

Case 1: The factors of $Q(x)$ are all linear and none are repeated. That is,

$$Q(x) = (x - a_1)(x - a_2) \cdots (x - a_n)$$

where no two of the a_i are identical.

In this case we write

(1) $$\frac{P(x)}{Q(x)} \equiv \frac{A_1}{x - a_1} + \frac{A_2}{x - a_2} + \cdots + \frac{A_n}{x - a_n}$$

where $A_1, A_2, \ldots, A_n$ are constants to be determined.

The reader will note we used "$\equiv$" (read: "identically equal") instead of "$=$" in (1). This is because (1) is an identity for the value of each A_i.

We shall illustrate by an example how we find the values of A_i.

EXAMPLE 1: *Find:* $\int [(x - 1)/(x^3 - x^2 - 2x)]\, dx.$
Solution: We factor the denominator, and we have

$$\frac{x - 1}{x^3 - x^2 - 2x} \equiv \frac{x - 1}{x(x - 2)(x + 1)}$$

So, we write

(2) $$\frac{x - 1}{x(x - 2)(x + 1)} \equiv \frac{A}{x} + \frac{B}{x - 2} + \frac{C}{x + 1}$$

Equation (2) is an identity for all x (except $x = 0, 2, -1$). From (2) we get

(3) $$x - 1 \equiv A(x - 2)(x + 1) + Bx(x + 1) + Cx(x - 2)$$

Equation (3) is an identity which is true for all values of x including 0, 2, and -1. We wish to find the constants A, B, and C. If we substitute 0 for x in (3), we obtain

$$-1 = -2A \quad \text{or} \quad A = 1/2$$

Substituting 2 for x in (3), we obtain

$$1 = 6B \quad \text{or} \quad B = 1/6$$

Substituting -1 for x in (3), we get

$$-2 = 3C \quad \text{or} \quad C = -2/3$$

There is another method for finding the values of A, B, and C. If on the right-hand side of (3) we combine terms, we obtain

(4) $$x - 1 \equiv (A + B + C)x^2 + (-A + B - 2C)x - 2A$$

In order for (3) to be an identity, the coefficients on the left must equal the corresponding coefficients on the right. So we obtain

$$A + B + C = 0$$
$$-A + B - 2C = 1$$
$$-2A = -1$$

Solving these equations simultaneously, we get $A = 1/2, B = 1/6$, and $C = -2/3$. Substituting these values in (2), we get

$$\frac{x-1}{x(x-2)(x+1)} = \frac{1/2}{x} + \frac{1/6}{x-2} + \frac{-2/3}{x+1}$$

So our given integral can be expressed as follows:

$$\int \frac{x-1}{x^3 - x^2 - 2x} dx = \frac{1}{2} \int \frac{dx}{x} + \frac{1}{6} \int \frac{dx}{x-2} - \frac{2}{3} \int \frac{dx}{x+1}$$

$$= \frac{1}{2} \ln |x| + \frac{1}{6} \ln |x-2| - \frac{2}{3} \ln |x+1| + \frac{1}{6} \ln C$$

$$= \frac{1}{6} (3 \ln |x| + \ln |x-2| - 4 \ln |x+1| + \ln C)$$

$$= \frac{1}{6} \ln \left| \frac{Cx^3(x-2)}{(x+1)^4} \right|$$

Case 2: The factors of $Q(x)$ are all linear and some are repeated.

Suppose $(x - a_i)$ is a p-fold factor. Then, corresponding to this factor, there will be the sum of p partial fractions

$$\frac{A_1}{(x-a_i)^p} + \frac{A_2}{(x-a_i)^{p-1}} + \cdots + \frac{A_{p-1}}{(x-a_i)^2} + \frac{A_p}{x-a_i}$$

where $A_1, A_2, \ldots, A_p$ are constants to be determined.

Example 2 illustrates this case and the method of determining each A_i.

EXAMPLE 2: *Find:* $\int [(x^3 - 1)/x^2(x-2)^3] \, dx$.

Solution: We write the fraction in the integrand as a sum of partial fractions as follows:

$$(5) \qquad \frac{x^3 - 1}{x^2(x-2)^3} \equiv \frac{A}{x^2} + \frac{B}{x} + \frac{C}{(x-2)^3} + \frac{D}{(x-2)^2} + \frac{E}{x-2}$$

The above is an identity for all x (except $x = 0, 2$). Multiplying both sides of (5) by the lowest common denominator, we have

$$x^3 - 1 \equiv A(x-2)^3 + Bx(x-2)^3 + Cx^2 + Dx^2(x-2) + Ex^2(x-2)^2$$

or

$$x^3 - 1 \equiv A(x^3 - 6x^2 + 12x - 8) + Bx(x^3 - 6x^2 + 12x - 8) + Cx^2 + Dx^3 - 2Cx^2 + Ex^2(x^2 - 4x + 4)$$

or

$$x^3 - 1 \equiv (B + E)x^4 + (A - 6B + D - 4E)x^3 + (-6A + 12B + C - 2D + 4E)x^2 + (12A - 8B)x - 8A$$

Equating the coefficients of like powers of x, we get

$$B + E = 0$$
$$A - 6B + D - 4E = 1$$
$$-6A + 12B + C - 2D + 4E = 0$$
$$12A - 8B = 0$$
$$-8A = -1$$

Solving, we get

$$A = \frac{1}{8} \quad B = \frac{3}{16} \quad C = \frac{7}{4} \quad D = \frac{5}{4} \quad E = -\frac{3}{16}$$

Therefore, from (5) we have

$$\frac{x^3 - 1}{x^2(x - 2)^3} \equiv \frac{1/8}{x^2} + \frac{3/16}{x} + \frac{7/4}{(x - 2)^3} + \frac{5/4}{(x - 2)^2} + \frac{-3/16}{x - 2}$$

So,

$$\int \frac{x^3 - 1}{x^2(x - 2)^2} \, dx = \frac{1}{8} \int \frac{dx}{x^2} + \frac{3}{16} \int \frac{dx}{x} + \frac{7}{4} \int \frac{dx}{(x - 2)^3}$$

$$+ \frac{5}{4} \int \frac{dx}{(x - 2)^2} - \frac{3}{16} \int \frac{dx}{x - 2}$$

$$= -\frac{1}{8x} + \frac{3}{16} \ln |x| - \frac{7}{8(x - 2)^2} - \frac{5}{4(x - 2)}$$

$$- \frac{3}{16} \ln |x - 2| + C$$

$$= \frac{-x^2 - 13x + 16}{8x(x - 2)^2} + \frac{3}{16} \ln \left| \frac{x}{x - 2} \right| + C$$

EXAMPLE 3: *Find:* $\int du/(u^2 - a^2)$.
Solution:

$$\frac{1}{u^2 - a^2} \equiv \frac{A}{u - a} + \frac{B}{u + a}$$

Multiplying by $(u - a)(u + a)$, we get

$$1 \equiv A(u + a) + B(u - a)$$

or $\quad 1 \equiv (A + B)u + Aa - Ba$

Equating coefficients, we have

$$A + B = 0$$

$$Aa - Ba = 1$$

Solving simultaneously, we get

$$A = \frac{1}{2a} \quad \text{and} \quad B = -\frac{1}{2a}$$

Therefore, $\quad \displaystyle\int \frac{du}{u^2 - a^2} = \frac{1}{2a} \int \frac{du}{u - a} - \frac{1}{2a} \int \frac{du}{u + a}$

$$= \frac{1}{2a} \ln |u - a| - \frac{1}{2a} \ln |u + a| + C$$

or $\quad \displaystyle\int \frac{du}{u^2 - a^2} = \frac{1}{2a} \ln \left| \frac{u - a}{u + a} \right| + C$

This type of integral occurs frequently enough for us to list it as a formula. It is not necessary to memorize it, since an integration by partial fractions is fairly simple.

$$I_{21} \quad \int \frac{du}{u^2 - a^2} = \frac{1}{2a} \ln \left| \frac{u - a}{u + a} \right| + C$$

If we have $\int du/(a^2 - u^2)$, we may write

$$\int \frac{du}{a^2 - u^2} = -\int \frac{du}{u^2 - a^2}$$

$$= -\frac{1}{2a} \ln \left| \frac{u - a}{u + a} \right| + C$$

$$= \frac{1}{2a} \ln \left| \frac{u + a}{u - a} \right| + C$$

We list this also as a formula:

$$I_{22} \quad \int \frac{du}{a^2 - u^2} = \frac{1}{2a} \ln \left| \frac{u + a}{u - a} \right| + C$$

Exercises 14.4

In Exercises 1 through 16, evaluate the indefinite integral.

1. $\int \dfrac{dx}{x^2 - 4}$

2. $\int \dfrac{x^2 \, dx}{x^2 + x - 6}$

3. $\int \dfrac{5x - 2}{x^2 - 4} \, dx$

4. $\int \dfrac{(4x - 2) \, dx}{x^3 - x^2 - 2x}$

5. $\int \dfrac{6x^2 - 2x - 1}{4x^3 - x} \, dx$

6. $\int \dfrac{x^2 + x + 2}{x^2 - 1} \, dx$

7. $\int \dfrac{dx}{x^3 + 3x^2}$

8. $\int \dfrac{3x^2 - x + 1}{x^3 - x^2} \, dx$

9. $\int \dfrac{dx}{(x + 2)^3}$

10. $\int \dfrac{dt}{(t + 2)^2(t + 1)}$

11. $\int \dfrac{x^2 - 3x - 7}{(2x + 3)(x + 1)^2} \, dx$

12. $\int \dfrac{(5x^2 - 11x + 5) \, dx}{x^3 - 4x^2 + 5x - 2}$

13. $\int \dfrac{x^4 + 3x^3 - 5x^2 - 4x + 17}{x^3 + x^2 - 5x + 3} \, dx$

14. $\int \dfrac{2x^4 - 2x + 1}{2x^5 - x^4} \, dx$

15. $\int \dfrac{-24x^3 + 30x^2 + 52x + 17}{9x^4 - 6x^3 - 11x^2 + 4x + 4} \, dx$

16. $\int \dfrac{dx}{16x^4 - 8x^2 + 1}$

In Exercises 17 through 24, evaluate the definite integral.

17. $\int_1^2 \dfrac{x - 3}{x^3 + x^2} \, dx$

18. $\int_0^4 \dfrac{(x - 2) \, dx}{2x^2 + 7x + 3}$

19. $\int_1^3 \dfrac{x^2 - 4x + 3}{x(x + 1)^2} \, dx$

20. $\int_1^4 \dfrac{(2x^2 + 13x + 18) \, dx}{x^3 + 6x^2 + 9x}$

21. $\int_1^2 \dfrac{5x^2 - 3x + 18}{9x - x^3}\, dx$

22. $\int_0^1 \dfrac{(3x^2 + 7x)\, dx}{x^3 + 6x^2 + 11x + 6}$

23. $\int_0^5 \dfrac{(x^2 - 3)\, dx}{x^3 + 4x^2 + 5x + 2}$

24. $\int_0^4 \dfrac{x^2\, dx}{2x^3 + 9x^2 + 12x + 4}$

25. Find the area of the region bounded by the curve $y = (x-1)/(x^2 - 5x + 6)$, the x axis, and the lines $x = 4$ and $x = 6$.

26. Find the abscissa of the centroid of the region in Exercise 25.

27. Find the volume of the solid of revolution generated by revolving the region in Exercise 25 about the y axis.

28. Find the area of the region in the first quadrant bounded by the curve $(x + 2)^2 y = 4 - x$.

29. Find the volume of the solid of revolution generated if the region in Exercise 28 is revolved about the x axis.

30. Find the volume of the solid of revolution generated if the region in Exercise 28 is revolved about the y axis.

31. A particle is moving along a straight line so that the number of feet per second in the velocity of the particle at t sec is given by

$$v = \frac{t + 3}{t^2 + 3t + 2}$$

Find the distance traveled by the particle from the time when $t = 0$ to the time when $t = 2$.

32. A particle is moving along a straight line so that the number of feet per second in the velocity of the particle at t sec is given by

$$v = \frac{t^2 - t + 1}{(t + 2)^2(t + 1)}$$

Find a formula for the distance traveled by the particle from the time when $t = 0$ to the time when $t = t_1$.

(14.5) Integration of rational functions by partial fractions. Cases 3 and 4: the denominator contains quadratic factors

Case 3: The factors of $Q(x)$ are linear and quadratic and none of the quadratic factors is repeated.

Corresponding to the quadratic factor $x^2 + px + q$ in the denominator is the partial fraction of the form

$$\frac{Ax + B}{x^2 + px + q}$$

EXAMPLE 1: *Find:* $\int \{(x^2 - 2x - 3)/[(x - 1)(x^2 + 2x + 2)]\} \, dx$.

Solution: The fraction in the integrand is written as a sum of partial fractions as follows:

(1) $$\frac{x^2 - 2x - 3}{(x - 1)(x^2 + 2x + 2)} \equiv \frac{Ax + B}{x^2 + 2x + 2} + \frac{C}{x - 1}$$

Multiplying both sides of (1) by the lowest common denominator, we have

$$x^2 - 2x - 3 \equiv (Ax + B)(x - 1) + C(x^2 + 2x + 2)$$

or $\quad x^2 - 2x - 3 \equiv (A + C)x^2 + (B - A + 2C)x + (2C - B)$

Equating coefficients of like powers of x gives us

$$A + C = 1$$
$$B - A + 2C = -2$$
$$2C - B = -3$$

Solving for A, B, and C, we obtain

$$A = \frac{9}{5} \qquad B = \frac{7}{5} \qquad C = -\frac{4}{5}$$

Substituting these values into (1), we get

$$\frac{x^2 - 2x - 3}{(x - 1)(x^2 + 2x + 2)} \equiv \frac{9x/5 + 7/5}{x^2 + 2x + 2} + \frac{-4/5}{x - 1}$$

So,

(2) $$\int \frac{x^2 - 2x - 3}{(x - 1)(x^2 + 2x + 2)} \, dx = \frac{9}{5} \int \frac{x \, dx}{x^2 + 2x + 2} + \frac{7}{5} \int \frac{dx}{x^2 + 2x + 2} - \frac{4}{5} \int \frac{dx}{x - 1}$$

To integrate $\int (x \, dx)/(x^2 + 2x + 2)$, we see that the differential of the denominator is $2(x + 1) \, dx$; so we add and subtract 1 in the numerator, giving us

(3) $$\frac{9}{5} \int \frac{x \, dx}{x^2 + 2x + 2} = \frac{9}{5} \int \frac{(x + 1) \, dx}{x^2 + 2x + 2} - \frac{9}{5} \int \frac{dx}{x^2 + 2x + 2}$$

Substituting (3) into (2) and combining terms on the right, we get

(4) $$\int \frac{x^2 - 2x - 3}{(x - 1)(x^2 + 2x + 2)} \, dx = \frac{9}{5} \cdot \frac{1}{2} \int \frac{2(x + 1) \, dx}{x^2 + 2x + 2} - \frac{2}{5} \int \frac{dx}{x^2 + 2x + 2} - \frac{4}{5} \int \frac{dx}{x - 1}$$

$$= \frac{9}{10} \ln |x^2 + 2x + 2| - \frac{2}{5} \int \frac{dx}{(x + 1)^2 + 1} - \frac{4}{5} \ln |x - 1|$$

$$= \frac{9}{10} \ln |x^2 + 2x + 2| - \frac{2}{5} \tan^{-1} (x + 1)$$

$$\qquad\qquad\qquad - \frac{8}{10} \ln |x - 1| + \frac{1}{10} \ln C$$

$$= \frac{1}{10} \ln \left| \frac{C(x^2 + 2x + 2)^9}{(x - 1)^8} \right| - \frac{2}{5} \tan^{-1} (x + 1)$$

In the above example we would have saved some steps if instead of (1) we had expressed our original fraction as

$$\frac{x^2 - 2x - 3}{(x - 1)(x^2 + 2x + 2)} \equiv \frac{D(2x + 2) + E}{x^2 + 2x + 2} + \frac{F}{x - 1}$$

NOTE: We write $D(2x + 2) + E$ instead of $Ax + B$, since

$$2x + 2 = D_x(x^2 + 2x + 2)$$

Then, solving for D, E, and F, we obtain

$$D = 9/10 \qquad E = -2/5 \qquad F = -4/5$$

giving us (4) directly.

Case 4: The factors of $Q(x)$ are linear and quadratic, and some of the quadratic factors are repeated.

If $x^2 + px + q$ is an n-fold quadratic factor of $Q(x)$, then, corresponding to this factor $(x^2 + px + q)^n$, we have the sum of the following n partial fractions:

$$\frac{A_1x + B_1}{(x^2 + px + q)^n} + \frac{A_2x + B_2}{(x^2 + px + q)^{n-1}} + \cdots + \frac{A_nx + B_n}{x^2 + px + q}$$

For example, if the denominator contains the factor $(x^2 - 5x + 2)^3$, we have, corresponding to this factor,

$$\frac{Ax + B}{(x^2 - 5x + 2)^3} + \frac{Cx + D}{(x^2 - 5x + 2)^2} + \frac{Ex + F}{x^2 - 5x + 2}$$

or, equivalently,

$$\frac{A(2x - 5) + B}{(x^2 - 5x + 2)^3} + \frac{C(2x - 5) + D}{(x^2 - 5x + 2)^2} + \frac{E(2x - 5) + F}{x^2 - 5x + 2}$$

EXAMPLE 2: *Find:* $\int [(x - 2)\,dx]/[x(x^2 - 4x + 5)^2]$.
Solution:

(5) $$\frac{x - 2}{x(x^2 - 4x + 5)^2} \equiv \frac{A}{x} + \frac{B(2x - 4) + C}{(x^2 - 4x + 5)^2} + \frac{D(2x - 4) + E}{x^2 - 4x + 5}$$

Multiplying both sides of (5) by the lowest common denominator, we have

$$x - 2 \equiv A(x^2 - 4x + 5)^2 + x(2Bx - 4B + C) + x(x^2 - 4x + 5)(2Dx - 4D + E)$$

or

$$x - 2 \equiv Ax^4 + 16Ax^2 + 25A - 8Ax^3 + 10Ax^2 - 40Ax + 2Bx^2 - 4Bx + Cx$$
$$+ 2Dx^4 - 12Dx^3 + Ex^3 + 26Dx^2 - 4Ex^2 - 20Dx + 5Ex$$

or

$$x - 2 \equiv (A + 2D)x^4 + (-8A - 12D + E)x^3 + (26A + 2B + 26D - 4E)x^2$$
$$+ (-40A - 4B + C - 20D + 5E)x + 25A$$

Equating coefficients of like powers of x, we have

$$A + 2D = 0 \qquad -8A - 12D + E = 0 \qquad 26A + 2B + 26D - 4E = 0$$
$$-40A - 4B + C - 20D + 5E = 1 \qquad 25A = -2$$

Solving simultaneously, we have

$$A = -\frac{2}{25} \qquad B = \frac{1}{5} \qquad C = \frac{1}{5} \qquad D = \frac{1}{25} \qquad E = -\frac{4}{25}$$

Therefore,

$$\int \frac{(x-2)\,dx}{x(x^2-4x+5)^2} = -\frac{2}{25}\int \frac{dx}{x} + \frac{1}{5}\int \frac{(2x-4)\,dx}{(x^2-4x+5)^2} + \frac{1}{5}\int \frac{dx}{(x^2-4x+5)^2}$$

$$+ \frac{1}{25}\int \frac{(2x-4)\,dx}{(x^2-4x+5)} - \frac{4}{25}\int \frac{dx}{x^2-4x+5}$$

or

(6) $$\int \frac{(x-2)\,dx}{x(x^2-4x+5)^2} = -\frac{2}{25}\ln|x| - \frac{1}{5(x^2-4x+5)} + \frac{1}{5}\int \frac{dx}{[(x^2-4x+4)+1]^2}$$

$$+ \frac{1}{25}\ln|x^2-4x+5| - \frac{4}{25}\int \frac{dx}{(x^2-4x+4)+1}$$

We evaluate separately the integrals in the third and fifth terms on the right-hand side of (6).

$$\int \frac{dx}{[(x^2-4x+4)+1]^2} = \int \frac{dx}{[(x-2)^2+1]^2}$$

Let $$x - 2 = \tan\theta \qquad -\frac{\pi}{2} < \theta < \frac{\pi}{2}$$

then $$dx = \sec^2\theta\,d\theta \qquad (x-2)^2 + 1 = \tan^2\theta + 1 = \sec^2\theta$$

So,

$$\int \frac{dx}{[(x-2)^2+1]^2} = \int \frac{\sec^2\theta\,d\theta}{(\tan^2\theta+1)^2} = \int \frac{\sec^2\theta\,d\theta}{\sec^4\theta} = \int \frac{d\theta}{\sec^2\theta}$$

$$= \int \cos^2\theta\,d\theta = \int \frac{1+\cos 2\theta}{2}\,d\theta = \frac{\theta}{2} + \frac{1}{4}\sin 2\theta + C_1$$

$$= \frac{\theta}{2} + \frac{1}{2}\sin\theta\cos\theta + C_1$$

Since $\theta = \tan^{-1}(x-2)$, we have either $0 \le \theta < \pi/2$ and $x - 2 \ge 0$ or $-\pi/2 < \theta \le 0$ and $x - 2 \le 0$. In the first case, we have the triangle as shown in Fig. 14.5.1, and in the second case we have the triangle as shown in Fig. 14.5.2. In either case,

$$\sin\theta = \frac{x-2}{\sqrt{x^2-4x+5}} \qquad \text{and} \qquad \cos\theta = \frac{1}{\sqrt{x^2-4x+5}}$$

So, we have

$$\int \frac{dx}{[(x-2)^2+1]^2} = \frac{1}{2}\tan^{-1}(x-2) + \frac{1}{2}\frac{x-2}{\sqrt{x^2-4x+5}}\cdot\frac{1}{\sqrt{x^2-4x+5}} + C_1$$

or

(7) $$\int \frac{dx}{[(x-2)^2+1]^2} = \frac{1}{2}\tan^{-1}(x-2) + \frac{x-2}{2(x^2-4x+5)} + C_1$$

Now, considering the other integral on the right-hand side of (6), we have

(8) $$\int \frac{dx}{(x^2-4x+4)+1} = \int \frac{dx}{(x-2)^2+1} = \tan^{-1}(x-2) + C_2$$

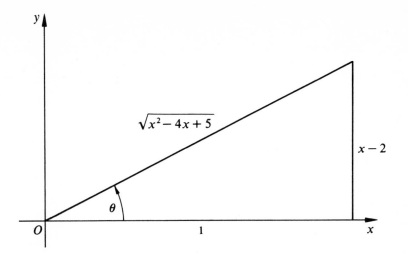

Figure 14.5.1

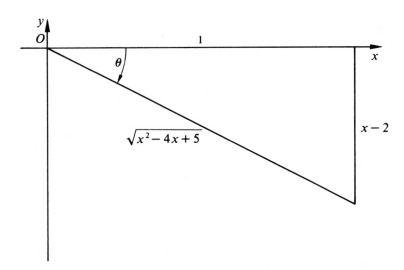

Figure 14.5.2

Substituting (7) and (8) into (6), we get

$$\int \frac{(x-2)\,dx}{x(x^2-4x+5)^2} = -\frac{2}{25}\ln|x| - \frac{1}{5(x^2-4x+5)} + \frac{1}{10}\tan^{-1}(x-2)$$

$$+ \frac{x-2}{10(x^2-4x+5)} + \frac{1}{25}\ln|x^2-4x+5| - \frac{4}{25}\tan^{-1}(x-2) + C$$

or

$$\int \frac{(x-2)\,dx}{x(x^2-4x+5)^2} = \frac{1}{25}\ln\left|\frac{x^2-4x+5}{x^2}\right| - \frac{3}{50}\tan^{-1}(x-2)$$

$$+ \frac{x-4}{10(x^2-4x+5)} + C$$

In Exercises 1 through 16, evaluate the indefinite integral.

1. $\int \dfrac{dx}{2x^3 + x}$

9. $\int \dfrac{(2x^2 - x + 2)\,dx}{x^5 + 2x^3 + x}$

2. $\int \dfrac{(x + 4)\,dx}{x(x^2 + 4)}$

10. $\int \dfrac{(2x^3 + 9x)\,dx}{(x^2 + 3)(x^2 - 2x + 3)}$

3. $\int \dfrac{dx}{16x^4 - 1}$

11. $\int \dfrac{(x^2 + 2x - 1)\,dx}{27x^3 - 1}$

4. $\int \dfrac{(x^2 - 4x - 4)\,dx}{x^3 - 2x^2 + 4x - 8}$

12. $\int \dfrac{dx}{(x^2 + 1)^3}$

5. $\int \dfrac{(x^2 + x)\,dx}{x^3 - x^2 + x - 1}$

13. $\int \dfrac{18\,dx}{(4x^2 + 9)^2}$

6. $\int \dfrac{dx}{9x^4 + x^2}$

14. $\int \dfrac{(2x^2 + 3x + 2)\,dx}{x^3 + 4x^2 + 6x + 4}$

7. $\int \dfrac{dx}{x^3 + x^2 + x}$

15. $\int \dfrac{(\sec^2 x + 1)\sec^2 x\,dx}{1 + \tan^3 x}$

8. $\int \dfrac{(x + 3)\,dx}{4x^4 + 4x^3 + x^2}$

16. $\int \dfrac{e^{5x}\,dx}{(e^{2x} + 1)^2}$

In Exercises 17 through 24, evaluate the definite integral.

17. $\int_1^4 \dfrac{(4 + 5x^2)\,dx}{x^3 + 4x}$

21. $\int_{-1}^0 \dfrac{x^2\,dx}{(2x^2 + 2x + 1)^2}$

18. $\int_0^1 \dfrac{x\,dx}{x^3 + 2x^2 + x + 2}$

22. $\int_0^{1/2} \dfrac{(x + 1)\,dx}{x^3 - 1}$

19. $\int_3^4 \dfrac{(5x^3 - 4x)\,dx}{x^4 - 16}$

23. $\int_0^1 \dfrac{(x^2 + 3x + 3)\,dx}{x^3 + x^2 + x + 1}$

20. $\int_0^1 \dfrac{9\,dx}{8x^3 + 1}$

24. $\int_{\pi/6}^{\pi/2} \dfrac{\cos x\,dx}{\sin x + \sin^3 x}$

25. Find the area of the region bounded by the curve $y = 4/(x^3 + 8)$, the x axis, the y axis, and the line $x = 2$.

26. Find the centroid of the region in Exercise 25.

27. Find the volume of the solid of revolution generated by revolving the region in Exercise 25 about the y axis.

(14.6)   **Integration of rational functions of sine and cosine**

If an integrand is a rational function of $\sin x$ and $\cos x$, it can be reduced to a rational function of z by the substitution

(1) $$z = \tan \dfrac{x}{2}$$

Using the identity $\cos 2y \equiv 2\cos^2 y - 1$ and letting $y = x/2$, we have

$$\cos x = 2\cos^2 \frac{x}{2} - 1 = \frac{2}{\sec^2 (x/2)} - 1 = \frac{2}{1 + \tan^2 (x/2)} - 1 = \frac{2}{1 + z^2} - 1$$

So,

(2) $$\cos x = \frac{1 - z^2}{1 + z^2}$$

Similarly from the identity $\sin 2y \equiv 2\sin y \cos y$, we have

$$\sin x = 2\sin \frac{x}{2} \cos \frac{x}{2} = 2\,\frac{\sin (x/2) \cos^2 (x/2)}{\cos (x/2)}$$

$$= 2\tan \frac{x}{2} \cdot \frac{1}{\sec^2 (x/2)} = \frac{2\tan (x/2)}{1 + \tan^2 (x/2)}$$

So,

(3) $$\sin x = \frac{2z}{1 + z^2}$$

Since $z = \tan (x/2)$,

$$dz = \frac{1}{2}\sec^2 \frac{x}{2}\,dx = \frac{1}{2}\left(1 + \tan^2 \frac{x}{2}\right) dx$$

So,

(4) $$dx = \frac{2\,dz}{1 + z^2}$$

EXAMPLE 1: *Find:* $\int dx/(1 - \sin x + \cos x)$.
Solution: Letting $z = \tan (x/2)$ and using (2), (3), and (4), we have

$$\int \frac{dx}{1 - \sin x + \cos x} = \int \frac{(2\,dz)/(1 + z^2)}{1 - 2z/(1 + z^2) + (1 - z^2)/(1 + z^2)}$$

$$= 2\int \frac{dz}{(1 + z^2) - 2z + (1 - z^2)}$$

$$= 2\int \frac{dz}{2 - 2z} = \int \frac{dz}{1 - z} = -\ln|1 - z| + C$$

$$= -\ln\left|1 - \tan \frac{x}{2}\right| + C$$

EXAMPLE 2: *Find:* $\int \sec x\,dx$ by using the substitution of this section.
Solution: $\int \sec x\,dx = \int dx/\cos x$.
Letting $z = \tan (x/2)$ and using (2) and (4), we have

$$\int \frac{dx}{\cos x} = \int \frac{2\,dz}{1 + z^2} \cdot \frac{1 + z^2}{1 - z^2} = 2\int \frac{dz}{1 - z^2}$$

Using formula I_{22} from Sec. 14.4, we have

$$2\int \frac{dz}{1 - z^2} = \ln\left|\frac{1 + z}{1 - z}\right| + C$$

Therefore,

(5)
$$\int \sec x \, dx = \ln \left| \frac{1 + \tan (x/2)}{1 - \tan (x/2)} \right| + C$$

Equation (5) may be written in another form by noting that $1 = \tan (\pi/4)$ and using the identity $\tan (\alpha + \beta) \equiv (\tan \alpha + \tan \beta)/(1 - \tan \alpha \tan \beta)$.
So, we have

$$\int \sec x \, dx = \ln \left| \frac{\tan (\pi/4) + \tan (x/2)}{1 - \tan (\pi/4) \tan (x/2)} \right| + C$$

or

(6)
$$\int \sec x \, dx = \ln \left| \tan\left(\frac{\pi}{4} + \frac{x}{2}\right) \right| + C$$

Formula (6) is an alternate form to formula I_{16}:

$$\int \sec x \, dx = \ln |\sec x + \tan x| + C$$

which is obtained by the trick of multiplying the numerator and denominator of the integrand by $\sec x + \tan x$.

It is worth noting that still another form for $\int \sec x \, dx$ may be obtained as follows:

$$\int \sec x \, dx = \int \frac{dx}{\cos x} = \int \frac{\cos x \, dx}{\cos^2 x} = \int \frac{\cos x \, dx}{1 - \sin^2 x}$$

Substituting $u = \sin x$, $du = \cos x \, dx$, we have

$$\int \sec x \, dx = \int \frac{du}{1 - u^2} = \frac{1}{2} \ln \left| \frac{1 + u}{1 - u} \right| + C = \ln \left| \frac{1 + \sin x}{1 - \sin x} \right|^{1/2} + C$$

Since $-1 \le \sin x \le 1$ for all x, $1 + \sin x$ and $1 - \sin x$ are nonnegative, and hence the absolute-value sign may be removed and we have

(7)
$$\int \sec x \, dx = \ln \left(\frac{1 + \sin x}{1 - \sin x} \right)^{1/2} + C = \ln \sqrt{\frac{1 + \sin x}{1 - \sin x}} + C$$

Exercises 14.6

In Exercises 1 through 12, evaluate the indefinite integral.

1. $\displaystyle\int \frac{dx}{5 + 4 \cos x}$

2. $\displaystyle\int \frac{dx}{3 - 5 \sin x}$

3. $\displaystyle\int \frac{dx}{\cos x - \sin x + 1}$

4. $\displaystyle\int \frac{dx}{\sin x - \cos x + 2}$

5. $\displaystyle\int \frac{dx}{\sin x + \tan x}$

6. $\displaystyle\int \frac{dx}{\tan x - 1}$

7. $\displaystyle\int \frac{8 \, dx}{3 \cos 2x + 1}$

8. $\displaystyle\int \frac{\cos x \, dx}{3 \cos x - 5}$

9. $\int \dfrac{5\,dx}{6 + 4\sec x}$

10. $\int \dfrac{dx}{\sin x - \tan x}$

11. $\int \dfrac{dx}{2\sin x + 2\cos x + 3}$

12. $\int \dfrac{dx}{\cot 2x(1 - \cos 2x)}$

In Exercises 13 through 18, evaluate the definite integral.

13. $\int_0^{\pi/2} \dfrac{dx}{5\sin x + 3}$

14. $\int_0^{\pi/4} \dfrac{8\,dx}{\tan x + 1}$

15. $\int_{-\pi/3}^{\pi/2} \dfrac{3\,dx}{2\cos x + 1}$

16. $\int_0^{\pi/2} \dfrac{dx}{3 + \cos 2x}$

17. $\int_{\pi/6}^{\pi/3} \dfrac{3\,dx}{2\sin 2x + 1}$

18. $\int_0^{\pi/2} \dfrac{\sin 2x\,dx}{2 + \cos x}$

19. Show that formula (7) of this section—

$$\int \sec x\,dx = \ln \sqrt{(1 + \sin x)/(1 - \sin x)} + C$$

is equivalent to formula $I_{16} - \int \sec x\,dx = \ln |\sec x + \tan x| + C$. HINT: Multiply numerator and denominator under the radical sign by $(1 + \sin x)$.

20. *Prove:* $\int \csc x\,dx = \ln\sqrt{(1 - \cos x)/(1 + \cos x)} + C$ by using the substitution $z = \tan (x/2)$.

21. Show that the result in Exercise 20 is equivalent to the result in formula $I_{17} - \int \csc x\,dx = \ln|\csc x - \cot x| + C$. HINT: Use a method similar to that suggested in the hint for Exercise 19.

(14.7)   Miscellaneous substitutions

If an integrand involves fractional powers of a variable x, the integrand may be simplified by the substitution

$$x = z^n$$

where n is the lowest common denominator of the denominators of the exponents. This is illustrated by the following example.

EXAMPLE 1: *Find:* $\int \sqrt{x}\,dx /(1 + \sqrt[3]{x})$.
Solution: We let $x = z^6$; then $dx = 6z^5\,dz$.

So, $\int \dfrac{x^{1/2}\,dx}{1 + x^{1/3}} = \int \dfrac{z^3(6z^5\,dz)}{1 + z^2} = 6\int \dfrac{z^8}{z^2 + 1}\,dz$

Dividing numerator by denominator, we have

$$\int \dfrac{x^{1/2}\,dx}{1 + x^{1/3}} = 6\int \left(z^6 - z^4 + z^2 - 1 + \dfrac{1}{z^2 + 1}\right) dz$$

$$= 6\left(\dfrac{z^7}{7} - \dfrac{z^5}{5} + \dfrac{z^3}{3} - z + \tan^{-1} z\right) + C$$

$$= \dfrac{6}{7}x^{7/6} - \dfrac{6}{5}x^{5/6} + 2x^{1/2} - 6x^{1/6} + 6\tan^{-1} x^{1/6} + C$$

No general rule may be given to determine a substitution that will result in a simpler integrand. Sometimes a substitution which does not rationalize the given integrand may still result in a simpler integrand.

EXAMPLE 2: *Evaluate:* $\int x^5\sqrt{x^2+4}\,dx$.

Solution: Let $z = \sqrt{x^2+4}$. Then $z^2 = x^2 + 4$, and $2z\,dz = 2x\,dx$. So, we have

$$\int x^5\sqrt{x^2+4}\,dx = \int (x^2)^2\sqrt{x^2+4}\,x\,dx = \int (z^2-4)^2\,z(z\,dz)$$

$$= \int (z^6 - 8z^4 + 16z^2)\,dz = z^7/7 - 8z^5/5 + 16z^3/3 + C$$

$$= (1/105)z^3[15z^4 - 168z^2 + 560] + C$$

$$= (1/105)(x^2+4)^{3/2}[15(x^2+4)^2 - 168(x^2+4) + 560] + C$$

$$= (1/105)(x^2+4)^{3/2}[15x^4 - 48x^2 + 128] + C$$

EXAMPLE 3: *Evaluate:* $\int dx/(x^2\sqrt{27x^2+6x-1})$ by using the reciprocal substitution $x = 1/z$.

Solution: If $x = 1/z$, then $dx = -dz/z^2$. We have then

$$(1) \quad \int \frac{dx}{x^2\sqrt{27x^2+6x-1}} = \int \frac{-dz/z^2}{(1/z^2)\sqrt{27/z^2+6/z-1}}$$

$$= -\int \frac{\sqrt{z^2}\,dz}{\sqrt{27+6z-z^2}} = -\int \frac{|z|\,dz}{\sqrt{27+6z-z^2}}$$

$$= \begin{cases} -\int \dfrac{z\,dz}{\sqrt{27+6z-z^2}} & \text{if } z > 0 \\[2mm] \int \dfrac{z\,dz}{\sqrt{27+6z-z^2}} & \text{if } z < 0 \end{cases}$$

We evaluate $\int z\,dz/\sqrt{27+6z-z^2}$.

$$\int \frac{z\,dz}{\sqrt{27+6z-z^2}} = -\frac{1}{2}\int \frac{(-2z+6)\,dz}{\sqrt{27+6z-z^2}} + 3\int \frac{dz}{\sqrt{27+6z-z^2}}$$

$$= -\frac{1}{2}\cdot 2\sqrt{27+6z-z^2} + 3\int \frac{dz}{\sqrt{27+9-(z^2-6z+9)}}$$

$$= -\sqrt{27+6z-z^2} + 3\int \frac{dz}{\sqrt{36-(z-3)^2}}$$

$$= -\sqrt{27+6z-z^2} + 3\sin^{-1}\frac{z-3}{6} + C$$

$$= -\sqrt{27+\frac{6}{x}-\frac{1}{x^2}} + 3\sin^{-1}\frac{1/x-3}{6} + C$$

$$= -\frac{\sqrt{27x^2+6x-1}}{\sqrt{x^2}} + 3\sin^{-1}\frac{1-3x}{6x} + C$$

$$(2) \qquad = -\frac{\sqrt{27x^2+6x-1}}{|x|} + 3\sin^{-1}\frac{1-3x}{6x} + C$$

Substitute (2) in (1) and we have

$$\int \frac{dx}{x^2\sqrt{27x^2 + 6x - 1}} = \begin{cases} \dfrac{\sqrt{27x^2 + 6x - 1}}{|x|} - 3\sin^{-1}\dfrac{1 - 3x}{6x} + C & \text{if } x > 0 \\[2ex] \dfrac{-\sqrt{27x^2 + 6x - 1}}{|x|} + 3\sin^{-1}\dfrac{1 - 3x}{6x} + C & \text{if } x < 0 \end{cases}$$

$$= \begin{cases} \dfrac{\sqrt{27x^2 + 6x - 1}}{x} - 3\sin^{-1}\dfrac{1 - 3x}{6x} + C & \text{if } x > 0 \\[2ex] \dfrac{\sqrt{27x^2 + 6x - 1}}{x} + 3\sin^{-1}\dfrac{1 - 3x}{6x} + C & \text{if } x < 0 \end{cases}$$

Exercises 14.7

In Exercises 1 through 16, evaluate the indefinite integral.

1. $\displaystyle\int \frac{x\,dx}{3 + \sqrt{x}}$

2. $\displaystyle\int \frac{dx}{\sqrt[3]{x} - x}$

3. $\displaystyle\int \frac{dx}{x\sqrt{1 + 4x}}$

4. $\displaystyle\int x(1 + x)^{2/3}\,dx$

5. $\displaystyle\int \frac{\sqrt{1 + x}}{1 - x}\,dx$

6. $\displaystyle\int \frac{dx}{3 + \sqrt{x + 2}}$

7. $\displaystyle\int \frac{dx}{1 + \sqrt[3]{x - 2}}$

8. $\displaystyle\int \frac{dx}{2\sqrt[3]{x} + \sqrt{x}}$

9. $\displaystyle\int \frac{dx}{\sqrt{2x} - \sqrt{x + 4}}$

10. $\displaystyle\int \frac{dx}{\sqrt{\sqrt{x} + 1}}$

11. $\displaystyle\int \frac{dx}{\sqrt{x}\sqrt[3]{x}(1 + \sqrt[3]{x})^2}$

12. $\displaystyle\int \frac{dx}{x\sqrt{x^2 + 2x - 1}}$

Use the reciprocal substitution $x = 1/z$.

13. Do Exercise 12 by using the substitution: $\sqrt{x^2 + 2x - 1} = z - x$.

14. $\displaystyle\int \frac{dx}{x\sqrt{x^2 + 4x - 4}}$

15. $\displaystyle\int \frac{dx}{x\sqrt{1 + x + x^2}}$

16. $\displaystyle\int \frac{dx}{x^2\sqrt{1 + 2x + 3x^2}}$

In Exercises 17 through 22, evaluate the definite integral.

17. $\displaystyle\int_0^4 \frac{dx}{1 + \sqrt{x}}$

18. $\displaystyle\int_0^1 \frac{x^{3/2}}{x + 1}\,dx$

19. $\int_{1/2}^{2} \dfrac{dx}{\sqrt{2x}(\sqrt{2x} + 9)}$

20. $\int_{16}^{18} \dfrac{dx}{\sqrt{x} - \sqrt[4]{x^3}}$

21. $\int_{1/3}^{3} \dfrac{\sqrt[3]{x - x^3}}{x^4} \, dx$

22. $\int_{1}^{2} \dfrac{dx}{x\sqrt{x^2 + 4x - 4}}$

(14.8) Review of techniques of integration

Often in practice, one will find it desirable to resort to a *table of integrals* instead of performing a complicated integration. However, it may be necessary to employ some of the techniques of integration found in this and previous chapters in order to express the integrand in a form which is found in a table. Therefore, it is necessary that the reader acquire proficiency in recognizing which technique to apply to a given integral. The problems in the exercises of this section embody a review of the techniques previously learned. The reader is advised to use a table of integrals only after he has mastered integration.

Exercises 14.8

In Exercises 1 through 60, evaluate the indefinite integral.

1. $\int \tan^2 4x \cos^4 4x \, dx$

2. $\int \dfrac{(5x^2 - 3)}{x^3 - x} \, dx$

3. $\int \dfrac{e^x \, dx}{\sqrt{4 - e^x}}$

4. $\int \dfrac{dx}{x^2\sqrt{a^2 + x^2}}$

5. $\int \tan^{-1} \sqrt{x} \, dx$

6. $\int \dfrac{dt}{t^4 + 1}$

7. $\int \cos^2 \left(\dfrac{x}{3}\right) dx$

8. $\int \dfrac{\sqrt{x + 1} + 1}{\sqrt{x + 1} - 1} \, dx$

9. $\int \dfrac{x^2 + 1}{(x - 1)^3} \, dx$

10. $\int \dfrac{dy}{\sqrt{y} + 1}$

11. $\int \sin x \sin 3x \, dx$

12. $\int \cos \theta \cos 2\theta \, d\theta$

13. $\int \dfrac{dx}{x + x^{4/3}}$

14. $\int t\sqrt{2t - t^2} \, dt$

15. $\int (\sec 3x + \csc 3x)^2 \, dx$

16. $\int \dfrac{dx}{\sqrt{e^x - 1}}$

17. $\int \dfrac{2t^3 + 11t + 8}{t^3 + 4t^2 + 4t} \, dt$

18. $\int x^3 e^{3x} \, dx$

19. $\int \dfrac{x^4 + 1}{x^4 - 1} \, dx$

20. $\int \dfrac{\sqrt{x^2 - 4}}{x^2} \, dx$

21. $\int \sin^4 3x \cos^2 3x \, dx$

22. $\int t \sin^2 2t \, dt$

23. $\displaystyle\int \frac{dr}{\sqrt{3 - 4r - r^2}}$

24. $\displaystyle\int \frac{4x^2 + x - 2}{x^3 - 5x^2 + 8x - 4}\, dx$

25. $\displaystyle\int x^n \ln x \, dx$

26. $\displaystyle\int \frac{y\, dy}{9 + 16y^4}$

27. $\displaystyle\int e^{t/2} \cos 2t \, dt$

28. $\displaystyle\int \frac{du}{u^{5/8} - u^{1/8}}$

29. $\displaystyle\int \frac{\sin x \cos x}{4 + \sin^4 x}\, dx$

30. $\displaystyle\int \frac{\sqrt{w - a}}{w}\, dw$

31. $\displaystyle\int \sin^5 nx \, dx$

32. $\displaystyle\int \frac{dx}{x \ln x(\ln x - 1)}$

33. $\displaystyle\int \csc^5 x \, dx$

34. $\displaystyle\int \frac{dx}{5 + 4 \sec x}$

35. $\displaystyle\int \frac{2y^2 + 1}{y^3 - 6y^2 + 12y - 8}\, dy$

36. $\displaystyle\int \frac{x^5\, dx}{(x^2 - a^2)^3}$

37. $\displaystyle\int \frac{\sin x \, dx}{1 + \cos^2 x}$

38. $\displaystyle\int \frac{dx}{x\sqrt{x^2 + x + 1}}$

39. $\displaystyle\int \sqrt{4t - t^2}\, dt$

40. $\displaystyle\int \frac{dx}{\sqrt{1 - x + 3x^2}}$

41. $\displaystyle\int \frac{dx}{x^4 - x}$

42. $\displaystyle\int \frac{\sqrt{t} - 1}{\sqrt{t} + 1}\, dt$

43. $\displaystyle\int \frac{e^x\, dx}{\sqrt{4 - 9e^{2x}}}$

44. $\displaystyle\int \frac{dx}{5 + 4 \cos 2x}$

45. $\displaystyle\int \cot^2 3x \csc^4 3x \, dx$

46. $\displaystyle\int \frac{\cot x \, dx}{3 + 2 \sin x}$

47. $\displaystyle\int x^2 \sin^{-1} x \, dx$

48. $\displaystyle\int \frac{dx}{x\sqrt{5x - 6 - x^2}}$

49. $\displaystyle\int \frac{dx}{\sin x - 2 \csc x}$

50. $\displaystyle\int \cos x \ln (\sin x) \, dx$

51. $\displaystyle\int \frac{\cos 3t \, dt}{\sin 3t \sqrt{\sin^2 3t - \frac{1}{4}}}$

52. $\displaystyle\int \frac{dx}{(x^2 + 6x + 34)^2}$

53. $\displaystyle\int \frac{\sqrt{x^2 + a^2}}{x^4}\, dx$

54. $\displaystyle\int \tan^n x \sec^4 x \, dx$

55. $\displaystyle\int \frac{\sin^{-1} \sqrt{2t}}{\sqrt{1 - 2t}}\, dt$

56. $\displaystyle\int \ln (x^2 + 1) \, dx$

57. $\displaystyle\int \frac{dx}{\sqrt{2 + \sqrt{x - 1}}}$

58. $\displaystyle\int \frac{dx}{2 + 2 \sin x + \cos x}$

59. $\displaystyle\int \sqrt{\tan x} \, dx$

60. $\displaystyle\int \frac{dx}{\sqrt{1 + \sqrt[3]{x}}}$

In Exercises 61 through 90, evaluate the definite integral.

61. $\displaystyle\int_0^\pi \sqrt{2 + 2 \cos x}\, dx$

62. $\displaystyle\int_{1/2}^1 \sqrt{\frac{1 - x}{x}}\, dx$

63. $\int_{1}^{2} \dfrac{2x^2 + x + 4}{x^3 + 4x^2}\, dx$

64. $\int_{0}^{1} \dfrac{dx}{e^x + e^{-x}}$

65. $\int_{0}^{2} \dfrac{t^3\, dt}{\sqrt{4 + t^2}}$

66. $\int_{0}^{\pi/2} \sin^3 t \cos^3 t\, dt$

67. $\int_{-2}^{2\sqrt{3}} \dfrac{x^2\, dx}{(16 - x^2)^{3/2}}$

68. $\int_{0}^{1} \dfrac{xe^x\, dx}{(1 + x)^2}$

69. $\int_{0}^{16} \sqrt{4 - \sqrt{x}}\, dx$

70. $\int_{0}^{2} \dfrac{(1 - x)\, dx}{x^2 + 3x + 2}$

71. $\int_{\pi/12}^{\pi/8} \cot^3 2y\, dy$

72. $\int_{0}^{2} (2^x + x^2)\, dx$

73. $\int_{a}^{a/2} \dfrac{\sqrt{(a^2 - x^2)^3}}{x^2}\, dx$

74. $\int_{1}^{2} (\ln x)^2\, dx$

75. $\int_{\sqrt{3}/3}^{1} \dfrac{(2x^2 - 2x + 1)\, dx}{x^3 + x}$

76. $\int_{\sqrt{2}/2}^{1} \dfrac{x^3\, dx}{\sqrt{2 - x^2}}$

77. $\int_{1}^{10} \log_{10} \sqrt{ex}\, dx$

78. $\int_{0}^{2\pi} |\sin x - \cos x|\, dx$

79. $\int_{1}^{2} \dfrac{x + 2}{(x + 1)^2}\, dx$

80. $\int_{2\pi/3}^{\pi} \dfrac{\sin (t/2)}{1 + \cos (t/2)}\, dt$

81. $\int_{0}^{\pi} |\cos^3 x|\, dx$

82. $\int_{-\pi/4}^{\pi/4} |\tan^5 x|\, dx$

83. $\int_{0}^{1/2} \dfrac{2x\, dx}{x^3 - x^2 - x + 1}$

84. $\int_{0}^{1} x^3\sqrt{1 + x^2}\, dx$

85. $\int_{0}^{1/2} \dfrac{x\, dx}{\sqrt{1 - 4x^4}}$

86. $\int_{0}^{\pi/12} \dfrac{dx}{\cos^4 3x}$

87. $\int_{0}^{1} \sqrt{2y + y^2}\, dy$

88. $\int_{0}^{4} \dfrac{x^2\, dx}{x^3 + 4x^2 + 5x + 2}$

89. $\int_{0}^{\pi/2} \dfrac{dt}{12 + 13 \cos t}$

90. $\int_{0}^{3} \dfrac{dr}{(r + 2)\sqrt{r + 1}}$

15 Approximate integration

(15.1) Introduction

We have seen previously how many problems in mechanics and geometry can be solved by evaluating definite integrals. In evaluating a definite integral by the fundamental theorem of integral calculus, it is necessary to find an indefinite integral (or antiderivative). There are many functions for which there is no known method for finding an indefinite integral. However, if a function f is continuous on a closed interval $[a,b]$, we know by Theorem 10.3.2 that the definite integral $\int_a^b f(x)\, dx$ exists and is a unique number. In this chapter we shall learn two methods for computing an approximate value of a definite integral. These methods can often give us fairly good accuracy and may be used for evaluating a definite integral by electronic computers. The first method is known as the *trapezoidal rule* and the second is known as *Simpson's rule*.

(15.2) The trapezoidal rule

We know that if f is continuous on the closed interval $[a,b]$, the definite integral $\int_a^b f(x)\, dx$ is the limit of a Riemann sum,

$$\int_a^b f(x)\, dx = \lim_{\|\Delta\| \to 0} \sum_{i=1}^{n} f(\xi_i)\, \Delta_i x$$

The geometrical interpretation of the Riemann sum,

$$\sum_{i=1}^{n} f(\xi_i)\, \Delta_i x$$

is that it is equal to the sum of the areas of the rectangles lying above the x axis plus the negatives of the areas of the rectangles lying below the x axis (see Fig. 10.3.3).

To approximate the area of a region bounded by a curve, let us use trapezoids instead of rectangles. Let us also use regular partitions and function values at equally spaced points.

So, if we are considering the definite integral $\int_a^b f(x)\, dx$, we divide the interval $[a,b]$ into n subintervals, each of length $\Delta x = (b - a)/n$. This gives us the following $(n + 1)$ points: $x_0 = a$, $x_1 = a + \Delta x$, $x_2 = a + 2\,\Delta x, \ldots, x_i = a + i\,\Delta x, \ldots, x_{n-1} = a + (n-1)\,\Delta x$, $x_n = b$. Then the definite integral $\int_a^b f(x)\,dx$ may be expressed as the sum of n definite integrals as follows:

(1) $\displaystyle \int_a^b f(x)\,dx = \int_a^{x_1} f(x)\,dx + \int_{x_1}^{x_2} f(x)\,dx + \cdots + \int_{x_{i-1}}^{x_i} f(x)\,dx + \cdots$

$$+ \int_{x_{n-1}}^b f(x)\,dx$$

To interpret (1) geometrically, refer to Fig. 15.2.1. In Fig. 15.2.1, we have taken $f(x) \geq 0$ for all x in $[a,b]$; however, (1) holds for any function which is continuous on $[a,b]$.

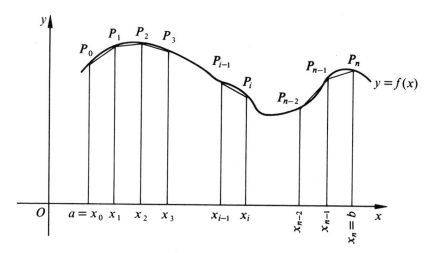

Figure 15.2.1

Then the integral $\int_a^{x_1} f(x)\,dx$ is the area of the region bounded by the x axis, the lines $x = a$ and $x = x_1$, and the portion of the curve from P_0 to P_1. This integral may be approximated by the area of the trapezoid formed by the lines $x = a$, $x = x_1$, P_0P_1, and the x axis. The area of this trapezoid is

$$\tfrac{1}{2}[f(x_0) + f(x_1)]\,\Delta x.$$

Similarly, the other integrals on the right-hand side may be approximated by the area of a trapezoid. Using the symbol "$\approx$" for "is approximately equal to," we have then for the ith integral

(2) $$\int_{x_{i-1}}^{x_i} f(x)\,dx \approx \tfrac{1}{2}[f(x_{i-1}) + f(x_i)]\,\Delta x$$

So, using (2) for each of the integrals on the right side of (1), we have

$$\int_a^b f(x)\,dx \approx \tfrac{1}{2}[f(x_0) + f(x_1)]\,\Delta x + \tfrac{1}{2}[f(x_1) + f(x_2)]\,\Delta x + \cdots$$

$$+ \tfrac{1}{2}[f(x_{n-2}) + f(x_{n-1})]\,\Delta x + \tfrac{1}{2}[f(x_{n-1}) + f(x_n)]\,\Delta x$$

or

(3) $$\int_a^b f(x)\,dx \approx \frac{\Delta x}{2}[f(x_0) + 2f(x_1) + 2f(x_2) + \cdots + 2f(x_{n-1}) + f(x_n)]$$

Formula (3) is known as the *trapezoidal rule*.

EXAMPLE 1: Compute $\int_0^3 dx/(16 + x^2)$ by using the trapezoidal rule with $n = 6$. Express the result to three decimal places. Check by finding the exact value of the definite integral.

Solution: Since $[a,b] = [0,3]$ and $n = 6$, we have

$$\Delta x = \frac{b - a}{n} = \frac{3}{6} = 0.5$$

Therefore,

$$(4) \quad \int_0^3 \frac{dx}{16 + x^2} \approx \frac{0.5}{2}[f(x_0) + 2f(x_1) + 2f(x_2) + 2f(x_3) + 2f(x_4) + 2f(x_5) + f(x_6)]$$

We show the computation of the sum in brackets in (4) in Table 15.2.1, where $f(x) = 1/(16 + x^2)$.

Table 15.2.1

i	x_i	$f(x_i)$	k	$k{\cdot}f(x_i)$
0	0	0.0625	1	0.0625
1	0.5	0.0615	2	0.1230
2	1	0.0588	2	0.1176
3	1.5	0.0548	2	0.1096
4	2	0.0500	2	0.1000
5	2.5	0.0450	2	0.0900
6	3	0.0400	1	0.0400
Sum:				0.6427

So, $\int_0^3 \frac{dx}{16 + x^2} \approx 0.25(0.6427)$

or $\int_0^3 \frac{dx}{16 + x^2} \approx 0.1607$

Rounding the result off to three decimal places, we get

$$\int_0^3 \frac{dx}{16 + x^2} \approx 0.161$$

We check by finding the exact value. We have

$$\int_0^3 \frac{dx}{16 + x^2} = \frac{1}{4} \tan^{-1} \frac{x}{4}\Big]_0^3$$

$$= \frac{1}{4} \tan^{-1} \frac{3}{4} - \frac{1}{4} \tan^{-1} 0$$

$$= \frac{1}{4}(0.6435) - \frac{1}{4}(0)$$

$$= 0.1609 \quad \text{to four decimal places}$$

Let us consider the accuracy of the approximation of a definite integral by the trapezoidal rule. First we shall prove that as Δx approaches zero and n approaches positive infinity, the limit of the approximation by the trapezoidal rule is the exact value of the definite integral.

Let

$$T = \frac{\Delta x}{2}[f(x_0) + 2f(x_1) + \cdots + 2f(x_{n-1}) + f(x_n)]$$

Then $T = [f(x_1) + f(x_2) + \cdots + f(x_n)]\,\Delta x + \frac{1}{2}[f(x_0) - f(x_n)]\,\Delta x$

or $T = \sum_{i=1}^{n} f(x_i)\,\Delta x + \frac{1}{2}[f(a) - f(b)]\,\Delta x$

Therefore, if $n \to +\infty$ and $\Delta x \to 0$, we have

$$\lim_{\Delta x \to 0} T = \lim_{\Delta x \to 0} \sum_{i=1}^{n} f(x_i)\,\Delta x + \lim_{\Delta x \to 0} \frac{1}{2}[f(a) - f(b)]\,\Delta x$$

$$= \int_a^b f(x)\,dx + 0$$

So, we can make the difference between T and the value of the definite integral as small as we please by taking n sufficiently large (and consequently Δx sufficiently small).

The following theorem, which is proved in advanced calculus, gives us a method for estimating the error obtained when using the trapezoidal rule. We denote the error by ϵ_T.

15.2.1 THEOREM   Let the function f be continuous on the closed interval $[a,b]$, and f' and f'' both exist on $[a,b]$. If

$$\epsilon_T = \int_a^b f(x)\,dx - T$$

where T is the approximate value of $\int_a^b f(x)\,dx$ found by the trapezoidal rule, then there is some number η in $[a,b]$ such that

(5) $$\epsilon_T = -\frac{(b-a)}{12}f''(\eta)\,(\Delta x)^2$$

EXAMPLE 2: Find the bounds for the error in the result of Example 1.

Solution: We first find the absolute minimum and absolute maximum values of $f''(x)$ on $[0,3]$.

$$f(x) = (16 + x^2)^{-1}$$
$$f'(x) = -2x(16 + x^2)^{-2}$$
$$f''(x) = 8x^2(16 + x^2)^{-3} - 2(16 + x^2)^{-2} = (6x^2 - 32)(16 + x^2)^{-3}$$
$$f'''(x) = -6x(6x^2 - 32)(16 + x^2)^{-4} + 12x(16 + x^2)^{-3}$$
$$= 24x(16 - x^2)(16 + x^2)^{-4}$$

Since $f'''(x) > 0$ for all x in the open interval $(0,3)$, then f'' is increasing on the open interval $(0,3)$. Therefore, the absolute minimum value of f'' on $[0,3]$ is $f''(0)$ and the absolute maximum value of f'' on $[0,3]$ is $f''(3)$.

$$f''(0) = -\frac{1}{128} \quad \text{and} \quad f''(3) = \frac{22}{15,625}$$

Taking $\eta = 0$ on the right side of (5), we get

$$-\frac{3}{12}\left(-\frac{1}{128}\right)\frac{1}{4} \quad \text{or} \quad \frac{1}{2,048}$$

Taking $\eta = 3$ on the right side of (5), we get

$$-\frac{3}{12}\left(\frac{22}{15,625}\right)\frac{1}{4} \quad \text{or} \quad -\frac{11}{45,000}$$

Therefore if ϵ_T is the error in the result of Example 1, we conclude

$$-\frac{11}{45,000} \leq \epsilon_T \leq \frac{1}{2,048}$$

or $\quad -0.0002 \leq \epsilon_T \leq 0.0005$

Exercises 15.2

In Exercises 1 through 14, compute the approximate value of the given definite integral by the trapezoidal rule for the indicated value of n. Express the result to three decimal places. In Exercises 1 through 8, find the exact value of the definite integral and compare the result with the approximation.

1. $\int_1^2 \frac{dx}{x}$; $n = 5$

2. $\int_2^{10} \frac{dx}{1+x}$; $n = 8$

3. $\int_0^2 x^3 \, dx$; $n = 4$

4. $\int_0^2 x\sqrt{4 - x^2} \, dx$; $n = 8$

5. $\int_0^1 \frac{dx}{\sqrt{1 + x^2}}$; $n = 5$

6. $\int_2^3 \sqrt{1 + x^2} \, dx$; $n = 6$

7. $\int_0^\pi \sin x \, dx$; $n = 6$

8. $\int_0^\pi x \cos x^2 \, dx$; $n = 4$

9. $\int_{\pi/2}^{3\pi/2} \frac{\sin x}{x} \, dx$; $n = 6$

10. $\int_2^3 \ln(1 + x^2) \, dx$; $n = 4$

11. $\int_0^1 e^{x^2} \, dx$; $n = 5$

12. $\int_0^4 e^{-x^2} \, dx$; $n = 4$

13. $\int_0^2 \sqrt{1 + x^4} \, dx$; $n = 6$

14. $\int_0^1 \sqrt{1 + x^3} \, dx$; $n = 4$

In Exercises 15 through 20, find the bounds for the error in the approximation of the indicated exercises.

15. Exercise 1

16. Exercise 2

17. Exercise 3

18. Exercise 6

19. Exercise 11

20. Exercise 12

21. The region bounded by the curve whose equation is $y = e^{-x/2}$, the x axis, the y axis, and the line $x = 2$ is revolved about the x axis. Find the volume of the solid of revolution generated. Approximate the definite integral by the trapezoidal rule to three decimal places, with $n = 5$.

22. Show that the exact value of $\int_0^2 \sqrt{4 - x^2}\, dx$ is π. Approximate the definite integral by the trapezoidal rule to three decimal places, with $n = 8$, and compare the value so obtained with the exact value.

23. Show that the exact value of $\frac{1}{2} \int_0^3 dx/(x + 1)$ is ln 2. Approximate the definite integral by the trapezoidal rule with $n = 6$ to three decimal places, and compare the value so obtained with the exact value of ln 2 as given in a table.

(15.3)   Simpson's rule

Another method for approximating the value of a definite integral is provided us by *Simpson's rule* (sometimes referred to as the *parabolic rule*). For a given partition of the closed interval $[a,b]$, Simpson's rule usually gives a better approximation than the trapezoidal rule. However, Simpson's rule requires more effort to apply. In the trapezoidal rule successive points on the graph of $y = f(x)$ are connected by segments of straight lines, while in Simpson's rule the points are connected by segments of parabolas.

Before we develop Simpson's rule, we shall state and prove a theorem which we need in the development.

15.3.1 THEOREM   If $P_0(x_0,y_0)$, $P_1(x_1,y_1)$, and $P_2(x_2,y_2)$ are three noncollinear points on the parabola, having the equation $y = Ax^2 + Bx + C$, where $y_0 \geq 0$, $y_1 \geq 0$, $y_2 \geq 0$, and $x_1 = x_0 + h$, and $x_2 = x_0 + 2h$, then the area of the region bounded by the parabola, the x axis, and the lines $x = x_0$ and $x = x_2$ is given by

$$(1) \qquad \qquad \text{Area} = \frac{h}{3}(y_0 + 4y_1 + y_2)$$

Proof: The parabola whose equation is $y = Ax^2 + Bx + C$ has a vertical axis. Refer to Fig. 15.3.1, which shows the region bounded by the parabola, the x axis, and the lines $x = x_0$ and $x = x_2$.

Since P_0, P_1, and P_2 are points on the parabola, their coordinates satisfy the equation of the parabola. So we have, replacing x_1 by $x_0 + h$, and x_2 by $x_0 + 2h$,

$y_0 = Ax_0^2 + Bx_0 + C$

$y_1 = A(x_0 + h)^2 + B(x_0 + h) + C = A(x_0^2 + 2hx_0 + h^2) + B(x_0 + h) + C$

$y_2 = A(x_0 + 2h)^2 + B(x_0 + 2h) + C = A(x_0^2 + 4hx_0 + 4h^2)$

$$+ B(x_0 + 2h) + C$$

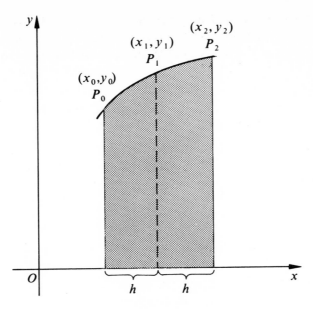

Figure 15.3.1

Therefore,

(2) $y_0 + 4y_1 + y_2 = A(6x_0^2 + 12hx_0 + 8h^2) + B(6x_0 + 6h) + 6C$

Now, if we compute the area of the region by the limit of a Riemann sum, we have

$$\text{Area} = \lim_{\Delta x \to 0} \sum_{i=1}^{n} f(\xi_i)\, \Delta x$$

$$= \int_{x_0}^{x_0+2h} f(x)\, dx$$

$$= \int_{x_0}^{x_0+2h} (Ax^2 + Bx + C)\, dx$$

or $\text{Area} = \dfrac{A}{3}x^3 + \dfrac{B}{2}x^2 + Cx \Big]_{x_0}^{x_0+2h}$

$$= \frac{A}{3}(x_0 + 2h)^3 + \frac{B}{2}(x_0 + 2h)^2 + C(x_0 + 2h)$$
$$- \left(\frac{A}{3}x_0^3 + \frac{B}{2}x_0^2 + Cx_0 \right)$$

(3) $= \dfrac{h}{3}[A(6x_0^2 + 12hx_0 + 6h^2) + B(6x_0 + 6h) + 6C]$

Substituting (2) in (3), we get

$$\text{Area} = \frac{h}{3}[y_0 + 4y_1 + y_2] \qquad\qquad \text{Q.E.D.}$$

Let the function f be continuous on the closed interval $[a,b]$. Consider a regular partition of the interval $[a,b]$ of $2n$ subintervals (we use $2n$ instead of n, since we want an even number of subintervals). The length of each subinterval is $\Delta x = (b - a)/2n$. Let the points on the curve $y = f(x)$ having these partitioning points as abscissas be denoted by $P_0(x_0,y_0)$, $P_1(x_1,y_1)$, ..., $P_{2n}(x_{2n},y_{2n})$ — see Fig. 15.3.2 where $f(x) \geq 0$ for all x in $[a,b]$.

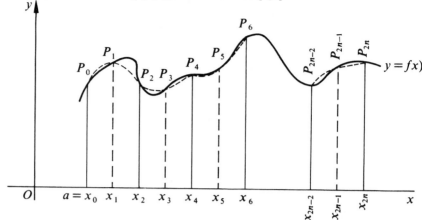

Figure 15.3.2

We approximate the segment of the curve $y = f(x)$ from P_0 to P_2 by the segment of the parabola, with vertical axis, through P_0, P_1, and P_2. Then the area of the region, bounded by this parabola, the x axis, and the lines $x = x_0$ and $x = x_2$ is given by Theorem 15.3.1 where $h = \Delta x$. We have

$$\frac{\Delta x}{3} (y_0 + 4y_1 + y_2) \quad \text{or} \quad \frac{\Delta x}{3} [f(x_0) + 4f(x_1) + f(x_2)]$$

Similarly, we approximate the segment of the curve $y = f(x)$ from P_2 to P_4 by the segment of the parabola, with vertical axis, through P_2, P_3, and P_4, and the area of the region bounded by this parabola, the x axis, and the lines $x = x_2$ and $x = x_4$ is given by

$$\frac{\Delta x}{3} (y_2 + 4y_3 + y_4) \quad \text{or} \quad \frac{\Delta x}{3} [f(x_2) + 4f(x_3) + f(x_4)]$$

We continue this process until we have n such regions, and the area of the last region is given by

$$\frac{\Delta x}{3} (y_{2n-2} + 4y_{2n-1} + y_{2n}) \quad \text{or} \quad \frac{\Delta x}{3} f(x_{2n-2}) + 4f(x_{2n-1}) + f(x_{2n})$$

The sum of the areas of these regions approximates the area of the region bounded by the curve whose equation is $y = f(x)$, the x axis, and the lines $x = a$ and $x = b$, and the area of this region is given by the definite integral $\int_a^b f(x)\, dx$.

So, we have

$$(4) \quad \int_a^b f(x)\, dx \approx \frac{\Delta x}{3} [f(x_0) + 4f(x_1) + 2f(x_2) + 4f(x_3) + 2f(x_4) + \cdots$$
$$+ 2f(x_{2n-2}) + 4f(x_{2n-1}) + f(x_{2n})]$$

where $\Delta x = (b - a)/2n$.

Formula (4) is known as *Simpson's rule.*

EXAMPLE 1: Use Simpson's rule to approximate the value of $\int_0^1 dx/(x+1)$, with $2n = 4$. Given the result to four decimal places.

Solution: Applying Simpson's rule with $2n = 4$, we have $\Delta x = (1 - 0)/4 = \frac{1}{4}$, and

$$(5) \qquad \int_0^1 \frac{dx}{x+1} \approx \frac{1}{12}[f(x_0) + 4f(x_1) + 2f(x_2) + 4f(x_3) + f(x_4)]$$

The computation of the expression in brackets on the right side of (5) is shown in Table 15.3.1, where $f(x) = 1/(x+1)$.

Table 15.3.1

i	x_i	$f(x_i)$	k	$k \cdot f(x_i)$
0	0	1.00000	1	1.00000
1	0.25	0.80000	4	3.20000
2	0.5	0.66667	2	1.33334
3	0.75	0.57143	4	2.28572
4	1	0.50000	1	0.50000
Sum:				8.31906

Substituting the sum from Table 15.3.1 in (5), we get

$$\int_0^1 \frac{dx}{x+1} \approx \frac{1}{12}(8.31906) \approx 0.69325+$$

Rounding off the result to four decimal places gives us

$$\int_0^1 \frac{dx}{x+1} \approx 0.6933$$

The exact value of $\int_0^1 dx/(x+1)$ is found as follows:

$$\int_0^1 \frac{dx}{x+1} = \ln|x+1| \Big]_0^1 = \ln 2 - \ln 1 = \ln 2$$

From a table of natural logarithms, the value of $\ln 2$ to four decimal places is 0.6931, which agrees with our approximation in the first three places. And the error in our approximation is -0.0002.

In applying Simpson's rule, the larger we take the value of $2n$, the smaller will be the value of Δx, and so geometrically it seems evident that the greater will be the accuracy of the approximation, since a parabola, passing through three points of a curve that are close to each other, will be close to the curve throughout the subinterval of width $2\,\Delta x$.

The following theorem, which is proved in advanced calculus, gives a method for determining the error in applying Simpson's rule. We denote the error by ϵ_S.

15.3.2 THEOREM   Let the function f be continuous on the closed interval $[a,b]$, and f', f'', f''', and $f^{(iv)}$ all exist on $[a,b]$. If

$$\epsilon_S = \int_a^b f(x)\, dx - S$$

where S is the approximate value of $\int_a^b f(x)\, dx$ found by Simpson's rule, then there is some number η in $[a,b]$ such that

(6) $$\epsilon_S = -\frac{(b-a)}{180} f^{(iv)}(\eta)\,(\Delta x)^4$$

EXAMPLE 2: Find the bounds for the error in Example 1.

Solution: $f(x) = (x+1)^{-1}$

$$f'(x) = -1(x+1)^{-2}$$

$$f''(x) = 2(x+1)^{-3}$$

$$f'''(x) = -6(x+1)^{-4}$$

$$f^{(iv)}(x) = 24(x+1)^{-5}$$

$$f^{(v)}(x) = -120(x+1)^{-6}$$

Since $f^{(v)}(x) < 0$ for all x in $[0,1]$, $f^{(iv)}$ is decreasing on $[0,1]$, and so the absolute minimum value of $f^{(iv)}$ on $[0,1]$ is at the right end point 1, and the absolute maximum value of $f^{(iv)}$ on $[0,1]$ is at the left end point 0.

$$f^{(iv)}(0) = 24 \quad \text{and} \quad f^{(iv)}(1) = \tfrac{3}{4}$$

Substituting 0 for η in the right side of (6), we get

$$-\frac{(b-a)}{180} f^{(iv)}(0)\,(\Delta x)^4 = -\frac{1}{180}(24)\left(\frac{1}{4}\right)^4 = -\frac{1}{1,920} = -0.00052$$

Substituting 1 for η in the right side of (6), we get

$$-\frac{(b-a)}{180} f^{(iv)}(1)\,(\Delta x)^4 = -\frac{1}{180}\cdot\frac{3}{4}\left(\frac{1}{4}\right)^4 = -\frac{1}{61,440} = -0.00002$$

So, we conclude that

(7) $$-0.00052 \leq \epsilon_S \leq -0.00002$$

The inequality (7) agrees with our previous discussion regarding the error in the approximation of $\int_0^1 dx/(x+1)$ by Simpson's rule, since $-0.00052 < -0.0002 < -0.00002$.

If $f(x)$ is a polynomial of degree three or less, then $f^{(iv)}(x) \equiv 0$ and therefore $\epsilon_S = 0$; or, in other words, Simpson's rule gives an exact result for a polynomial of the third degree or lower. This statement is geometrically obvious if $f(x)$ is of the second or first degree, since in the first case, the graph of $y = f(x)$ is a parabola, and in the second case, the graph is a straight line (a degenerate parabola).

Let us apply Simpson's rule to the definite integral $\int_a^b f(x)\, dx$, where $f(x)$ is a third-degree polynomial, and take $2n = 2$. Simpson's rule gives an exact value for the definite integral in this case. Since $2n = 2$, $x_0 = a$, $x_1 = (a+b)/2$, and $x_2 = b$; and $\Delta x = (b - a)/2$. So, we have

(8) $$\int_a^b f(x)\, dx = \frac{b-a}{6}\left[f(a) + 4f\left(\frac{a+b}{2}\right) + f(b) \right]$$

Formula (8) is known as the *prismoidal formula*.

In Sec. 11.9, we learned that $\int_a^b f(x)\, dx$ gives the volume of a solid for which $f(x)$ is the area of a plane section formed by a plane perpendicular to the x axis at a distance x units from the origin. Therefore, if $f(x)$ is a polynomial of the third degree or less, the prismoidal formula will give the exact volume of such a solid.

EXAMPLE 3: Find the volume of a right-circular cone of height h and base radius r by the prismoidal formula.

Solution: Figure 15.3.3 illustrates a right-circular cone having its vertex at the origin and its axis along the positive side of the x axis. The area of the plane

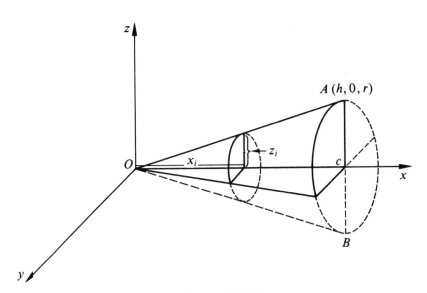

Figure 15.3.3

section x_i units from the origin is $\pi z_i{}^2$. The equation of line OA in the xz plane is $z = (r/h)x$. Therefore the area of the plane section is

$$\pi \frac{r^2}{h^2} x_i{}^2 = f(x_i)$$

So,

$$\text{Volume} = \int_0^h f(x)\,dx = \int_0^h \pi\frac{r^2}{h^2}x^2\,dx = \frac{\pi r^2}{h^2}\int_0^h x^2\,dx$$

If we evaluate $\int_0^h x^2\,dx$ by the prismoidal formula, we have $f(x) = x^2$; $b = h$; $a = 0$; $(a+b)/2 = h/2$.
So,

$$\text{Volume} = \frac{\pi r^2}{h^2}\cdot\frac{h}{6}\left(0 + 4\cdot\frac{h^2}{4} + h^2\right) = \frac{\pi r^2}{6h}(2h^2) = \frac{1}{3}\pi r^2 h$$

Exercises 15.3

In Exercises 1 through 6, approximate the definite integral by Simpson's rule, using the indicated value of $2n$. Express the answers to three decimal places. Also, find the exact value of the definite integral and compare the results.

1. $\int_0^2 x^2\,dx$; $2n = 4$

2. $\int_1^2 \dfrac{dx}{x+1}$; $2n = 8$

3. $\int_0^1 \dfrac{dx}{\sqrt{1+x^2}}$; $2n = 4$

4. $\int_{-1/2}^0 \dfrac{dx}{\sqrt{1-x^2}}$; $2n = 4$

5. $\int_0^1 \dfrac{dx}{x^2 + x + 1}$; $2n = 4$

6. $\int_0^\pi \sin x\,dx$; $2n = 6$

In Exercises 7 through 9, find bounds for the error in the indicated exercise.

7. Exercise 1   8. Exercise 2   9. Exercise 6

Each of the definite integrals in Exercises 10 through 15 cannot be evaluated exactly in terms of elementary functions. Use Simpson's rule, with the indicated value of $2n$, to find an approximate value of the given definite integral. Express results to three decimal places.

10. $\int_0^{\pi/2} \sqrt{\sin x}\,dx$; $2n = 6$

11. $\int_{\pi/2}^{3\pi/2} (\sin x/x)\,dx$; $2n = 6$

12. $\int_0^1 \sqrt[3]{1+x^2}\,dx$; $2n = 4$

13. $\int_0^4 e^{-x^2}\,dx$; $2n = 4$

14. $\int_0^2 \sqrt{1+x^4}\,dx$; $2n = 6$

15. $\int_0^2 \dfrac{dx}{\sqrt{1+x^3}}$; $2n = 8$

In Exercises 16 through 19, use the prismoidal formula to find the exact volume of the given solid.

16. A sphere of radius r.
17. A right-circular cylinder of height h and base radius r.
18. A right pyramid of height h and base a square having a side of length s.
19. A frustrum of a right-circular cone of height h_1 and base radii r_1 and r_2.

20. Show that the exact value of $4 \int_0^1 \sqrt{1 - x^2} \, dx$ is π. Then use Simpson's rule with $2n = 6$ to get an approximate value of $4 \int_0^1 \sqrt{1 - x^2} \, dx$ to three decimal places. Compare the results.

21. Find an approximate value to four decimal places of the definite integral $\int_0^{\pi/3} \log_{10} \cos x \, dx$, (a) by the prismoidal formula; (b) by Simpson's rule, taking $\Delta x = \pi/12$; (c) by the trapezoidal rule, taking $\Delta x = \pi/12$.

22. Find the area of the region enclosed by the loop of the curve whose equation is $y^2 = 8x^2 - x^5$. Evaluate the definite integral by Simpson's rule, with $2n = 8$. Express the result to three decimal places.

16 Polar coordinates

(16.1) The polar coordinate system

Until now we have located a point in a plane by its rectangular cartesian coordinates. There are other coordinate systems that may be used. Probably the next in importance to the cartesian coordinate system is the *polar coordinate system*. In the cartesian coordinate system, the coordinates are numbers called the abscissa and the ordinate, and these numbers are directed distances from two fixed lines. In the polar coordinate system, the coordinates consist of a distance and an angle relative to a fixed point and a fixed ray (or half line).

We call the fixed point the *pole* (or origin), and we designate it by the letter "O." The fixed ray is called the *polar axis* (or polar line), and we shall designate it by OA. The ray OA is usually drawn horizontally and to the right, and it extends indefinitely far (see Fig. 16.1.1).

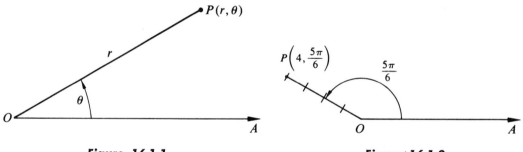

Figure 16.1.1   Figure 16.1.2

Let P be any point in the plane distinct from O. Let θ be the directed angle AOP, positive when measured counterclockwise and negative when measured clockwise, having as its initial side the ray OA and, as its terminal side, the ray OP. Then, if r is the undirected distance from O to P; that is, $r = |\overline{OP}|$; one set of polar coordinates of P is given by the numbers r and θ and we write these coordinates as (r, θ).

For example, the point $P(4, 5\pi/6)$ is determined by first drawing the angle $5\pi/6$, having its vertex at the pole and its initial side along the polar axis. Then the point on the terminal side, which is four units from the pole, is the point P (see Fig. 16.1.2). Another set of polar coordinates for this same point is

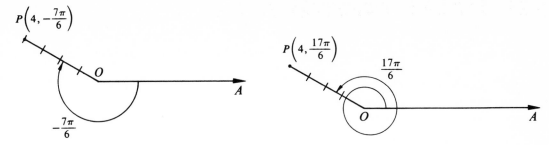

Figure 16.1.3   **Figure 16.1.4**

$(4, -7\pi/6)$ (see Fig. 16.1.3). Furthermore, the polar coordinates $(4, 17\pi/6)$ would also give us the same point, as shown in Fig. 16.1.4.

Actually the coordinates $(4, 5\pi/6 + 2n\pi)$ where n is any integer will give us the same point as $(4, 5\pi/6)$. So, a given point has indefinitely many sets of polar coordinates. This is unlike the rectangular cartesian coordinate system, since there is a one-to-one correspondence between the rectangular cartesian coordinates and the position of points in the plane, while there is no such one-to-one correspondence between the polar coordinates and the position of points in the plane. A further illustration of this is obtained by considering sets of polar coordinates for the pole. If $r = 0$ and θ is any real number, we have the pole, which then may be designated by $(0, \theta)$.

We may consider polar coordinates for which r is negative. In this case, instead of taking the point on the terminal side of the angle θ, we take the point on the extension of the terminal side, which is the ray from the pole extending in the opposite direction to the terminal side. So, if P is on the extension of the terminal side of θ, a set of polar coordinates of P is (r, θ) where $r = -|\overline{OP}|$. For example, the point $(-4, -\pi/6)$ shown in Fig. 16.1.5, is the same point as $(4, 5\pi/6), (4, -7\pi/6)$, and $(17\pi/6)$, as shown above. Still another set of polar coordinates for this same point is $(-4, 11\pi/6)$ — see Fig. 16.1.6.

The angle θ is usually given in radians, and so a set of polar coordinates of a point is an ordered pair of real numbers. To each ordered pair of real numbers there is a unique point having this set of polar coordinates. However, we have

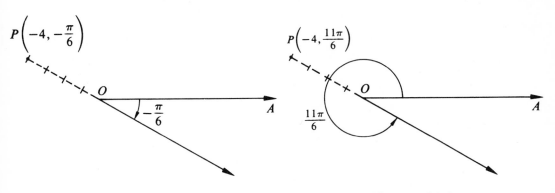

Figure 16.1.5   **Figure 16.1.6**

seen that a particular point may be given by indefinitely many ordered pairs of real numbers. If the point P is not the pole, and we restrict r and θ so that $r > 0$ and $0 \leq \theta < 2\pi$, then there is a unique set of polar coordinates for P.

EXAMPLE 1: (a) Plot the point having polar coordinates $(3, -2\pi/3)$. Find another set of polar coordinates of this point, for which (b) r is negative and $0 < \theta < 2\pi$; (c) r is positive and $0 < \theta < 2\pi$; (d) r is negative and $-2\pi < \theta < 0$.

Solution: (a) The point is plotted by drawing the angle $-2\pi/3$ in the clockwise direction from the polar axis. Since $r > 0$, P is on the terminal side of the angle, three units from the pole; see Fig. 16.1.7a. The answers to (b), (c), and (d) are, respectively, $(-3, \pi/3)$, $(3, 4\pi/3)$, and $(-3, -5\pi/3)$, and they are illustrated in Figs. 16.1.7b, c, and d.

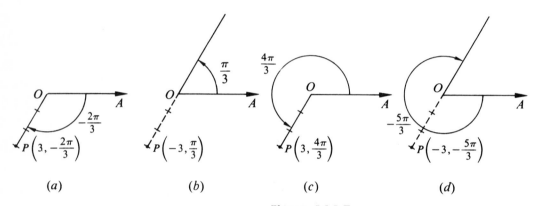

(a)   (b)   (c)   (d)

Figure 16.1.7

Often we wish to refer to both the rectangular cartesian coordinates and the polar coordinates of a point. To do this, we take the origin of the first system and the pole of the second system coincident, the polar axis as the positive side of the x axis, and the ray for which $\theta = \pi/2$ as the positive side of the y axis.

Suppose P is a point whose representation in the rectangular cartesian coordinate system is (x,y). Then if (r,θ) is a polar-coordinate representation of P, we shall distinguish two cases, $r > 0$ and $r < 0$. In the first case, if $r > 0$, then the point P is on the terminal side of θ and $r = |\overline{OP}|$. Such a case is shown in Fig. 16.1.8.

Then, $\cos \theta = x/|\overline{OP}| = x/r$ and $\sin \theta = y/|\overline{OP}| = y/r$; and so

(1) $$x = r \cos \theta \qquad \text{and} \qquad y = r \sin \theta$$

In the second case, if $r < 0$, then the point P is on the extension cf the terminal side of θ and $r = -|\overline{OA}|$ (see Fig. 16.1.9). Then if $\overline{P}$ is the point $(-x,-y)$, we have

$$\cos \theta = \frac{-x}{|\overline{OP}|} = \frac{-x}{|\overline{OP}|} = \frac{-x}{-r} = \frac{x}{r}$$

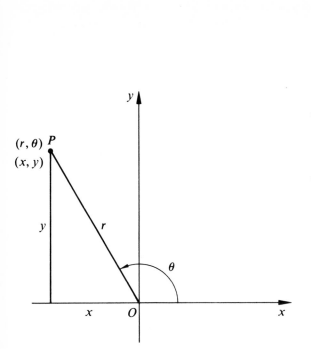

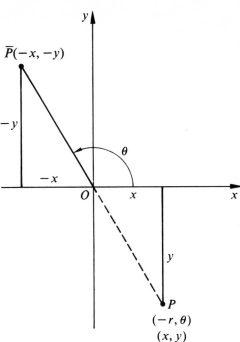

Figure 16.1.8   **Figure 16.1.9**

So,

(2) $$x = r \cos \theta$$

Also

$$\sin \theta = \frac{-y}{\overline{|OP|}} = \frac{-y}{|\overline{OP}|} = \frac{-y}{-r} = \frac{y}{r}$$

So,

(3) $$y = r \sin \theta$$

Formulas (2) and (3) are the same as the formulas in (1), and so the formulas (1) hold in all cases.

From formulas (1) we may obtain the rectangular cartesian coordinates of a point when its polar coordinates are known. Also, from the formulas we may obtain a polar equation of a curve if a rectangular cartesian equation is known.

To obtain formulas which will give us a set of polar coordinates of a point when its rectangular cartesian coordinates are known, we square both sides of each equation in (1), and we have

$$x^2 = r^2 \cos^2 \theta \quad \text{and} \quad y^2 = r^2 \sin^2 \theta$$

Equating the sum of the left members of the above to the sum of the right members, we have

$$x^2 + y^2 = r^2 \cos^2 \theta + r^2 \sin^2 \theta$$

or, equivalently,

$$x^2 + y^2 = r^2 (\sin^2 \theta + \cos^2 \theta)$$

which gives us

$$x^2 + y^2 = r^2$$

and so

(4)
$$r = \pm \sqrt{x^2 + y^2}$$

From the equations in (1) and dividing, we have

$$\frac{r \sin \theta}{r \cos \theta} = \frac{y}{x}$$

or, equivalently,

(5)
$$\tan \theta = \frac{y}{x}$$

EXAMPLE 2: Plot the point whose polar coordinates are $(-6, 7\pi/4)$ and find its rectangular cartesian coordinates.

Solution: The point is plotted in Fig. 16.1.10. From (1) we have

$$x = r \cos \theta \qquad\qquad y = r \sin \theta$$

$$= -6 \cos \frac{7\pi}{4} \qquad\qquad = -6 \sin \frac{7\pi}{4}$$

$$= -6 \frac{\sqrt{2}}{2} \qquad\qquad = -6 \left(-\frac{\sqrt{2}}{2} \right)$$

$$= -3\sqrt{2} \qquad\qquad = 3\sqrt{2}$$

So the point is $(-3\sqrt{2}, 3\sqrt{2})$.

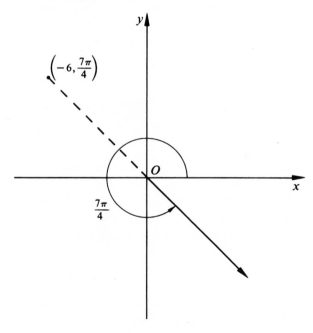

Figure 16.1.10

The graph of an equation in polar coordinates r and θ consists of all those points and only those points P having at least one pair of coordinates which satisfy the equation. If an equation of a graph is given in polar coordinates, we call it a *polar equation*, to distinguish it from a *cartesian equation*, which is the term used when an equation is given in rectangular cartesian coordinates.

EXAMPLE 3: *Given:* a polar equation of a graph is $r^2 = 4 \sin 2\theta$. *Find:* a cartesian equation.

Solution: Since $r^2 = x^2 + y^2$ and $\sin 2\theta = 2 \sin \theta \cos \theta = 2(y/r)(x/r)$, from (1) we have, upon substituting in the given polar equation,

$$x^2 + y^2 = 4(2)\frac{y}{r} \cdot \frac{x}{r}$$

or

$$x^2 + y^2 = \frac{8xy}{r^2}$$

or, equivalently,

$$x^2 + y^2 = \frac{8xy}{x^2 + y^2}$$

or

$$(x^2 + y^2)^2 = 8xy$$

EXAMPLE 4: *Find:* (r,θ), if $r > 0$ and $0 \le \theta < 2\pi$, for the point whose rectangular cartesian coordinate representation is $(-\sqrt{3}, -1)$.

Solution: The point $(-\sqrt{3}, -1)$ is plotted in Fig. 16.1.11.

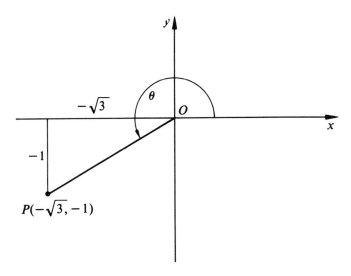

Figure 16.1.11

From (4), since $r > 0$, we have

$$r = \sqrt{1 + 3} = 2$$

From (5), $\tan \theta = -1/(-\sqrt{3})$, and since $\pi/2 < \theta < 3\pi/2$, we have

$$\theta = \frac{7}{6}\pi$$

So the point is $(2, 7\pi/6)$.

EXAMPLE 5: *Given:* a cartesian equation of a graph is $x^2 + y^2 - 4x = 0$. *Find:* a polar equation.

Solution: Substituting $x = r \cos \theta$ and $y = r \sin \theta$ in

$$x^2 + y^2 - 4x = 0$$

we have $r^2 \cos^2 \theta + r^2 \sin^2 \theta - 4r \cos \theta = 0$

or $r^2 - 4r \cos \theta = 0$

or $r(r - 4 \cos \theta) = 0$

Therefore, we have

$$r = 0 \quad \text{or} \quad r - 4 \cos \theta = 0$$

The graph of $r = 0$ is the pole. However, the pole is a point on the graph of $r - 4 \cos \theta = 0$, since $r = 0$ when $\theta = \pi/2$.

Therefore, a polar equation of the graph is

$$r = 4 \cos \theta$$

The graph of $x^2 + y^2 - 4x = 0$ is a circle. The equation may be written in the form

$$(x - 2)^2 + y^2 = 4$$

which is an equation of the circle with center at $(2,0)$ and radius 2.

Exercises 16.1

In Exercises 1 through 6, plot the point having the given set of polar coordinates; then find another set of polar coordinates for the same point for which (a) $r < 0$ and $0 \leq \theta < 2\pi$; (b) $r > 0$ and $-2\pi < \theta \leq 0$; (c) $r < 0$ and $-2\pi < \theta \leq 0$.

1. $\left(4, \dfrac{\pi}{4}\right)$

2. $\left(3, \dfrac{5\pi}{6}\right)$

3. $\left(2, \dfrac{\pi}{2}\right)$

4. $\left(3, \dfrac{3\pi}{2}\right)$

5. $\left(\sqrt{2}, \dfrac{7\pi}{4}\right)$

6. $\left(2, \dfrac{4\pi}{3}\right)$

In Exercises 7 through 12, plot the point having the given set of polar coordinates; then give two other sets of polar coordinates of the same point, one with the same value of r and one with an r having opposite sign.

7. $\left(3, \dfrac{-2\pi}{3}\right)$

8. $\left(\sqrt{2}, \dfrac{-\pi}{4}\right)$

9. $\left(-4, \dfrac{5\pi}{6}\right)$ 11. $\left(-2, \dfrac{-5\pi}{4}\right)$

10. $\left(-2, \dfrac{4\pi}{3}\right)$ 12. $(-3, -\pi)$

13. Find the rectangular cartesian coordinates of each of the following points:
(a) $(3, \pi)$; (b) $(\sqrt{2}, -3\pi/4)$; (c) $(-4, 2\pi/3)$; (d) $(-2, -\pi/2)$; (e) $(-2, 7\pi/4)$; (f) $(-1, -7\pi/6)$.

14. Find a set of polar coordinates for each of the following points, taking $r > 0$ and $0 \le \theta < 2\pi$: (a) $(1, -1)$; (b) $(-\sqrt{3}, 1)$; (c) $(2, 2)$; (d) $(-5, 0)$; (e) $(0, -2)$; (f) $(-2, -2\sqrt{3})$.

In Exercises 15 through 22, find a polar equation of the graph having the given cartesian equation.

15. $x^2 + y^2 = a^2$ 19. $(x^2 + y^2)^2 = 4(x^2 - y^2)$

16. $x^3 = 4y^2$ 20. $2xy = a^2$

17. $y^2 = 4(x + 1)$ 21. $x^2 + y^2 - 9x + 8y = 0$

18. $x^2 - y^2 = 16$ 22. $y = \dfrac{2x}{x^2 + 1}$

In Exercises 23 through 30, find a cartesian equation of the graph having the given polar equation.

23. $r^2 = 2 \sin 2\theta$ 27. $r^2 = 4 \cos 2\theta$

24. $r^2 \cos 2\theta = 10$ 28. $r^2 = \theta$

25. $r^2 = \cos \theta$ 29. $r = 9 \sin^2 \dfrac{\theta}{2}$

26. $r = a \tan^2 \theta$ 30. $r = 2 \sin 3\theta$

(16.2)   The slope of a tangent line to a polar curve

Let $r = f(\theta)$ be a polar equation of a curve. To find the slope of the tangent line to the curve at a point (r, θ) on the curve, we consider a rectangular cartesian coordinate system and a polar coordinate system in the same plane and having the positive side of the x axis coincident with the polar axis. In the previous section, we saw that the two sets of coordinates are related by the equations

$$x = r \cos \theta \qquad \text{and} \qquad y = r \sin \theta$$

x and y may be considered as functions of θ, since $r = f(\theta)$. If we differentiate these equations with respect to θ, we get, by applying the chain rule,

(1) $$\frac{dx}{d\theta} = \cos \theta \frac{dr}{d\theta} - r \sin \theta$$

and

(2) $$\frac{dy}{d\theta} = \sin \theta \frac{dr}{d\theta} + r \cos \theta$$

If α is the inclination of the tangent line, then

$$\tan \alpha = \frac{dy}{dx}$$

and if $dx/d\theta \neq 0$, we have

(3)
$$\frac{dy}{dx} = \frac{dy/d\theta}{dx/d\theta}$$

Substituting (1) and (2) into (3), we obtain

(4)
$$\frac{dy}{dx} = \frac{\sin \theta \, dr/d\theta + r \cos \theta}{\cos \theta \, dr/d\theta - r \sin \theta}$$

If $\cos \theta \neq 0$, we divide numerator and denominator of the right-hand side of (4) by $\cos \theta$ and replace dy/dx by $\tan \alpha$, giving us

(5)
$$\tan \alpha = \frac{\tan \theta \, dr/d\theta + r}{dr/d\theta - r \tan \theta}$$

EXAMPLE 1: Find the slope of the tangent line to the curve whose equation is $r = 1 - \cos \theta$ at the point $(1 - \sqrt{2}/2, \pi/4)$.

Solution: Since $r = 1 - \cos \theta$, $dr/d\theta = \sin \theta$. So at the point $(1 - \sqrt{2}/2, \pi/4)$, $dr/d\theta = \sqrt{2}/2$ and $\tan \theta = 1$; so from (5) we obtain

$$\tan \alpha = \frac{(1)\sqrt{2}/2 + (1 - \sqrt{2}/2)}{\sqrt{2}/2 - (1 - \sqrt{2}/2)(1)} = \frac{1}{\sqrt{2} - 1} = \sqrt{2} + 1$$

(16.3) Graphs of equations in polar coordinates

If we are to draw a sketch of the graph of a polar equation, it will be helpful to consider properties of *symmetry* of a graph. Two points P and Q are said to be *symmetric with respect to a line* if the line is the perpendicular bisector of the line segment PQ. Two points P and Q are said to be *symmetric with respect to a third point* if the third point is the midpoint of the line segment PQ. For example, using cartesian coordinates, the points (x,y) and $(x,-y)$ are symmetric with respect to the x axis, the points (x,y) and $(-x,y)$ are symmetric with respect to the y axis, and the points (x,y) and $(-x,-y)$ are symmetric with respect to the origin. Using polar coordinates, the points $(2,\pi/3)$ and $(2,2\pi/3)$ are symmetric with respect to the $\pi/2$ axis and the points $(2,\pi/3)$ and $(2,-2\pi/3)$ are symmetric with respect to the pole. The graph of an equation is symmetric with respect to a line l if for every point P on the graph there is a point Q, also on the graph, such that P and Q are symmetric with respect to l. Similarly, the graph of an equation is symmetric with respect to a point R if for every point P on the graph there is a point S, also on the graph, such that P and S are symmetric with respect to R. We have the following rules of symmetry for graphs of polar equations.

Rule 1. If an equation in polar coordinates remains unchanged when (r,θ) is replaced by either $(r, -\theta + 2n\pi)$ or $(-r, \pi - \theta + 2n\pi)$, where n is any integer, the graph of the equation is symmetric with respect to the polar axis.

Rule 2. If an equation in polar cordoinates remains unchanged when (r,θ) is replaced by either $(r, \pi - \theta + 2n\pi)$ or $(-r, -\theta + 2n\pi)$, where n is any integer, the graph of the equation is symmetric with respect to the $\pi/2$ axis.

Rule 3. If an equation in polar coordinates remains unchanged when (r,θ) is replaced by either $(-r, \theta + 2n\pi)$ or $(r, \pi + \theta + 2n\pi)$, where n is any integer, the graph of the equation is symmetric with respect to the pole.

The proof of rule 1 is as follows: If the point $P(r,\theta)$ is a point on the graph of an equation, then the graph will be symmetric with respect to the polar axis if there is a point $P_1(r_1,\theta_1)$ on the graph so that the polar axis is the perpendicular bisector of the line segment P_1P (see Fig. 16.3.1). So, if $r_1 = r$, then θ_1 must equal $-\theta + 2n\pi$, where n is an integer, and if $r_1 = -r$, then θ_1 must be $\pi - \theta + 2n\pi$. The proofs of Rules 2 and 3 are similar, and are omitted.

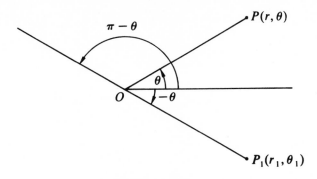

Figure 16.3.1

EXAMPLE 1: Test for symmetry with respect to the polar axis, the $\pi/2$ axis, and the pole, the graph of the equation $r = 4 \cos 2\theta$.

Solution: Using Rule 1 to test for symmetry with respect to the polar axis, we replace (r,θ) by $(r,-\theta)$, and we obtain $r = 4 \cos (-2\theta)$, which is equivalent to $r = 4 \cos 2\theta$. So the graph is symmetric with respect to the polar axis.

Using Rule 2 to test for symmetry with respect to the $\pi/2$ axis, we replace (r,θ) by $(r, \pi - \theta)$, and we obtain $r = 4 \cos (2(\pi - \theta))$ or, equivalently, $r = 4 \cos (2\pi - 2\theta)$, which is the same equation as $r = 4 \cos 2\theta$. Therefore, the graph is symmetric with respect to the $\pi/2$ axis.

To test for symmetry with respect to the pole, replace (r,θ) by $(-r,\theta)$ and we obtain the equation $-r = 4 \cos 2\theta$, which is not the same equation. However, we must also check to see if the other set of coordinates will work. Replace (r,θ) by $(r, \pi + \theta)$ and we obtain $r = 4 \cos 2(\pi + \theta)$ or, equivalently, $r = 4 \cos (2\pi + 2\theta)$, which is the same equation as $r = 4 \cos 2\theta$. Therefore, the graph is symmetric with respect to the pole.

When drawing a sketch of a graph, it is desirable to determine if the pole is on the graph. This is done by substituting 0 for r and solving for θ. Also, it is advantageous to plot the points for which r has a relative maximum or relative minimum value. As a further aid in plotting, if a curve contains the pole it is sometimes helpful to find the equations of the tangent lines to the graph at the pole.

In Sec. 16.2 we learned that the slope of the tangent line at a point (r,θ) is given by

$$\tan \alpha = \frac{\tan \theta \; dr/d\theta + r}{dr/d\theta - r \tan \theta}$$

where α is the inclination of the tangent line.

At the pole, $r = 0$, and so if $dr/d\theta \neq 0$, we have

(1) $$\tan \alpha = \tan \theta$$

From (1) we conclude that the values of θ, where $0 \leq \theta < \pi$, which satisfy a polar equation of the curve when $r = 0$, are the inclinations of the tangent lines to the curve at the pole. So, if $\theta_1, \theta_2, \ldots, \theta_k$ are these values of θ, then equations of the tangent lines to the curve at the pole are

$$\theta = \theta_1, \theta = \theta_2, \ldots, \theta = \theta_k$$

EXAMPLE 2: Draw a sketch of the graph of

$$r = 1 - 2 \cos \theta$$

Solution: Replacing (r,θ) by $(r,-\theta)$, we obtain the same equation and so the graph is symmetric with respect to the polar axis.

Table 16.3.1 gives the coordinates of some points on the graph. From these points we draw half of the graph and the remainder is drawn from its symmetry with respect to the polar axis.

If $r = 0$, we obtain $\cos \theta = 1/2$, and if $0 \leq \theta < \pi$, $\theta = \pi/3$. Therefore, the point $(0,\pi/3)$ is on the graph and an equation of the tangent line there is $\theta = \pi/3$.

Table 16.3.1

θ	0	$\pi/6$	$\pi/3$	$\pi/2$	$2\pi/3$	$5\pi/6$	π
r	-1	$1-\sqrt{3}$	0	1	2	$1+\sqrt{3}$	3

A sketch of the graph is shown in Fig. 16.3.2. It is called a *limaçon*.

The graph of an equation of the form

$$r = a \pm b \cos \theta$$

or $$r = a \pm b \sin \theta$$

is a limaçon. If $b > a$, as is the case in Example 2, the limaçon has a loop. If $a = b$, the limaçon is a cardioid, which is heartshaped. If $a > b$, the limaçon has a similar shape to the one in Example 3.

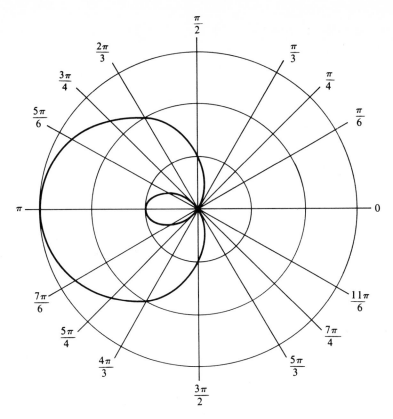

Figure 16.3.2

EXAMPLE 3: Draw a sketch of the graph of

$$r = 3 + 2 \sin \theta$$

Solution: The graph is symmetric with respect to the $\pi/2$ axis since if (r,θ) is replaced by $(r, \pi - \theta)$, the equation remains unchanged.

Table 16.3.2 gives the coordinates of some of the points on the graph.

Table 16.3.2

θ	0	$\pi/6$	$\pi/3$	$\pi/2$	π	$7\pi/6$	$4\pi/3$	$3\pi/2$
r	3	4	$3 + \sqrt{3}$	5	3	2	$3 - \sqrt{3}$	1

A sketch of the graph is shown in Fig. 16.3.3. It is drawn by plotting the points whose coordinates are given in Table 16.3.2 and using the symmetry property.

The graph of an equation of the form

$$r = a \cos n\theta \qquad \text{or} \qquad r = a \sin n\theta$$

is a rose, having n leaves if n is odd and $2n$ leaves if n is even.

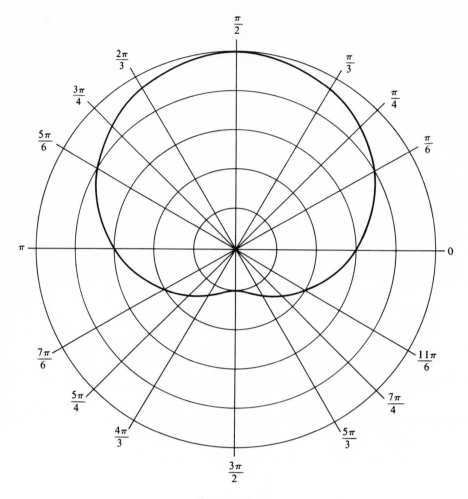

Figure 16.3.3

EXAMPLE 4: Draw a sketch of the graph of the four-leafed rose

$$r = 4 \cos 2\theta$$

Solution: In Example 1 we proved that the graph is symmetric with respect to the polar axis, the $\pi/2$ axis, and the pole.

Substituting 0 for r in the given equation, we get

$$\cos 2\theta = 0$$

from which we obtain, for $0 \leq \theta < 2\pi$, $\theta = \pi/4$, $3\pi/4$, $7\pi/4$, and $11\pi/4$.

Table 16.3.3 gives values of r for some values of θ from 0 to $\pi/2$. From these values and the symmetry properties, we draw a sketch of the graph as shown in Fig. 16.3.4.

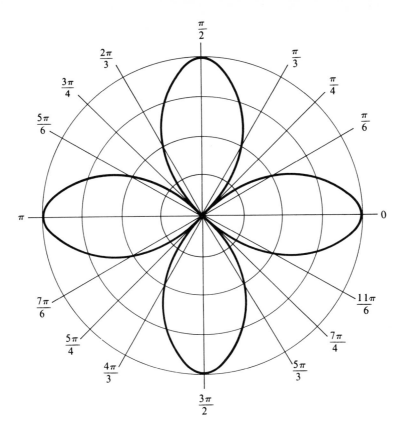

Figure 16.3.4

Table 16.3.3

θ	0	$\pi/12$	$\pi/6$	$\pi/4$	$\pi/3$	$5\pi/12$	$\pi/2$
r	4	$2\sqrt{3}$	2	0	-2	$-2\sqrt{3}$	-4

The graph of the equation

$$\theta = C$$

where C is any constant, is a straight line through the pole and making an angle of C with the polar axis. The same line is given by the equation

$$\theta = C \pm n\pi$$

where n is any integer.

In general, the polar form of an equation of a line is not so simple as the cartesian form. However, if the line is parallel to either the polar axis or the $\pi/2$ axis, the equation is fairly simple.

If a line is parallel to the polar axis and contains the point B whose cartesian coordinates are $(0,b)$ and polar coordinates are $(b,\pi/2)$, then a cartesian equation is $y = b$. If we replace y by $r \sin \theta$, we have

$$r \sin \theta = b$$

which is a polar equation of any line parallel to the polar axis. If b is positive, the line is above the polar axis, and if b is negative, it is below the polar axis.

If a line is parallel to the $\pi/2$ axis or, equivalently, perpendicular to the polar axis, and goes through the point A whose cartesian coordinates are $(a,0)$ and polar coodinates are $(a,0)$, a cartesian equation is $x = a$. Replacing x by $r \cos \theta$, we obtain

$$r \cos \theta = a$$

which is an equation of any line perpendicular to the polar axis. If a is positive, the line is to the right of the $\pi/2$ axis, and if a is negative, the line is to the left of the $\pi/2$ axis.

EXAMPLE 5: Draw a sketch of the graph of each of the following equations: (a) $r \sin \theta = 3$; (b) $r \cos \theta = 3$; (c) $r \sin \theta = -3$; (d) $r \cos \theta = -3$.

Solution: Each graph is a line, and they are shown in Figs. 16.3.5a, b, c, and d.

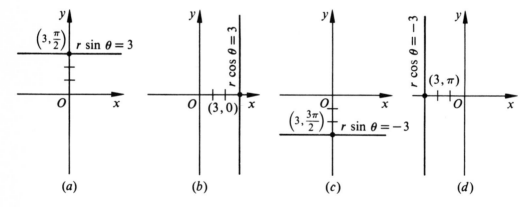

Figure 16.3.5

The graph of the equation

$$r = C$$

where C is any constant, is a circle whose center is at the pole and radius is $|C|$. The same circle is given by the equation

$$r = -C$$

As was the case with the straight line, the general polar equation of a circle is not so simple as the cartesian form. However, there are special cases of an equation of a circle which are worth considering in polar form.

If a circle has its center on the polar axis at the point having polar coordinates $(a,0)$ and is tangent to the $\pi/2$ axis, then its radius is $|a|$. The points of intersection of such a circle with the polar axis are the pole (0,0) and the point (2a,0) (see Fig. 16.3.6).

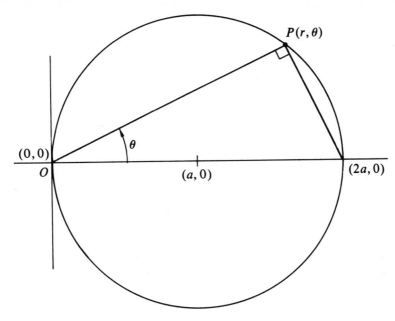

Figure 16.3.6

Then if $P(r,\theta)$ is any point on the circle, the angle at P inscribed in the circle is a right angle. Therefore, $\cos \theta = r/2a$ or, equivalently,

$$r = 2a \cos \theta$$

which is a polar equation of the circle having its center on the polar axis or its extension, and tangent to the $\pi/2$ axis. If a is a positive number, the circle is to the right of the pole, and if a is a negative number, the circle is to the left of the pole.

In a similar manner, it may be shown that

$$r = 2b \sin \theta$$

is a polar equation of the circle having its center on the $\pi/2$ axis or its extension, and tangent to the polar axis. If b is positive, the circle is above the pole, and if b is negative, the circle is below the pole.

EXAMPLE 6: Draw a sketch of the graph of

$$r = \theta \qquad \theta \geq 0$$

Solution: When $\theta = n\pi$, where n is any integer, the graph intersects the polar axis, and when $\theta = n\pi/2$, where n is any odd integer, the graph intersects the $\pi/2$ axis.

When $r = 0$, $\theta = 0$, and so the tangent line to the curve at the pole is the polar axis.

A sketch of the graph is shown in Fig. 16.3.7. The curve is called a *spiral of Archimedes.*

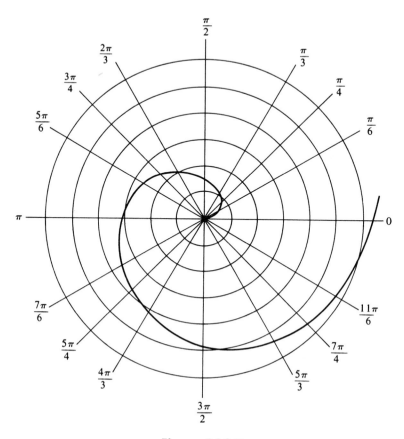

Figure 16.3.7

Exercises 16.3

In Exercises 1 through 40, draw a sketch of the graph of the given equation.

1. $r \cos \theta = 4$

2. $r \sin \theta = 2$

3. $r = 4 \cos \theta$

4. $r = 2 \sin \theta$

5. $\theta = 5$

6. $\theta = -4$

7. $r = 5$

8. $r = -4$

9. $r \sin \theta = -4$

10. $r \cos \theta = -5$

11. $r = -4 \sin \theta$

12. $r = -5 \cos \theta$

13. $r = e^{\theta}$ (logarithmic spiral)

14. $r = e^{\theta/3}$ (logarithmic spiral)

15. $r = 1/\theta$ (reciprocal spiral)

16. $r = 2/\theta$ (reciprocal spiral)

17. $r = 2\theta$ (spiral of Archimedes)

18. $r = \frac{1}{3}\theta$ (spiral of Archimedes)

19. $r = 2 \sin 3\theta$ (three-leafed rose)

20. $r = 3 \cos 2\theta$ (four-leafed rose)

21. $r = 2 \cos 4\theta$ (eight-leafed rose)

22. $r = 4 \sin 5\theta$ (five-leafed rose)

23. $r = 4 \sin 2\theta$ (four-leafed rose)

24. $r = 3 \cos 3\theta$ (three-leafed rose)

25. $r = 2 + 2 \sin \theta$ (cardioid)

26. $r = 3 + 3 \cos \theta$ (cardioid)

27. $r = 4 - 4 \cos \theta$ (cardioid)

28. $r = 3 - 3 \sin \theta$ (cardioid)

29. $r = 4 - 3 \cos \theta$ (limaçon)

30. $r = 3 - 4 \cos \theta$ (limaçon)

31. $r = 4 + 2 \sin \theta$ (limaçon)

32. $r = 2 - 3 \sin \theta$ (limaçon)

33. $r^2 = 9 \sin 2\theta$ (lemniscate)

34. $r^2 = - 4 \sin 2\theta$ (lemniscate)

35. $r^2 = - 25 \cos 2\theta$ (lemniscate)

36. $r^2 = 16 \cos 2\theta$ (lemniscate)

37. $r = 2 \sin \theta \tan \theta$ (cissoid)

38. $(r - 2)^2 = 8\theta$ (parabolic spiral)

39. $r = 2 \sec \theta - 1$ (conchoid of Nicomedes)

40. $r = 2 \csc \theta + 3$ (conchoid of Nicomedes)

In Exercises 41 through 46, find an equation of each of the tangent lines to the given curve at the pole.

41. $r = 4 \cos \theta + 2$

42. $r = 3 - 3 \sin \theta$

43. $r = 4 \cos 2\theta$

44. $r = 2 \sin 3\theta$

45. $r^2 = 4 \cos 2\theta$

46. $r^2 = 9 \sin 2\theta$

47. Find the slope of the tangent line to the curve $r = 4$ at the point $(4, \pi/4)$.

48. Find the slope of the tangent line to the curve $r = 6 \cos \theta - 2$ at the point $(1, 5\pi/3)$

49. Find a polar equation of the tangent line to the curve $r = \theta$ at the point (π, π).

50. Find a polar equation of the tangent line to the curve $r = -6 \sin \theta$ at the point $(6, 3\pi/2)$.

(16.4) Intersection of graphs in polar coordinates

To find the points of intersection of two curves whose equations are in cartesian coodinates, we solve the two equations simultaneously, and the common solutions give us all the points of intersection. However, since a point P has indefinitely many sets of polar coordinates, it is possible to have as the intersection of two curves a point for which no single pair of polar coordinates satisfies both equations.

For example, consider the two curves having the equations $r = 2 \sin 2\theta$ and $r = 1$. The graph of the first equation is a four-leafed rose and the graph of the second equation is the circle with center at the pole and radius 1. Solving the two equations simultaneously, we have

$$1 = 2 \sin 2\theta \quad \text{or} \quad \sin 2\theta = \tfrac{1}{2}$$

Therefore $\quad 2\theta = \dfrac{\pi}{6} \quad \dfrac{5\pi}{6} \quad \dfrac{13\pi}{6} \quad$ and $\quad \dfrac{17\pi}{6}$

or $\quad\quad\quad \theta = \dfrac{\pi}{12} \quad \dfrac{5\pi}{12} \quad \dfrac{13\pi}{12} \quad$ and $\quad \dfrac{17\pi}{12}$

So we obtain the points of intersection $(1,\pi/12)$, $(1,5\pi/12)$, $(1,13\pi/12)$, and $(1,17\pi/12)$.

The two curves are shown in Fig. 16.4.1. Eight points of intersection are shown. The other four points are obtained if we take another form of the equation of the circle $r = 1$; that is, $r = -1$. Solving this equation simultaneously with the equation of the four-leafed rose, we have

$$\sin 2\theta = -\dfrac{1}{2}$$

$$2\theta = \dfrac{7\pi}{6} \quad \dfrac{11\pi}{6} \quad \dfrac{19\pi}{6} \quad \text{and} \quad \dfrac{23\pi}{6}$$

or $\quad \theta = \dfrac{7\pi}{12} \quad \dfrac{11\pi}{12} \quad \dfrac{19\pi}{12} \quad$ and $\quad \dfrac{23\pi}{12}$

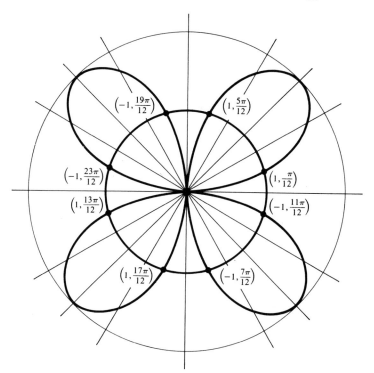

Figure 16.4.1

Thus we have the four points $(-1,7\pi/12)$, $(-1,11\pi/12)$, $(-1,19\pi/12)$, and $(-1,23\pi/12)$. Incidentally, $(-1,7\pi/12)$ may also be written $(1,19\pi/12)$, $(-1,11\pi/12)$ may be written $(1,23\pi/12)$, $(-1,19\pi/12)$ may be written $(1,7\pi/12)$, and $(-1,23\pi/12)$ may be written $(1,11\pi/12)$.

Since $(0,\theta)$ represents the pole for any θ, we determine if the pole is a point of intersection by setting $r = 0$ in each equation and solving for θ.

Often the coordinates of the points of intersection of two curves may be found directly from their graphs. However, we outline a general method.

If an equation of a curve in polar coordinates is given by

(1) $F(r,\theta) = 0$

then the same curve is given by the equation

(2) $F((-1)^n r, \theta + n\pi) = 0$

where n is any integer.

For example, the graph of the equation $r = 2 \sin 2\theta$ also has the equation, taking $n = 1$ in (2),

$$(-1)r = 2 \sin 2(\theta + \pi)$$
$$\text{or} \quad -r = 2 \sin 2\theta$$

Taking $n = 2$, we have

$$(-1)^2 r = 2 \sin 2(\theta + 2\pi)$$
$$\text{or} \quad r = 2 \sin 2\theta$$

which is the same as the original equation. Taking n any other integer, we get either $r = 2 \sin 2\theta$ or $r = -2 \sin 2\theta$.

The equation $r = 1$ gives us, from $n = 1$ in (2),

$$(-1)r = 1 \quad \text{or} \quad r = -1$$

Other integer values of n give us either

$$r = 1 \quad \text{or} \quad r = -1$$

So, if we are given the two equations

$$F(r,\theta) = 0 \quad \text{and} \quad G(r,\theta) = 0$$

we obtain all the points of intersection of the graphs of the two equations by doing the following.

(a) Use (2) to determine all the distinct equations of the two curves:

(3) $F_1(r,\theta) = 0, \; F_2(r,\theta) = 0, \; F_3(r,\theta) = 0, \ldots$

(4) $G_1(r,\theta) = 0, \; G_2(r,\theta) = 0, \; G_3(r,\theta) = 0, \ldots$

(b) Solve each equation in (3) simultaneously with each equation in (4).

(c) Check to see if the pole is a point of intersection by setting $r = 0$ in each equation, giving

(5) $F(0,\theta) = 0 \quad \text{and} \quad G(0,\theta) = 0$

If equations (5) each have a solution for θ, not necessarily the same θ, then the pole lies on both curves.

EXAMPLE 1: Find the points of intersection of the two curves $r = 2 - 2 \cos\theta$ and $r = 2 \cos\theta$.

Solution: To find other equations of the curve represented by $r = 2 - 2 \cos \theta$, we have

$$(-1)r = 2 - 2 \cos (\theta + \pi)$$

or $\qquad -r = 2 + 2 \cos \theta$

$$(-1)^2 r = 2 - 2 \cos (\theta + 2\pi)$$

or $\qquad r = 2 - 2 \cos \theta$

which is the same as the original equation.

Similarly, we find other equations of the curve given by $r = 2 \cos \theta$:

$$(-1)r = 2 \cos (\theta + \pi)$$

or $\qquad -r = -2 \cos \theta$

$$r = 2 \cos \theta,$$

which is the same as the original equation.

So we have two possible equations for the first curve: $r = 2 - 2 \cos \theta$ and $-r = 2 + 2 \cos \theta$; and one equation for the second curve: $r = 2 \cos \theta$. Solving simultaneously $r = 2 - 2 \cos \theta$ and $r = 2 \cos \theta$, we have

$$2 \cos \theta = 2 - 2 \cos \theta$$

$$4 \cos \theta = 2$$

$$\cos \theta = \tfrac{1}{2}$$

So, $\theta = \pi/3$ and $5\pi/3$, giving the points $(1, \pi/3)$ and $(1, 5\pi/3)$.

Solving simultaneously $-r = 2 + 2 \cos \theta$ and $r = 2 \cos \theta$, we have

$$2 + 2 \cos \theta = -2 \cos \theta$$

$$4 \cos \theta = -2$$

$$\cos \theta = -\tfrac{1}{2}$$

So, $\theta = 2\pi/3$ and $\theta = 4\pi/3$, giving us the points $(-1, 2\pi/3)$ and $(-1, 4\pi/3)$. However, $(-1, 2\pi/3)$ is the same point as $(1, 5\pi/3)$, and $(-1, 4\pi/3)$ is the same point as $(1, \pi/3)$.

We check to see if the pole is on each curve. Substituting $r = 0$ in the equation $r = 2 - 2 \cos \theta$, we have

$$0 = 2 - 2 \cos \theta$$

$$\cos \theta = 1$$

$$\theta = 0$$

Therefore the pole lies on the first curve. Similarly, substituting $r = 0$ in $r = 2 \cos \theta$, we have

$$0 = 2 \cos \theta$$

$$\cos \theta = 0$$

$$\theta = \frac{\pi}{2} \quad \text{or} \quad \frac{3\pi}{2}$$

So the pole lies on the second curve.

Therefore, the points of intersection of the two curves are $(1, \pi/3)$, $(1, 5\pi/3)$, and the pole. Sketches of the two curves are shown in Fig. 16.4.2.

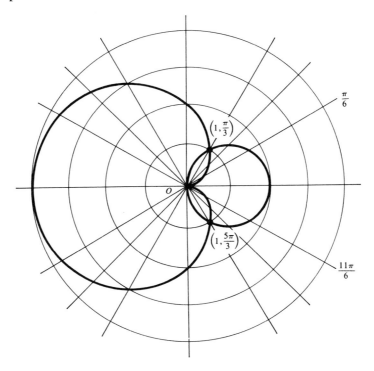

Figure 16.4.2

Exercises 16.4

In Exercises 1 through 12, find the points of intersection of the graphs of the given pair of equations. Draw a sketch of each pair of graphs with the same pole and polar axis.

1. $\begin{cases} 2r = 3 \\ r = 3 \sin \theta \end{cases}$

2. $\begin{cases} 2r = 3 \\ r = 1 + \cos \theta \end{cases}$

3. $\begin{cases} r = 2 \cos \theta \\ r = 2 \sin \theta \end{cases}$

4. $\begin{cases} r = 2 \cos 2\theta \\ r = 2 \sin \theta \end{cases}$

5. $\begin{cases} r = 4\theta \\ r = \dfrac{\pi}{2} \end{cases}$

6. $\begin{cases} \theta = \dfrac{\pi}{6} \\ r = 2 \end{cases}$

7. $\begin{cases} r = \cos \theta - 1 \\ r = \cos 2\theta \end{cases}$

8. $\begin{cases} r = 1 - \sin \theta \\ r = \cos 2\theta \end{cases}$

9. $\begin{cases} r = \tan \theta \\ r = 4 \sin \theta \end{cases}$

10. $\begin{cases} r = 4 \tan \theta \sin \theta \\ r = 4 \cos \theta \end{cases}$

11. $\begin{cases} r = 4(1 + \sin \theta) \\ r(1 - \sin \theta) = 3 \end{cases}$

12. $\begin{cases} r^2 \sin 2\theta = 8 \\ r \cos \theta = 2 \end{cases}$

In Exercises 13 and 14, the graph of the given equation intersects itself. Find the points at which this occurs.

13. $r = \sin \frac{3}{2}\theta$

14. $r = 1 + 2 \cos 2\theta$

(16.5)   Tangent lines of polar curves

In Sec. 16.2, we derived a formula for finding the slope of a tangent line to a polar curve whose equation is $r = f(\theta)$. If α is the inclination of the tangent line to the curve at (r,θ), we have

(1)
$$\tan \alpha = \frac{\tan \theta \ dr/d\theta + r}{dr/d\theta - r \tan \theta}$$

In most cases, formula (1) is complicated. We get a simpler formula if we consider the angle between the line OP and the tangent line. We call this angle χ, and χ is measured from the line OP counterclockwise to the tangent line, $0 \le \chi < \pi$.

There are two possible cases: $\alpha \ge \theta$ and $\alpha < \theta$. These two cases are illustrated in Figs. 16.5.1 and 16.5.2. In Fig. 16.5.1, $\alpha > \theta$ and $\chi = \alpha - \theta$. In Fig. 16.5.2, $\alpha < \theta$ and $\chi = \pi - (\theta - \alpha)$. In each case,

$$\tan \chi = \tan (\alpha - \theta)$$

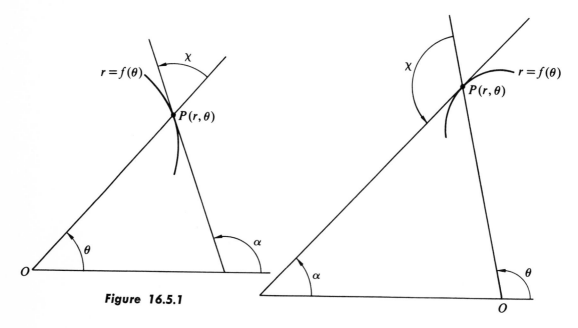

Figure 16.5.1

Figure 16.5.2

or, equivalently,

$$(2) \qquad \tan \chi = \frac{\tan \alpha - \tan \theta}{1 + \tan \alpha \tan \theta}$$

Substituting the value of $\tan \alpha$ from (1) in (2), we get

$$\tan \chi = \frac{(\tan \theta \, dr/d\theta + r)/(dr/d\theta - r \tan \theta) - \tan \theta}{1 + [(\tan \theta \, dr/d\theta + r)/(dr/d\theta - r \tan \theta)] (\tan \theta)}$$

$$= \frac{\tan \theta \, dr/d\theta + r - \tan \theta \, dr/d\theta + r \tan^2 \theta}{dr/d\theta - r \tan \theta + \tan^2 \theta \, dr/d\theta + r \tan \theta}$$

$$= \frac{r \, (1 + \tan^2 \theta)}{(1 + \tan^2 \theta) \, dr/d\theta}$$

or

$$(3) \qquad \tan \chi = \frac{r}{dr/d\theta}$$

Comparing formula (3) with formula (1), the reader can see why it is more desirable to consider the angle χ instead of the angle α when working with polar coodinates.

EXAMPLE 1: Find the angle χ for the cardioid $r = a + a \sin \theta$ at the point $(3a/2, \pi/6)$.

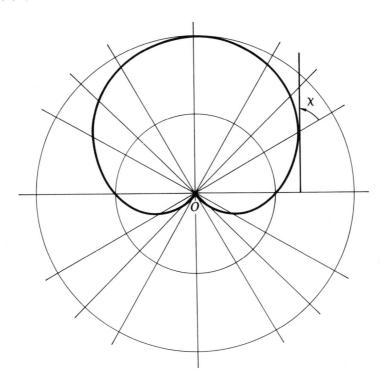

Figure 16.5.3

Solution: See Fig. 16.5.3. Since $r = a + a \sin \theta$, we have

$$\frac{dr}{d\theta} = a \cos \theta$$

So, applying (3), we get

$$\tan \chi = \frac{a + a \sin \theta}{a \cos \theta} = \frac{1 + \sin \theta}{\cos \theta}$$

Therefore, at the point $(3a/2, \pi/6)$,

$$\tan \chi = \frac{1 + \frac{1}{2}}{\sqrt{3}/2} = \frac{3}{\sqrt{3}} = \sqrt{3}$$

So $\chi = \dfrac{\pi}{3}$

EXAMPLE 2: Find the angle between the tangent lines to the curves $r = 3 \cos 2\theta$ and $r = 3 \sin 2\theta$ at the point $P(3\sqrt{2}/2, \pi/8)$.

Solution: Let χ_1 be the angle between the line OP and the tangent line to the curve $r = 3 \cos 2\theta$, and let χ_2 be the angle between the line OP and the tangent line to the curve $r = 3 \sin 2\theta$. The graph of each equation is a four-leafed rose (see Fig. 16.5.4).

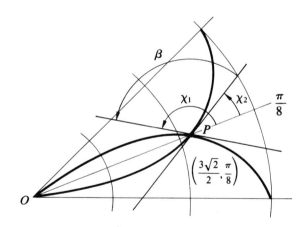

Figure 16.5.4

Let β be the angle between the tangent lines at $P(3\sqrt{2}/2, \pi/8)$.

$$\beta = \chi_1 - \chi_2$$

So $\tan \beta = \tan (\chi_1 - \chi_2)$

or, equivalently,

(4) $$\tan \beta = \frac{\tan \chi_1 - \tan \chi_2}{1 + \tan \chi_1 \tan \chi_2}$$

We find $\tan \chi_1$ and $\tan \chi_2$ from formula (3). For $\tan \chi_1$, $r = 3 \cos 2\theta$ and $dr/d\theta = -6 \sin 2\theta$. So

$$\tan \chi_1 = \frac{3 \cos 2\theta}{-6 \sin 2\theta} = -\frac{1}{2} \cot 2\theta$$

When $\theta = \pi/8$, $\tan \chi_1 = (-1/2) \cot (\pi/4) = -1/2$.

For $\tan \chi_2$, $r = 3 \sin 2\theta$ and $\dfrac{dr}{d\theta} = 6 \cos 2\theta$.

$$\text{So} \quad \tan \chi_2 = \frac{3 \sin 2\theta}{6 \cos 2\theta} = \frac{1}{2} \tan 2\theta$$

When $\theta = \pi/8$, $\tan \chi_2 = (1/2) \tan (\pi/4) = 1/2$.

Substituting $\tan \chi_1 = -1/2$ and $\tan \chi_2 = 1/2$ in (4), we obtain

$$\tan \beta = \frac{-1/2 - 1/2}{1 + (-1/2)(1/2)} = \frac{-1}{1 - 1/4} = -\frac{4}{3}$$

The measure of angle β to the nearest 10 min is $126°50'$. So the acute angle between the two tangent lines is $180° - 126°50' = 53°10'$.

Exercises 16.5

In Exercises 1 through 8, find the angle χ at the point indicated.

1. $r\theta = a$; $(a,1)$

2. $r = a\theta$; $\left(\dfrac{5\pi}{2}a, \dfrac{5\pi}{2}\right)$

3. $r = a \sec 2\theta$; $\left(\sqrt{2}a, -\dfrac{\pi}{8}\right)$

4. $r = a \sin \dfrac{1}{2}\theta$; $\left(\dfrac{a}{2}, \dfrac{\pi}{3}\right)$

5. $r = \theta^2$; $\left(\dfrac{\pi^2}{4}, \dfrac{\pi}{2}\right)$

6. $r = a \cos 2\theta$; $\left(\dfrac{\sqrt{3}}{2}a, \dfrac{\pi}{12}\right)$

7. $r^2 = a^2 \cos 2\theta$; $\left(\dfrac{a}{\sqrt{2}}, \dfrac{\pi}{6}\right)$

8. $r = a(1 - \sin \theta)$; (a,π)

In Exercises 9 through 12, find the angle between the tangent lines of the given pair of curves at the indicated point of intersection.

9. $\begin{cases} r = a \cos \theta \\ r = a \sin \theta \end{cases}$ $\left(\dfrac{\sqrt{2}}{2}a, \dfrac{\pi}{4}\right)$

10. $\begin{cases} r = a \\ r = 2a \sin \theta \end{cases}$ $\left(a, \dfrac{\pi}{6}\right)$

11. $\begin{cases} r = 4 \cos \theta \\ r = 4 \cos^2 \theta - 3 \end{cases}$ $\left(-2, \dfrac{2\pi}{3}\right)$

12. $\begin{cases} r = -a \sin \theta \\ r = a \cos 2\theta \end{cases}$ the pole

In Exercises 13 through 16, find the angle between the tangent lines of the given pair of curves at all points of intersection.

13. $\begin{cases} r = 1 - \sin\theta \\ r = 1 + \sin\theta \end{cases}$

15. $\begin{cases} r = \cos\theta \\ r = \sin 2\theta \end{cases}$

14. $\begin{cases} r = 3\cos\theta \\ r = 1 + \cos\theta \end{cases}$

16. $\begin{cases} r = 2\sec\theta \\ r = \csc^2(\theta/2) \end{cases}$

17. Prove that $\tan\chi = \tan\frac{1}{2}\theta$ at all points of the cardioid $r = 2(1 - \cos\theta)$.

18. Prove that at each point of the logarithmic spiral $r = be^{a\theta}$, χ is the same.

19. Prove that the graphs of $r = a\theta$ and $r\theta = a$ have infinitely many points of intersection. Also prove that the tangent lines are perpendicular at only two of these points of intersection, and find these points.

20. Prove that at the points of intersection of the two curves $r = a\sec^2(\theta/2)$ and $r = b\csc^2(\theta/2)$, their tangent lines are perpendicular.

(16.6)   Area of a region in polar coordinates

In this section we shall develop a method for finding the area of a region bounded by a curve whose equation is given in polar coordinates and by two lines through the pole.

Let the function f be continuous and nonnegative on the closed interval $[\alpha,\beta]$ and let R be the region bounded by the curve whose equation is $r = f(\theta)$ and by the lines $\theta = \alpha$ and $\theta = \beta$. The region R then is the region AOB shown in Fig. 16.6.1.

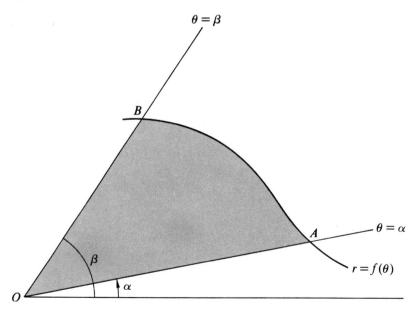

Figure 16.6.1

Let us consider a partition Δ of $[\alpha,\beta]$ defined by $\alpha = \theta_0 < \theta_1 < \theta_2 < \cdots < \theta_{i-1} < \theta_i < \cdots < \theta_{n-1} < \theta_n = \beta$.

Therefore, we have n subintervals of the form $[\theta_{i-1}, \theta_i]$, where $i = 1, 2, \ldots, n$. Let ξ_i be a value of θ in the ith subinterval $[\theta_{i-1}, \theta_i]$. See Fig. 16.6.2 where the ith subinterval is shown together with $\theta = \xi_i$. The angle between the lines $\theta =$

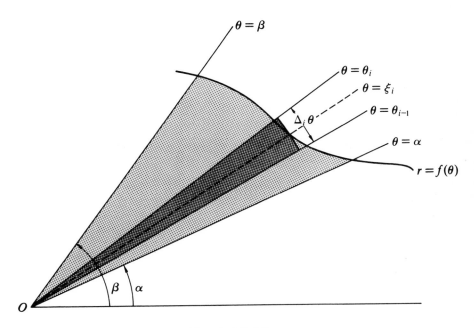

Figure 16.6.2

θ_{i-1} and $\theta = \theta_i$ we denote by $\Delta_i\theta$. The area of the circular sector of radius $f(\xi_i)$ and central angle $\Delta_i\theta$ is given by

$$\tfrac{1}{2}[f(\xi_i)]^2 \, \Delta_i\theta$$

For each of the n subintervals, we have such a circular sector, and the sum of the areas of these n circular sectors is

$$\tfrac{1}{2}[f(\xi_1)]^2 \, \Delta_1\theta + \tfrac{1}{2}[f(\xi_2)]^2 \, \Delta_2\theta + \tfrac{1}{2}[f(\xi_3)]^2 \, \Delta_3\theta + \cdots$$
$$+ \tfrac{1}{2}[f(\xi_i)]^2 \, \Delta_i\theta + \cdots + \tfrac{1}{2}[f(\xi_n)]^2 \, \Delta_n\theta$$

which may be written, using sigma notation, as

$$\sum_{i=1}^{n} \tfrac{1}{2}[f(\xi_i)]^2 \, \Delta_i\theta$$

Let $\|\Delta\|$ be the norm of the partition Δ, that is, $\|\Delta\|$ is the measure of the largest $\Delta_i\theta$. Then if we let A be the number which is to be the area of the region R, we define

$$(1) \qquad\qquad A = \lim_{\|\Delta\| \to 0} \sum_{i=1}^{n} \tfrac{1}{2}[f(\xi_i)]^2 \, \Delta_i\theta$$

The limit in (1) is a definite integral, and we have

(2) $$A = \tfrac{1}{2} \int_{\alpha}^{\beta} [f(\theta)]^2 \, d\theta$$

EXAMPLE 1: Find the area of the region bounded by the graph of $r = 2 + 2 \cos \theta$.

The region together with an element of area is shown in Fig. 16.6.3. Since the curve is symmetric with respect to the polar axis, we shall take the θ limits from 0 to π which will give us the area of the region bounded by the curve above the polar axis. The area of the entire region then will be obtained by multiplying that area by 2. So we have

$$A = 2 \lim_{\|\Delta\| \to 0} \sum_{i=1}^{n} \tfrac{1}{2}[f(\xi_i)]^2 \, \Delta_i\theta$$

$$= 2 \cdot \tfrac{1}{2} \int_{0}^{\pi} [f(\theta)]^2 \, d\theta = \int_{0}^{\pi} (2 + 2 \cos \theta)^2 \, d\theta$$

$$= 4 \int_{0}^{\pi} (1 + 2 \cos \theta + \cos^2 \theta) \, d\theta = 4\left[\theta + 2 \sin \theta + \frac{\theta}{2} + \frac{\sin 2\theta}{4} \right]_{0}^{\pi}$$

$$= 4\left(\pi + 0 + \frac{\pi}{2} + 0 - 0 \right) = 4\left(\frac{3\pi}{2} \right) = 6\pi$$

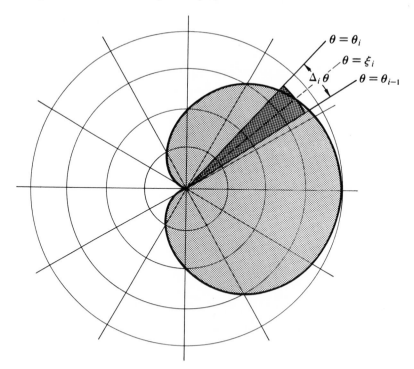

Figure 16.6.3

EXAMPLE 2: Find the area of the region inside the circle $r = 3 \sin \theta$ and outside the limaçon $r = 2 - \sin \theta$.

Solution: To find the points of intersection, we set

$$3 \sin \theta = 2 - \sin \theta$$

$$\sin \theta = \frac{1}{2}$$

So $\theta = \dfrac{\pi}{6}$ and $\dfrac{5\pi}{6}$

The curves are sketched and the region is shown together with an element of area in Fig. 16.6.4.

If we let $f(\theta) = 3 \sin \theta$ and $g(\theta) = 2 - \sin \theta$, then the equation of the circle is $r = f(\theta)$ and the equation of the limaçon is $r = g(\theta)$.

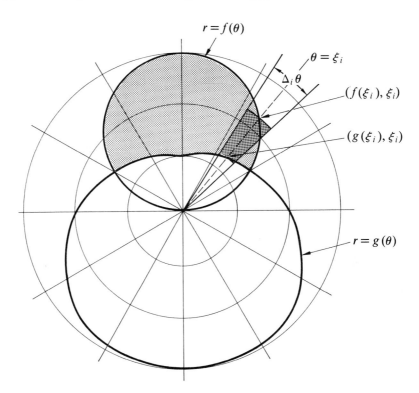

Figure 16.6.4

The area of the element of area is given by the difference of the areas of two circular sectors.

$$\tfrac{1}{2}[f(\xi_i)]^2 \, \Delta_i\theta - \tfrac{1}{2}[g(\xi_i)]^2 \, \Delta_i\theta = \tfrac{1}{2}([f(\xi_i)]^2 - [g(\xi_i)]^2) \, \Delta_i\theta$$

The sum of the areas of n such elements is given by

$$\sum_{i=1}^{n} \tfrac{1}{2}([f(\xi_i)]^2 - [g(\xi_i)]^2) \, \Delta_i\theta$$

So, if A is the area of the region desired, we have

$$A = \lim_{||\Delta|| \to 0} \sum_{i=1}^{n} \tfrac{1}{2}([f(\xi_i)]^2 - [g(\xi_i)]^2)\, \Delta_i\theta$$

This limit is a definite integral. Instead of taking the limits $\pi/6$ to $5\pi/6$, we shall use the property of symmetry with respect to the $\pi/2$ axis and take the limits from $\pi/6$ to $\pi/2$ and multiply by 2. So we have

$$A = 2 \cdot \frac{1}{2} \int_{\pi/6}^{\pi/2} ([f(\theta)]^2 - [g(\theta)]^2)\, d\theta$$

$$= \int_{\pi/6}^{\pi/2} [9 \sin^2 \theta - (2 - \sin \theta)^2]\, d\theta$$

$$= 10 \int_{\pi/6}^{\pi/2} \sin^2 \theta\, d\theta + 4 \int_{\pi/6}^{\pi/2} \sin \theta\, d\theta - 4 \int_{\pi/6}^{\pi/2} d\theta$$

$$= \frac{10}{2} \int_{\pi/6}^{\pi/2} (1 - \cos 2\theta)\, d\theta + \left[-4 \cos \theta - 4\theta \right]_{\pi/6}^{\pi/2}$$

$$= 5\theta - \frac{5}{2} \sin 2\theta - 4 \cos \theta - 4\theta \Big]_{\pi/6}^{\pi/2}$$

$$= \theta - \frac{5}{2} \sin 2\theta - 4 \cos \theta \Big]_{\pi/6}^{\pi/2}$$

$$= \left(\frac{\pi}{2} - \frac{5}{2} \sin \pi - 4 \cos \frac{\pi}{2} \right) - \left(\frac{\pi}{6} - \frac{5}{2} \sin \frac{\pi}{3} - 4 \cos \frac{\pi}{6} \right)$$

$$= \frac{\pi}{2} - \frac{\pi}{6} + \frac{5}{2} \cdot \frac{\sqrt{3}}{2} + 4 \cdot \frac{\sqrt{3}}{2}$$

$$= \frac{\pi}{3} + \frac{13}{4} \cdot \sqrt{3}$$

Exercises 16.6

In Exercises 1 through 6, find the area of the region enclosed by the graph of the given equation.

1. $r = 3 \cos \theta$

2. $r = 2 - \sin \theta$

3. $r = 4 \cos 3\theta$

4. $r = 4 \sin^2 \dfrac{\theta}{2}$

5. $r^2 = 4 \sin 2\theta$

6. $r = 4 \sin^2 \theta \cos \theta$

In Exercises 7 through 10, find the area of the region bounded by one loop of the graph of the given equation.

7. $r = 3 \cos 2\theta$

8. $r = a \sin 3\theta$

9. $r = 1 + 3 \sin \theta$

10. $r = a(1 - 2 \cos \theta)$

In Exercises 11 through 14, find the area of the region which is enclosed by both of the graphs of the two given equations.

11. $\begin{cases} r = 2 \\ r = 3 - 2 \cos \theta \end{cases}$

13. $\begin{cases} r = 3 \sin 2\theta \\ r = 3 \cos 2\theta \end{cases}$

12. $\begin{cases} r = 4 \sin \theta \\ r = 4 \cos \theta \end{cases}$

14. $\begin{cases} r^2 = 2 \cos 2\theta \\ r = 1 \end{cases}$

In Exercises 15 through 18, find the area of the region which is inside the graph of the first equation and outside the graph of the second equation.

15. $\begin{cases} r = a \\ r = a(1 - \cos \theta) \end{cases}$

17. $\begin{cases} r = 2 \sin \theta \\ r = \sin \theta + \cos \theta \end{cases}$

16. $\begin{cases} r = 2a \sin \theta \\ r = a \end{cases}$

18. $\begin{cases} r^2 = 4 \sin 2\theta \\ r = \sqrt{2} \end{cases}$

19. The face of a bow tie is the region enclosed by the graph of the equation $r^2 = 4 \cos 2\theta$. How much material is necessary to cover the face of the tie?

20. Find the area of the region swept out by the radius vector of the spiral $r = a\theta$ during its second revolution that was not swept out during its first revolution.

17 The conic sections

(17.1) Some properties of conics

In Sec. 2.9 we stated that a *conic section* (or *conic*) is a curve of intersection of a plane with a right-circular cone of two nappes, and three types of curves of intersection that occur are the *parabola*, the *ellipse*, and the *hyperbola*. The Greek mathematician Apollonius studied conic sections geometrically by this concept. We studied the parabola in Sec. 2.9, where we gave an analytic definition (2.9.1) of a parabola. In this chapter, we shall give an analytic definition of a conic section, and as special cases of this definition, we shall obtain the three types of curves.

In considering conic sections geometrically, a cone is thought of as having two nappes, extending indefinitely far in both directions. A portion of a right-circular cone of two nappes is shown in Fig. 17.1.1. A *generator* (or element) of the cone is a line lying in the cone, and all the generators of a cone contain the point V, called the *vertex* of the cone.

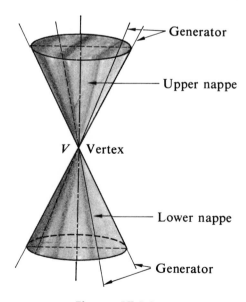

Figure 17.1.1

In Fig. 17.1.2 we have a cone and a cutting plane, which is parallel to one and only one generator of the cone. This conic is a *parabola*. If the cutting plane is parallel to two generators, it intersects both nappes of the cone, and a *hyperbola* is obtained. This is shown in Fig. 17.1.3. An *ellipse* is obtained if the cutting plane is parallel to no generator, in which case the cutting plane intersects each generator, as is shown in Fig. 17.1.4.

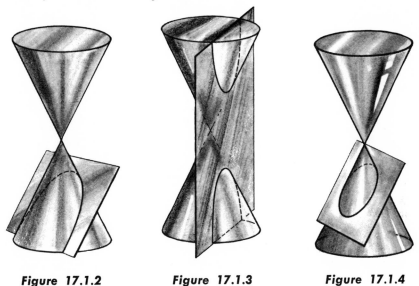

Figure 17.1.2   **Figure 17.1.3**   **Figure 17.1.4**

A special case of the ellipse is a *circle*, which is obtained if the cutting plane, which intersects each generator, is also perpendicular to the axis of the cone. Degenerate cases of the conic sections include a point, a straight line, and two intersecting straight lines. A point is obtained if the cutting plane contains the vertex of the cone but does not contain a generator. This is a degenerate ellipse. If the cutting plane contains the vertex of the cone and only one generator, then a straight line is obtained, and this is a degenerate parabola. A degenerate hyperbola is obtained when the cutting plane contains the vertex of the cone and two generators, giving us two intersecting straight lines.

There are many applications of conic sections to both pure and applied mathematics. We shall mention a few of them. The orbits of planets and satellites are ellipses. Ellipses are used in making machine gears. Arches of bridges are sometimes elliptical or parabolic in shape. The path of a projectile is a parabola if motion is considered to be in a plane and air resistance is neglected. Parabolas are used in the design of parabolic mirrors, searchlights, and automobile headlights. Hyperbolas are used in combat in "sound ranging" to locate the position of enemy guns by the sound of the firing of those guns. If a quantity varies inversely as another quantity, such as pressure and volume in Boyle's law for a perfect gas at a constant temperature, the graph is a hyperbola.

To discuss conics analytically, as plane curves, we first state a definition which gives a property common to all conics.

17.1.1 DEFINITION   A *conic* is the set of all points P in a plane such that the undirected distance of P from a fixed point is in a constant ratio to the undirected distance of P from a fixed line which does not contain the fixed point.

The constant ratio in the above definition is called the *eccentricity* of the conic and is denoted by e. e is a nonnegative number, since it is the ratio of two undirected distances. Actually for nondegenerate conics, $e > 0$. (We shall see later that when $e = 0$, we have a point.) If $e = 1$, we see by comparing Definitions 17.1.1 and 2.9.1 that the conic is a parabola. If $e < 1$, the conic is an ellipse, and if $e > 1$, the conic is a hyperbola.

The fixed point, referred to in Definition 17.1.1, is called a *focus* of the conic, and the fixed line is called the corresponding *directrix*. The plural of focus is *foci*, and the plural of directrix is *directrices*. We learned in Sec. 2.9 that a parabola has one focus and one directrix. We shall learn later that an ellipse and a hyperbola each have two foci and two directrices, with each focus corresponding to a particular directrix.

The line through a focus of a conic perpendicular to its directrix is called the *principal axis* of the conic, and the points of intersection of the conic and its principal axis are called the *vertices* of the conic. From our study of the parabola, we know that a parabola has one vertex. However, both the ellipse and the hyperbola have two vertices. This is proved in the following theorem.

17.1.2 THEOREM   If e is the eccentricity of a nondegenerate conic, then if $e \neq 1$, the conic has two vertices, and if $e = 1$, the conic has only one vertex.

Proof: Let F denote the focus of the conic and D denote the point of intersection of the directrix and the principal axis. Let d denote the undirected distance between the focus and its directrix. In Fig. 17.1.5, F is to the right of the directrix, and in Fig. 17.1.6, F is to the left of the directrix. Let V denote a vertex of the conic. We wish to show that if $e \neq 1$, there are two possible vertices V, and if $e = 1$, there is only one vertex V.

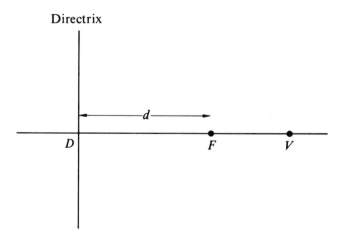

Figure 17.1.5

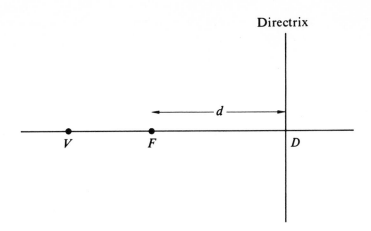

Figure 17.1.6

From Definition 17.1.1, we have

$$|\overline{FV}| = e|\overline{DV}|$$

Removing the absolute-value bars, we obtain

(1) $$\overline{FV} = \pm e(\overline{DV})$$

Since D, F, and V are all on the principal axis, we have

$$\overline{DV} = \overline{DF} + \overline{FV}$$

If F is to the right of D, $\overline{DF} = d$, and so we have from the above

(2) $$\overline{DV} = d + \overline{FV}$$

Substituting (1) in (2), we obtain

$$\overline{DV} = d \pm e(\overline{DV})$$

from which we get

(3) $$\overline{DV} = \frac{d}{1 \pm e}$$

If $e = 1$, we must reject the minus sign in the above equation, since we would be dividing by zero. So, if $e \neq 1$, we obtain two points V, and if $e = 1$, we obtain only one point V.

If F is to the left of D, $\overline{DF} = -d$, and instead of (3), we get

$$\overline{DV} = \frac{-d}{1 \mp e}$$

from which the same conclusion follows. So the theorem is proved.

A point on the principal axis of an ellipse or a hyperbola which lies halfway between the two vertices is called the *center* of the conic. The ellipse and the hyperbola are called *central conics*, in contrast to the parabola which has no center, since it has only one vertex.

17.1.3 THEOREM   A conic is symmetric with respect to its principal axis.

The proof of this theorem is left for the reader (see Exercise 1 at the end of this section).

Exercises 17.1

1. Prove Theorem 17.1.3.

2. Find an equation whose graph consists of all points P in a plane such that the undirected distance of P from the point $(ae,0)$ is in a constant ratio e to the undirected distance of P from the line $x = a/e$. Let $a^2(1 - e^2) = \pm b^2$, and consider the three cases: $e = 1$, $e < 1$, and $e > 1$.

3. Solve Exercise 2 if the point is $(-ae,0)$ and the line is $x = -a/e$.

(17.2)   Polar equations of the conics

Fairly simple polar equations of conics are obtained by taking the pole at a focus and the polar axis and its extension along the principal axis. We shall first consider this situation when the directrix corresponding to the focus at the pole is to the left of the focus. Let D be the point of intersection of this directrix with the principal axis, and let d denote the undirected distance between a focus and its directrix (refer to Fig. 17.2.1). Let $P(r,\theta)$ be any point on the conic to the right of the directrix and on the terminal side of θ, and draw

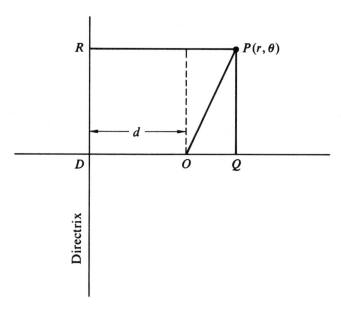

Figure 17.2.1

perpendiculars PQ and PR to the principal axis and the directrix, respectively. By Definition 17.1.1, the point P is on the conic if and only if

(1) $$|\overline{OP}| = e|\overline{RP}|$$

Since P is to the right of the directrix, $\overline{RP} > 0$, and so $|\overline{RP}| = \overline{RP}$. $|\overline{OP}| = r$, because $r > 0$ since P is on the terminal side of θ. So from (1) we have

(2) $$r = e(\overline{RP})$$

However, $\overline{RP} = \overline{DQ} = \overline{DO} + \overline{OQ} = d + r\cos\theta$. Substituting this expression for $\overline{RP}$ in (2), we get

$$r = e(d + r\cos\theta)$$

from which we obtain

(3) $$r = \frac{ed}{1 - e\cos\theta}$$

In a similar manner, we may derive an equation of a conic if the directrix corresponding to the focus at the pole is to the right of the focus, and we obtain

(4) $$r = \frac{ed}{1 + e\cos\theta}$$

The derivation of (4) is left for the reader (see Exercise 1 at the end of this section).

If a focus of a conic is at the pole and the polar axis is parallel to the corresponding directrix, then the $\pi/2$ axis and its extension are along the principal axis, and we obtain the following equation:

(5) $$r = \frac{ed}{1 \pm e\sin\theta}$$

where e and d are, respectively, the eccentricity and the undirected distance between the focus and the corresponding directrix. The positive sign is taken when the directrix corresponding to the focus at the pole is above the focus, and the negative sign is taken when it is below the focus. The derivation of equations (5) is left for the reader (see Exercises 2 and 3 at the end of this section).

We shall now discuss the graph of equation (3) for each of the three cases: $e = 1$, $e < 1$, and $e > 1$.

Case 1: $e = 1$. The conic is a parabola.

Equation (3) becomes

(6) $$r = \frac{d}{1 - \cos\theta}$$

r is not defined when $\theta = 0$; however, r is defined for all other values of θ for which $0 < \theta < 2\pi$. Differentiating (6), we obtain

$$D_\theta r = \frac{-d\sin\theta}{(1 - \cos\theta)^2}$$

Setting $D_\theta r = 0$, for values of θ in the interval $(0,2\pi)$ we obtain $\theta = \pi$. Since when $0 < \theta < \pi$, $D_\theta r < 0$, and when $\pi < \theta < 2\pi$, $D_\theta r > 0$, r has an absolute minimum value at $\theta = \pi$.

By Theorem 17.1.3, the parabola is symmetric with respect to its principal axis, and by Theorem 17.1.2, there is one vertex. When $\theta = \pi$, $r = d/2$, and so the point $(d/2,\pi)$ is the vertex. We note that the curve does not contain the pole, since there is no value of θ which will give a value of 0 for r. A sketch of the parabola is shown in Fig. 17.2.2.

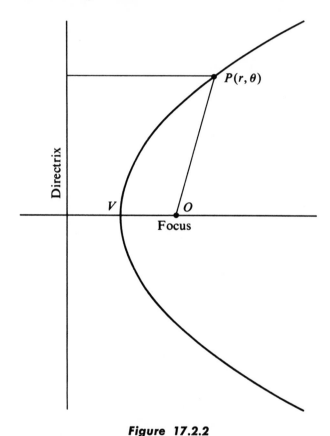

Figure 17.2.2

Case 2: $e < 1$. The conic is an ellipse.

When $e < 1$, the denominator of (3) is never zero, and so r exists for all values of θ. To find the absolute extrema of r on the interval $[0,2\pi)$, we find $D_\theta r$, and we obtain

(7) $$D_\theta r = \frac{-e^2 d \sin \theta}{(1 - e \cos \theta)^2}$$

For θ in the interval $[0,2\pi)$, $D_\theta r = 0$ when $\theta = 0$ and π. r has an absolute maximum value of $ed/(1 - e)$ when $\theta = 0$ and an absolute minimum value of $ed/(1 + e)$ when $\theta = \pi$. The points $(ed(1 - e), 0)$ and $(ed/(1 + e), \pi)$ are the vertices of the ellipse, and we shall denote them by V_1 and V_2, respectively.

The ellipse is symmetric with respect to its principal axis, by Theorem 17.1.3. There is no value of θ which will give a value of 0 for r, and so the curve does not contain the pole. A sketch of the ellipse is shown in Fig. 17.2.3.

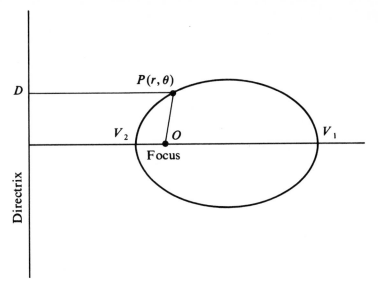

Figure 17.2.3

Case 3: $e > 1$. The conic is a hyperbola.

In the derivation of equation (3), we assumed that the point P on the conic is to the right of the given directrix and that P is on the terminal side of θ, making r positive. In the previous two cases, when the conic is an ellipse or a parabola, we obtain the entire curve with these assumptions. However, in this case, when $e > 1$, we obtain only one branch of a hyperbola, and this branch is to the right of the directrix. There is also a branch to the left of the given directrix, and this is obtained by letting r assume negative values as well as positive values, as θ takes on values in the interval $[0,2\pi)$.

When $e > 1$ in equation (3), r is undefined when $\cos \theta = 1/e$. There are two values of θ in $[0,2\pi)$ which satisfy this equation, and they are

$$\theta_1 = \cos^{-1} \frac{1}{e} \qquad \text{and} \qquad \theta_2 = 2\pi - \cos^{-1} \frac{1}{e}$$

Let us investigate the values of r as θ increases from 0 to θ_1. When $\theta = 0$, $r = ed/(1 - e)$, and since $e > 1$, $r < 0$. So the point $(ed/(1 - e), 0)$ is the left vertex of the hyperbola. For values of θ in the interval $(0,\theta_1)$, $r < 0$. r is undefined when $\theta = \theta_1$; however,

$$\lim_{\theta \to \theta_1^-} r = \lim_{\theta \to \theta_1^-} \frac{ed}{1 - e \cos \theta} = -\infty$$

We conclude then that as θ increases from 0 to θ_1, $|r|$ increases without bound. For values of θ in the interval $[0,\theta_1)$, we obtain the lower half of the left branch.

We shall show later that the hyperbola has two asymptotes. For this hyperbola, one of the asymptotes is parallel to the line $\theta = \theta_1$.

Now let us consider the points on the hyperbola as θ increases through values between θ_1 and θ_2. For θ in the interval (θ_1,θ_2), $r > 0$. When $\theta = \pi$, $r = ed/(1 + e)$. The point $(ed/(1 + e), 0)$ is then the right vertex of the hyperbola.

$$\lim_{\theta \to \theta_1^+} r = +\infty \qquad \text{and} \qquad \lim_{\theta \to \theta_2^-} r = +\infty$$

For values of θ in the interval (θ_1,θ_2), we obtain the entire right branch of the hyperbola from the top half to the lower half. The other asymptote of the hyperbola is parallel to the line $\theta = \theta_2$.

As θ increases through values between θ_2 and 2π, $r < 0$.

$$\lim_{\theta \to \theta_2^+} r = -\infty$$

For values of θ in the interval $(\theta_2,2\pi)$, we obtain the upper half of the left branch, and the curve is complete.

The asymptotes of a hyperbola intersect at the center of the hyperbola. This will be shown later. A sketch of the hyperbola is shown in Fig. 17.2.4.

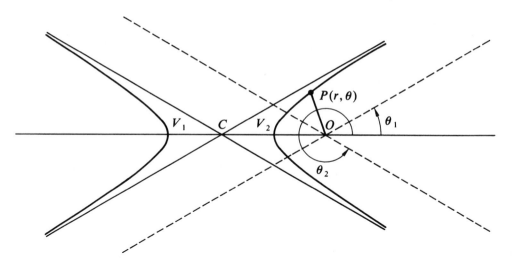

Figure 17.2.4

EXAMPLE 1: Given the equation of a conic, $r = 5/(3 - 2 \cos \theta)$, (a) find the eccentricity; (b) write an equation of the directrix; (c) identify the conic and draw a sketch of the curve.

Solution: We write the given equation in the form:

$$r = \frac{5/3}{1 - (2/3) \cos \theta}$$

which is of the form of equation (3). $e = 2/3 < 1$, and so the conic is an ellipse. Since $ed = 5/3$, $d = 5/3 \div 2/3 = 5/2$. Since the directrix is to the left of the

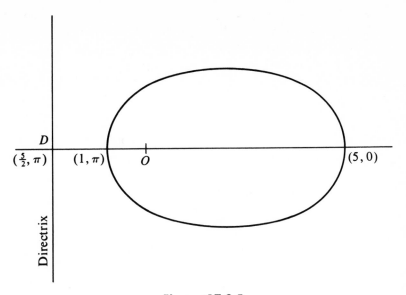

Figure 17.2.5

pole, an equation is $r \cos \theta = -5/2$. A sketch of the curve is shown in Fig. 17.2.5.

EXAMPLE 2: Find a polar equation of the conic having the line $r \sin \theta = 4$ as the directrix corresponding to a focus at the pole, and $e = 3/2$.

Solution: The given directrix is perpendicular to the $\pi/2$ axis and is four units above the pole. Therefore an equation of the conic is of the form

$$r = \frac{ed}{1 + e \sin \theta}$$

Since $d = 4$ and $e = 3/2$, the equation becomes

$$r = \frac{(3/2)4}{1 + (3/2) \sin \theta}$$

$$\text{or} \qquad r = \frac{12}{2 + 3 \sin \theta}$$

Exercises 17.2

1. Show that an equation of a conic having its principal axis along the polar axis and its extension, a focus at the pole, and the corresponding directrix to the right of the focus is $r = ed/(1 + e \cos \theta)$.

2. Show that an equation of a conic having its principal axis along the $\pi/2$ axis and its extension, a focus at the pole, and the corresponding directrix above the focus is $r = ed/(1 + e \sin \theta)$.

3. Show that an equation of a conic having its principal axis along the $\pi/2$ axis and its extension, a focus at the pole, and the corresponding directrix below the focus is $r = ed/(1 - e \sin \theta)$.

4. Show that the equation $r = k \csc^2 (\theta/2)$, where k is a constant, is a polar equation of a parabola.

In Exercises 5 through 14, the equation is that of a conic having a focus at the pole. In each Exercise, (a) find the eccentricity; (b) identify the conic; (c) write an equation of the directrix which corresponds to the focus at the pole; (d) draw a sketch of the curve.

5. $r = \dfrac{2}{1 - \cos \theta}$

6. $r = \dfrac{4}{1 + \cos \theta}$

7. $r = \dfrac{5}{2 + \sin \theta}$

8. $r = \dfrac{4}{1 - 3 \cos \theta}$

9. $r = \dfrac{6}{3 - 2 \cos \theta}$

10. $r = \dfrac{1}{2 + \sin \theta}$

11. $r = \dfrac{9}{5 - 6 \sin \theta}$

12. $r = \dfrac{1}{1 - 2 \sin \theta}$

13. $r = \dfrac{10}{7 - 2 \sin \theta}$

14. $r = \dfrac{7}{3 + 4 \cos \theta}$

In Exercises 15 through 19, find an equation of the conic having a focus at the pole and satisfying the given conditions.

15. Parabola; vertex at the point $(4,3\pi/2)$.

16. Hyperbola; $e = 4/3$; $r \cos \theta = 9$ is the directrix corresponding to the focus at the pole.

17. Hyperbola; vertices at $(1,\pi/2)$ and $(3,\pi/2)$.

18. Parabola; vertex on the polar axis; directrix to the left of the focus; containing the point $(2,\pi/3)$.

19. Ellipse; $e = \frac{1}{2}$; a vertex at $(4,\pi)$.

20. Find the area of the region enclosed by the two parabolas: $r = 2/(1 - \cos \theta)$ and $r = 2/(1 + \cos \theta)$.

21. Find the area of the region inside the ellipse $r = 6/(2 - \sin \theta)$ and above the parabola $r = 3/(1 + \sin \theta)$.

22. For the ellipse and the parabola of Exercise 21, find the area of the region inside the ellipse and below the parabola.

23. A focal chord of a conic is a line segment passing through a focus and having its end points on the conic. Prove that if two focal chords of a parabola are perpendicular, the sum of the reciprocals of their lengths is a constant.

24. A focal chord of a conic is divided into two segments by the focus. Prove that the sum of the reciprocals of the lengths of the two segments is the same, regardless of what chord is taken.

25. Using Definition 17.1.1, find a polar equation of a central conic for which the center is at the pole, the principal axis is along the polar axis and its extension, and the distance from the pole to a directrix is a/e.

(17.3) Cartesian equations of the conics

In Sec. 17.2, we learned that a polar equation of a conic is

$$r = \frac{ed}{1 - e \cos \theta}$$

or, equivalently,

(1)
$$r = e(r \cos \theta + d)$$

We may obtain a cartesian representation of equation (1) by replacing r by $\pm\sqrt{x^2 + y^2}$ and $r \cos \theta$ by x. Making these substitutions, we get

$$\pm\sqrt{x^2 + y^2} = e(x + d)$$

Squaring both sides of the above equation, we obtain

$$x^2 + y^2 = e^2x^2 + 2e^2dx + e^2d^2$$

or, equivalently,

(2)
$$y^2 + x^2(1 - e^2) = 2e^2dx + e^2d^2$$

If $e = 1$, equation (2) becomes

(3)
$$y^2 = 2d\left(x + \frac{d}{2}\right)$$

Translating the origin to the point $(-d/2, 0)$, we replace x by $\bar{x} - d/2$ and y by $\bar{y}$, and equation (3) becomes

(4)
$$\bar{y}^2 = 2d\bar{x}$$

Equation (4) resembles equation (1) of Sec. 2.9.

$$y^2 = 4px$$

which is an equation of the parabola having focus at $(p,0)$ and directrix the line $x = -p$. Therefore, relative to the $\bar{x}$ and $\bar{y}$ axes, (4) is an equation of a parabola having focus at $(d/2, 0)$, which is the origin relative to the x and y axes. The parabola having its axis parallel to one of the coordinate axes was discussed in detail in Secs. 2.9 and 2.10.

If $e \neq 1$, we may divide both sides of equation (2) by $1 - e^2$, and we obtain

$$x^2 - \frac{2e^2d}{1 - e^2} x + \frac{1}{1 - e^2} y^2 = \frac{e^2d^2}{1 - e^2}$$

Completing the square for the terms involving x by adding $e^4d^2/(1 - e^2)^2$ to both sides of the above equation, we get

(5)
$$\left(x - \frac{e^2d}{1 - e^2}\right)^2 + \frac{1}{1 - e^2} y^2 = \frac{e^2d^2}{(1 - e^2)^2}$$

If the origin is translated to the point $(e^2d/(1 - e^2), 0)$, (5) becomes

$$\bar{x}^2 + \frac{1}{1 - e^2}\, \bar{y}^2 = \frac{e^2d^2}{(1 - e^2)^2}$$

or, equivalently,

(6)
$$\frac{\bar{x}^2}{e^2d^2/(1 - e^2)^2} + \frac{\bar{y}^2}{e^2d^2/(1 - e^2)} = 1$$

Now, let $e^2d^2/(1 - e^2)^2 = a^2$, where $a > 0$. Then

(7)
$$a = \begin{cases} \dfrac{ed}{1 - e^2} & \text{if } 0 < e < 1 \\[2mm] \dfrac{ed}{e^2 - 1} & \text{if } e > 1 \end{cases}$$

Equation (6) then may be written as

$$\frac{\bar{x}^2}{a^2} + \frac{\bar{y}^2}{a^2(1 - e^2)} = 1$$

Replacing $\bar{x}$ and $\bar{y}$ by x and y, we get

(8)
$$\frac{x^2}{a^2} + \frac{y^2}{a^2(1 - e^2)} = 1$$

Equation (8) is a standard form of a cartesian equation of a central conic having its principal axis on the x axis. Since (5) is an equation of a conic having a focus at the origin (pole), and (8) is obtained from (5) by translating the origin to the point $(e^2d/(1 - e^2), 0)$, it follows that the central conic having equation (8) has a focus at the point $(-e^2d/(1 - e^2), 0)$. However, from (7) it follows that

$$\frac{-e^2d}{1 - e^2} = \begin{cases} -ae & \text{if } 0 < e < 1 \\ ae & \text{if } e > 1 \end{cases}$$

Therefore, we may conclude that if (8) is an equation of an ellipse ($0 < e < 1$), there is a focus at the point $(-ae, 0)$, and if (8) is an equation of a hyperbola ($e > 1$), there is a focus at $(ae, 0)$, and in each case the corresponding directrix is d units to the left of the focus. So, if the graph of (8) is an ellipse, the directrix corresponding to the focus at $(-ae, 0)$ has as an equation

$$x = -ae - d$$

Since when $0 < e < 1$, $d = a(1 - e^2)/e$, this equation becomes

$$x = -ae - \frac{a(1 - e^2)}{e}$$

or $\quad x = -\dfrac{a}{e}$

Similarly, if the graph of (8) is a hyperbola, the directrix corresponding to the focus at $(ae, 0)$ has as an equation

$$x = ae - d$$

When $e > 1$, $d = a(e^2 - 1)/e$, and so the above equation of the directrix may be written as

$$x = \frac{a}{e}$$

So, we have shown that if (8) is an equation of an ellipse, a focus and its corresponding directrix are $(-ae,0)$ and $x = -a/e$; and if (8) is an equation of a hyperbola, a focus and its corresponding directrix are $(ae,0)$ and $x = a/e$.

Since equation (8) contains only even powers of x and y, its graph is symmetric with respect to both the x and y axes. Therefore, if there is a focus at $(-ae,0)$ having a corresponding directrix of $x = -a/e$, by symmetry there is also a focus at $(ae,0)$ having a corresponding directrix of $x = a/e$. Similarly for a focus at $(ae,0)$ and a corresponding directrix of $x = a/e$, there is also a focus at $(-ae,0)$ and a corresponding directrix of $x = -a/e$. These results are summarized in the following theorem.

17.3.1 THEOREM   The central conic having as an equation

(9)
$$\frac{x^2}{a^2} + \frac{y^2}{a^2(1 - e^2)} = 1$$

where $a > 0$, has a focus at $(-ae,0)$, whose corresponding directrix is $x = -a/e$, and a focus at $(ae,0)$, whose corresponding directrix is $x = a/e$.

Figures 17.3.1 and 17.3.3 show sketches of the graph of equation (9) together with the foci and directrices in the respective cases of an ellipse and a hyperbola.

Suppose that in equation (9) $0 < e < 1$. Then the conic is an ellipse. Since in this case, $1 - e^2 > 0$, we may conclude that $\sqrt{1 - e^2}$ is a real number. Therefore, we may let

(10)
$$b = a\sqrt{1 - e^2}$$

Since $a > 0$, it follows that $b > 0$. Substituting (10) in (9), we obtain

(11)
$$\frac{x^2}{a^2} + \frac{y^2}{b^2} = 1$$

Equation (11) is an equation of an ellipse having its principal axis on the x axis. Since the vertices are the points of intersection of the ellipse with its principal axis, they are $(-a,0)$ and $(a,0)$. The center of the ellipse is the origin, since it is the point midway between the vertices. Figure 17.3.1 shows a sketch of this ellipse. Refer to this figure as you read the next two paragraphs.

If we denote the vertices $(-a,0)$ and $(a,0)$ by A' and A, respectively, the segment $A'A$ of the principal axis is called the *major axis* of the ellipse, and its length is $2a$. a is then the length of the semimajor axis of the ellipse.

The ellipse having equation (11) intersects the y axis at the points $(-b,0)$ and $(b,0)$, which we shall denote by B' and B, respectively. The segment $B'B$ is

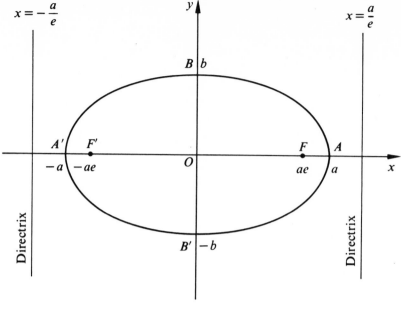

Figure 17.3.1

called the *minor axis* of the ellipse, and its length is $2b$. b is the length of the semiminor axis of the ellipse. Since a and b are positive numbers and $0 < e < 1$, it follows from (10) that $b < a$.

EXAMPLE 1: *Given:* the ellipse $x^2/25 + y^2/16 = 1$. *Find:* the vertices, foci, directrices, eccentricity, and extremities of the minor axis. Draw a sketch of the curve and show the foci and the directrices.

Solution: From the equation of the ellipse, we have $a^2 = 25$ and $b^2 = 16$, and so $a = 5$ and $b = 4$. Therefore, the vertices are the points $(-5,0)$ and $(5,0)$, and the extremities of the minor axis are the points $(0,-4)$ and $(0,4)$. From (10) we have $4 = 5\sqrt{1 - e^2}$, from which it follows that $e = 3/5$. We obtain the foci and the directrices by applying Theorem 17.3.1. Since $ae = 3$, and $a/e = 25/3$, we conclude that one focus and its corresponding directrix are $(3,0)$ and $x = 25/3$, and the other focus and its corresponding directrix are $(-3,0)$ and $x = -25/3$. A sketch of the ellipse, the foci F and F', and the directrices are shown in Fig. 17.3.2.

Let us now consider the central conic of Theorem 17.3.1 for the case when $e > 1$; that is, when the conic is a hyperbola. Since $e > 1$, $1 - e^2 < 0$, and so $e^2 - 1 > 0$. So, for a hyperbola, we let

(12) $$b = a\sqrt{e^2 - 1}$$

It follows from (12) that b is a positive number. Also from (12), if $1 < e < \sqrt{2}$, $b < a$; if $e = \sqrt{2}$, $b = a$; and if $e > \sqrt{2}$, $b > a$. Substituting (12) in (9), we get

(13) $$\frac{x^2}{a^2} - \frac{y^2}{b^2} = 1$$

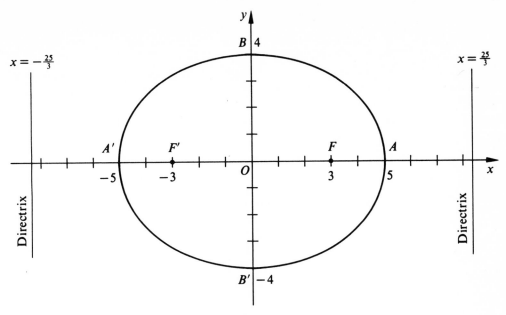

Figure 17.3.2

Equation (13) is an equation of a hyperbola having its principal axis on the x axis, its vertices the points $(-a,0)$ and $(a,0)$, and its center at the origin. A sketch of this hyperbola is shown in Fig. 17.3.3. If we denote the vertices $(-a,0)$

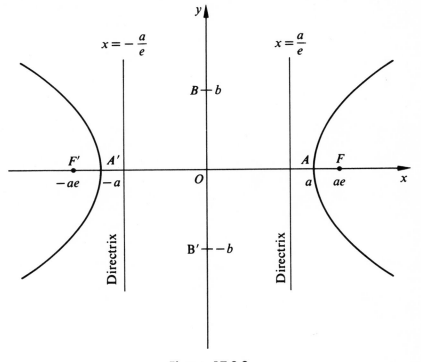

Figure 17.3.3

and $(a,0)$ by A' and A, the segment $A'A$ is called the transverse axis of the hyperbola. The length of the transverse axis is then $2a$, and so a is the length of the semitransverse axis.

If we substitute 0 for x in equation (13), we obtain $y^2 = -b^2$, which has no real roots. Consequently, the hyperbola does not intersect the y axis. However, the line segment having extremeties at the points $(0,-b)$ and $(0,b)$ is called the conjugate axis of the hyperbola, and its length is $2b$. b is then the length of the semiconjugate axis.

If we solve equation (13) for y in terms of x, we obtain

(14) $$y = \pm \frac{b}{a}\sqrt{x^2 - a^2}$$

We conclude from (14) that if $|x| < a$, there is no real value of y. Therefore there are no points (x,y) on the hyperbola for which $-a < x < a$. We also see from (14) that if $|x| \geq a$, then y has two real values. As we previously learned, the hyperbola has two branches. One branch contains the vertex $A(a,0)$ and extends indefinitely far to the right of A, and the other branch contains the vertex $A'(-a,0)$ and extends indefinitely far to the left of A'.

EXAMPLE 2: *Given:* the hyperbola: $x^2/9 - y^2/16 = 1$. *Find:* the vertices, foci, directrices, eccentricity, and the lengths of the transverse and conjugate axes. Draw a sketch of the hyperbola and show the foci and the directrices.

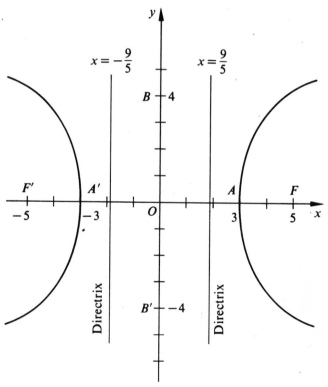

Figure 17.3.4

Solution: The given equation is of the form of equation (13), and so $a = 3$ and $b = 4$. The vertices are therefore the points $(-3,0)$ and $(3,0)$. The length of the transverse axis is $2a = 6$, and the length of the conjugate axis is $2b = 8$. Since from (12), $b = a\sqrt{e^2 - 1}$, we have $4 = 3\sqrt{e^2 - 1}$, and so $e = 5/3$. Therefore $ae = 5$ and $a/e = 9/5$. Hence the foci are $(-5,0)$ and $(5,0)$, and the corresponding directrices are, respectively, $x = -9/5$ and $x = 9/5$. A sketch of the hyperbola and the foci and directrices are shown in Fig. 17.3.4.

Exercises 17.3

In Exercises 1 through 4, find the vertices, foci, directrices, eccentricity, and extremities of the minor axis of the given ellipse. Draw a sketch of the curve and show the foci and the directrices.

1. $4x^2 + 9y^2 = 36$

2. $4x^2 + 9y^2 = 4$

3. $2x^2 + 3y^2 = 18$

4. $3x^2 + 4y^2 = 9$

In Exercises 5 through 9, find the vertices, foci, directrices, eccentricity, and lengths of the transverse and conjugate axes of the given hyperbola. Draw a sketch of the curve and show the foci and the directrices.

5. $9x^2 - 4y^2 = 36$

6. $x^2 - 9y^2 = 9$

7. $9x^2 - 16y^2 = 1$

8. $25x^2 - 25y^2 = 1$

In Exercises 9 through 14, find an equation of the given conic satisfying the given conditions and draw a sketch of the graph.

9. Hyperbola having vertices $(-2,0)$ and $(2,0)$ and a conjugate axis of length 6.
10. Ellipse having foci $(-5,0)$ and $(5,0)$ and one directrix the line $x = -20$.
11. Ellipse having vertices $(-5/2,0)$ and $(5/2,0)$ and one focus $(3/2,0)$.
12. Hyperbola having the ends of its conjugate axis $(0,-3)$ and $(0,3)$ and $e = 2$.
13. Hyperbola having its center at the origin, its foci on the x axis, and passing through the points $(4,-2)$ and $(7,-6)$.
14. Ellipse having its center at the origin, its foci on the x axis, the length of the semimajor axis equal to three times the length of the semiminor axis, and passing through the point $(3,3)$.

15. Find an equation of the tangent line to the ellipse $4x^2 + 9y^2 = 72$ at the point $(3,2)$.

16. Find an equation of the normal line to the hyperbola $4x^2 - 3y^2 = 24$ at the point $(3,2)$.

17. Find an equation of the hyperbola whose foci are the vertices of the ellipse $7x^2 + 11y^2 = 77$ and whose vertices are the foci of this ellipse.

18. Find an equation of the ellipse whose foci are the vertices of the hyperbola $11x^2 - 7y^2 = 77$ and whose vertices are the foci of this hyperbola.

19. An arch is in the form of a semiellipse, and it is 48 ft wide at the base and has a height of 20 ft. How wide is the arch at a height of 10 ft above the base?

20. Prove that there is no tangent line to the hyperbola $x^2 - y^2 = 1$ which passes through the origin.

21. An equilateral hyperbola is one for which the transverse axis and the conjugate axis have the same length. Prove that the eccentricity of an equilateral hyperbola is equal to $\sqrt{2}$.

22. A football is 16 in. long, and a plane section containing a seam is an ellipse, of which the length of the semiminor axis is 8 in. Find the volume of the football if the leather is so stiff that every cross section is a square.

23. Solve Exercise 22 if every cross section is a circle.

24. Find the volume of the solid of revolution generated by revolving the region bounded by the hyperbola $x^2/a^2 - y^2/b^2 = 1$ and the line $x = 2a$ about the x axis.

25. Find the volume of the solid of revolution generated if the region in Exercise 24 is revolved about the y axis.

26. Find the centroid of the solid of revolution of Exericse 24.

(17.4) The ellipse and the hyperbola

In the previous section we considered ellipses and hyperbolas having centers at the origin and principal axes on the x axis. We shall now consider more general equations of the central conics.

If an ellipse has its center at the origin and its principal axis on the y axis, then an equation of the ellipse is of the form

(1)
$$\frac{y^2}{a^2} + \frac{x^2}{b^2} = 1$$

which is obtained from equation (11) of Sec. 17.3 by interchanging x and y. Since, for an ellipse, $a > b$, it follows that the ellipse having the equation $x^2/16 + y^2/25 = 1$ has its foci on the y axis. This ellipse has the same shape as the ellipse of Example 1, Sec. 17.3. The vertices are $(0,-5)$ and $(0,5)$, and the foci are $(0,-3)$ and $(0,3)$, and their corresponding directrices are $y = -25/3$ and $y = 25/3$, respectively.

If the center of an ellipse is at the point (h,k) rather than at the origin and the principal axis is parallel to one of the coordinate axes, then by a translation of axes, so that the point (h,k) is the new origin, an equation of the ellipse is $\bar{x}^2/a^2 + \bar{y}^2/b^2 = 1$ if the principal axis is horizontal, and $\bar{y}^2/a^2 + \bar{x}^2/b^2 = 1$ if the principal axis is vertical. Since $\bar{x} = x - h$ and $\bar{y} = y - k$, these equations become the following in x and y:

(2)
$$\frac{(x - h)^2}{a^2} + \frac{(y - k)^2}{b^2} = 1$$

if the principal axis is horizontal, and

(3)
$$\frac{(y - k)^2}{a^2} + \frac{(x - h)^2}{b^2} = 1$$

if the principal axis is vertical.

In Sec. 2.8 we discussed the general equation of the second degree in two variables:

(4)
$$Ax^2 + Bxy + Cy^2 + Dx + Ey + F = 0$$

when $B = 0$ and $A = C$. In such a case, the graph of (4) is either a circle or a degenerate case of a circle, which is either a point-circle or no real locus. If we clear of fractions and combine terms in equations (2) and (3), we obtain an equation of the form

(5)
$$Ax^2 + Cy^2 + Dx + Ey + F = 0$$

where $A \neq C$, if $a \neq b$ and $AC > 0$. It can be shown by completing the squares in x and y that an equation of the form (5) can be put in the form

(6)
$$\frac{(x - h)^2}{1/A} + \frac{(y - k)^2}{1/C} = G$$

If $AC > 0$, then A and C are of the same sign. If G has the same sign as A and C, then equation (6) is of the form of (2) or (3) and so the graph of (5) is an ellipse. If G has a sign opposite to that of A and C, then (6) is not satisfied by any real values of x and y and hence the graph of (5) is no real locus. If $G = 0$, then (6) is satisfied by only the point (h,k) and so the graph of (5) is a single point, which we call a point-ellipse. In the case of a point-ellipse or no real locus, we say the graph is degenerate.

If $A = C$ in (5) we have either a circle or a degenerate circle, as mentioned above. A circle is a limiting form of an ellipse. This can be shown by considering the formula relating a, b, and e for an ellipse:

$$b^2 = a^2(1 - e^2)$$

From this formula, we see that as e approaches zero, b^2 approaches a^2. If $b^2 = a^2$, equations (2) and (3) become

$$(x - h)^2 + (y - k)^2 = a^2$$

which is an equation of a circle having center at (h,k) and radius a. We see that the results of Sec. 2.8 for a circle are the same as those obtained for equation (5) applied to an ellipse. We summarize these results in the following theorem.

17.4.1 THEOREM   If in the general second-degree equation (4), $B = 0$ and $AC > 0$, then the graph is either an ellipse, a point-ellipse, or no real locus. If in addition, $A = C$, then the graph is either a circle, a point-circle, or no real locus.

EXAMPLE 1: Determine the graph of the equation

$$25x^2 + 16y^2 + 150x - 128y - 1{,}119 = 0$$

Solution: From Theorem 17.4.1, since $B = 0$ and $AC > 0$, the graph is either an ellipse or is degenerate. Completing the squares in x and y, we get

$$25(x^2 + 6x + 9) + 16(y^2 - 8y + 16) = 1{,}119 + 225 + 256$$

or $\quad 25(x + 3)^2 + 16(y - 4)^2 = 1600$

or

(7) $$\frac{(x + 3)^2}{64} + \frac{(y - 4)^2}{100} = 1$$

Equation (7) is of the form of equation (3), and so the graph is an ellipse having its principal axis parallel to the y axis and its center at $(-3,4)$.

EXAMPLE 2: For the ellipse of Example 1, find the vertices, foci, directrices, eccentricity, and extremities of the minor axis.

Solution: From equation (7), we have $a = 10$ and $b = 8$. Since the center of the ellipse is at $(-3,4)$ and the principal axis is vertical, the vertices are the points $(-3,-6)$ and $(-3,14)$. The extremities of the minor axis are the points $(-11,4)$ and $(5,4)$. Since $b = a\sqrt{1 - e^2}$, we have

$$8 = 10\sqrt{1 - e^2}$$

and, solving for e, we get $e = 3/5$. Consequently, $ae = 6$ and $a/e = 50/3$. Therefore, the foci are the points $(-3,-2)$ and $(-3,10)$, and the corresponding directrices are, respectively, $y = -14/3$ and $y = 86/3$. 62/3

In Sec. 17.3 we learned that an equation of a hyperbola having its center at the origin and its principal axis on the x axis is of the form $x^2/a^2 - y^2/b^2 = 1$. Interchanging x and y in this equation, we obtain

(8) $$\frac{y^2}{a^2} - \frac{x^2}{b^2} = 1$$

which is an equation of a hyperbola having its center at the origin and its principal axis on the y axis. For example, the hyperbola, having as an equation $y^2/9 - x^2/16 = 1$, has its foci on the y axis since the equation is of the form (8). The reader should note that there is no general inequality involving a and b corresponding to the inequality $a > b$ for an ellipse. That is, for a hyperbola, it is possible to have $a < b$, as in the case of the example just mentioned where $a = 3$ and $b = 4$; or it is possible to have $a > b$, as in the case of the hyperbola having equation $y^2/25 - x^2/16 = 1$ where $a = 5$ and $b = 4$. If, for a hyperbola, $a = b$, then the hyperbola is said to be *equilateral*.

We learned in Sec. 17.2 that a hyperbola has asymptotes. We shall now show how to obtain equations of the asymptotes of a hyperbola. In Sec. 4.5 we defined horizontal and vertical asymptotes of the graph of a function. Following is a more general definition, of which the definitions in Sec. 4.5 are special cases.

17.4.2 DEFINITION   The graph of the equation $y = f(x)$ has the line $y = mx + b$ as an *asymptote* if either of the following statements is true:

(i) $\lim\limits_{x \to +\infty} [f(x) - (mx + b)] = 0$

(ii) $\lim\limits_{x \to -\infty} [f(x) - (mx + b)] = 0$

Statement (i) says that for any $\epsilon > 0$, there exists a number $N > 0$ such that

$$|f(x) - (mx + b)| < \epsilon \qquad \text{whenever} \qquad x > N$$

that is, we can make the function value $f(x)$ as close to the value of $mx + b$ as we please by taking x large enough. This is consistent with our intuitive notion of an asymptote of a graph. A similar statement may be made for part (ii) of Definition 17.4.2.

For the hyperbola $x^2/a^2 - y^2/b^2 = 1$, upon solving for y we get

$$y = \pm \frac{b}{a} \sqrt{x^2 - a^2}$$

So, if

$$f(x) = \frac{b}{a} \sqrt{x^2 - a^2}$$

we have

$$\lim\limits_{x \to +\infty} \left[f(x) - \frac{b}{a} x \right] = \lim\limits_{x \to +\infty} \left[\frac{b}{a} \sqrt{x^2 - a^2} - \frac{b}{a} x \right]$$

$$= \frac{b}{a} \lim\limits_{x \to +\infty} \frac{(\sqrt{x^2 - a^2} - x)(\sqrt{x^2 - a^2} + x)}{\sqrt{x^2 - a^2} + x}$$

$$= \frac{b}{a} \lim\limits_{x \to +\infty} \frac{-a^2}{\sqrt{x^2 - a^2} + x} = 0$$

Therefore, by Definition 17.4.2, we may conclude that the line $y = bx/a$ is an asymptote of the graph of $y = b\sqrt{x^2 - a^2}/a$. Similarly, we can show that the line $y = bx/a$ is an asymptote of the graph of $y = -b\sqrt{x^2 - a^2}/a$. Consequently, the line $y = bx/a$ is an asymptote of the hyperbola $x^2/a^2 - y^2/b^2 = 1$. In an analogous manner, we may show that the line $y = -bx/a$ is an asymptote of this same hyperbola. We have then the following theorem.

17.4.3 THEOREM   The lines

$$y = \frac{b}{a} x \qquad \text{and} \qquad y = -\frac{b}{a} x$$

are asymptotes of the hyperbola

$$\frac{x^2}{a^2} - \frac{y^2}{b^2} = 1$$

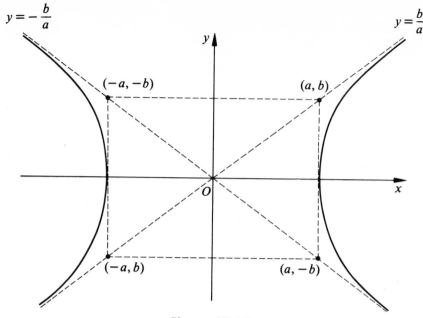

Figure 17.4.1

Figure 17.4.1 shows a sketch of the hyperbola of Theorem 17.4.3 together with its asymptotes. In the figure, the reader should note that the diagonals of the rectangle having vertices at (a,b), $(a,-b)$, $(-a,b)$ and $(-a,-b)$ are on the asymptotes of the hyperbola. This rectangle is called the *auxiliary rectangle* of the hyperbola. The vertices of the hyperbola are the points of intersection of the principal axis and the auxiliary rectangle. A fairly good sketch of a hyperbola may be made by first drawing the auxiliary rectangle and then drawing the branch of the hyperbola through each vertex tangent to the side of the auxiliary rectangle there and approaching asymptotically the lines on which the diagonals of the rectangle lie.

There is a mnemonic device for obtaining the equations of the asymptotes of a hyperbola. For example, for the hyperbola having equation $x^2/a^2 - y^2/b^2 = 1$, if the right-hand side is replaced by zero, we obtain $x^2/a^2 - y^2/b^2 = 0$, and upon factoring this equation becomes $(x/a - y/b)(x/a + y/b) = 0$, which is equivalent to the two equations $x/a - y/b = 0$ and $x/a + y/b = 0$, which, by Theorem 17.4.3, are equations of the asymptotes of the given hyperbola. Using this device for the hyperbola having equation (8), we see that the asymptotes are lines having equations $y/a - x/b = 0$ and $y/a + x/b = 0$, which are the same lines as the asymptotes of the hyperbola $x^2/b^2 - y^2/a^2 = 1$. These two hyperbolas are called *conjugate hyperbolas*.

The asymptotes of an equilateral hyperbola ($a = b$) are perpendicular to each other. The auxiliary rectangle for such a hyperbola is a square, and the transverse and conjugate axes have equal lengths.

If the center of a hyperbola is at (h,k) and its principal axis is parallel to the

x axis, then if we translate the axes so that the point (h,k) is the new origin, an equation of the hyperbola relative to this new coordinate system is

$$\frac{\bar{x}^2}{a^2} - \frac{\bar{y}^2}{b^2} = 1.$$

If we replace $\bar{x}$ by $x - h$ and $\bar{y}$ by $y - k$, this equation becomes

(9)
$$\frac{(x - h)^2}{a^2} - \frac{(y - k)^2}{b^2} = 1$$

Similarly, an equation of a hyperbola having center at (h,k) and principal axis parallel to the y axis is

(10)
$$\frac{(y - k)^2}{a^2} - \frac{(x - h)^2}{b^2} = 1$$

EXAMPLE 3: The vertices of a hyperbola are $(-5, -3)$ and $(-5, -1)$, and the eccentricity is $\sqrt{5}$. Find an equation of the hyperbola and equations of the asymptotes. Draw a sketch of the hyperbola and the asymptotes.

Solution: The distance between the vertices is $2a$, and so we get $a = 1$. For a hyperbola, $b = a\sqrt{e^2 - 1}$, and therefore $b = 1\sqrt{5 - 1} = 2$. Since the principal axis is parallel to the y axis, an equation of the hyperbola is of the form (10). The center (h,k) is halfway between the vertices and is therefore the point $(-5, -2)$. We have then as an equation of the hyperbola

$$\frac{(y + 2)^2}{1} - \frac{(x + 5)^2}{4} = 1$$

Using the mnemonic device to obtain equations of the asymptotes, we have

$$\left(\frac{y + 2}{1} - \frac{x + 5}{2}\right)\left(\frac{y + 2}{1} + \frac{x + 5}{2}\right) = 0$$

which gives us

$$y + 2 = \tfrac{1}{2}(x + 5) \qquad \text{and} \qquad y + 2 = -\tfrac{1}{2}(x + 5)$$

A sketch of the hyperbola and the asymptotes is shown in Fig. 17.4.2.

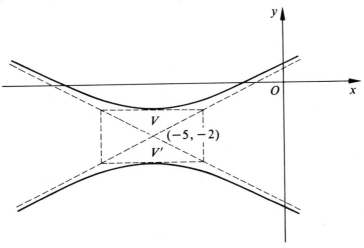

Figure 17.4.2

If in equations (9) and (10) we clear of fractions and combine terms, the resulting equations will be of the form (5) where A and C have different signs; that is, $AC < 0$. We now wish to show that the graph of an equation of the form (5), where $AC < 0$, is either a hyperbola or degenerates. Completing the squares in x and y in equation (5), where $AC < 0$, the resulting equation is of the form

(11) $$\alpha^2(x - h)^2 - \beta^2(y - k)^2 = H$$

If $H > 0$, equation (11) may be written as

$$\frac{(x - h)^2}{H/\alpha^2} - \frac{(y - k)^2}{H/\beta^2} = 1$$

which is of the form of equation (9). If $H < 0$, then (11) may be written as

$$\frac{(y - k)^2}{|H|/\alpha^2} - \frac{(x - h)^2}{|H|/\beta^2} = 1$$

which is of the form of equation (10). If $H = 0$, (11) is equivalent to the two equations

$$(x - h) - (y - k) = 0 \quad \text{and} \quad (x - h) + (y - k) = 0$$

which are equations of two straight lines through the point (h,k). This is the degenerate case of the hyperbola. We summarize these results in a theorem.

17.4.4 THEOREM   If in the general second-degree equation (4), $B = 0$ and $AC < 0$, then the graph is either a hyperbola or two intersecting straight lines.

We have discussed the graph of the general second-degree equation (4) when $B = 0$ for the cases $AC > 0$ and $AC < 0$. Now, if $AC = 0$, then either $A = 0$ or $C = 0$. We shall not consider both A and C equal to zero, in addition to $B = 0$, since then we would not have a quadratic equation. Suppose in (4), $B = 0$, $A = 0$, and $C \neq 0$. The equation becomes

(12) $$Cy^2 + Dx + Ey + F = 0$$

If $D \neq 0$, (12) is an equation of a parabola. If $D = 0$, then the graph of (12) may be two parallel lines, one line, or no real locus. For example, $4y^2 - 9 = 0$ is an equation of two parallel lines; $9y^2 + 6y + 1 = 0$ is an equation of one line; and $2y^2 + y + 1 = 0$ is satisfied by no real values of y. These are the degenerate cases of the parabola. A similar discussion holds if $B = 0$, $C = 0$, and $A \neq 0$. Again the results are summarized in a theorem.

17.4.5 THEOREM   If in the general second-degree equation (4), $B = 0$ and either $A = 0$ and $C \neq 0$ or $C = 0$ and $A \neq 0$, then the graph is one of the following: a parabola, two parallel lines, one line, or no real locus.

From Theorems 17.4.1, 17.4.4, and 17.4.5, we may conclude that the graph of the general quadratic equation in two unknowns when $B = 0$ is either a conic or a degenerate conic. We can also determine the type of conic from the product of A and C. We have the following theorem.

$q^2 \qquad \dfrac{100}{6} = 16$

17.4.6 THEOREM The graph of the equation $Ax^2 + Cy^2 + Dx + Ey + F = 0$, where not both A and C are zero, is either a conic or a degenerate conic; if it is a conic, then the graph is

    (i)   a *parabola* if either $A = 0$ or $C = 0$; that is, if $AC = 0$

    (ii) an *ellipse* if A and C have the same sign; that is, if $AC > 0$

    (iii) a *hyperbola* if A and C have opposite signs; that is, if $AC < 0$

A discussion of the graph of the general quadratic equation, when $B \neq 0$, is given in the next section.

We conclude this section with two theorems that give alternate definitions of each of the two central conics. The theorems are based on characteristic properties of the ellipse and the hyperbola.

17.4.7 THEOREM An ellipse may be defined as the set of points such that the sum of the distances from any point of the set to two given points (the foci) is a constant.

Proof: The proof consists of two parts. In the first part we shall show that the set of points defined in the theorem is an ellipse. In the second part we shall show that any ellipse is such a set of points. Refer to Fig. 17.4.3 in both parts of the proof.

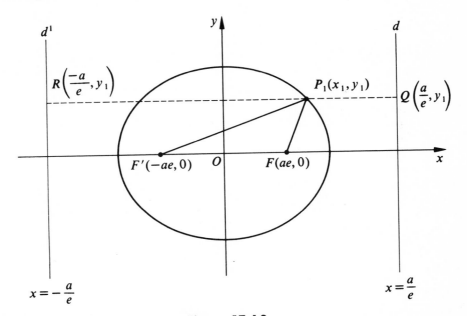

Figure 17.4.3

Let the point $P_1(x_1, y_1)$ be any point in the given set. Let the foci be the points $F'(-ae, 0)$ and $F(ae, 0)$, and let the constant sum of the distances be $2a$. Then

$$|\overline{FP_1}| + |\overline{F'P_1}| = 2a$$

Using the distance formula, we get

$$\sqrt{(x_1 - ae)^2 + y_1^2} + \sqrt{(x_1 + ae)^2 + y_1^2} = 2a$$

or

$$\sqrt{(x_1 - ae)^2 + y_1^2} = 2a - \sqrt{(x_1 + ae)^2 + y_1^2}$$

Squaring both sides of the above equation, we obtain

$$x_1^2 - 2aex_1 + a^2e^2 + y_1^2 = 4a^2 - 4a\sqrt{(x_1 + ae)^2 + y_1^2}$$
$$+ x_1^2 + 2aex_1 + a^2e^2 + y_1^2$$

or

$$\sqrt{(x_1 + ae)^2 + y_1^2} = a + ex_1$$

Squaring both sides again, we get

$$x_1^2 + 2aex_1 + a^2e^2 + y_1^2 = a^2 + 2aex_1 + e^2x_1^2$$

or

$$(1 - e^2)x_1^2 + y_1^2 = a^2(1 - e^2)$$

or

$$\frac{x_1^2}{a^2} + \frac{y_1^2}{a^2(1 - e^2)} = 1$$

Since $b^2 = a^2(1 - e^2)$ and replacing x_1 and y_1 by x and y, respectively, we obtain

$$\frac{x^2}{a^2} + \frac{y^2}{b^2} = 1$$

which is the required form of an equation of an ellipse.

Now consider the ellipse shown in Fig. 17.4.3; $P_1(x_1,y_1)$ is any point on the ellipse. Through P_1 draw a line parallel to the x axis and intersecting the directrices d and d' at the points Q and R, respectively. From Definition 17.1.1 we have

$$|\overline{F'P_1}| = e|\overline{RP_1}| \quad \text{and} \quad |\overline{FP_1}| = e|\overline{P_1Q}|$$

Therefore,

(13)
$$|\overline{F'P_1}| + |\overline{FP_1}| = e[|\overline{RP_1}| + |\overline{P_1Q}|]$$

$\overline{RP_1}$ and $\overline{P_1Q}$ are both positive because an ellipse lies between its directrices. Hence,

(14)
$$|\overline{RP_1}| + |\overline{P_1Q}| = \overline{RP_1} + \overline{P_1Q} = \overline{RQ} = \frac{a}{e} - \left(-\frac{a}{e}\right) = \frac{2a}{e}$$

Substituting (14) into (13), we get

$$|\overline{F'P_1}| + |\overline{FP_1}| = 2a$$

which proves that an ellipse is a set of points as described in the theorem.

17.4.8 THEOREM   A hyperbola may be defined as the set of points such that the difference of the distances from any point of the set to two given points (the foci) is a constant.

The proof of this theorem is left for the reader (see Exercises 26 and 27 at the end of this section). In the proof, take as the foci the points $F'(-ae,0)$ and $F(ae,0)$ and let the constant difference of the distances be $2a$ (see Fig. 17.4.4).

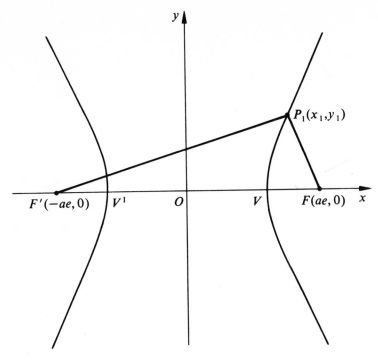

Figure 17.4.4

Exercises 17.4

In Exercises 1 through 6, find the eccentricity, center, foci, and directrices of each of the given ellipses and draw a sketch of the graph.

1. $6x^2 + 9y^2 - 24x - 54y + 51 = 0$ *Complete* ☐

2. $9x^2 + 4y^2 - 18x + 16y - 11 = 0$

3. $5x^2 + 3y^2 - 3y - 12 = 0$

4. $2x^2 + 2y^2 - 2x + 18y + 33 = 0$

5. $4x^2 + 4y^2 + 20x - 32y + 89 = 0$

6. $3x^2 + 4y^2 - 30x + 16y + 100 = 0$

In Exercises 7 through 12, find the eccentricity, center, foci, directrices, and equations of the asymptotes of the given hyperbolas and draw a sketch of the graph.

7. $9x^2 - 18y^2 + 54x - 36y + 79 = 0$

8. $x^2 - y^2 + 6x + 10y - 4 = 0$

9. $3y^2 - 4x^2 - 8x - 24y - 40 = 0$

10. $4x^2 - y^2 + 56x + 2y + 195 = 0$

11. $4y^2 - 9x^2 + 16y + 18x = 29$

12. $y^2 - x^2 + 2y - 2x - 1 = 0$

In Exercises 13 through 18, find an equation of the ellipse satisfying the given conditions and draw a sketch of the graph.

13. Foci at $(5,0)$ and $(-5,0)$; one directrix is the line $x = -20$.

14. Vertices at $(0,5)$ and $(0,-5)$ and passing through the point $(2, -5\sqrt{5}/3)$.

15. Center at $(4,-2)$, a vertex at $(9,-2)$, and one focus at $(0,-2)$.

16. Foci at $(2,3)$ and $(2,-7)$ and eccentricity is $2/3$.

17. Foci at $(-1,-1)$ and $(-1,7)$ and the semimajor axis of length 8 units.

18. Directrices the lines $y = 3 \pm 169/12$ and a focus at $(0,-2)$.

In Exercises 19 through 24, find an equation of the hyperbola satisfying the given conditions and draw a sketch of the graph.

19. One focus at $(26,0)$ and asymptotes the lines $12y = \pm 5x$.

20. Center at $(3,-5)$, a vertex at $(7,-5)$, and a focus at $(8,-5)$.

21. Center at $(-2,-1)$, a focus at $(-2,14)$, and a directrix the line $5y = -53$.

22. Foci at $(3,6)$ and $(3,0)$ and passing through the point $(5, 3 + 6/\sqrt{5})$.

23. One focus at $(-3-3\sqrt{13},1)$, asymptotes intersecting at $(-3,1)$, and one asymptote passing through the point $(1,7)$.

24. Foci at $(-1,4)$ and $(7,4)$ and eccentricity of 3.

25. The following graphical method for sketching the graph of an ellipse is based on Theorem 17.4.7. To draw a sketch of the graph of the ellipse $4x^2 + y^2 = 16$, first locate the points of intersection with the axes and then locate the foci on the y axis by use of compasses set with center at one point of intersection with the x axis and with radius of 4. Then fasten thumbtacks at each focus and tie one end of a string at one thumbtack and the other end of the string at the second thumbtack in such a way that the length of the string between the tacks is $2a = 8$ units. Place a pencil against the string, drawing it taut, and describe a curve with the point of the pencil by moving it against the taut string. When the curve is completed, it will necessarily be an ellipse, since the pencil point describes a locus of points whose sum of distances from the two tacks is a constant.

26. Prove that the set of points such that the difference of the distances from any point of the set to two given points (the foci) is a constant, is a hyperbola.

27. Prove that any hyperbola is a set of points such that the difference of the distances from any point of the set to two given points (the foci) is a constant.

28. Three listening posts are located at the points $A(0,0)$, $B(0,21/4)$, and $C(25/3,0)$, the unit being one mile. Microphones located at these points show that a gun is $5/3$ miles closer to A than to C, $7/4$ miles closer to B than to A, and $41/12$ miles closer to B than to C. Locate the position of the gun by use of Theorem 17.4.8.

(17.5) Rotation of axes

We have previously shown how a translation of coordinate axes may be used to simplify the form of certain equations. A translation of axes gives a new coordinate system whose axes are parallel to the original axes. We shall now consider a rotation of coordinate axes.

Suppose we have two rectangular cartesian coordinate systems with the same origin. Let one system be the xy system and the other the $\bar{x}\bar{y}$ system. Suppose further that the $\bar{x}$ axis makes an angle of α with the x axis. Then, of course, the $\bar{y}$ axis makes an angle of α with the y axis. In such a case, we say that the xy system of coordinates is *rotated* through an angle of α to form the $\bar{x}\bar{y}$ system of coordinates. A point P having coordinates (x,y) with respect to the original coordinate system will have coordinates $(\bar{x},\bar{y})$ with respect to the new one. We shall now obtain relationships between these two sets of coordinates. To do this, we introduce two polar coordinate systems, each system having the pole at the origin. In the first polar coordinate system we take the positive side of the x axis as the polar axis, and in the second polar coordinate system we take the positive side of the $\bar{x}$ axis as the polar axis — see Fig. 17.5.1. Point P has two sets of polar coordinates: (r,θ) and $(\bar{r},\bar{\theta})$, where

(1) $\bar{r} = r$ and $\bar{\theta} = \theta - \alpha$

The following equations hold:

(2) $\bar{x} = \bar{r} \cos \bar{\theta}$ and $\bar{y} = \bar{r} \sin \bar{\theta}$

Substituting (1) into (2), we get

(3) $\bar{x} = r \cos (\theta - \alpha)$ and $\bar{y} = r \sin (\theta - \alpha)$

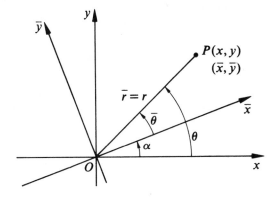

Figure 17.5.1

If we use the trigonometric identities for the sine and cosine of the difference of two angles, equations (3) become

$$\bar{x} = r \cos \theta \cos \alpha + r \sin \theta \sin \alpha$$

and $$\bar{y} = r \sin \theta \cos \alpha - r \cos \theta \sin \alpha$$

Since $r \cos \theta = x$ and $r \sin \theta = y$, we obtain from the above two equations

(4) $$\bar{x} = x \cos \alpha + y \sin \alpha$$

and

(5) $$\bar{y} = -x \sin \alpha + y \cos \alpha$$

If we solve equations (4) and (5) simultaneously for x and y in terms of $\bar{x}$ and $\bar{y}$, we obtain

(6) $$x = \bar{x} \cos \alpha - \bar{y} \sin \alpha$$

and

(7) $$y = \bar{x} \sin \alpha + \bar{y} \cos \alpha$$

It is left for the reader to fill in the steps in going from (4) and (5) to (6) and (7) (see Exercise 1 at the end of this section).

EXAMPLE 1: *Given:* the equation $xy = 1$. *Find:* an equation of the graph with respect to the $\bar{x}$ and $\bar{y}$ axes after a rotation of axes through an angle of $\pi/4$.

Solution: Taking $\alpha = \pi/4$ in equations (6) and (7), we obtain

$$x = \frac{1}{\sqrt{2}} \bar{x} - \frac{1}{\sqrt{2}} \bar{y} \qquad \text{and} \qquad y = \frac{1}{\sqrt{2}} \bar{x} + \frac{1}{\sqrt{2}} \bar{y}$$

Substituting these expressions for x and y in the equation $xy = 1$, we get

$$\left(\frac{1}{\sqrt{2}} \bar{x} - \frac{1}{\sqrt{2}} \bar{y} \right)\left(\frac{1}{\sqrt{2}} \bar{x} + \frac{1}{\sqrt{2}} \bar{y} \right) = 1$$

or, equivalently,

$$\frac{\bar{x}^2}{2} - \frac{\bar{y}^2}{2} = 1$$

This is an equation of an equilateral hyperbola whose asymptotes are the bisectors of the quadrants in the $\bar{x}\bar{y}$ system. So we may conclude that the graph of the equation $xy = 1$ is an equilateral hyperbola lying in the first and third quadrants whose asymptotes are the x and y axes — see Fig. 17.5.2.

In Sec. 17.4 we showed that when $B = 0$ and A and C are not both zero, the graph of the general second-degree equation in two unknowns,

(8) $$Ax^2 + Bxy + Cy^2 + Dx + Ey + F = 0$$

is either a conic or a degenerate conic. We shall now show that if $B \neq 0$, then

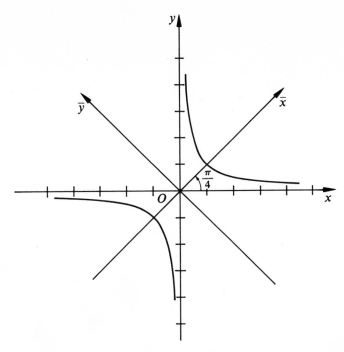

Figure 17.5.2

any equation of the form (8) can be transformed by a suitable rotation of axes into an equation of the form

(9) $$\bar{A}\bar{x}^2 + \bar{C}\bar{y}^2 + \bar{D}\bar{x} + \bar{E}\bar{y} + \bar{F} = 0$$

where $\bar{A}$ and $\bar{C}$ are not both zero.

If the xy system is rotated through an angle α, then to obtain an equation of the graph of (8) with respect to the $\bar{x}\bar{y}$ system, we replace x by $\bar{x} \cos \alpha - \bar{y} \sin \alpha$ and y by $\bar{x} \sin \alpha + \bar{y} \cos \alpha$, and we get

(10) $$\bar{A}\bar{x}^2 + \bar{B}\bar{x}\bar{y} + \bar{C}\bar{y}^2 + \bar{D}\bar{x} + \bar{E}\bar{y} + \bar{F} = 0$$

where

$$\bar{A} = A \cos^2 \alpha + B \sin \alpha \cos \alpha + C \sin^2 \alpha$$

(11) $$\bar{B} = -2A \sin \alpha \cos \alpha + B(\cos^2 \alpha - \sin^2 \alpha) + 2C \sin \alpha \cos \alpha$$

$$\bar{C} = A \sin^2 \alpha - B \sin \alpha \cos \alpha + C \cos^2 \alpha$$

We wish to find an angle α so that the rotation will transform equation (8) into an equation of the form (9). Setting $\bar{B}$ from (11) equal to zero, we have

$$B(\cos^2 \alpha - \sin^2 \alpha) + (C - A)(2 \sin \alpha \cos \alpha) = 0$$

or, equivalently, using trigonometric identities,

$$B \cos 2\alpha + (C - A) \sin 2\alpha = 0$$

Since $B \neq 0$, this gives us

(12)
$$\cot 2\alpha = \frac{A - C}{B}$$

We have shown then that an equation of the form (8), where $B \neq 0$, may be transformed to an equation of the form (9) by a rotation of axes through an angle α satisfying (12). We wish to show that $\bar{A}$ and $\bar{C}$ in (9) are not both zero. To prove this, we notice that equation (10) is obtained from (8) by rotating the axes through the angle α. Also equation (8) may be obtained from (10) by rotating the axes back through the angle $(-\alpha)$. If $\bar{A}$ and $\bar{C}$ in (10) are both zero, then the substitutions

$$\bar{x} = x \cos \alpha + y \sin \alpha \qquad \text{and} \qquad \bar{y} = -x \sin \alpha + y \cos \alpha$$

in (10) would result in the equation

$$\bar{D}(x \cos \alpha + y \sin \alpha) + \bar{E}(-x \sin \alpha + y \cos \alpha) + \bar{F} = 0$$

which is an equation of the first degree and hence different from (8), since we have assumed that at least $B \neq 0$. We have therefore proved the following theorem.

17.5.1 THEOREM   If $B \neq 0$, the equation $Ax^2 + Bxy + Cy^2 + Dx + Ey + F = 0$ may be transformed into the equation $\bar{A}\bar{x}^2 + \bar{C}\bar{y}^2 + \bar{D}\bar{x} + \bar{E}\bar{y} + \bar{F} = 0$, where $\bar{A}$ and $\bar{C}$ are not both zero, by a rotation of axes through an angle α for which $\cot 2\alpha = (A - C)/B$.

By Theorems 17.5.1 and 17.4.6, it follows that the graph of an equation of the form (8) is either a conic or a degenerate conic. To determine which type of conic is the graph of a particular equation, we make use of the fact that A, B, and C of equation (8) and $\bar{A}, \bar{B}$, and $\bar{C}$ of equation (10) satisfy the relation

(13)
$$B^2 - 4AC = \bar{B}^2 - 4\bar{A}\bar{C}$$

which may be proved by substituting the expressions for $\bar{A}$, $\bar{B}$, and $\bar{C}$ given in equations (11) in the right-hand side of (13). This is left for the reader (see Exercise 15 at the end of this section).

The expression $B^2 - 4AC$ is called the *discriminant* of equation (8). Equation (13) states that the discriminant of the general quadratic equation in two variables is *invariant* under a rotation of axes. If the angle of rotation is chosen so that $\bar{B} = 0$, then (13) becomes

(14)
$$B^2 - 4AC = -4\bar{A}\bar{C}$$

From Theorem 17.4.6, it follows that if the graph of (9) is not degenerate, then it is a parabola if $\bar{A}\bar{C} = 0$, an ellipse if $\bar{A}\bar{C} > 0$, and a hyperbola if $\bar{A}\bar{C} < 0$. So we may conclude that the graph of (9) is a parabola, an ellipse, or a hyperbola, according as $-4\bar{A}\bar{C}$ is zero, negative, or positive. Since the graph of (8) is the same as the graph of (9), it follows from (14) that if the graph of (8) is not degenerate, then it is a parabola, an ellipse, or a hyperbola, according to whether the discriminant $B^2 - 4AC$ is zero, negative, or positive. We have proved the following theorem.

(handwritten margin notes)
$\tan 2\theta = \dfrac{B}{A-C}$

(handwritten) 1.333

3)4.0000

3.0

17.5.2 THEOREM   The graph of the equation $Ax^2 + Bxy + Cy^2 + Dx + Ey + F = 0$ is either a conic or a degenerate conic. If it is a conic, then it is

   (i) a *parabola* if $B^2 - 4AC = 0$

   (ii) an *ellipse* if $B^2 - 4AC < 0$

   (iii) a *hyperbola* if $B^2 - 4AC > 0$

EXAMPLE 2: *Given:* the equation $17x^2 - 12xy + 8y^2 - 80 = 0$. Simplify the equation by a rotation of axes. Draw a sketch of the graph of the equation showing both sets of axes.

Solution: $B^2 - 4AC = (-12)^2 - 4(17)(8) = -400 < 0$. Therefore, by Theorem 17.5.2, the graph is an ellipse or else it is degenerate. To eliminate the xy term by a rotation of axes, we must choose an angle α such that

$$\cot 2\alpha = \frac{A - C}{B} = \frac{17 - 8}{-12} = -\frac{3}{4}$$

(handwritten) $-\dfrac{4}{3}$

We may choose an angle 2α in the interval $(0, \pi)$ for which $\cot 2\alpha = -3/4$. Therefore, α is in the interval $(0, \pi/2)$. To apply (6) and (7), it is not necessary to find α as long as we find $\cos \alpha$ and $\sin \alpha$. We may find these functions from the value of $\cot 2\alpha$ by the trigonometric identities

$$\cos \alpha = \sqrt{\frac{1 + \cos 2\alpha}{2}} \qquad \text{and} \qquad \sin \alpha = \sqrt{\frac{1 - \cos 2\alpha}{2}}$$

Since $\cot 2\alpha = -3/4$ and $0 < \alpha < \pi/2$, it follows that $\cos 2\alpha = -3/5$. So,

$$\cos \alpha = \sqrt{\frac{1 - 3/5}{2}} = \frac{1}{\sqrt{5}}$$

$$\text{and} \qquad \sin \alpha = \sqrt{\frac{1 + 3/5}{2}} = \frac{2}{\sqrt{5}}$$

Substituting $x = \bar{x}/\sqrt{5} - 2\bar{y}/\sqrt{5}$ and $y = 2\bar{x}/\sqrt{5} + \bar{y}/\sqrt{5}$ in the given equation, we obtain

$$17\left(\frac{\bar{x}^2 - 4\bar{x}\bar{y} + 4\bar{y}^2}{5}\right) - 12\left(\frac{2\bar{x}^2 - 3\bar{x}\bar{y} - 2\bar{y}^2}{5}\right)$$
$$+ 8\left(\frac{4\bar{x}^2 + 4\bar{x}\bar{y} + \bar{y}^2}{5}\right) - 80 = 0$$

Upon simplification, this equation becomes

$$\bar{x}^2 + 4\bar{y}^2 = 16$$

(handwritten) -68 $+36$ -32

or, equivalently,

$$\frac{\bar{x}^2}{16} + \frac{\bar{y}^2}{4} = 1$$

So the graph is an ellipse whose major axis is 8 units long and whose minor axis is 4 units long. A sketch of the ellipse with both sets of axes is shown in Fig. 17.5.3.

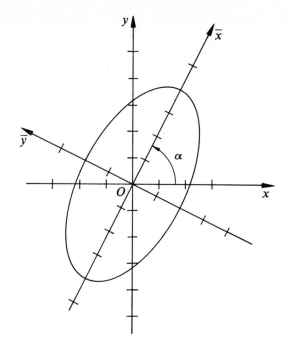

Figure 17.5.3

Exercises 17.5

1. Derive equations (6) and (7) of this section by solving equations (4) and (5) for x and y in terms of $\bar{x}$ and $\bar{y}$.

In Exercises 2 through 8, remove the xy term from the given equation by a rotation of axes. Draw a sketch of the graph and show both sets of axes.

2. $x^2 + xy + y^2 = 3$

3. $24xy - 7y^2 + 36 = 0$

4. $4xy + 3x^2 = 4$

5. $xy = 8$

6. $5x^2 + 6xy + 5y^2 = 9$

7. $31x^2 + 10\sqrt{3}xy + 21y^2 = 144$

8. $6x^2 + 20\sqrt{3}\,xy + 26y^2 = 324$

In Exercises 9 through 14, simplify the given equation by a rotation and translation of axes. Draw a sketch of the graph and show the three sets of axes.

9. $x^2 + xy + y^2 - 3y - 6 = 0$

10. $x^2 - 10xy + y^2 + x + y + 1 = 0$

11. $17x^2 - 12xy + 8y^2 - 68x + 24y - 12 = 0$

12. $3x^2 - 4xy + 8x - 1 = 0$

13. $11x^2 - 24xy + 4y^2 + 30x + 40y - 45 = 0$

14. $19x^2 + 6xy + 11y^2 - 26x + 38y + 31 = 0$

15. Show that for the general second-degree equation in two variables, the discriminant $B^2 - 4AC$ is invariant under a rotation of axes.

18 Vectors in the plane and parametric equations

(18.1)   Introduction

In the application of mathematics to physics and engineering, we are often concerned with quantities that possess both *magnitude* and *direction;* examples of these are *force, velocity, acceleration,* and *displacement.* Such quantities may be represented geometrically by a *directed line segment.* The physicists and engineers refer to a directed line segment as a *vector,* and the quantities that have both magnitude and direction are called *vector quantities.* The study of vectors is called *vector analysis.*

The approach to vector analysis may be on either a geometric or analytic basis. If the geometric approach is taken, we first define a directed line segment as a line segment from a point P to a point Q and denote this directed line segment by $\overrightarrow{PQ}$. The point P is called the *initial point*, and the point Q is called the *terminal point*. Then two directed line segments $\overrightarrow{PQ}$ and $\overrightarrow{RS}$ are said to be equal if they have the same *length* and *direction*, and we write $\overrightarrow{PQ} = \overrightarrow{RS}$ — see Fig. 18.1.1. The directed line segment $\overrightarrow{PQ}$ is called the *vector* from P to Q. A

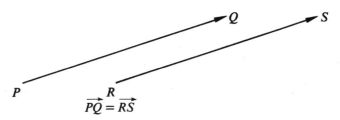

$$\overrightarrow{PQ} = \overrightarrow{RS}$$

Figure 18.1.1

vector will be denoted by a single letter, set in boldface type, such as **A**. In some books, a letter in lightface type, with an arrow above it, is used to indicate a vector — for example, $\vec{A}$. Continuing with the geometric approach to vector analysis, if the directed line segment $\overrightarrow{PQ}$ is the vector **A**, and $\overrightarrow{PQ} = \overrightarrow{RS}$, the directed line segment $\overrightarrow{RS}$ is also the vector **A**. Then a vector is considered to be remaining unchanged if it is moved parallel to itself. With this interpretation of

593

a vector, we may assume for convenience that every vector has its initial point at some fixed reference point. By taking this point as the origin of a rectangular cartesian coordinate system, we may define a vector analytically in terms of real numbers. Such a definition enables us to study vector analysis from a purely mathematical viewpoint. In this book, we shall use the mathematical approach; however, the geometric interpretation will be given for illustrative purposes.

(18.2) Vectors in the plane

We shall denote a vector in the plane by an ordered pair of real numbers and use the notation $\langle x,y \rangle$ instead of (x,y) to avoid confusing the notation for a vector with the notation for a point. We shall let V^2 be the set of all such ordered pairs. Following is the formal definition.

18.2.1 DEFINITION   *A vector in the plane* is an ordered pair of real numbers $\langle x,y \rangle$.
x and y are called the *components* of the vector $\langle x,y \rangle$.

There is a one-to-one correspondence between the vectors $\langle x,y \rangle$ in the plane and the points (x,y) in the plane. Let the vector **A** be the ordered pair of real numbers $\langle a_1,a_2 \rangle$. If we let A denote the point (a_1,a_2), then the vector **A** may be represented geometrically by the directed line segment $\overrightarrow{OA}$. Such a directed line segment is called a *representation* of vector **A**. Any directed line segment which is equal to $\overrightarrow{OA}$ is also a representation of vector **A**. The particular representation of a vector which has its initial point at the origin is called the *position representation* of the vector. For example, the vector $\langle 2,3 \rangle$ has as its position representation the directed line segment from the origin to the point $(2,3)$. The representation of the vector $\langle 2,3 \rangle$ whose initial point is (h,k) has as its terminal point $(h + 2, 3 + k)$ — refer to Fig. 18.2.1.
The vector $\langle 0,0 \rangle$ is called the *zero vector*, and we denote it by **0**; that is

$$\mathbf{0} = \langle 0,0 \rangle$$

Any point is a representation of the zero vector. The direction of the zero vector is indeterminate.

18.2.2 DEFINITION   The *magnitude* of a vector is the length of any of its representations, and the *direction* of a vector is the direction of any of its representations.

We shall denote the magnitude of the vector **A** by $|\mathbf{A}|$.

18.2.3 THEOREM   If **A** is the vector $\langle a_1,a_2 \rangle$, then $|\mathbf{A}| = \sqrt{a_1{}^2 + a_2{}^2}$.

Proof: Since by Definition 18.2.2, $|\mathbf{A}|$ is the length of any of the representations of **A**, then $|\mathbf{A}|$ will be the length of the position representation of **A**, which is the distance from the origin to the point (a_1,a_2). So, from the formula for the distance between two points, we have

$$|\mathbf{A}| = \sqrt{(a_1 - 0)^2 + (a_2 - 0)^2} = \sqrt{a_1{}^2 + a_2{}^2} \qquad \text{Q.E.D.}$$

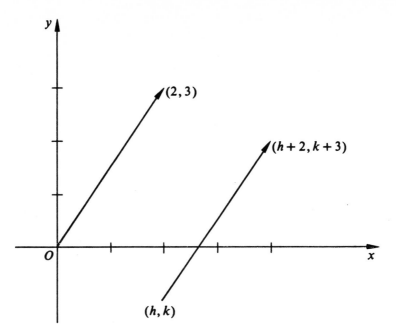

Figure 18.2.1

It should be noted that $|\mathbf{A}|$ is a nonnegative number and not a vector. The magnitude of the zero vector is given by $|\mathbf{0}| = 0$.

EXAMPLE 1: Find the magnitude of the vector $\mathbf{A} = \langle -3,5 \rangle$.

Solution: $|\mathbf{A}| = \sqrt{(-3)^2 + 5^2} = \sqrt{34}$.

We give the direction of any nonzero vector by giving the angle $\theta, 0 \le \theta < 2\pi$, measured from the positive x axis counterclockwise to the position representation of the vector. So, if $\mathbf{A} = \langle a_1, a_2 \rangle$, then $\tan \theta = a_2/a_1$ if $a_1 \ne 0$. If $a_1 = 0$, and $a_2 > 0$, then $\theta = \pi/2$. If $a_1 = 0$ and $a_2 < 0$, then $\theta = 3\pi/2$. Figures 18.2.2, 18.2.3, and 18.2.4 show θ for specific vectors $\langle a_1, a_2 \rangle$ whose position representations are drawn.

EXAMPLE 2: Find the direction of each of the following vectors: (a) $\langle -1,1 \rangle$; (b) $\langle 0, -5 \rangle$; (c) $\langle 1, -2 \rangle$.

Solution: The position representation of each of the vectors in (a), (b), and (c) is shown in Figs. 18.2.5, 18.2.6, and 18.2.7, respectively.

(a) $\tan \theta = -1$; so $\theta = 3\pi/4$
(b) $\tan \theta$ does not exist and $a_2 < 0$; $\theta = 3\pi/2$
(c) $\tan \theta = -2$; $\theta = \tan^{-1}(-2) + 2\pi$

If the vector $\mathbf{A} = \langle a_1, a_2 \rangle$, then the representation of $\mathbf{A}$ whose initial point is (x,y) has as its end point $(x + a_1, y + a_2)$. In this way a vector may be thought of as a translation of the plane into itself. Figure 18.2.8 illustrates five representations of the vector $\mathbf{A} = \langle a_1, a_2 \rangle$. In each case, $\mathbf{A}$ translates the point (x_i, y_i)

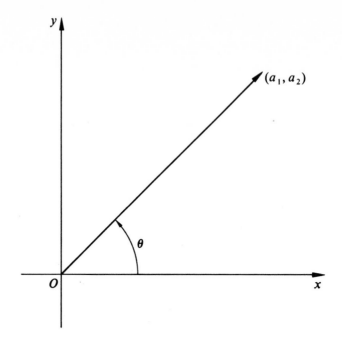

Figure 18.2.2

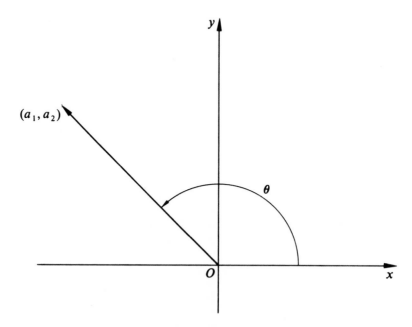

Figure 18.2.3

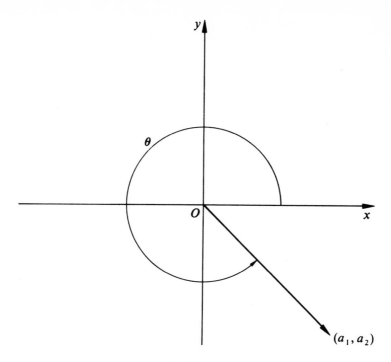

Figure 18.2.4

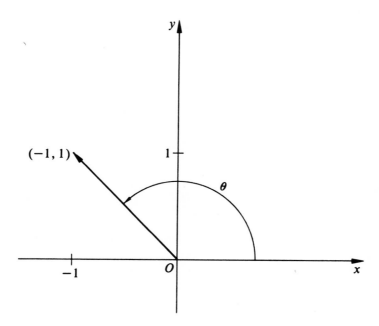

Figure 18.2.5

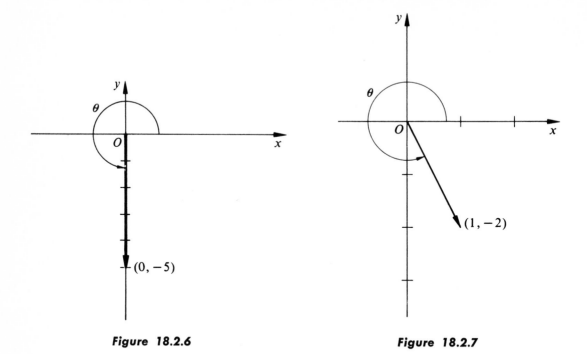

Figure 18.2.6

Figure 18.2.7

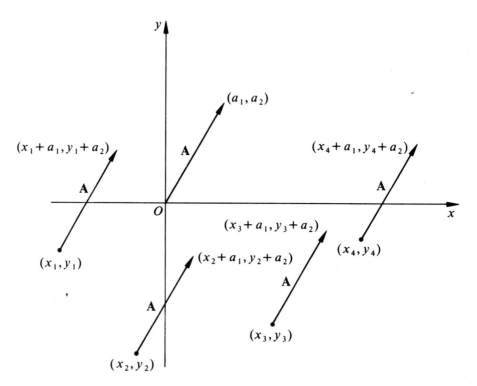

Figure 18.2.8

into the point $(x_i + a_1,\ y_i + a_2)$. A two-dimensional vector, then, may be considered as a function whose domain and range are the set of points in the plane. If $\mathbf{A}$ is the vector which translates the point P into the point Q, we write $\mathbf{A}(P) = Q$. So if P is the point (x,y) and $\mathbf{A} = \langle a_1, a_2 \rangle$, then

$$\mathbf{A}(P) = (x + a_1,\ y + a_2) = Q$$

EXAMPLE 3: *Given:* $\mathbf{A} = \langle 3, -4 \rangle$; $P_1 = (0,0)$; $P_2 = (1,4)$; $P_3 = (-6,5)$. *Find:* $\mathbf{A}(P_1)$; $\mathbf{A}(P_2)$; $\mathbf{A}(P_3)$.

  Solution: $\mathbf{A}(P_1) = (3,-4)$; $\mathbf{A}(P_2) = (4,0)$; $\mathbf{A}(P_3) = (-3,1)$.

It should be noted that $\mathbf{A}(P) = P$ if and only if $\mathbf{A} = \langle 0,0 \rangle$. Also, if $P = (x_1, y_1)$ and $Q = (x_2, y_2)$, there exists a unique vector $\mathbf{B}$ for which $\mathbf{B}(P) = Q$; and $\mathbf{B} = \langle x_2 - x_1,\ y_2 - y_1 \rangle$.

Exercises 18.2

In Exercises 1 through 6, draw the position representation of the given vector $\mathbf{A}$ and also the particular representation through the given point P; find the magnitude of $\mathbf{A}$.

1. $\mathbf{A} = \langle 3,4 \rangle$; $P = (2,1)$
4. $\mathbf{A} = \langle 4,0 \rangle$; $P = (2,6)$

2. $\mathbf{A} = \langle -2,5 \rangle$; $P = (3,-4)$
5. $\mathbf{A} = \langle 3, \sqrt{2} \rangle$; $P = (4, -\sqrt{2})$

3. $\mathbf{A} = \langle 0,-2 \rangle$; $P = (-3,4)$
6. $\mathbf{A} = \langle e, -\frac{1}{2} \rangle$; $P = (-2,-e)$

In Exercises 7 through 12, find $\mathbf{A}(P)$ for the given value of $\mathbf{A}$ and P. If $Q = \mathbf{A}(P)$, draw $\overrightarrow{PQ}$.

7. $\mathbf{A} = \langle 2,6 \rangle$; $P = (1,3)$
10. $\mathbf{A} = \langle -3,0 \rangle$; $P = (-1,-6)$

8. $\mathbf{A} = \langle -4,1 \rangle$; $P = (-2,-3)$
11. $\mathbf{A} = \langle \frac{1}{2}, \frac{1}{3} \rangle$; $P = (-\frac{1}{3}, -\frac{1}{2})$

9. $\mathbf{A} = \langle 0,4 \rangle$; $P = (3,-4)$
12. $\mathbf{A} = \langle -3,-7 \rangle$; $P = (3,7)$

In Exercises 13 through 18, find the vector $\mathbf{A}$ having $\overrightarrow{PQ}$ as a representation. Draw $\overrightarrow{PQ}$ and the position representation of $\mathbf{A}$.

13. $P = (3,7)$; $Q = (5,4)$
16. $P = (0,\sqrt{3})$; $Q = (2,3\sqrt{3})$

14. $P = (5,4)$; $Q = (3,7)$
17. $P = (-5,-3)$; $Q = (0,3)$

15. $P = (-3,5)$; $Q = (-5,-2)$
18. $P = (-\sqrt{2},0)$; $Q = (0,0)$

In Exercises 19 through 22, find the point S so that $\overrightarrow{PQ}$ and $\overrightarrow{RS}$ are each representations of the same vector.

19. $P = (2,5)$; $Q = (1,6)$; $R = (-3,2)$

20. $P = (-1,4)$; $Q = (2,-3)$; $R = (-5,-2)$

21. $P = (0,3)$; $Q = (5,-2)$; $R = (7,0)$

22. $P = (-2,0)$; $Q = (-3,-4)$; $R = (4,2)$

(18.3) Vector addition, subtraction, and scalar multiplication

The following definition gives us the method for adding two vectors.

18.3.1 DEFINITION   The sum of two vectors $\mathbf{A} = \langle a_1, a_2 \rangle$ and $\mathbf{B} = \langle b_1, b_2 \rangle$ is the vector $\mathbf{A} + \mathbf{B}$, defined by

$$\mathbf{A} + \mathbf{B} = \langle a_1 + b_1,\, a_2 + b_2 \rangle$$

EXAMPLE 1: *Given:* $\mathbf{A} = \langle 3, -1 \rangle$; $\mathbf{B} = \langle -4, 5 \rangle$. *Find:* $\mathbf{A} + \mathbf{B}$.
Solution: $\mathbf{A} + \mathbf{B} = \langle 3 + (-4), -1 + 5 \rangle = \langle -1, 4 \rangle$.

The following laws involving addition of vectors follow from Definition 18.3.1 and the properties of real numbers.

18.3.2 THEOREM   If $\mathbf{A}$, $\mathbf{B}$, and $\mathbf{C}$ are any vectors and $\mathbf{0}$ is the zero vector, then

  (i) $\mathbf{A} + \mathbf{B} = \mathbf{B} + \mathbf{A}$ commutative law

  (ii) $\mathbf{A} + (\mathbf{B} + \mathbf{C}) = (\mathbf{A} + \mathbf{B}) + \mathbf{C}$ associative law

  (iii) $\mathbf{A} + \mathbf{0} = \mathbf{A}$

  (iv)   There is a vector, called the *negative* of $\mathbf{A}$ and denoted by $-\mathbf{A}$, such that

$$\mathbf{A} + (-\mathbf{A}) = \mathbf{0}$$

Proof of (i): Let $\mathbf{A} = \langle a_1, a_2 \rangle$ and $\mathbf{B} = \langle b_1, b_2 \rangle$.

$a_1 + b_1 = b_1 + a_1$ and $a_2 + b_2 = b_2 + a_2$ by the commutative law for real numbers. So,

$$\mathbf{A} + \mathbf{B} = \langle a_1, a_2 \rangle + \langle b_1, b_2 \rangle = \langle b_1 + a_1,\, b_2 + a_2 \rangle$$
$$= \mathbf{B} + \mathbf{A}$$

Proof of (iv): If $\mathbf{A} = \langle a_1, a_2 \rangle$, then the vector $\langle -a_1, -a_2 \rangle$ will be the vector $-\mathbf{A}$, since

$$\mathbf{A} + (-\mathbf{A}) = \langle a_1, a_2 \rangle + \langle -a_1, -a_2 \rangle = \langle a_1 + (-a_1),\, a_2 + (-a_2) \rangle = \langle 0, 0 \rangle = \mathbf{0}$$

The proofs of (ii) and (iii) are left for the reader (see Exercises 13 and 14 at the end of this section).

If the directed line segment $\overrightarrow{PQ}$ is a representation of the vector $\mathbf{A}$, then the directed line segment $\overrightarrow{QP}$ is a representation of $-\mathbf{A}$. Any directed line segment which is parallel to $\overrightarrow{PQ}$, has the same length as $\overrightarrow{PQ}$, and has a direction opposite to that of $\overrightarrow{PQ}$ is also a representation of $-\mathbf{A}$ — see Fig. 18.3.1.

The geometric interpretation of the sum of two vectors is shown in Fig. 18.3.2. Let $\mathbf{A} = \langle a_1, a_2 \rangle$ and $\mathbf{B} = \langle b_1, b_2 \rangle$ and P be the point (x, y). Then

$$\mathbf{A}(P) = (x + a_1,\, y + a_2) = Q$$
$$\mathbf{B}(Q) = ((x + a_1) + b_1,\, (y + a_2) + b_2)$$
$$= (x + (a_1 + b_1),\, y + (a_2 + b_2))$$
$$= R$$

But
$$\mathbf{A} + \mathbf{B} = \langle a_1 + b_1, a_2 + b_2 \rangle$$
So, $(\mathbf{A} + \mathbf{B})(P) = (x + (a_1 + b_1), y + (a_2 + b_2))$
$$= R$$

So, in Fig. 18.3.2, $\overrightarrow{PQ}$ is a representation of the vector $\mathbf{A}$, $\overrightarrow{QR}$ is a representation of the vector $\mathbf{B}$, and $\overrightarrow{PR}$ is a representation of the vector $\mathbf{A} + \mathbf{B}$. The representations of the vectors $\mathbf{A}$ and $\mathbf{B}$ are adjacent sides of a parallelogram and the representation of the vector $\mathbf{A} + \mathbf{B}$ is a diagonal of the parallelogram. Thus the rule for the addition of vectors is sometimes referred to as the *parallelogram law*.

We now define subtraction of two vectors.

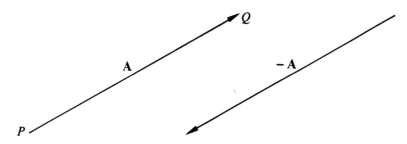

Figure 18.3.1

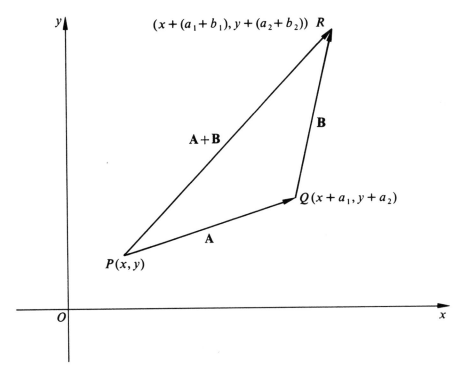

Figure 18.3.2

18.3.3 DEFINITION   The difference of the two vectors **A** and **B**, denoted by **A** − **B**, is the vector obtained by adding **A** to the negative of **B**; that is,

$$\mathbf{A} - \mathbf{B} = \mathbf{A} + (-\mathbf{B})$$

So, if $\mathbf{A} = \langle a_1, a_2 \rangle$ and $\mathbf{B} = \langle b_1, b_2 \rangle$, then $-\mathbf{B} = \langle -b_1, -b_2 \rangle$, and so

$$\mathbf{A} - \mathbf{B} = \langle a_1 - b_1, a_2 - b_2 \rangle$$

EXAMPLE 2: *Given:* $\mathbf{A} = \langle 4, -2 \rangle$; $\mathbf{B} = \langle 6, -3 \rangle$. *Find:* **A** − **B**.

Solution: $\mathbf{A} - \mathbf{B} = \langle 4, -2 \rangle - \langle 6, -3 \rangle$

$$= \langle 4, -2 \rangle + \langle -6, 3 \rangle$$

$$= \langle -2, 1 \rangle.$$

To interpret the difference of two vectors geometrically, let the representations of the vectors **A** and **B** have the same initial point; then, the directed line segment from the end point of the representation of **B** to the end point of the representation of **A** is a representation of the vector **A** − **B**. This obeys the parallelogram law **B** + (**A** − **B**) = **A** — see Fig. 18.3.3.

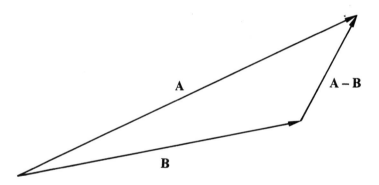

Figure 18.3.3

Another operation with vectors is *scalar multiplication*. A *scalar* is a real number. Following is the definition of the multiplication of a vector by a scalar.

18.3.4 DEFINITION   If c is a scalar and **A** is the vector $\langle a_1, a_2 \rangle$, then the product of c and **A**, denoted by $c\mathbf{A}$, is a vector and is given by

$$c\mathbf{A} = c\langle a_1, a_2 \rangle = \langle ca_1, ca_2 \rangle$$

The geometric interpretation of the vector $c\mathbf{A}$ is given in Fig. 18.3.4 and 18.3.5. If $c > 0$, then $c\mathbf{A}$ is a vector whose representation has a length c times the magnitude of **A** and the same direction as **A**; a case of this is shown in Fig. 18.3.4, where $c = 3$. If $c < 0$, then $c\mathbf{A}$ is a vector whose representation has a length which is $|c|$ times the magnitude of **A** and a direction opposite to that of **A**. This is shown in Fig. 18.3.5, where $c = -\frac{1}{2}$.

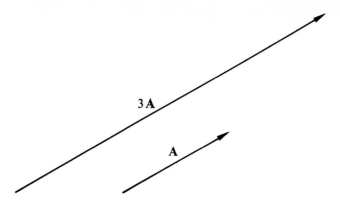

Figure 18.3.4

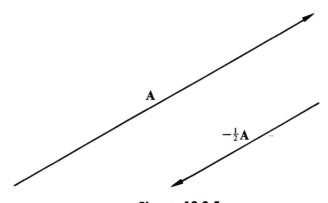

Figure 18.3.5

The following laws for multiplying scalars and vectors follow from Definition 18.3.4 and properties of real numbers.

18.3.5 THEOREM   If **A** and **B** are any two vectors and c and d are any two scalars, then

 (i) $c(\mathbf{A} + \mathbf{B}) = c\mathbf{A} + c\mathbf{B}$

 (ii) $(c + d)\mathbf{A} = c\mathbf{A} + d\mathbf{A}$

 (iii) $(cd)\mathbf{A} = c(d\mathbf{A})$

 (iv) $(-c)\mathbf{A} = -(c\mathbf{A})$

 (v) $1(\mathbf{A}) = \mathbf{A}$

 (vi) $0(\mathbf{A}) = \mathbf{0}$

 (vii) $c(\mathbf{0}) = \mathbf{0}$

Proof of (i): Let $\mathbf{A} = \langle a_1,a_2 \rangle$ and $\mathbf{B} = \langle b_1,b_2 \rangle$.

$$\begin{aligned}
\text{Then,} \quad c(\mathbf{A} + \mathbf{B}) &= c(\langle a_1,a_2 \rangle + \langle b_1,b_2 \rangle) \\
&= c(\langle a_1 + b_1, \ a_2 + b_2 \rangle) \\
&= \langle c(a_1 + b_1), \ c(a_2 + b_2) \rangle \\
&= \langle ca_1 + cb_1, \ ca_2 + cb_2 \rangle \\
&= \langle ca_1,ca_2 \rangle + \langle cb_1,cb_2 \rangle \\
&= c\langle a_1,a_2 \rangle + c\langle b_1,b_2 \rangle \\
&= c\mathbf{A} + c\mathbf{B} \qquad\qquad\qquad \text{Q.E.D.}
\end{aligned}$$

The proofs of (ii) to (vii) are left for the reader (see Exercises 16 to 19 at the end of this section).

EXAMPLE 3: *Given:* $\mathbf{A} = \langle 2,-3 \rangle$; $\mathbf{B} = \langle -1,4 \rangle$. *Find:* (a) $5(\mathbf{A} + \mathbf{B})$; (b) $(\sqrt{3} + 4)\mathbf{A}$.

Solution:

$$\begin{aligned}
(a) \quad 5(\mathbf{A} + \mathbf{B}) &= 5\mathbf{A} + 5\mathbf{B} = 5\langle 2,-3 \rangle + 5\langle -1,4 \rangle \\
&= \langle 10,-15 \rangle + \langle -5,20 \rangle = \langle 5,5 \rangle
\end{aligned}$$

$$\begin{aligned}
(b) \quad (\sqrt{3} + 4)\mathbf{A} &= (\sqrt{3} + 4)(\langle 2,-3 \rangle) \\
&= \sqrt{3}\langle 2,-3 \rangle + 4\langle 2,-3 \rangle \\
&= \langle 2\sqrt{3},-3\sqrt{3} \rangle + \langle 8,-12 \rangle \\
&= \langle 2\sqrt{3} + 8, \ -3\sqrt{3} - 12 \rangle
\end{aligned}$$

We shall now take an arbitrary two-dimensional vector and write it in a special form.

$$\mathbf{A} = \langle a_1,a_2 \rangle = \langle a_1,0 \rangle + \langle 0,a_2 \rangle = a_1\langle 1,0 \rangle + a_2\langle 0,1 \rangle$$

We have shown that every two-dimensional vector may be written as the sum of the two vectors $\langle 1,0 \rangle$ and $\langle 0,1 \rangle$, each multiplied by a suitably chosen scalar. Since the magnitude of each of the two vectors $\langle 1,0 \rangle$ and $\langle 0,1 \rangle$ is one unit, they are called *unit vectors*. We introduce the following notations for these two unit vectors:

$$\mathbf{i} = \langle 1,0 \rangle \qquad \mathbf{j} = \langle 0,1 \rangle$$

The position representation of each of these unit vectors is shown in Fig. 18.3.6. Every vector $\mathbf{A} = \langle a_1,a_2 \rangle$ may be written as

$$\mathbf{A} = a_1\mathbf{i} + a_2\mathbf{j}$$

EXAMPLE 4: Express the vector $\langle 3,-4 \rangle$ in terms of $\mathbf{i}$ and $\mathbf{j}$.

Solution: $\langle 3,-4 \rangle = 3\langle 1,0 \rangle + (-4)\langle 0,1 \rangle = 3\mathbf{i} - 4\mathbf{j}$.

Let $\mathbf{A}$ be the vector $\langle a_1,a_2 \rangle$ and θ be the angle giving the direction of $\mathbf{A}$ — see Fig. 18.3.7 where (a_1,a_2) is in the second quadrant. $a_1 = |\mathbf{A}| \cos \theta$ and $a_2 = |\mathbf{A}| \sin \theta$. Since $\mathbf{A} = a_1\mathbf{i} + a_2\mathbf{j}$, we may write

$$\mathbf{A} = |\mathbf{A}| \cos \theta\mathbf{i} + |\mathbf{A}| \sin \theta\mathbf{j}$$

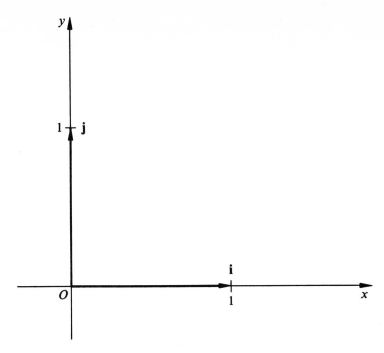

Figure 18.3.6

or, equivalently,

(1) $$\mathbf{A} = |\mathbf{A}| \, (\cos \theta \mathbf{i} + \sin \theta \mathbf{j})$$

Equation (1) expresses the vector $\mathbf{A}$ in terms of its magnitude, the angle θ giving the direction of $\mathbf{A}$, and the unit vectors $\mathbf{i}$ and $\mathbf{j}$.

EXAMPLE 5: If $\mathbf{A}$ is the vector $\langle -5, -2 \rangle$, express $\mathbf{A}$ in terms of its magnitude and the angle θ giving the direction of $\mathbf{A}$.

Solution: Refer to Fig. 18.3.8, which shows the position representation of $\mathbf{A}$.

$$|\mathbf{A}| = \sqrt{(-5)^2 + (-2)^2} = \sqrt{25 + 4} = \sqrt{29}$$

$$\sin \theta = -2/\sqrt{29} \quad \text{and} \quad \cos \theta = -5/\sqrt{29}$$

So from (1), we have

$$\mathbf{A} = \sqrt{29}\left(-\frac{5}{\sqrt{29}}\mathbf{i} - \frac{2}{\sqrt{29}}\mathbf{j} \right)$$

The following theorem enables us to find the unit vector in the same direction as a given nonzero vector.

18.3.6 THEOREM   If the nonzero vector $\mathbf{A} = a_1\mathbf{i} + a_2\mathbf{j}$, then the unit vector $\mathbf{U}$ having the same direction as $\mathbf{A}$ is given by

(2) $$\mathbf{U} = \frac{a_1}{|\mathbf{A}|}\mathbf{i} + \frac{a_2}{|\mathbf{A}|}\mathbf{j}$$

Proof: From (2),

$$\mathbf{U} = \frac{1}{|\mathbf{A}|}(a_1\mathbf{i} + a_2\mathbf{j}) = \frac{1}{|\mathbf{A}|}(\mathbf{A})$$

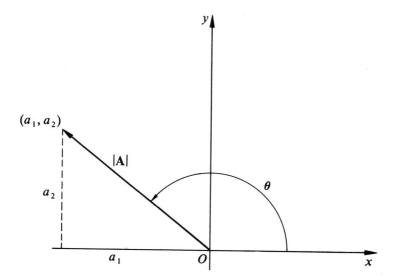

Figure 18.3.7

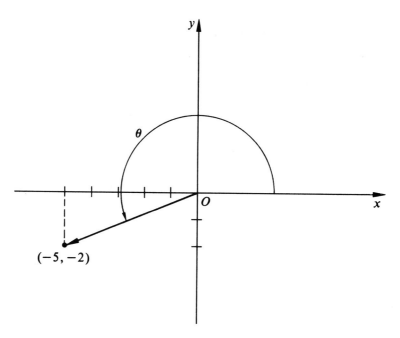

Figure 18.3.8

Therefore **U** is a positive scalar times the vector **A**, and so the direction of **U** is the same as the direction of **A**. Furthermore,

$$|\mathbf{U}| = \sqrt{\left(\frac{a_1}{|\mathbf{A}|}\right)^2 + \left(\frac{a_2}{|\mathbf{A}|}\right)^2} = \frac{\sqrt{a_1^2 + a_2^2}}{|\mathbf{A}|}$$

$$= \frac{|\mathbf{A}|}{|\mathbf{A}|} = 1$$

Therefore, **U** is the unit vector having the same direction as **A**, and the theorem is proved.

EXAMPLE 6: *Given:* $\mathbf{A} = \langle 3,1 \rangle$ and $\mathbf{B} = \langle -2,4 \rangle$. *Find:* the unit vector having the same direction as $\mathbf{A} - \mathbf{B}$.

 Solution: $\mathbf{A} - \mathbf{B} = \langle 3,1 \rangle - \langle -2,4 \rangle = \langle 5,-3 \rangle$. So, we may write

$$\mathbf{A} - \mathbf{B} = 5\mathbf{i} - 3\mathbf{j}$$

Then,

$$|\mathbf{A} - \mathbf{B}| = \sqrt{5^2 + (-3)^2} = \sqrt{34}$$

By Theorem 18.3.6, the desired unit vector is given by

$$\mathbf{U} = \frac{5}{\sqrt{34}}\mathbf{i} - \frac{3}{\sqrt{34}}\mathbf{j}$$

Exercises 18.3

In Exercises 1 through 6, find the sum of the given pairs of vectors and illustrate geometrically.

1. $\langle 2,4 \rangle; \langle -3,5 \rangle$

2. $\langle 0,3 \rangle; \langle -2,3 \rangle$

3. $\langle -3,0 \rangle; \langle 4,-5 \rangle$

4. $\langle 2,3 \rangle; \langle -\sqrt{2},-1 \rangle$

5. $\langle 0,0 \rangle; \langle -2,2 \rangle$

6. $\langle 2,5 \rangle; \langle 2,5 \rangle$

In Exercises 7 through 12, subtract the second vector from the first, and illustrate geometrically.

7. $\langle 4,5 \rangle; \langle -3,2 \rangle$

8. $\langle 0,5 \rangle; \langle 2,8 \rangle$

9. $\langle -3,-4 \rangle; \langle 6,0 \rangle$

10. $\langle 1,e \rangle; \langle -3,2e \rangle$

11. $\langle 0,\sqrt{3} \rangle; \langle -\sqrt{2},0 \rangle$

12. $\langle 3,7 \rangle; \langle 3,7 \rangle$

13. Prove Theorem 18.3.2(ii).

14. Prove Theorem 18.3.2(iii).

15. *Given:* $\mathbf{A} = \langle 2,-5 \rangle$; $\mathbf{B} = \langle 3,1 \rangle$; $\mathbf{C} = \langle -4,2 \rangle$. (*a*) *Find:* $\mathbf{A} + (\mathbf{B} + \mathbf{C})$ and illustrate geometrically. (*b*) *Find:* $(\mathbf{A} + \mathbf{B}) + \mathbf{C}$ and illustrate geometrically.

16. Prove Theorem 18.3.5(ii).

17. Prove Theorem 18.3.5(iii).

18. Prove Theorem 18.3.5(iv).

19. Prove Theorem 18.3.5(v)–(vii).

In Exercises 20 through 25, take $\mathbf{A} = \langle 2,4 \rangle$, $\mathbf{B} = \langle 4,-3 \rangle$, and $\mathbf{C} = \langle -3,2 \rangle$.

20. *Find:* $\mathbf{A} + \mathbf{B}$ 23. *Find:* $|\mathbf{C} - \mathbf{B}|$

21. *Find:* $\mathbf{A} - \mathbf{B}$ 24. *Find:* $2\mathbf{A} + 3\mathbf{B}$

22. *Find:* $|\mathbf{C}|$ 25. *Find:* $|3\mathbf{A} - \mathbf{B}|$

In Exercises 26 through 33, take $\mathbf{A} = 2\mathbf{i} + 3\mathbf{j}$ and $\mathbf{B} = 4\mathbf{i} - \mathbf{j}$.

26. *Find:* $\mathbf{A} + \mathbf{B}$ 30. *Find:* $|\mathbf{A} + \mathbf{B}|$

27. *Find:* $\mathbf{A} - \mathbf{B}$ 31. *Find:* $|\mathbf{A}| + |\mathbf{B}|$

28. *Find:* $2\mathbf{A} - 3\mathbf{B}$ 32. *Find:* $|3\mathbf{A} - 2\mathbf{B}|$

29. *Find:* $|\mathbf{A}|\,|\mathbf{B}|$ 33. *Find:* $|3\mathbf{A}| - |2\mathbf{B}|$

34. *Given:* $\mathbf{A} = \langle 3,2 \rangle$; $\mathbf{C} = \langle 8,8 \rangle$; $\mathbf{A} + \mathbf{B} = \mathbf{C}$. *Find:* $|\mathbf{B}|$.

35. *Given:* $\mathbf{A} = 2\mathbf{i} + 5\mathbf{j}$ and $\mathbf{B} = 3\mathbf{i} - \mathbf{j}$; *Find:* a unit vector having the same direction as $\mathbf{A} + \mathbf{B}$.

36. *Given:* $\mathbf{A} = -2\mathbf{i} + 3\mathbf{j}$; $\mathbf{B} = 3\mathbf{i} - 4\mathbf{j}$; $\mathbf{C} = -\mathbf{i} - \mathbf{j}$. *Find:* $|2\mathbf{A} - 3\mathbf{B} - \mathbf{C}|$.

37. *Given:* $\mathbf{A} = -2\mathbf{i} + \mathbf{j}$; $\mathbf{B} = 3\mathbf{i} - 2\mathbf{j}$; $\mathbf{C} = 5\mathbf{i} - 4\mathbf{j}$. *Find:* scalars h and k such that $\mathbf{C} = h\mathbf{A} + k\mathbf{B}$.

38. Write each of the following vectors in the form $r(\cos \theta \, \mathbf{i} + \sin \theta \, \mathbf{j})$, where r is the magnitude of the vector and θ is the angle giving the direction of the vector: (*a*) $\mathbf{A} = 3\mathbf{i} - 3\mathbf{j}$; (*b*) $\mathbf{B} = -4\mathbf{i} + 4\sqrt{3}\mathbf{j}$; (*c*) $\mathbf{C} = -16\mathbf{i}$; (*d*) $\mathbf{D} = 2\mathbf{j}$.

39. For each of the vectors in Exercise 38, find a unit vector having the same direction.

40. Let $\overrightarrow{PQ}$ be a representation of vector $\mathbf{A}$, $\overrightarrow{QR}$ be a representation of vector $\mathbf{B}$, and $\overrightarrow{RS}$ be a representation of vector $\mathbf{C}$. Prove that if $\overrightarrow{PQ}$, $\overrightarrow{QR}$, and $\overrightarrow{RS}$ are sides of a triangle, then $\mathbf{A} + \mathbf{B} + \mathbf{C} = \mathbf{0}$.

41. Prove analytically the triangle inequality for vectors $|\mathbf{A} + \mathbf{B}| \leq |\mathbf{A}| + |\mathbf{B}|$.

42. The vectors $\mathbf{i}$ and $\mathbf{j}$ form a *basis* for vectors in the plane, since every other vector may be written in terms of these two vectors. Is this the only possible set of vectors which forms a basis for vectors in the plane? If your answer is yes, prove it. If your answer is no, give an example of another set.

(18.4) Dot product

18.4.1 DEFINITION   If $A = \langle a_1, a_2 \rangle$ and $B = \langle b_1, b_2 \rangle$ are two vectors, then the dot product of A and B, denoted by $A \cdot B$, is given by

$$A \cdot B = \langle a_1, a_2 \rangle \cdot \langle b_1, b_2 \rangle = a_1 b_1 + a_2 b_2$$

The dot product of two vectors is a real number (or scalar) and not a vector. The dot product is sometimes called the *scalar product* or the *inner product*.

EXAMPLE 1: *Given:* $A = \langle 2, -3 \rangle, B = \langle -\frac{1}{2}, 4 \rangle$. *Find:* $A \cdot B$.
Solution: $A \cdot B = \langle 2, -3 \rangle \cdot \langle -\frac{1}{2}, 4 \rangle = (2)(-\frac{1}{2}) + (-3)(4) = -13$.

The following dot products will be useful and are easily verified (see Exercise 5 at the end of this section).

(1) $i \cdot i = 1$

(2) $j \cdot j = 1$

(3) $i \cdot j = 0$

Laws for dot multiplication of vectors are given in the following theorem.

18.4.2 THEOREM   If A, B, and C are any vectors and k is a scalar, then

(i) $A \cdot B = B \cdot A$ commutative law

(ii) $A \cdot (B + C) = A \cdot B + A \cdot C$ distributive law

(iii) $k(A \cdot B) = (kA) \cdot B$

(iv) $0 \cdot A = 0$

(v) $A \cdot A = |A|^2$

The proofs are left for the reader (see Exercises 6 through 10 at the end of this section).

We now consider what is meant by the angle between two vectors, and this will lead us to another expression for the dot product of two vectors.

18.4.3 DEFINITION   Let A and B be two nonzero vectors such that A is not a scalar multiple of B. If $\overrightarrow{OP}$ is the position representation of A and $\overrightarrow{OQ}$ is the position representation of B, then the angle α between the two vectors A and B is defined to be the positive angle between $\overrightarrow{OP}$ and $\overrightarrow{OQ}$ interior to the triangle POQ. If $A = cB$, where c is a scalar, then the angle $\alpha = 0$ if $c > 0$ and $\alpha = \pi$ if $c < 0$.

From the above definition, we conclude that $0 \leq \alpha \leq \pi$. Figure 18.4.1 shows α if A is not a scalar multiple of B.

The following theorem is perhaps the most important fact about the dot product of two vectors.

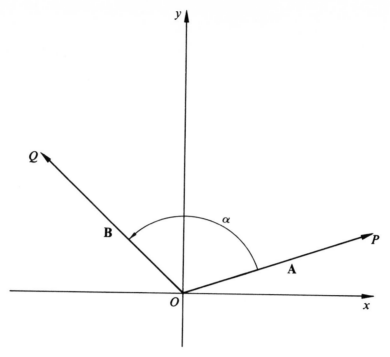

Figure 18.4.1

18.4.4 THEOREM   If α is the angle between the two nonzero vectors **A** and **B**, then

(4) $\mathbf{A} \cdot \mathbf{B} = |\mathbf{A}||\mathbf{B}| \cos \alpha$

Proof: Let $\mathbf{A} = a_1\mathbf{i} + a_2\mathbf{j}$ and $\mathbf{B} = b_1\mathbf{i} + b_2\mathbf{j}$. Let $\overrightarrow{OP}$ be the position representation of **A** and $\overrightarrow{OQ}$ be the position representation of **B**. Then α is the angle at the origin in triangle POQ — see Fig. 18.4.2.

P is the point (a_1, a_2) and Q is the point (b_1, b_2). In triangle OPQ, $|\mathbf{A}|$ is the length of the side OP and $|\mathbf{B}|$ is the length of the side OQ. So, from the law of cosines we obtain

$$\cos \alpha = \frac{|\mathbf{A}|^2 + |\mathbf{B}|^2 - |\overrightarrow{PQ}|^2}{2|\mathbf{A}||\mathbf{B}|}$$

$$= \frac{(a_1{}^2 + a_2{}^2) + (b_1{}^2 + b_2{}^2) - [(a_1 - b_1)^2 - (a_2 - b_2)^2]}{2|\mathbf{A}||\mathbf{B}|}$$

$$= \frac{2a_1b_1 + 2a_2b_2}{2|\mathbf{A}||\mathbf{B}|} = \frac{a_1b_1 + a_2b_2}{|\mathbf{A}||\mathbf{B}|}$$

So, $\cos \alpha = \dfrac{\mathbf{A} \cdot \mathbf{B}}{|\mathbf{A}||\mathbf{B}|}$

from which we obtain

$$\mathbf{A} \cdot \mathbf{B} = |\mathbf{A}||\mathbf{B}| \cos \alpha \qquad\qquad \text{Q.E.D.}$$

Theorem 18.4.4 states that the dot product of two vectors is the product of the magnitudes of the vectors and the cosine of the angle between them.

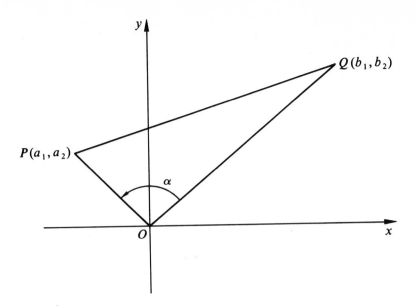

Figure 18.4.2

EXAMPLE 2: *Given:* $\mathbf{A} = 3\mathbf{i} - 2\mathbf{j}$; $\mathbf{B} = 2\mathbf{i} + \mathbf{j}$. *Find:* $\cos \alpha$, if α is the angle between $\mathbf{A}$ and $\mathbf{B}$.

Solution: From Theorem 18.4.4, we have

$$\cos \alpha = \frac{\mathbf{A} \cdot \mathbf{B}}{|\mathbf{A}||\mathbf{B}|} = \frac{(3)(2) + (-2)(1)}{\sqrt{9 + 4} \ \sqrt{4 + 1}}$$

$$= \frac{6 - 2}{\sqrt{13}\sqrt{5}} = \frac{4}{\sqrt{65}}$$

18.4.5 DEFINITION   Two nonzero vectors are said to be *parallel* if the angle between them is zero or π.

18.4.6 DEFINITION   Two vectors are said to be *orthogonal* if and only if the angle between them is $\pi/2$.

The following theorem gives us a method for determining if two vectors are orthogonal.

18.4.7 THEOREM   Two nonzero vectors $\mathbf{A}$ and $\mathbf{B}$ are orthogonal if and only if $\mathbf{A} \cdot \mathbf{B} = 0$.

Proof: From Definition 18.4.6, if α is the angle between the two vectors $\mathbf{A}$ and $\mathbf{B}$, $\mathbf{A}$ and $\mathbf{B}$ are orthogonal if and only if $\alpha = \pi/2$. Since $0 \leq \alpha \leq \pi$, it follows that

(5) $\mathbf{A}$ and $\mathbf{B}$ are orthogonal if and only if $\cos \alpha = 0$

But from Theorem 18.4.4, we have

(6) $\mathbf{A} \cdot \mathbf{B} = |\mathbf{A}||\mathbf{B}| \cos \alpha$

Since neither **A** nor **B** is the zero vector, $|\mathbf{A}| \neq 0$ and $|\mathbf{B}| \neq 0$. Therefore, from (6) we conclude that

(7) $\qquad\qquad \mathbf{A} \cdot \mathbf{B} = 0 \qquad$ if and only if $\qquad \cos \alpha = 0$

From (5) and (7) we have the desired result:

$$\text{A and B are orthogonal if and only if } \mathbf{A} \cdot \mathbf{B} = 0$$

EXAMPLE 3: *Given:* $\mathbf{A} = 3\mathbf{i} + 2\mathbf{j}$; $\mathbf{B} = 2\mathbf{i} + k\mathbf{j}$ where k is a scalar. *Find:* (*a*) k so that **A** and **B** are orthogonal; (*b*) k so that **A** and **B** are parallel.

Solution: (*a*) By Theorem 18.4.7, **A** and **B** are orthogonal if and only if

$$\mathbf{A} \cdot \mathbf{B} = 0$$

or $\qquad (3)(2) + 2(k) = 0$

So $\qquad k = -3$

(*b*) If α is the angle between **A** and **B**, **A** and **B** are parallel if either $\alpha = 0$ or $\alpha = \pi$. So, if $\alpha = 0$ or $\alpha = \pi$,

(8) $\qquad\qquad\qquad \cos \alpha = \pm 1$

Substituting (8) into (4), we obtain

$$\mathbf{A} \cdot \mathbf{B} = \pm |\mathbf{A}||\mathbf{B}|$$

or $\qquad 6 + 2k = \pm\sqrt{13}\sqrt{4 + k^2}$

Squaring both sides of this equation gives us

$$36 + 24k + 4k^2 = 52 + 13k^2$$
$$9k^2 - 24k + 16 = 0$$
$$(3k - 4)^2 = 0$$
$$k = 4/3$$

Vectors have geometric representations which are independent of the coordinate system used. Because of this, vector analysis may be used to prove certain theorems of plane geometry. This is illustrated in the following two examples.

EXAMPLE 4: Prove by vector analysis that the altitudes of a triangle meet in a point.

Solution: Let ABC be a triangle having altitudes AP and BQ intersecting at point S. Draw a line through C and S intersecting AB at point R. We wish to prove that RC is perpendicular to AB — see Fig. 18.4.3.

Let $\overrightarrow{AB}, \overrightarrow{BC}, \overrightarrow{AC}, \overrightarrow{AS}, \overrightarrow{BS}, \overrightarrow{CS}$ be representations of vectors. Let $\mathbf{V}[\overrightarrow{AB}]$ be the vector having directed line segment $\overrightarrow{AB}$ as a representation. Similarly, let $\mathbf{V}[\overrightarrow{BC}], \mathbf{V}[\overrightarrow{AC}], \mathbf{V}[\overrightarrow{AS}], \mathbf{V}[\overrightarrow{BS}],$ and $\mathbf{V}[\overrightarrow{CS}]$ be the vectors having the directed line segment in brackets as a representation.

Since AP is an altitude of the triangle,

(9) $\qquad\qquad\qquad \mathbf{V}[\overrightarrow{AS}] \cdot \mathbf{V}[\overrightarrow{BC}] = 0$

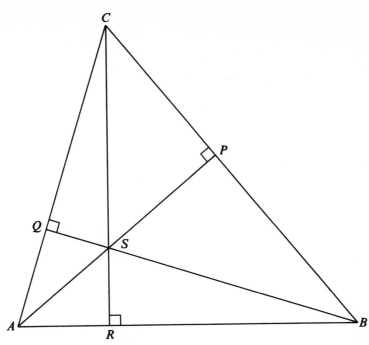

Figure 18.4.3

Also, since BQ is an altitude of the triangle,

(10) $$\text{V}[\overrightarrow{BS}] \cdot \text{V}[\overrightarrow{AC}] = 0$$

In order to prove RC is perpendicular to AB, we shall show that

$$\text{V}[\overrightarrow{CS}] \cdot \text{V}[\overrightarrow{AB}] = 0$$
$$\text{V}[\overrightarrow{CS}] \cdot \text{V}[\overrightarrow{AB}] = \text{V}[\overrightarrow{CS}] \cdot (\text{V}[\overrightarrow{AC}] + \text{V}[\overrightarrow{CB}])$$
$$= \text{V}[\overrightarrow{CS}] \cdot \text{V}[\overrightarrow{AC}] + \text{V}[\overrightarrow{CS}] \cdot \text{V}[\overrightarrow{CB}]$$
$$= (\text{V}[\overrightarrow{CB}] + \text{V}[\overrightarrow{BS}]) \cdot \text{V}[\overrightarrow{AC}] + (\text{V}[\overrightarrow{CA}] + \text{V}[\overrightarrow{AS}]) \cdot \text{V}[\overrightarrow{CB}]$$
$$= \text{V}[\overrightarrow{CB}] \cdot \text{V}[\overrightarrow{AC}] + \text{V}[\overrightarrow{BS}] \cdot \text{V}[\overrightarrow{AC}] + \text{V}[\overrightarrow{CA}] \cdot \text{V}[\overrightarrow{CB}]$$
$$+ \text{V}[\overrightarrow{AS}] \cdot \text{V}[\overrightarrow{CB}]$$

Replacing $\text{V}[\overrightarrow{CA}]$ by $-\text{V}[\overrightarrow{AC}]$ and using (9) and (10), we obtain

$$\text{V}[\overrightarrow{CS}] \cdot \text{V}[\overrightarrow{AB}] = \text{V}[\overrightarrow{CB}] \cdot \text{V}[\overrightarrow{AC}] + 0 + (-\text{V}[\overrightarrow{AC}]) \cdot \text{V}[\overrightarrow{CB}] + 0$$
$$= 0$$

Therefore, altitudes AP, BQ, and RC meet in a point.   Q.E.D.

EXAMPLE 5: Prove by vector analysis that a line drawn from a vertex of a parallelogram to a midpoint of an opposite side is trisected by a diagonal and also trisects the diagonal.

Solution: Let $ABCD$ be the parallelogram, having diagonal BD — see Fig. 18.4.4.

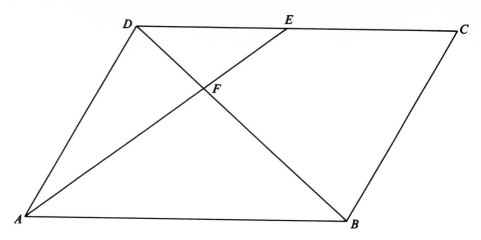

Figure 18.4.4

Let E be the midpoint of DC.

Since $\overrightarrow{DE}$ and $\overrightarrow{EC}$ are equal in length and have the same direction, they are representations of the same vector.

So

$$(11) \qquad \mathbf{V}[\overrightarrow{DE}] = \mathbf{V}[\overrightarrow{EC}]$$

Also,

$$(12) \qquad \mathbf{V}[\overrightarrow{AB}] = 2\mathbf{V}[\overrightarrow{DE}]$$

Let F be the point of intersection of AE and BD. Since $\overrightarrow{AF}$ and $\overrightarrow{AE}$ lie along the same line,

$$(13) \qquad \mathbf{V}[\overrightarrow{AF}] = a\mathbf{V}[\overrightarrow{AE}]$$

where a is a scalar.

Similarly,

$$(14) \qquad \mathbf{V}[\overrightarrow{DF}] = b\mathbf{V}[\overrightarrow{DB}]$$

where b is a scalar.

In order to prove the theorem, we must show that $a = \frac{2}{3}$ and $b = \frac{1}{3}$. Since $\mathbf{V}[\overrightarrow{AE}] = \mathbf{V}[\overrightarrow{AD}] + \mathbf{V}[\overrightarrow{DE}]$, we have from (13)

$$(15) \qquad \mathbf{V}[\overrightarrow{AF}] = a(\mathbf{V}[\overrightarrow{AD}] + \mathbf{V}[\overrightarrow{DE}])$$

Also,

$$(16) \qquad \mathbf{V}[\overrightarrow{AF}] = \mathbf{V}[\overrightarrow{AD}] + \mathbf{V}[\overrightarrow{DF}]$$

Substituting from (14) into (16), we obtain

$$(17) \qquad \mathbf{V}[\overrightarrow{AF}] = \mathbf{V}[\overrightarrow{AD}] + b\mathbf{V}[\overrightarrow{DB}]$$

But

$$(18) \qquad \mathbf{V}[\overrightarrow{DB}] = \mathbf{V}[\overrightarrow{AB}] - \mathbf{V}[\overrightarrow{AD}]$$

Substituting from (18) into (17), we get

$$(19) \qquad \mathbf{V}[\overrightarrow{AF}] = \mathbf{V}[\overrightarrow{AD}] + b(\mathbf{V}[\overrightarrow{AB}] - \mathbf{V}[\overrightarrow{AD}])$$

Equations (15) and (19) give us two expressions for $\mathbf{V}[\overrightarrow{AF}]$. Equating the right-hand sides of (15) and (19) gives us

$$(20) \qquad a\mathbf{V}[\overrightarrow{AD}] + a\mathbf{V}[\overrightarrow{DE}] = \mathbf{V}[\overrightarrow{AD}] + b\mathbf{V}[\overrightarrow{AB}] - b\mathbf{V}[\overrightarrow{AD}]$$

Substituting from (12) into (20), we obtain

$$a\mathbf{V}[\overrightarrow{AD}] + a\mathbf{V}[\overrightarrow{DE}] = \mathbf{V}[\overrightarrow{AD}] + 2b\mathbf{V}[\overrightarrow{DE}] - b\mathbf{V}[\overrightarrow{AD}]$$

Regrouping terms gives us

$$(21) \qquad (a + b - 1)\mathbf{V}[\overrightarrow{AD}] = (2b - a)\mathbf{V}[\overrightarrow{DE}]$$

Since in (21) the coefficients of $\mathbf{V}[\overrightarrow{AD}]$ and $\mathbf{V}[\overrightarrow{DE}]$ are both scalars, these coefficients must both be zero; otherwise $\mathbf{V}[\overrightarrow{AD}]$ would be parallel to $\mathbf{V}[\overrightarrow{DE}]$, which is impossible.

$$\text{Therefore,} \qquad a + b - 1 = 0$$

$$\text{and} \qquad\qquad 2b - a = 0$$

Solving these two equations simultaneously, we obtain $a = \frac{2}{3}$ and $b = \frac{1}{3}$. So, the theorem is proved.

Exercises 18.4

In Exercises 1 through 4, find $\mathbf{A} \cdot \mathbf{B}$.

1. $\mathbf{A} = \langle -1,2 \rangle$; $\mathbf{B} = \langle -4,3 \rangle$ 3. $\mathbf{A} = 2\mathbf{i} - \mathbf{j}$; $\mathbf{B} = \mathbf{i} + 3\mathbf{j}$

2. $\mathbf{A} = \langle 1/3, -1/2 \rangle$; $\mathbf{B} = \langle 5/2, 4/3 \rangle$ 4. $\mathbf{A} = -2\mathbf{i}$; $\mathbf{B} = -\mathbf{i} + \mathbf{j}$

5. Show that $\mathbf{i} \cdot \mathbf{i} = 1$; $\mathbf{j} \cdot \mathbf{j} = 1$; $\mathbf{i} \cdot \mathbf{j} = 0$.

6. Prove Theorem 18.4.2(i).

7. Prove Theorem 18.4.2(ii).

8. Prove Theorem 18.4.2(iii).

9. Prove Theorem 18.4.2(iv).

10. Prove Theorem 18.4.2(v).

In Exercises 11 through 14, if α is the angle between $\mathbf{A}$ and $\mathbf{B}$, find $\cos \alpha$.

11. $\mathbf{A} = \langle 4,3 \rangle$; $\mathbf{B} = \langle 1,-1 \rangle$ 13. $\mathbf{A} = 5\mathbf{i} - 12\mathbf{j}$; $\mathbf{B} = 4\mathbf{i} + 3\mathbf{j}$

12. $\mathbf{A} = \langle -2,-3 \rangle$; $\mathbf{B} = \langle 3,2 \rangle$ 14. $\mathbf{A} = 2\mathbf{i} + 4\mathbf{j}$; $\mathbf{B} = -5\mathbf{j}$

15. Find k so that the angle between the vectors in Example 3 of this section is $\pi/4$.

16. *Given:* $\mathbf{A} = k\mathbf{i} - 2\mathbf{j}$; $\mathbf{B} = 4\mathbf{i} + 6\mathbf{j}$, where k is a scalar. *Find:* k so that $\mathbf{A}$ and $\mathbf{B}$ are orthogonal.

17. Find k so that the vectors given in Exercise 16 have opposite directions.

18. *Given:* $\mathbf{A} = 2\mathbf{i} - k\mathbf{j}$; $\mathbf{B} = k\mathbf{i} + 2\mathbf{j}$, where k is a scalar. *Find:* k so that $\mathbf{A}$ and $\mathbf{B}$ are parallel.

19. *Given:* $\mathbf{A} = 5\mathbf{i} + 12\mathbf{j}$; $\mathbf{B} = \mathbf{i} + k\mathbf{j}$, where k is a scalar. *Find:* k so that the angle between $\mathbf{A}$ and $\mathbf{B}$ is $\pi/3$.

20. Given the vector $\mathbf{A} = \langle a_1, a_2 \rangle$. Find the unit vectors which are orthogonal to $\mathbf{A}$.

21. If $\mathbf{A}$ and $\mathbf{B}$ are vectors, prove that

$$(\mathbf{A} + \mathbf{B}) \cdot (\mathbf{A} + \mathbf{B}) = \mathbf{A} \cdot \mathbf{A} + 2\mathbf{A} \cdot \mathbf{B} + \mathbf{B} \cdot \mathbf{B}$$

22. Prove by vector analysis that the line segment joining the midpoints of two sides of a triangle is parallel to the third side and its length is one-half the length of the third side.

23. Prove by vector analysis that the line segment joining the midpoints of the nonparallel sides of a trapezoid is parallel to the parallel sides and its length is one-half the sum of the lengths of the parallel sides.

24. Prove by vector analysis that the medians of a triangle meet in a point and the point of intersection is two-thirds of the distance from each vertex to the midpoint of the opposite side.

25. Prove by vector analysis that if the diagonals of a parallelogram are perpendicular, then the parallelogram is a rhombus.

26. Prove by vector analysis that the diagonals of a rhombus are perpendicular.

27. Prove by vector analysis that the diagonals of a parallelogram bisect each other.

28. *Given:* triangle ABC, points D, E, and F are on sides AB, BC, and AC, respectively, and $\mathbf{V}[\overrightarrow{AD}] = \frac{1}{3}\mathbf{V}[\overrightarrow{AB}]$; $\mathbf{V}[\overrightarrow{BE}] = \frac{1}{3}\mathbf{V}[\overrightarrow{BC}]$; $\mathbf{V}[\overrightarrow{CF}] = \frac{1}{3}\mathbf{V}[\overrightarrow{CA}]$. *Prove:* $\mathbf{V}[\overrightarrow{AE}] + \mathbf{V}[\overrightarrow{BF}] + \mathbf{V}[\overrightarrow{CD}] = \mathbf{0}$.

29. Prove that the conclusion of Exercise 28 holds when the fraction $\frac{1}{3}$ is replaced by any scalar k.

(18.5) Vector-valued functions and parametric equations

We shall now consider a function whose domain is a set of real numbers and whose range is a set of vectors. Such a function is called a *vector-valued function*. Following is the precise definition.

18.5.1 DEFINITION   Let f and g be two real-valued functions of a real variable t. Then, for every number t in the domain common to f and g, there is a vector **R** defined by

(1) $$\mathbf{R}(t) = f(t)\mathbf{i} + g(t)\mathbf{j}$$

and **R** is called a vector-valued function.

EXAMPLE 1: *Given:* $\mathbf{R}(t) = \sqrt{t-2}\,\mathbf{i} + (t-3)^{-1}\mathbf{j}$. *Find:* the domain of **R**.
  Solution: $f(t) = \sqrt{t-2}$ and $g(t) = (t-3)^{-1}$.
  The domain of **R** is the set of values of t for which both $f(t)$ and $g(t)$ are defined. $f(t)$ is defined for $t \geq 2$ and $g(t)$ is defined for all real numbers except 3. Therefore, the domain of **R** is given by $t \geq 2$, $t \neq 3$.

  If **R** is the vector-valued function defined by (1), as t assumes all values of t in the domain of **R**, the end point of the position representation of the vector $\mathbf{R}(t)$ traces a curve C, and for each such value of t, we obtain a point (x,y) on C, for which

(2) $$x = f(t) \qquad \text{and} \qquad y = g(t)$$

  If we eliminate t from the pair of equations (2), we obtain one equation in x and y, which we may write in the form

(3) $$F(x,y) = 0$$

  The curve C may be defined by either (1), (2), or (3). Equation (1) is called a *vector equation* of C. Equations (2) are called *parametric equations* of C, and t is called a *parameter*. (3) is called a *cartesian equation* of the curve C.
  The curve C is also called a *graph*. The set of all points (x,y) satisfying (2) is called the *graph* of the vector-valued function **R** or the *graph* of either equation (1), equations (2), or equation (3).
  A vector equation of a curve, as well as parametric equations of a curve, gives the curve a direction. That is, if we think of the curve as being traced by a particle, we may consider the positive direction along a curve as the direction in which the particle moves as the parameter t increases. In such a case as this, t may be taken to be the time, and the vector $\mathbf{R}(t)$ is called the *position vector*. Sometimes $\mathbf{R}(t)$ is referred to as the *radius vector*.

EXAMPLE 2: Given the vector equation $\mathbf{R}(t) = 2\cos t\,\mathbf{i} + 2\sin t\,\mathbf{j}$, (*a*) draw a sketch of the graph of this equation, (*b*) find a cartesian equation of the graph.
  Solution: We could tabulate values for x and y for particular values of t. However, if we find the magnitude of the position vector, we have for every t

$$|\mathbf{R}(t)| = \sqrt{4\cos^2 t + 4\sin^2 t} = 2\sqrt{\cos^2 t + \sin^2 t} = 2$$

  Therefore, the end point of the position representation of each vector $\mathbf{R}(t)$ is two units from the origin. Since t may be any number in the closed interval

$[0,2\pi]$, the graph is the circle having center at the origin and radius 2. A sketch of the graph is shown in Fig. 18.5.1. Parametric equations of the graph are

$$x = 2 \cos t \qquad \text{and} \qquad y = 2 \sin t$$

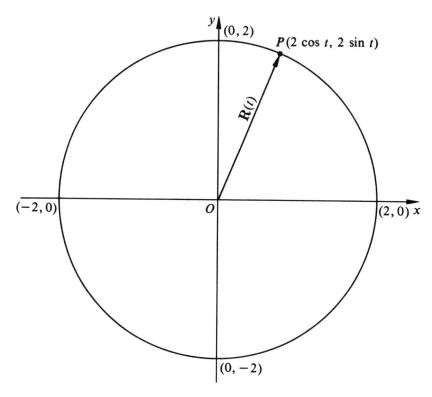

Figure 18.5.1

A cartesian equation of the graph may be found by eliminating t from the two parametric equations, which, upon squaring both sides of each equation and adding, gives

$$x^2 + y^2 = 4$$

As previously stated, upon eliminating t from parametric equations (2) we obtain a cartesian equation (3). Equation (3) defines y as one or more functions of x, either implicitly or explicitly. That is, if $x = f(t)$ and $y = g(t)$, then

$$y = h(x)$$

If h is a differentiable function of x and f is a differentiable function of t, we have from the chain rule,

$$D_t y = (D_x y)(D_t x)$$

$$\text{or} \qquad g'(t) = (h'(x))(f'(t))$$

or, using differential notation,

$$\frac{dy}{dt} = \frac{dy}{dx}\,\frac{dx}{dt}$$

If $dx/dt \neq 0$, we may divide both sides of the above equation by dx/dt and we obtain

(4)
$$\frac{dy}{dx} = \frac{dy/dt}{dx/dt}$$

Equation (4) enables us to find the derivative of y with respect to x directly from the parametric equations.

EXAMPLE 3: *Given:* $x = 3t^2$, $y = 4t^3$. *Find:* dy/dx and d^2y/dx^2 without eliminating t.

Solution: Applying (4), we have

$$\frac{dy}{dx} = \frac{dy/dt}{dx/dt} = \frac{12t^2}{6t} = 2t$$

$$\frac{d^2y}{dx^2} = \frac{d(y')}{dx} = \frac{d(y')/dt}{dx/dt}$$

Since $y' = 2t$, $d(y')/dt = 2$, and so we have from the above

$$\frac{d^2y}{dx^2} = \frac{2}{6t} = \frac{1}{3t}$$

EXAMPLE 4: (*a*) Draw a sketch of the graph of the curve defined by the parametric equations of Example 3; (*b*) find a cartesian equation of the graph in (*a*).

Solution: Since $x = 3t^2$, we conclude that x is never negative. Table 18.5.1 gives values for x and y for particular values of t. Since $D_x y = 2t$, we see that when $t = 0$, $D_x y = 0$, and so the tangent line is horizontal at the point (0,0). A sketch of the graph is shown in Fig. 18.5.2.

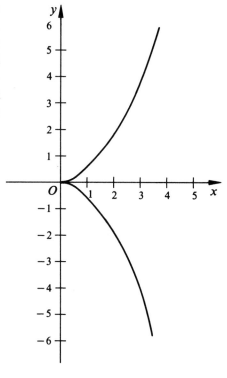

Figure 18.5.2

Table 18.5.1

t	x	y
0	0	0
½	¾	½
1	3	4
2	12	32
−½	¾	−½
−1	3	−4
−2	12	−32

From the two parametric equations $x = 3t^2$ and $y = 4t^3$, we get

$$x^3 = 27t^6 \quad \text{and} \quad y^2 = 16t^6$$

Therefore, $\quad \dfrac{x^3}{27} = \dfrac{y^2}{16}$

or

(5) $$16x^3 = 27y^2$$

which is the cartesian equation desired.

If we take the differential of both sides of equation (5), we have

$$48x^2 \, dx = 54y \, dy$$

Solving for dy/dx, we get

$$\frac{dy}{dx} = \frac{8x^2}{9y}$$

Substituting for x and y in terms of t from the given parametric equations, we obtain

$$\frac{dy}{dx} = \frac{8(3t^2)^2}{9(4t^3)} = 2t$$

which agrees with the value of dy/dx found in Example 3.

We shall now show how parametric equations may be used to define a curve which is described by a physical motion. The curve we shall consider is a *cycloid*, which is the curve traced by a point on the circumference of a circle as the circle rolls along a straight line. Suppose the circle has radius a. Let the fixed straight line on which the circle rolls be the x axis, and let the origin be one of the points at which the given point P comes in contact with the x axis. See Fig. 18.5.3, in which we have the circle after it has rolled through an angle of t radians.

We see from Fig. 18.5.3 that

(6) $$\mathbf{V}(\overrightarrow{OT}) + \mathbf{V}(\overrightarrow{TA}) + \mathbf{V}(\overrightarrow{AP}) = \mathbf{V}(\overrightarrow{OP})$$

$|\mathbf{V}(\overrightarrow{OT})|$ = length of the arc $PT = at$. Since the direction of $\mathbf{V}(\overrightarrow{OT})$ is along the positive x axis, we conclude that

(7) $$\mathbf{V}(\overrightarrow{OT}) = at\mathbf{i}$$

Also, $|\mathbf{V}(\overrightarrow{TA})| = a - a \cos t$, and since the direction of $\mathbf{V}(\overrightarrow{TA})$ is the same as the direction of $\mathbf{j}$, we have

(8) $$\mathbf{V}(\overrightarrow{TA}) = a(1 - \cos t)\mathbf{j}$$

$|\mathbf{V}(\overrightarrow{AP})| = a \sin t$, and the direction of $\mathbf{V}(\overrightarrow{AP})$ is the same as the direction of $-\mathbf{i}$, and so we have

(9) $$\mathbf{V}(\overrightarrow{AP}) = -a \sin t\mathbf{i}$$

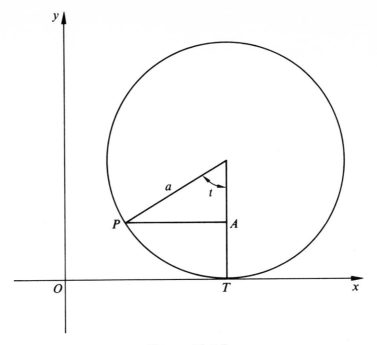

Figure 18.5.3

Substituting (7), (8), and (9) into (6), we obtain

$$at\mathbf{i} + a(1 - \cos t)\mathbf{j} - a \sin t\mathbf{i} = \mathbf{V}(\overrightarrow{OP})$$

or, equivalently,

(10) $$\mathbf{V}(\overrightarrow{OP}) = a(t - \sin t)\mathbf{i} + a(1 - \cos t)\mathbf{j}$$

Equation (10) is a vector equation of the cycloid, and so parametric equations of the cycloid are

(11) $$x = a(t - \sin t) \qquad \text{and} \qquad y = a(1 - \cos t)$$

where t may be any real number. A sketch of a portion of the cycloid is shown in Fig. 18.5.4.

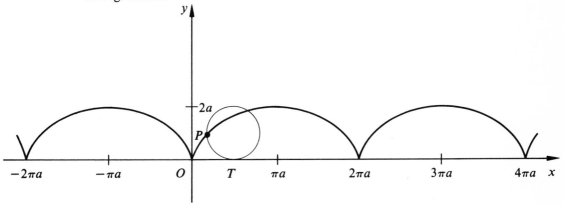

Figure 18.5.4

Exercises 18.5

In Exercises 1 through 6, find the domain of the vector-valued function **R**.

1. $\mathbf{R}(t) = (1/t)\,\mathbf{i} + \sqrt{4 - t}\,\mathbf{j}$

2. $\mathbf{R}(t) = (t^2 + 3)\mathbf{i} + (t - 1)\mathbf{j}$

3. $\mathbf{R}(t) = (\sin^{-1} t)\mathbf{i} + (\cos^{-1} t)\mathbf{j}$

4. $\mathbf{R}(t) = \ln (t + 1)\mathbf{i} + (\tan^{-1} t)\mathbf{j}$

5. $\mathbf{R}(t) = \sqrt{t^2 - 9}\,\mathbf{i} + \sqrt{t^2 + 2t - 8}\,\mathbf{j}$

6. $\mathbf{R}(t) = \sqrt{t - 4}\,\mathbf{i} + \sqrt{4 - t}\,\mathbf{j}$

In Exercises 7 through 12, find dy/dx and d^2y/dx^2 without eliminating the parameter.

7. $x = 3t,\ y = 2t^2$

8. $x = 1 - t^2,\ y = 1 + t$

9. $x = a \sin t,\ y = b \sin t$

10. $x = e^{2t},\ y = 1 + \cos t$

11. $x = t^2 e^t,\ y = t \ln t$

12. $x = a \sin^3 t,\ y = a \cos^3 t$

In Exercises 13 through 16, draw a sketch of the graph of the given vector equation. Also, find a cartesian equation of the graph.

13. $\mathbf{R}(t) = t^2\mathbf{i} + (t + 1)\mathbf{j}$

14. $\mathbf{R}(t) = \dfrac{4}{t^2}\mathbf{i} + \dfrac{4}{t}\mathbf{j}$

15. $\mathbf{R}(t) = e^t\mathbf{i} + e^{-t}\mathbf{j}$

16. $\mathbf{R}(t) = \cos t\,\mathbf{i} + \cos t\,\mathbf{j};\ t$ in $\left[0, \dfrac{\pi}{2}\right]$

In Exercises 17 and 18, find equations of the horizontal tangent lines by finding the values of t for which $dy/dt = 0$, and find equations of the vertical tangent lines by finding the values of t for which $dx/dt = 0$. Then draw a sketch of the graph of the given pair of parametric equations.

17. $x = 4t^2 - 4t,\ y = 1 - 4t^2$

18. $x = \dfrac{3at}{1 + t^3},\ y = \dfrac{3at^2}{1 + t^3}$

19. Find an equation of the tangent line to the curve, $y = 5 \cos \theta,\ x = 2 \sin \theta$, at the point where $\theta = \pi/3$.

20. A projectile moves so that the coordinates of its position at any time t are given by the equations $x = 60t$ and $y = 80t - 16t^2$. Draw a sketch of the path of the projectile.

21. Find dy/dx, d^2y/dx^2, and d^3y/dx^3 at the point on the cycloid having equations (11) for which y has its largest value when x is in the closed interval $[0, 2\pi a]$.

22. A *hypocycloid* is the curve traced by a point P on the circumference of a circle of radius b which is rolling inside a fixed circle of radius a, $a > b$. If the origin is at the center of the fixed circle of radius a, $A(a,0)$ is one of the points at which the given point P comes in contact with the fixed circle, B is the moving point of tangency of the two circles, and the parameter t is

the number of radians in the angle AOB, prove that parametric equations of the hypocycloid are

$$x = (a - b) \cos t + b \cos \frac{a - b}{b} t$$

and $$y = (a - b) \sin t - b \sin \frac{a - b}{b} t$$

23. If $a = 4b$ in Exercise 22, we have a *hypocycloid of four cusps*. Find a cartesian equation of a hypocycloid of four cusps from the parametric equations in Exercise 22, and draw a sketch of the graph of the resulting equation.

(18.6)   Derivatives of vector-valued functions

18.6.1 DEFINITION   Let $\mathbf{R}$ be a vector-valued function whose function values are given by

$$\mathbf{R}(t) = f(t)\mathbf{i} + g(t)\mathbf{j}$$

Then the limit of $\mathbf{R}(t)$ as t approaches t_1 is defined by

$$\lim_{t \to t_1} \mathbf{R}(t) = \left[\lim_{t \to t_1} f(t) \right]\mathbf{i} + \left[\lim_{t \to t_1} g(t) \right]\mathbf{j}$$

if $\lim_{t \to t_1} f(t)$ and $\lim_{t \to t_1} g(t)$ both exist.

EXAMPLE 1: *Given:* $\mathbf{R}(t) = \cos t\mathbf{i} + 2e^t\mathbf{j}$. *Find:* $\lim_{t \to 0} \mathbf{R}(t)$, if it exists.

Solution:

$$\lim_{t \to 0} \mathbf{R}(t) = (\lim_{t \to 0} \cos t)\mathbf{i} + (\lim_{t \to 0} 2e^t)\mathbf{j} = \mathbf{i} + 2\mathbf{j}$$

18.6.2 DEFINITION   The vector-valued function $\mathbf{R}$ is *continuous* at t_1 if and only if the following three conditions are satisfied:

  (i) $\mathbf{R}(t_1)$ exists

  (ii) $\lim_{t \to t_1} \mathbf{R}(t)$ exists

  (iii) $\lim_{t \to t_1} \mathbf{R}(t) = \mathbf{R}(t_1)$

From Definitions 18.6.1 and 18.6.2, it follows that the vector-valued function $\mathbf{R}$, defined by $\mathbf{R}(t) = f(t)\mathbf{i} + g(t)\mathbf{j}$, is continuous at t_1 if and only if f and g are continuous there.

18.6.3 DEFINITION   If $\mathbf{R}$ is a vector-valued function, then the derivative of $\mathbf{R}$ is another vector-valued function, denoted by $\mathbf{R}'$ and defined by

$$\mathbf{R}'(t) = \lim_{\Delta t \to 0} \frac{\mathbf{R}(t + \Delta t) - \mathbf{R}(t)}{\Delta t}$$

if this limit exists.

NOTE: We haven't defined the division of a vector by a scalar; however by the expression

$$\frac{\mathbf{R}(t + \Delta t) - \mathbf{R}(t)}{\Delta t} \qquad \text{we mean} \qquad \frac{1}{\Delta t} [\mathbf{R}(t + \Delta t) - \mathbf{R}(t)]$$

The notation $D_t \mathbf{R}(t)$ is sometimes used in place of $\mathbf{R}'(t)$.

The following theorem follows from Definition 18.6.3 and the definition of the derivative of a real-valued function.

18.6.4 THEOREM   If $\mathbf{R}$ is a vector-valued function defined by

(1) $$\mathbf{R}(t) = f(t)\mathbf{i} + g(t)\mathbf{j}$$

then $$\mathbf{R}'(t) = f'(t)\mathbf{i} + g'(t)\mathbf{j}$$

if $f'(t)$ and $g'(t)$ exist.

Proof: From Definition 18.6.3,

$$\mathbf{R}'(t) = \lim_{\Delta t \to 0} \frac{\mathbf{R}(t + \Delta t) - \mathbf{R}(t)}{\Delta t}$$

$$= \lim_{\Delta t \to 0} \frac{[f(t + \Delta t)\mathbf{i} + g(t + \Delta t)\mathbf{j}] - [f(t)\mathbf{i} + g(t)\mathbf{j}]}{\Delta t}$$

$$= \lim_{\Delta t \to 0} \frac{[f(t + \Delta t) - f(t)]}{\Delta t} \mathbf{i} + \lim_{\Delta t \to 0} \frac{[g(t + \Delta t) - g(t)]}{\Delta t} \mathbf{j}$$

$$= f'(t)\mathbf{i} + g'(t)\mathbf{j} \qquad\qquad\qquad \text{Q.E.D.}$$

The direction of $\mathbf{R}'(t)$ is given by the angle $\theta (0 \leq \theta < 2\pi)$, where

$$\tan \theta = \frac{g'(t)}{f'(t)} = \frac{dy/dt}{dx/dt} = dy/dx$$

From the above, we see that the direction of $\mathbf{R}'(t)$ is along the tangent line to the curve, having vector equation (1), at the point $(f(t), g(t))$.

EXAMPLE 2: *Given:* $\mathbf{R}(t) = (2 + \sin t)\mathbf{i} + \cos t\mathbf{j}$. *Find:* $\mathbf{R}'(t)$.

Solution: $\mathbf{R}'(t) = \cos t\mathbf{i} - \sin t\mathbf{j}$.

Higher-order derivatives of vector-valued functions are defined as for higher-order derivatives of real-valued functions. So, if $\mathbf{R}$ is a vector-valued function defined by $\mathbf{R}(t) = f(t)\mathbf{i} + g(t)\mathbf{j}$, the second derivative of $\mathbf{R}$, denoted by $\mathbf{R}''(t)$, is given by

$$\mathbf{R}''(t) = D_t[\mathbf{R}'(t)]$$

We also have the notation $D_t{}^2 \mathbf{R}(t)$ in place of $\mathbf{R}''(t)$. By applying Theorem 18.6.4 to $\mathbf{R}'(t)$, we obtain

$$\mathbf{R}''(t) = f''(t)\mathbf{i} + g''(t)\mathbf{j}$$

if $f''(t)$ and $g''(t)$ exist.

EXAMPLE 3: *Given:* $\mathbf{R}(t) = (\ln t)\mathbf{i} + (1/t)\mathbf{j}$. *Find:* $\mathbf{R}''(t)$.
Solution:

$$\mathbf{R}'(t) = \frac{1}{t}\mathbf{i} - \frac{1}{t^2}\mathbf{j}$$

$$\mathbf{R}''(t) = -\frac{1}{t^2}\mathbf{i} + \frac{2}{t^3}\mathbf{j}$$

18.6.5 DEFINITION   A vector-valued function $\mathbf{R}$ is said to be *differentiable* on an interval if $\mathbf{R}'(t)$ exists for all values of t in the interval.

The following theorems give differentiation formulas for vector-valued functions. The proofs are based on Theorem 18.6.4 and theorems on differentiation of real-valued functions.

18.6.6 THEOREM   If $\mathbf{R}$ and $\mathbf{Q}$ are differentiable vector-valued functions on an interval, then $\mathbf{R} + \mathbf{Q}$ is differentiable on the interval, and

$$D_t[\mathbf{R}(t) + \mathbf{Q}(t)] = D_t\mathbf{R}(t) + D_t\mathbf{Q}(t)$$

The proof of this theorem is left for the reader (see Exercise 17 at the end of this section).

18.6.7 THEOREM   If $\mathbf{R}$ and $\mathbf{Q}$ are differentiable vector-valued functions on an interval, then $\mathbf{R}\cdot\mathbf{Q}$ is differentiable on the interval, and

$$D_t[\mathbf{R}(t)\cdot\mathbf{Q}(t)] = [D_t\mathbf{R}(t)]\cdot\mathbf{Q}(t) + \mathbf{R}(t)\cdot[D_t\mathbf{Q}(t)]$$

Proof: Let $\mathbf{R}(t) = f_1(t)\mathbf{i} + g_1(t)\mathbf{j}$ and $\mathbf{Q}(t) = f_2(t)\mathbf{i} + g_2(t)\mathbf{j}$.
Then, by Theorem 18.6.4,

$$D_t\mathbf{R}(t) = f_1'(t)\mathbf{i} + g_1'(t)\mathbf{j} \quad \text{and} \quad D_t\mathbf{Q}(t) = f_2'(t)\mathbf{i} + g_2'(t)\mathbf{j}$$
$$\mathbf{R}(t)\cdot\mathbf{Q}(t) = [f_1(t)][f_2(t)] + [g_1(t)][g_2(t)]$$

So,

$$D_t[\mathbf{R}(t)\cdot\mathbf{Q}(t)] = [f_1'(t)][f_2(t)] + [f_1(t)][f_2'(t)] + [g_1'(t)][g_2(t)] + [g_1(t)][g_2'(t)]$$
$$= \{[f_1'(t)][f_2(t)] + [g_1'(t)][g_2(t)]\} + \{[f_1(t)][f_2'(t)] + [g_1(t)][g_2'(t)]\}$$
$$= [D_t\mathbf{R}(t)]\cdot\mathbf{Q}(t) + \mathbf{R}(t)\cdot[D_t\mathbf{Q}(t)] \qquad \text{Q.E.D.}$$

18.6.8 THEOREM   If $\mathbf{R}$ is a differentiable vector-valued function on an interval and f is a differentiable real-valued function on the interval, then

$$D_t\{[f(t)][\mathbf{R}(t)]\} = [D_t f(t)]\mathbf{R}(t) + f(t)\, D_t\mathbf{R}(t)$$

The proof is left for the reader (see Exercise 18 at the end of this section). The following theorem will be useful later.

18.6.9 THEOREM   If $\mathbf{R}$ is a differentiable vector-valued function on an interval and $\mathbf{R}(t)$ is a nonzero vector of constant magnitude and variable direction for all t in the interval, then the vectors $\mathbf{R}(t)$ and $D_t\mathbf{R}(t)$ are orthogonal.

Proof: Let the magnitude of $\mathbf{R}(t)$ be k, a constant. Then by Theorem 18.4.2(v),

$$\mathbf{R}(t) \cdot \mathbf{R}(t) = k^2$$

Differentiating both sides with respect to t and using Theorem 18.6.7, we obtain

$$[D_t\mathbf{R}(t)] \cdot \mathbf{R}(t) + \mathbf{R}(t) \cdot [D_t\mathbf{R}(t)] = 0$$

So, $$2\mathbf{R}(t) \cdot D_t\mathbf{R}(t) = 0$$

Since the dot product of $\mathbf{R}(t)$ and $D_t\mathbf{R}(t)$ is zero, either $\mathbf{R}(t)$ and $D_t\mathbf{R}(t)$ are orthogonal, or either $\mathbf{R}(t)$ or $D_t\mathbf{R}(t)$ is the zero vector. By hypothesis, $\mathbf{R}(t)$ is not the zero vector. If $D_t\mathbf{R}(t)$ is the zero vector, then $\mathbf{R}(t)$ is constant. But $\mathbf{R}(t)$ is not constant, since its direction changes, even though its length is constant. Therefore, $\mathbf{R}(t)$ and $D_t\mathbf{R}(t)$ are orthogonal.   Q.E.D.

The geometric interpretation of Theorem 18.6.9 is evident. If the vector $\mathbf{R}(t)$ has constant magnitude, then the position representation $\overrightarrow{OP}$ of $\mathbf{R}(t)$ has its terminal point P on the circle with center at the origin and radius k. So the graph of $\mathbf{R}$ is this circle. Since $D_t\mathbf{R}(t)$ and $\mathbf{R}(t)$ are orthogonal, $\overrightarrow{OP}$ is perpendicular to a representation of $D_t\mathbf{R}(t)$. Figure 18.6.1 shows a sketch of a quarter circle, the position representation $\overrightarrow{OP}$ of $\mathbf{R}(t)$, and the representation $\overrightarrow{PB}$ of $D_t\mathbf{R}(t)$.

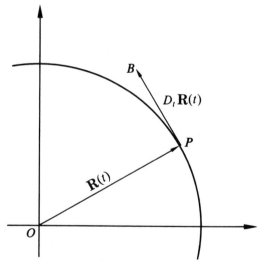

Figure 18.6.1

Exercises 18.6

In Exercises 1 through 4, find the indicated limit, if it exists.

1. $\mathbf{R}(t) = (t - 2)\mathbf{i} + \dfrac{t^2 - 4}{t - 2}\mathbf{j}$; $\lim\limits_{t \to 2} \mathbf{R}(t)$

2. $\mathbf{R}(t) = e^{t+1}\mathbf{i} + |t + 1|\,\mathbf{j}$; $\lim\limits_{t \to -1} \mathbf{R}(t)$

3. $\mathbf{R}(t) = 2 \sin t\mathbf{i} + \cos t\mathbf{j}; \lim_{t \to \pi/2} \mathbf{R}(t)$

4. $\mathbf{R}(t) = \dfrac{t^2 - 2t - 3}{t - 3}\mathbf{i} + \dfrac{t^2 - 5t + 6}{t - 3}\mathbf{j}; \lim_{t \to 3} \mathbf{R}(t)$

In Exercises 5 through 10, find $\mathbf{R}'(t)$ and $\mathbf{R}''(t)$.

5. $\mathbf{R}(t) = (t^2 - 3)\mathbf{i} + (2t + 1)\mathbf{j}$ 8. $\mathbf{R}(t) = \cos 2t\,\mathbf{i} + \tan t\,\mathbf{j}$

6. $\mathbf{R}(t) = \dfrac{t - 1}{t + 1}\mathbf{i} + \dfrac{t - 2}{t}\mathbf{j}$ 9. $\mathbf{R}(t) = \tan^{-1} t\,\mathbf{i} + 2^t\,\mathbf{j}$

7. $\mathbf{R}(t) = e^{2t}\,\mathbf{i} + \ln t\,\mathbf{j}$ 10. $\mathbf{R}(t) = \sqrt{2t + 1}\,\mathbf{i} + (t - 1)^2\,\mathbf{j}$

In Exercises 11 and 12, find $D_t|\mathbf{R}(t)|$.

11. $\mathbf{R}(t) = (t - 1)\mathbf{i} + (2 - t)\mathbf{j}$ 12. $\mathbf{R}(t) = (e^t + 1)\mathbf{i} + (e^t - 1)\mathbf{j}$

In Exercises 13 through 16, find $\mathbf{R}'(t) \cdot \mathbf{R}''(t)$.

13. $\mathbf{R}(t) = (2t^2 - 1)\mathbf{i} + (t^2 + 3)\mathbf{j}$ 15. $\mathbf{R}(t) = -\cos 2t\mathbf{i} + \cos 2t\mathbf{j}$

14. $\mathbf{R}(t) = -\cos 2t\mathbf{i} + \sin 2t\mathbf{j}$ 16. $\mathbf{R}(t) = e^{2t}\mathbf{i} + e^{-2t}\mathbf{j}$

17. Prove Theorem 18.6.6.

18. Prove Theorem 18.6.8.

19. *Given:* the vector equation $\mathbf{R}(t) = \cos t\mathbf{i} + \sin t\mathbf{j}$. *Find:* a cartesian equation of the curve which is traced by the end point of the position representation of $\mathbf{R}'(t)$. *Find:* $\mathbf{R}(t) \cdot \mathbf{R}'(t)$. Interpret the result geometrically.

20. *Given:* $\mathbf{R}(t) = 2t\mathbf{i} + (t^2 - 1)\mathbf{j}$ and $\mathbf{Q}(t) = 3t\mathbf{i}$. If $\alpha(t)$ is the angle between $\mathbf{R}(t)$ and $\mathbf{Q}(t)$, find $D_t\alpha(t)$.

21. Suppose $\mathbf{R}$ and $\mathbf{R}'$ are vector-valued functions defined on an interval and $\mathbf{R}'$ is differentiable on the interval. *Prove:*

$$D_t[\mathbf{R}'(t) \cdot \mathbf{R}(t)] = |\mathbf{R}'(t)|^2 + \mathbf{R}(t) \cdot \mathbf{R}''(t)$$

22. If $|\mathbf{R}(t)| = h(t)$, prove that $\mathbf{R}(t) \cdot \mathbf{R}'(t) = [h(t)][h'(t)]$.

23. If the vector-valued function $\mathbf{R}$ and the real-valued function f are both differentiable on an interval and $f(t) \neq 0$ on the interval, prove that $\mathbf{R}/f$ is also differentiable on the interval and

$$D_t\left[\frac{\mathbf{R}(t)}{f(t)}\right] = \frac{f(t)\mathbf{R}'(t) - f'(t)\mathbf{R}(t)}{[f(t)]^2}$$

(18.7)   Length of arc

In Sec. 11.10, we obtained a formula for finding the length of arc of a curve having an equation of the form $y = f(x)$. This is a special kind of curve, since the graph of a function f cannot be intersected by a vertical line in more than one point.

We shall now develop a method for finding the length of arc of some other kinds of curves. Let C be the curve having parametric equations

(1) $$x = f(t) \quad \text{and} \quad y = g(t)$$

and suppose f and g are continuous on the closed interval $[a,b]$. Also suppose no two values of t give the same point (x,y) on C; that is, the curve does not intersect itself. We wish to assign a number L to represent the length of arc of C from $t = a$ to $t = b$. We proceed in a manner similar to that in Sec. 11.10.

Let Δ be a partition of the closed interval $[a,b]$ formed by dividing the interval into n subintervals by choosing $n - 1$ numbers between a and b. Let $t_0 = a$ and $t_n = b$, and let $t_1, t_2, \ldots, t_{n-1}$ be the intermediate numbers, so that

$$t_0 < t_1 < \cdots < t_{n-1} < t_n$$

The ith subinterval is $[t_{i-1},t_i]$ and its length, denoted by $\Delta_i t$, is $t_i - t_{i-1}$, where $i = 1, 2, \ldots, n$. Let $||\Delta||$ be the norm of the partition; so, each $\Delta_i t \leq ||\Delta||$.

Associated with each number t_i is a point $P_i(f(t_i),g(t_i))$ on C. From each point P_{i-1} draw a line segment to the next point P_i — see Fig. 18.7.1. The

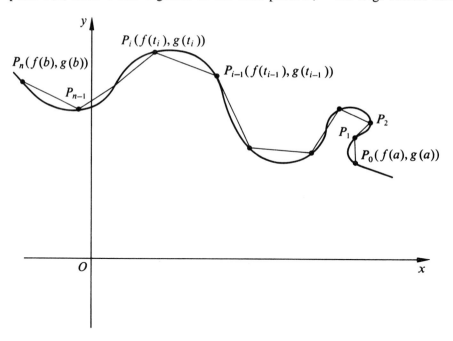

Figure 18.7.1

length of the line segment from P_{i-1} to P_i is denoted by $|\overline{P_{i-1}P_i}|$, and from the distance formula we have

(2) $$|\overline{P_{i-1}P_i}| = \sqrt{[f(t_i) - f(t_{i-1})]^2 + [g(t_i) - g(t_{i-1})]^2}$$

The sum of the lengths of the n line segments is

$$(3) \qquad \sum_{i=1}^{n} |\overline{P_{i-1}P_i}|$$

Our intuitive notion of the length of the arc from $t = a$ to $t = b$ leads us to define the length of arc as the limit of the sum in (3) as $||\Delta||$ approaches zero.

18.7.1 DEFINITION   Let the curve C have parametric equations $x = f(t)$ and $y = g(t)$, and suppose that no two values of t give the same point (x,y) on C. Then, if there exists a number L having the property that for any $\epsilon > 0$, there is a $\delta > 0$ such that

$$\left| \sum_{i=1}^{n} |\overline{P_{i-1}P_i}| - L \right| < \epsilon$$

for every partition Δ of the interval $[a,b]$ for which $||\Delta|| < \delta$, then we write

$$(4) \qquad L = \lim_{||\Delta|| \to 0} \sum_{i=1}^{n} |\overline{P_{i-1}P_i}|$$

and L is called the length of arc of the curve C from the point $(f(a),g(a))$ to the point $(f(b),g(b))$.

The arc of the curve is rectifiable if the limit in (4) exists.

If f' and g' are continuous on $[a,b]$, we can find a formula for evaluating the limit in (4). We proceed as follows.

Since f' and g' are continuous on $[a,b]$, they are continuous on each subinterval of the partition Δ. So, the hypothesis of the mean-value theorem (Theorem 8.5.1) is satisfied by f and g on each $[t_{i-1},t_i]$, and therefore there are numbers z_i and w_i in the open interval (t_{i-1},t_i) such that

$$(5) \qquad f(t_i) - f(t_{i-1}) = f'(z_i) \Delta_i t$$

and

$$(6) \qquad g(t_i) - g(t_{i-1}) = g'(w_i) \Delta_i t$$

Substituting from (5) and (6) into (2), we obtain

$$|\overline{P_{i-1}P_i}| = \sqrt{[f'(z_i) \Delta_i t]^2 + [g'(w_i) \Delta_i t]^2}$$

or, equivalently,

$$(7) \qquad |\overline{P_{i-1}P_i}| = \sqrt{[f'(z_i)]^2 + [g'(w_i)]^2} \, \Delta_i t$$

where z_i and w_i are in the open interval (t_{i-1},t_i). Then from (4) and (7), if the limit exists,

$$(8) \qquad L = \lim_{||\Delta|| \to 0} \sum_{i=1}^{n} \sqrt{[f'(z_i)]^2 + [g'(w_i)]^2} \, \Delta_i t$$

The sum in (8) is not a Riemann sum, since z_i and w_i are not necessarily the same numbers. So we cannot apply the definition of a definite integral to evaluate the limit in (8). However, there is a theorem which we can apply to evaluate this limit. We state the theorem, but a proof is not given since it is beyond the scope of this book. The reader will find a proof in most advanced calculus texts.

18.7.2 THEOREM If the functions F and G are continuous on the closed interval $[a,b]$, then the function $\sqrt{F^2 + G^2}$ is also continuous on $[a,b]$, and if Δ is a partition of the interval $[a,b]$(Δ: $a = t_0 < t_1 < \cdots < t_{i-1} < t_i < \cdots < t_n = b$) and z_i and w_i are any numbers in (t_{i-1}, t_i), then

(9)
$$\lim_{\|\Delta\| \to 0} \sum_{i=1}^{n} \sqrt{[F(z_i)]^2 + [G(w_i)]^2}\, \Delta_i t = \int_a^b \sqrt{[F(t)]^2 + [G(t)]^2}\, dt$$

Applying (9) to (8) where F is f' and G is g', we have

$$L = \int_a^b \sqrt{[f'(t)]^2 + [g'(t)]^2}\, dt$$

We state this result as a theorem.

18.7.3 THEOREM Let the curve C have parametric equations $x = f(t)$ and $y = g(t)$, and suppose f' and g' are continuous on the closed interval $[a,b]$. Further, suppose that no two values of t give the same point (x,y) on C. Then the length of arc L of the curve C from the point $(f(a), g(a))$ to the point $(f(b),g(b))$ is given by

(10)
$$L = \int_a^b \sqrt{[f'(t)]^2 + [g'(t)]^2}\, dt$$

EXAMPLE 1: Find the length of the arc of the curve having parametric equations $x = t^3$ and $y = 2t^2$ in each of the following cases: (a) from $t = 0$ to $t = 1$; (b) from $t = -2$ to $t = 0$.

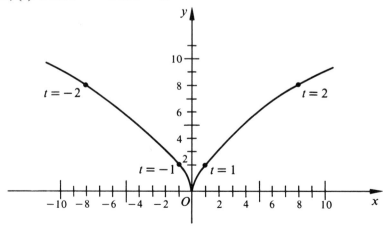

Figure 18.7.2

Solution: A sketch of the curve is shown in Fig. 18.7.2.

(a) Letting $x = f(t), f'(t) = D_t x = 3t^2$, and letting $y = g(t), g'(t) = D_t y = 4t$. So, from Theorem 18.7.3, if L is the length of the arc of the curve from $t = 0$ to $t = 1$,

$$L = \int_0^1 \sqrt{9t^4 + 16t^2}\, dt = \int_0^1 t\sqrt{9t^2 + 16}\, dt$$

$$= \frac{1}{18} \cdot \frac{2}{3}(9t^2 + 16)^{3/2}\Big]_0^1 = \frac{1}{27}[(25)^{3/2} - (16)^{3/2}]$$

$$= \frac{1}{27}(125 - 64) = \frac{61}{27}$$

(b) If L is the length of the arc of the curve from $t = -2$ to $t = 0$, we have from Theorem 18.7.3,

$$L = \int_{-2}^0 \sqrt{9t^4 + 16t^2}\, dt = \int_{-2}^0 \sqrt{t^2}\, \sqrt{9t^2 + 16}\, dt$$

Since $-2 \le t \le 0$, $\sqrt{t^2} = -t$, and so we have

$$L = \int_{-2}^0 -t\sqrt{9t^2 + 16}\, dt = -\frac{1}{27}(9t^2 + 16)^{3/2}\Big]_{-2}^0$$

$$= -\frac{1}{27}[(16)^{3/2} - (50)^{3/2}] = \frac{1}{27}(250\sqrt{2} - 64) \approx 10.7$$

C is the curve having parametric equations (1). Let s be the length of arc of C from the point $(f(t_0), g(t_0))$ to the point $(f(t), g(t))$, and let s increase as t increases. Then, s is a function of t and is given by

$$(11) \qquad\qquad s = \int_{t_0}^t \sqrt{[f'(u)]^2 + [g'(u)]^2}\, du$$

From Theorem 10.6.1, we have

$$(12) \qquad\qquad \frac{ds}{dt} = \sqrt{[f'(t)]^2 + [g'(t)]^2}$$

A vector equation of C is

$$(13) \qquad\qquad \mathbf{R}(t) = f(t)\mathbf{i} + g(t)\mathbf{j}$$

Since

$$\mathbf{R}'(t) = f'(t)\mathbf{i} - g'(t)\mathbf{j}$$

we have

$$(14) \qquad\qquad |\mathbf{R}'(t)| = \sqrt{[f'(t)]^2 + [g'(t)]^2}$$

Substituting from (14) into (12), we obtain

$$(15) \qquad\qquad |\mathbf{R}'(t)| = \frac{ds}{dt}$$

From (15) we conclude that if s is the length of arc of curve C having vector equation (13) measured from some fixed point to the point $(f(t), g(t))$ where s increases as t increases, then the derivative of s with respect to t is the magnitude of the derivative of the position vector at the point $(f(t), g(t))$.

If we substitute from (14) into (10), we obtain $L = \int_a^b |\mathbf{R}'(t)|\, dt$. So Theorem 18.7.3 may be stated in terms of vectors in the following way.

18.7.4 THEOREM   Let the curve C have the vector equation $\mathbf{R}(t) = f(t)\mathbf{i} + g(t)\mathbf{j}$, and suppose f' and g' are continuous on the closed interval $[a,b]$. Then the length of arc of C, traced by the terminal point of the position representation of $\mathbf{R}(t)$ as t increases from a to b, is given by

(16) $$L = \int_a^b |\mathbf{R}'(t)|\, dt$$

EXAMPLE 2: Find the length of the arc traced by the terminal point of the position representation of $\mathbf{R}(t)$ as t increases from 1 to 4 if

$$\mathbf{R}(t) = e^t \sin t\mathbf{i} + e^t \cos t\mathbf{j}.$$

Solution: $\mathbf{R}'(t) = (e^t \sin t + e^t \cos t)\mathbf{i} + (e^t \cos t - e^t \sin t)\mathbf{j}$. Therefore,

$$|\mathbf{R}'(t)| = e^t\sqrt{\sin^2 t + 2\sin t \cos t + \cos^2 t + \cos^2 t - 2\sin t \cos t + \sin^2 t}$$

$$= e^t\sqrt{2}$$

From (16), we have

$$L = \int_1^4 \sqrt{2}e^t\, dt = \sqrt{2}e^t\Big]_1^4 = \sqrt{2}(e^4 - e)$$

An alternate form of (10) for the length of an arc of a curve C, having parametric equations $x = f(t)$ and $y = g(t)$, is obtained by replacing $f'(t)$ by dx/dt and $g'(t)$ by dy/dt, and we have

(17) $$L = \int_a^b \sqrt{\left(\frac{dx}{dt}\right)^2 + \left(\frac{dy}{dt}\right)^2}\, dt$$

Now suppose we wish to find the length of arc of a curve C whose polar equation is $r = F(\theta)$. If (x,y) is the cartesian representation of a point P on C and (r,θ) is a polar representation of P, then

(18) $$x = r\cos\theta \qquad \text{and} \qquad y = r\sin\theta$$

Replacing r by $F(\theta)$ in equations (18), we have

(19) $$x = \cos\theta F(\theta) \qquad \text{and} \qquad y = \sin\theta F(\theta)$$

Equations (19) may be considered as parametric equations of C where θ is the parameter instead of t. Therefore, if F' is continuous on the closed interval $[\alpha,\beta]$, the formula for the length of arc L of the curve C whose polar equation is $r = F(\theta)$ is obtained from (17) by taking $t = \theta$. So we have

(20) $$L = \int \sqrt{\left(\frac{dx}{d\theta}\right)^2 + \left(\frac{dy}{d\theta}\right)^2}\, d\theta$$

From (18), we have

$$\frac{dx}{d\theta} = \cos\theta\frac{dr}{d\theta} - r\sin\theta \qquad \text{and} \qquad \frac{dy}{d\theta} = \sin\theta\frac{dr}{d\theta} + r\cos\theta$$

Therefore,

$$\sqrt{\left(\frac{dx}{d\theta}\right)^2 + \left(\frac{dy}{d\theta}\right)^2}$$

$$= \sqrt{\left(\cos\theta\,\frac{dr}{d\theta} - r\sin\theta\right)^2 + \left(\sin\theta\,\frac{dr}{d\theta} + r\cos\theta\right)^2}$$

$$= \sqrt{\cos^2\theta\left(\frac{dr}{d\theta}\right)^2 - 2r\sin\theta\cos\theta\,\frac{dr}{d\theta} + r^2\sin^2\theta + \sin^2\theta\left(\frac{dr}{d\theta}\right)^2 + 2r\sin\theta\cos\theta\,\frac{dr}{d\theta} + r^2\cos^2\theta}$$

$$= \sqrt{(\cos^2\theta + \sin^2\theta)\left(\frac{dr}{d\theta}\right)^2 + (\sin^2\theta + \cos^2\theta)r^2} = \sqrt{\left(\frac{dr}{d\theta}\right)^2 + r^2}$$

Substituting this into (20), we obtain

$$(21) \qquad\qquad L = \int_{\alpha}^{\beta} \sqrt{\left(\frac{dr}{d\theta}\right)^2 + r^2}\, d\theta$$

EXAMPLE 3: Find the length of the cardioid $r = 2(1 + \cos\theta)$.

Solution: A sketch of the curve is shown in Fig. 18.7.3.

To obtain the length of the entire curve, we may let θ take on values from 0 to 2π or we may make use of the symmetry of the curve and find half the length by letting θ take on values from 0 to π.

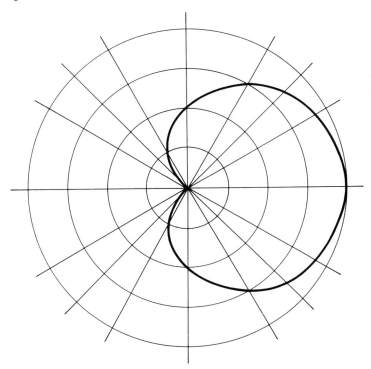

Figure 18.7.3

Since $r = 2(1 + \cos \theta)$, $dr/d\theta = -2 \sin \theta$. Substituting into (21), integrating from 0 to π, and multiplying by 2, we have

$$L = 2 \int_0^\pi \sqrt{(-2 \sin \theta)^2 + 4 (1 + \cos \theta)^2} \, d\theta$$

$$= 4 \int_0^\pi \sqrt{\sin^2 \theta + 1 + 2 \cos \theta + \cos^2 \theta} \, d\theta$$

$$= 4\sqrt{2} \int_0^\pi \sqrt{1 + \cos \theta} \, d\theta$$

To evaluate this integral, we use the identity $\cos^2 (\theta/2) = (1 + \cos \theta)/2$, which gives us $\sqrt{1 + \cos \theta} = \sqrt{2} \, |\cos (\theta/2)|$. Since $0 \leq \theta \leq \pi, 0 \leq \theta/2 \leq \pi/2$, and so $\cos \theta/2 \geq 0$. Therefore, $\sqrt{1 + \cos \theta} = \sqrt{2} \cos (\theta/2)$. So, we have

$$L = 4\sqrt{2} \int_0^\pi \sqrt{2} \cos \frac{\theta}{2} \, d\theta = 16 \sin \frac{\theta}{2} \Big]_0^\pi = 16$$

Exercises 18.7

Find the length of arc in each of the following Exercises.

1. $x = \frac{1}{2}t^2 + t, y = \frac{1}{2}t^2 - t$; from $t = 0$ to $t = 1$.

2. $x = t^3, y = 3t^2$; from $t = -2$ to $t = 0$.

3. $\mathbf{R}(t) = 2t^2\mathbf{i} + 2t^3\mathbf{j}$; from $t = 1$ to $t = 2$.

4. $\mathbf{R}(t) = a (\cos t + t \sin t)\mathbf{i} + a(\sin t - t \cos t)\mathbf{j}$; from $t = 0$ to $t = \pi/3$.

5. The entire hypocycloid: $x = a \cos^3 t, y = a \sin^3 t$.

6. $x = e^{-t} \cos t, y = e^{-t} \sin t$; from $t = 0$ to $t = \pi$.

7. One arch of the cycloid: $x = a(t - \sin t), y = a(1 - \cos t)$.

8. The circumference of the circle: $\mathbf{R}(t) = a \cos t\mathbf{i} + a \sin t\mathbf{j}$.

9. The circumference of the circle: $r = a \sin \theta$.

10. The circumference of the circle: $r = a$.

11. The entire curve: $r = 3 \cos^2 \frac{1}{2}\theta$.

12. The entire curve: $r = 1 - \sin \theta$.

13. $r = a\theta$; from $\theta = 0$ to $\theta = 2\pi$.

14. $r = 3 \sec \theta$; from $\theta = 0$ to $\theta = \pi/4$.

15. $r = a \sin^3 \frac{1}{3}\theta$; from $\theta = 0$ to $\theta = \theta_1$.

16. $r = a\theta^2$; from $\theta = 0$ to $\theta = \pi$.

(18.8)   Plane motion

In our previous discussion of the motion of a particle, we confined ourselves to straight-line motion. In this connection, we defined the velocity and acceleration of a particle moving along a straight line. We shall now consider the motion of a particle along a curve in the plane.

Suppose C is the plane curve having parametric equations $x = f(t), y = g(t)$, where t denotes time. Then

$$\mathbf{R}(t) = f(t)\mathbf{i} + g(t)\mathbf{j}$$

is the vector equation of C. As t varies, the end point $P(f(t),g(t))$ of $\overrightarrow{OP}$ moves along the curve C. The position at time t of a particle moving along C is the point $P(f(t),g(t))$. The *velocity vector* of the particle at time t is defined to be $\mathbf{R}'(t)$. We denote the velocity vector by the symbol $\mathbf{V}(t)$, instead of $\mathbf{R}'(t)$.

18.8.1 DEFINITION   Let C be the curve having parametric equations $x = f(t)$ and $y = g(t)$. If a particle is moving along C, so that its position at any time t is the point (x,y), then the *instantaneous velocity* of the particle at time t is given by the velocity vector

$$\mathbf{V}(t) = f'(t)\mathbf{i} + g'(t)\mathbf{j}$$

if $f'(t)$ and $g'(t)$ exist.

In Sec. 18.6, we saw that the direction of $\mathbf{R}'(t)$ at the point $P(f(t),g(t))$ is along the tangent line to the curve C at P. Therefore the velocity vector $\mathbf{V}(t)$ has this direction at P.

The magnitude of the velocity vector is called the *speed* of the particle at time t and is given by

$$(1) \qquad\qquad |\mathbf{V}(t)| = \sqrt{[f'(t)]^2 + [g'(t)]^2}$$

Note that the velocity is a vector and the speed is a scalar.

As shown in Sec. 18.7, the expression on the right-hand side of (1) is ds/dt. So the speed is the rate of change of arc length s with respect to t, and we write

$$(2) \qquad\qquad |\mathbf{V}(t)| = \frac{ds}{dt}$$

The *acceleration vector* of the particle at time t is defined to be the derivative of the velocity vector or, equivalently, the second derivative of the position vector. The acceleration vector is denoted by $\mathbf{A}(t)$.

18.8.2 DEFINITION   The *instantaneous acceleration* at time t of a particle moving along a curve C, having parametric equations $x = f(t)$ and $y = g(t)$, is given by the acceleration vector

$$\mathbf{A}(t) = \mathbf{V}'(t) = \mathbf{R}''(t)$$

where $\mathbf{R}(t) = f(t)\mathbf{i} + g(t)\mathbf{j}$ and $\mathbf{R}''(t)$ exists.

Figure 18.8.1 shows the representations of the velocity vector and the acceleration vector whose initial point is the point P on C.

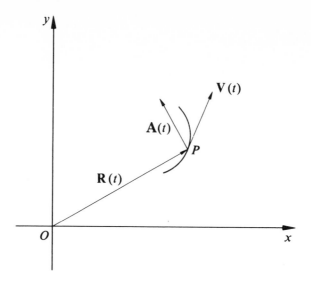

Figure 18.8.1

EXAMPLE 1: A particle is moving along the curve whose parametric equations are $x = 4 \cos \tfrac{1}{2}t$ and $y = 4 \sin \tfrac{1}{2}t$. If t is the number of seconds in the time and x and y represent number of feet, find the speed and the magnitude of the acceleration vector of the particle at time t. Draw a sketch of the path of the particle and also draw the representations of the velocity and acceleration vectors having initial point where $t = \pi/3$.

Solution: The vector equation of C is

$$\mathbf{R}(t) = 4 \cos \tfrac{1}{2}t\,\mathbf{i} + 4 \sin \tfrac{1}{2}t\,\mathbf{j}$$

$$\mathbf{V}(t) = \mathbf{R}'(t) = -2 \sin \tfrac{1}{2}t\,\mathbf{i} + 2 \cos \tfrac{1}{2}t\,\mathbf{j}$$

$$\mathbf{A}(t) = \mathbf{V}'(t) = -\cos \tfrac{1}{2}t\,\mathbf{i} - \sin \tfrac{1}{2}t\,\mathbf{j}$$

$$|\mathbf{V}(t)| = \sqrt{(-2 \sin \tfrac{1}{2}t)^2 + (2 \cos \tfrac{1}{2}t)^2}$$

$$= \sqrt{4 \sin^2 \tfrac{1}{2}t + 4 \cos^2 \tfrac{1}{2}t} = 2$$

$$|\mathbf{A}(t)| = \sqrt{(-\cos \tfrac{1}{2}t)^2 + (-\sin \tfrac{1}{2}t)^2} = 1$$

Therefore the speed of the particle is constant and is 2 ft/sec. The magnitude of the acceleration vector is also constant and is 1 ft/sec².

Eliminating t between the parametric equations of C, we obtain the cartesian equation $x^2 + y^2 = 16$, which is a circle with center at O and radius 4.

$$\mathbf{V}(t) \cdot \mathbf{A}(t) = (-2 \sin \tfrac{1}{2}t)(-\cos \tfrac{1}{2}t) + (2 \cos \tfrac{1}{2}t)(-\sin \tfrac{1}{2}t) = 0$$

So the velocity vector and the acceleration vector are orthogonal at every point of C. Since the direction of the velocity vector is along the tangent line to C, the acceleration vector will have direction toward the center of the circle. When $t = \pi/3$, the direction of $\mathbf{V}(t)$ is given by $\tan \theta = -\cos (\pi/6) = -\sqrt{3}$.

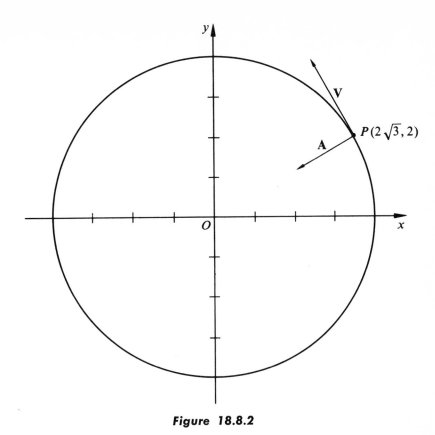

Figure 18.8.2

Figure 18.8.2 shows the representations of the velocity and acceleration vectors having initial point where $t = \pi/3$.

EXAMPLE 2: The position of a moving particle at time t is given by the vector equation

$$\mathbf{R}(t) = e^{-2t}\mathbf{i} + 3e^t\mathbf{j}$$

Find: $\mathbf{V}(t)$, $\mathbf{A}(t)$, $|\mathbf{V}(t)|$, $|\mathbf{A}(t)|$.

Draw a sketch of the path of the particle and the representations of the velocity and acceleration vectors having initial point where $t = \frac{1}{2}$.

Solution:

$$\mathbf{V}(t) = \mathbf{R}'(t) = -2e^{-2t}\mathbf{i} + 3e^t\mathbf{j}$$

$$\mathbf{A}(t) = \mathbf{V}'(t) = 4e^{-2t}\mathbf{i} + 3e^t\mathbf{j}$$

$$|\mathbf{V}(t)| = \sqrt{4e^{-4t} + 9e^{2t}}$$

$$|\mathbf{A}(t)| = \sqrt{16e^{-4t} + 9e^{2t}}$$

$$|\mathbf{V}(\tfrac{1}{2})| = \sqrt{4e^{-2} + 9e} \approx 5.01$$

$$|\mathbf{A}(\tfrac{1}{2})| = \sqrt{16e^{-2} + 9e} \approx 5.15$$

Parametric equations of the path of the particle are $x = e^{-2t}$ and $y = 3e^t$. Eliminating t between these two equations, we obtain

$$xy^2 = 9$$

Since $x > 0$ and $y > 0$, the path of the particle is the portion of the curve $xy^2 = 9$ in the first quadrant. Figure 18.8.3 shows the path of the particle and the velocity and acceleration vectors when $t = \frac{1}{2}$. The slope of $\mathbf{V}(\frac{1}{2})$ is $-3e^{3/2}/2 \approx -6.7$ and the slope of $\mathbf{A}(1/2)$ is $3e^{3/2}/4 \approx 3.4$.

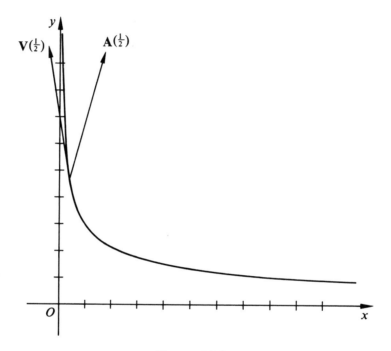

Figure 18.8.3

Exercises 18.8

In Exercises 1 through 6, a particle is moving along the curve having the given parametric equations, where t is the time. *Find:* (a) the velocity vector $\mathbf{V}(t)$; (b) the acceleration vector $\mathbf{A}(t)$; (c) the speed at $t = t_1$; (d) the magnitude of the acceleration vector at $t = t_1$. Draw a sketch of the path of the particle and the representations of the velocity vector and the acceleration vector at $t = t_1$.

1. $x = t^2 + 4$, $y = t - 2$; $t_1 = 3$
2. $x = 2\cos t$, $y = 3\sin t$; $t_1 = \pi/3$
3. $x = t$, $y = \ln \sec t$; $t_1 = \pi/4$
4. $x = 2/t$, $y = -t/4$; $t_1 = 4$
5. $x = \sin t$, $y = \tan t$; $t_1 = \pi/6$
6. $x = e^{2t}$, $y = e^{3t}$; $t_1 = 0$

In Exercises 7 through 12, the position of a moving particle at time t is given by a vector equation. *Find:* (a) $\mathbf{V}(t_1)$; (b) $\mathbf{A}(t_1)$; (c) $|\mathbf{V}(t_1)|$; (d) $|\mathbf{A}(t_1)|$ at the given time $t = t_1$. Draw a sketch of a portion of the path of the particle containing the position of the particle at $t = t_1$, and draw the representations of $\mathbf{V}(t_1)$ and $\mathbf{A}(t_1)$ having initial point where $t = t_1$.

7. $\mathbf{R}(t) = (2t - 1)\mathbf{i} + (t^2 + 1)\mathbf{j}$; $t_1 = 3$

8. $\mathbf{R}(t) = (t^2 + 3t)\mathbf{i} + (1 - 3t^2)\mathbf{j}$; $t_1 = \dfrac{1}{2}$

9. $\mathbf{R}(t) = \cos 2t\mathbf{i} - 3 \sin t\mathbf{j}$; $t_1 = \pi$

10. $\mathbf{R}(t) = e^{-t}\mathbf{i} + e^{2t}\mathbf{j}$; $t_1 = \ln 2$

11. $\mathbf{R}(t) = 2(1 - \cos t)\mathbf{i} + 2(1 - \sin t)\mathbf{j}$; $t_1 = 5\pi/6$

12. $\mathbf{R}(t) = \ln (t + 2)\mathbf{i} + \frac{1}{3}t^2\mathbf{j}$; $t_1 = 1$

(18.9)   Indefinite integration of vector-valued functions

In the next section we shall learn how vector analysis may be used to derive the equations of motion of a projectile. In this connection, we shall need to find an indefinite integral (or anti-derivative) of a vector-valued function. We make the following definition.

18.9.1 DEFINITION   If $\mathbf{Q}$ is the vector-valued function given by

$$\mathbf{Q}(t) = f(t)\mathbf{i} + g(t)\mathbf{j}$$

then the indefinite integral of $\mathbf{Q}(t)$ is defined by

(1) $$\int \mathbf{Q}(t)\, dt = \mathbf{i} \int f(t)\, dt + \mathbf{j} \int g(t)\, dt$$

This definition is consistent with the definition of an indefinite integral of a real-valued function, since if we take the derivative of both sides of (1) with respect to t, we have

$$D_t \int \mathbf{Q}(t)\, dt = \mathbf{i}\, D_t \int f(t)\, dt + \mathbf{j}\, D_t \int g(t)\, dt$$

which gives us

$$D_t \int \mathbf{Q}(t)\, dt = \mathbf{i} f(t) + \mathbf{j} g(t)$$

For each of the indefinite integrals on the right-hand side of (1), there occurs an arbitrary scalar constant, and when each of these scalars is multiplied by either $\mathbf{i}$ or $\mathbf{j}$, there occurs an arbitrary constant vector in the sum. So we have

$$\int \mathbf{Q}(t)\, dt = \mathbf{R}(t) + \mathbf{C}$$

where $D_t\mathbf{R}(t) = \mathbf{Q}(t)$ and $\mathbf{C}$ is an arbitrary constant vector.

EXAMPLE 1: Find the most general vector-valued function whose derivative is $Q(t) = \sin t \mathbf{i} - 3 \cos t \mathbf{j}$.

Solution: If $D_t R(t) = Q(t)$, then $R(t) = Q(t) \, dt$, or

$$R(t) = \mathbf{i} \int \sin t \, dt - 3\mathbf{j} \int \cos t \, dt$$

$$= \mathbf{i}(-\cos t + C_1) - 3\mathbf{j}(\sin t + C_2)$$

$$= -\cos t \mathbf{i} - 3 \sin t \mathbf{j} + (C_1 \mathbf{i} - 3 C_2 \mathbf{j})$$

$$= -\cos t \mathbf{i} - 3 \sin t \mathbf{j} + \mathbf{C}$$

EXAMPLE 2: Find the vector $R(t)$ for which $D_t R(t) = e^{-t}\mathbf{i} + e^t\mathbf{j}$, and for which $R(0) = \mathbf{i} + \mathbf{j}$.

Solution: $R(t) = \mathbf{i} \int e^{-t} \, dt + \mathbf{j} \int e^t \, dt$.

So $\qquad R(t) = \mathbf{i}(-e^{-t} + C_1) + \mathbf{j}(e^t + C_2)$

Since $R(0) = \mathbf{i} + \mathbf{j}$, we have

$$\mathbf{i} + \mathbf{j} = \mathbf{i}(-1 + C_1) + \mathbf{j}(1 + C_2)$$

So, $\qquad C_1 - 1 = 1 \qquad$ and $\qquad C_2 + 1 = 1$.

Therefore, $\qquad C_1 = 2 \quad$ and $\qquad C_2 = 0$

So, $\qquad R(t) = (-e^{-t} + 2)\mathbf{i} + e^t\mathbf{j}$

Exercises 18.9

In Exercises 1 through 6, find the most general vector whose derivative is the given vector-valued function.

1. $\tan t \mathbf{i} - \dfrac{1}{t}\mathbf{j}$

2. $3^t\mathbf{i} - 2^t\mathbf{j}$

3. $\sin^2 t \mathbf{i} + 2 \cos^2 t \mathbf{j}$

4. $\dfrac{1}{4 + t^2}\mathbf{i} - \dfrac{4}{1 - t^2}\mathbf{j}$

5. $\ln t \mathbf{i} + t^2\mathbf{j}$

6. $e^t \sin t \mathbf{i} + e^t \cos t \mathbf{j}$

7. Find the position vector $R(t)$ if the velocity vector

$$V(t) = \frac{1}{(t - 1)^2}\mathbf{i} - (t + 1)\mathbf{j} \qquad \text{and} \qquad R(0) = 3\mathbf{i} + 2\mathbf{j}$$

8. Find the position vector $R(t)$ if the acceleration vector

$$A(t) = 2 \cos 2t \mathbf{i} + 2 \sin 2t \mathbf{j}$$

and $V(0) = \mathbf{i} + \mathbf{j}$, and $R(0) = \frac{1}{2}\mathbf{i} - \frac{1}{2}\mathbf{j}$.

9. Prove that if $\mathbf{A}$ and $\mathbf{B}$ are constant vectors, then

$$\int [\mathbf{A}f(t) + \mathbf{B}g(t)] \, dt = \mathbf{A} \int f(t) \, dt + \mathbf{B} \int g(t) \, dt$$

HINT: Express $\mathbf{A}$ and $\mathbf{B}$ in terms of $\mathbf{i}$ and $\mathbf{j}$.

(18.10) The motion of a projectile

We now derive the equations of motion of a projectile. We assume that the projectile is moving in a vertical plane. We also assume that the only force acting on the projectile is its weight, which has a downward direction and a magnitude of *mg*, where m is its mass and g is the constant of acceleration due to gravity, and we are neglecting the force due to air resistance (which for heavy bodies traveling at small speeds has no noticeable effect). We take the positive direction vertically upward and horizontally to the right.

Suppose then that a projectile is shot from a gun having an angle of elevation α. Let the number of feet per second in the initial speed, or *muzzle speed*, be denoted by v_0. We shall set up the coordinate axes so that the gun is located at the origin (refer to Fig. 18.10.1). The initial velocity of the projectile, denoted by the vector $\mathbf{V}_0$, is given by

(1) $$\mathbf{V}_0 = v_0 \cos \alpha \mathbf{i} + v_0 \sin \alpha \mathbf{j}$$

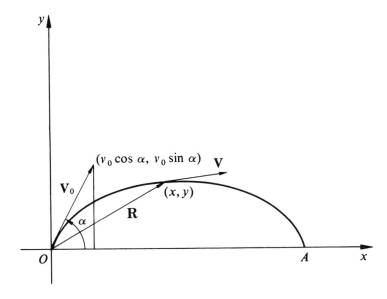

Figure 18.10.1

Let t = the number of seconds in the time that has elapsed since the gun was fired

Let x = the number of feet in the horizontal distance of the projectile from the starting point at t sec

Let y = the number of feet in the vertical distance of the projectile from the starting point at t sec

Let $\mathbf{R}(t)$ = the position vector of the projectile at t sec

Let $\mathbf{V}(t)$ = the velocity vector of the projectile at t sec

Let $\mathbf{A}(t) = $ the acceleration vector of the projectile at t sec

x is a function of t; so we write $x(t)$. Similarly, y is a function of t; so we write $y(t)$.

Then

(2)
$$\mathbf{R}(t) = x(t)\mathbf{i} + y(t)\mathbf{j}$$

(3)
$$\mathbf{V}(t) = \mathbf{R}'(t)$$

(4)
$$\mathbf{A}(t) = \mathbf{V}'(t)$$

Since the only force acting on the projectile has a magnitude of mg and is in the downward direction, then if $\mathbf{F}$ denotes this force, we have

(5)
$$\mathbf{F} = -mg\mathbf{j}$$

Newton's law of motion states that the net force which is acting on a body is its "mass times acceleration." So,

(6)
$$\mathbf{F} = m\mathbf{A}$$

From (5) and (6) we obtain

$$m\mathbf{A} = mg\mathbf{j}$$

Dividing by m, we have

(7)
$$\mathbf{A} = -g\mathbf{j}$$

Since $\mathbf{A}(t) = \mathbf{V}'(t)$, we have from (7)

(8)
$$\mathbf{V}'(t) = -g\mathbf{j}$$

Integrating the vector equation (8) with respect to t, we obtain

(9)
$$\mathbf{V}(t) = -gt\mathbf{j} + \mathbf{C}_1$$

where $\mathbf{C}_1$ is a vector constant of integration.

When $t = 0$, $\mathbf{V} = \mathbf{V}_0$. So, $\mathbf{C}_1 = \mathbf{V}_0$. Therefore, from (9) we have

$$\mathbf{V}(t) = gt\mathbf{j} + \mathbf{V}_0$$

or, since $\mathbf{V}(t) = \mathbf{R}'(t)$, we have

(10)
$$\mathbf{R}'(t) = -gt\mathbf{j} + \mathbf{V}_0$$

Integrating the vector equation (10) with respect to t, we obtain

$$\mathbf{R}(t) = -\tfrac{1}{2}gt^2\mathbf{j} + \mathbf{V}_0 t + \mathbf{C}_2$$

where $\mathbf{C}_2$ is a vector constant of integration.

When $t = 0$, $\mathbf{R} = \mathbf{0}$, since the projectile is at the origin at the start. So, $\mathbf{C}_2 = \mathbf{0}$. Therefore,

(11)
$$\mathbf{R}(t) = -\tfrac{1}{2}gt^2\mathbf{j} + \mathbf{V}_0 t$$

Substituting the value of $\mathbf{V}_0$ from equation (1) into (11), we obtain

$$\mathbf{R}(t) = -\tfrac{1}{2}gt^2\mathbf{j} + (v_0 \cos \alpha \mathbf{i} + v_0 \sin \alpha \mathbf{j})t$$

or, equivalently,

(12)
$$\mathbf{R}(t) = tv_0 \cos \alpha \mathbf{i} + (tv_0 \sin \alpha - \tfrac{1}{2}gt^2)\mathbf{j}$$

Equation (12) gives the position vector of the projectile at time t. From this equation, we may discuss the motion of the projectile. We are usually concerned with the following questions:

1. What is the *range* of the projectile? The *range* is the distance $|\overline{OA}|$ along the x axis — see Fig. 18.10.1.
2. What is the total time of flight? That is, the time it takes the projectile to go from O to A.
3. What is the maximum height of the projectile?
4. What is a cartesian equation of the curve traveled by the projectile?
5. What is the velocity of the projectile at impact?

These questions are answered in the following example.

EXAMPLE 1: A projectile is shot from a gun at an angle of elevation of 30°. Its muzzle speed is 480 ft/sec. *Find:* (a) the position vector of the projectile at any time; (b) the time of flight; (c) the range; (d) the maximum height; (e) the velocity of the projectile at impact; (f) the position vector and the velocity vector at 2 sec; (g) the speed at 2 sec; (h) a cartesian equation of the curve traveled by the projectile.

Solution: $v_0 = 480$ and $\alpha = 30°$.
So,

$$\mathbf{V_0} = 480 \cos 30° \, \mathbf{i} + 480 \sin 30° \mathbf{j}$$

$$= 240\sqrt{3} \, \mathbf{i} + 240\mathbf{j}$$

(a) The position vector at time t is given by equation (12), which in this case is

(13) $$\mathbf{R}(t) = 240\sqrt{3}t\mathbf{i} + (240t - \tfrac{1}{2}gt^2)\mathbf{j}$$

So if (x,y) is the position of the projectile at time t, $x = 240\sqrt{3}t$ and $y = 240t - \tfrac{1}{2}gt^2$.

(b) To find the time of flight, we find t when $y = 0$. From part (a), we get $y = 0$ and have

$$240t - \tfrac{1}{2}gt^2 = 0$$

$$t(240 - \tfrac{1}{2}gt) = 0$$

$$t = 0 \quad \text{and} \quad t = \frac{480}{g}$$

The value $t = 0$ is when the projectile is fired, since $y = 0$ then.

If we take $g = 32$, the time of flight is given by $t = 480/g = 480/32 = 15$. So the time of flight is 15 sec.

(c) To find the range, we must find x when $t = 15$. From part (a), $x = 240\sqrt{3}t$. So, when $t = 15$, $x = 3,600\sqrt{3}$. Therefore, the range is 6,235 ft (approximately).

(*d*) The maximum height is attained when $D_t y = 0$, that is, when the vertical component of the velocity vector is 0.

Since

$$y = 240t - \tfrac{1}{2}gt^2$$

$$D_t y = 240 - gt$$

So $D_t y = 0$ when $t = 240/g$. Taking $g = 32$, the maximum height is attained when $t = 7\tfrac{1}{2}$, which is half the total time of flight. When $t = 7\tfrac{1}{2}$, $y = 900$. So the maximum height attained is 900 ft.

(*e*) Since the time of flight is 15 sec, the velocity at impact is **V**(15). Finding **V**(*t*) by using (13), we have

$$\mathbf{V}(t) = D_t\mathbf{R}(t) = 240\sqrt{3}\,\mathbf{i} + (240 - gt)\mathbf{j}$$

Taking $g = 32$, we get

$$\mathbf{V}(15) = 240\sqrt{3}\,\mathbf{i} - 480\mathbf{j}$$

(*f*) Taking $t = 2$ in equation (13), we obtain

$$\mathbf{R}(2) = 480\sqrt{3}\,\mathbf{i} + 416\mathbf{j}$$

Since $\mathbf{V}(t) = \mathbf{R}'(t)$, we have

$$\mathbf{V}(t) = 240\sqrt{3}\,\mathbf{i} + (240 - gt)\mathbf{j}$$

So, $$\mathbf{V}(2) = 240\sqrt{3}\,\mathbf{i} + 176\mathbf{j}$$

(*g*) The speed when $t = 2$ is given by

$$|\mathbf{V}(2)| = \sqrt{(240\sqrt{3})^2 + (176)^2}$$

$$= 16\sqrt{166}$$

So, at 2 sec, the speed is approximately 12.9 ft/sec.

(*h*) To find a cartesian equation, we eliminate *t* between the parametric equations

$$x = 240\sqrt{3}\,t$$

$$y = 240t - \tfrac{1}{2}gt^2$$

Solving the first equation for *t* and substituting into the second equation, we obtain

$$y = \frac{1}{\sqrt{3}}\,x - \frac{1}{21{,}600}x^2$$

which is an equation of a parabola.

Exercises 18.10

1. A projectile is shot from a gun at an angle of elevation of 45° with a muzzle speed of 2,500 ft/sec. Find the range of the projectile, the maximum height reached, and the velocity at impact.

2. A projectile is shot from a gun at an angle of elevation of 60°. The muzzle speed is 160 ft/sec. *Find:* (*a*) the position vector of the projectile at *t* sec; (*b*) the time of flight; (*c*) the range; (*d*) the maximum height reached; (*e*) the velocity at impact; (*f*) the speed at 4 sec.

3. A projectile is shot from the top of a building 96 ft high from a gun at an angle of 30° with the horizontal. If the muzzle speed is 1,600 ft/sec, find the time of flight and the distance from the base of the building to the point where the projectile lands.

4. A boy throws a ball horizontally from the top of a cliff 256 ft high with an initial speed of 50 ft/sec. Find the time of flight of the ball and the distance from the base of the cliff to the point where the ball lands.

5. A boy throws a ball with an initial speed of 60 ft/sec at an angle of elevation of 60° towards a tall building which is 25 ft from the boy. If the boy's hand is 5 ft from the ground, does the ball hit the building? What is the direction of the ball when it hits the building?

6. At what angle of elevation should a gun be fired to obtain the maximum range for a given muzzle speed?

7. For a given muzzle speed of v_0 ft/sec and a given angle of elevation α, find a formula for obtaining the maximum height reached by a projectile fired from the gun.

8. The muzzle speed of a gun is 160 ft/sec. At what angle of elevation should the gun be fired so that a projectile will hit an object on the same level as the gun and a distance of 400 ft from it?

9. What is the muzzle speed of a gun if the range of a projectile fired from it has a range of 2,000 ft and reaches a maximum height of 1,000 ft?

(18.11) The unit tangent and unit normal vectors and arc length as a parameter

We previously noted that a unit vector is a vector having a magnitude of 1, examples of which are the two unit vectors **i** and **j**. With each point on a curve in the plane we shall now associate two other unit vectors, the *unit tangent vector* and the *unit normal vector*.

18.11.1 DEFINITION   If $\mathbf{R}(t)$ is the position vector of curve C at a point P on C, then the *unit tangent vector* of C at P, denoted by $\mathbf{T}(t)$, is the unit vector in the direction of $D_t\mathbf{R}(t)$, if $D_t\mathbf{R}(t) \neq \mathbf{0}$.

The unit vector in the direction of $D_t\mathbf{R}(t)$ is given by $D_t\mathbf{R}(t)/|D_t\mathbf{R}(t)|$; so we may write

(1) $$\mathbf{T}(t) = \frac{D_t\mathbf{R}(t)}{|D_t\mathbf{R}(t)|}$$

Since $\mathbf{T}(t)$ is a unit vector, it follows from Theorem 18.6.9 that $D_t\mathbf{T}(t)$ must be orthogonal to $\mathbf{T}(t)$. $D_t\mathbf{T}(t)$ is not necessarily a unit vector. However, the vector $D_t\mathbf{T}(t)/|D_t\mathbf{T}(t)|$ is of unit magnitude and has the same direction as $D_t\mathbf{T}(t)$. Therefore, $D_t\mathbf{T}(t)/|D_t\mathbf{T}(t)|$ is a unit vector which is orthogonal to $\mathbf{T}(t)$, and it is called the unit normal vector.

18.11.2 DEFINITION   If $\mathbf{T}(t)$ is the unit tangent vector of curve C at a point P on C, then the *unit normal vector*, denoted by $\mathbf{N}(t)$, is the unit vector in the direction of $D_t\mathbf{T}(t)$.

From Definition 18.11.2 and the previous discussion, we conclude that

$$(2) \qquad\qquad \mathbf{N}(t) = \frac{D_t\mathbf{T}(t)}{|D_t\mathbf{T}(t)|}$$

From (1) we obtain

$$(3) \qquad\qquad D_t\mathbf{R}(t) = |D_t\mathbf{R}(t)|\, \mathbf{T}(t)$$

The right-hand side of (3) is the product of a scalar and a vector. So to differentiate this product, we apply Theorem 18.6.8, and we have

$$(4) \qquad D_t{}^2\mathbf{R}(t) = [D_t|D_t\mathbf{R}(t)|]\, \mathbf{T}(t) + |D_t\mathbf{R}(t)|[D_t\mathbf{T}(t)]$$

From (2) we obtain

$$(5) \qquad\qquad D_t\mathbf{T}(t) = |D_t\mathbf{T}(t)|\, \mathbf{N}(t)$$

Substituting (5) into (4), we get

$$(6) \qquad D_t{}^2\mathbf{R}(t) = [D_t|D_t\mathbf{R}(t)|]\, \mathbf{T}(t) + |D_t\mathbf{R}(t)|\, |D_t\mathbf{T}(t)|\, \mathbf{N}(t)$$

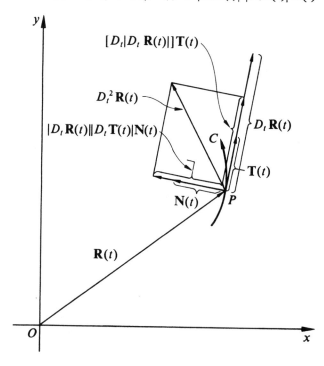

Figure 18.11.1

Equation (3) expresses the vector $D_t\mathbf{R}(t)$ as a scalar times the unit tangent vector, and equation (6) expresses the vector $D_t^2\mathbf{R}(t)$ as a scalar times the unit tangent vector plus a scalar times the unit normal vector. The coefficient of $\mathbf{T}(t)$ on the right-hand side of (6) is the component of the vector $D_t^2\mathbf{R}(t)$ in the direction of the unit tangent vector, and the coefficient of $\mathbf{N}(t)$ on the right-hand side of (6) is the component of $D_t^2\mathbf{R}(t)$ in the direction of the unit normal vector. Figure 18.11.1 shows a portion of a curve C with the position representation of $\mathbf{R}(t)$ and the representations of $\mathbf{T}(t)$, $\mathbf{N}(t)$, $D_t\mathbf{R}(t)$, $D_t^2\mathbf{R}(t)$, $[D_t|D_t\mathbf{R}(t)|]\,\mathbf{T}(t)$, and $|D_t\mathbf{R}(t)|\,|D_t\mathbf{T}(t)|\mathbf{N}(t)$, all of whose initial points are at the point P on C. The reader should note that the representation of the unit normal vector $\mathbf{N}$ is on the concave side of the curve. This is proved in general in Sec. 18.12.

EXAMPLE 1: *Given:* the curve having parametric equations $x = t^3 - 3t$ and $y = 3t^2$. *Find:* $\mathbf{T}(t)$ and $\mathbf{N}(t)$. Draw a sketch of a portion of the curve at $t = 2$ and draw the representations of $\mathbf{T}(2)$ and $\mathbf{N}(2)$ having their initial point at $t = 2$.

Solution: A vector equation of the curve is

$$\mathbf{R}(t) = (t^3 - 3t)\mathbf{i} + 3t^2\mathbf{j}$$

So, $D_t\mathbf{R}(t) = (3t^2 - 3)\mathbf{i} + 6t\mathbf{j}$

Then

$$|D_t\mathbf{R}(t)| = \sqrt{(3t^2 - 3)^2 + 36t^2} = \sqrt{9(t^4 + 2t^2 + 1)} = 3(t^2 + 1)$$

Applying (1), we get

$$\mathbf{T}(t) = \frac{t^2 - 1}{t^2 + 1}\mathbf{i} + \frac{2t}{t^2 + 1}\mathbf{j}$$

Differentiating $\mathbf{T}(t)$ with respect to t, we obtain

$$D_t\mathbf{T}(t) = \frac{4t}{(t^2 + 1)^2}\mathbf{i} + \frac{2 - 2t^2}{(t^2 + 1)^2}\mathbf{j}$$

Therefore,

$$|D_t\mathbf{T}(t)| = \sqrt{\frac{16t^2}{(t^2 + 1)^4} + \frac{4 - 8t^2 + 4t^4}{(t^2 + 1)^4}} = \sqrt{\frac{4 + 8t^2 + 4t^4}{(t^2 + 1)^4}}$$

$$= \sqrt{\frac{4(t^2 + 1)^2}{(t^2 + 1)^4}} = \frac{2}{t^2 + 1}$$

Applying (2), we have

$$\mathbf{N}(t) = \frac{2t}{t^2 + 1}\mathbf{i} + \frac{1 - t^2}{t^2 + 1}\mathbf{j}$$

Finding $\mathbf{R}(t)$, $\mathbf{T}(t)$, and $\mathbf{N}(t)$, when $t = 2$, we obtain

$$\mathbf{R}(2) = 2\mathbf{i} + 12\mathbf{j} \qquad \mathbf{T}(2) = \frac{3}{5}\mathbf{i} + \frac{4}{5}\mathbf{j} \qquad \mathbf{N}(2) = \frac{4}{5}\mathbf{i} - \frac{3}{5}\mathbf{j}$$

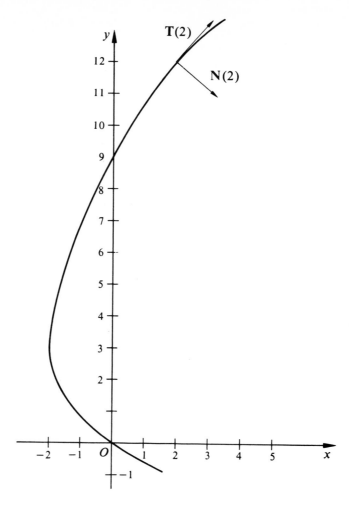

Figure 18.11.2

The required sketch is shown in Fig. 18.11.2.

Sometimes instead of a parameter t, we wish to use as a parameter the arc length s, where s is measured from an arbitrarily chosen point $P_0(x_0,y_0)$ on curve C to the point $P(x,y)$ on C. Let s increase as t increases, so that s is positive if the length of arc is measured in the direction of increasing t and s is negative if the length of arc is measured in the opposite direction. Therefore, s is a directed distance. Also $D_t s > 0$. To each value of s there corresponds a unique point P on the curve C. Consequently, the coordinates of P are functions of s and s is a function of t. In Sec. 18.7 we showed that

(7)
$$|D_t\mathbf{R}(t)| = D_t s$$

Substituting (7) into (1), we get

$$\mathbf{T}(t) = \frac{D_t\mathbf{R}(t)}{D_t s}$$

So, $\quad D_t\mathbf{R}(t) = D_t s\, \mathbf{T}(t)$

If the parameter is s instead of t, we have from the above, by taking $t = s$ and noting that $D_s s = 1$,

$$D_s \mathbf{R}(s) = \mathbf{T}(s)$$

This result is stated as a theorem.

18.11.3 THEOREM   If the vector equation of a curve C is $\mathbf{R}(s) = f(s)\mathbf{i} + g(s)\mathbf{j}$, where s is the length of arc measured from a particular point P_0 on C to the point P, then the unit tangent vector of C at P is given by

$$\mathbf{T}(s) = D_s \mathbf{R}(s)$$

Now suppose that the parametric equations of a curve C involve a parameter t, and we wish to find parametric equations of C, with the arc length s, measured from some fixed point, as the parameter. Often the operations involved are quite complicated. However, the method used is illustrated in the following example.

EXAMPLE 2: Suppose parametric equations of the curve C are $x = t^3$ and $y = t^2$, where $t \geq 0$. Find parametric equations of C having the arc length s as a parameter, where s is measured from the point where $t = 0$.

Solution: If P_0 is the point where $t = 0$, P_0 is the origin. The vector equation of C is

$$\mathbf{R}(t) = t^3 \mathbf{i} + t^2 \mathbf{j}$$

Since $D_t s = |D_t \mathbf{R}(t)|$, we differentiate the above and obtain

$$D_t \mathbf{R}(t) = 3t^2 \mathbf{i} + 2t \mathbf{j}$$

So, $|D_t \mathbf{R}(t)| = \sqrt{9t^4 + 4t^2} = \sqrt{t^2}\sqrt{9t^2 + 4}$

Since $t \geq 0$, $\sqrt{t^2} = t$ and we have

$$|D_t \mathbf{R}(t)| = t\sqrt{9t^2 + 4}$$

Therefore, $D_t s = t\sqrt{9t^2 + 4}$

and so $s = \displaystyle\int_0^t u\sqrt{9u^2 + 4}\, du$

$$= \frac{1}{18}\int_0^t 18u\sqrt{9u^2 + 4}\, du = \frac{1}{27}(9u^2 + 4)^{3/2}\Big]_0^t$$

We obtain

(8) $$s = \frac{1}{27}(9t^2 + 4)^{3/2} - \frac{8}{27}$$

Solving equation (8) for t in terms of s, we have

$$(9t^2 + 4)^{3/2} = 27s + 8$$

$$9t^2 + 4 = (27s + 8)^{2/3}$$

Since $t \geq 0$, we get

$$t = \tfrac{1}{3}\sqrt{(27s + 8)^{2/3} - 4}$$

Substituting this value of t into the given parametric equations for C, we obtain

(9) $\quad x = \dfrac{1}{27}[(27s + 8)^{2/3} - 4]^{3/2} \qquad$ and $\qquad y = \dfrac{1}{9}[(27s + 8)^{2/3} - 4]$

Now, since $D_s\mathbf{R}(s) = \mathbf{T}(s)$, it follows that if $\mathbf{R}(s) = x(s)\mathbf{i} + y(s)\mathbf{j}$, then $\mathbf{T}(s) = (D_sx)\,\mathbf{i} + (D_sy)\mathbf{j}$, and since $\mathbf{T}(s)$ is a unit vector, we have

(10) $\qquad\qquad\qquad\qquad (D_sx)^2 + (D_sy)^2 = 1$

Equation (10) may be used to check equations (9). This check is left for the reader (see Exercise 11 below).

Exercises 18.11

In Exercises 1 through 8, for the given curve, find $\mathbf{T}(t)$ and $\mathbf{N}(t)$, and at $t = t_1$, draw a sketch of a portion of the curve and draw the representations of $\mathbf{T}(t_1)$ and $\mathbf{N}(t_1)$ having initial point at $t = t_1$.

1. $x = \frac{1}{3}t^3 - t,\ y = t^2;\ t_1 = 2$

2. $x = \frac{1}{2}t^2,\ y = \frac{1}{3}t^3;\ t_1 = 1$

3. $\mathbf{R}(t) = e^t\mathbf{i} + e^{-t}\mathbf{j};\ t_1 = 0$

4. $\mathbf{R}(t) = 3\cos t\mathbf{i} + 3\sin t\mathbf{j};\ t_1 = \pi/2$

5. $x = \cos kt,\ y = \sin kt,\ k > 0;\ t_1 = \pi/k$

6. $x = t - \sin t,\ y = 1 - \cos t;\ t_1 = \pi$

7. $\mathbf{R}(t) = \ln \cos t\mathbf{i} + \ln \sin t\mathbf{j},\ 0 < t < \pi/2;\ t_1 = \pi/4$

8. $\mathbf{R}(t) = t\cos t\mathbf{i} + t\sin t\mathbf{j};\ t_1 = 0$

9. If the vector equation of curve C is $\mathbf{R}(t) = 3t^2\mathbf{i} + (t^3 - 3t)\mathbf{j}$, find the angle between the vectors $\mathbf{R}(2)$ and $\mathbf{T}(2)$.

10. If the vector equation of curve C is $\mathbf{R}(t) = (4 - 3t^2)\mathbf{i} + (t^3 - 3t)\mathbf{j}$, find the angle between the vectors $\mathbf{N}(1)$ and $D_t^2\mathbf{R}(1)$.

11. Check equations (9) of the solution of Example 2 by using (10).

In Exercises 12 through 15, find parametric equations of the curve having arc length s as a parameter, where s is measured from the point where $t = 0$. Check your result by using (10).

12. $x = a\cos t,\ y = a\sin t$

13. $x = 2 + \cos t,\ y = 3 + \sin t$

14. $x = 2(\cos t + t\sin t),\ y = 2(\sin t - t\cos t)$

15. One cusp of the hypocycloid of four cusps: $\mathbf{R}(t) = a \cos^3 t\mathbf{i} + a \sin^3 t\mathbf{j}$, $0 \le t \le \pi/2$.

16. Given the cycloid $x = 2(t - \sin t)$, $y = 2(1 - \cos t)$. Express the arc length s as a function of t, where s is measured from the point where $t = 0$.

(18.12) Curvature

In Sec. 18.3, we expressed a vector $\mathbf{A}$ in terms of its magnitude and the angle θ ($0 \le \theta < 2\pi$), giving the direction of the vector, as

(1) $$\mathbf{A} = |\mathbf{A}| (\cos \theta \mathbf{i} + \sin \theta \mathbf{j})$$

If we are considering a unit tangent vector associated with a curve C, we shall let the angle θ be denoted by ϕ. So, ϕ is the angle measured counterclockwise from the direction of the positive x axis to the direction of the unit tangent vector $\mathbf{T}$ — see Fig. 18.12.1.

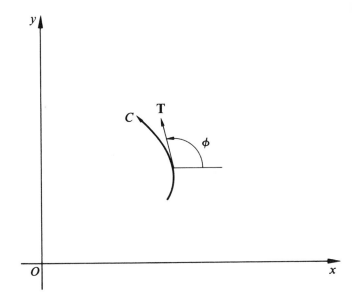

Figure 18.12.1

Since $|\mathbf{T}| = 1$, we have from (1)

(2) $$\mathbf{T} = \cos \phi \mathbf{i} + \sin \phi \mathbf{j}$$

Differentiating (2) with respect to ϕ, we obtain

(3) $$D_\phi \mathbf{T} = -\sin \phi \mathbf{i} + \cos \phi \mathbf{j}$$

Since $|D_\phi \mathbf{T}| = \sqrt{(-\sin \phi)^2 + (\cos \phi)^2} = 1$, $D_\phi \mathbf{T}$ is a unit vector. By Theorem 18.6.9 because $\mathbf{T}$ is of constant length, $D_\phi \mathbf{T}$ is orthogonal to $\mathbf{T}$.

Replacing $-\sin\phi$ by $\cos(\pi/2+\phi)$ and $\cos\phi$ by $\sin(\pi/2+\phi)$, we write (3) as

(4)
$$D_\phi\mathbf{T} = \cos\left(\frac{\pi}{2}+\phi\right)\mathbf{i} + \sin\left(\frac{\pi}{2}+\phi\right)\mathbf{j}$$

From (4) and the previous discussion, the vector $D_\phi\mathbf{T}$ is a unit vector orthogonal to $\mathbf{T}$ in the direction $\pi/2$ counterclockwise from the direction of $\mathbf{T}$. The unit normal vector $\mathbf{N}$ is also orthogonal to $\mathbf{T}$.

By the chain rule (which is valid for vector-valued functions, although we won't prove it), we have

(5)
$$D_t\mathbf{T} = [D_\phi\mathbf{T}]\, D_t\phi$$

Since the direction of $\mathbf{N}$ is the same as the direction of $D_t\mathbf{T}$, we see from (5) that the direction of $\mathbf{N}$ is the same as the direction of $D_\phi\mathbf{T}$ if $D_t\phi > 0$ (that is, if $\mathbf{T}$ turns counterclockwise as t increases), and the direction of $\mathbf{N}$ is opposite that of $D_\phi\mathbf{T}$ if $D_t\phi < 0$ (that is, if $\mathbf{T}$ turns clockwise as t increases). Since both $D_\phi\mathbf{T}$ and $\mathbf{N}$ are unit vectors, we may conclude that

(6)
$$D_\phi\mathbf{T} = \begin{cases} \mathbf{N} & \text{if } D_t\phi > 0 \\ -\mathbf{N} & \text{if } D_t\phi < 0 \end{cases}$$

In Figs. 18.12.2, 18.12.3, 18.12.4, and 18.12.5, various cases are illustrated, In Figs. 18.12.2 and 18.12.3, $D_t\phi > 0$, and in Figs. 18.12.4 and 18.12.5. $D_t\phi < 0$. The positive direction along the curve C is indicated by the tip of the arrow on C. In each figure, the angle ϕ and representations of the vectors $\mathbf{T}$,

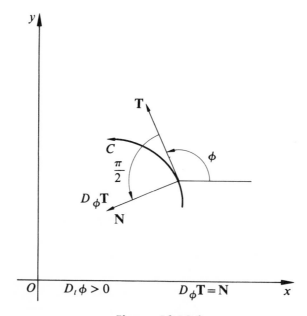

Figure 18.12.2

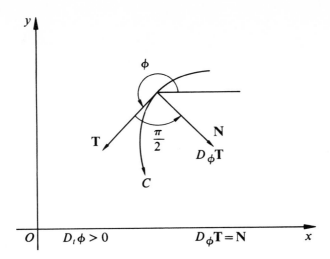

Figure 18.12.3

$D_\phi\mathbf{T}$, and $\mathbf{N}$ are shown. *The representation of the unit normal vector* $\mathbf{N}$ *is always on the concave side of the curve.*

From (5) and (6) we have

(7) $$D_t\mathbf{T} = |D_t\phi|\ \mathbf{N}$$

By the chain rule we have

$$|D_t\phi| = |D_s\phi\ D_t s| = |D_s\phi|\ |D_t s|$$

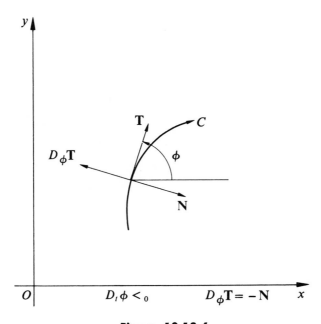

Figure 18.12.4

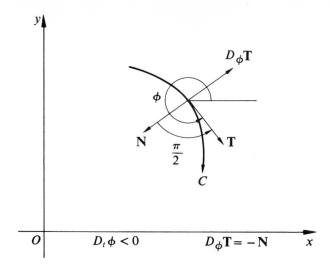

Figure 18.12.5

But, since $D_t s$ is nonnegative, we write

(8) $$|D_t \phi| = D_t s \, |D_s \phi|$$

Substituting (8) into (7), we obtain

(9) $$D_t \mathbf{T} = D_t s \, |D_s \phi| \, \mathbf{N}$$

The number $|D_s \phi|$ measures the absolute value of the rate of change of the direction of the unit tangent vector $\mathbf{T}$ at a point on a curve with respect to the arc length s along the curve. This number is called the *curvature* of the curve at the point.

18.12.1 DEFINITION   Let C be the curve having vector equation $\mathbf{R}(t) = f(t)\mathbf{i} + g(t)\mathbf{j}$. $\mathbf{T}$ is the unit tangent vector at a point P on C, and ϕ is the angle measured counterclockwise from the direction of the positive x axis to the vector $\mathbf{T}$. If s is the arc length measured from an arbitrarily chosen point on C to point P, and s increases as t increases, then the *curvature* of the curve C at point P, denoted by K, is defined to be

$$K = |D_s \phi|$$

if this derivative exists.

The above definition of the curvature of a curve at a point is consistent with what we should intuitively think of as the curvature. For example, at point P on C, let ϕ be the angle giving the direction of the unit tangent vector $\mathbf{T}$ at P and s be the arc length from a point P_0 on C to P. Let Q be a point on C for which the angle giving the direction of $\mathbf{T}$ at Q is $\phi + \Delta\phi$, and $s + \Delta s$ is the arc length from P_0 to Q. Then the arc length from P to Q is Δs, and the ratio $\Delta\phi/\Delta s$ seems like a good measure of what we would intuitively think of as the

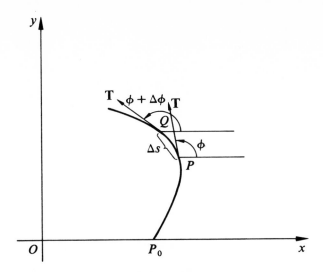

Figure 18.12.6

average curvature along arc PQ — see Figs. 18.12.6 ($\Delta\phi > 0$, $\Delta s > 0$), 18.12.7 ($\Delta\phi > 0$, $\Delta s < 0$), and 18.12.8 ($\Delta\phi < 0$, $\Delta s > 0$).

Another formula for the curvature K follows by considering $D_s\mathbf{T}$.

By the chain rule,

(10) $$D_s\mathbf{T} = D_\phi\mathbf{T}\, D_s\phi$$

So, $$|D_s\mathbf{T}| = |D_\phi\mathbf{T}\, D_s\phi| = |D_\phi\mathbf{T}|\,|D_s\phi|$$

But, since $D_\phi\mathbf{T}$ is a unit vector, $|D_\phi\mathbf{T}| = 1$, and so we have

$$|D_s\mathbf{T}| = |D_s\phi|$$

or, equivalently,

(11) $$K = |D_s\mathbf{T}|$$

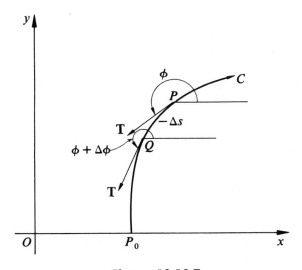

Figure 18.12.7

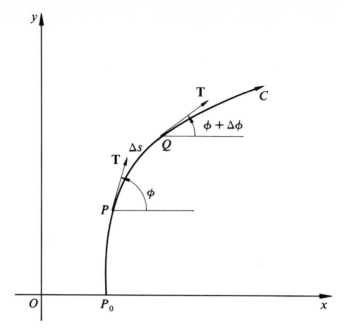

Figure 18.12.8

The vector $D_s\mathbf{T}$ at a point P on the curve C is called the *curvature vector*, and we see from (11) that its magnitude is the curvature of C at P.

To calculate K for a particular curve, it is convenient to have a formula expressing the curvature vector in terms of derivatives with respect to time t.

By the chain rule,

$$D_t\mathbf{T} = D_s\mathbf{T}\ D_t s$$

Letting $D_t s = |D_t\mathbf{R}(t)|$ and dividing by this, we obtain

$$D_s\mathbf{T}(t) = \frac{D_t\mathbf{T}(t)}{|D_t\mathbf{R}(t)|}$$

Since $K(t) = |D_s\mathbf{T}(t)|$, we have

⟪ (12) $$K(t) = \left|\frac{D_t\mathbf{T}(t)}{|D_t\mathbf{R}(t)|}\right|$$

EXAMPLE 1: *Given:* the circle $x = a\cos t$, $y = a\sin t$, $a > 0$. *Find:* the curvature vector and the curvature at any time t.

Solution: The vector equation of the circle is

$$\mathbf{R}(t) = a\cos t\mathbf{i} + a\sin t\mathbf{j}$$

So, $$D_t\mathbf{R}(t) = -a\sin t\mathbf{i} + a\cos t\mathbf{j}$$

$$|D_t\mathbf{R}(t)| = \sqrt{(-a\sin t)^2 + (a\cos t)^2} = a$$

So $$\mathbf{T}(t) = \frac{D_t\mathbf{R}(t)}{|D_t\mathbf{R}(t)|} = -\sin t\mathbf{i} + \cos t\mathbf{j}$$

$$D_t\mathbf{T}(t) = -\cos t\mathbf{i} - \sin t\mathbf{j}$$

$$\frac{D_t\mathbf{T}(t)}{|D_t\mathbf{R}(t)|} = -\frac{\cos t}{a}\mathbf{i} - \frac{\sin t}{a}\mathbf{j}$$

So, the curvature vector

$$D_s\mathbf{T}(t) = -\frac{1}{a}\cos t\mathbf{i} - \frac{1}{a}\sin t\mathbf{j}$$

$$K(t) = |D_s\mathbf{T}(t)| = \frac{1}{a}$$

The result of Example 1 states that the curvature of a circle is constant and is the reciprocal of the radius.

Suppose we are given a curve C, and at a particular point P the curvature exists and is K, where $K \neq 0$. Suppose, furthermore, we wish to find the circle which is tangent to curve C at P and has curvature K at P. From Example 1, we know that the radius of this circle is $1/K$ and its center is on a line perpendicular to the tangent line in the direction of $\mathbf{N}$. This circle is called the *circle of curvature* and its radius is the *radius of curvature* of C at P. The circle of curvature is sometimes referred to as the *osculating circle*.

18.12.2 DEFINITION   If K is the curvature of a curve C at point P and $K \neq 0$, then the *radius of curvature* of C at P, denoted by ρ, is defined by

$$\rho = \frac{1}{K}$$

EXAMPLE 2: *Given:* a vector equation of a curve C is

$$\mathbf{R}(t) = 2t\mathbf{i} + (t^2 - 1)\mathbf{j}$$

Find: the curvature K and the radius of curvature ρ at $t = 1$.

Draw a sketch of a portion of the curve, the unit tangent vector, and the circle of curvature at $t = 1$.

Solution:

$$\mathbf{R}(t) = 2t\mathbf{i} + (t^2 - 1)\mathbf{j}$$

$$D_t\mathbf{R}(t) = 2\mathbf{i} + 2t\mathbf{j}$$

$$|D_t\mathbf{R}(t)| = 2\sqrt{1 + t^2}$$

$$\mathbf{T}(t) = \frac{D_t\mathbf{R}(t)}{|D_t\mathbf{R}(t)|} = \frac{1}{\sqrt{1 + t^2}}\mathbf{i} + \frac{t}{\sqrt{1 + t^2}}\mathbf{j}$$

$$D_t\mathbf{T}(t) = -\frac{t}{(1 + t^2)^{3/2}}\mathbf{i} + \frac{1}{(1 + t^2)^{3/2}}\mathbf{j}$$

$$\frac{D_t\mathbf{T}(t)}{|D_t\mathbf{R}(t)|} = -\frac{t}{2(1 + t^2)^2}\mathbf{i} + \frac{1}{2(1 + t^2)^2}\mathbf{j}$$

$$K(t) = \left|\frac{D_t\mathbf{T}(t)}{|D_t\mathbf{R}(t)|}\right| = \sqrt{\frac{t^2}{4(1 + t^2)^4} + \frac{1}{4(1 + t^2)^4}}$$

$$K(t) = \frac{1}{2(1 + t^2)^{3/2}}$$

So, $K(1) = \dfrac{1}{4\sqrt{2}}$

$\rho(1) = 4\sqrt{2}$

$T(1) = \dfrac{1}{\sqrt{2}}\mathbf{i} + \dfrac{1}{\sqrt{2}}\mathbf{j}$

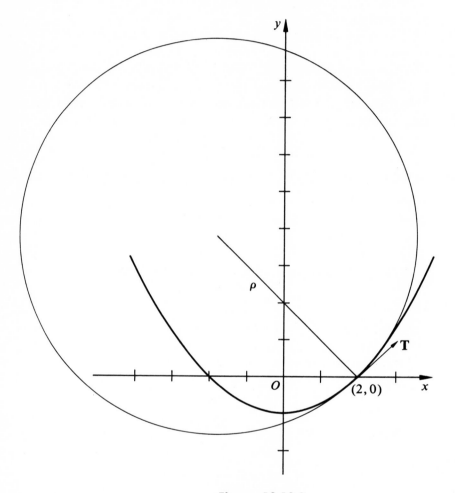

Figure 18.12.9

Figure 18.12.9 shows the required sketch. The accompanying Table 18.12.1 gives corresponding values of x and y for $t = 0$, 1, and 2.

Table 18.12.1

t	x	y
0	0	−1
1	2	0
2	4	3

We shall now find a formula for computing the curvatuve K directly from parametric equations of the curve, $x = f(t)$, $y = g(t)$. From Definition 18.12.1,

$$K = |D_s\phi|$$

Assuming s and t increase together, we have

$$D_s\phi = \frac{d\phi}{ds} = \frac{d\phi/dt}{ds/dt} = \frac{d\phi/dt}{\sqrt{[f'(t)]^2 + [g'(t)]^2}}$$

So,

(13) $$D_s\phi = \frac{d\phi/dt}{\sqrt{(dx/dt)^2 + (dy/dt)^2}}$$

To find $d\phi/dt$, we observe that since ϕ is the direction of the unit tangent vector,

(14) $$\tan \phi = \frac{dy}{dx} = \frac{dy/dt}{dx/dt}$$

Differentiating the left and right members of (14) implicitly with respect to t, we obtain

$$\sec^2 \phi \frac{d\phi}{dt} = \frac{(dx/dt)(d^2y/dt^2) - (dy/dt)(d^2x/dt^2)}{(dx/dt)^2}$$

So,

(15) $$\frac{d\phi}{dt} = \frac{(dx/dt)(d^2y/dt^2) - (dy/dt)(d^2x/dt^2)}{\sec^2 \phi(dx/dt)^2}$$

But $\sec^2 \phi = 1 + \tan^2 \phi = 1 + \dfrac{(dy/dt)^2}{(dx/dt)^2}$

Substituting this expression for $\sec^2 \phi$ in (15), we get

(16) $$\frac{d\phi}{dt} = \frac{(dx/dt)(d^2y/dt^2) - (dy/dt)(d^2x/dt^2)}{(dx/dt)^2 + (dy/dt)^2}$$

Substituting (16) into (13) and since $K = |D_s\phi|$, we have

◖◖ (17) $$K = \frac{|(dx/dt)(d^2y/dt^2) - (dy/dt)(d^2x/dt^2)|}{[(dx/dt)^2 + (dy/dt)^2]^{3/2}}$$

EXAMPLE 3: Find the curvature of the curve in Example 2 by using (17).
Solution: Parametric equations of C are $x = 2t$ and $y = t^2 - 1$. So,

$$\frac{dx}{dt} = 2 \qquad \frac{d^2x}{dt^2} = 0 \qquad \frac{dy}{dt} = 2t \qquad \frac{d^2y}{dt^2} = 2$$

From (17) we have, then,

$$K = \frac{|2(2) - 2t(0)|}{[(2)^2 + (2t)^2]^{3/2}} = \frac{4}{(4 + 4t^2)^{3/2}} = \frac{1}{2(1 + t^2)^{3/2}}$$

Suppose we are given a cartesian equation of a curve, either in the form

$y = F(x)$ or $x = G(y)$. Special cases of formula (17) may be used to find the curvature of the curve in such situations.

If $y = F(x)$ is an equation of a curve C, a set of parametric equations of C is $x = t$ and $y = F(t)$. Then $dx/dt = 1$, $d^2x/dt^2 = 0$, $dy/dt = dy/dx$, and $d^2y/dt^2 = d^2y/dx^2$. Substituting into (17), we obtain

(((18)
$$K = \frac{|d^2y/dx^2|}{[1 + (dy/dx)^2]^{3/2}}$$

Similarly, if an equation of a curve C is $x = G(y)$, we obtain

(((19)
$$K = \frac{|d^2x/dy^2|}{[1 + (dx/dy)^2]^{3/2}}$$

EXAMPLE 4: If the curve C has an equation $xy = 1$, find the radius of curvature of C at the point $(1,1)$ and draw a sketch of the curve and the circle of curvature at $(1,1)$.

Solution: Solving for y, we obtain $y = 1/x$. So, $dy/dx = -1/x^2$ and $d^2y/dx^2 = 2/x^3$. Applying formula (18), we have

$$K = \frac{|2/x^3|}{[1 + (1/x^4)]^{3/2}} = \frac{2x^6}{|x^3| (x^4 + 1)^{3/2}} = \frac{2x^4}{|x| (x^4 + 1)^{3/2}}$$

Since $\rho = 1/K$, we have

$$\rho = \frac{|x| (x^4 + 1)^{3/2}}{2x^4}$$

So at $(1,1)$, $\rho = \sqrt{2}$. The required sketch is shown in Fig. 18.12.10.

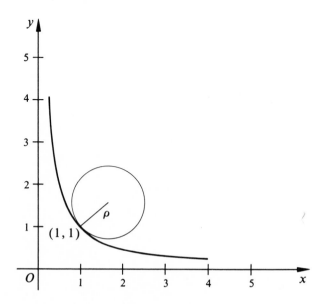

Figure 18.12.10

Exercises 18.12

In Exercises 1 through 4, find the curvature K and the radius of curvature ρ at the point where $t = t_1$. Use formula (12) to find K. Draw a sketch showing a portion of the curve, the unit tangent vector, and the circle of curvature at $t = t_1$.

1. $\mathbf{R}(t) = 2t\mathbf{i} + (t^2 - 1)\mathbf{j}$; $t_1 = 1$

2. $\mathbf{R}(t) = (t^2 - 2t)\mathbf{i} + (t^3 - t)\mathbf{j}$; $t_1 = 1$

3. $\mathbf{R}(t) = 2e^t\mathbf{i} + 2e^{-t}\mathbf{j}$; $t_1 = 0$

4. $\mathbf{R}(t) = \sin t\mathbf{i} + \sin 2t\mathbf{j}$; $t_1 = \pi/2$

In Exercises 5 and 6, find the curvature K by using formula (17). Then find K and ρ at the point where $t = t_1$ and draw a sketch showing a portion of the curve, the unit tangent vector, and the circle of curvature at $t = t_1$.

5. $x = \dfrac{1}{1+t}$, $y = \dfrac{1}{1-t}$; $t_1 = 0$

6. $x = e^t + e^{-t}$, $y = e^t - e^{-t}$; $t_1 = 0$

In Exercises 7 through 12, find the curvature K and the radius of curvature ρ at the given point. Draw a sketch showing a portion of the curve, a piece of the tangent line, and the circle of curvature at the given point.

7. $y = 2\sqrt{x}$; $(0,0)$

8. $y^2 = x^3$; $(\frac{1}{4}, \frac{1}{8})$

9. $y = e^x$; $(0,1)$

10. $4x^2 + 9y^2 = 36$; $(0,2)$

11. $x = \sin y$; $(1/2, \pi/6)$

12. $x = \tan y$; $(1, \pi/4)$

In Exercises 13 through 18, find the radius of curvature at any point on the given curve.

13. $y = \sin^{-1} x$

14. $y = \ln \sec x$

15. $x^{1/2} + y^{1/2} = a^{1/2}$

16. $\mathbf{R}(t) = e^t \sin t\mathbf{i} + e^t \cos t\mathbf{j}$

17. $x = a(t - \sin t)$, $y = a(1 - \cos t)$

18. $x = a(\cos t + t \sin t)$, $y = a(\sin t - t \cos t)$

In Exercises 19 through 22, find a point on the given curve at which the curvature is an absolute maximum.

19. $y = 6x - x^2$

20. $y = e^x$

21. $\mathbf{R}(t) = (2t - 3)\mathbf{i} + (t^2 - 1)\mathbf{j}$

22. $y = \sin x$

23. If a polar equation of a curve is $r = F(\theta)$, prove that the curvature K is given by the formula

$$K = \frac{|r^2 + 2(dr/d\theta)^2 - r(d^2r/d\theta^2)|}{[r^2 + (dr/d\theta)^2]^{3/2}}$$

In Exercises 24 through 27, find the curvature K and the radius of curvature ρ at the indicated point. Use the formula of Exercise 23 to find K.

24. $r = 1 - \sin \theta$; $\theta = 0$ 26. $r = a\theta$; $\theta = 1$

25. $r = 4 \cos 2\theta$; $\theta = \pi/12$ 27. $r = a \sec^2 \tfrac{1}{2}\theta$; $\theta = 2\pi/3$

28. The center of the circle of curvature of a curve C at a point P is called the *center of curvature* at P. Prove that the coordinates of the center of curvature of a curve at $P(x,y)$ are given by

$$x_c = x - \frac{(dy/dx)[1 + (dy/dx)^2]}{d^2y/dx^2} \qquad y_c = y + \frac{(dy/dx)^2 + 1}{d^2y/dx^2}$$

In Exercises 29 through 32, find the curvature K, the radius of curvature ρ, and the center of curvature at the given point. Draw a sketch of the curve and the circle of curvature.

29. $y = x^4 - x^2$; $(0,0)$ 31. $y = \ln x$; $(1,0)$

30. $y = \cos x$; $(\pi/3, 1/2)$ 32. $y = e^{-x}$; $(0,1)$

In Exercises 33 through 36, find the coordinates of the center of curvature at any point.

33. $y^2 = 4px$ 35. $\mathbf{R}(t) = a \cos t\mathbf{i} + b \sin t\mathbf{j}$

34. $y^3 = a^2 x$ 36. $\mathbf{R}(t) = a \cos^3 t\mathbf{i} + a \sin^3 t\mathbf{j}$

(18.13) Tangential and normal components of acceleration

If a particle is moving along a curve C having the vector equation

$$(1) \qquad\qquad \mathbf{R}(t) = f(t)\mathbf{i} + g(t)\mathbf{j}$$

from Definition 18.8.1, the velocity vector at P is given by

$$(2) \qquad\qquad \mathbf{V}(t) = D_t\mathbf{R}(t)$$

From Sec. 18.11, if $\mathbf{T}(t)$ is the unit tangent vector at P and s is the length of arc of C from a fixed point P_0 to P and s increases as t increases, we have

$$(3) \qquad\qquad D_t\mathbf{R}(t) = D_t s[\mathbf{T}(t)]$$

Substituting (3) into (2), we have

$$(4) \qquad\qquad \mathbf{V}(t) = D_t s[\mathbf{T}(t)]$$

Equation (4) expresses the velocity vector at a point as a scalar times the unit tangent vector at the point. We now proceed to express the acceleration vector at a point in terms of the unit tangent and unit normal vectors at the point. From Definition 18.8.2, the acceleration vector at P is given by

$$(5) \qquad\qquad \mathbf{A}(t) = D_t^2\mathbf{R}(t)$$

From equation (6), Sec. 18.11, we have

(6) $\qquad D_t{}^2\mathbf{R}(t) = [D_t|D_t\mathbf{R}(t)|]\ \mathbf{T}(t) + |D_t\mathbf{R}(t)|\ |D_t\mathbf{T}(t)|\ \mathbf{N}(t)$

Since

(7) $\qquad\qquad\qquad\qquad D_t s = |D_t\mathbf{R}(t)|$

if we differentiate with respect to t, we obtain

(8) $\qquad\qquad\qquad\qquad D_t{}^2 s = D_t|D_t\mathbf{R}(t)|$

Furthermore,

(9) $\qquad\qquad |D_t\mathbf{R}(t)|\ |D_t\mathbf{T}(t)| = |D_t\mathbf{R}(t)|^2 \left|\dfrac{D_t\mathbf{T}(t)}{|D_t\mathbf{R}(t)|}\right|$

Applying (7) above and equation (12) of Sec. 18.12 to the right-hand side of (9), we have

(10) $\qquad\qquad |D_t\mathbf{R}(t)|\ |D_t\mathbf{T}(t)| = (D_t s)^2\ K(t)$

Substituting (5), (8), and (10) into (6), we obtain

(11) $\qquad\qquad \mathbf{A}(t) = (D_t{}^2 s)\ \mathbf{T}(t) + (D_t s)^2\ K(t)\mathbf{N}(t)$

Equation (11) expresses the acceleration vector as the sum of a scalar times the unit tangent vector and a scalar times the unit normal vector. The coefficient of $\mathbf{T}(t)$ is called the *tangential component* of the acceleration vector and is denoted by A_T, while the coefficient of $\mathbf{N}(t)$ is called the *normal component* of the acceleration vector and is denoted by A_N. So,

(12) $\qquad\qquad\qquad\qquad A_T = D_t{}^2 s$

and

(13) $\qquad\qquad\qquad\qquad A_N = (D_t s)^2\ K(t)$

or, equivalently,

(14) $\qquad\qquad\qquad\qquad A_N = \dfrac{(D_t s)^2}{\rho(t)}$

Since the speed of the particle at time t is $|\mathbf{V}(t)| = D_t s$, A_T is the derivative of the speed of the particle and A_N is the square of the speed divided by the radius of curvature.

From Newton's second law of motion,

$$\mathbf{F} = m\mathbf{A}$$

where $\mathbf{F}$ is the force vector applied to the moving object, m is the mass of the object, and $\mathbf{A}$ is the acceleration vector of the object. In curvilinear motion, the normal component of $\mathbf{F}$ is the force normal to the curve necessary to keep the object on the curve. For example, if an automobile is going around a curve at a high speed, then the normal force must have a large magnitude in order to keep the car on the road. Also, if the curve is sharp, the radius of curvature is a small number, and so the magnitude of the normal force must be a large number.

Equation (4) tells us that the tangential component of the velocity vector is $D_t s$ and the normal component of the velocity vector is zero.

Substituting (12) and (13) into (11), we have

(15) $$\mathbf{A}(t) = A_T \mathbf{T}(t) + A_N \mathbf{N}(t)$$

from which it follows that

$$|\mathbf{A}(t)| = \sqrt{(A_T)^2 + (A_N)^2}$$

and solving for A_N, noting from (13) that A_N is nonnegative,

(16) $$A_N = \sqrt{|\mathbf{A}(t)|^2 - (A_T)^2}$$

EXAMPLE 1: A particle is moving along the curve having the vector equation

$$\mathbf{R}(t) = (t^2 - 1)\mathbf{i} + (\tfrac{1}{3}t^3 - t)\mathbf{j}$$

Find each of the following vectors: $\mathbf{V}(t)$, $\mathbf{A}(t)$, $\mathbf{T}(t)$, and $\mathbf{N}(t)$. Also, find the following scalars at time t: $|\mathbf{V}(t)|$, A_T, A_N, $K(t)$. Find the particular values of these quantities when $t = 2$. Draw a sketch showing a portion of the curve at the point where $t = 2$, representations of $\mathbf{V}(2)$, $\mathbf{A}(2)$, $A_T\mathbf{T}(2)$, and $A_N\mathbf{N}(2)$, having their initial point at $t = 2$.

Solution:

$$\mathbf{V}(t) = D_t\mathbf{R}(t) = 2t\mathbf{i} + (t^2 - 1)\mathbf{j}$$
$$\mathbf{A}(t) = D_t\mathbf{V}(t) = 2\mathbf{i} + 2t\mathbf{j}$$
$$|\mathbf{V}(t)| = \sqrt{4t^2 + t^4 - 2t^2 + 1} = \sqrt{t^4 + 2t^2 + 1} = t^2 + 1$$
$$|\mathbf{A}(t)| = \sqrt{4 + 4t^2} = 2\sqrt{1 + t^2}$$
$$D_t s = |\mathbf{V}(t)| = t^2 + 1$$
$$A_T = D_t^2 s = 2t$$

From (16),

$$A_N = \sqrt{|\mathbf{A}(t)|^2 - (A_T)^2} = \sqrt{4 + 4t^2 - 4t^2} = 2$$
$$\mathbf{T}(t) = \frac{\mathbf{V}(t)}{|\mathbf{V}(t)|} = \frac{2t}{t^2 + 1}\mathbf{i} + \frac{t^2 - 1}{t^2 + 1}\mathbf{j}$$

To find $\mathbf{N}(t)$, we make use of the following formula which comes from (11):

(17) $$\mathbf{N}(t) = \frac{1}{(D_t s)^2 K(t)} [\mathbf{A}(t) - (D_t^2 s)\,\mathbf{T}(t)]$$

$$\mathbf{A}(t) - (D_t^2 s)\,\mathbf{T}(t) = 2\mathbf{i} + 2t\mathbf{j} - 2t\left(\frac{2t}{t^2 + 1}\mathbf{i} + \frac{t^2 - 1}{t^2 + 1}\mathbf{j}\right)$$

(18) $$\mathbf{A}(t) - (D_t^2 s)\,\mathbf{T}(t) = \frac{2}{t^2 + 1}[(1 - t^2)\mathbf{i} + 2t\mathbf{j}]$$

From (17), we see that $\mathbf{N}(t)$ is a scalar times the vector in (18). Since $\mathbf{N}(t)$ is a unit vector, we may obtain $\mathbf{N}(t)$ by dividing the vector in (18) by its magnitude, and we have

$$\mathbf{N}(t) = \frac{(1 - t^2)\mathbf{i} + 2t\mathbf{j}}{\sqrt{(1 - t^2)^2 + (2t)^2}} = \frac{1 - t^2}{1 + t^2}\mathbf{i} + \frac{2t}{1 + t^2}\mathbf{j}$$

We find $K(t)$ from (13), and we have

$$K(t) = \frac{A_N}{(D_t s)^2} = \frac{2}{(t^2 + 1)^2}$$

When $t = 2$, we obtain $\mathbf{V}(2) = 4\mathbf{i} + 3\mathbf{j}$, $\mathbf{A}(2) = 2\mathbf{i} + 4\mathbf{j}$, $|\mathbf{V}(2)| = 5$, $A_T = 4$, $A_N = 2$, $\mathbf{T}(2) = (4/5)\mathbf{i} + (3/5)\mathbf{j}$, $\mathbf{N}(2) = (-3/5)\mathbf{i} + (4/5)\mathbf{j}$, $K(2) = 2/25$. The required sketch is shown in Fig. 18.13.1.

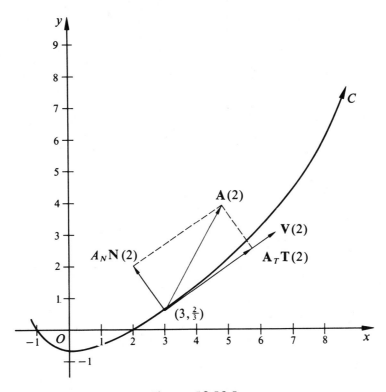

Figure 18.13.1

Exercises 18.13

In Exercises 1 through 6, a particle is moving along the curve having the given vector equation. In each problem, find the vectors $\mathbf{V}(t)$, $\mathbf{A}(t)$, $\mathbf{T}(t)$, and $\mathbf{N}(t)$, and the following scalars at time t: $|\mathbf{V}(t)|$, A_T, A_N, $K(t)$. Also find the particular values of these quantities when $t = t_1$. At $t = t_1$, draw a sketch of a portion of the curve and representations of the vectors $\mathbf{V}(t_1)$, $\mathbf{A}(t_1)$, $A_T\mathbf{T}(t_1)$, and $A_N\mathbf{N}(t_1)$.

1. $\mathbf{R}(t) = (2t + 3)\mathbf{i} + (t^2 - 1)\mathbf{j}$; $t_1 = 2$

2. $\mathbf{R}(t) = (t - 1)\mathbf{i} + t^2\mathbf{j}$; $t_1 = 1$

3. $\mathbf{R}(t) = 5 \cos 3t\mathbf{i} + 5 \sin 3t\mathbf{j}$; $t_1 = \pi/3$

4. $\mathbf{R}(t) = \cos t^2 \mathbf{i} + \sin t^2 \mathbf{j}; \ t_1 = \sqrt{\pi}/2$

5. $\mathbf{R}(t) = e^t \mathbf{i} + e^{-t} \mathbf{j}; \ t_1 = 0$

6. $\mathbf{R}(t) = 3t^2 \mathbf{i} + 2t^3 \mathbf{j}; \ t_1 = 1$

7. A particle is moving along the parabola $y^2 = 8x$ and its speed is constant. Find each of the following when the particle is at (2,4): the position vector, the velocity vector, the acceleration vector, the unit tangent vector, the unit normal vector, A_T, and A_N.

8. A particle is moving along the top branch of the hyperbola $y^2 - x^2 = 9$, such that $D_t x$ is a positive constant. Find each of the following when the particle is at (4,5): the position vector, the velocity vector, the acceleration vector, the unit tangent vector, the unit normal vector, A_T, and A_N.

19 The hyperbolic functions

(19.1)   The hyperbolic functions

Certain combinations of e^x and e^{-x} appear so frequently in applications of mathematics that they are given special names. Two of these functions are the *hyperbolic sine function* and the *hyperbolic cosine function*. The function values are related to the coordinates of the points of an equilateral hyperbola in a manner similar to that in which the values of the corresponding trigonometric functions are related to the coordinates of points of a circle (see Sec. 19.3). Following are the definitions of the hyperbolic sine function and the hyperbolic cosine function.

19.1.1 DEFINITION   The hyperbolic sine function is defined by

$$\sinh x = \frac{e^x - e^{-x}}{2} \qquad \text{where } x \text{ is a real number}$$

The domain and range are the set of all real numbers.

19.1.2 DEFINITION   The hyperbolic cosine function is defined by

$$\cosh x = \frac{e^x + e^{-x}}{2} \qquad \text{where } x \text{ is a real number}$$

The domain is the set of all real numbers and the range is the set of all numbers in the interval $[1, +\infty)$.

Sketches of the graphs of the hyperbolic sine function and the hyperbolic cosine function are shown in Figs. 19.1.1 and 19.1.2, respectively. The graphs are easily sketched by using values in a table of hyperbolic functions found in the Appendix.

The remaining four hyperbolic functions may be defined in terms of the hyperbolic sine and hyperbolic cosine functions. The reader should note that each satisfies a relation analogous to one satisfied by corresponding trigonometric functions.

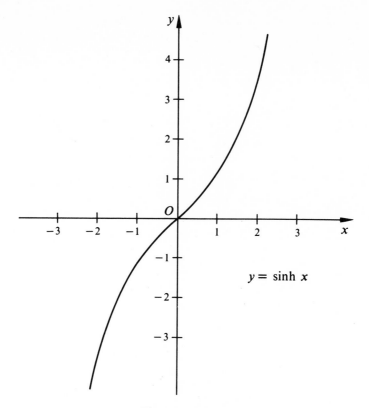

Figure 19.1.1

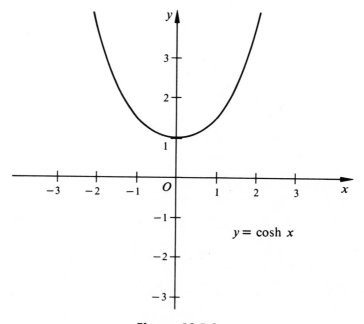

Figure 19.1.2

19.1.3 DEFINITION The *hyperbolic tangent function*, *hyperbolic cotangent function*, *hyperbolic secant function*, and *hyperbolic cosecant function* are defined, respectively, as follows:

(1) $$\tanh x = \frac{\sinh x}{\cosh x} = \frac{e^x - e^{-x}}{e^x + e^{-x}}$$

(2) $$\coth x = \frac{\cosh x}{\sinh x} = \frac{e^x + e^{-x}}{e^x - e^{-x}}$$

(3) $$\operatorname{sech} x = \frac{1}{\cosh x} = \frac{2}{e^x + e^{-x}}$$

(4) $$\operatorname{csch} x = \frac{1}{\sinh x} = \frac{2}{e^x - e^{-x}}$$

A sketch of the graph of the hyperbolic tangent function is shown in Fig. 19.1.3.

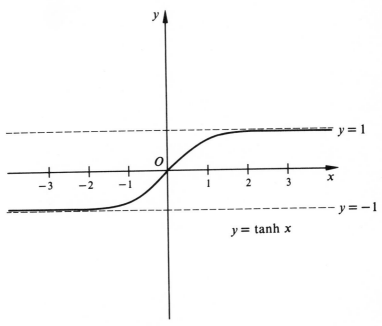

Figure 19.1.3

There are identities that are satisfied by the hyperbolic functions which are similar to those satisfied by the trigonometric functions. Four of the fundamental identities are given in Definition 19.1.3. The other four fundamental identities are as follows:

(5) $$\tanh x = \frac{1}{\coth x}$$

(6) $$\cosh^2 x - \sinh^2 x = 1$$

(7) $$1 - \tanh^2 x = \operatorname{sech}^2 x$$

(8) $$1 - \coth^2 x = -\operatorname{csch}^2 x$$

Equation (5) follows immediately from (1) and (2). Following is the proof of (6).

$$\cosh^2 x - \sinh^2 x = \left(\frac{e^x + e^{-x}}{2}\right)^2 - \left(\frac{e^x - e^{-x}}{2}\right)^2$$

$$= \frac{e^{2x} + 2e^0 + e^{-2x} - e^{2x} + 2e^0 - e^{-2x}}{4} = 1$$

Equation (7) may be proved by using the definitions of $\tanh x$ and $\operatorname{sech} x$ in terms of e^x and e^{-x} as in the proof above, or an alternate proof is obtained by using other identities as follows:

$$1 - \tanh^2 x = 1 - \frac{\sinh^2 x}{\cosh^2 x} = \frac{\cosh^2 x - \sinh^2 x}{\cosh^2 x} = \frac{1}{\cosh^2 x} = \operatorname{sech}^2 x$$

The proof of (8) is left for the reader (see Exercise 1 at the end of this section). From the eight fundamental identities, it is possible to prove others. Some of these are given in the exercises that follow. Other identities, such as the hyperbolic functions of the sum or difference of two numbers and the hyperbolic functions of twice a number or one-half a number, are similar to the corresponding trigonometric identities. In some cases, it is helpful to make use of the following two relations, which follow from Definitions 19.1.1 and 19.1.2.

(9) $$\cosh x + \sinh x = e^x$$

(10) $$\cosh x - \sinh x = e^{-x}$$

We shall use them in proving the following identity:

(11) $$\sinh (x + y) = \sinh x \cosh y + \cosh x \sinh y$$

From Definition 19.1.1 we have

$$\sinh (x + y) = \frac{e^{x+y} - e^{-(x+y)}}{2} = \frac{e^x e^y - e^{-x} e^{-y}}{2}$$

Applying (9) and (10) to the right-hand side of the above, we obtain

$$\sinh (x + y) = \tfrac{1}{2}[(\cosh x + \sinh x)(\cosh y + \sinh y)$$
$$- (\cosh x - \sinh x)(\cosh y - \sinh y)]$$

Expanding the right-hand side of the above and combining terms, we obtain (11).

In a similar manner we may prove

(12) $$\cosh (x + y) = \cosh x \cosh y + \sinh x \sinh y$$

If in (11) and (12) we replace y by x, we obtain the following two formulas:

(13) $$\sinh 2x = 2 \sinh x \cosh x$$

and

(14) $$\cosh 2x = \cosh^2 x + \sinh^2 x$$

Formula (14) combined with the identity (6) gives us two alternate formulas for cosh 2x, which are

(15) $\cosh 2x = 2 \sinh^2 x + 1$

and

(16) $\cosh 2x = 2 \cosh^2 x - 1$

Solving (15) and (16) for sinh x and cosh x, respectively, and replacing x by $x/2$, we get

(17) $\sinh \dfrac{x}{2} = \pm\sqrt{\dfrac{\cosh x - 1}{2}}$

and

(18) $\cosh \dfrac{x}{2} = \sqrt{\dfrac{\cosh x + 1}{2}}$

We do not have a $\pm$ sign on the right-hand side of (18) since the range of the hyperbolic cosine function is $[1, +\infty)$.

The details of the proofs of equations (12) through (18) are left for the reader (see Exercises 2 and 4 through 7 at the end of this section).

The formulas for the derivatives of the hyperbolic sine and hyperbolic cosine functions may be obtained by applying Definitions 19.1.1 and 19.1.2 and differentiating the resulting expressions involving exponential functions. For example,

$$D_x(\cosh x) = D_x \left(\frac{e^x + e^{-x}}{2}\right) = \frac{e^x - e^{-x}}{2} = \sinh x$$

In a similar manner, we find $D_x(\sinh x) = \cosh x$ (see Exercise 21). To find the derivative of the hyperbolic tangent function, we shall make use of some of the identities we have previously proved.

$$D_x(\tanh x) = D_x \left(\frac{\sinh x}{\cosh x}\right) = \frac{\cosh^2 x - \sinh^2 x}{\cosh^2 x} = \frac{1}{\cosh^2 x} = \operatorname{sech}^2 x$$

The formulas for the derivatives of the remaining three hyperbolic functions are as follows: $D_x(\coth x) = -\operatorname{csch}^2 x$; $D_x(\operatorname{sech} x) = -\operatorname{sech} x \tanh x$; $D_x(\operatorname{csch} x) = -\operatorname{csch} x \coth x$. The proofs of these formulas are left for the reader (see Exercises 22 through 24 at the end of the section).

From the above formulas and the chain rule, if u is a differentiable function of x, we have the following more general formulas:

(((19) $D_x(\sinh u) = \cosh u \, D_x u$

(((20) $D_x(\cosh u) = \sinh u \, D_x u$

(((21) $D_x(\tanh u) = \operatorname{sech}^2 u \, D_x u$

(((22) $D_x(\coth u) = -\operatorname{csch}^2 u \, D_x u$

(((23) $D_x(\operatorname{sech} u) = -\operatorname{sech} u \tanh u \, D_x u$

(((24) $D_x(\operatorname{csch} u) = -\operatorname{csch} u \coth u \, D_x u$

The reader should notice that the formulas for the derivatives of the hyperbolic sine, cosine, and tangent all have a plus sign, while the formulas for the derivatives of the hyperbolic cotangent, secant, and cosecant all have a minus sign. Otherwise the formulas are similar to the corresponding formulas for the derivatives of the trigonometric functions.

EXAMPLE 1: *Given:* $y = \tanh(1 - x^2)$. *Find:* $D_x y$.
Solution: $D_x y = -2x \operatorname{sech}^2(1 - x^2)$.

EXAMPLE 2: *Given:* $y = \ln \sinh x$. *Find:* $D_x y$.
Solution: $D_x y = (1/\sinh x) \cosh x = (\cosh x/\sinh x) = \coth x$.

Formulas (19) through (24) give rise to the following indefinite integration formulas:

(((25)
$$\int \sinh u \, du = \cosh u + C$$

(((26)
$$\int \cosh u \, du = \sinh u + C$$

(((27)
$$\int \operatorname{sech}^2 u \, du = \tanh u + C$$

(((28)
$$\int \operatorname{csch}^2 u \, du = -\coth u + C$$

(((29)
$$\int \operatorname{sech} u \tanh u \, du = -\operatorname{sech} u + C$$

(((30)
$$\int \operatorname{csch} u \coth u \, du = -\operatorname{csch} u + C$$

EXAMPLE 3: *Evaluate:* $\int \sinh^3 x \cosh^2 x \, dx$.
Solution:

$$\int \sinh^3 x \cosh^2 x \, dx = \int \sinh^2 x \cosh^2 x \, (\sinh x \, dx)$$

$$= \int (\cosh^2 x - 1) \cosh^2 x \, (\sinh x \, dx)$$

$$= \int \cosh^4 x \, (\sinh x \, dx) - \int \cosh^2 x \, (\sinh x \, dx)$$

$$= \frac{1}{5} \cosh^5 x - \frac{1}{3} \cosh^3 x + C$$

EXAMPLE 4: Find the volume generated by revolving the region bounded by $y = \sinh x$, the x axis, and the line $x = 1$ about the x axis.
Solution: The region and a rectangular element of area are shown in Fig. 19.1.4. If V is the number of cubic units in the volume of the solid, then

$$V = \lim_{\|\Delta\| \to 0} \sum_{i=1}^{n} \pi [f(\xi_i)]^2 \, \Delta_i x = \pi \int_0^1 \sinh^2 x \, dx$$

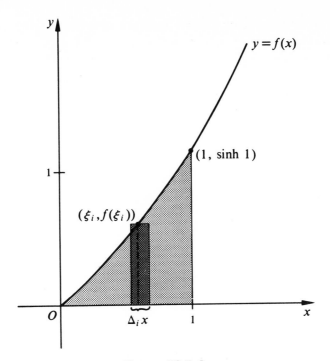

Figure 19.1.4

To evaluate this integral, we use (17), replacing $x/2$ by x; so we have

$$\frac{V}{\pi} = \int_0^1 \frac{\cosh 2x - 1}{2}\, dx = \frac{1}{4} \sinh 2x - \frac{x}{2}\Big]_0^1 = \frac{1}{4} \sinh 2 - \frac{1}{2} - \frac{1}{4} \sinh 0$$

$$= \frac{1}{4}(3.6269) - \frac{1}{2} - \frac{1}{4}(0) = 0.4067. \text{ So, } V = 0.4067\pi$$

Exercises 19.1

In Exercises 1 through 13, prove the given identity.

1. $1 - \coth^2 x = -\operatorname{csch}^2 x$

2. $\cosh (x + y) = \cosh x \cosh y + \sinh x \sinh y$

3. $\tanh (x + y) = \dfrac{\tanh x + \tanh y}{1 + \tanh x \tanh y}$

4. $\sinh 2x = 2 \sinh x \cosh x$

5. $\cosh 2x = \cosh^2 x + \sinh^2 x = 2 \sinh^2 x + 1 = 2 \cosh^2 x - 1$

6. $\cosh \dfrac{x}{2} = \sqrt{\dfrac{\cosh x + 1}{2}}$

7. $\sinh \dfrac{x}{2} = \pm\sqrt{\dfrac{\cosh x - 1}{2}}$

8. $\operatorname{csch} 2x = \frac{1}{2} \operatorname{sech} x \operatorname{csch} x$

9. $\tanh(-x) = -\tanh x$

10. $\operatorname{sech}(-x) = \operatorname{sech} x$

11. $\sinh 3x = 3 \sinh x + 4 \sinh^3 x$

12. $\cosh 3x = 4 \cosh^3 x - 3 \cosh x$

13. $\sinh^2 x - \sinh^2 y = \sinh(x + y)\sinh(x - y)$

14. *Prove:* $(\sinh x + \cosh x)^n = \cosh nx + \sinh nx$. HINT: Use formula (9).

15. Prove that the hyperbolic sine function is an odd function and the hyperbolic cosine function is an even function.

16. *Prove:* $\tanh(\ln x) = \dfrac{x^2 - 1}{x^2 + 1}$.

17. *Prove:* $\dfrac{1 + \tanh x}{1 - \tanh x} = e^{2x}$.

18. *Prove:* $\sin^{-1}(\tanh x) = \tan^{-1}(\sinh x)$.

19. Show that $x = \cosh t$ and $y = \sinh t$ are parametric equations of a branch of an equilateral hyperbola.

20. Draw a sketch of the curve having parametric equations $x = t - \tanh t$ and $y = \operatorname{sech} t$. The curve is called a *tractrix*.

21. *Prove:* $D_x(\sinh x) = \cosh x$.

22. *Prove:* $D_x(\coth x) = -\operatorname{csch}^2 x$.

23. *Prove:* $D_x(\operatorname{sech} x) = -\operatorname{sech} x \tanh x$.

24. *Prove:* $D_x(\operatorname{csch} x) = -\operatorname{csch} x \coth x$.

In Exercises 25 through 36, find the derivative of the given function.

25. $f(x) = \tanh \dfrac{4x + 1}{5}$

26. $g(x) = \ln(\sinh x^3)$

27. $F(r) = \cosh(e^r)$

28. $G(t) = \exp(\sinh t)$

29. $f(x) = e^x \cosh x$

30. $g(x) = \coth \dfrac{1}{x}$

31. $h(t) = \ln(\tanh t)$

32. $F(x) = \tan^{-1}(\sinh x^2)$

33. $G(x) = \sin^{-1}(\tanh x^2)$

34. $f(x) = \ln(\coth 3x - \operatorname{csch} 3x)$

35. $f(x) = x^{\sinh x}$

36. $g(x) = (\cosh x)^x$

37. *Prove:* $\displaystyle\int \tanh u \, du = \ln|\cosh u| + C$.

38. *Prove:* $\displaystyle\int \coth u \, du = \ln|\sinh u| + C$.

39. *Prove:* $\displaystyle\int \operatorname{sech} u \, du = 2 \tan^{-1} e^u + C$.

40. *Prove:* $\int \operatorname{csch} u \, du = \ln|\tanh(u/2)| + C.$

In Exercises 41 through 50, evaluate the indefinite integral.

41. $\int \sinh^4 x \cosh^3 x \, dx$

42. $\int \tanh^2 x \, dx$

43. $\int \tanh x \ln(\cosh x) \, dx$

44. $\int \sinh^2 x \, dx$

45. $\int \cosh^4 x \, dx$

46. $\int \operatorname{sech} x \tanh^3 x \, dx$

47. $\int \operatorname{sech}^4 3x \, dx$

48. $\int \dfrac{\sinh\sqrt{x}}{\sqrt{x}} dx$

49. $\int \sinh x \sin x \, dx$

50. $\int x \cosh x \, dx$

In Exercises 51 through 54, evaluate the definite integral.

51. $\int_0^2 \sinh^3 x \, dx$

52. $\int_{-1}^1 \cosh^2 x \, dx$

53. $\int_0^1 \tanh x \, dx$

54. $\int_0^1 e^x \cosh x \, dx$

55. Draw a sketch of the graph of the hyperbolic cotangent function. Find equations of the asymptotes.

56. Draw a sketch of the graph of the hyperbolic secant function. Find the relative extrema of the function, the points of inflection of the graph, the intervals on which the graph is concave upward, and the intervals on which the graph is concave downward.

57. Prove that the hyperbolic sine function is continuous and increasing on its entire domain.

58. Prove that the hyperbolic tangent function is continuous and increasing on its entire domain.

59. Prove that the hyperbolic cosine function is continuous on its entire domain but is not monotonic on its entire domain. Find the intervals on which the function is increasing and the intervals on which the function is decreasing.

60. Find the area of the region of Example 4 of this section.

61. Find the centroid of the region of Example 4 of this section.

62. A catenary is the curve formed by a homogeneous flexible cable hanging from two points under its own weight. If the lowest point of the catenary is the point $(0,a)$, its equation is $y = a \cosh(x/a)$, $a > 0$. Find the length of arc of the catenary from the point $(0,a)$ to the point (x_1, y_1), where $x_1 > 0$.

63. Find the area of the region bounded by the catenary of Exercise 62, the y axis, the x axis, and the line $x = x_1$ where $x_1 > 0$.

64. Find the centroid of the region of Exercise 63.

65. Find the volume of the solid of revolution generated if the region of Exercise 63 is revolved about the x axis.

(19.2)   The inverse hyperbolic functions

From the graph of the hyperbolic sine function (Fig. 19.1.1), we see that a horizontal line intersects the graph in one and only one point, and therefore to each number in the range of the function there corresponds one and only one number in the domain. The hyperbolic sine function is continuous and increasing on its domain (see Exercise 57 in Sec. 19.1), and so by Theorem 12.4.2, the function has an inverse function.

19.2.1 DEFINITION   The *inverse hyperbolic sine function,* denoted by $\sinh^{-1}$, is defined as follows:

$$y = \sinh^{-1} x \qquad \text{if and only if} \qquad x = \sinh y$$

A sketch of the graph of the inverse hyperbolic sine function is shown in Fig. 19.2.1. Its domain is the set of all real numbers, and its range is the set of all real numbers.

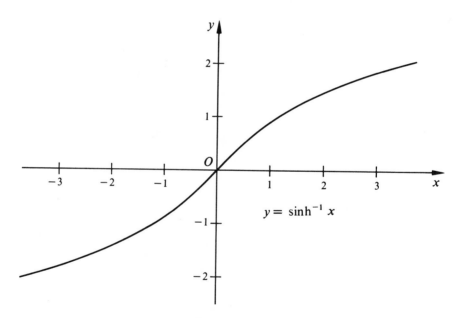

Figure 19.2.1

It follows from Definition 19.2.1 that

(1) $\sinh (\sinh^{-1} x) = x$

and

(2) $\sinh^{-1} (\sinh y) = y$

From Fig. 19.1.2, we notice that a horizontal line $y = k$, where $k > 1$, intersects the graph of the hyperbolic cosine function in two points. Therefore, for each number greater than 1 in the range of this function, there correspond two numbers in the domain. So the hyperbolic cosine function does not have an inverse function. However, let us define a function F as follows:

(3) $$F(x) = \cosh x \qquad \text{for } x \geq 0$$

The domain of F is the interval $[0, +\infty)$ and the range is the interval $[1, +\infty)$. A sketch of the graph of F is shown in Fig. 19.2.2. The function F is continuous and increasing on its entire domain (see Exercise 1 at the end of this section), and so by Theorem 12.4.2, F has an inverse function, which we call the inverse hyperbolic cosine function.

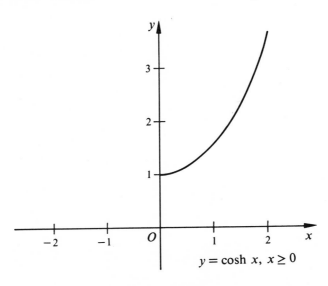

$$y = \cosh x, \ x \geq 0$$

Figure 19.2.2

19.2.2 DEFINITION   The *inverse hyperbolic cosine function*, denoted by $\cosh^{-1}$, is defined as follows:

$$y = \cosh^{-1} x \qquad \text{if and only if} \qquad x = \cosh y \text{ and } y \geq 0$$

A sketch of the graph of the inverse hyperbolic cosine function is shown in Fig. 19.2.3. The domain of this function is the interval $[1, +\infty)$, and the range is the interval $[0, +\infty)$. From Definition 19.2.2, we may conclude that

(4) $$\cosh (\cosh^{-1} x) = x \qquad \text{if } x \geq 1$$

and

(5) $$\cosh^{-1} (\cosh y) = y \qquad \text{if } y \geq 0$$

As with the hyperbolic sine function, a horizontal line intersects each of the graphs of the hyperbolic tangent function, the hyperbolic cotangent function, and the hyperbolic cosecant function in one and only one point. For the hyperbolic tangent function, this may be seen in Fig. 19.1.3. Each of the above three functions is continuous and monotonic on its domain, and hence each has an inverse function.

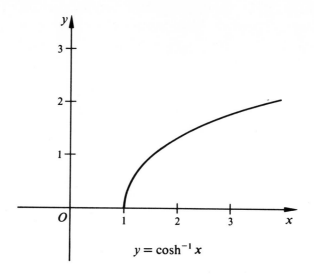

$$y = \cosh^{-1} x$$

Figure 19.2.3

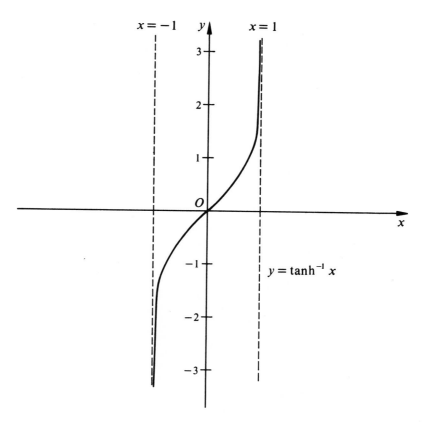

$$y = \tanh^{-1} x$$

Figure 19.2.4

19.2.3 DEFINITION   The *inverse hyperbolic tangent function*, the *inverse hyperbolic cotangent function*, and the *inverse hyperbolic cosecant function*, denoted respectively by tanh^{-1}, coth^{-1}, and csch^{-1}, are defined as follows:

$$y = \tanh^{-1} x \qquad \text{if and only if} \qquad x = \tanh y$$
$$y = \coth^{-1} x \qquad \text{if and only if} \qquad x = \coth y$$
$$y = \operatorname{csch}^{-1} x \qquad \text{if and only if} \qquad x = \operatorname{csch} y$$

The hyperbolic secant function does not have an inverse function. However, we may proceed as we did with the hyperbolic cosine function and define a new function which has an inverse function. Let the function G be defined by

(6) $$G(x) = \operatorname{sech} x \qquad \text{for } x \geq 0$$

It can be shown that G is continuous and monotonic on its entire domain (see Exercise 2 at the end of this section), and therefore G has an inverse function, which we call the *inverse hyperbolic secant function*.

19.2.4 DEFINITION   The *inverse hyperbolic secant function*, denoted by sech^{-1}, is defined as follows:

(7) $$y = \operatorname{sech}^{-1} x \qquad \text{if and only if} \qquad x = \operatorname{sech} y \text{ and } y \geq 0$$

The inverse hyperbolic functions may be expressed in terms of natural logarithms. This should not be surprising, since the hyperbolic functions were defined in terms of the exponential function, and the natural logarithmic function is the inverse of the exponential function. Following are these expressions for sinh^{-1}, cosh^{-1}, tanh^{-1}, and coth^{-1}.

(8) $$\sinh^{-1} x = \ln (x + \sqrt{x^2 + 1}) \qquad x \text{ any real number}$$

(9) $$\cosh^{-1} x = \ln (x + \sqrt{x^2 - 1}) \qquad x \geq 1$$

(10) $$\tanh^{-1} x = \frac{1}{2} \ln \frac{1 + x}{1 - x} \qquad |x| < 1$$

(11) $$\coth^{-1} x = \frac{1}{2} \ln \frac{x + 1}{x - 1} \qquad |x| > 1$$

We shall prove (9) and leave the proofs of the other three formulas for the reader (see Exercises 3 through 5 at the end of this section).

To prove (9), let $y = \cosh^{-1} x$, $x \geq 1$. Then, by Definition 19.2.2, $x = \cosh y$, $y \geq 0$. Applying Definition 19.1.2 to cosh y, we get

$$x = \frac{e^y + e^{-y}}{2} \qquad y \geq 0$$

from which we obtain

$$e^{2y} - 2xe^y + 1 = 0 \qquad y \geq 0$$

Solving this equation for e^y by the quadratic formula, we obtain

$$e^y = \frac{2x \pm \sqrt{4x^2 - 4}}{2} = x \pm \sqrt{x^2 - 1} \qquad y \geq 0$$

We know that $y \geq 0$ and $x \geq 1$. Therefore, $e^y \geq 1$. Hence, we may safely reject the minus sign in the above, since when $x = 1$, $x + \sqrt{x^2 - 1} = x - \sqrt{x^2 - 1} = 1$, and when $x > 1$, $x - \sqrt{x^2 - 1} < 1$. Since $y = \cosh^{-1} x$, we have

$$\cosh^{-1} x = \ln(x + \sqrt{x^2 - 1}) \qquad x \geq 1$$

which is (9).

EXAMPLE 1: Express each of the following in terms of a natural logarithm: (a) $\tanh^{-1}(-4/5)$; (b) $\sinh^{-1} 2$.

Solution: (a) From (10), we obtain

$$\tanh^{-1}\left(-\frac{4}{5}\right) = \frac{1}{2} \ln \frac{1/5}{9/5} = \frac{1}{2} \ln \frac{1}{9} = \ln \frac{1}{3} = -\ln 3$$

(b) From (8), we get

$$\sinh^{-1} 2 = \ln(2 + \sqrt{5})$$

To obtain a formula for the derivative of the inverse hyperbolic sine function, let $y = \sinh^{-1} x$, and then $x = \sinh y$. So, since $D_y x = \cosh y$ and $D_x y = 1/D_y x$, we have

$$(12) \qquad\qquad D_x y = \frac{1}{\cosh y}$$

From the identity $\cosh^2 y - \sinh^2 y = 1$, it follows that $\cosh y = \sqrt{\sinh^2 y + 1}$. (NOTE: When taking the square root, the minus sign is rejected, since $\cosh y \geq 1$). So since $x = \sinh y$, $\cosh y = \sqrt{x^2 + 1}$. Substituting this in (12), we obtain

(((13) $$\qquad\qquad D_x(\sinh^{-1} x) = \frac{1}{\sqrt{x^2 + 1}}$$

If u is a differentiable function of x, we have from (13) and the chain rule,

(((14) $$\qquad\qquad D_x(\sinh^{-1} u) = \frac{1}{\sqrt{u^2 + 1}} D_x u$$

Formula (13) may also be derived by using (8), as follows.

$$D_x(\sinh^{-1} x) = D_x \ln(x + \sqrt{x^2 + 1}) = \frac{1 + x/\sqrt{x^2 + 1}}{x + \sqrt{x^2 + 1}}$$

$$= \frac{\sqrt{x^2 + 1} + x}{\sqrt{x^2 + 1}(x + \sqrt{x^2 + 1})} = \frac{1}{\sqrt{x^2 + 1}}$$

The following differentiation formulas may be obtained in analogous ways. Their proofs are left for the reader (see Exercises 6 through 10 at the end of this section). In each formula u is a differentiable function of x.

$$\mathbf{(\!(}\quad (15) \qquad\qquad D_x(\cosh^{-1} u) = \frac{1}{\sqrt{u^2 - 1}}\, D_x u \qquad\qquad u > 1$$

$$\mathbf{(\!(}\quad (16) \qquad\qquad D_x(\tanh^{-1} u) = \frac{1}{1 - u^2}\, D_x u \qquad\qquad |u| < 1$$

$$\mathbf{(\!(}\quad (17) \qquad\qquad D_x(\coth^{-1} u) = \frac{1}{1 - u^2} D_x u \qquad\qquad |u| > 1$$

$$\mathbf{(\!(}\quad (18) \qquad\qquad D_x(\text{sech}^{-1} u) = -\frac{1}{u\sqrt{1 - u^2}}\, D_x u \qquad\qquad 0 < u < 1$$

$$\mathbf{(\!(}\quad (19) \qquad\qquad D_x(\text{csch}^{-1} u) = -\frac{1}{|u|\sqrt{1 + u^2}}\, D_x u \qquad\qquad u \neq 0$$

EXAMPLE 2: *Given:* $y = \tanh^{-1}(\cos 2x)$. *Find:* $D_x y$.

Solution: Applying formula (16), we get

$$D_x y = \frac{-2 \sin 2x}{1 - \cos^2 2x} = \frac{-2 \sin 2x}{\sin^2 2x} = -2 \csc 2x$$

From differentiation formulas (14) through (17) and formulas (8) through (11), we obtain the following indefinite integration formulas:

$$\mathbf{(\!(}\quad (20) \qquad \int \frac{du}{\sqrt{u^2 + 1}} = \sinh^{-1} u + C = \ln(u + \sqrt{u^2 + 1}) + C$$

$$\mathbf{(\!(}\quad (21) \qquad \int \frac{du}{\sqrt{u^2 - 1}} = \cosh^{-1} u + C = \ln(u + \sqrt{u^2 - 1}) + C \quad u > 1$$

$$\mathbf{(\!(}\quad (22) \qquad \int \frac{du}{1 - u^2} = \begin{cases} \tanh^{-1} u + C & \text{if } |u| < 1 \\ \coth^{-1} u + C & \text{if } |u| > 1 \end{cases} = \frac{1}{2} \ln \left| \frac{1 + u}{1 - u} \right| + C \quad \text{if } u \neq 1$$

We also have the following formulas:

$$\mathbf{(\!(}\quad (23) \qquad \int \frac{du}{\sqrt{u^2 + a^2}} = \sinh^{-1} \frac{u}{a} + C = \ln \left(\frac{u + \sqrt{u^2 + a^2}}{a} \right) + C \quad a > 0$$

$$\mathbf{(\!(}\quad (24) \qquad \int \frac{du}{\sqrt{u^2 - a^2}} = \cosh^{-1} \frac{u}{a} + C = \ln \left(\frac{u + \sqrt{u^2 - a^2}}{a} \right) + C \quad u > a > 0$$

$$\mathbf{(\!(}\quad (25) \qquad \int \frac{du}{a^2 - u^2} = \begin{cases} \dfrac{1}{a} \tanh^{-1} \dfrac{u}{a} + C & \text{if } |u| < a \\ \dfrac{1}{a} \coth^{-1} \dfrac{u}{a} + C & \text{if } |u| > a \end{cases} = \frac{1}{2a} \ln \left| \frac{a + u}{a - u} \right| + C$$

$$u \neq a \text{ and } a \neq 0$$

These formulas may be proved by finding the differential of the right-hand side and obtaining the integrand. We illustrate this by proving (24).

$$d\left(\cosh^{-1}\frac{u}{a}\right) = \frac{1}{\sqrt{(u/a)^2 - 1}}\left(\frac{1}{a}\right)du$$

$$= \frac{\sqrt{a^2}}{\sqrt{u^2 - a^2}}\left(\frac{1}{a}\right)du = \frac{a}{\sqrt{u^2 - a^2}}\left(\frac{1}{a}\right)du \quad \text{if } a > 0$$

$$= \frac{du}{\sqrt{u^2 - a^2}} \quad \text{if } a > 0$$

The proofs of (23) and (25) are left for the reader (see Exercises 11 and 12 at the end of this section).

EXAMPLE 3: *Evaluate:* $\int dx/\sqrt{x^2 - 6x + 8}$.
Solution:

$$\int \frac{dx}{\sqrt{x^2 - 6x + 8}} = \int \frac{dx}{\sqrt{(x^2 - 6x + 9) - 1}} = \int \frac{dx}{\sqrt{(x - 3)^2 - 1}}$$

$$= \cosh^{-1}(x - 3) + C \quad \text{for } x - 3 > 1$$

$$= \ln(x - 3 + \sqrt{x^2 - 6x + 8}) + C \quad \text{for } x > 4$$

Exercises 19.2

1. If $F(x) = \cosh x$ and $x \geq 0$, prove that F is continuous and increasing on its entire domain.

2. If $G(x) = \operatorname{sech} x$ and $x \geq 0$, prove that G is continuous and monotonic on its entire domain.

In Exercises 3 through 12, prove the indicated formula of this section.

3. Formula (8)	7. Formula (16)	11. Formula (23)
4. Formula (10)	8. Formula (17)	12. Formula (25)
5. Formula (11)	9. Formula (18)	
6. Formula (15)	10. Formula (19)	

In Exercises 13 through 16, draw a sketch of the graph of the indicated function.

13. The inverse hyperbolic tangent function

14. The inverse hyperbolic cotangent function

15. The inverse hyperbolic secant function

16. The inverse hyperbolic cosecant function

In Exercises 17 through 20, express the given quantity in terms of a natural logarithm.

17. $\sinh^{-1} \frac{1}{4}$

18. $\cosh^{-1} 3$

19. $\tanh^{-1} \frac{1}{2}$

20. $\coth^{-1} (-2)$

In Exercises 21 through 34, find the derivative of the given function.

21. $f(x) = \sinh^{-1} x^2$

22. $G(x) = \cosh^{-1} \frac{x}{3}$

23. $F(x) = \tanh^{-1} 4x$

24. $h(w) = \tanh^{-1} w^3$

25. $g(x) = \coth^{-1} (3x + 1)$

26. $f(r) = \operatorname{csch}^{-1} (r^2/2)$

27. $f(x) = x^2 \cosh^{-1} x^2$

28. $h(x) = (\operatorname{sech}^{-1} x)^2$

29. $f(x) = \sinh^{-1} (\tan x)$

30. $g(x) = \tanh^{-1} (\sin 3x)$

31. $h(x) = \cosh^{-1} (\csc x)$

32. $F(x) = \coth^{-1} (\cosh x)$

33. $G(x) = x \sinh^{-1} x - \sqrt{1 + x^2}$

34. $H(x) = \ln \sqrt{x^2 - 1} - x \tanh^{-1} x$

In Exercises 35 through 44, express the indefinite integral in terms of an inverse hyperbolic function and as a natural logarithm.

35. $\int \dfrac{dx}{\sqrt{4 + x^2}}$

36. $\int \dfrac{dx}{\sqrt{4x^2 - 9}}$

37. $\int \dfrac{x\,dx}{\sqrt{x^4 - 1}}$

38. $\int \dfrac{dx}{25 - x^2}$

39. $\int \dfrac{dx}{9x^2 - 16}$

40. $\int \dfrac{dx}{4e^x - e^{-x}}$

41. $\int \dfrac{\cos x\,dx}{\sqrt{4 - \cos^2 x}}$

42. $\int \dfrac{dx}{\sqrt{x^2 - 4x + 1}}$

43. $\int \dfrac{dx}{2 - 4x - x^2}$

44. $\int \dfrac{3x\,dx}{\sqrt{x^4 + 6x^2 + 5}}$

In Exercises 45 through 50, evaluate the definite integral and express the answer in terms of a natural logarithm.

45. $\displaystyle\int_3^5 \dfrac{dx}{\sqrt{x^2 - 4}}$

46. $\displaystyle\int_1^2 \dfrac{dx}{\sqrt{x^2 + 2x}}$

47. $\displaystyle\int_{-1/2}^{1/2} \dfrac{dx}{1 - x^2}$

48. $\displaystyle\int_{-4}^{-3} \dfrac{dx}{1 - x^2}$

49. $\displaystyle\int_2^3 \dfrac{dx}{\sqrt{9x^2 - 12x - 5}}$

50. $\displaystyle\int_{-2}^2 \dfrac{dx}{\sqrt{16 + x^2}}$

(19.3)   Geometric interpretation of the hyperbolic functions

We shall now see how the function values of the hyperbolic sine and hyperbolic cosine functions have the same relationship to the equilateral hyperbola as the trigonometric sine and cosine functions have to the circle. The equations

(1) $x = \cos \theta$ and $y = \sin \theta$

are a set of parametric equations of the unit circle, since if θ is eliminated from them, by squaring each and adding, we obtain

$$x^2 + y^2 = \cos^2 \theta + \sin^2 \theta = 1$$

The parameter θ in equations (1) may be interpreted as the number of radians in the angle between the x axis and a line from the origin to $P(\cos \theta, \sin \theta)$ on the unit circle — refer to Fig. 19.3.1.

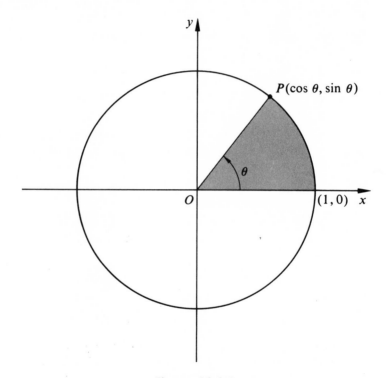

Figure 19.3.1

Since the area of a circular sector of radius r units and having a central angle of θ radians is given by $\frac{1}{2}r^2\theta$ square units, the area of the circular sector shown in Fig. 19.3.1 is $\frac{1}{2}\theta$, because $r = 1$.

Now consider the pair of parametric equations

(2) $x = \cosh t$ and $y = \sinh t$

Squaring both sides of these equations and subtracting, we obtain

$$x^2 - y^2 = \cosh^2 t - \sinh^2 t = 1$$

We may conclude then that equations (2) are a set of parametric equations of the right-hand branch of the equilateral hyperbola $x^2 - y^2 = 1$. This hyperbola is called the *unit hyperbola.*

Let $P(\cosh t, \sinh t)$ be a point on the unit hyperbola, and let us calculate the area of the sector AOP shown in Fig. 19.3.2. The sector AOP is the region bounded by the x axis, the line OP, and the arc AP of the unit hyperbola. Since

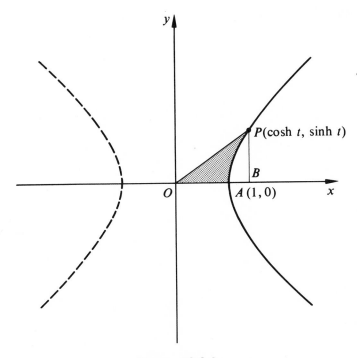

Figure 19.3.2

the area of the sector AOP is equal to the area of triangle OBP minus the area of region ABP, we have

(3)   Area of sector $AOP = \frac{1}{2} \cosh t \sinh t -$ area of region ABP

We now find the area of region ABP by integration.

$$\text{Area of region } ABP = \int_0^t \sinh u \, d(\cosh u)$$

$$= \int_0^t \sinh^2 u \, du = \frac{1}{2} \int_0^t (\cosh 2u - 1) \, du$$

$$= \frac{1}{4} \sinh 2u - \frac{1}{2}u \Big]_0^t = \frac{1}{2} \cosh t \sinh t - \frac{1}{2}t$$

Substituting this result into (3), we get

$$\text{Area of sector } AOP = \frac{1}{2} \cosh t \sinh t - (\frac{1}{2} \cosh t \sinh t - \frac{1}{2}t)$$

$$= \frac{1}{2}t$$

So we see that the area of circular sector AOP of Fig. 19.3.1 and the area of sector AOP of Fig. 19.3.2 in each case is one-half the value of the parameter associated with the point P. For the circle, the parameter θ is the number of radians in the angle AOP. The parameter t, for the unit hyperbola, is not interpreted as an angle; however, sometimes the term *hyperbolic radian* is used in connection with t.

20 Indeterminate forms and improper integrals

(20.1) Cauchy's mean-value theorem

In Chap. 8 we stated and proved two important theorems, Rolle's theorem (8.4.1) and the mean-value theorem (8.5.1). We have seen how useful these theorems are in proving other theorems. Each theorem involved a single function. The mean-value theorem was extended to two functions f and g by the French mathematician Augustin L. Cauchy (1789–1857), and it is known as *Cauchy's mean-value theorem.*

20.1.1 THEOREM (*Cauchy's Mean-value Theorem*)   If f and g are two functions such that

   (i) f and g are continuous on the closed interval $[a,b]$

   (ii) f and g are differentiable on the open interval (a,b)

   (iii) $g'(x) \neq 0$ for all x in the open interval (a,b)

then there exists a number z in the open interval (a,b) such that

$$\frac{f(b) - f(a)}{g(b) - g(a)} = \frac{f'(z)}{g'(z)}$$

Proof: We first show that $g(b) \neq g(a)$. Assume $g(b) = g(a)$. Since g satisfies the two conditions in the hypothesis of the mean-value theorem (8.5.1), there is some number c in (a,b) such that $g'(c) = [g(b) - g(a)]/(b - a)$. But if $g(b) = g(a)$, then there is some number c in (a,b) such that $g'(c) = 0$. But condition (iii) of the hypothesis of this theorem states that $g'(x) \neq 0$ for all x in (a,b). Therefore, we have a contradiction. Therefore our assumption that $g(b) = g(a)$ is false. So, $g(b) \neq g(a)$, and consequently $g(b) - g(a) \neq 0$.

Now, let us consider the function h defined by

$$h(x) = f(x) - f(a) - \frac{f(b) - f(a)}{g(b) - g(a)}[g(x) - g(a)]$$

Then,

(1) $$h'(x) = f'(x) - \frac{f(b) - f(a)}{g(b) - g(a)} g'(x)$$

Therefore, h is differentiable on (a,b), since f and g are differentiable there. The function h is continuous on $[a,b]$, since f and g are continuous there.

$$h(a) = f(a) - f(a) - \frac{f(b) - f(a)}{g(b) - g(a)}[g(a) - g(a)] = 0$$

$$h(b) = f(b) - f(a) - \frac{f(b) - f(a)}{g(b) - g(a)}[g(b) - g(a)] = 0$$

Hence, the three conditions in the hypothesis of Rolle's theorem are satisfied by the function h. So, there exists a number z in the open interval (a,b) such that $h'(z) = 0$. Thus from (1) we have

(2) $$f'(z) - \frac{f(b) - f(a)}{g(b) - g(a)} g'(z) = 0$$

Since $g'(z) \neq 0$ on (a,b), we have from (2)

$$\frac{f(b) - f(a)}{g(b) - g(a)} = \frac{f'(z)}{g'(z)}$$

where z is some number in (a,b). This proves the theorem.

It should be noted that if g is the function such that $g(x) = x$, then the conclusion of Cauchy's mean-value theorem becomes the conclusion of our former mean-value theorem, since then $g'(z) = 1$. So, the former mean-value theorem is a special case of Cauchy's mean-value theorem.

To interpret Theorem 20.1.1 geometrically, consider a curve having the parametric equations $x = g(t)$, $y = f(t)$, where $a \leq t \leq b$ (see Fig. 20.1.1).

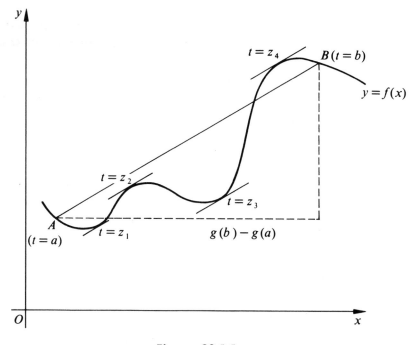

Figure 20.1.1

The slope of the curve in Fig. 20.1.1 at a particular point is given by

$$\frac{dy}{dx} = \frac{f'(t)}{g'(t)}$$

The slope of the line segment through points $A(t = a)$ and $B(t = b)$ is given by

$$\frac{f(b) - f(a)}{g(b) - g(a)}$$

Theorem 20.1.1 says that the slopes are equal for at least one value of t between a and b. For the curve shown in Fig. 20.1.1, there are four values of t satisfying the conclusion of Theorem 20.1.1: $t = z_1$, $t = z_2$, $t = z_3$, and $t = z_4$.

(20.2) Indeterminate forms

Limit theorem 8 (4.2.8) states that if $\lim_{x \to a} f(x)$ and $\lim_{x \to a} g(x)$ both exist, then

$$\lim_{x \to a} \frac{f(x)}{g(x)} = \frac{\lim_{x \to a} f(x)}{\lim_{x \to a} g(x)}$$

provided $\lim_{x \to a} g(x) \neq 0$.

There are various cases for which we cannot apply this theorem — in particular, if $\lim_{x \to a} g(x) = 0$ and $\lim_{x \to a} f(x) = k$, where k is a constant $\neq 0$. For example, consider $\lim_{x \to 3} [(x + 5)/(x - 3)]$.

$$\lim_{x \to 3} (x + 5) = 8 \qquad \text{and} \qquad \lim_{x \to 3} (x - 3) = 0$$

To apply limit theorem 12 (4.4.12), we must consider the left- and right-hand limits separately, since when $x \to 3^-$, $(x - 3)$ approaches 0 through negative values, and when $x \to 3^+$, $(x - 3)$ approaches 0 through positive values.

$$\text{So,} \qquad \lim_{x \to 3^-} \frac{x + 5}{x - 3} = -\infty \qquad \text{and} \qquad \lim_{x \to 3^+} \frac{x + 5}{x - 3} = +\infty$$

So, the two-sided limit

$$\lim_{x \to 3} \frac{x + 5}{x - 3} = \infty$$

Now, take the case when both $\lim_{x \to a} f(x) = 0$, and $\lim_{x \to a} g(x) = 0$. We have previously considered some particular limits of this type. For example,

$$\lim_{x \to 4} \frac{x^2 - x - 12}{x^2 - 3x - 4}$$

$$\lim_{x \to 4} (x^2 - x - 12) = 0 \qquad \text{and} \qquad \lim_{x \to 4} (x^2 - 3x - 4) = 0$$

However, we may factor the numerator and denominator, and we have

$$\lim_{x \to 4} \frac{x^2 - x - 12}{x^2 - 3x - 4} = \lim_{x \to 4} \frac{(x - 4)(x + 3)}{(x - 4)(x + 1)}$$

and since $x \neq 4$, we divide numerator and denominator by $(x - 4)$, and we obtain

$$\lim_{x \to 4} \frac{x^2 - x - 12}{x^2 - 3x - 4} = \lim_{x \to 4} \frac{x + 3}{x + 1} = \frac{7}{5}$$

Another example of this case is $\lim\limits_{x \to 0} (\sin x/x)$, which equals, 1, by the Theorem 13.2.1.

20.2.1 DEFINITION   If f and g are two functions such that $\lim\limits_{x \to a} f(x) = 0$ and $\lim\limits_{x \to a} g(x) = 0$, we say that the function f/g has the *indeterminate form 0/0 at a*.

So, $(x^2 - x - 12)/(x^2 - 3x - 4)$ has the indeterminate form 0/0 at 4; however, we saw above that $\lim\limits_{x \to 4} [(x^2 - x - 12)/(x^2 - 3x - 4)] = 7/5$. Also, $(\sin x/x)$ has the indeterminate form 0/0 at 0, while $\lim\limits_{x \to 0} (\sin x/x) = 1$.

We shall now consider a general method for finding the limit, if it exists, of a function at a number where it has the indeterminate form 0/0. This method is attributed to the French mathematician Guillaume Francois de L'Hôpital (1661–1707), who wrote the first calculus textbook, published in 1696. It is known as *L'Hôpital's rule*.

20.2.2 THEOREM (*L'Hôpital's Rule*)   Let f and g be functions which are differentiable on an open interval I, except possibly at the number a in I, and let $g'(x) \neq 0$ for all $x \neq a$ in I. Then

$$\text{if} \quad \lim_{x \to a} f(x) = 0 \quad \text{and} \quad \lim_{x \to a} g(x) = 0$$

$$\text{and if} \quad \lim_{x \to a} \frac{f'(x)}{g'(x)} = L \quad \text{then} \quad \lim_{x \to a} \frac{f(x)}{g(x)} = L$$

The theorem is valid if all the limits are right-hand limits or all the limits are left-hand limits.

Proof: We shall distinguish three cases: (i) $x \to a^+$; (ii) $x \to a^-$; (iii) $x \to a$.

Proof of (i): Since in the hypothesis we did not assume that f and g are defined at a, we shall consider two new functions F and G for which

(1)
$$F(x) = f(x), \text{ if } x \neq a, \text{ and } F(a) = 0$$
$$G(x) = g(x), \text{ if } x \neq a, \text{ and } G(a) = 0$$

Let b be the right end point of the open interval I given in the hypothesis. Since f and g are both differentiable on I, except possible at a, we may conclude that F and G are both differentiable on the interval $(a,x]$, where $a < x < b$. Therefore, F and G are both continuous on $(a,x]$. F and G are also both continuous from the right at a since $\lim\limits_{x \to a^+} F(x) = \lim\limits_{x \to a^+} f(x) = 0 = F(a)$, and

$\lim\limits_{x\to a^+} G(x) = \lim\limits_{x\to a^+} g(x) = 0 = G(a)$. Therefore, F and G are continuous on the closed interval $[a,x]$. So, F and G satisfy the three conditions of the hypothesis of Cauchy's mean-value theorem (Theorem 20.1.1) on the interval $[a,x]$. Hence, we have

$$(2) \qquad \frac{F(x) - F(a)}{G(x) - G(a)} = \frac{F'(z)}{G'(z)}$$

where z is some number such that $a < z < x$. From (1) and (2) we have

$$(3) \qquad \frac{f(x)}{g(x)} = \frac{f'(z)}{g'(z)}$$

Since $a < z < x$, it follows that as $x \to a^+$, $z \to a^+$, and therefore

$$(4) \qquad \lim_{x\to a^+} \frac{f(x)}{g(x)} = \lim_{x\to a^+} \frac{f'(z)}{g'(z)} = \lim_{z\to a^+} \frac{f'(z)}{g'(z)}$$

But by hypothesis, the limit on the right-hand side of (4) is L. Therefore,

$$\lim_{x\to a^+} \frac{f(x)}{g(x)} = L$$

which proves case (i).

The proof of case (ii) is similar to the proof of case (i) and is left for the reader (see Exercise 31 at the end of this section). The proof of case (iii) is based upon the results of cases (i) and (ii) and is also left for the reader (see Exercise 32 at the end of this section).

20.2.3 THEOREM (*L'Hôpital's Rule*)   Let f and g be functions which are differentiable for all $x > N$, where N is a positive constant, and let $g'(x) \neq 0$ for all $x > N$. Then

$$\text{if} \qquad \lim_{x\to +\infty} f(x) = 0 \qquad \text{and} \qquad \lim_{x\to +\infty} g(x) = 0$$

$$\text{and if} \qquad \lim_{x\to +\infty} \frac{f'(x)}{g'(x)} = L \qquad \text{then} \qquad \lim_{x\to +\infty} \frac{f(x)}{g(x)} = L$$

The theorem is also valid if $+\infty$ is replaced by either $-\infty$ or ∞.

Proof: We shall prove the theorem for $x \to +\infty$. The proofs for $x \to -\infty$ and $x \to \infty$ are left for the reader (see Exercises 34 and 35 at the end of this section).

For all $x > N$, let $x = 1/t$; then $t = 1/x$. Let F and G be the functions defined by $F(t) = f(1/t)$ and $G(t) = g(1/t)$, if $t \neq 0$. Then $f(x) = F(t)$ and $g(x) = G(t)$, where $x > N$ and $0 < t < 1/N$. By using Definitions 4.3.1 and 4.4.1, it may be shown that the statements

$$\lim_{x\to +\infty} f(x) = M \qquad \text{and} \qquad \lim_{t\to 0^+} F(t) = M$$

have the same meaning. It is left for the reader to prove this (see Exercise 33 at the end of this section). Since by hypothesis $\lim\limits_{x \to +\infty} f(x) = 0$ and $\lim\limits_{x \to +\infty} g(x) = 0$, we may conclude that

(5) $$\lim_{t \to 0^+} F(t) = 0 \qquad \text{and} \qquad \lim_{t \to 0^+} G(t) = 0$$

Considering the quotient $F'(t)/G'(t)$, we have, using the chain rule,

$$\frac{F'(t)}{G'(t)} = \frac{(-1/t^2)f'(1/t)}{(-1/t^2)g'(1/t)} = \frac{f'(1/t)}{g'(1/t)} = \frac{f'(x)}{g'(x)}$$

Since by hypothesis $\lim\limits_{x \to +\infty} f'(x)/g'(x) = L$, it follows from the above that

(6) $$\lim_{t \to 0^+} \frac{F'(t)}{G'(t)} = L$$

Since $g'(x) \neq 0$ for all $x > N$,

(7) $$G'(t) \neq 0 \qquad \text{for all } 0 < t < \frac{1}{N}$$

From (5), (6), and (7), it follows from Theorem 20.2.2 that

$$\lim_{t \to 0^+} \frac{F(t)}{G(t)} = L$$

But since $F(t)/G(t) = f(x)/g(x)$ for all $x > N$ and $t \neq 0$, we have

$$\lim_{x \to +\infty} \frac{f(x)}{g(x)} = L$$

and the theorem is proved.

EXAMPLE 1: *Find:* $\lim\limits_{x \to 0} [x/(1 - e^x)]$, if it exists.

Solution: Since $\lim\limits_{x \to 0} x = 0$ and $\lim\limits_{x \to 0} (1 - e^x) = 0$, we apply L'Hôpital's rule and we get

$$\lim_{x \to 0} \frac{x}{1 - e^x} = \lim_{x \to 0} \frac{1}{-e^x} = \frac{1}{-1} = -1$$

EXAMPLE 2: *Find:* $\lim\limits_{x \to 1} [(1 - x + \ln x)/(x^3 - 3x + 2)]$, if it exists.

Solution:

$$\lim_{x \to 1} (1 - x + \ln x) = 1 - 1 + 0 = 0$$

and $$\lim_{x \to 1} (x^3 - 3x + 2) = 1 - 3 + 2 = 0$$

Therefore, we apply L'Hôpital's rule and we have

$$\lim_{x \to 1} \frac{1 - x + \ln x}{x^3 - 3x + 2} = \lim_{x \to 1} \frac{-1 + 1/x}{3x^2 - 3}$$

Now, since $\lim\limits_{x \to 1} (-1 + 1/x) = 0$ and $\lim\limits_{x \to 1} (3x^2 - 3) = 0$, we apply L'Hôpital's rule again and we have

$$\lim_{x \to 1} \frac{(-1 + 1/x)}{3x^2 - 3} = \lim_{x \to 1} \frac{-1/x^2}{6x} = -\frac{1}{6}$$

Therefore, we conclude

$$\lim_{x \to 1} \frac{1 - x + \ln x}{x^3 - 3x + 2} = -\frac{1}{6}$$

EXAMPLE 3: *Find:* $\lim\limits_{x \to \infty} [\sin(1/x)/\tan^{-1}(1/x)]$, if it exists.

Solution: $\lim\limits_{x \to \infty} \sin(1/x) = 0$ and $\lim\limits_{x \to \infty} \tan^{-1}(1/x) = 0$. So we apply L'Hôpital's rule and we get

$$\lim_{x \to \infty} \frac{\sin(1/x)}{\tan^{-1}(1/x)} = \lim_{x \to \infty} \frac{(-1/x^2)\cos(1/x)}{\dfrac{1}{1 + (1/x)^2}(-1/x^2)} = \lim_{x \to \infty} \frac{\cos(1/x)}{x^2/(x^2 + 1)}$$

$$\lim_{x \to \infty} \cos \frac{1}{x} = 1 \qquad \text{and} \qquad \lim_{x \to \infty} \frac{x^2}{x^2 + 1} = \lim_{x \to \infty} \frac{1}{1 + 1/x^2} = 1$$

So

$$\lim_{x \to \infty} \frac{\cos(1/x)}{x^2/(x^2 + 1)} = 1$$

Therefore,

$$\lim_{x \to \infty} \frac{\sin(1/x)}{\tan^{-1}(1/x)} = 1$$

We shall now consider another type of indeterminate form. Suppose we wish to evaluate $\lim\limits_{x \to \pi/2} [\sec^2 x / \sec^2 3x]$. We cannot apply the theorem involving the limit of a quotient, since $\lim\limits_{x \to \pi/2} \sec^2 x = +\infty$ and $\lim\limits_{x \to \pi/2} \sec^2 3x = +\infty$. In this case we say that the function defined by $\sec^2 x / \sec^2 3x$ has the indeterminate form, $(+\infty/+\infty)$ at $x = \pi/2$. L'Hôpital's rule also applies to an indeterminate form of this type, as well as to $(-\infty/-\infty)(-\infty/+\infty), (-\infty/-\infty)$, or (∞/∞). This is given by the following theorems, for which we omit the proofs since they are beyond the scope of this book.

20.2.4 THEOREM (*L'Hôpital's Rule*)   Let f and g be functions which are differentiable on an open interval I, except possibly at the number a in I, and let $g'(x) \neq 0$ for all $x \neq a$ in I. Then

$$\text{if} \quad \lim_{x \to a} f(x) = +\infty, \ -\infty, \text{ or } \infty \quad \text{and} \quad \lim_{x \to a} g(x) = +\infty, \ -\infty, \text{ or } \infty$$

$$\text{and if} \quad \lim_{x \to a} \frac{f'(x)}{g'(x)} = L \qquad\qquad \text{then} \quad \lim_{x \to a} \frac{f(x)}{g(x)} = L$$

The theorem is valid if all the limits are right-hand limits or all the limits are left-hand limits.

20.2.5 THEOREM (*L'Hôpital's Rule*)   Let f and g be functions which are differentiable for all $x > N$, where N is a positive constant, and let $g'(x) \neq 0$ for all $x > N$. Then

$$\text{if} \quad \lim_{x \to +\infty} f(x) = +\infty, \ -\infty, \text{ or } \infty \quad \text{and} \quad \lim_{x \to +\infty} g(x) = +\infty, \ -\infty, \text{ or } \infty$$

$$\text{and if} \quad \lim_{x \to +\infty} \frac{f'(x)}{g'(x)} = L \qquad\qquad \text{then} \quad \lim_{x \to +\infty} \frac{f(x)}{g(x)} = L$$

The theorem is valid if $x \to +\infty$ is replaced by either $x \to -\infty$ or $x \to \infty$.

Theorems 20.2.2, 20.2.3, 20.2.4, and 20.2.5 also hold when L is replaced by $+\infty$, $-\infty$, or ∞. The proofs for these cases are omitted.

EXAMPLE 4: *Find:* $\lim\limits_{x \to 0^+} [\ln x/(1/x)]$, if it exists.

Solution: Since $\lim\limits_{x \to 0^+} \ln x = -\infty$ and $\lim\limits_{x \to 0^+} 1/x = +\infty$, we apply L'Hôpital's rule and we get

$$\lim_{x \to 0^+} \frac{\ln x}{1/x} = \lim_{x \to 0^+} \frac{1/x}{-1/x^2} = \lim_{x \to 0^+} (-x) = 0$$

EXAMPLE 5: *Find:* $\lim\limits_{x \to +\infty} (x^2/e^x)$, if it exists.

Solution: Since $\lim\limits_{x \to +\infty} x^2 = +\infty$ and $\lim\limits_{x \to +\infty} e^x = +\infty$, we apply L'Hôpital's rule and we obtain

$$\lim_{x \to +\infty} \frac{x^2}{e^x} = \lim_{x \to +\infty} \frac{2x}{e^x}$$

Now, since $\lim\limits_{x \to +\infty} 2x = +\infty$ and $\lim\limits_{x \to +\infty} e^x = +\infty$, we apply L'Hôpital's rule again and we get

$$\lim_{x \to +\infty} \frac{2x}{e^x} = \lim_{x \to +\infty} \frac{2}{e^x}$$
$$= 0$$

since $\lim\limits_{x \to +\infty} 2 = 2$ and $\lim\limits_{x \to +\infty} e^x = +\infty$. Therefore,

$$\lim_{x \to +\infty} \frac{x^2}{e^x} = 0$$

EXAMPLE 6: *Find:* $\lim\limits_{x \to \pi/2} (\sec^2 x/\sec^2 3x)$, if it exists.

Solution: $\lim\limits_{x \to \pi/2} \sec^2 x = +\infty$ and $\lim\limits_{x \to \pi/2} \sec^2 3x = +\infty$. So, we apply L'Hôpital's rule and we get

$$\lim_{x \to \pi/2} \frac{\sec^2 x}{\sec^2 3x} = \lim_{x \to \pi/2} \frac{2 \sec^2 x \tan x}{6 \sec^2 3x \tan 3x}$$

$$\lim_{x \to \pi/2} 2 \sec^2 x \tan x = \infty \quad \text{and} \quad \lim_{x \to \pi/2} 6 \sec^2 3x \tan 3x = \infty$$

It may be seen that further applications of L'Hôpital's rule will not help us. However, we may rewrite our original quotient and we have

$$\lim_{x \to \pi/2} \frac{\sec^2 x}{\sec^2 3x} = \lim_{x \to \pi/2} \frac{\cos^2 3x}{\cos^2 x}$$

Now, since $\lim\limits_{x\to\pi/2} \cos^2 3x = 0$ and $\lim\limits_{x\to\pi/2} \cos^2 x = 0$, we may apply L'Hôpital's rule and we have

$$\lim_{x\to\pi/2} \frac{\cos^2 3x}{\cos^2 x} = \lim_{x\to\pi/2} \frac{-6\cos 3x \sin 3x}{-2\cos x \sin x}$$

$$= \lim_{x\to\pi/2} \frac{3(2\cos 3x \sin 3x)}{(2\cos x \sin x)}$$

$$= \lim_{x\to\pi/2} \frac{3\sin 6x}{\sin 2x}$$

Since $\lim\limits_{x\to\pi/2} 3\sin 6x = 0$ and $\lim\limits_{x\to\pi/2} \sin 2x = 0$, we apply L'Hôpital's rule again and we have

$$\lim_{x\to\pi/2} \frac{3\sin 6x}{\sin 2x} = \lim_{x\to\pi/2} \frac{18\cos 6x}{2\cos 2x} = \frac{18(-1)}{2(-1)} = 9$$

Therefore, $\lim\limits_{x\to\pi/2} \dfrac{\sec^2 x}{\sec^2 3x} = 9$

Exercises 20.2

In Exercises 1 through 28, evaluate the limit, if it exists.

1. $\lim\limits_{x\to 0} \dfrac{x}{\tan x}$

2. $\lim\limits_{x\to 0} \dfrac{\tan x - x}{x - \sin x}$

3. $\lim\limits_{x\to\infty} \dfrac{x^2}{e^x}$

4. $\lim\limits_{x\to 2} \dfrac{\sin \pi x}{2 - x}$

5. $\lim\limits_{x\to\infty} \dfrac{\sin (2/x)}{1/x}$

6. $\lim\limits_{x\to 0} \dfrac{\sin^{-1} x}{x}$

7. $\lim\limits_{x\to 0^+} \dfrac{e^{-1/x}}{x}$

8. $\lim\limits_{x\to 0} \dfrac{e^x - \cos x}{x \sin x}$

9. $\lim\limits_{x\to 0} \dfrac{\tan 2x}{\sin^2 x}$

10. $\lim\limits_{x\to 0} \dfrac{e^{2x^2} - 1}{\sin^2 x}$

11. $\lim\limits_{x\to 0} \dfrac{2^x - 3^x}{x}$

12. $\lim\limits_{x\to 2} \dfrac{x^n - 2^n}{x - 2}$

13. $\lim\limits_{\theta\to 0} \dfrac{\theta - \sin \theta}{\tan^3 \theta}$

14. $\lim\limits_{x\to\pi/2^-} \dfrac{\ln (\cos x)}{\ln (\tan x)}$

15. $\lim\limits_{x\to 0} \dfrac{\sin^2 x}{\sin x^2}$

16. $\lim\limits_{x\to +\infty} \dfrac{(\ln x)^3}{x}$

17. $\lim\limits_{x\to\pi} \dfrac{1 + \cos 2x}{1 - \sin x}$

18. $\lim\limits_{x\to 0} \dfrac{\coth 2x}{\coth x}$

19. $\lim\limits_{x\to\frac{1}{2}} \dfrac{\ln (1 - 2x)}{\tan \pi x}$

20. $\lim\limits_{x\to +\infty} \dfrac{3^x}{x^3}$

21. $\lim\limits_{x\to +\infty} \dfrac{\ln (1 + e^{2x}/x)}{x^{1/2}}$

22. $\lim\limits_{x\to 0} \dfrac{e^x - 10^x}{x}$

23. $\displaystyle\lim_{x\to 0} \frac{(1+x)^{1/5} - (1-x)^{1/5}}{(1+x)^{1/3} - (1-x)^{1/3}}$

26. $\displaystyle\lim_{x\to 0} \frac{e - (1+x)^{1/x}}{x}$

24. $\displaystyle\lim_{x\to +\infty} \frac{x^{100}}{e^x}$

27. $\displaystyle\lim_{x\to 0} \frac{\cos x - \cosh x}{x^2}$

25. $\displaystyle\lim_{x\to \pi/2} \frac{\tan x + 3}{\sec x - 1}$

28. $\displaystyle\lim_{x\to 0} \frac{x - \tan^{-1} x}{4x^3}$

29. (a) Prove that $\displaystyle\lim_{x\to 0} (e^{-1/x^2}/x^n) = 0$ for n any positive integer. (b) If $f(x) = e^{-1/x^2}$, use the result of (a) to prove that the limit of f and all of its derivatives, as x approaches 0, is 0.

30. (a) Prove that $\displaystyle\lim_{x\to +\infty} (x^n/e^x) = 0$, for n any positive integer. (b) Find $\displaystyle\lim_{x\to 0} (e^{-1/x}/x^n)$, where $x > 0$ and n is any positive integer, by letting $x = 1/t$ and using the result of (a).

31. Prove Theorem 20.2.2, case (ii) (L'Hôpital's rule).

32. Prove Theorem 20.2.2, case (iii) (L'Hôpital's rule).

33. Suppose that f is a function defined for all $x > N$, where N is a positive constant. If $t = 1/x$ and $F(t) = f(1/t)$, where $t \neq 0$, prove that the statements $\displaystyle\lim_{x\to +\infty} f(x) = M$ and $\displaystyle\lim_{t\to 0^+} F(t) = M$ have the same meaning.

34. Prove Theorem 20.2.3 for $x \to -\infty$.

35. Prove Theorem 20.2.3 for $x \to \infty$.

(20.3)   More indeterminate forms

In addition to 0/0 and $\pm(\infty/\infty)$, other indeterminate forms are $0 \cdot \infty$, $\infty - \infty$, 0^0, ∞^0, 1^∞, and corresponding forms where ∞ is replaced by either $+\infty$ or $-\infty$. These indeterminate forms are defined analogously to the other two. For example, if $\displaystyle\lim_{x\to a} f(x) = \infty$ and $\displaystyle\lim_{x\to a} g(x) = 0$, then the function defined by $f(x)^{g(x)}$ has the indeterminate form ∞^0 at a. To find the limit of a function having one of these indeterminate forms, we must change it to either the form 0/0 or $\pm(\infty/\infty)$ before we can apply L'Hôpital's rule. The following examples illustrate the method.

EXAMPLE 1: *Find:* $\displaystyle\lim_{x\to 0^+} x \ln x$, if it exists.

Solution: Since $\displaystyle\lim_{x\to 0^+} x = 0$ and $\displaystyle\lim_{x\to 0^+} \ln x = -\infty$, the function defined by $x \ln x$ has the indeterminate form $0(-\infty)$. Before we can apply L'Hôpital's rule, we rewrite $x \ln x$ as $\ln x/(1/x)$, and consider $\displaystyle\lim_{x\to 0^+} [\ln x/(1/x)]$. Now,

$\lim\limits_{x \to 0^+} \ln x = -\infty$ and $\lim\limits_{x \to 0^+} 1/x = +\infty$. So we have the indeterminate form $-\infty/+\infty$. Therefore, we may apply L'Hôpital's rule, giving us

$$\lim_{x \to 0^+} \frac{\ln x}{1/x} = \lim_{x \to 0^+} \frac{1/x}{-1/x^2} = \lim_{x \to 0^+} (-x) = 0$$

EXAMPLE 2: *Find:* $\lim\limits_{x \to 0} [1/x^2 - 1/(x^2 \sec x)]$, if it exists.

Solution: Since

$$\lim_{x \to 0} \frac{1}{x^2} = +\infty \qquad \text{and} \qquad \lim_{x \to 0} \frac{1}{x^2 \sec x} = +\infty$$

we have the indeterminate form $+\infty - (+\infty)$. We rewrite the expression and we have

$$\lim_{x \to 0} \left(\frac{1}{x^2} - \frac{1}{x^2 \sec x} \right) = \lim_{x \to 0} \frac{\sec x - 1}{x^2 \sec x}$$

$\lim\limits_{x \to 0} (\sec x - 1) = 0$ and $\lim\limits_{x \to 0} (x^2 \sec x) = 0$; so we apply L'Hopital's rule and we get

$$\lim_{x \to 0} \frac{\sec x - 1}{x^2 \sec x} = \lim_{x \to 0} \frac{\sec x \tan x}{2x \sec x + x^2 \sec x \tan x}$$

$$= \lim_{x \to 0} \frac{\tan x}{2x + x^2 \tan x}$$

$$\lim_{x \to 0} \tan x = 0 \qquad \text{and} \qquad \lim_{x \to 0} (2x + x^2 \tan x) = 0$$

and so we apply the rule again and we obtain

$$\lim_{x \to 0} \frac{\tan x}{2x + x^2 \tan x} = \lim_{x \to 0} \frac{\sec^2 x}{2 + 2x \tan x + x^2 \sec^2 x} = \frac{1}{2}$$

$$\text{Therefore,} \qquad \lim_{x \to 0} \left(\frac{1}{x^2} - \frac{1}{x^2 \sec x} \right) = \frac{1}{2}$$

If we have one of the following indeterminate forms: 0^0, ∞^0, or 1^∞, the procedure for evaluating the limit is illustrated in Example 3.

EXAMPLE 3: *Find:* $\lim\limits_{x \to 0} (x + 1)^{\cot x}$, if it exists.

Solution: Since $\lim\limits_{x \to 0} (x + 1) = 1$ and $\lim\limits_{x \to 0} \cot x = \infty$, we have the indeterminate form 1^∞. Let

(1) $$y = (x + 1)^{\cot x}$$

Then $$\ln y = \cot x \ln (x + 1)$$

or $$\ln y = \frac{\ln (x + 1)}{\tan x}$$

So

(2) $$\lim_{x \to 0} \ln y = \lim_{x \to 0} \frac{\ln (x + 1)}{\tan x}$$

Since $\lim_{x \to 0} \ln (x + 1) = 0$ and $\lim_{x \to 0} \tan x = 0$, we may apply L'Hôpital's rule to the right-hand side of (2) and we obtain

$$\lim_{x \to 0} \frac{\ln (x + 1)}{\tan x} = \lim_{x \to 0} \frac{1/(x + 1)}{\sec^2 x} = 1$$

Therefore, substituting 1 on the right-hand side of (2), we have

(3)
$$\lim_{x \to 0} \ln y = 1$$

Since the natural logarithmic function is continuous on its entire domain, which is the set of all positive numbers, we may apply Theorem 5.2.5 and we have from (3)

$$\ln \lim_{x \to 0} y = 1$$

Therefore, $\lim_{x \to 0} y = e^1$

But from (1), $y = (x + 1)^{\cot x}$, and so we have

$$\lim_{x \to 0} (x + 1)^{\cot x} = e$$

Exercises 20.3

In Exercises 1 through 20, evaluate the limit if it exists.

1. $\lim_{x \to 0} x \csc 2x$

2. $\lim_{x \to 0} \sin^{-1} x \csc x$

3. $\lim_{x \to 1} \left[\dfrac{1}{\ln x} - \dfrac{1}{x - 1} \right]$

4. $\lim_{x \to 0} (\sinh x)^{\tan x}$

5. $\lim_{x \to 0^+} x^{\sin x}$

6. $\lim_{x \to 0} (x + e^{2x})^{1/x}$

7. $\lim_{x \to \infty} (x^2 - \sqrt{x^4 - x^2 + 2})$

8. $\lim_{x \to 2} \left(\dfrac{5}{x^2 + x - 6} - \dfrac{1}{x - 2} \right)$

9. $\lim_{x \to + \infty} x^{1/x}$

10. $\lim_{x \to 0^+} (1 + x)^{\ln x}$

11. $\lim_{x \to 0} (\csc^2 x - x^{-2})$

12. $\lim_{x \to + \infty} \left(1 + \dfrac{1}{2x} \right)^{x^2}$

13. $\lim_{x \to 0} (1 + ax)^{1/x}; \ a \neq 0$

14. $\lim_{x \to 2} (x - 2) \tan \dfrac{\pi x}{4}$

15. $\lim_{x \to 0} (1 + \sinh x)^{2/x}$

16. $\lim_{x \to + \infty} x \ln \dfrac{x + 1}{x - 1}$

17. $\lim_{x \to 0} [(\cos x)e^{x^2/2}]^{4/x^4}$

18. $\lim_{x \to 0} (\cos x)^{1/x^2}$

19. $\lim_{x \to + \infty} \dfrac{\ln (\ln x)}{\ln (x - \ln x)}$

20. $\lim_{x \to 0^+} x^{x^x}$

(20.4)   Improper integrals with infinite limits of integration

In defining the definite integral $\int_a^b f(x)\,dx$, the function f was assumed to be continuous on the finite closed interval $[a,b]$. We shall now extend the definition of the definite integral to consider an infinite interval of integration; and in the next section we shall discuss a definite integral in which the integrand is discontinuous at some points in the interval. In either case we say that the definite integral is an *improper integral*.

Consider the problem of finding the area of the region bounded by the curve whose equation is $y = 1/(1 + x^2)$, the x axis, the y axis, and the line $x = b$, where $b > 0$. This region is shown in Fig. 20.4.1.

$$A = \lim_{\Delta x \to 0} \sum_{i=1}^{n} f(\xi_i)\,\Delta x = \int_0^b f(x)\,dx$$

or $A = \int_0^b \dfrac{dx}{1 + x^2} = \tan^{-1} x\Big]_0^b = \tan^{-1} b$

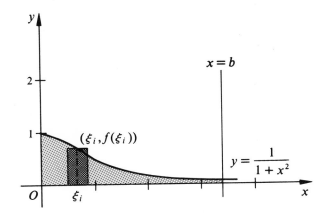

Figure 20.4.1

If we let b approach positive infinity, then

$$\lim_{b \to +\infty} \int_0^b \frac{dx}{1 + x^2} = \lim_{b \to +\infty} \tan^{-1} b$$

or

(1) $$\lim_{b \to +\infty} \int_0^b \frac{dx}{1 + x^2} = \frac{\pi}{2}$$

Equation (1) says that if $b > 0$, for any $\epsilon > 0$ there exists a $N > 0$ such that

$$\left| \int_0^b \frac{dx}{1 + x^2} - \frac{\pi}{2} \right| < \epsilon \qquad \text{whenever} \qquad b > N$$

In place of (1), we write

$$\int_0^{+\infty} \frac{dx}{1 + x^2} = \frac{\pi}{2}$$

We have the following definition, in general.

20.4.1 DEFINITION   If f is continuous for all $x \geq a$, then

$$\int_a^{+\infty} f(x)\, dx = \lim_{b \to +\infty} \int_a^b f(x)\, dx$$

if this limit exists.

If the lower limit of integration is infinite, we have the following definition.

20.4.2 DEFINITION   If f is continuous for all $x \leq b$, then

$$\int_{-\infty}^b f(x)\, dx = \lim_{a \to -\infty} \int_a^b f(x)\, dx$$

if this limit exists.

Finally we have the case when both limits of integration are infinite.

20.4.3 DEFINITION   If f is continuous for all values of x, then

$$\int_{-\infty}^{+\infty} f(x)\, dx = \lim_{a \to -\infty} \int_a^0 f(x)\, dx + \lim_{b \to +\infty} \int_0^b f(x)\, dx$$

if these limits exist.

In Definitions 20.4.1, 20.4.2, and 20.4.3, if the limits exist and are finite, we say that the improper integral is *convergent*. If the limits do not exist or are infinite, we say that the improper integral is *divergent*.

EXAMPLE 1: *Evaluate:* $\int_{-\infty}^0 e^{2x}\, dx$, if it converges.
Solution:

$$\int_{-\infty}^0 e^{2x}\, dx = \lim_{a \to -\infty} \int_a^0 e^{2x}\, dx$$

$$= \lim_{a \to -\infty} [\tfrac{1}{2} e^{2x}]_a^0 = \lim_{a \to -\infty} (\tfrac{1}{2} - \tfrac{1}{2} e^{2a})$$

$$= \tfrac{1}{2} - 0 = \tfrac{1}{2}$$

EXAMPLE 2: *Evaluate:* $\int_{-\infty}^{+\infty} [dx/(x^2 + 6x + 12)]$, if it converges.
Solution:

$$\int_{-\infty}^{+\infty} \frac{dx}{x^2 + 6x + 12}$$

$$= \lim_{a \to -\infty} \int_a^0 \frac{dx}{(x+3)^2 + 3} + \lim_{b \to +\infty} \int_0^b \frac{dx}{(x+3)^2 + 3}$$

$$= \lim_{a \to -\infty} \left[\frac{1}{\sqrt{3}} \tan^{-1} \frac{x+3}{\sqrt{3}} \right]_a^0 + \lim_{b \to +\infty} \left[\frac{1}{\sqrt{3}} \tan^{-1} \frac{x+3}{\sqrt{3}} \right]_0^b$$

$$= \lim_{a \to -\infty} \left(\frac{1}{\sqrt{3}} \tan^{-1} 3 - \frac{1}{\sqrt{3}} \tan^{-1} \frac{a+3}{\sqrt{3}} \right) + \lim_{b \to +\infty} \left(\frac{1}{\sqrt{3}} \tan^{-1} \frac{b+3}{\sqrt{3}} - \frac{1}{\sqrt{3}} \tan^{-1} \sqrt{3} \right)$$

$$= \frac{1}{\sqrt{3}} \left[\lim_{a \to -\infty} \left(-\tan^{-1} \frac{a+3}{\sqrt{3}} \right) + \lim_{b \to +\infty} \tan^{-1} \frac{b+3}{\sqrt{3}} \right]$$

$$= \frac{1}{\sqrt{3}} \left[-\left(-\frac{\pi}{2} \right) + \frac{\pi}{2} \right] = \frac{\pi}{\sqrt{3}}$$

EXAMPLE 3: Is it possible to assign a finite number to represent the area of the region bounded by the graphs of the equations $y = 1/x$, $y = 0$, and $x = 1$?

Solution: The region is shown in Fig. 20.4.2. Let L be the number we should wish to assign to the area, if possible. Let A be the area of the region bounded by the graphs of the equations

$$y = 1/x, \ y = 0, \ x = 1, \qquad \text{and} \qquad x = b, \ b > 1$$

Then

$$A = \lim_{\Delta x \to 0} \sum_{i=1}^{n} f(\xi_i) \, \Delta x = \int_{1}^{b} \frac{dx}{x}$$

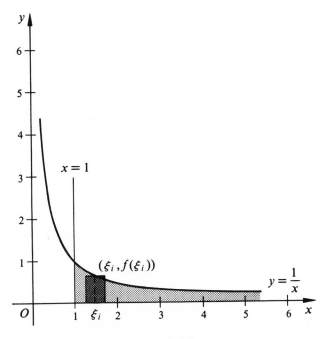

Figure 20.4.2

So, we shall let $L = \lim_{b \to +\infty} A$, if this limit exists. But

$$\lim_{b \to +\infty} A = \lim_{b \to +\infty} \int_{1}^{b} \frac{dx}{x}$$

$$= \lim_{b \to +\infty} [\ln b - \ln 1] = +\infty$$

Therefore, the region does not have a finite area.

Therefore it is not possible to assign a finite number to represent the area of the region.

EXAMPLE 4: Is it possible to assign a finite number to represent the volume of the solid formed by revolving the region as defined in Example 3 about the x axis?

Solution: The element of volume is a circular disk, having thickness Δx and base radius $f(\xi_i)$. Let L be the number we wish to assign to the volume. Let V be the volume of the solid formed by revolving about the x axis the region bounded by the graphs of the equations $y = 1/x$, $y = 0$, $x = 1$, and $x = b$, $b > 1$.

$$V = \lim_{\Delta x \to 0} \sum_{i=1}^{n} \pi[f(\xi_i)]^2 \, \Delta x$$

$$= \pi \int_1^b [f(x)]^2 \, dx$$

So, we shall let

$$L = \lim_{b \to +\infty} V$$

$$= \lim_{b \to +\infty} \pi \int_1^b \frac{dx}{x^2} = \pi \lim_{b \to +\infty} \left[-\frac{1}{x} \right]_1^b$$

$$= \pi \lim_{b \to +\infty} \left[-\frac{1}{b} + 1 \right] = \pi$$

Therefore we assign the number π to represent the volume of the solid.

Exercises 20.4

In Exercises 1 through 12, determine whether the improper integral is convergent or divergent. If it is convergent, evaluate it.

1. $\int_0^{+\infty} e^{-x} \, dx$

2. $\int_{-\infty}^1 e^x \, dx$

3. $\int_0^{+\infty} x e^{-x} \, dx$

4. $\int_5^{+\infty} \frac{dx}{\sqrt{x-1}}$

5. $\int_{-\infty}^0 x^2 e^x \, dx$

6. $\int_0^{+\infty} \frac{dx}{\sqrt{e^x}}$

7. $\int_{-\infty}^{+\infty} x \cosh x \, dx$

8. $\int_{-\infty}^{+\infty} \frac{dx}{16 + x^2}$

9. $\int_e^{+\infty} \frac{dx}{x(\ln x)^2}$

10. $\int_0^{+\infty} e^{-x} \cos x \, dx$

11. $\int_1^{+\infty} \ln x \, dx$

12. $\int_1^{+\infty} \frac{dx}{x^4 + x^2}$

13. Find the area of the region bounded by the curve whose equation is $y = 1/(e^x + e^{-x})$ and the x axis.

14. Find the area of the region in the first quadrant and below the curve whose equation is $y = e^{-x}$.

15. Find the area of the region bounded by the x axis, the y axis, and the curve whose equation is $y = 1/(x^2 + 1)$.

16. Determine if it is possible to assign a finite number to represent the volume of the solid formed by revolving about the x axis the region to the right of the line $x = 1$ and bounded by the curve whose equation is $y = 1/x\sqrt{x}$ and the x axis. If a finite number can be assigned to this volume, find it.

17. Prove that the improper integral $\int_1^{+\infty} dx/x^n$ is convergent if and only if $n > 1$.

(20.5)   Improper integrals with discontinuous integrand

In Fig. 20.5.1, we have the region bounded by the curve whose equation is $y = 1/\sqrt{x}$, the x axis, the y axis, and the line $x = 4$.

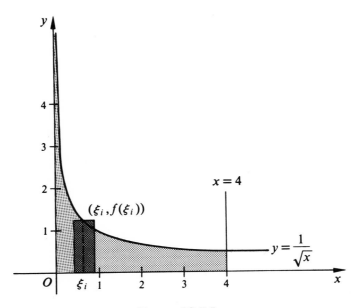

Figure 20.5.1

Is it possible to assign a finite number to represent the area of this region? If A is to be the number, then

$$A = \lim_{\Delta x \to 0} \sum_{i=1}^{n} f(\xi_i)\, \Delta x = \int_0^4 \frac{dx}{\sqrt{x}}$$

The integrand is discontinuous at the lower limit zero, since if $f(x) = 1/\sqrt{x}$, $f(0)$ does not exist. So, $\int_0^4 dx/\sqrt{x}$ is an improper integral. We make the following definition.

20.5.1 DEFINITION   If f is continuous at all x in the interval half open on the left $(a, b]$, then

$$\int_a^b f(x)\, dx = \lim_{\epsilon \to 0^+} \int_{a+\epsilon}^b f(x)\, dx$$

if this limit exists.

Applying Definition 20.5.1 to the improper integral above, we have

$$\int_0^4 \frac{dx}{\sqrt{x}} = \lim_{\epsilon \to 0^+} \int_\epsilon^4 \frac{dx}{\sqrt{x}} = \lim_{\epsilon \to 0^+} 2x^{1/2} \Big]_\epsilon^4$$

$$= \lim_{\epsilon \to 0^+} [4 - 2\sqrt{\epsilon}] = 4 - 0 = 4$$

Therefore, we assign 4 to the area of the region shown in Fig. 20.5.1.

If the integrand is discontinuous at the upper limit of integration, we use the following definition.

20.5.2 DEFINITION   If f is continuous at all x in the interval half open on the right, $[a,b)$, then

$$\int_a^b f(x)\, dx = \lim_{\epsilon \to 0^+} \int_a^{b-\epsilon} f(x)\, dx$$

if this limit exists.

If the integrand is discontinuous at an interior point of the interval of integration, we use the following definition.

20.5.3 DEFINITION   If f is continuous at all x in the interval $[a,b]$ except c where $a < c < b$, then

$$\int_a^b f(x)\, dx = \lim_{\epsilon \to 0^+} \int_a^{c-\epsilon} f(x)\, dx + \lim_{\delta \to 0^+} \int_{c+\delta}^b f(x)\, dx$$

if these limits exist.

If the limits in Definitions 20.5.1, 20.5.2, and 20.5.3 exist and are finite, we say that the improper integral is *convergent;* otherwise it is *divergent.*

EXAMPLE 1: *Evaluate:* $\int_0^2 dx/(x-1)^2$, if it converges.
Solution: The integrand is discontinuous at 1, and so we have

$$\int_0^2 \frac{dx}{(x-1)^2} = \lim_{\epsilon \to 0^+} \int_0^{1-\epsilon} \frac{dx}{(x-1)^2} + \lim_{\delta \to 0^+} \int_{1+\delta}^2 \frac{dx}{(x-1)^2}$$

$$= \lim_{\epsilon \to 0^+} \left[-\frac{1}{x-1} \right]_0^{1-\epsilon} + \lim_{\delta \to 0^+} \left[-\frac{1}{x-1} \right]_{1+\delta}^2$$

$$= \lim_{\epsilon \to 0^+} \left[\frac{1}{\epsilon} - 1 \right] + \lim_{\delta \to 0^+} \left[-1 + \frac{1}{\delta} \right]$$

Since neither of these limits exist, the integral is divergent.

EXAMPLE 2: *Evaluate:* $\int_0^1 x \ln x \, dx$, if it converges.

Solution: The integrand is discontinuous at the lower limit 0 since $\ln 0$ does not exist. So we have

$$\int_0^1 x \ln x \, dx = \lim_{\epsilon \to 0^+} \int_\epsilon^1 x \ln x \, dx$$

$$= \lim_{\epsilon \to 0^+} \left[\frac{x^2}{2} \ln x - \frac{x^2}{4} \right]_\epsilon^1$$

$$= \lim_{\epsilon \to 0^+} \left[\frac{1}{2} \ln 1 - \frac{1}{4} - \frac{\epsilon^2}{2} \ln \epsilon - \frac{\epsilon^2}{4} \right]$$

or

(1) $$\int_0^1 x \ln x \, dx = 0 - \tfrac{1}{4} - \tfrac{1}{2} \lim_{\epsilon \to 0^+} \epsilon^2 \ln \epsilon - 0$$

To evaluate,

$$\lim_{\epsilon \to 0^+} \epsilon^2 \ln \epsilon = \lim_{\epsilon \to 0^+} \frac{\ln \epsilon}{1/\epsilon^2}$$

we apply L'Hôpital's rule, since $\lim_{\epsilon \to 0^+} \ln \epsilon = -\infty$ and $\lim_{\epsilon \to 0^+} 1/\epsilon^2 = +\infty$, and we have

$$\lim_{\epsilon \to 0^+} \frac{\ln \epsilon}{1/\epsilon^2} = \lim_{\epsilon \to 0^+} \frac{1/\epsilon}{-2/\epsilon^3} = \lim_{\epsilon \to 0^+} \left[-\frac{\epsilon^2}{2} \right] = 0$$

Therefore, from (1) we have

$$\int_0^1 x \ln x \, dx = -\tfrac{1}{4}$$

EXAMPLE 3: *Evaluate:* $\int_1^{+\infty} dx/(x\sqrt{x^2 - 1})$, if it converges.

Solution: For this integral, we have both an infinite upper limit, as well as an infinite discontinuity at the lower limit. We proceed as follows:

$$\int_1^{+\infty} \frac{dx}{x\sqrt{x^2 - 1}} = \lim_{a \to 1^+} \int_a^2 \frac{dx}{x\sqrt{x^2 - 1}} + \lim_{b \to +\infty} \int_2^b \frac{dx}{x\sqrt{x^2 - 1}}$$

$$= \lim_{a \to 1^+} [\sec^{-1} x]_a^2 + \lim_{b \to +\infty} [\sec^{-1} x]_2^b$$

$$= \lim_{a \to 1^+} (\sec^{-1} 2 - \sec^{-1} a) + \lim_{b \to +\infty} (\sec^{-1} b - \sec^{-1} 2)$$

$$= -\lim_{a \to 1^+} \sec^{-1} a + \lim_{b \to +\infty} \sec^{-1} b = 0 + \frac{\pi}{2} = \frac{\pi}{2}$$

Exercises 20.5

In Exercises 1 through 22, determine whether the improper integral is convergent or divergent. If it is convergent, evaluate it.

1. $\int_0^1 \dfrac{dx}{\sqrt{1 - x}}$

2. $\int_0^2 \dfrac{dx}{\sqrt{4 - x^2}}$

3. $\int_{\pi/4}^{\pi/2} \sec \theta \, d\theta$

4. $\int_0^4 \frac{x \, dx}{\sqrt{16 - x^2}}$

5. $\int_0^{\pi/2} \tan \theta \, d\theta$

6. $\int_0^{+\infty} \frac{dx}{x^3}$

7. $\int_0^{\pi/2} \frac{d\theta}{1 - \sin \theta}$

8. $\int_0^2 \frac{dx}{(x - 1)^{2/3}}$

9. $\int_2^{+\infty} \frac{dx}{x\sqrt{x^2 - 4}}$

10. $\int_{-2}^0 \frac{dx}{(x + 1)^{1/3}}$

11. $\int_0^4 \frac{dx}{x^2 - 2x - 3}$

12. $\int_{-1}^1 \frac{dx}{x^2}$

13. $\int_{-2}^2 \frac{dx}{x^3}$

14. $\int_0^2 \frac{dx}{\sqrt{2x - x^2}}$

15. $\int_{-2}^0 \frac{dx}{2x + 3}$

16. $\int_0^{+\infty} \frac{e^{-\sqrt{x}}}{\sqrt{x}} \, dx$

17. $\int_{1/2}^2 \frac{dx}{x(\ln x)^{1/5}}$

18. $\int_2^4 \frac{x \, dx}{\sqrt{x - 2}}$

19. $\int_1^2 \frac{dx}{x\sqrt{x^2 - 1}}$

20. $\int_0^2 \frac{x \, dx}{1 - x}$

21. $\int_0^1 \cot^2 \theta \, d\theta$

22. $\int_0^1 \frac{dx}{x\sqrt{4 - x^2}}$

21 Vectors in three-dimensional space and solid analytic geometry

(21.1) Three-dimensional cartesian coordinates

The position of a point in three-dimensional space is determined by its directed distances from three mutually perpendicular planes. The planes are formed by first considering three mutually perpendicular lines which intersect at a point which we call the *origin* and denote by the letter O. These lines, called the coordinate axes, are designated as the *x axis*, the *y axis*, and the *z axis*. Usually the

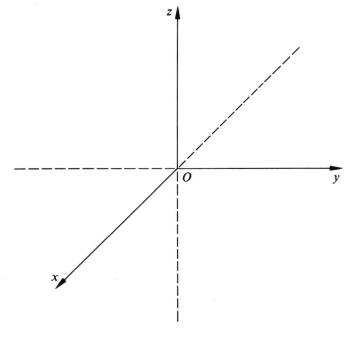

Figure 21.1.1

x axis and the *y* axis are taken in a horizontal plane, and the *z* axis is vertical. A positive direction is selected on each axis. If the positive directions are chosen as in Fig. 21.1.1, the coordinate system is called a *right-handed system*. This terminology follows from the fact that if the right hand is placed so that the thumb is pointed in the positive direction of the *x* axis and the index finger is pointed in the positive direction of the *y* axis, then the middle finger is pointed in the positive direction of the *z* axis. If the middle finger is pointed in the negative direction of the *z* axis, then the coordinate system is called *left-handed*. A left-handed system is shown in Fig. 21.1.2. In general we shall use a right-

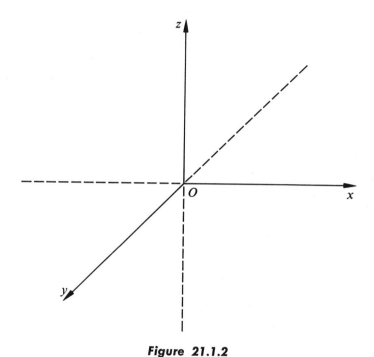

Figure 21.1.2

handed coordinate system. The three axes determine three coordinate planes: the *xy* plane containing the *x* and *y* axes, the *xz* plane containing the *x* and *z* axes, and the *yz* plane containing the *y* and *z* axes.

An ordered triple of real numbers (x,y,z) is associated with each point P in three-dimensional space. The directed distance of P from the *yz* plane is called the *x coordinate*, the directed distance of P from the *xz* plane is called the *y coordinate*, and the *z coordinate* is the directed distance of P from the *xy* plane. These three coordinates are called the *rectangular cartesian coordinates* of a point in three-dimensional space, and there is a one-to-one correspondence between all such ordered triples of real numbers and the points in three-dimensional space. The point $(3,2,4)$ is shown in Fig. 21.1.3 and the point $(4,-2,-5)$ is shown in Fig. 21.1.4.

The three coordinate planes divide the space into eight parts, called *oc-*

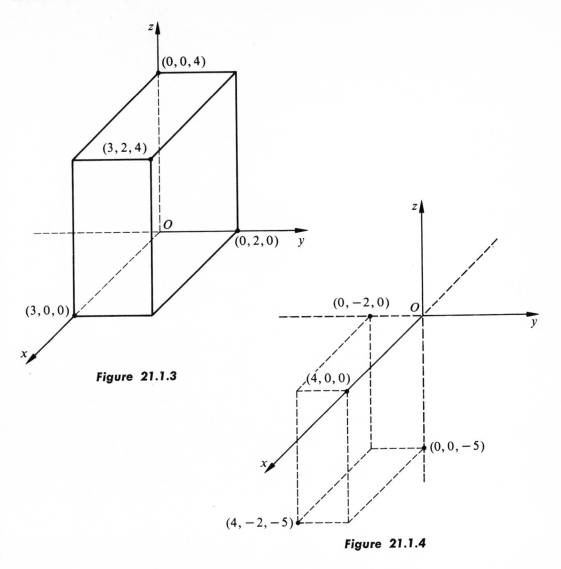

Figure 21.1.3

Figure 21.1.4

tants. The *first octant* is the one in which all three coordinates are positive. The other octants are usually numbered so that the x coordinate is positive in the first four octants, the numbering being in the counterclockwise direction. The remaining four octants are those for which the x coordinate is negative, the fifth octant being the one for which the y and z coordinates are positive. So the point $(4, -2, -5)$ shown in Fig. 21.1.4 is in the third octant, and the point $(-3, -1, 6)$ is in the sixth octant. The point $(-2, -4, -7)$ is in the seventh octant.

  If a line is parallel to a plane, the distance from any point on the line to the plane is the same. Conversely, if the distance from any point on a given line to a given plane is always the same, the line and the plane are parallel. We shall consider all lines lying in a given plane as being parallel to the plane. In this case the distance from any point on the line to the plane is zero. We may therefore conclude the following theorem.

21.1.1 THEOREM

    (i)   A line is parallel to the yz plane if and only if all points on the line have equal x coordinates.

    (ii)   A line is parallel to the xz plane if and only if all points on the line have equal y coordinates.

    (iii)   A line is parallel to the xy plane if and only if all points on the line have equal z coordinates.

In three-dimensional space, if a line is parallel to each of two intersecting planes, it is parallel to the line of intersection of the two planes. Also, if a given line is parallel to a second line, then the given line is parallel to any plane containing the second line. Theorem 21.1.2 follows from these two facts from solid geometry and from Theorem 21.1.1.

21.1.2 THEOREM

    (i)   A line is parallel to the x axis if and only if all points on the line have equal y coordinates and equal z coordinates.

    (ii)   A line is parallel to the y axis if and only if all points on the line have equal x coordinates and equal z coordinates.

    (iii)   A line is parallel to the z axis if and only if all points on the line have equal x coordinates and equal y coordinates.

The formulas for finding the directed distance from one point to another point on a line parallel to a coordinate axis follow from the definition of directed distance given in Sec. 2.2 and are stated in the following theorem.

21.1.3 THEOREM

    (i)   If $A(x_1,y,z)$ and $B(x_2,y,z)$ are two points on a line parallel to the x axis, then the directed distance from A to B, denoted by $\overline{AB}$, is given by

$$\overline{AB} = x_2 - x_1$$

    (ii)   If $C(x,y_1,z)$ and $D(x,y_2,z)$ are two points on a line parallel to the y axis, then the directed distance from C to D, denoted by $\overline{CD}$, is given by

$$\overline{CD} = y_2 - y_1$$

    (iii)   If $E(x,y,z_1)$ and $F(x,y,z_2)$ are two points on a line parallel to the z axis, then the directed distance from E to F, denoted by $\overline{EF}$, is given by

$$\overline{EF} = z_2 - z_1$$

EXAMPLE 1: Find the directed distance from the point $P(2,-5,-4)$ to the point $Q(2,-3,-4)$.

Solution: From Theorem 21.1.3(ii), we have

$$\overline{PQ} = (-3) - (-5) = 2$$

The following theorem gives a formula for finding the undirected distance between any two points in three-dimensional space.

21.1.4 THEOREM   The undirected distance between the two points $P_1(x_1,y_1,z_1)$ and $P_2(x_2,y_2,z_2)$ is given by

$$|\overline{P_1P_2}| = \sqrt{(x_2 - x_1)^2 + (y_2 - y_1)^2 + (z_2 - z_1)^2}$$

Proof: Construct a rectangular parallelepiped having P_1 and P_2 as opposite vertices and faces parallel to the coordinate planes — see Fig. 21.1.5.

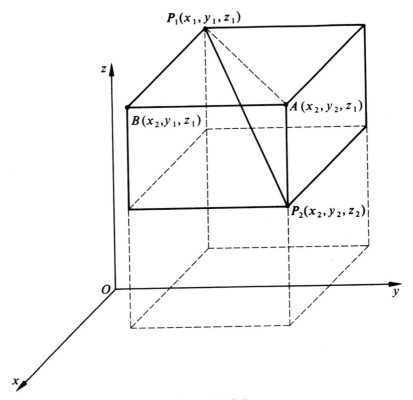

Figure 21.1.5

By the pythagorean theorem we have

(1) $$|\overline{P_1P_2}|^2 = |\overline{P_1A}|^2 + |\overline{AP_2}|^2$$

Since

(2) $$|\overline{P_1A}|^2 = |\overline{P_1B}|^2 + |\overline{BA}|^2$$

we obtain, by substituting from (2) into (1),

(3) $$|\overline{P_1P_2}|^2 = |\overline{P_1B}|^2 + |\overline{BA}|^2 + |\overline{AP_2}|^2$$

Applying Theorem 21.1.3(i), (ii), and (iii) to the right-hand side of (3), we obtain

$$|\overline{P_1P_2}|^2 = (x_2 - x_1)^2 + (y_2 - y_1)^2 + (z_2 - z_1)^2$$

So

$$|\overline{P_1P_2}| = \sqrt{(x_2 - x_1)^2 + (y_2 - y_1)^2 + (z_2 - z_1)^2}$$

and the theorem is proved.

EXAMPLE 2: Find the undirected distance between the points $P(-3,4,-1)$ and $Q(2,5,-4)$.

Solution: From Theorem 21.1.4, we have

$$|\overline{PQ}| = \sqrt{(2 + 3)^2 + (5 - 4)^2 + (-4 + 1)^2} = \sqrt{25 + 1 + 9} = \sqrt{35}$$

21.1.5 DEFINITION A *sphere* is the set of all points in three-dimensional space equidistant from a fixed point. The fixed point is called the *center* of the sphere and the constant distance is called the *radius* of the sphere.

21.1.6 THEOREM An equation of the sphere of radius r and center at (h,k,l) is

$$(4) \qquad (x - h)^2 + (y - k)^2 + (z - l)^2 = r^2$$

Proof: Let the point (h,k,l) be denoted by C — see Fig. 21.1.6.

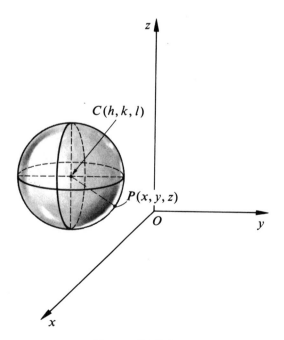

Figure 21.1.6

The point $P(x,y,z)$ is a point on the sphere if and only if

$$\overline{|CP|} = r$$

or, equivalently,

$$\sqrt{(x - h)^2 + (y - k)^2 + (z - l)^2} = r$$

Squaring both sides of the above equation, we obtain the desired result.

If the center of the sphere is at the origin, then $h = k = l = 0$, and so an equation of this sphere is

$$x^2 + y^2 + z^2 = r^2$$

If we expand the terms of equation (4) and regroup the terms, we have

$$x^2 + y^2 + z^2 - 2hx - 2ky - 2lz + (h^2 + k^2 + l^2 - r^2) = 0$$

This equation is of the form

(5) $$x^2 + y^2 + z^2 + Gx + Hy + Iz + J = 0$$

where G, H, I, and J are constants. Equation (5) is called the *general form* of an equation of a sphere, while equation (4) is called the *center-radius* form. Since every sphere has a center and a radius, its equation may be put in the center-radius form and hence the general form.

It can be shown that any equation of the form (5) may be put in the form

(6) $$(x - h)^2 + (y - k)^2 + (z - l)^2 = K$$

where

$$h = -\frac{G}{2} \qquad k = -\frac{H}{2} \qquad l = -\frac{I}{2} \qquad K = \frac{G^2 + H^2 + I^2 - 4J}{4}$$

It is left as an exercise for the reader to show this (see Exercise 6 at the end of this section).

If $K > 0$, then equation (6) is of the form of equation (4), and so the graph of the equation is a sphere having center at (h,k,l) and radius $\sqrt{K}$. If $K = 0$, the graph of the equation is the point (h,k,l). This is called a *point-sphere*. If $K < 0$, there is no real locus, since the sum of the squares of three real numbers is nonnegative. We state this result as a theorem.

21.1.7 THEOREM   The graph of any second-degree equation in x, y, and z, of the form

$$x^2 + y^2 + z^2 + Gx + Hy + Iz + J = 0$$

is either a sphere, a point-sphere, or no real locus.

EXAMPLE 3: Draw a sketch of the graph of the equation

$$x^2 + y^2 + z^2 - 6x - 4y + 2z - 2 = 0$$

Solution: Regrouping terms and completing the squares, we have

$$x^2 - 6x + 9 + y^2 - 4y + 4 + z^2 + 2z + 1 = 2 + 9 + 4 + 1$$

$$\text{or} \quad (x - 3)^2 + (y - 2)^2 + (z + 1)^2 = 16$$

So the graph is a sphere having center at $(3, 2, -1)$ and radius 4. A sketch of the graph is shown in Fig. 21.1.7.

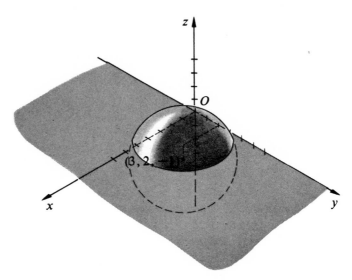

Figure 21.1.7

The formulas for the coordinates of the midpoint of a line segment are derived by forming congruent triangles and proceeding in a manner analogous to the two-dimensional case. These formulas are given in Theorem 21.1.8, and the proof is left for the reader (see Exercise 7 at the end of this section).

21.1.8 THEOREM   The coordinates of the midpoint of the line segment having end points $P_1(x_1, y_1, z_1)$ and $P_2(x_2, y_2, z_2)$ are given by

$$\bar{x} = \frac{x_1 + x_2}{2} \qquad \bar{y} = \frac{y_1 + y_2}{2} \qquad \bar{z} = \frac{z_1 + z_2}{2}$$

EXAMPLE 4: Find an equation of the sphere having the points $A(-5, 6, -2)$ and $B(9, -4, 0)$ as end points of a diameter.

Solution: The center of the sphere will be the midpoint of the line segment AB. Let this point be C $(\bar{x}, \bar{y}, \bar{z})$. By Theorem 21.1.8, we get

$$\bar{x} = \frac{9 - 5}{2} = 2 \qquad \bar{y} = \frac{-4 + 6}{2} = 1 \qquad \bar{z} = \frac{0 - 2}{2} = -1$$

So, C is the point $(2, 1, -1)$. The radius of the sphere is given by

$$r = |\overline{CB}| = \sqrt{(9 - 2)^2 + (-4 - 1)^2 + (0 + 1)^2} = \sqrt{75}$$

Therefore from Theorem 21.1.6, an equation of the sphere is

$$(x - 2)^2 + (y - 1)^2 + (z + 1)^2 = 75$$

or, equivalently,

$$x^2 + y^2 + z^2 - 4x - 2y + 2z - 69 = 0$$

Exercises 21.1

In Exercises 1 through 4, the given points A and B are opposite vertices of a rectangular parallelepiped, having its faces parallel to the coordinate planes. In each problem (a) draw a sketch of the figure, (b) find the coordinates of the other six vertices, (c) find the length of the diagonal AB.

1. $A(0,0,0)$; $B(7,2,3)$ 3. $A(-1,1,2)$; $B(2,3,5)$

2. $A(1,1,1)$; $B(3,4,2)$ 4. $A(2,-1,-3)$; $B(4,0,-1)$

5. The vertex opposite one corner of a room is 18 ft east, 15 ft south, and 12 ft up from the first corner. (a) Draw a sketch of the figure, (b) determine the length of the diagonal joining two opposite vertices, (c) find the coordinates of all eight vertices of the room.

6. Show that any equation of the form (5) may be put in the form (6).

7. Prove Theorem 21.1.8.

In Exercises 8 through 11, find (a) the undirected distance between the points A and B, and (b) the midpoint of the line segment joining A and B.

8. $A(3,4,2)$; $B(1,6,3)$ 10. $A(4,-3,2)$; $B(-2,3,-5)$

9. $A(2,-4,1)$; $B(\frac{1}{2},2,3)$ 11. $A(-2,-\frac{1}{2},5)$; $B(5,1,-4)$

12. Prove that the three points $(1,-1,3)$, $(2,1,7)$, and $(4,2,6)$ are the vertices of a right triangle, and find its area.

13. A line is drawn through the point $(6,4,2)$ perpendicular to the yz plane. Find the coordinates of the points on this line at a distance of 10 units from the point $(0,4,0)$.

14. Solve Exercise 13 if the line is drawn perpendicular to the xy plane.

In Exercises 15 through 19, determine the graph of the given equation.

15. $x^2 + y^2 + z^2 - 8x + 4y + 2z - 4 = 0$

16. $x^2 + y^2 + z^2 - 8y + 6z - 25 = 0$

17. $x^2 + y^2 + z^2 - 6z + 9 = 0$

18. $x^2 + y^2 + z^2 - x - y - 3z + 2 = 0$

19. $x^2 + y^2 + z^2 - 6x + 2y - 4z + 19 = 0$

In Exercises 20 through 22, find an equation of the sphere satisfying the given conditions.

20. A diameter is the line segment having end points at $(6,2,-5)$ and $(-4,0,7)$.

21. It is concentric with the sphere having equation

$$x^2 + y^2 + z^2 - 2y + 8z - 9 = 0.$$

22. It passes through the points $(0,0,4)$, $(2,1,3)$, and $(0,2,6)$ and has its center in the yz plane.

23. Find the vertices of the triangle whose sides have midpoints at $(3,2,3)$, $(-1,1,5)$, and $(0,3,4)$.

In Exercises 24 through 30, describe in words the locus of the given equation or the given pair of equations.

24. $y = 5$

25. $x^2 + z^2 = 4$

26. $\begin{cases} x^2 + z^2 = 4 \\ \qquad y = 0 \end{cases}$

27. $\begin{cases} y = 0 \\ z = 0 \end{cases}$

28. $\begin{cases} x = 6 \\ y = 3 \end{cases}$

29. $x = y$

30. $\begin{cases} x = z \\ y = z \end{cases}$

31. Prove analytically that the four diagonals joining opposite vertices of a rectangular parallelepiped bisect each other.

32. If P, Q, R, and S are four points in three-dimensional space and A, B, C, and D are the midpoints of PQ, QR, RS, and SP, respectively, prove analytically that $ABCD$ is a parallelogram.

(21.2)   Algebra of vectors in three-dimensional space

The presentation of topics in solid analytic geometry is simplified by the use of vectors in three-dimensional space. In this section, we shall confine ourselves to the algebra of vectors in three-dimensional space. In Sec. 21.3, we shall discuss the geometry of these vectors by using directed line segments as representations of the vectors. The definitions and theorems given in Secs. 18.2 to 18.4 for vectors in the plane are easily extended.

21.2.1 DEFINITION   A *vector in three-dimensional space* is an order triple of real numbers $\langle x, y, z \rangle$.

x, y, and z are called the components of the vector $\langle x, y, z \rangle$. We shall let V^3 be the set of all ordered triples $\langle x, y, z \rangle$ for which x, y, and z are real numbers. In this chapter, a vector will always be in V^3 unless otherwise stated.

The *zero vector* is the vector $\langle 0, 0, 0 \rangle$ and is denoted by $\mathbf{0}$.

21.2.2 DEFINITION   If the vector $\mathbf{A} = \langle a_1, a_2, a_3 \rangle$, the *magnitude* of $\mathbf{A}$, denoted by $|\mathbf{A}|$, is given by

$$|\mathbf{A}| = \sqrt{a_1{}^2 + a_2{}^2 + a_3{}^2}$$

The operations of addition, scalar multiplication, and dot product are given definitions analogous to the corresponding definitions for vectors in V^2. Associated with each of these operations is a theorem which gives laws involving the operations. The statements of these theorems, as well as their proofs, are similar to those for vectors in V^2, and so we shall not prove them in the text. The proofs are left for the reader (see Exercises 1 through 10 at the end of this section).

21.2.3 DEFINITION   If $\mathbf{A} = \langle a_1, a_2, a_3 \rangle$ and $\mathbf{B} = \langle b_1, b_2, b_3 \rangle$, then the sum of these vectors is given by

$$\mathbf{A} + \mathbf{B} = \langle a_1 + b_1,\ a_2 + b_2,\ a_3 + b_3 \rangle$$

21.2.4 THEOREM   If $\mathbf{A}$, $\mathbf{B}$, and $\mathbf{C}$ are any vectors in V^3 and $\mathbf{0}$ is the zero vector, then

  (i) $\mathbf{A} + \mathbf{B} = \mathbf{B} + \mathbf{A}$ commutative law

  (ii) $\mathbf{A} + (\mathbf{B} + \mathbf{C}) = (\mathbf{A} + \mathbf{B}) + \mathbf{C}$ associative law

  (iii) $\mathbf{A} + \mathbf{0} = \mathbf{A}$

  (iv)   There is a vector, called the *negative* of $\mathbf{A}$, denoted by $-\mathbf{A}$, such that

$$\mathbf{A} + (-\mathbf{A}) = \mathbf{0}$$

In the proof of part (iv) of the above theorem, if $\mathbf{A} = \langle a_1, a_2, a_3 \rangle$, we define the negative of $\mathbf{A}$ by

$$-\mathbf{A} = \langle -a_1, -a_2, -a_3 \rangle$$

21.2.5 DEFINITION   The difference of the two vectors $\mathbf{A}$ and $\mathbf{B}$, denoted by $\mathbf{A} - \mathbf{B}$, is the vector obtained by adding $\mathbf{A}$ to the negative of $\mathbf{B}$; that is,

$$\mathbf{A} - \mathbf{B} = \mathbf{A} + (-\mathbf{B})$$

21.2.6 DEFINITION   If c is a scalar and $\mathbf{A}$ is the vector $\langle a_1, a_2, a_3 \rangle$, then the product of c and $\mathbf{A}$, denoted by $c\mathbf{A}$, is a vector and is given by

$$c\mathbf{A} = c\langle a_1, a_2, a_3 \rangle = \langle ca_1, ca_2, ca_3 \rangle$$

21.2.7 THEOREM   If $\mathbf{A}$ and $\mathbf{B}$ are any two vectors in V^3 and c and d are any two scalars, then

  (i) $c(\mathbf{A} + \mathbf{B}) = c\mathbf{A} + c\mathbf{B}$

  (ii) $(c + d)\mathbf{A} = c\mathbf{A} + d\mathbf{A}$

  (iii) $(cd)\mathbf{A} = c(d\mathbf{A})$

  (iv) $(-c)\mathbf{A} = -(c\mathbf{A})$

  (v) $1(\mathbf{A}) = \mathbf{A}$

  (vi) $0(\mathbf{A}) = \mathbf{0}$

  (vii) $c(\mathbf{0}) = \mathbf{0}$

21.2.8 DEFINITION   If $A = \langle a_1, a_2, a_3 \rangle$ and $B = \langle b_1, b_2, b_3 \rangle$, then the *dot product* of A and B, denoted by $A \cdot B$, is given by

$$A \cdot B = \langle a_1, a_2, a_3 \rangle \cdot \langle b_1, b_2, b_3 \rangle = a_1 b_1 + a_2 b_2 + a_3 b_3$$

21.2.9 THEOREM   If A, B, and C are any vectors in V^3 and c is a scalar, then

   (i) $A \cdot B = B \cdot A$ commutative law

   (ii) $A \cdot (B + C) = A \cdot B + A \cdot C$ distributive law

   (iii) $c(A \cdot B) = (cA) \cdot B$

   (iv) $0 \cdot A = 0$

   (v) $A \cdot A = |A|^2$

A *unit vector* is a vector of magnitude 1. In V^3, three important unit vectors, denoted by i, j, and k, are defined by

(1) $i = \langle 1,0,0 \rangle$ $j = \langle 0,1,0 \rangle$ $k = \langle 0,0,1 \rangle$

It is possible to express each vector in V^3 in terms of i, j, and k. For example, if $A = \langle a_1, a_2, a_3 \rangle$, then by applying Definitions 21.2.3 and 21.2.6 we have

$$
\begin{aligned}
A &= \langle a_1, 0, 0 \rangle + \langle 0, a_2, 0 \rangle + \langle 0, 0, a_3 \rangle \\
&= a_1 \langle 1,0,0 \rangle + a_2 \langle 0,1,0 \rangle + a_3 \langle 0,0,1 \rangle \\
&= a_1 i + a_2 j + a_3 k
\end{aligned}
$$

We have a vector operation for vectors in V^3 that we did not have for vectors in V^2. This operation is called the *cross product*.

21.2.10 DEFINITION   If $A = \langle a_1, a_2, a_3 \rangle$ and $B = \langle b_1, b_2, b_3 \rangle$, then the *cross product* of A and B, denoted by $A \times B$, is given by

(2) $A \times B = \langle a_2 b_3 - a_3 b_2, \ a_3 b_1 - a_1 b_3, \ a_1 b_2 - a_2 b_1 \rangle$

Since the cross product of two vectors is a vector, the cross product is also called the *vector product*. The operation of obtaining the cross product is called *cross multiplication*.

21.2.11 THEOREM   If A is any vector in V^3, then

   (i) $A \times A = 0$

   (ii) $0 \times A = 0$

   (iii) $A \times 0 = 0$

Proof of (i): If $A = \langle a_1, a_2, a_3 \rangle$, then by Definition 21.2.10 we have

$$
\begin{aligned}
A \times A &= \langle a_2 a_3 - a_3 a_2, \ a_3 a_1 - a_1 a_3, \ a_1 a_2 - a_2 a_1 \rangle \\
&= \langle 0,0,0 \rangle = 0
\end{aligned}
$$

The proofs of (ii) and (iii) are left for the reader (see Exercise 11 at the end of this section).

By applying Definition 21.2.10 to pairs of unit vectors **i**, **j**, and **k**, we obtain the following:

(3)
$$\mathbf{i} \times \mathbf{i} = \mathbf{j} \times \mathbf{j} = \mathbf{k} \times \mathbf{k} = \mathbf{0}$$
$$\mathbf{i} \times \mathbf{j} = \mathbf{k} \qquad \mathbf{j} \times \mathbf{k} = \mathbf{i} \qquad \mathbf{k} \times \mathbf{i} = \mathbf{j}$$
$$\mathbf{j} \times \mathbf{i} = -\mathbf{k} \qquad \mathbf{k} \times \mathbf{j} = -\mathbf{i} \qquad \mathbf{i} \times \mathbf{k} = -\mathbf{j}$$

As an aid in remembering the above cross products, we first notice that the cross product of any one of the unit vectors **i**, **j**, or **k** with itself is the zero vector. The other six cross products may be obtained from Fig. 21.2.1 by applying

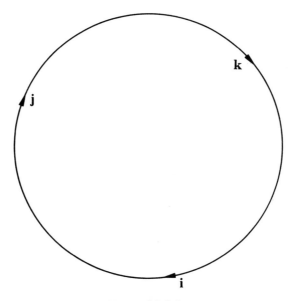

Figure 21.2.1

the following rule: the cross product of two consecutive vectors, in the clockwise direction, is the next vector; and the cross product of two consecutive vectors, in the counterclockwise direction, is the negative of the next vector.

It can easily be seen that cross multiplication of two vectors is not commutative, since in particular $\mathbf{i} \times \mathbf{j} \neq \mathbf{j} \times \mathbf{i}$. However, $\mathbf{i} \times \mathbf{j} = \mathbf{k}$ and $\mathbf{j} \times \mathbf{i} = -\mathbf{k}$; and so $\mathbf{i} \times \mathbf{j} = -(\mathbf{j} \times \mathbf{i})$. It is true in general that $\mathbf{A} \times \mathbf{B} = -(\mathbf{B} \times \mathbf{A})$, which we state and prove as a theorem.

21.2.12 THEOREM   If **A** and **B** are any two vectors in V^3,

$$\mathbf{A} \times \mathbf{B} = -(\mathbf{B} \times \mathbf{A})$$

Proof: If $\mathbf{A} = \langle a_1, a_2, a_3 \rangle$ and $\mathbf{B} = \langle b_1, b_2, b_3 \rangle$, then by Definition 21.2.10, we have

$$\mathbf{A} \times \mathbf{B} = \langle a_2 b_3 - a_3 b_2, \, a_3 b_1 - a_1 b_3, \, a_1 b_2 - a_2 b_1 \rangle$$
$$= -1 \langle a_3 b_2 - a_2 b_3, \, a_1 b_3 - a_3 b_1, \, a_2 b_1 - a_1 b_2 \rangle$$
$$= -(\mathbf{B} \times \mathbf{A})$$

Cross multiplication of vectors is not associative. This is shown by the following particular example.

$$\mathbf{i} \times (\mathbf{i} \times \mathbf{j}) = \mathbf{i} \times \mathbf{k} = -\mathbf{j}$$
$$(\mathbf{i} \times \mathbf{i}) \times \mathbf{j} = \mathbf{0} \times \mathbf{j} = \mathbf{0}$$

So $\quad \mathbf{i} \times (\mathbf{i} \times \mathbf{j}) \neq (\mathbf{i} \times \mathbf{i}) \times \mathbf{j}$

Cross multiplication of vectors is distributive with respect to vector addition. This is given by the following theorem.

21.2.13 THEOREM   If $\mathbf{A}$, $\mathbf{B}$, and $\mathbf{C}$ are any three vectors in V^3, then

(4) $$\mathbf{A} \times (\mathbf{B} + \mathbf{C}) = \mathbf{A} \times \mathbf{B} + \mathbf{A} \times \mathbf{C}$$

This theorem may be proved by letting $\mathbf{A} = \langle a_1, a_2, a_3 \rangle$, $\mathbf{B} = \langle b_1, b_2, b_3 \rangle$, and $\mathbf{C} = \langle c_1, c_2, c_3 \rangle$, and then showing that the components of the vector on the left-hand side of (4) are the same as the components of the vector on the right-hand side of (4). The details are left for the reader (see Exercise 12 at the end of this section).

The following theorem gives two properties of cross multiplication of vectors.

21.2.14 THEOREM   If $\mathbf{A}$ and $\mathbf{B}$ are any two vectors in V^3 and c is a scalar, then

(i) $\quad (c\mathbf{A}) \times \mathbf{B} = \mathbf{A} \times (c\mathbf{B})$

and

(ii) $\quad (c\mathbf{A}) \times \mathbf{B} = c(\mathbf{A} \times \mathbf{B})$

The proof of Theorem 21.2.14 is left for the reader (see Exercises 13 and 14).

Repeated applications of Theorems 21.2.13 and 21.2.14 enable us to compute the cross product of two vectors by using laws of algebra, provided we do not change the order of the vectors in cross multiplication, which is prohibited by Theorem 21.2.12. The following example illustrates this.

EXAMPLE 1: *Given:* $\mathbf{A} = \langle 2, 1, -3 \rangle$; $\mathbf{B} = \langle 3, -1, 4 \rangle$. *Find:* $\mathbf{A} \times \mathbf{B}$ *(a)* by applying Theorems 21.2.13 and 21.2.14; *(b)* by using only Definition 21.2.12.
Solution:

(a) $\mathbf{A} \times \mathbf{B} = (2\mathbf{i} + \mathbf{j} - 3\mathbf{k}) \times (3\mathbf{i} - \mathbf{j} + 4\mathbf{k})$
$$= 6(\mathbf{i} \times \mathbf{i}) - 2(\mathbf{i} \times \mathbf{j}) + 8(\mathbf{i} \times \mathbf{k}) + 3(\mathbf{j} \times \mathbf{i}) - 1(\mathbf{j} \times \mathbf{j})$$
$$+ 4(\mathbf{j} \times \mathbf{k}) - 9(\mathbf{k} \times \mathbf{i}) + 3(\mathbf{k} \times \mathbf{j}) - 12(\mathbf{k} \times \mathbf{k})$$
$$= 6(\mathbf{0}) - 2(\mathbf{k}) + 8(-\mathbf{j}) + 3(-\mathbf{k}) - 1(\mathbf{0}) + 4(\mathbf{i}) - 9(\mathbf{j})$$
$$+ 3(-\mathbf{i}) - 12(\mathbf{0})$$
$$= -2\mathbf{k} - 8\mathbf{j} - 3\mathbf{k} + 4\mathbf{i} - 9\mathbf{j} - 3\mathbf{i} = \mathbf{i} - 17\mathbf{j} - 5\mathbf{k}$$

(b) $\mathbf{A} \times \mathbf{B} = \langle 2,1,-3 \rangle \times \langle 3,-1,4 \rangle$

$$= \langle (1)(4) - (-3)(-1), \ (-3)(3) - (2)(4), \ (2)(-1) - (1)(3) \rangle$$

$$= \langle 4 - 3, \ -9 - 8, \ -2 - 3 \rangle = \langle 1,-17,-5 \rangle = \mathbf{i} - 17\mathbf{j} - 5\mathbf{k}$$

Since the expressions for finding the components of the cross product of two vectors as given by equation (2) in Definition 21.2.10 are not easily remembered in that form, part *(a)* of the above solution shows how the cross product may be obtained without using (2). Actually all the steps shown above in part *(a)* need not be included, since the various cross products of the unit vectors may be obtained immediately by using Fig. 21.2.1 and the corresponding rule.

EXAMPLE 2: Prove that if $\mathbf{A}$ and $\mathbf{B}$ are any two vectors in V^3,

$$|\mathbf{A} \times \mathbf{B}|^2 = |\mathbf{A}|^2 \, |\mathbf{B}|^2 - (\mathbf{A} \cdot \mathbf{B})^2$$

Solution: Let $\mathbf{A} = \langle a_1, a_2, a_3 \rangle$ and $\mathbf{B} = \langle b_1, b_2, b_3 \rangle$.

Then

$$|\mathbf{A} \times \mathbf{B}|^2 = (a_2 b_3 - a_3 b_2)^2 + (a_3 b_1 - a_1 b_3)^2 + (a_1 b_2 - a_2 b_1)^2$$
$$= a_2{}^2 b_3{}^2 - 2 a_2 a_3 b_2 b_3 + a_3{}^2 b_2{}^2 + a_3{}^2 b_1{}^2 - 2 a_1 a_3 b_1 b_3 + a_1{}^2 b_3{}^2$$
$$+ a_1{}^2 b_2{}^2 - 2 a_1 a_2 b_1 b_2 + a_2{}^2 b_1{}^2$$

$$|\mathbf{A}|^2 \, |\mathbf{B}|^2 - (\mathbf{A} \cdot \mathbf{B})^2 = (a_1{}^2 + a_2{}^2 + a_3{}^2)(b_1{}^2 + b_2{}^2 + b_3{}^2)$$
$$- (a_1 b_1 + a_2 b_2 + a_3 b_3)^2$$
$$= a_1{}^2 b_2{}^2 + a_1{}^2 b_3{}^2 + a_2{}^2 b_1{}^2 + a_2{}^2 b_3{}^2 + a_3{}^2 b_1{}^2 + a_3{}^2 b_2{}^2$$
$$- 2 a_1 a_3 b_1 b_3 - 2 a_2 a_3 b_2 b_3 - 2 a_1 a_2 b_1 b_2$$

Comparing the two expressions, we conclude that

$$|\mathbf{A} \times \mathbf{B}|^2 = |\mathbf{A}|^2 \, |\mathbf{B}|^2 - (\mathbf{A} \cdot \mathbf{B})^2$$

The formula proved in the above example will be useful to us in proving Theorem 21.3.9 in the next section.

The product $\mathbf{A} \cdot (\mathbf{B} \times \mathbf{C})$ is called the *triple scalar product* of the vectors $\mathbf{A}$, $\mathbf{B}$, and $\mathbf{C}$. Actually, the parentheses are not needed since $\mathbf{A} \cdot \mathbf{B}$ is a scalar, and therefore $\mathbf{A} \cdot \mathbf{B} \times \mathbf{C}$ can only be interpreted in one way. The following theorem regarding the triple scalar product will be useful later.

21.2.15 THEOREM   If $\mathbf{A}$, $\mathbf{B}$, and $\mathbf{C}$ are three vectors in V^3, then

$$\mathbf{A} \cdot \mathbf{B} \times \mathbf{C} = \mathbf{A} \times \mathbf{B} \cdot \mathbf{C}$$

The proof of this theorem is left for the reader (see Exercise 36 below).

Exercises 21.2

1. Prove Theorem 21.2.4(i).

2. Prove Theorem 21.2.4(ii).

3. Prove Theorem 21.2.4(iii) and (iv).

4. Prove Theorem 21.2.7(i) and (ii).

5. Prove Theorem 21.2.7(iii) and (iv).

6. Prove Theorem 21.2.7(v), (vi), and (vii).

7. Prove Theorem 21.2.9(i).

8. Prove Theorem 21.2.9(ii).

9. Prove Theorem 21.2.9(iii).

10. Prove Theorem 21.2.9(iv) and (v).

11. Prove Theorem 21.2.11(ii) and (iii).

12. Prove Theorem 21.2.13.

13. Prove Theorem 21.2.14(i).

14. Prove Theorem 21.2.14(ii).

In Exercises 15 through 35, take $\mathbf{A} = \langle 1,2,3 \rangle$, $\mathbf{B} = \langle 4,-3,-1 \rangle$, $\mathbf{C} = \langle -5,-3,5 \rangle$, $\mathbf{D} = \langle -2,1,6 \rangle$, $\mathbf{E} = \langle 4,0,-7 \rangle$, $\mathbf{F} = \langle 0,2,1 \rangle$, and find the indicated quantity.

15. $\mathbf{A} + \mathbf{B}$

16. $2\mathbf{A} - \mathbf{C}$

17. $\mathbf{C} + 3\mathbf{D} - 2\mathbf{E}$

18. $3\mathbf{A} - 2\mathbf{B} + \mathbf{C} - 2\mathbf{D} + \mathbf{E}$

19. $\mathbf{A} \times \mathbf{B}$

20. $\mathbf{E} \times \mathbf{F}$

21. $\mathbf{A} \cdot (\mathbf{B} + \mathbf{C})$

22. $\mathbf{A} \cdot \mathbf{B} + \mathbf{A} \cdot \mathbf{C}$

23. $\mathbf{A} \times (\mathbf{B} + \mathbf{C})$

24. $(\mathbf{A} \times \mathbf{B}) + (\mathbf{A} \times \mathbf{C})$

25. $(\mathbf{A} \times \mathbf{B}) \times \mathbf{C}$

26. $\mathbf{A} \times (\mathbf{B} \times \mathbf{C})$

27. $(\mathbf{C} \times \mathbf{D}) \cdot (\mathbf{E} \times \mathbf{F})$

28. $(\mathbf{C} \times \mathbf{E}) \cdot (\mathbf{D} \times \mathbf{F})$

29. $(\mathbf{C} \times \mathbf{F}) \cdot (\mathbf{D} \times \mathbf{E})$

30. $(\mathbf{C} \cdot \mathbf{D})(\mathbf{E} \cdot \mathbf{F})$

31. $(\mathbf{A} + \mathbf{B}) \times (\mathbf{C} - \mathbf{D})$

32. $(\mathbf{D} - \mathbf{C}) \times (\mathbf{A} + \mathbf{B})$

33. $|\mathbf{A} \times \mathbf{B}| \, |\mathbf{C} \times \mathbf{D}|$

34. $|\mathbf{A}| \, |\mathbf{B}| \, |\mathbf{C}| \, |\mathbf{D}|$

35. $(\mathbf{A} \cdot \mathbf{B})(\mathbf{C} \cdot \mathbf{D})$

36. Prove Theorem 21.2.15.

37. If $\mathbf{A}$ and $\mathbf{B}$ are any two vectors in V^3, prove that $(\mathbf{A} - \mathbf{B}) \times (\mathbf{A} + \mathbf{B}) = 2(\mathbf{A} \times \mathbf{B})$.

(21.3) Geometry of vectors in three-dimensional space

Just as for vectors in V^2, a vector in V^3 may be represented by a directed line segment. If $\mathbf{A} = \langle a_1,a_2,a_3 \rangle$, then the directed line segment having its initial point at the origin and its terminal point at the point (a_1,a_2,a_3) is called the *position representation* of **A**. A directed line segment having its initial point at (x, y, z) and its terminal point at $(x + a_1, y + a_2, z + a_3)$ is also a representation of the vector **A**.

The *direction* of a nonzero vector in V^3 is given by three angles, called the *direction angles* of the vector.

21.3.1 DEFINITION   The *direction angles* of a nonzero vector are the three angles α, β, and γ, which are the smallest nonnegative angles measured from the positive x, y, and z axes, respectively, to the position representation of the vector.

Each direction angle of a vector is greater than or equal to 0 and less than or equal to π. The direction angles α, β, and γ of the vector $\mathbf{A} = \langle a_1, a_2, a_3 \rangle$ are shown in Fig. 21.3.1. In this figure, the components of **A** are all positive numbers and the position representation is $\overrightarrow{OP}$.

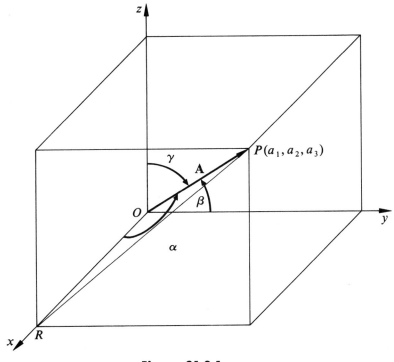

Figure 21.3.1

The length of any representation of a vector is the magnitude of the vector. In Fig. 21.3.1 we see that the length of $\overrightarrow{OP}$ is $\sqrt{a_1{}^2 + a_2{}^2 + a_3{}^2}$, which is equal to $|\mathbf{A}|$.

Referring again to the vector **A** of Fig. 21.3.1, the direction angles of this vector are all positive and less than $\pi/2$. α is an acute angle in right triangle *POR*, and so

$$\cos \alpha = \frac{|\overrightarrow{OR}|}{|\overrightarrow{OP}|} = \frac{a_1}{|\mathbf{A}|}$$

It can be shown that the same formula holds if $\pi/2 \leq \alpha \leq \pi$. Similar formulas may be found for $\cos \beta$ and $\cos \gamma$, and we have

(1) $\cos \alpha = \dfrac{a_1}{|\mathbf{A}|}$ $\cos \beta = \dfrac{a_2}{|\mathbf{A}|}$ and $\cos \gamma = \dfrac{a_3}{|\mathbf{A}|}$

The three numbers $\cos \alpha$, $\cos \beta$, and $\cos \gamma$ are called the *direction cosines* of vector $\mathbf{A}$. The zero vector has no direction angles and hence no direction cosines. The three direction cosines of a vector are not independent of each other, as we see by the following theorem.

21.3.2 THEOREM   If $\cos \alpha$, $\cos \beta$, and $\cos \gamma$ are the direction cosines of a vector, then

$$\cos^2 \alpha + \cos^2 \beta + \cos^2 \gamma = 1$$

Proof: If $\mathbf{A} = \langle a_1, a_2, a_3 \rangle$, then the direction cosines of $\mathbf{A}$ are given by (1) and we have

$$\cos^2 \alpha + \cos^2 \beta + \cos^2 \gamma = \frac{a_1{}^2}{|\mathbf{A}|^2} + \frac{a_2{}^2}{|\mathbf{A}|^2} + \frac{a_3{}^2}{|\mathbf{A}|^2}$$

$$= \frac{a_1{}^2 + a_2{}^2 + a_3{}^2}{|\mathbf{A}|^2} = \frac{|\mathbf{A}|^2}{|\mathbf{A}|^2} = 1$$

If we are given the magnitude of a vector and its direction cosines, the vector is uniquely determined. For example, if $\mathbf{A} = \langle a_1, a_2, a_3 \rangle$, then from (1)

$$a_1 = |\mathbf{A}| \cos \alpha \qquad a_2 = |\mathbf{A}| \cos \beta \qquad \text{and} \qquad a_3 = |\mathbf{A}| \cos \gamma$$

Therefore, since $\mathbf{A} = a_1 \mathbf{i} + a_2 \mathbf{j} + a_3 \mathbf{k}$, we have

$$\mathbf{A} = |\mathbf{A}| \cos \alpha \mathbf{i} + |\mathbf{A}| \cos \beta \mathbf{j} + |\mathbf{A}| \cos \gamma \mathbf{k}$$

or, equivalently,

(2) $$\mathbf{A} = |\mathbf{A}| (\cos \alpha \mathbf{i} + \cos \beta \mathbf{j} + \cos \gamma \mathbf{k})$$

EXAMPLE 1: *Given:* $\mathbf{A} = \langle 3, 2, -6 \rangle$. Express $\mathbf{A}$ in terms of its magnitude and direction cosines.

Solution:

$$|\mathbf{A}| = \sqrt{(3)^2 + (2)^2 + (-6)^2} = \sqrt{9 + 4 + 36} = \sqrt{49} = 7$$

$$\cos \alpha = 3/7 \qquad \cos \beta = 2/7 \qquad \cos \gamma = -6/7$$

So, from (2)

$$\mathbf{A} = 7 \left(\frac{3}{7} \mathbf{i} + \frac{2}{7} \mathbf{j} - \frac{6}{7} \mathbf{k} \right)$$

The geometric interpretation of the sum of two vectors in V^3 is similar to that for vectors in V^2. If P is the point (x,y,z), $\mathbf{A} = \langle a_1,a_2,a_3 \rangle$ and $\overrightarrow{PQ}$ is a representation of $\mathbf{A}$, then Q is the point $(x + a_1, y + a_2, z + a_3)$. Let $\mathbf{B} = \langle b_1,b_2,b_3 \rangle$ and let $\overrightarrow{QR}$ be a representation of $\mathbf{B}$. Then R is the point $(x + (a_1 + b_1),$ $y + (a_2 + b_2), z + (a_3 + b_3))$. Therefore, $\overrightarrow{PR}$ is a representation of the vector $\mathbf{A} + \mathbf{B}$, and the parallelogram law holds — see Fig. 21.3.2.

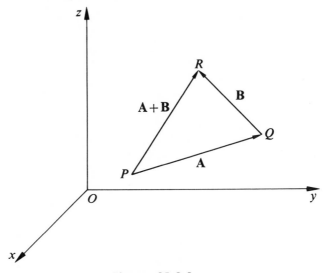

Figure 21.3.2

The difference of two vectors in V^3 is also interpreted geometrically as it is in V^2. A representation of the vector $\mathbf{A} - \mathbf{B}$ is obtained by choosing representations of $\mathbf{A}$ and $\mathbf{B}$ having the same initial point. Then a representation of the vector $\mathbf{A} - \mathbf{B}$ is the directed line segment from the terminal point of the representation of $\mathbf{B}$ to the terminal point of the representation of $\mathbf{A}$ — see Fig. 21.3.3.

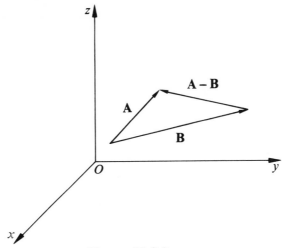

Figure 21.3.3

Now suppose that $\mathbf{A}$ is a nonzero vector having direction cosines $\cos \alpha$, $\cos \beta$, and $\cos \gamma$, and c is any scalar except zero. Let us obtain the direction cosines of the vector $c\mathbf{A}$. If $\mathbf{A} = \langle a_1, a_2, a_3 \rangle$, then $c\mathbf{A} = \langle ca_1, ca_2, ca_3 \rangle$. Let $\cos \alpha_1$, $\cos \beta_1$, and $\cos \gamma_1$ be the direction cosines of $c\mathbf{A}$, and so from equations (1) we have

$$\cos \alpha_1 = \frac{ca_1}{|c\mathbf{A}|} \qquad \cos \beta_1 = \frac{ca_2}{|c\mathbf{A}|} \qquad \cos \gamma_1 = \frac{ca_3}{|c\mathbf{A}|}$$

or, equivalently,

$$(3) \qquad \cos \alpha_1 = \frac{ca_1}{|c|\,|\mathbf{A}|} \qquad \cos \beta_1 = \frac{ca_2}{|c|\,|\mathbf{A}|} \qquad \cos \gamma_1 = \frac{ca_3}{|c|\,|\mathbf{A}|}$$

Since

$$\frac{a_1}{|\mathbf{A}|} = \cos \alpha \qquad \frac{a_2}{|\mathbf{A}|} = \cos \beta \qquad \frac{a_3}{|\mathbf{A}|} = \cos \gamma$$

we have from (3)

$$(4) \qquad \cos \alpha_1 = \frac{c}{|c|} \cos \alpha \qquad \cos \beta_1 = \frac{c}{|c|} \cos \beta \qquad \cos \gamma_1 = \frac{c}{|c|} \cos \gamma$$

So, if $c > 0$, it follows from equations (4) that the direction cosines of vector $c\mathbf{A}$ are the same as the direction cosines of $\mathbf{A}$, and if $c < 0$, the direction cosines of $c\mathbf{A}$ are the negatives of the direction cosines of $\mathbf{A}$. Therefore, we may conclude that if c is a nonzero scalar, then the vector $c\mathbf{A}$ is a vector whose magnitude is $|c|$ times the magnitude of $\mathbf{A}$, and if $c > 0$, $c\mathbf{A}$ has the same direction as $\mathbf{A}$, while if $c < 0$, the direction of $c\mathbf{A}$ is opposite that of $\mathbf{A}$.

21.3.3 THEOREM   If the nonzero vector $\mathbf{A} = a_1\mathbf{i} + a_2\mathbf{j} + a_3\mathbf{k}$, then the unit vector $\mathbf{U}$ having the same direction as $\mathbf{A}$ is given by

$$\mathbf{U} = \frac{a_1}{|\mathbf{A}|}\mathbf{i} + \frac{a_2}{|\mathbf{A}|}\mathbf{j} + \frac{a_3}{|\mathbf{A}|}\mathbf{k}$$

The proof of this theorem is analogous to the proof of Theorem 18.3.6 for a vector in V^2 and is left for the reader (see Exercise 1 at the end of this section).

21.3.4 DEFINITION   Let $\mathbf{A}$ and $\mathbf{B}$ be two nonzero vectors in V^3 such that $\mathbf{A}$ is not a scalar multiple of $\mathbf{B}$. If $\overrightarrow{OP}$ is the position representation of $\mathbf{A}$ and $\overrightarrow{OQ}$ is the position representation of $\mathbf{B}$, then the angle θ between the two vectors $\mathbf{A}$ and $\mathbf{B}$ is defined to be the positive angle betweeen $\overrightarrow{OP}$ and $\overrightarrow{OQ}$ interior to the triangle POQ. If $\mathbf{A} = c\mathbf{B}$, where c is a scalar, then if $c > 0$, $\theta = 0$, and if $c < 0$, $\theta = \pi$.

Figure 21.3.4 shows θ if $\mathbf{A}$ is not a scalar multiple of $\mathbf{B}$.

21.3.5 THEOREM   If θ is the angle between the two nonzero vectors $\mathbf{A}$ and $\mathbf{B}$, then

$$(5) \qquad \mathbf{A} \cdot \mathbf{B} = |\mathbf{A}|\,|\mathbf{B}|\cos\theta$$

The proof of Theorem 21.3.5 is left for the reader (see Exercise 2 at the end of this section). It is analogous to the proof of Theorem 18.4.4 for vectors in V^2.

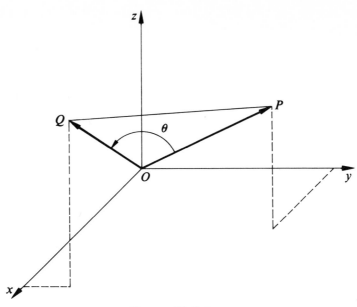

Figure 21.3.4

21.3.6 DEFINITION   Two nonzero vectors in V^3 are said to be *parallel* if the angle between them is zero or π.

21.3.7 DEFINITION   Two nonzero vectors in V^3 are said to be *orthogonal* if the angle between them is $\pi/2$.

By the above definition and Theorem 21.3.5 the following theorem may be proved.

21.3.8 THEOREM   If $\mathbf{A}$ and $\mathbf{B}$ are two nonzero vectors in V^3, $\mathbf{A}$ and $\mathbf{B}$ are orthogonal if and only if $\mathbf{A} \cdot \mathbf{B} = 0$.

The proof of Theorem 21.3.8 is left for the reader (see Exercise 3).
The following theorem gives the criterion for two nonzero vectors to be parallel.

21.3.9 THEOREM   If $\mathbf{A}$ and $\mathbf{B}$ are two nonzero vectors in V^3, $\mathbf{A}$ and $\mathbf{B}$ are parallel if and only if $\mathbf{A} \times \mathbf{B} = \mathbf{0}$.

Proof: From Example 2 in the previous section, we have

(6) $$|\mathbf{A} \times \mathbf{B}|^2 = |\mathbf{A}|^2\,|\mathbf{B}|^2 - (\mathbf{A} \cdot \mathbf{B})^2$$

Let θ be the angle between vectors $\mathbf{A}$ and $\mathbf{B}$. Substituting (5) into (6), we obtain

$$|\mathbf{A} \times \mathbf{B}|^2 = |\mathbf{A}|^2\,|\mathbf{B}|^2 - |\mathbf{A}|^2\,|\mathbf{B}|^2 \cos^2 \theta$$
$$= |\mathbf{A}|^2\,|\mathbf{B}|^2\,(1 - \cos^2 \theta)$$

So

(7) $$|\mathbf{A} \times \mathbf{B}|^2 = |\mathbf{A}|^2\,|\mathbf{B}|^2 \sin^2 \theta$$

Since $0 \leq \theta \leq \pi$, $\sin \theta \geq 0$. Therefore, taking the square root of both sides of (7), we get

(8) $|\mathbf{A} \times \mathbf{B}| = |\mathbf{A}|\,|\mathbf{B}|\,\sin \theta$

Since neither $\mathbf{A}$ nor $\mathbf{B}$ is the zero vector, $|\mathbf{A}| \neq 0$ and $|\mathbf{B}| \neq 0$. Therefore, $|\mathbf{A} \times \mathbf{B}| = 0$ if and only if $\sin \theta = 0$. Since $|\mathbf{A} \times \mathbf{B}| = 0$ if and only if $\mathbf{A} \times \mathbf{B} = \mathbf{0}$, and $\sin \theta = 0$ $(0 \leq \theta \leq \pi)$ if and only if $\theta = 0$ or π, we may conclude from (8) that

$$\mathbf{A} \times \mathbf{B} = \mathbf{0} \qquad \text{if and only if} \qquad \theta = 0 \text{ or } \pi$$

However, from Definition 21.3.6, if the angle between two vectors is zero or π, the two vectors are parallel and so the theorem follows.

From (8) we obtain a geometric interpretation of $|\mathbf{A} \times \mathbf{B}|$. Let $\overrightarrow{PR}$ be a representation of $\mathbf{A}$ and let $\overrightarrow{PQ}$ be a representation of $\mathbf{B}$. Then since θ is the angle between the vectors $\mathbf{A}$ and $\mathbf{B}$, θ is the angle at P in triangle RPQ (see Fig. 21.3.5). Therefore, the area of the parallelogram having $\overrightarrow{PR}$ and $\overrightarrow{PQ}$

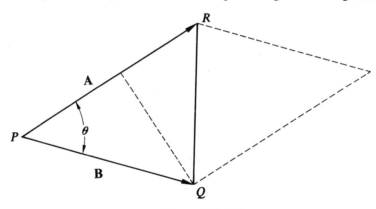

Figure 21.3.5

as adjacent sides is $|\mathbf{A}|\,|\mathbf{B}|\,\sin \theta$, since the altitude of the parallelogram has length $|\mathbf{B}|\,\sin \theta$ and the length of the base is $|\mathbf{A}|$. So from (8) it follows that $|\mathbf{A} \times \mathbf{B}|$ is the area of this parallelogram.

21.3.10 THEOREM   If $\mathbf{A}$ and $\mathbf{B}$ are two nonzero and nonparallel vectors in V^3, then the vector $\mathbf{A} \times \mathbf{B}$ is orthogonal to both $\mathbf{A}$ and $\mathbf{B}$.

Proof: From Theorem 21.2.15 we have

$$\mathbf{A} \cdot \mathbf{A} \times \mathbf{B} = \mathbf{A} \times \mathbf{A} \cdot \mathbf{B}$$

From Theorem 21.2.11(i), $\mathbf{A} \times \mathbf{A} = \mathbf{0}$. Therefore, from the above we have

$$\mathbf{A} \cdot \mathbf{A} \times \mathbf{B} = \mathbf{0} \cdot \mathbf{B} = 0$$

Since the dot product of $\mathbf{A}$ and $\mathbf{A} \times \mathbf{B}$ is zero and neither $\mathbf{A}$ nor $\mathbf{A} \times \mathbf{B}$ is the zero vector, it follows from Theorem 21.3.8 that $\mathbf{A}$ and $\mathbf{A} \times \mathbf{B}$ are orthogonal. We also have from Theorem 21.2.15 that

$$\mathbf{A} \times \mathbf{B} \cdot \mathbf{B} = \mathbf{A} \cdot \mathbf{B} \times \mathbf{B}$$

Again applying Theorem 21.2.11(i), we get $\mathbf{B} \times \mathbf{B} = \mathbf{0}$, and so from the above we have

$$\mathbf{A} \times \mathbf{B} \cdot \mathbf{B} = \mathbf{A} \cdot \mathbf{0} = 0$$

Therefore, since the dot product of $\mathbf{A} \times \mathbf{B}$ and $\mathbf{B}$ is zero and neither $\mathbf{A}$ nor $\mathbf{A} \times \mathbf{B}$ is $\mathbf{0}$, $\mathbf{A} \times \mathbf{B}$ and $\mathbf{B}$ are orthogonal and the theorem is proved.

From Theorem 21.3.10 we may conclude that if representations of the vectors $\mathbf{A}$, $\mathbf{B}$, and $\mathbf{A} \times \mathbf{B}$, have the same initial point, then the representation of $\mathbf{A} \times \mathbf{B}$ is perpendicular to the plane formed by the representations of $\mathbf{A}$ and $\mathbf{B}$.

EXAMPLE 2: *Given:* the points $P(-1,-2,-3)$, $Q(-2,1,0)$, and $R(0,5,1)$. *Find:* a unit vector whose representations are perpendicular to the plane through points P, Q, and R.

Solution: Let $\mathbf{A}$ be the vector having $\overrightarrow{PQ}$ as a representation, and let $\mathbf{B}$ be the vector having $\overrightarrow{PR}$ as a representation. Let $\mathbf{V}(\overrightarrow{OP})$, $\mathbf{V}(\overrightarrow{OQ})$, and $\mathbf{V}(\overrightarrow{OR})$ be the vectors whose position representations are, respectively, $\overrightarrow{OP}$, $\overrightarrow{OQ}$, and $\overrightarrow{OR}$. Then

$$\mathbf{A} = \mathbf{V}(\overrightarrow{OQ}) - \mathbf{V}(\overrightarrow{OP}) = \langle -2,1,0 \rangle - \langle -1,-2,-3 \rangle = \langle -1,3,3 \rangle$$

and

$$\mathbf{B} = \mathbf{V}(\overrightarrow{OR}) - \mathbf{V}(\overrightarrow{OP}) = \langle 0,5,1 \rangle - \langle -1,-2,-3 \rangle = \langle 1,7,4 \rangle$$

The plane through P, Q, and R is the plane formed by $\overrightarrow{PQ}$ and $\overrightarrow{PR}$, which are, respectively, representations of vectors $\mathbf{A}$ and $\mathbf{B}$. Therefore any representation of the vector $\mathbf{A} \times \mathbf{B}$ is perpendicular to this plane.

$$\mathbf{A} \times \mathbf{B} = (-\mathbf{i} + 3\mathbf{j} + 3\mathbf{k}) \times (\mathbf{i} + 7\mathbf{j} + 4\mathbf{k}) = -9\mathbf{i} + 7\mathbf{j} - 10\mathbf{k}$$

The desired vector is a unit vector parallel to $\mathbf{A} \times \mathbf{B}$. To find this unit vector, we apply Theorem 21.3.3 and divide $\mathbf{A} \times \mathbf{B}$ by $|\mathbf{A} \times \mathbf{B}|$, and we obtain

$$\frac{\mathbf{A} \times \mathbf{B}}{|\mathbf{A} \times \mathbf{B}|} = -\frac{9}{\sqrt{230}}\mathbf{i} + \frac{7}{\sqrt{230}}\mathbf{j} - \frac{10}{\sqrt{230}}\mathbf{k}$$

Exercises 21.3

1. Prove Theorem 21.3.3.

2. Prove Theorem 21.3.5.

3. Prove Theorem 21.3.8.

In Exercises 4 through 7, find the direction cosines of the vector $\mathbf{V}(\overrightarrow{P_1 P_2})$ and check your answers by verifying that the sum of their squares is 1.

4. $P_1(1,3,5)$; $P_2(2,-1,4)$ 6. $P_1(-2,6,5)$; $P_2(2,4,1)$

5. $P_1(3,-1,-4)$; $P_2(7,2,4)$ 7. $P_1(4,-3,-1)$; $P_2(-2,-4,-8)$

In Exercises 8 through 11, express the given vector in terms of its magnitude and direction cosines.

8. $\mathbf{A} = \langle 2,-2,1 \rangle$

9. $\mathbf{B} = \langle -6,2,3 \rangle$

10. $\mathbf{C} = 3\mathbf{i} + 4\mathbf{j} - 5\mathbf{k}$

11. $\mathbf{A} = -2\mathbf{i} + \mathbf{j} - 3\mathbf{k}$

12. Find the cosine of the angle between the vectors $\mathbf{A}$ and $\mathbf{B}$ of Exercises 8 and 9.

13. Find the cosine of the angle between the vectors $\mathbf{C}$ and $\mathbf{A}$ of Exercises 10 and 11.

14. If the three direction angles of a vector are equal, what is the angle?

15. Prove by using vectors that the three points $(4,-1,1)$, $(2,1,-3)$, and $(6,-3,5)$ are collinear.

16. Prove by using vectors that the points $(4,9,1)$, $(-2,6,3)$, and $(6,3,-2)$ are the vertices of a right triangle.

17. Prove by using vectors that the points $(2,2,2)$, $(2,0,1)$, $(4,1,-1)$, and $(4,3,0)$ are the vertices of a rectangle.

18. Prove by using vectors that the points $(2,2,2)$, $(0,1,2)$, $(-1,3,3)$, and $(3,0,1)$ are the vertices of a parallelogram.

19. *Given:* the two unit vectors

$$\mathbf{A} = (4/9)\mathbf{i} + (7/9)\mathbf{j} - (4/9)\mathbf{k} \quad \text{and} \quad \mathbf{B} = -(2/3)\mathbf{i} + (2/3)\mathbf{j} + (1/3)\mathbf{k}$$

If θ is the angle between the two vectors, find $\sin \theta$ in two ways: (*a*) by finding $\cos \theta$ using the dot product, and then using the identity

$$\sin^2 \theta + \cos^2 \theta = 1$$

(*b*) by using the cross product HINT: Use formula (8) of this section.

20. Follow the instructions of Exercise 19 for the two unit vectors:

$$\mathbf{A} = \frac{1}{\sqrt{3}}\mathbf{i} - \frac{1}{\sqrt{3}}\mathbf{j} + \frac{1}{\sqrt{3}}\mathbf{k} \quad \text{and} \quad \mathbf{B} = \frac{1}{3\sqrt{3}}\mathbf{i} + \frac{5}{3\sqrt{3}}\mathbf{j} + \frac{1}{3\sqrt{3}}\mathbf{k}$$

21. Find the area of the parallelogram $PQRS$ if $\mathbf{V}(\overrightarrow{PQ}) = 3\mathbf{i} - 2\mathbf{j}$ and $\mathbf{V}(\overrightarrow{PS}) = 3\mathbf{j} + 4\mathbf{k}$.

22. Find the area of the parallelogram having vertices at $(1,1,3)$, $(-2,1,-1)$, $(-5,4,0)$, and $(-8,4,-4)$.

23. Find the area of the parallelogram having vertices at $(1,-2,3)$, $(4,3,-1)$, $(2,2,1)$, and $(5,7,-3)$.

24. Find the area of the triangle having vertices at $(4,5,6)$, $(4,4,5)$, and $(3,5,5)$.

25. Find the area of the triangle having vertices at $(0,2,2)$, $(8,8,-2)$, and $(9,12,6)$.

26. Let $\overrightarrow{OP}$ be the position representation of vector $\mathbf{A}$, $\overrightarrow{OQ}$ be the position representation of vector $\mathbf{B}$, and $\overrightarrow{OR}$ be the position representation of vector $\mathbf{C}$. Prove that the area of triangle PQR is $\frac{1}{2} |(\mathbf{B} - \mathbf{A}) \times (\mathbf{C} - \mathbf{A})|$.

27. *Given:* the points $P(5,2,-1)$, $Q(2,4,-2)$, and $R(11,1,4)$. *Find:* a unit vector whose representations are perpendicular to the plane through points P, Q, and R.

28. *Find:* a unit vector whose representations are perpendicular to the plane containing $\overrightarrow{PQ}$ and $\overrightarrow{PR}$ if $\overrightarrow{PQ}$ is a representation of the vector $\mathbf{i} + 3\mathbf{j} - 2\mathbf{k}$ and $\overrightarrow{PR}$ is a representation of the vector $2\mathbf{i} - \mathbf{j} - \mathbf{k}$.

29. Suppose $\overrightarrow{PQ}$, $\overrightarrow{PR}$, and $\overrightarrow{PS}$ are three edges of a parallelepiped and $\overrightarrow{PQ}$ is a representation of vector $\mathbf{A}$, $\overrightarrow{PR}$ is a representation of vector $\mathbf{B}$, and $\overrightarrow{PS}$ is a representation of vector $\mathbf{C}$. Prove that the volume of the parallelepiped is the absolute value of the triple scalar product $\mathbf{A} \cdot \mathbf{B} \times \mathbf{C}$.

30. Using the result of Exercise 29, find the volume of the parallelepiped if the points P, Q, R, and S are, respectively, $(1,3,4)$, $(3,5,3)$, $(2,1,6)$, and $(2,2,5)$.

31. Using the result of Exercise 29, find the volume of the parallelepiped if the vectors $\mathbf{A}$, $\mathbf{B}$, and $\mathbf{C}$ are, respectively, $\mathbf{i} + 3\mathbf{j} + 2\mathbf{k}$, $2\mathbf{i} + \mathbf{j} - \mathbf{k}$, and $\mathbf{i} - 2\mathbf{j} + \mathbf{k}$.

32. Let P, Q, and R be three noncollinear points and $\overrightarrow{OP}$, $\overrightarrow{OQ}$, and $\overrightarrow{OR}$ be the position representations of vectors $\mathbf{A}$, $\mathbf{B}$, and $\mathbf{C}$, respectively. Prove that the representations of the vector $\mathbf{A} \times \mathbf{B} + \mathbf{B} \times \mathbf{C} + \mathbf{C} \times \mathbf{A}$ are perpendicular to the plane containing the points P, Q, and R.

(21.4) Planes

The graph of an equation in two variables, x and y, is a curve in the xy plane. The simplest kind of curve in two-dimensional space is a straight line, and the general equation of a straight line is of the form $Ax + By + C = 0$, which is an equation of the first degree. In three-dimensional space, the graph of an equation in three variables, x, y, and z, is a surface. The simplest kind of surface is a *plane*, and we shall see that an equation of a plane is an equation of the first degree in three variables.

21.4.1 DEFINITION   If $\mathbf{N}$ is a given nonzero vector and P_0 is a given point, then the set of all points P for which $\mathbf{V}(\overrightarrow{P_0P})$ and $\mathbf{N}$ are orthogonal is defined to be a *plane* through P_0 having $\mathbf{N}$ as a *normal vector*.

Figure 21.4.1 shows a portion of a plane through the point $P_0(x_0,y_0,z_0)$ and the representation of the normal vector $\mathbf{N}$ having its initial point at P_0.

In plane analytic geometry we may obtain an equation of a line if we are given a point on the line and its direction (slope). Analogously, in solid analytic geometry, an equation of a plane may be determined by knowing a point in the plane and the direction of a normal vector.

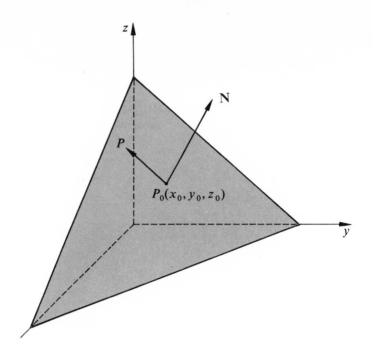

Figure 21.4.1

21.4.2 THEOREM   If $P_0(x_0,y_0,z_0)$ is a point in a plane and a normal vector to the plane is $\mathbf{N} = \langle a,b,c \rangle$, then an equation of the plane is

(1) $$a(x - x_0) + b(y - y_0) + c(z - z_0) = 0$$

Proof: Let $P(x,y,z)$ be any point in the plane. $\mathbf{V}(\overrightarrow{P_0P})$ is the vector having P_0P as a representation, and so

(2) $$\mathbf{V}(\overrightarrow{P_0P}) = \langle x - x_0, y - y_0, z - z_0 \rangle$$

From Definition 21.4.1 and Theorem 21.3.8, it follows that

$$\mathbf{V}(\overrightarrow{P_0P}) \cdot \mathbf{N} = 0$$

Since $\mathbf{N} = \langle a,b,c \rangle$, from (2) and the above we obtain

(3) $$a(x - x_0) + b(y - y_0) + c(z - z_0) = 0$$

which is the desired equation.

21.4.3 THEOREM   If a, b, and c, are not all zero, the graph of an equation of the form

(4) $$ax + by + cz + d = 0$$

is a plane and $\langle a,b,c \rangle$ is a normal vector to the plane.

Proof: Suppose $b \neq 0$. Then the point $(0,-d/b,0)$ is on the graph of the equation, since its coordinates satisfy the equation. The given equation may be written as

$$a(x - 0) + b\left(y + \frac{d}{b}\right) + c(z - 0) = 0$$

which from Theorem 21.4.2 is an equation of a plane through the point $(0,-d/b,0)$ and for which $\langle a,b,c \rangle$ is a normal vector. This proves the theorem, if $b \neq 0$. A similar argument holds if $b = 0$ and either $a \neq 0$ or $c \neq 0$.

Equations (3) and (4) are called *cartesian equations* of a plane. Equation (3) is analogous to the point-slope form of an equation of a line in two dimensions. Equation (4) is the general first-degree equation in three variables. It is called a *linear equation*, even though its graph is a plane. This is because the graph of the general first-degree equation in two variables is a straight line.

EXAMPLE 1: Find an equation of the plane containing the point $(2,1,3)$ and having $3\mathbf{i} - 4\mathbf{j} + \mathbf{k}$ as a normal vector.

Solution: Using (3) with the point $(x_0, y_0, z_0) = (2,1,3)$ and the vector $\langle a,b,c \rangle = \langle 3,-4,1 \rangle$, we have as an equation of the required plane

$$3(x - 2) - 4(y - 1) + (z - 3) = 0$$

or, equivalently,

$$3x - 4y + z - 5 = 0$$

A plane is determined by three noncollinear points, by a line and a point not on the line, by two intersecting lines, or by two parallel lines. To draw a sketch of a plane from its equation, it is convenient to find the points at which the plane intersects each of the coordinate axes. The x coordinate of the point at which the plane intersects the x axis is called the x *intercept* of the plane; the y coordinate of the point at which the plane intersects the y axis is called the y *intercept* of the plane; and the z *intercept* of the plane is the z coordinate of the point at which the plane intersects the z axis.

EXAMPLE 2: Draw a sketch of the plane having equation $2x + 4y + 3z = 8$.

Solution: By substituting zero for y and z, we obtain $x = 4$; so, the x intercept of the plane is 4. Similarly we obtain the y intercept and the z intercept, which are 2 and 8/3, respectively. Plotting the points corresponding to these intercepts and connecting them with lines, we have the sketch of the plane shown in Fig. 21.4.2. It should be noted that only a portion of the plane is shown in the figure.

EXAMPLE 3: Draw a sketch of the plane having equation $3x + 2y - 6z = 0$.

Solution: Since the equation is satisfied when x, y, and z are all zero, the plane intersects each of the axes at the origin. If we set $x = 0$ in the given equation, we obtain $y - 3z = 0$, which is a line in the yz plane, and it is the line of intersection of the yz plane with the given plane. Similarly, the line of intersection of the xz plane with the given plane is obtained by setting $y = 0$, and we get $x - 2z = 0$. Drawing a sketch of each of these two lines and drawing a line segment from a point on one of the lines to a point on the other line, we obtain Fig. 21.4.3.

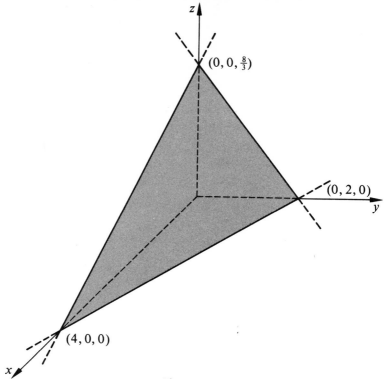

Figure 21.4.2

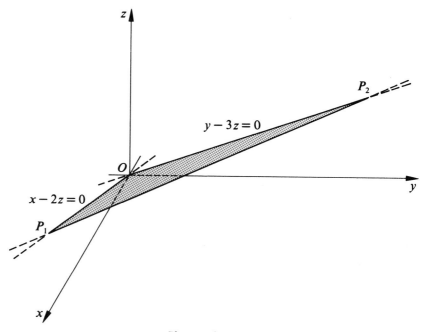

Figure 21.4.3

In the above example, the line in the yz plane and the line in the xz plane used to draw the sketch of the plane are called the *traces* of the given plane in the yz plane and the xz plane, respectively.

The equation $x = 0$ is an equation of the yz plane, since the point (x,y,z) is in the yz plane if and only if $x = 0$. A plane parallel to the yz plane has an equation of the form $x = k$, where k is a constant. Similarly the equations $y = 0$ and $z = 0$ are equations of the xz plane and the xy plane, respectively. A plane parallel to the xz plane has an equation of the form $y = k$, and a plane parallel to the xy plane has an equation of the form $z = k$.

21.4.4 DEFINITION   The angle between two planes is defined to be the angle between the normal vectors of the two planes.

> **EXAMPLE 4:** Find the angle between the two planes $5x - 2y + 5z - 12 = 0$ and $2x + y - 7z + 11 = 0$.
>
> **Solution:** Let $\mathbf{N}_1$ be a normal vector to the first plane and $\mathbf{N}_1 = 5\mathbf{i} - 2\mathbf{j} + 5\mathbf{k}$. Let $\mathbf{N}_2$ be a normal vector to the second plane and $\mathbf{N}_2 = 2\mathbf{i} + \mathbf{j} - 7\mathbf{k}$.
>
> If θ is the angle between the two planes, then by Definition 21.4.4, θ is the angle between $\mathbf{N}_1$ and $\mathbf{N}_2$, and so by Theorem 21.3.5,
>
> $$\cos \theta = \frac{\mathbf{N}_1 \cdot \mathbf{N}_2}{|\mathbf{N}_1||\mathbf{N}_2|} = \frac{(5\mathbf{i} - 2\mathbf{j} + 5\mathbf{k}) \cdot (2\mathbf{i} + \mathbf{j} - 7\mathbf{k})}{\sqrt{25 + 4 + 25} \ \sqrt{4 + 1 + 49}} = \frac{-27}{54} = -\frac{1}{2}$$
>
> Therefore, $\theta = 2\pi/3$.

21.4.5 DEFINITION   Two planes are *parallel* if and only if their normal vectors are parallel.

From Definitions 21.4.4 and 21.4.5, it follows that two planes are parallel if and only if the angle between their normal vectors is 0 or π; or, equivalently, if and only if their normal vectors have the same or opposite direction. So, if we have two planes with equations

(5) $a_1x + b_1y + c_1z + d_1 = 0$

                and

(6) $a_2x + b_2y + c_2z + d_2 = 0$

and normal vectors $\mathbf{N}_1 = \langle a_1,b_1,c_1 \rangle$ and $\mathbf{N}_2 = \langle a_2,b_2,c_2 \rangle$, respectively, then the two planes are parallel if and only if

$$\mathbf{N}_1 = k\mathbf{N}_2 \qquad \text{where } k \text{ is a constant}$$

21.4.6 DEFINITION   Two planes are *perpendicular* if and only if their normal vectors are orthogonal.

Therefore, the two planes having equations (5) and (6) are perpendicular if and only if

$$\mathbf{N_1} \cdot \mathbf{N_2} = 0$$

or, equivalently,

(7) $$a_1 a_2 + b_1 b_2 + c_1 c_2 = 0$$

Since an equation of the xy plane is $z = 0$, the plane having an equation of the form

$$ax + by + d = 0$$

is perpendicular to the xy plane, since (7) holds if a_1, b_1, and c_1 are, respectively, 0, 0, and 1, and a_2, b_2, and c_2 are, respectively, a, b, and 0. So, we may conclude that a plane having an equation with no z term is perpendicular to the xy plane. Similarly, we may conclude that a plane having an equation with no x term is perpendicular to the yz plane, and a plane having an equation with no y term is perpendicular to the xz plane.

In Sec. 21.3, we learned that if representations of two vectors $\mathbf{A}$ and $\mathbf{B}$ have the same initial point, then the representation of the vector $\mathbf{A} \times \mathbf{B}$, also having that common initial point, is perpendicular to the plane formed by the representations of $\mathbf{A}$ and $\mathbf{B}$. Therefore, the vector $\mathbf{A} \times \mathbf{B}$ is a normal vector to the plane formed by the representations of $\mathbf{A}$ and $\mathbf{B}$. We may use this fact to find an equation of a plane determined by three points. This is illustrated in the following example.

EXAMPLE 5: Find an equation of the plane through the points $P(1,3,2)$, $Q(3,-2,2)$, and $R(2,1,3)$.

Solution: $\mathbf{V}(\overrightarrow{RQ}) = -\mathbf{i} + 3\mathbf{j} + \mathbf{k}$ and $\mathbf{V}(\overrightarrow{RP}) = \mathbf{i} - 2\mathbf{j} + \mathbf{k}$. A normal vector to the required plane is the cross product $\mathbf{V}(\overrightarrow{RQ}) \times \mathbf{V}(\overrightarrow{RP})$, which is

$$(-\mathbf{i} + 3\mathbf{j} + \mathbf{k}) \times (\mathbf{i} - 2\mathbf{j} + \mathbf{k}) = 5\mathbf{i} + 2\mathbf{j} - \mathbf{k}$$

So if $P_0 = (1,3,2)$ and $\mathbf{N} = \langle 5,2,-1 \rangle$, we have from equation (3)

$$5(x - 1) + 2(y - 3) - (z - 2) = 0$$

or, equivalently,

$$5x + 2y - z - 9 = 0$$

The following example illustrates the method used to find the undirected distance from a plane to a point.

EXAMPLE 6: Find the distance from the plane $2x - y + 2z + 10 = 0$ to the point $(1,4,6)$.

Solution: Let P be the point $(1,4,6)$ and choose any point Q in the plane. For simplicity, choose the point Q as the point where the plane intersects the x axis; that is, the point $(-5,0,0)$. The vector having $\overrightarrow{QP}$ as a representation is given by

$$\mathbf{V}(\overrightarrow{QP}) = 6\mathbf{i} + 4\mathbf{j} + 6\mathbf{k}$$

A normal vector to the given plane is

$$\mathbf{N} = 2\mathbf{i} - \mathbf{j} + 2\mathbf{k}$$

The negative of $\mathbf{N}$ is also a normal vector to the given plane and

$$-\mathbf{N} = -2\mathbf{i} + \mathbf{j} - 2\mathbf{k}$$

We are not certain which of the two vectors, $\mathbf{N}$ or $-\mathbf{N}$, makes the smaller angle with vector $\mathbf{V}(\overrightarrow{QP})$. Let $\mathbf{N}'$ be the one of the two vectors $\mathbf{N}$ or $-\mathbf{N}$ which makes an angle $\theta < \pi/2$ with $\mathbf{V}(\overrightarrow{QP})$. In Fig. 21.4.4, we show a portion of the given

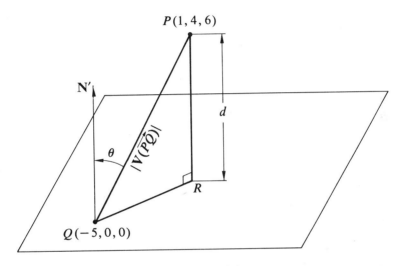

Figure 21.4.4

plane containing the point $Q(-5,0,0)$, the representation of the vector $\mathbf{N}'$ having its initial point at Q, the point $P(1,4,6)$, the directed line segment $\overrightarrow{QP}$, and the point R, which is the foot of the perpendicular from P to the plane. For simplicity, we did not include the coordinate axes in this figure. The distance $|\overrightarrow{RP}|$ is the required distance, which we shall call d. We see from Fig. 21.4.4 that

$$(8) \qquad\qquad d = |\mathbf{V}(\overrightarrow{QP})| \cos \theta$$

Since θ is the angle between $\mathbf{N}'$ and $\mathbf{V}(\overrightarrow{QP})$, we have

$$(9) \qquad\qquad \cos \theta = \frac{\mathbf{N}' \cdot \mathbf{V}(\overrightarrow{QP})}{|\mathbf{N}'||\mathbf{V}(\overrightarrow{QP})|}$$

Substituting from (9) into (8) and replacing $|\mathbf{N}'|$ by $|\mathbf{N}|$, we obtain

$$d = \frac{|\mathbf{V}(\overrightarrow{QP})|(\mathbf{N}' \cdot \mathbf{V}(\overrightarrow{QP}))}{|\mathbf{N}||\mathbf{V}(\overrightarrow{QP})|} = \frac{\mathbf{N}' \cdot \mathbf{V}(\overrightarrow{QP})}{|\mathbf{N}|}$$

Since d is an undirected distance, it is nonnegative, and so we can replace the numerator in the above expression by the absolute value of the dot product of $\mathbf{N}$ and $\mathbf{V}(\overrightarrow{QP})$. Therefore,

$$d = \frac{|\mathbf{N} \cdot \mathbf{V}(\overrightarrow{QP})|}{|\mathbf{N}|} = \frac{|(2\mathbf{i} - \mathbf{j} + 2\mathbf{k}) \cdot (6\mathbf{i} + 4\mathbf{j} + 6\mathbf{k})|}{\sqrt{4 + 1 + 4}} = \frac{20}{3}$$

Exercises 21.4

In Exercises 1 through 4, find an equation of the plane containing the given point P and having the given vector $\mathbf{N}$ as a normal vector.

1. $P(3,1,2)$; $\mathbf{N} = \langle 1,2,-3 \rangle$ 3. $P(2,1,-1)$; $\mathbf{N} = -\mathbf{i} + 3\mathbf{j} + 4\mathbf{k}$
2. $P(-1,8,3)$; $\mathbf{N} = \langle -7,-1,1 \rangle$ 4. $P(1,0,0)$; $\mathbf{N} = \mathbf{i} + \mathbf{k}$

In Exercises 5 through 8, find an equation of the plane containing the given three points.

5. $(3,4,1)$, $(1,7,1)$, $(-1,-2,5)$ 7. $(-2,2,2)$, $(-8,1,6)$, $(3,4,-1)$
6. $(0,0,2)$, $(2,4,1)$, $(-2,3,3)$ 8. $(a,b,0)$, $(a,0,c)$, $(0,b,c)$

In Exercises 9 through 14, draw a sketch of the given plane and find two unit vectors which are normal to the plane.

9. $2x - y + 2z - 6 = 0$ 12. $y + 2z - 4 = 0$
10. $4x - 4y - 2z - 9 = 0$ 13. $3x + 2z - 6 = 0$
11. $4x + 3y - 12z = 0$ 14. $z = 5$

In Exercises 15 through 19, find an equation of the plane satisfying the given conditions.

15. Perpendicular to the line through the points $(2,2,-4)$ and $(7,-1,3)$ and containing the point $(-5,1,2)$.
16. Parallel to the plane $4x - 2y + z - 1 = 0$ and containing the point $(2,6,-1)$.
17. Perpendicular to the plane $x + 3y - z - 7 = 0$ and containing the points $(2,0,5)$ and $(0,2,-1)$.
18. Perpendicular to each of the planes $x - y + z = 0$ and $2x + y - 4z - 5 = 0$ and containing the point $(4,0,-2)$.
19. Perpendicular to the yz plane, containing the point $(2,1,1)$, and making an angle of $\cos^{-1}$ ($\frac{2}{3}$) with the plane $2x - y + 2z - 3 = 0$.

20. Find the cosine of the angle between the planes $2x - y - 2z - 5 = 0$ and $6x - 2y + 3z + 8 = 0$.

21. Find the cosine of the angle between the planes $3x + 4y = 0$ and $4x - 7y + 4z - 6 = 0$.

22. Find the distance from the plane $2x + 2y - z - 6 = 0$ to the point $(2,2,-4)$.

23. Find the distance from the plane $5x + 11y + 2z - 30 = 0$ to the point $(-2,6,3)$.

24. Find the perpendicular distance between the parallel planes

$$4x - 8y - z + 9 = 0 \quad \text{and} \quad 4x - 8y - z - 6 = 0.$$

25. Find the perpendicular distance between the parallel planes $4y - 3z - 6 = 0$ and $8y - 6z - 27 = 0$.

26. Prove that the undirected distance from the plane $ax + by + cz + d = 0$ to the point (x_0, y_0, z_0) is given by

$$\frac{|ax_0 + by_0 + cz_0 + d|}{\sqrt{a^2 + b^2 + c^2}}$$

27. Prove that the perpendicular distance between the two parallel planes $ax + by + cz + d_1 = 0$ and $ax + by + cz + d_2 = 0$ is given by

$$\frac{|d_1 - d_2|}{\sqrt{a^2 + b^2 + c^2}}$$

28. If a, b, and c are nonzero and are the x intercept, y intercept, and z intercept, respectively, of a plane, prove that an equation of the plane is

$$\frac{x}{a} + \frac{y}{b} + \frac{z}{c} = 1$$

This is called the *intercept form* of an equation of a plane.

(21.5) Lines in space

Let L be a line in three-dimensional space such that it contains a given point $P_0(x_0, y_0, z_0)$ and is parallel to the representations of a given vector $\mathbf{R} = \langle a,b,c \rangle$. Then L is the set of all points $P(x,y,z)$ such that $\mathbf{V}(\overrightarrow{P_0P})$ is parallel to the vector $\mathbf{R}$. So, P is on the line L if and only if there is a nonzero scalar t such that

(1) $$\mathbf{V}(\overrightarrow{P_0P}) = t\,\mathbf{R}$$

Since $\quad \mathbf{V}(\overrightarrow{P_0P}) = \langle x - x_0, y - y_0, z - z_0 \rangle$

we obtain from (1)

$$\langle x - x_0, y - y_0, z - z_0 \rangle = t\langle a,b,c \rangle$$

from which it follows that

$$x - x_0 = ta \qquad y - y_0 = tb \qquad z - z_0 = tc$$

or, equivalently,

(2) $$x = x_0 + ta \qquad y = y_0 + tb \qquad z = z_0 + tc$$

Letting the parameter t be any real number [that is, t takes on all values in the interval $(-\infty, +\infty)$], the point P may be any point on the line L. Therefore, equations (2) represent the line L, and we call these equations *parametric equations* of the line.

If none of the numbers a, b, or c is zero, we eliminate t from equations (2) and obtain

(3) $$\frac{x - x_0}{a} = \frac{y - y_0}{b} = \frac{z - z_0}{c}$$

These equations are called *symmetric equations* of the line.

If one of the numbers a, b, or c is zero, we do not use symmetric equations (3). However, suppose for example that $b = 0$ and neither a nor c is zero. We may then write as equations of the line

$$\frac{x - x_0}{a} = \frac{z - z_0}{c} \quad \text{and} \quad y = y_0$$

The vector $\mathbf{R} = \langle a, b, c \rangle$ determines the direction of the line, and the numbers a, b, and c are called *direction numbers* of the line. Any vector parallel to $\mathbf{R}$ has either the same or the opposite direction as $\mathbf{R}$, and hence such a vector may be used in place of $\mathbf{R}$ in the above discussion. Since the components of any vector parallel to $\mathbf{R}$ are proportional to the components of $\mathbf{R}$, we may conclude that any set of three numbers proportional to a, b, and c may also serve as a set of direction numbers of the line. So, a line has an unlimited number of sets of direction numbers. We shall write a set of direction numbers of a line in brackets as $[a, b, c]$. In particular, if $[2, 3, -4]$ represents a set of direction numbers of a line, other sets of direction numbers of the same line may be represented as $[4, 6, -8]$, $[1, 3/2, -2]$, and $[2/\sqrt{29}, 3/\sqrt{29}, -4/\sqrt{29}]$.

EXAMPLE 1: Find symmetric equations of the line through the two points $(-3, 2, 4)$ and $(6, 1, 2)$.

Solution: Let P_1 be the point $(-3, 2, 4)$ and P_2 be the point $(6, 1, 2)$. Then the required line is parallel to the representations of the vector $\mathbf{V}(\overrightarrow{P_1 P_2})$, and so the components of this vector constitute a set of direction numbers of the line. $\mathbf{V}(\overrightarrow{P_1 P_2}) = \langle 9, -1, -2 \rangle$. Taking P_0 as the point $(-3, 2, 4)$, we have from (3) the equations

$$\frac{x + 3}{9} = \frac{y - 2}{-1} = \frac{z - 4}{-2}$$

Another set of symmetric equations of this line is obtained by taking P_0 as the point $(6, 1, 2)$ and we have

$$\frac{x - 6}{9} = \frac{y - 1}{-1} = \frac{z - 2}{-2}$$

Equations (3) are equivalent to the system of three equations

(4) $b(x - x_0) = a(y - y_0)$ $\qquad c(x - x_0) = a(z - z_0)$ $\qquad c(y - y_0) = b(z - z_0)$

Actually, the three equations in (4) are not independent, since any one of them may be derived from the other two. Each of the equations in (4) is an equation of a plane containing the line L represented by equations (3). Any two of these planes have as their intersection the line L, and hence any two of the equations

(4) define the line. However, there is an unlimited number of planes which contain a given line, and since any two of them will determine the line, we may conclude that there is an unlimited number of pairs of equations which represent a line.

EXAMPLE 2: *Given:* the two planes

$$x + 3y - z - 9 = 0 \quad \text{and} \quad 2x - 3y + 4z + 3 = 0.$$

For the line of intersection of these two planes, find (*a*) a set of symmetric equations, and (*b*) a set of parametric equations.

Solution: If we solve the two given equations for x and y in terms of z, we obtain

$$x = -z + 2 \qquad y = (2/3)z + 7/3$$

from which we get

$$\frac{x - 2}{-1} = \frac{y - 7/3}{2/3} = \frac{z - 0}{1}$$

or, equivalently,

$$\frac{x - 2}{-3} = \frac{y - 7/3}{2} = \frac{z - 0}{3}$$

which is a set of symmetric equations of the line. A set of parametric equations may be obtained by setting each of the above ratios equal to t, and we obtain

$$x = 2 - 3t \qquad y = 7/3 + 2t \qquad z = 3t$$

EXAMPLE 3: Find the direction cosines of a vector whose representations are parallel to the line of Example 2.

Solution: From the symmetric equations of the line, found in Example 2, we see that a set of direction numbers of the line is $[-3,2,3]$. Therefore the vector $\langle -3,2,3 \rangle$ is a vector whose representations are parallel to the line. The direction cosines of this vector are as follows: $\cos \alpha = -3/\sqrt{22}$, $\cos \beta = 2/\sqrt{22}$, $\cos \gamma = 3/\sqrt{22}$.

Exercises 21.5

In Exercises 1 through 6, find symmetric equations for the line satisfying the given conditions.

1. Through the two points $(1,2,1)$ and $(5,-1,1)$.

2. Through the point $(5,3,2)$ with direction numbers $[4,1,-1]$.

3. Through the point $(4,-5,20)$ and perpendicular to the plane
$$x + 3y - 6z - 8 = 0$$

4. Through the origin and perpendicular to the lines having direction numbers $[4, 2, 1]$ and $[-3, -2, 1]$.

5. Through the origin and perpendicular to the line $(x - 10)/4 = y/3 = z/2$.

6. Through the point $(2, 0, -4)$ and parallel to each of the planes $2x + y - z = 0$ and $x + 3y + 5z = 0$.

The planes through a line which are perpendicular to the coordinate planes are called the *projecting planes* of the line. In Exercises 7 through 10, find equations of the projecting planes of the given line and draw a sketch of the line.

7. $3x - 2y + 5z - 30 = 0$
   $2x + 3y - 10z - 6 = 0$

9. $x - 2y - 3z + 6 = 0$
   $x + y + z - 1 = 0$

8. $x + y - 3z + 1 = 0$
   $2x - y - 3z + 14 = 0$

10. $2x - y + z - 7 = 0$
    $4x - y + 3z - 13 = 0$

11. Find the cosine of the smallest angle between the two lines $x = 2y + 4$, $z = -y + 4$, and $x = y + 7$, $2z = y + 2$.

12. Find an equation of the plane determined by the point $(6, 2, 4)$ and the line $(x - 1)/5 = (y + 2)/6 = (z - 3)/7$.

13. Find an equation of the plane determined by the intersecting lines $(x - 2)/4 = (y + 3)/-1 = (z + 2)/3$ and $3x + 2y + z + 2 = 0$, $x - y + 2z - 1 = 0$.

14. Find equations for the line through the point $(1, -1, 1)$, perpendicular to the line $3x = 2y = z$, and parallel to the plane $x + y - z = 0$.

15. Find equations for the line through the point $(3, 6, 4)$, intersecting the z axis, and parallel to the plane $x - 3y + 5z - 6 = 0$.

16. Find the perpendicular distance from the origin to the line

$$x = -2 + \frac{6}{7}t \qquad y = 7 - \frac{2}{7}t \qquad z = 4 + \frac{3}{7}t$$

17. Find equations of the line through the origin, perpendicular to the line $x = y - 5$, $z = 2y - 3$, and intersecting the line $y = 2x + 1$, $z = x + 2$.

(21.6)   Cylinders and surfaces of revolution

As mentioned previously, the graph of an equation in three variables is a *surface*. A surface is represented by an equation if the coordinates of every point on the surface satisfy the equation and if every point whose coordinates satisfy the equation lies on the surface. We have already discussed two kinds of surfaces, a plane and a sphere. Another kind of surface that is fairly simple is a *cylinder*. The reader is probably familiar with right-circular cylinders from previous experience. We now consider a more general cylindrical surface.

21.6.1 DEFINITION   A *cylinder* is a surface which is generated by a line, moving along a given plane curve in such a way that it always remains parallel to a fixed line not lying in the plane of the given curve.

The moving line is called a *generator* of the cylinder, and the given plane curve is called a *directrix* of the cylinder. Any position of a generator is called a *ruling* of the cylinder. We shall confine ourselves to cylinders having a directrix in a coordinate plane and rulings perpendicular to that plane. If the rulings of a cylinder are perpendicular to the plane of a directrix, the cylinder is said to be perpendicular to the plane.

The familiar right-circular cylinder is one for which a directrix is a circle in a plane perpendicular to the cylinder. In Fig. 21.6.1, we show a cylinder whose

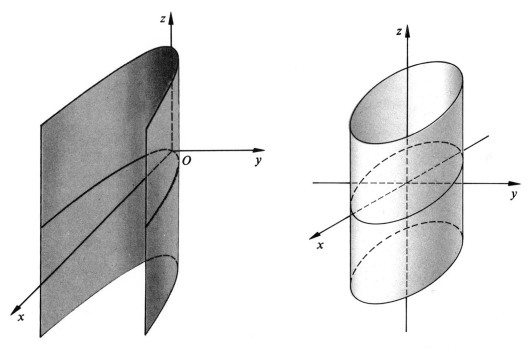

Figure 21.6.1   **Figure 21.6.2**

directrix is the parabola $y^2 = 4px$ in the xy plane and whose rulings are parallel to the z axis. This cylinder is called a *parabolic cylinder*. An *elliptic cylinder* is shown in Fig. 21.6.2; its directrix is the ellipse $b^2x^2 + a^2y^2 = a^2b^2$ in the xy plane and its rulings are parallel to the z axis. Figure 21.6.3 shows a *hyperbolic cylinder* having as directrix the hyperbola $b^2x^2 - a^2y^2 = a^2b^2$ in the xy plane and rulings parallel to the z axis.

Let us consider the problem of finding an equation of a cylinder having a directrix in a coordinate plane and rulings parallel to the coordinate axis not in that plane. To be specific, we shall take the directrix in the xy plane and the rulings parallel to the z axis. Suppose an equation of the directrix in the xy plane is $f(x,y) = 0$. If the point $(x_0,y_0,0)$ in the xy plane satisfies this equation, then any point (x_0,y_0,z) in three-dimensional space, where z is any real number, will satisfy the same equation, since z does not appear in the equation. The points having representations (x_0,y_0,z) all lie on the line parallel to the z axis

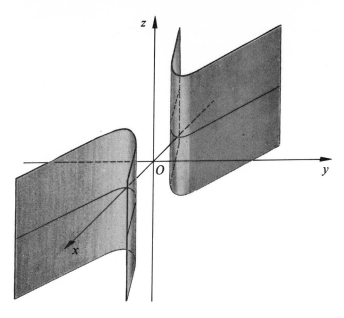

Figure 21.6.3

through the point $(x_0, y_0, 0)$, and this line is a ruling of the cylinder. Hence any point whose x and y coordinates satisfy the equation $f(x,y) = 0$ lies on the cylinder. Conversely, if the point $P(x,y,z)$ lies on the cylinder, then the point $(x,y,0)$ lies on the directrix of the cylinder in the xy plane, and hence the x and y coordinates of P satisfy the equation $f(x,y) = 0$. Therefore, if $f(x,y) = 0$ is considered as an equation of a graph in three-dimensional space, the graph is a cylinder whose rulings are parallel to the z axis and which has as a directrix the curve $f(x,y) = 0$ in the plane $z = 0$. A similar discussion pertains when the directrix is in either of the other coordinate planes. We summarize the results in the following theorem.

21.6.2 THEOREM In three-dimensional space, the graph of an equation in two of the three variables x, y, and z is a cylinder whose rulings are parallel to the axis associated with the missing variable and whose directrix is a curve in the plane associated with the two variables appearing in the equation.

Therefore, an equation of the parabolic cylinder of Fig. 21.6.1 is $y^2 = 4px$, considered as an equation in three-dimensional space. Similarly, equations of the elliptic cylinder of Fig. 21.6.2 and the hyperbolic cylinder of Fig. 21.6.3 are, respectively, $b^2x^2 + a^2y^2 = a^2b^2$ and $b^2x^2 - a^2y^2 = a^2b^2$, both considered as equations in three-dimensional space.

A *cross section* of a surface in a plane is the set of all points of the surface which lie in the given plane. If a plane is parallel to the plane of the directrix of a cylinder, the cross section of the cylinder is the same as the directrix. For example, the cross section of the elliptic cylinder of Fig. 21.6.2 in any plane parallel to the xy plane is an ellipse.

EXAMPLE 1: Draw a sketch of the graph of the equation $y = \ln z$.

Solution: The graph is a cylinder whose directrix in the yz plane is the curve $y = \ln z$ and whose rulings are parallel to the x axis. A sketch of the graph is shown in Fig. 21.6.4.

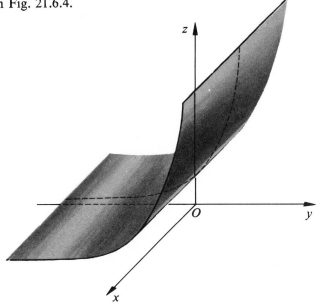

Figure 21.6.4

21.6.3 DEFINITION   If a plane curve is revolved about a fixed line lying in the plane of the curve, the surface generated is called a *surface of revolution*.

The fixed line is called the *axis* of the surface of revolution and the plane curve is called the *generating curve*. A sphere is a particular example of a surface of revolution, since a sphere may be generated by revolving a circle about a diameter. Another example is a right-circular cylinder for which the generating curve and the axis are parallel straight lines.

We shall now find an equation of the surface generated by revolving about the y axis the curve in the yz plane having the two-dimensional equation

(1) $$z = f(y)$$

Refer to Fig. 21.6.5. Let $P(x,y,z)$ be any point on the surface of revolution. Through P, pass a plane perpendicular to the y axis. Denote the point of intersection of this plane with the y axis by $Q(0,y,0)$ and let $P_0(0,y,z)$ be a point of intersection of the plane with the generating curve. Since the cross section of the surface with the plane through P is a circle, P is on the surface if and only if

(2) $$|\overline{QP}|^2 = |\overline{QP_0}|^2$$

Since $|\overline{QP}| = \sqrt{x^2 + z^2}$ and $|\overline{QP_0}| = z_0$, we obtain from (2)

(3) $$x^2 + z^2 = z_0^2$$

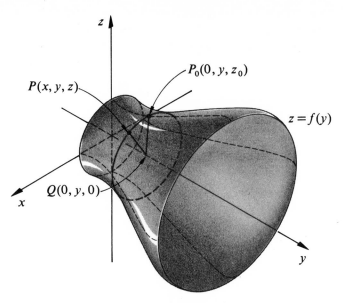

Figure 21.6.5

The point P_0 is on the generating curve, and so its coordinates must satisfy (1). Therefore we have

(4) $$z_0 = f(y)$$

From equations (3) and (4), we may conclude that the point P is on the surface of revolution if and only if

(5) $$x^2 + z^2 = [f(y)]^2$$

Equation (5) is the desired equation of the surface of revolution. Since (5) is equivalent to

$$\pm \sqrt{x^2 + z^2} = f(y)$$

we may obtain (5) by replacing z in (1) by $\pm \sqrt{x^2 + z^2}$.

In a similar manner we may show that if the curve in the yz plane having the two-dimensional equation

(6) $$y = g(z)$$

is revolved about the z axis, an equation of the surface of revolution generated is obtained by replacing y in (6) by $\pm \sqrt{x^2 + y^2}$. Analogous remarks hold when a curve in any coordinate plane is revolved about either one of the coordinate axes in that plane. In summary, the graphs of any of the following equations are surfaces of revolution having the indicated axis: $x^2 + y^2 = [F(z)]^2$ — z axis; $x^2 + z^2 = [F(y)]^2$ — y axis; $y^2 + z^2 = [F(x)]^2$ — x axis. In each case, cross sections of the surface in planes perpendicular to the axis are circles having centers on the axis.

EXAMPLE 2: Find an equation of the surface of revolution generated by revolving the parabola $y^2 = 4x$ in the xy plane about the x axis. Draw a sketch of the graph of the surface.

Solution: In the equation of the parabola, we replace y by $\pm\sqrt{y^2 + z^2}$ and we obtain

$$y^2 + z^2 = 4x$$

A sketch of the graph is shown in Fig. 21.6.6. It should be noted that the same surface is generated if the parabola $z^2 = 4x$ in the xz plane is revolved about the x axis.

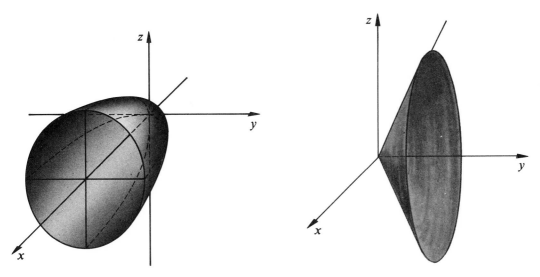

Figure 21.6.6   **Figure 21.6.7**

The surface obtained in Example 2 is called a *paraboloid of revolution*. If an ellipse is revolved about one of its axes, the surface obtained is called an *ellipsoid of revolution*, and a *hyperboloid of revolution* is obtained when a hyperbola is revolved about an axis.

EXAMPLE 3: Draw a sketch of the surface $x^2 + z^2 - 4y^2 = 0$.

Solution: The given equation is of the form $x^2 + z^2 = [F(y)]^2$ and so its graph is a surface of revolution having the y axis as axis. If we solve the given equation for y, we obtain

$$2y = \pm\sqrt{x^2 + z^2}$$

Hence the generating curve may be either the straight line $2y = x$ in the xy plane or the straight line $2y = z$ in the yz plane. By drawing sketches of the two possible generating curves and using the fact that cross sections of the surface in planes perpendicular to the y axis are circles having centers on the y axis, we obtain the surface shown in Fig. 21.6.7. It is called a *right-circular cone*.

Exercises 21.6

In Exercises 1 through 8, draw a sketch of the cylinder having the given equation.

1. $4x^2 + 9y^2 = 36$

2. $x^2 - z^2 = 4$

3. $y = |z|$

4. $z = \sin y$

5. $z = 2x^2$

6. $x^2 = y^3$

7. $4y^2 - x^2 = 4$

8. $z^2 = 4y^2$

In Exercises 9 through 14, find an equation of the surface of revolution generated by revolving the given plane curve about the indicated axis. Draw a sketch of the surface.

9. $x^2 = 4y$ in the xy plane, about the y axis.

10. $x^2 = 4y$ in the xy plane, about the x axis.

11. $x^2 + 4z^2 = 16$ in the xz plane, about the x axis.

12. $x^2 + 4z^2 = 16$ in the xz plane, about the z axis.

13. $y = \sin x$ in the xy plane, about the x axis.

14. $y^2 = z^3$ in the yz plane, about the z axis.

In Exercises 15 through 18, find the generating curve and the axis for the given surface of revolution. Draw a sketch of the surface.

15. $x^2 + y^2 - z^2 = 4$

16. $y^2 + z^2 = e^{2x}$

17. $x^2 + z^2 = |y|$

18. $4x^2 + 9y^2 + 4z^2 = 36$

(21.7) Quadric surfaces

The graph of a second-degree equation in three variables x, y, and z is called a *quadric surface*. These surfaces correspond to the conics in the plane.

The simplest type of quadric surfaces are the parabolic, elliptic, and hyperbolic cylinders, which were discussed in the previous section. There are six other types of quadric surfaces, which we shall now consider. We shall choose the coordinate axes so that the equations are in their simplest form. In our discussion of each of these surfaces, we shall refer to the cross sections of the surfaces in planes parallel to the coordinate planes. These cross sections will help the reader to visualize the surface.

The Ellipsoid:

$$\frac{x^2}{a^2} + \frac{y^2}{b^2} + \frac{z^2}{c^2} = 1$$

where a, b, and c are positive — see Fig. 21.7.1.

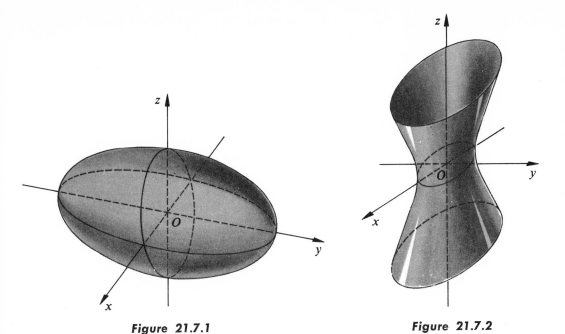

Figure 21.7.1   **Figure 21.7.2**

If in this equation we replace z by zero, we obtain the cross section of the ellipsoid in the xy plane, which is the ellipse $x^2/a^2 + y^2/b^2 = 1$. To obtain the cross sections of the surface with the planes $z = k$, we replace z by k in the equation of the ellipsoid and we get

$$\frac{x^2}{a^2} + \frac{y^2}{b^2} = 1 - \frac{k^2}{c^2}$$

If $|k| < c$, the cross section is an ellipse and the lengths of the semiaxes decrease to zero as $|k|$ increases to the value c. If $|k| = c$, the intersection of a plane $z = k$ with the ellipsoid is the single point $(0,0,k)$. If $|k| > c$, there is no intersection. We may have a similar discussion if we consider cross sections formed by planes parallel to either of the other coordinate planes.

The numbers a, b, and c are the lengths of the semiaxes of the ellipsoid. If any two of these three numbers are equal, we have an ellipsoid of revolution, which is also called a *spheroid*. If we have a spheroid and the third number is greater than the two equal numbers, the spheroid is said to be *prolate*. A prolate spheroid is shaped like a football. An *oblate* spheroid is obtained if the third number is less than the two equal numbers. If all three numbers a, b, and c in the equation of an ellipsoid are equal, the ellipsoid is a *sphere*.

The Elliptic Hyperboloid of One Sheet:

$$\frac{x^2}{a^2} + \frac{y^2}{b^2} - \frac{z^2}{c^2} = 1$$

where a, b, and c are positive — see Fig. 21.7.2.

The cross sections in the planes $z = k$ are ellipses $x^2/a^2 + y^2/b^2 = 1 + k^2/c^2$. When $k = 0$, the lengths of the semiaxes of the ellipse are smallest, and these lengths increase as $|k|$ increases. The cross sections in the planes $x = k$ are hyperbolas $y^2/b^2 - z^2/c^2 = 1 - k^2/a^2$. If $|k| < a$, the transverse axis of the hyperbola is parallel to the y axis, and if $|k| > a$, the transverse axis is parallel to the z axis. If $k = a$, the hyperbola degenerates into two straight lines: $y/b - z/c = 0$ and $y/b + z/c = 0$. Analogously, the cross sections in the planes $y = k$ are also hyperbolas. The axis of this hyperboloid is the z axis.

If $a = b$, the surface is a hyperboloid of revolution for which the axis is the line containing the conjugate axis.

The Elliptic Hyperboloid of Two Sheets:

$$-\frac{x^2}{a^2} - \frac{y^2}{b^2} + \frac{z^2}{c^2} = 1$$

where a, b, and c are positive — see Fig. 21.7.3.

Replacing z by k in the equation of the surface, we obtain $x^2/a^2 + y^2/b^2 = k^2/c^2 - 1$. If $|k| < c$, there is no intersection of the plane $z = k$ with the surface; hence, there are no points of the surface between the planes $z = -c$ and $z = c$. If $|k| = c$, the intersection of the plane $z = k$ with the surface is the single point $(0,0,k)$. When $|k| > c$, the cross section of the surface in the plane

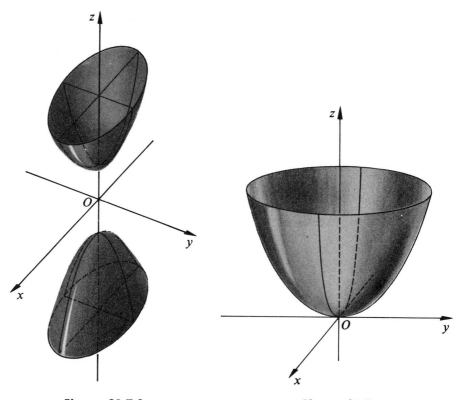

Figure 21.7.3   **Figure 21.7.4**

$z = k$ is an ellipse and the lengths of the semiaxes of the ellipse increase as $|k|$ increases.

The cross sections of the surface in the planes $x = k$ are the hyperbolas $z^2/c^2 - y^2/b^2 = 1 + k^2/a^2$ whose transverse axes are parallel to the z axis. Similarly, the cross sections in the planes $y = k$ are the hyperbolas given by $z^2/c^2 - x^2/a^2 = 1 + k^2/b^2$ for which the transverse axes are also parallel to the z axis.

If $a = b$, the surface is a hyperboloid of revolution in which the axis is the line containing the transverse axis of the hyperbola.

Each of the above three quadric surfaces is symmetric with respect to each of the coordinate planes and symmetric with respect to the origin. Their graphs are called *central quadrics* and their center is at the origin. The graph of any equation of the form

$$\pm \frac{x^2}{a^2} \pm \frac{y^2}{b^2} \pm \frac{z^2}{c^2} = 1$$

where a, b, and c are positive, is a central quadric.

The following two quadrics are called *noncentral quadrics*.

The Elliptic Paraboloid:

$$\frac{x^2}{a^2} + \frac{y^2}{b^2} = \frac{z}{c}$$

where a and b are positive and $c \neq 0$. Figure 21.7.4 shows the surface if $c > 0$.

Substituting k for z in the equation of the surface, we obtain the equation $x^2/a^2 + y^2/b^2 = k/c$. When $k = 0$, this equation becomes $x^2/a^2 + y^2/b^2 = 0$, which represents a single point, the origin. If $k \neq 0$ and k and c have the same sign, the equation is that of an ellipse. So, we conclude that cross sections of the surface in the planes $z = k$, where k and c have the same sign, are ellipses and the lengths of the semiaxes increase as $|k|$ increases. If k and c have opposite signs, the planes $z = k$ do not intersect the surface. The cross sections of the surface with the planes $x = k$ and $y = k$ are parabolas. When $c > 0$, the parabolas open upward, as shown in Fig. 21.7.4, and when $c < 0$, the parabolas open downward.

If $a = b$, the surface is a paraboloid of revolution.

The Hyperbolic Paraboloid:

$$\frac{y^2}{b^2} - \frac{x^2}{a^2} = \frac{z}{c}$$

where a and b are positive and $c \neq 0$. The surface is shown in Fig. 21.7.5 for $c > 0$.

The cross sections of the surface in the planes $z = k$, $k \neq 0$, are hyperbolas having their transverse axes parallel to the y axis if k and c have the same sign and parallel to the x axis if k and c have opposite signs. The cross section of the surface in the plane $z = 0$ consists of two straight lines through the origin. The cross sections in the planes $x = k$ are parabolas opening upward if $c > 0$ and

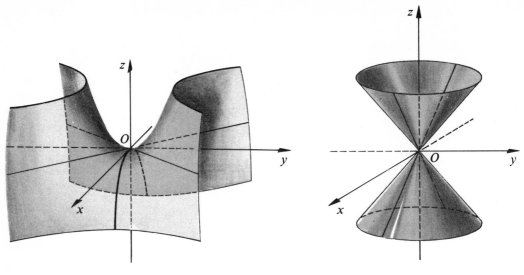

Figure 21.7.5   **Figure 21.7.6**

opening downward if $c < 0$. The cross sections in the planes $y = k$ are parabolas opening downward if $c > 0$ and opening upward if $c < 0$.

The Elliptic Cone:

$$\frac{x^2}{a^2} + \frac{y^2}{b^2} - \frac{z^2}{c^2} = 0$$

where a, b, and c are positive — see Fig. 21.7.6.

The intersection of the plane $z = 0$ with the surface is a single point, the origin. The cross sections of the surface in the planes $z = k$, $k \neq 0$, are ellipses, and the lengths of the semiaxes increase as k increases. Cross sections in the planes $x = 0$ and $y = 0$ are pairs of intersecting lines, and in the planes $x = k$ and $y = k$, $k \neq 0$, the cross sections are hyperbolas.

The general equation of the second degree in x, y, and z is of the form

$$ax^2 + by^2 + cz^2 + dxy + exz + fyz + gx + hy + iz + j = 0$$

where $a, b, \ldots, j$ are constants. It can be shown that by translation and rotation of the three-dimensional coordinate axes (the study of which is beyond the scope of this book) that this equation can be reduced to one of the following two forms:

(1) $$Ax^2 + By^2 + Cz^2 + J = 0$$

                    or

(2) $$Ax^2 + By^2 + Iz = 0$$

The graphs of the equations of the second degree will either be one of the above six types of quadrics or else will degenerate into a cylinder, plane, line, point, or no real locus.

The nondegenerate curves associated with equations of the form (1) are the central quadrics and the elliptic cone, while those associated with equations of the form (2) are the noncentral quadrics. Following are examples of some degenerate cases:

$x^2 - y^2 = 0$; two planes, $x - y = 0$ and $x + y = 0$

$z^2 = 0$; one plane, the xy plane

$x^2 + y^2 = 0$; one line, the z axis

$x^2 + y^2 + z^2 = 0$; a single point, the origin

$x^2 + y^2 + z^2 + 1 = 0$; no real locus

Exercises 21.7

Draw a sketch of the graph of each of the following equations and name the surface.

1. $4x^2 + 9y^2 + z^2 = 36$

2. $4x^2 - 9y^2 - z^2 = 36$

3. $4x^2 + 9y^2 - z^2 = 36$

4. $4x^2 - 9y^2 + z^2 = 36$

5. $\dfrac{x^2}{36} + \dfrac{z^2}{25} = 4y$

6. $\dfrac{y^2}{25} + \dfrac{x^2}{36} = 4$

7. $\dfrac{x^2}{36} - \dfrac{z^2}{25} = 9y$

8. $x^2 = y^2 + z^2$

9. $x^2 = y^2 - z^2$

10. $x^2 = 2y + 4z$

(21.8)   Curves in three-dimensional space

21.8.1 DEFINITION   Let f_1, f_2, and f_3 be three real-valued functions of a real variable t. Then for every number t in the domain common to f_1, f_2, and f_3, there is a vector $\mathbf{R}$ defined by

(1) $$\mathbf{R}(t) = f_1(t)\mathbf{i} + f_2(t)\mathbf{j} + f_3(t)\mathbf{k}$$

and $\mathbf{R}$ is called a *vector-valued function*.

The graph of a vector-valued function in three-dimensional space is obtained in a way analogous to the way we obtained the graph of a vector-valued function in two dimensions in Sec. 18.5. As t assumes all values in the domain of $\mathbf{R}$, the terminal point of the position representation of the vector $\mathbf{R}(t)$ traces a curve C, and this curve is called the graph of (1). A point on the curve C has the cartesian representation (x,y,z) where

(2) $$x = f_1(t) \qquad y = f_2(t) \qquad z = f_3(t)$$

Equations (2) are called *parametric equations* of C, whereas equation (1) is called a *vector equation* of C. *Cartesian equations* of C may be obtained by eliminating t from equations (2), which gives two equations of the form

(3) $$F(x,y,z) = 0 \qquad \text{and} \qquad G(x,y,z) = 0$$

EXAMPLE 1: Draw a sketch of the curve having the vector equation

$$\mathbf{R}(t) = a\cos t\mathbf{i} + b\sin t\mathbf{j} + t\mathbf{k}$$

Solution: Parametric equations of the required curve are

$$x = a\cos t \qquad y = b\sin t \qquad z = t$$

Eliminating t from the first two equations, we obtain $x^2/a^2 + y^2/b^2 = 1$. Therefore, the curve lies entirely on the elliptical cylinder whose directrix is an ellipse in the xy plane and whose rulings are parallel to the z axis. Table 21.8.1 gives sets of values of x, y, and z for specific values of t. A sketch of the curve is shown in Fig. 21.8.1.

Table 21.8.1

t	x	y	z
0	a	0	0
$\pi/4$	$a/\sqrt{2}$	$b/\sqrt{2}$	$\pi/4$
$\pi/2$	0	b	$\pi/2$
$3\pi/4$	$-a/\sqrt{2}$	$b/\sqrt{2}$	$3\pi/4$
π	$-a$	0	π
$3\pi/2$	0	$-b$	$3\pi/2$

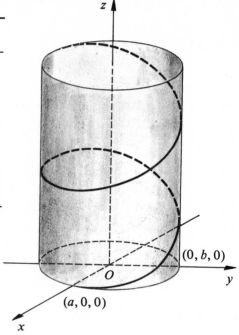

Figure 21.8.1

The curve of Example 1 is called a *helix*. If $a = b$, the helix is called a *circular helix* and it lies on the right-circular cylinder $x^2 + y^2 = a^2$.

Many of the definitions and theorems pertaining to vector-valued functions in two dimensions may be extended to vector-valued functions in three dimensions.

21.8.2 DEFINITION   If $\mathbf{R}(t) = f_1(t)\mathbf{i} + f_2(t)\mathbf{j} + f_3(t)\mathbf{k}$, then

$$\lim_{t\to t_1} \mathbf{R}(t) = \lim_{t\to t_1} f_1(t)\mathbf{i} + \lim_{t\to t_1} f_2(t)\mathbf{j} + \lim_{t\to t_1} f_3(t)\mathbf{k}$$

if $\lim\limits_{t\to t_1} f_1(t)$, $\lim\limits_{t\to t_1} f_2(t)$, and $\lim\limits_{t\to t_1} f_3(t)$ all exist.

21.8.3 DEFINITION   The vector-valued function $\mathbf{R}$ is continuous at t_1 if and only if

   (i) $\mathbf{R}(t_1)$ exists

   (ii) $\lim\limits_{t \to t_1} \mathbf{R}(t)$ exists

   (iii) $\lim\limits_{t \to t_1} \mathbf{R}(t) = \mathbf{R}(t_1)$

21.8.4 DEFINITION   The derivative of the vector-valued function $\mathbf{R}$ is another vector-valued function, denoted by $\mathbf{R}'$ and defined by

$$\mathbf{R}'(t) = \lim_{\Delta t \to 0} \frac{\mathbf{R}(t + \Delta t) - \mathbf{R}(t)}{\Delta t}$$

if this limit exists.

21.8.5 THEOREM   If $\mathbf{R}$ is the vector-valued function defined by

$$\mathbf{R}(t) = f_1(t)\mathbf{i} + f_2(t)\mathbf{j} + f_3(t)\mathbf{k}$$

and $\mathbf{R}'(t)$ exists, then

$$\mathbf{R}'(t) = f'_1(t)\mathbf{i} + f'_2(t)\mathbf{j} + f'_3(t)\mathbf{k}$$

The proof of this theorem is left to the reader (see Exercise 1 at the end of this section).

Theorems 18.6.6, 18.6.7, and 18.6.8 regarding derivatives of sums and products of two-dimensional vector-valued functions also hold for vectors in three dimensions. The following theorem regarding the derivative of the cross product of two vector-valued functions is similar to the corresponding formula for the derivative of the product of real-valued functions; however, it is important to maintain the correct order of the vector-valued functions, since the cross product is not commutative.

21.8.6 THEOREM   If $\mathbf{R}$ and $\mathbf{Q}$ are vector-valued functions, then

$$D_t[\mathbf{R}(t) \times \mathbf{Q}(t)] = \mathbf{R}(t) \times \mathbf{Q}'(t) + \mathbf{R}'(t) \times \mathbf{Q}(t)$$

for all values of t for which $\mathbf{R}'(t)$ and $\mathbf{Q}'(t)$ exist.

The proof of this theorem is left for the reader (see Exercise 2 below).

We may define the length of an arc of a curve C in three-dimensional space in exactly the same way as we defined the length of an arc of a curve in the plane (see Definition 18.7.1). If C is the curve having parametric equations (2), f'_1, f'_2, f'_3 are continuous on the closed interval $[a,b]$, and no two values of t give the same point (x,y,z) on C, then we may prove (as we did in the plane) a theorem similar to Theorem 18.7.3, which states that the length of arc L of the curve C from the point $(f_1(a), f_2(a), f_3(a))$ to the point $(f_1(b), f_2(b), f_3(b))$ is given by

(4) $$L = \int_a^b \sqrt{[f'_1(t)]^2 + [f'_2(t)]^2 + [f'_3(t)]^2}\, dt$$

If s is the length of arc of C from the fixed point $(f_1(t_0), f_2(t_0), f_3(t_0))$ to the variable point $(f_1(t), f_2(t), f_3(t))$ and s increases as t increases, then s is a function of t and is given by

$$(5) \qquad s = \int_{t_0}^{t} \sqrt{[f_1'(u)]^2 + [f_2'(u)]^2 + [f_3'(u)]^2} \, du$$

As we showed in Sec. 18.7 for plane curves, we may show that if (1) is a vector equation of C, then

$$(6) \qquad D_t s = |D_t \mathbf{R}(t)|$$

and the length of arc L, given by (4), may also be given by

$$(7) \qquad L = \int_{a}^{b} |D_t \mathbf{R}(t)| \, dt$$

EXAMPLE 2: *Given:* the circular helix $\mathbf{R}(t) = a \cos t\mathbf{i} + a \sin t\mathbf{j} + t\mathbf{k}$, $a > 0$. *Find:* the length of arc from $t = 0$ to $t = 2\pi$.

Solution: $D_t \mathbf{R}(t) = -a \sin t\mathbf{i} + a \cos t\mathbf{j} + \mathbf{k}$. So from (7), we obtain

$$L = \int_{0}^{2\pi} \sqrt{(-a \sin t)^2 + (a \cos t)^2 + 1} \, dt$$

$$= \int_{0}^{2\pi} \sqrt{a^2 + 1} \, dt = 2\pi\sqrt{a^2 + 1}$$

The definition of the unit tangent vector is analogous to Definition 18.11.1 for vectors in the plane. So if $\mathbf{T}(t)$ denotes the unit tangent vector to curve C having equation (1), then

$$(8) \qquad \mathbf{T}(t) = \frac{D_t \mathbf{R}(t)}{|D_t \mathbf{R}(t)|}$$

21.8.7 DEFINITION   If $\mathbf{T}(t)$ is the unit tangent vector to a curve C at a point P, s is the arc length measured from an arbitrarily chosen point on C to P, and s increases as t increases, then the *curvature vector* of C at P, denoted by $\mathbf{K}(t)$, is given by

$$(9) \qquad \mathbf{K}(t) = D_s \mathbf{T}(t)$$

and the *curvature* of C at P, denoted by $K(t)$, is the magnitude of the curvature vector; that is,

$$K(t) = |D_s \mathbf{T}(t)|$$

By the chain rule, $D_t \mathbf{T}(t) = D_s \mathbf{T}(t) \, [D_t s]$, and so we may write $D_s \mathbf{T}(t) = D_t \mathbf{T}(t)/D_t s$. Since $D_t s = |D_t \mathbf{R}(t)|$, we have from (9)

$$(10) \qquad \mathbf{K}(t) = \frac{D_t \mathbf{T}(t)}{|D_t \mathbf{R}(t)|}$$

Therefore, a formula for finding the curvature is

$$(11) \qquad K(t) = \frac{|D_t \mathbf{T}(t)|}{|D_t \mathbf{R}(t)|}$$

Taking the dot product of $\mathbf{K}(t)$ and $\mathbf{T}(t)$ and using (10), we get

$$(12) \qquad \mathbf{K}(t) \cdot \mathbf{T}(t) = \frac{D_t \mathbf{T}(t)}{|D_t \mathbf{R}(t)|} \cdot \mathbf{T}(t) = \frac{1}{|D_t \mathbf{R}(t)|} D_t \mathbf{T}(t) \cdot \mathbf{T}(t)$$

Theorem 18.6.9 states that if a vector-valued function in a plane has a constant magnitude, it is orthogonal to its derivative. This theorem and its proof also hold for vectors in three dimensions. Therefore, since $|\mathbf{T}(t)| = 1$, we may conclude from (12) that $\mathbf{K}(t) \cdot \mathbf{T}(t) = 0$, and so the curvature vector and the unit tangent vector of a curve at a point are orthogonal.

We shall define the *unit normal vector* as the unit vector having the same direction as the curvature vector, provided the curvature vector is not the zero vector. So, if $\mathbf{N}(t)$ denotes the unit normal vector to a curve C at a point P, then if $\mathbf{K}(t) \neq \mathbf{0}$,

$$(13) \qquad\qquad \mathbf{N}(t) = \frac{\mathbf{K}(t)}{|\mathbf{K}(t)|}$$

From (13) and the previous discussion, it follows that the unit normal vector and the unit tangent vector are orthogonal. So the angle between these two vectors is $\pi/2$, and we have from equation (8), Sec. 21.3,

$$|\mathbf{T}(t) \times \mathbf{N}(t)| = |\mathbf{T}(t)||\mathbf{N}(t)| \sin \frac{\pi}{2} = (1)(1)(1) = 1$$

Therefore, the cross product of $\mathbf{T}(t)$ and $\mathbf{N}(t)$ is a unit vector. By Theorem 21.3.10, $\mathbf{T}(t) \times \mathbf{N}(t)$ is orthogonal to both $\mathbf{T}(t)$ and $\mathbf{N}(t)$, and so the vector $\mathbf{B}(t)$, defined by

$$(14) \qquad\qquad \mathbf{B}(t) = \mathbf{T}(t) \times \mathbf{N}(t)$$

is a unit vector orthogonal to $\mathbf{T}(t)$ and $\mathbf{N}(t)$ and is called the *unit binormal vector* to the curve C at P.

The three mutually orthogonal unit vectors $\mathbf{T}(t)$, $\mathbf{N}(t)$, and $\mathbf{B}(t)$ of a curve C are called the *moving trihedral* of C — see Fig. 21.8.2.

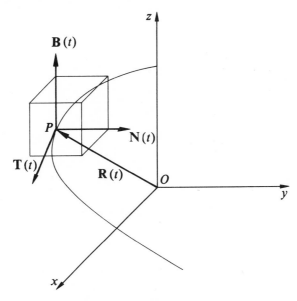

Figure 21.8.2

EXAMPLE 3: Find the moving trihedral and the curvature at any point of the circular helix of Example 2.

Solution: A vector equation of the circular helix is

$$\mathbf{R}(t) = a \cos t\mathbf{i} + a \sin t\mathbf{j} + t\mathbf{k}$$

So, $D_t\mathbf{R}(t) = -a \sin t\mathbf{i} + a \cos t\mathbf{j} + \mathbf{k}$ and $|D_t\mathbf{R}(t)| = \sqrt{a^2 + 1}$. From (8) we get

$$\mathbf{T}(t) = \frac{1}{\sqrt{a^2 + 1}}(-a \sin t\mathbf{i} + a \cos t\mathbf{j} + \mathbf{k})$$

So $$D_t\mathbf{T}(t) = \frac{1}{\sqrt{a^2 + 1}}(-a \cos t\mathbf{i} - a \sin t\mathbf{j})$$

Applying (10), we obtain

$$\mathbf{K}(t) = \frac{1}{a^2 + 1}(-a \cos t\mathbf{i} - a \sin t\mathbf{j})$$

The curvature, then, is given by

$$K(t) = |\mathbf{K}(t)| = \frac{a}{a^2 + 1}$$

and so the curvature of the circular helix is constant.
From (13), we get

$$\mathbf{N}(t) = -\cos t\mathbf{i} - \sin t\mathbf{j}$$

Applying (14), we have

$$\mathbf{B}(t) = \frac{1}{\sqrt{a^2 + 1}}(-a \sin t\mathbf{i} + a \cos t\mathbf{j} + \mathbf{k}) \times (-\cos t\mathbf{i} - \sin t\mathbf{j})$$

$$= \frac{1}{\sqrt{a^2 + 1}}(\sin t\mathbf{i} - \cos t\mathbf{j} + a\mathbf{k})$$

A thorough study of curves and surfaces by means of calculus forms the subject of *differential geometry*. The use of the calculus of vectors further enhances this subject. The previous discussion has been but a short introduction.

We now consider briefly the motion of a particle along a curve in three-dimensional space. If the parameter t in the vector equation (1) measures time, then the position at time t of a particle moving along the curve C, having vector equation (1), is the point $P(f_1(t), f_2(t), f_3(t))$. The *velocity vector* $\mathbf{V}(t)$, and the *acceleration vector*, $\mathbf{A}(t)$, are defined as in the plane. The vector $\mathbf{R}(t)$ is called the *position vector*, and

(15) $$\mathbf{V}(t) = D_t\mathbf{R}(t)$$

and

(16) $$\mathbf{A}(t) = D_t\mathbf{V}(t) = D_t^2\mathbf{R}(t)$$

The *speed* of the particle at time t is the magnitude of the velocity vector, and by applying (6) we may write

$$|\mathbf{V}(t)| = D_t s$$

EXAMPLE 4: A particle is moving along the curve having parametric equations $x = 3t$, $y = t^2$, $z = \frac{2}{3}t^3$. Find the velocity and acceleration vectors and the speed of the particle at $t = 1$. Draw a sketch of a portion of the curve at $t = 1$, and draw the velocity and acceleration vectors there.

Solution: A vector equation of the curve is

$$\mathbf{R}(t) = 3t\mathbf{i} + t^2\mathbf{j} + \tfrac{2}{3} t^3 \mathbf{k}$$

Therefore, $$\mathbf{V}(t) = D_t\mathbf{R}(t) = 3\mathbf{i} + 2t\mathbf{j} + 2t^2\mathbf{k}$$

and $$\mathbf{A}(t) = D_t\mathbf{V}(t) = 2\mathbf{j} + 4t\mathbf{k}$$

Also, $$|\mathbf{V}(t)| = \sqrt{9 + 4t^2 + 4t^4}$$

So, when $t = 1$, $\mathbf{V} = 3\mathbf{i} + 2\mathbf{j} + 2\mathbf{k}$, $\mathbf{A} = 2\mathbf{j} + 4\mathbf{k}$, and $|\mathbf{V}(1)| = \sqrt{17}$. The required sketch is shown in Fig. 21.8.3.

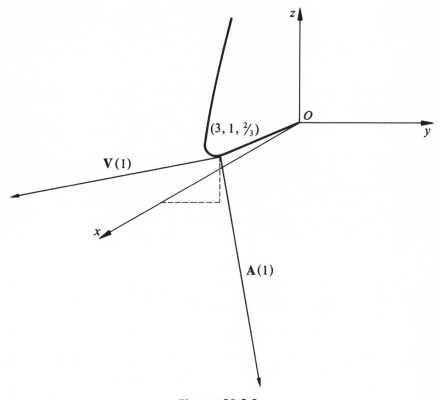

Figure 21.8.3

Exercises 21.8

1. Prove Theorem 21.8.5.

2. Prove Theorem 21.8.6.

In Exercises 3 through 6, find the unit tangent vector for the curve having the given vector equation.

3. $\mathbf{R}(t) = t\mathbf{i} + t^2\mathbf{j} + t^3\mathbf{k}$

4. $\mathbf{R}(t) = \sin 2t\mathbf{i} + \cos 2t\mathbf{j} + 2t^{3/2}\mathbf{k}$

5. $\mathbf{R}(t) = e^t \cos t\mathbf{i} + e^t \sin t\mathbf{j} + e^t\mathbf{k}$

6. $\mathbf{R}(t) = t^2\mathbf{i} + (t + \frac{1}{3}t^3)\mathbf{j} + (t - \frac{1}{3}t^3)\mathbf{k}$

7. The curve of Exercise 3 is called a *twisted cubic*. Show that this curve lies on the cylinder $y = x^2$, and draw a sketch of the curve from $t = 0$ to $t = 2$.

In Exercises 8 through 11, find the length of arc of the curve from t_1 to t_2.

8. The curve of Exercise 4; $t_1 = 0$, $t_2 = 1$.

9. The curve of Exercise 5; $t_1 = 0$, $t_2 = 3$.

10. The curve of Exercise 6; $t_1 = 0$, $t_2 = 1$.

11. $x = t \cos t$, $y = t \sin t$, $z = t$; $t_1 = 0$, $t_2 = \pi/2$.

12. Prove that the unit tangent vector of the circular helix of Example 2 makes a constant angle with the unit vector $\mathbf{k}$.

In Exercises 13 through 16, find the moving trihedral and the curvature of the given curve at $t = t_1$.

13. The curve of Exercise 3; $t_1 = 1$.   15. The curve of Exercise 5; $t_1 = 0$.

14. The curve of Exercise 4; $t_1 = 0$.   16. The curve of Exercise 6; $t_1 = 1$.

In Exercises 17 through 20, a particle is moving along the given curve. Find the velocity vector, the acceleration vector, and the speed at time t_1. Draw a sketch of a portion of the curve at $t = t_1$ and draw the velocity and acceleration vectors there.

17. The circular helix of Example 2; $t_1 = \pi/2$.

18. $x = t$, $y = \frac{1}{2}t^2$, $z = \frac{1}{3}t^3$; $t_1 = 2$.

19. The curve of Exercise 11; $t_1 = \pi/2$.

20. $x = 1/2(t^2 + 1)$, $y = \ln (1 + t^2)$, $z = \tan^{-1} t$; $t_1 = 1$.

21. Prove that if the speed of a moving particle is constant, its acceleration vector is always orthogonal to its velocity vector.

22. Prove that for the twisted cubic of Exercise 3, if $t \neq 0$, no two of the vectors $\mathbf{R}(t)$, $\mathbf{V}(t)$, and $\mathbf{A}(t)$ are orthogonal.

23. Prove that if $\mathbf{R}(t) = f_1(t)\mathbf{i} + f_2(t)\mathbf{j} + f_3(t)\mathbf{k}$ is a vector equation of curve C, and $K(t)$ is the curvature of C, then

$$K(t) = \frac{|D_t\mathbf{R}(t) \times D_t^2\mathbf{R}(t)|}{|D_t\mathbf{R}(t)|^3}$$

24. Use the formula of Exercise 23 to show that the curvature of the circular helix of Example 2 is $a/(a^2 + 1)$.

25. Prove that if $\mathbf{R}(t) = f_1(t)\mathbf{i} + f_2(t)\mathbf{j} + f_3(t)\mathbf{k}$ is a vector equation of curve C, $K(t)$ is the curvature of C at a point P, and s is in the arc length measured from an arbitrarily chosen point on C to P, then

$$D_s \mathbf{R}(t) \cdot D_s{}^3 \mathbf{R}(t) = - [K(t)]^2$$

26. If $\mathbf{R}(t)$, $\mathbf{Q}(t)$, and $\mathbf{W}(t)$ are three vector-valued functions whose derivatives with respect to t exist, prove that

$$D_t[\mathbf{R}(t) \cdot \mathbf{Q}(t) \times \mathbf{W}(t)]$$
$$= D_t \mathbf{R}(t) \cdot \mathbf{Q}(t) \times \mathbf{W}(t) + \mathbf{R}(t) \cdot D_t \mathbf{Q}(t) \times \mathbf{W}(t) + \mathbf{R}(t) \cdot \mathbf{Q}(t) \times D_t \mathbf{W}(t)$$

22 Differential calculus of functions of several variables

(22.1) Introduction

In this chapter the concept of a function is extended to functions of n variables. Along with this, we also extend to functions of n variables the concepts of the *limit* of a function, *continuity* of a function, and the *derivative* of a function. A thorough treatment of these topics belongs to a course in advanced calculus. In this book, we confine most of our discussion of functions of more than one variable to those of two and three variables; however, we make our definitions for functions of n variables and then show the applications of these definitions to functions of two and three variables. We also show that when each of these definitions is applied to a function of one variable, we have the definition previously given.

(22.2) Functions of more than one variable

In Sec. 1.1, we stated that there is a one-to-one correspondence between the points on the real line and the real numbers. A point on the real line is represented by x, where x is a real number. We shall let E^1 denote the set of all points on the real line, or equivalently, the set of all real numbers, and this set is called a *one-dimensional euclidean space*. A point in the xy plane is represented by an ordered pair of real numbers (x,y). The set of all points in the xy plane, or equivalently, the set of all ordered pairs of real numbers (x,y), is denoted by E^2 and is called a *two-dimensional euclidean space*. The set of all points in *three-dimensional euclidean space*, or equivalently, the set of all ordered triples of real numbers (x,y,z), is denoted by E^3. Extending this notation, we shall represent a point in *n-dimensional euclidean space* by an ordered n-tuple of real numbers customarily denoted by $P = (x_1, x_2, \ldots, x_n)$. In particular, if $n = 1$, we shall let $P = x$; if $n = 2$, $P = (x,y)$; if $n = 3$, $P = (x,y,z)$; if $n = 6$, $P = (x_1, x_2, x_3, x_4, x_5, x_6)$.

In Chap. 3, we had the following definition (3.1.1) of a function: "A function is a set of ordered pairs of real numbers (x,y) in which no two distinct ordered pairs have the same first number; the totality of all possible values of x is called the domain of the function and the totality of all possible values of y is called the range of the function." This is the definition of a function of one variable. We now extend the concept of a function to include functions of any number of variables.

22.2.1 DEFINITION   A *function* of *n variables* is a set of ordered pairs of the form (P,w) in which no two distinct ordered pairs have the same first element. P is a point in n-dimensional euclidean space and w is a real number. The totality of all possible values of P is called the *domain* of the function, and the totality of all possible values of w is called the *range* of the function.

From this definition, we see that the domain of a function of n variables is a set of points in E^n and the range is a set of real numbers or, equivalently, a set of points in E^1. When $n = 1$, we have a function of one variable, and so the domain is a set of points in E^1 or, equivalently, a set of real numbers, and the range is a set of real numbers. Hence, we see that Definition 3.1.1 is a special case of Definition 22.2.1. If $n = 2$, we have a function of two variables, and the domain is a set of points in E^2 or, equivalently, a set of ordered pairs of real numbers (x,y). The range is a set of real numbers.

EXAMPLE 1: Let the function f of two variables x and y be the set of all ordered pairs of the form (P,z) such that

$$z = \sqrt{9 - x^2 - y^2}$$

Find the domain and range of f and draw a sketch showing as a shaded region in E^2 the set of points in the domain of f.

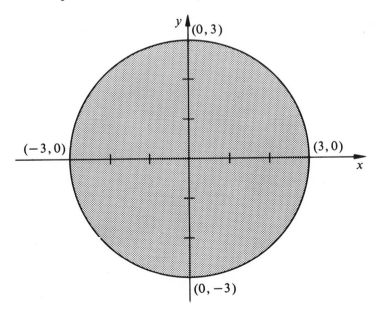

Figure 22.2.1

Solution: The domain of f is the set of all ordered pairs (x,y) for which $9 - x^2 - y^2 \geq 0$. This is the set of all points in the xy plane interior to and on the circumference of the circle $x^2 + y^2 = 9$.

Since $z = \sqrt{9 - (x^2 + y^2)}$, we see that $0 \leq z \leq 3$, and therefore, the range of f is the set of all real numbers in the closed interval $[0,3]$. The required sketch is shown in Fig. 22.2.1.

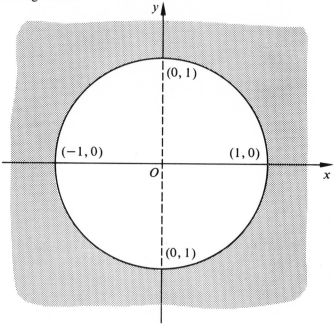

Figure 22.2.2

EXAMPLE 2: The function f of two variables x and y is the set of all ordered pairs of the form (P,z) such that

$$z = y\sqrt{x^2 + y^2 - 1}$$

Find the domain of f and draw a sketch showing as a shaded region in E^2 the set of points in the domain of f.

Solution: The domain of f consists of all ordered pairs (x,y) for which either $y = 0$ or $x^2 + y^2 - 1 \geq 0$. This is the set of all points on the x axis and all points on the circumference of and exterior to the circle $x^2 + y^2 = 1$. The required sketch is shown in Fig. 22.2.2.

If f is a function of n variables, then according to Definition 22.2.1, f is a set of ordered pairs of the form (P,w), where $P = (x_1, x_2, \ldots, x_n)$ is a point in E^n and w is a real number. We shall denote the particular value of w, which corresponds to a point P, by the symbol $f(P)$ or $f(x_1, x_2, \ldots, x_n)$. In particular, if $n = 2$ and we let $P = (x,y)$, we may denote the function value by either $f(P)$ or $f(x,y)$. Similarly, if $n = 3$ and $P = (x,y,z)$, we may denote the function value by either $f(P)$ or $f(x,y,z)$. Note that if $n = 1$, $P = x$, and so if f is a function of one variable, $f(P) = f(x)$. Therefore, this notation is consistent with our notation for function values of one variable.

A function f of n variables may be defined by the equation

$$w = f(x_1, x_2, \ldots, x_n)$$

The variables x_1, x_2, $\ldots$, x_n are called the *independent variables* and w is called the *dependent variable*.

EXAMPLE 3: The domain of a function f is the set of all ordered triples of real numbers (x,y,z) such that $f(x,y,z) = x^2 - 5xz + yz^2$. *Find:* (a) $f(1,4,-2)$; (b) $f(2a,-b,3c)$; (c) $f(x^2,y^2,z^2)$; (d) $f(y,z,-x)$.
   Solution:

   (a) $f(1,4,-2) = 1^2 - 5(1)(-2) + 4(-2)^2 = 1 + 10 + 16 = 27$

   (b) $f(2a,-b,3c) = (2a)^2 - 5(2a)(3c) + (-b)(3c)^2 = 4a^2 - 30ac - 9bc^2$

   (c) $f(x^2,y^2,z^2) = (x^2)^2 - 5(x^2)(z^2) + (y^2)(z^2)^2 = x^4 - 5x^2z^2 + y^2z^4$

   (d) $f(y,z,-x) = y^2 - 5y(-x) + z(-x)^2 = y^2 + 5xy + x^2z$

The graph of a function f of one variable consists of the set of points (x,y) in E^2 for which $y = f(x)$. Similarly, the *graph* of a function of two variables is a set of points in E^3. That is, if f is a function of the two variables x and y, then if all the ordered triples of real numbers (x,y,z) for which (x,y) is any point in the domain of f and $z = f(x,y)$ are plotted as the cartesian coordinates of a point in three-dimensional space, then the totality of all such points is called the graph of f. Since the domain of a function of two variables is a set of points in the xy plane, and since for each ordered pair (x,y) in the domain of f there corresponds a unique value of z, no line perpendicular to the xy plane can intersect the graph of f in more than one point.

EXAMPLE 4: Draw a sketch of the graph of the function of Example 1.
   Solution: The function of Example 1 is the function f which is the set of all ordered pairs of the form (P,z) such that

$$z = \sqrt{9 - x^2 - y^2}$$

So the graph of f is the hemisphere on and above the xy plane having a radius of 3 and center at the origin. A sketch of the graph of this hemisphere is shown in Fig. 22.2.3.

Extending the notion of the graph of a function to a function of n variables, we have the following definition.

22.2.2 DEFINITION   If the function f of n variables is the set of ordered pairs of the form (P,w) where $P = (x_1, x_2, \ldots, x_n)$, then the *graph* of f is the set of points in E^{n+1} of the form $(x_1, x_2, \ldots, x_n, w)$.

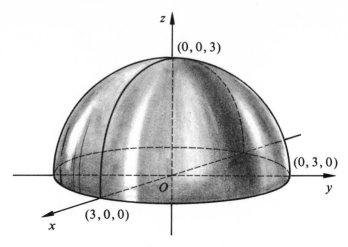

Figure 22.2.3

Exercises 22.2

1. Let the function f of two variables x and y be the set of all ordered pairs of the form (P,z) such that $z = (x + y)/(x - y)$. *Find:* (a) $f(-3,4)$; (b) $f(x^2,y^2)$; (c) $[f(x,y)]^2$; (d) $f(-x,y) - f(x,-y)$; (e) the domain of f; (f) the range of f. Draw a sketch showing as a shaded region in E^2 the set of points in the domain of f.

2. Let the function g of three variables, x, y, and z, be the set of all ordered pairs of the form (P,w) such that $w = \sqrt{4 - x^2 - y^2 - z^2}$. *Find:* (a) $g(1,-1,-1)$; (b) $g(-a,2b,\tfrac{1}{2}c)$; (c) $g(y,-x,-y)$; (d) the domain of g; (e) the range of g; (f) $[g(x,y,z)]^2 - [g(x + 2, y + 2, z)]^2$. Draw a sketch showing as a shaded solid in E^3 the set of points in the domain of g.

In Exercises 3 through 10, find the domain and range of the function f, and draw a sketch showing as a shaded region in E^2 the set of points in the domain of f.

3. $f(x,y) = \dfrac{x^2 - y^2}{x - y}$

4. $f(x,y) = \sqrt{\dfrac{x - y}{x + y}}$

5. $f(x,y) = \dfrac{x}{\sqrt{4 - x^2 - y^2}}$

6. $f(x,y) = \sin^{-1}(x + y)$

7. $f(x,y) = \sin^{-1}\sqrt{1 - x^2 - y^2}$

8. $f(x,y) = \tan^{-1}\sqrt{x^2 - y^2}$

9. $f(x,y) = \ln(xy - 1)$

10. $f(x,y) = [\![x]\!] + [\![\sqrt{1 - y^2}]\!]$

In Exercises 11 through 14, find the domain and range of the function f.

11. $f(x,y,z) = (x + y)\sqrt{z - 2}$

12. $f(x,y,z) = xy/\sqrt{z}$

13. $f(x,y,z) = \sin^{-1}x + \cos^{-1}y + \tan^{-1}z$

14. $f(x,y,z) = |x|e^{y/z}$

In Exercises 15 through 18, find the domain and range of the function f and draw a sketch of the graph of f.

15. $f(x,y) = 4x^2 + 9y^2$

16. $f(x,y) = \sqrt{100 - 25x^2 - 4y^2}$

17. $f(x,y) = x\sqrt{y}$

18. $f(x,y) = \begin{cases} 2 & \text{if } x \neq y \\ 0 & \text{if } x = y \end{cases}$

19. *Given:* $f(x,y) = x - y$, $g(t) = \sqrt{t}$, $h(s) = s^2$. *Find:* (a) $(g \circ f)(5,1)$; (b) $f(h(3), g(9))$; (c) $f(g(x), h(y))$; (d) $g((h \circ f)(x,y))$.

(22.3)   Limits of functions of more than one variable

In E^1 the distance between two points is the absolute value of the difference of two real numbers. That is, $|x - a|$ is the distance between the points x and a. In E^2, the distance between the two points $P(x,y)$ and $P_0(x_0,y_0)$ is given by $\sqrt{(x - x_0)^2 + (y - y_0)^2}$, and in E^3 the distance between the two points $P(x,y,z)$ and $P_0(x_0,y_0,z_0)$ is given by $\sqrt{(x - x_0)^2 + (y - y_0)^2 + (z - z_0)^2}$. In E^n we define the *distance* between two points analogously as follows.

22.3.1 DEFINITION   If $P(x_1,x_2,\ldots,x_n)$ and $A(a_1,a_2,\ldots,a_n)$ are two points in E^n, then the *distance* between P and A, denoted by $\|P - A\|$, is given by

(1) $$\|P - A\| = \sqrt{(x_1 - a_1)^2 + (x_2 - a_2)^2 + \cdots + (x_n - a_n)^2}$$

If in E^1 we take $P = x$, and $A = a$, (1) becomes

(2) $$\|x - a\| = \sqrt{(x - a)^2} = |x - a|$$

If in E^2 we take $P = (x,y)$ and $A = (x_0,y_0)$, (1) becomes

(3) $$\|(x,y) - (x_0,y_0)\| = \sqrt{(x - x_0)^2 + (y - y_0)^2}$$

And, if in E^3 we take $P = (x,y,z)$ and $A = (x_0,y_0,z_0)$, (1) becomes

(4) $$\|(x,y,z) - (x_0,y_0,z_0)\| = \sqrt{(x - x_0)^2 + (y - y_0)^2 + (z - z_0)^2}$$

$\|P - A\|$ is read: "the distance between P and A." It is a nonnegative number.

22.3.2 DEFINITION   If A is a point in E^n and r is a positive number, then the *open ball* $B(A;r)$ is defined to be the set of all points P in E^n such that $\|P - A\| < r$.

22.3.3 DEFINITION   If A is a point in E^n and r is a positive number, then the *closed ball* $B[A;r]$ is defined to be the set of all points in E^n such that $\|P - A\| \leq r$.

To illustrate these definitions, we show what they mean in E^1, E^2, and E^3. First of all, if a is a point in E^1, then the open ball $B(a;r)$ is the set of all points x in E^1 such that

(5) $$|x - a| < r$$

The set of all points x satisfying (5) is the set of all points in the open interval $(a - r, a + r)$; so the open ball $B(a;r)$ in E^1 is simply an open interval having its midpoint at a and its end points at $a - r$ and $a + r$. The closed ball $B[a;r]$ in E^1 is the closed interval $[a - r, a + r]$.

If (x_0,y_0) is a point in E^2, then the open ball $B((x_0,y_0);r)$ is the set of all points (x,y) in E^2 such that

$$(6) \qquad ||(x,y) - (x_0,y_0)|| < r$$

From (3) we see that (6) is equivalent to

$$\sqrt{(x - x_0)^2 + (y - y_0)^2} < r$$

So the open ball $B((x_0,y_0);r)$ in E^2 consists of all points interior to the circle having center at (x_0,y_0) and radius r. An open ball in E^2 is sometimes called an *open disk*. The closed ball, or closed disk, $B[(x_0,y_0);r]$ in E^2 is the set of all points interior to and on the circumference of the circle having center at (x_0,y_0) and radius r.

If (x_0,y_0,z_0) is a point in E^3, then the open ball $B((x_0,y_0,z_0);r)$ is the set of all points (x,y,z) in E^3 such that

$$(7) \qquad ||(x,y,z) - (x_0,y_0,z_0)|| < r$$

From (4) and (7) we see that the open ball $B((x_0,y_0,z_0); r)$ in E^3 consists of all points interior to the sphere having center at P_0 and radius r. Similarly, the closed ball $B[(x_0,y_0,z_0);r]$ in E^3 consists of all points interior to and on the surface of the sphere having center at (x_0,y_0,z_0) and radius r. We are now in a position to define what is meant by the limit of a function of n variables.

22.3.4 DEFINITION   Let f be a function of n variables which is defined on some open ball $B(A;r)$, except possibly at the point A itself. Then the limit of $f(P)$ as P approaches A, is L, written as,

$$(8) \qquad \lim_{P \to A} f(P) = L$$

if for any $\epsilon > 0$, however small, there exists a $\delta > 0$ such that

$$(9) \qquad |f(P) - L| < \epsilon \qquad \text{whenever} \qquad 0 < ||P - A|| < \delta$$

If f is a function of one variable and if in the above definition we take $A = a$ in E^1 and $P = x$, then (8) becomes

$$\lim_{x \to a} f(x) = L$$

and (9) becomes

$$|f(x) - L| < \epsilon \qquad \text{whenever} \qquad 0 < |x - a| < \delta$$

So we see that the definition (4.1.1) of the limit of a function of one variable is a special case of Definition 22.3.4.

We shall now state the definition of the limit of a function of two variables. It is the special case of Definition 22.3.4 where A is the point (x_0,y_0) and P is the point (x,y).

22.3.5 DEFINITION   Let f be a function of two variables which is defined on some open disk $B((x_0,y_0);r)$, except possibly at the point (x_0,y_0) itself. Then

$$\lim_{(x,y)\to(x_0,y_0)} f(x,y) = L$$

if for any $\epsilon > 0$, however small, there exists a $\delta > 0$ such that

(10) $|f(x,y) - L| < \epsilon$ whenever $0 < \sqrt{(x-x_0)^2 + (y-y_0)^2} < \delta$

In words, Definition 22.3.5 states: the function values $f(x,y)$ approach a limit L as the point (x,y) approaches the point (x_0,y_0), if the absolute value of the difference between $f(x,y)$ and L can be made as small as we please by taking the point (x,y) sufficiently close to (x_0,y_0) but not equal to (x_0,y_0). The reader should note that in Definition 22.3.5, nothing is said about the function value at the point (x_0,y_0); that is, it is not necessary that the function be defined at (x_0,y_0) in order for $\lim_{(x,y)\to(x_0,y_0)} f(x,y)$ to exist.

EXAMPLE 1: Prove that $\lim_{(x,y)\to(1,3)} (2x + 3y) = 11$ by applying Definition 22.3.5

Solution: We wish to show that for any $\epsilon > 0$, there exists a $\delta > 0$ such that

$|(2x + 3y) - 11| < \epsilon$ whenever $0 < \sqrt{(x-1)^2 + (y-3)^2} < \delta$

Applying the triangle inequality, we get

$$|2x + 3y - 11| = |2x - 2 + 3y - 9| \le 2|x-1| + 3|y-3|$$

Since $|x-1| \le \sqrt{(x-1)^2 + (y-3)^2}$ and $|y-3| \le \sqrt{(x-1)^2 + (y-3)^2}$, we may conclude that

$$2|x-1| + 3|y-3| < 2\delta + 3\delta$$

whenever $0 < \sqrt{(x-1)^2 + (y-3)^2} < \delta$. So, if we take $\delta = \epsilon/5$, we have

$$|2x + 3y - 11| \le 2|x-2| + 3|y-3| < 5\delta = \epsilon$$

whenever

$$0 < \sqrt{(x-1)^2 + (y-3)^2} < \delta$$

This proves that $\lim_{(x,y)\to(1,3)} (2x + 3y) = 11$.

EXAMPLE 2: Prove that $\lim_{(x,y)\to(1,2)} (3x^2 + y) = 5$ by applying Definition 22.3.5.

Solution: We wish to show that for any $\epsilon > 0$, there exists a $\delta > 0$ such that

$|(3x^2 + y) - 5| < \epsilon$ whenever $0 < \sqrt{(x-1)^2 + (y-2)^2} < \delta$

Applying the triangle inequality, we get

(11) $|3x^2 + y - 5| = |3x^2 - 3 + y - 2| \le 3|x-1|\,|x+1| + |y-2|$

If we require the δ, for which we are looking, to be less than or equal to 1, then $|x - 1| < \delta \le 1$ and $|y - 2| < \delta \le 1$ whenever

$$0 < \sqrt{(x - 1)^2 + (y - 2)^2} < \delta \le 1.$$

Furthermore, whenever $|x - 1| < 1$, then $-1 < x - 1 < 1$, and so $1 < x + 1 < 3$. Hence,

(12) $$3|x - 1| \, |x + 1| + |y - 2| < 3 \cdot \delta \cdot 3 + \delta = 10\delta$$

whenever

$$0 < \sqrt{(x - 1)^2 + (y - 2)^2} < \delta \le 1.$$

So, if for any $\epsilon > 0$ we take $\delta = \min(1, \epsilon/10)$, we have from (11) and (12)

$$|3x^2 + y - 5| < 10\delta \le \epsilon \qquad \text{whenever} \qquad 0 < \sqrt{(x - 1)^2 + (y - 2)^2} < \delta$$

This proves that $\lim\limits_{(x,y)\to(1,2)} (3x^2 + y) = 5$.

We now introduce the concept of an *accumulation point*, which we shall need in order to continue our discussion of limits of functions of two variables.

22.3.6 DEFINITION   A point P_0 is said to be an *accumulation point* of a set S of points in E^n if every open ball $B(P_0;r)$ contains infinitely many points of S.

For example, if S is the set of all points in E^2 on the positive side of the x axis, the origin will be an accumulation point of S, because no matter how small we

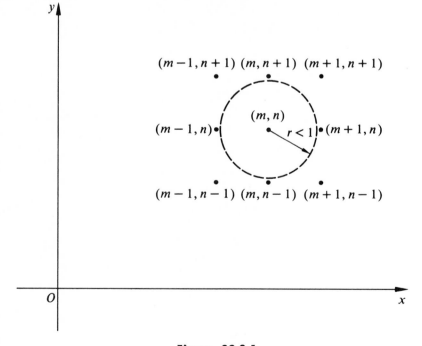

Figure 22.3.1

take the value of r, every open disk having center at the origin and radius r will contain infinitely many points of S. This is an example of a set having an accumulation point for which the accumulation point is not a point of the set. Any point of this set S will also be an accumulation point of S.

If S is the set of all points in E^2 for which the cartesian coordinates are positive integers, then this set has no accumulation point. This can be seen by considering the point (m,n) where m and n are positive integers. Then an open disk having center at (m,n) and radius less than 1 will contain no points of S other than (m,n), and therefore Definition 22.3.6 will not be satisfied — see Fig. 22.3.1.

We now consider the limit of a function of two variables as a point (x,y) approaches a point (x_0,y_0) where (x,y) is restricted to a specific set of points.

22.3.7 DEFINITION   Let f be a function defined on a set of points S in E^2, and let (x_0,y_0) be an accumulation point of S. Then the limit of $f(x,y)$, as (x,y) approaches (x_0,y_0) in S, is L, written as

$$(13) \qquad \lim_{\substack{(x,y)\to(x_0,y_0)\\(P \text{ in } S)}} f(x,y) = L$$

if for any $\epsilon > 0$, however small, there exists a $\delta > 0$ such that

$$|f(x,y) - L| < \epsilon \qquad \text{whenever} \qquad 0 < ||(x,y) - (x_0,y_0)|| < \delta$$

and (x,y) is in S.

A special case of (13) occurs when S is a set of points on a curve containing (x_0,y_0). In such cases the limit in (13) becomes the limit of a function of one variable. For example, let us consider $\lim_{(x,y)\to(0,0)} f(x,y)$. Then if S_1 is the set of all points on the positive side of the x axis, we have

$$\lim_{\substack{(x,y)\to(0,0)\\(P \text{ in } S_1)}} f(x,y) = \lim_{x\to 0^+} f(x,0)$$

If S_2 is the set of all points on the negative side of the y axis.

$$\lim_{\substack{(x,y)\to(0,0)\\(P \text{ in } S_2)}} f(x,y) = \lim_{y\to 0^-} f(0,y)$$

If S_3 is the set of all points on the x axis,

$$\lim_{\substack{(x,y)\to(0,0)\\(P \text{ in } S_3)}} f(x,y) = \lim_{x\to 0} f(x,0)$$

If S_4 is the set of all points on the parabola $y = x^2$,

$$\lim_{\substack{(x,y)\to(0,0)\\(P \text{ in } S_4)}} f(x,y) = \lim_{x\to 0} f(x,x^2)$$

22.3.8 THEOREM   Suppose the function f is defined for all points on an open disk having center at (x_0,y_0), except possibly at (x_0,y_0) itself, and $\lim_{(x,y)\to(x_0,y_0)} f(x,y) = L$.

Then if S is any set of points in E^2 having (x_0, y_0) as an accumulation point,

$$\lim_{\substack{(x,y) \to (x_0, y_0) \\ (P \text{ in } S)}} f(x,y)$$

exists and always has the value L.

Proof: Since $\lim\limits_{(x,y) \to (x_0, y_0)} f(x,y) = L$, then by Definition 22.3.5, for any $\epsilon > 0$, there exists a $\delta > 0$ such that

$$|f(x,y) - L| < \epsilon \qquad \text{whenever} \qquad 0 < ||(x,y) - (x_0, y_0)|| < \delta$$

The above will be true if we further restrict (x,y) by the requirement that (x,y) be in a set S, where S is any set of points having (x_0, y_0) as an accumulation point. Therefore, by Definition 22.3.7,

$$\lim_{\substack{(x,y) \to (x_0, y_0) \\ (P \text{ in } S)}} f(x,y) = L$$

and L does not depend upon the set S through which (x,y) is approaching (x_0, y_0). This proves the theorem.

The following is an immediate consequence of Theorem 22.3.8.

22.3.9 THEOREM   If the function f has different limits as (x,y) approaches (x_0, y_0) through two distinct sets of points having (x_0, y_0) as an accumulation point, then $\lim\limits_{(x,y) \to (x_0, y_0)} f(x,y)$ does not exist.

Proof: Let S_1 and S_2 be two distinct sets of points in E^2 and let

$$\lim_{\substack{(x,y) \to (x_0, y_0) \\ (P \text{ in } S_1)}} f(x,y) = L_1 \qquad \text{and} \qquad \lim_{\substack{(x,y) \to (x_0, y_0) \\ (P \text{ in } S_2)}} f(x,y) = L_2$$

Now assume $\lim\limits_{(x,y) \to (x_0, y_0)} f(x,y)$ exists. Then by Theorem 23.3.8, L_1 must equal L_2, but by hypothesis, $L_1 \neq L_2$, and so we have a contradiction. Therefore, $\lim\limits_{(x,y) \to (x_0, y_0)} f(x,y)$ does not exist.

EXAMPLE 3: *Given:* $f(x,y) = xy/(x^2 + y^2)$. *Find:* $\lim\limits_{(x,y) \to (0,0)} f(x,y)$, if it exists.

Solution: Let S_1 be the set of all points on the x axis. Then

$$\lim_{\substack{(x,y) \to (0,0) \\ (P \text{ in } S_1)}} f(x,y) = \lim_{x \to 0} f(x,0) = \lim_{x \to 0} \frac{0}{x^2 + 0} = 0$$

Let S_2 be the set of all points on the line $y = x$. Then

$$\lim_{\substack{(x,y) \to (0,0) \\ (P \text{ in } S_2)}} f(x,y) = \lim_{x \to 0} \frac{x^2}{x^2 + x^2} = \lim_{x \to 0} \frac{1}{2} = \frac{1}{2}$$

Since

$$\lim_{\substack{(x,y) \to (0,0) \\ (P \text{ in } S_1)}} f(x,y) \neq \lim_{\substack{(x,y) \to (0,0) \\ (P \text{ in } S_2)}} f(x,y)$$

it follows from Theorem 22.3.9 that $\lim\limits_{(x,y) \to (0,0)} f(x,y)$ does not exist.

In the solution of Example 3, instead of taking S_1 to be the set of all the points on the x axis, we could just as well have restricted the points of S_1 to be on the positive side of the x axis, since the origin is an accumulation point of this set.

EXAMPLE 4: *Given:* $f(x,y) = 3x^2y/(x^2 + y^2)$. *Find:* $\lim\limits_{(x,y)\to(0,0)} f(x,y)$, if it exists.

Solution: Let S_1 be the set of all points on the x axis.

$$\text{Then} \quad \lim_{\substack{(x,y)\to(0,0) \\ (P\ in\ S_1)}} f(x,y) = \lim_{x\to 0} \frac{0}{x^2 + 0} = 0$$

Let S_2 be the set of all points on any line through the origin; that is, for any point (x,y) in S_2, $y = mx$.

$$\lim_{\substack{(x,y)\to(0,0) \\ (P\ in\ S_2)}} f(x,y) = \lim_{x\to 0} \frac{3x^2(mx)}{x^2 + m^2x^2} = \lim_{x\to 0} \frac{3mx}{1 + m^2} = 0$$

Even though we obtain the same limit of 0, if (x,y) approaches $(0,0)$ through a set of points on any line through the origin, we cannot make the conclusion that $\lim\limits_{(x,y)\to(0,0)} f(x,y)$ exists and is zero (see Example 5). However, let us attempt to prove that $\lim\limits_{(x,y)\to(0,0)} f(x,y) = 0$. From Definition 22.3.5, if we can show that for any $\epsilon > 0$, there exists a $\delta > 0$, such that

$$(14) \qquad \left| \frac{3x^2y}{x^2 + y^2} \right| < \epsilon \qquad \text{whenever} \qquad 0 < \sqrt{x^2 + y^2} < \delta$$

then we shall have proved that $\lim\limits_{(x,y)\to(0,0)} f(x,y) = 0$.

Since $x^2 \leq x^2 + y^2$ and $|y| \leq \sqrt{x^2 + y^2}$, we have

$$\left| \frac{3x^2y}{x^2 + y^2} \right| = \frac{3x^2\,|y|}{x^2 + y^2} \leq \frac{3(x^2 + y^2)\sqrt{x^2 + y^2}}{x^2 + y^2} = 3\sqrt{x^2 + y^2}$$

So, if $\delta = \epsilon/3$, we may conclude that

$$\left| \frac{3x^2y}{x^2 + y^2} \right| < \epsilon \qquad \text{whenever} \qquad 0 < \sqrt{x^2 + y^2} < \delta$$

which is (14), and hence we have proved that $\lim\limits_{(x,y)\to(0,0)} f(x,y) = 0$.

EXAMPLE 5: *Given:* $f(x,y) = x^2y/(x^4 + y^2)$. *Find:* $\lim\limits_{(x,y)\to(0,0)} f(x,y)$, if it exists.

Solution: Let S_1 be the set of all points on either the x axis or the y axis. So if (x,y) is in S_1, $xy = 0$. Therefore,

$$\lim_{\substack{(x,y)\to(0,0) \\ (P\ in\ S_1)}} f(x,y) = 0$$

Let S_2 be the set of all points on any line through the origin; so if (x,y) is a point in S_2, $y = mx$. We have, then,

$$\lim_{\substack{(x,y)\to(0,0)\\(P \text{ in } S_2)}} f(x,y) = \lim_{x\to 0} \frac{mx^3}{x^4 + m^2x^2} = \lim_{x\to 0} \frac{mx}{x^2 + m^2} = 0$$

Let S_3 be the set of all points on the parabola $y = x^2$. Then

$$\lim_{\substack{(x,y)\to(0,0)\\(P \text{ in } S_3)}} f(x,y) = \lim_{x\to 0} \frac{x^4}{x^4 + x^4} = \lim_{x\to 0} \frac{1}{2} = \frac{1}{2}$$

Since

$$\lim_{\substack{(x,y)\to(0,0)\\(P \text{ in } S_3)}} f(x,y) \neq \lim_{\substack{(x,y)\to(0,0)\\(P \text{ in } S_1)}} f(x,y)$$

it follows that $\displaystyle\lim_{(x,y)\to(0,0)} f(x,y)$ does not exist.

EXAMPLE 6: *Given:*

$$f(x,y) = \begin{cases} (x + y) \sin \dfrac{1}{x} & \text{if } x \neq 0 \\ 0 & \text{if } x = 0 \end{cases}$$

Find:

$$\lim_{(x,y)\to(0,0)} f(x,y) \qquad \text{if it exists}$$

Solution: Let S_1 be the set of all points on the y axis. Then

$$\lim_{\substack{(x,y)\to(0,0)\\(P \text{ in } S_1)}} f(x,y) = \lim_{y\to 0} 0 = 0$$

Let S_2 be the set of all points on any line through the origin except points on the y axis; that is, if (x,y) is a point in S_2, $y = kx$, where $x \neq 0$. Then

$$\lim_{\substack{(x,y)\to(0,0)\\(P \text{ in } S_2)}} f(x,y) = \lim_{x\to 0} (x + kx) \sin \frac{1}{x} = 0$$

Let S_3 be the set of all points (x,y) for which $y = kx^n$, where n is any positive integer and $x \neq 0$. Then

$$\lim_{\substack{(x,y)\to(0,0)\\(P \text{ in } S_3)}} f(x,y) = \lim_{x\to 0} (x + kx^n) \sin \frac{1}{x} = 0$$

We shall now attempt to find a $\delta > 0$ for any $\epsilon > 0$ such that

(15) $\qquad |f(x,y) - 0| < \epsilon \qquad \text{whenever} \qquad 0 < ||(x,y) - (0,0)|| < \delta$

which will prove $\displaystyle\lim_{(x,y)\to(0,0)} f(x,y) = 0$.

We distinguish two cases: $x = 0$ and $x \neq 0$.

Case 1: If $x = 0$, $|f(x,y) - 0| = 0$, which is less than ϵ for any $\delta > 0$.

Case 2: If $x \neq 0$, $|f(x,y) - 0| = |(x + y) \sin (1/x)|$.

$$\left|(x + y) \sin \frac{1}{x}\right| = |x + y| \left|\sin \frac{1}{x}\right| \leq |x + y| (1)| \leq |x| + |y|$$

$$\leq \sqrt{x^2 + y^2} + \sqrt{x^2 + y^2} = 2\sqrt{x^2 + y^2}$$

Therefore,

$$\left|(x + y) \sin \frac{1}{x}\right| < 2 \cdot \frac{\epsilon}{2} \qquad \text{whenever} \qquad 0 < \sqrt{x^2 + y^2} < \frac{\epsilon}{2}$$

So, take $\delta = \epsilon/2$.

Therefore in both cases we have found a $\delta > 0$ for any $\epsilon > 0$ such that (15) holds. So we have proved that $\lim\limits_{(x,y)\to(0,0)} f(x,y) = 0$.

The limit theorems of Chap. 4 and their proofs, with minor modifications, apply to functions of several variables. We shall make use of these theorems without restating them and their proofs.

EXAMPLE 7: *Find:* $\lim\limits_{(x,y)\to(-2,1)} (x^3 + 2x^2y - y^2 + 2)$.

Solution: By applying the limit theorems on sums and products, we have

$$\lim\limits_{(x,y)\to(-2,1)} (x^3 + 2x^2y - y^2 + 2) = (-2)^3 + 2(-2)^2(1) - (1)^2 + 2 = 1$$

Exercises 22.3

In Exercises 1 through 6, establish the limit by finding a $\delta > 0$ for any $\epsilon > 0$ so that Definition 22.3.5 holds.

1. $\lim\limits_{(x,y)\to(3,2)} (3x - 4y) = 1$

2. $\lim\limits_{(x,y)\to(2,4)} (5x - 3y) = -2$

3. $\lim\limits_{(x,y)\to(1,1)} (x^2 + y^2) = 2$

4. $\lim\limits_{(x,y)\to(2,3)} (2x^2 - y^2) = -1$

5. $\lim\limits_{(x,y)\to(2,4)} (x^2 + 2x - y) = 4$

6. $\lim\limits_{(x,y)\to(3,-1)} (x^2 + y^2 - 4x + 2y) = -4$

In Exercises 7 through 12, prove that for the given function f, $\lim\limits_{(x,y)\to(0,0)} f(x,y)$ does not exist.

7. $f(x,y) = \dfrac{x^2 - y^2}{x^2 + y^2}$

8. $f(x,y) = \dfrac{x^2}{x^2 + y^2}$

9. $f(x,y) = \dfrac{x^3 + y^3}{x^2 + y}$

10. $f(x,y) = \dfrac{x^4 + 3x^2y^2 + 2xy^3}{(x^2 + y^2)^2}$

11. $f(x,y) = \dfrac{x^4y^4}{(x^2 + y^4)^3}$

12. $f(x,y) = \dfrac{x^2y^2}{x^3 + y^3}$

In Exercises 13 through 16, prove that $\lim\limits_{(x,y)\to(0,0)} f(x,y)$ exists.

13. $f(x,y) = \dfrac{xy}{\sqrt{x^2 + y^2}}$

14. $f(x,y) = \dfrac{x^3 + y^3}{x^2 + y^2}$

15. $f(x,y) = \begin{cases} (x + y) \sin \dfrac{1}{x} \sin \dfrac{1}{y} & \text{if } x \neq 0 \text{ and } y \neq 0 \\ 0 & \text{if either } x = 0 \text{ or } y = 0 \end{cases}$

16. $f(x,y) = \begin{cases} \dfrac{1}{x} \sin(xy) & \text{if } x \neq 0 \\ y & \text{if } x = 0 \end{cases}$

In Exercises 17 through 20, evaluate the given limit by the use of limit theorems.

17. $\lim\limits_{(x,y)\to(2,3)} (3x^2 + xy - 2y^2)$

19. $\lim\limits_{(x,y)\to(0,0)} \dfrac{e^x + e^y}{\cos x + \sin y}$

18. $\lim\limits_{(x,y)\to(-2,4)} y\sqrt{x^3 + 2y}$

20. $\lim\limits_{(x,y)\to(2,2)} \tan^{-1}\dfrac{y}{x}$

In Exercises 21 through 26, determine if the indicated limit exists.

21. $\lim\limits_{(x,y)\to(0,0)} \dfrac{x^2 y^2}{x^2 + y^2}$

23. $\lim\limits_{(x,y)\to(0,0)} \dfrac{x^2 + y}{x^2 + y^2}$

22. $\lim\limits_{(x,y)\to(0,0)} \dfrac{x^2 y^2}{x^4 + y^4}$

24. $\lim\limits_{(x,y)\to(2,-2)} \dfrac{\sin(x + y)}{x + y}$

25. $f(x,y) = \begin{cases} x \sin \dfrac{1}{y} + y \sin \dfrac{1}{x} & \text{if } x \neq 0 \text{ and } y \neq 0 \\ 0 & \text{if either } x = 0 \text{ or } y = 0 \end{cases} \quad \lim\limits_{(x,y)\to(0,0)} f(x,y)$

26. $f(x,y) = \begin{cases} \dfrac{xy}{x^2 + y^2} + y \sin \dfrac{1}{x} & \text{if } x \neq 0 \\ 0 & \text{if } x = 0 \end{cases} \quad \lim\limits_{(x,y)\to(0,0)} f(x,y)$

27. (a) Give a definition, similar to Definition 22.3.5, of the limit of a function of three variables as a point (x,y,z) approaches a point (x_0,y_0,z_0). (b) Give a definition, similar to Definition 22.3.7, of the limit of a function of three variables as a point (x,y,z) approaches a point (x_0,y_0,z_0) in a specific set of points S in E^3.

28. (a) State and prove a theorem similar to Theorem 22.3.8 for a function f of three variables. (b) State and prove a theorem similar to Theorem 22.3.9 for a function f of three variables.

In Exercises 29 through 32, use the definitions and theorems of Exercises 27 and 28 to prove that $\lim\limits_{(x,y,z)\to(0,0,0)} f(x,y,z)$ does not exist.

29. $f(x,y,z) = \dfrac{x^2 + y^2 - z^2}{x^2 + y^2 + z^2}$

30. $f(x,y,z) = \dfrac{x^4 + yx^3 + z^2 x^2}{x^4 + y^4 + z^4}$

31. $f(x,y,z) = \dfrac{x^2 y^2 z^2}{x^6 + y^6 + z^6}$ 32. $f(x,y,z) = \dfrac{x^3 + yz^2}{x^4 + y^2 + z^4}$

In Exercises 33 and 34, use the definition in Exercise 27a to prove that $\lim\limits_{(x,y,z)\to(0,0,0)} f(x,y,z)$ exists.

33. $f(x,y,z) = \dfrac{y^3 + xz^2}{x^2 + y^2 + z^2}$

34. $f(x,y,z) = \begin{cases} (x + y + z) \sin \dfrac{1}{x} \sin \dfrac{1}{y} & \text{if } x \neq 0 \text{ and } y \neq 0 \\ 0 & \text{if either } x = 0 \text{ or } y = 0 \end{cases}$

(22.4)   Continuity of functions of more than one variable

22.4.1 DEFINITION   Suppose f is a function of n variables and A is a point in E^n. Then f is said to be *continuous* at the point A if and only if the following three conditions are satisfied:

    (i) $f(A)$ exists

    (ii) $\lim\limits_{P\to A} f(P)$ exists

    (iii) $\lim\limits_{P\to A} f(P) = f(A)$

If one or more of these three conditions fails to hold at the point A, then f is said to be *discontinuous* at A.

Definition 5.1.1 of continuity of a function of one variable at a number a is a special case of Definition 22.4.1.

If f is a function of two variables, A is the point (x_0, y_0), and P is a point (x,y), then Definition 22.4.1 becomes the following.

22.4.2 DEFINITION   The function f of two variables x and y is said to be continuous at the point (x_0, y_0) if and only if the following three conditions are satisfied:

    (i) $f(x_0, y_0)$ exists

    (ii) $\lim\limits_{(x,y)\to(x_0,y_0)} f(x,y)$ exists

    (iii) $\lim\limits_{(x,y)\to(x_0,y_0)} f(x,y) = f(x_0, y_0)$

EXAMPLE 1: *Given:*

$$f(x,y) = \begin{cases} (x + y) \sin \dfrac{1}{x} & \text{if } x \neq 0 \\ 0 & \text{if } x = 0 \end{cases}$$

Determine if f is continuous at $(0,0)$.

Solution: We check the three conditions of Definition 22.4.2 at the point $(0,0)$.

(i) $f(0,0) = 0$. Therefore condition (i) holds.

(ii) $\lim\limits_{(x,y)\to(0,0)} f(x,y) = 0$. This was proved in Example 6 of Sec. 22.3. Therefore, condition (ii) holds.

(iii) $\lim\limits_{(x,y)\to(0,0)} f(x,y) = f(0,0)$.

So we conclude that f is continuous at $(0,0)$.

The theorems about continuity for functions of one variable may be extended to functions of two variables.

22.4.3 THEOREM   If f and g are two functions which are continuous at the point (x_0,y_0), then

(i) $f + g$ is continuous at (x_0,y_0)

(ii) $f - g$ is continuous at (x_0,y_0)

(iii) fg is continuous at (x_0,y_0)

(iv) f/g is continuous at (x_0,y_0), provided $g(x_0,y_0) \neq 0$

The proof of this theorem is analogous to the proof of the corresponding theorem (5.2.1) for functions of one variable, and it will be omitted.

A *polynomial function* of two variables x and y is a function f such that $f(x,y)$ is the sum of terms of the form cx^ny^m, where c is a real number and n and m are nonnegative integers. A *rational function* of two variables is a function h such $h(x,y) = f(x,y)/g(x,y)$, where f and g are polynomial functions.

22.4.4 THEOREM   A polynomial function of two variables is continuous at every point in E^2.

The proof of this theorem is analogous to the proof of the corresponding theorem (5.2.2) for functions of one variable, and it will be omitted.

22.4.5 THEOREM   A rational function of two variables is continuous at every point in its domain.

Again we shall omit the proof since it is analogous to the proof of the corresponding theorem (5.2.3) for rational functions of one variable.

22.4.6 DEFINITION   The function f of n variables is said to be continuous on an open ball if it is continuous at every point of the open ball.

EXAMPLE 2: Let the function f be defined by

$$f(x,y) = \begin{cases} x^2 + y^2 & \text{if } \sqrt{x^2 + y^2} \leq 1 \\ 0 & \text{if } \sqrt{x^2 + y^2} > 1 \end{cases}$$

Discuss the continuity of f. What is the region of continuity of f?

Solution: The function f is defined at all points in E^2. By Theorem 22.4.4, f is continuous at all points (x_0, y_0) for which $\sqrt{x_0^2 + y_0^2} \neq 1$.

To determine the continuity of f at points (x_0, y_0) for which $\sqrt{x_0^2 + y_0^2} = 1$, we apply Definition 22.4.2 and check the three conditions. Condition (i) holds since f is defined at all points in E^2. We shall now determine if $\lim\limits_{(x,y) \to (x_0, y_0)} f(x,y)$ exists.

Let S_1 be the set of all points (x,y) such that $\sqrt{x^2 + y^2} \leq 1$. Then

$$\lim_{\substack{(x,y) \to (x_0, y_0) \\ (P \text{ in } S_1)}} f(x,y) = 1$$

Let S_2 be the set of all points (x,y) such that $\sqrt{x^2 + y^2} > 1$. Then

$$\lim_{\substack{(x,y) \to (x_0, y_0) \\ (P \text{ in } S_2)}} f(x,y) = 0$$

Since
$$\lim_{\substack{(x,y) \to (x_0, y_0) \\ (P \text{ in } S_1)}} f(x,y) \neq \lim_{\substack{(x,y) \to (x_0, y_0) \\ (P \text{ in } S_2)}} f(x,y)$$

we conclude that $\lim\limits_{(x,y) \to (x_0, y_0)} f(x,y)$ does not exist.

So, f is discontinuous at all points (x_0, y_0) for which $\sqrt{x_0^2 + y_0^2} = 1$. The region of continuity of f consists of all points in the xy plane except those on the circumference of the circle $x^2 + y^2 = 1$.

Let F be a function of one variable having function values $F(t)$, and let G be a function of two variables having function values $G(x,y)$. Then the composite function $F \circ G$ is a function of two variables. For example, if $F(t) = \ln t$ and $G(x,y) = x^2 + y$, then $(F \circ G)(x,y) = F(G(x,y)) = F(x^2 + y) = \ln (x^2 + y)$. If $g(t) = \sqrt{t}$ and $h(x,y) = 1 - x^2 - y^2$, then $(g \circ h)(x,y) = g(h(x,y)) = g(1 - x^2 - y^2) = \sqrt{1 - x^2 - y^2}$.

The following theorem states that a continuous function of a continuous function is continuous.

22.4.7 THEOREM   Suppose f is a function of one variable and g is a function of two variables. Suppose further that g is continuous at (x_0, y_0) and f is continuous at $g(x_0, y_0)$. Then, the composite function $f \circ g$ is continuous at (x_0, y_0).

The proof of this theorem is similar to the proof of Theorem 5.2.10 and is left for the reader (see Exercise 9 at the end of this section).

EXAMPLE 3: *Given:* $f(x,y) = \ln (xy - 1)$ Discuss the continuity of f. Draw a sketch showing as a shaded region in E^2 the region of continuity of f.

Solution: If g is the function defined by $g(x,y) = xy - 1$, g is continuous at all points in E^2. The natural logarithm function is continuous on its entire domain, which is the set of all positive numbers. So, if h is the function defined by $h(t) = \ln t$, h is continuous for all $t > 0$. f is the composite function $h \circ g$ and, by Theorem 22.4.7, is continuous at all points (x,y) in E^2 for which $xy - 1 > 0$ or, equivalently, $xy > 1$.

The shaded region in Fig. 22.4.1 is the region of continuity of f.

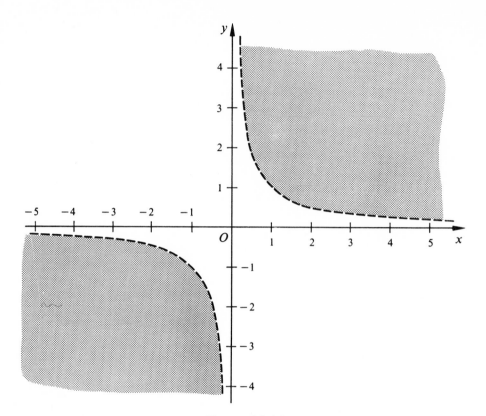

Figure 22.4.1

EXAMPLE 4: *Given:* $f(x,y) = y/\sqrt{x^2 + y^2 - 9}$. Discuss the continuity of f. Draw a sketch showing as a shaded region in E^2 the region of continuity of f.

Solution: The domain of f consists of all points in E^2 for which $x^2 + y^2 - 9 > 0$ and the points for which $y = 0$ and $x \neq \pm 3$; these are the points in E^2 exterior to the circle $x^2 + y^2 = 9$ and the points on the x axis for which $-3 < x < 3$. The function f is continuous at all points in its domain except those points on the x axis for which $-3 < x < 3$. It is easily shown that f is discontinuous at $(a,0)$ if $-3 < a < 3$, since if S_1 is the set of points on the line $x = a$,

$$\lim_{\substack{(x,y)\to(a,0) \\ (P \text{ in } S_1)}} f(x,y)$$

does not exist.

The shaded region of Fig. 22.4.2 is the region of continuity of f.

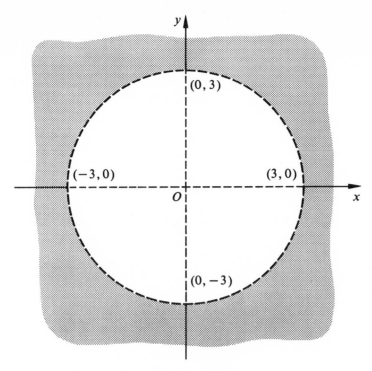

Figure 22.4.2

Exercises 22.4

In Exercises 1 through 8, discuss the continuity of f.

1. $f(x,y) = \begin{cases} \dfrac{xy}{x^2 + y^2} & \text{if } (x,y) \neq (0,0) \\ 0 & \text{if } (x,y) = (0,0) \end{cases}$ (HINT: See Example 3, Sec. 22.3)

2. $f(x,y) = \begin{cases} \dfrac{xy}{\sqrt{x^2 + y^2}} & \text{if } (x,y) \neq (0,0) \\ 0 & \text{if } (x,y) = (0,0) \end{cases}$ (HINT: See Exercise 13, Sec. 22.3)

3. $f(x,y) = \begin{cases} \dfrac{3x^2 y}{x^2 + y^2} & \text{if } (x,y) \neq (0,0) \\ 0 & \text{if } (x,y) = (0,0) \end{cases}$ (HINT: See Example 4, Sec. 22.3)

4. $f(x,y) = \begin{cases} \dfrac{x^2 y}{x^4 + y^2} & \text{if } (x,y) \neq (0,0) \\ 0 & \text{if } (x,y) = (0,0) \end{cases}$ (HINT: See Example 5, Sec. 22.3)

5. $f(x,y) = \begin{cases} \dfrac{x + y}{x^2 + y^2} & \text{if } (x,y) \neq (0,0) \\ 0 & \text{if } (x,y) = (0,0) \end{cases}$

6. $f(x,y) = \begin{cases} \dfrac{x^3 + y^3}{x^2 + y^2} & \text{if } (x,y) \neq (0,0) \\ 0 & \text{if } (x,y) = (0,0) \end{cases}$

7. $f(x,y) = \begin{cases} \dfrac{xy}{|x| + |y|} & \text{if } (x,y) \neq (0,0) \\ 0 & \text{if } (x,y) = (0,0) \end{cases}$

8. $f(x,y) = \begin{cases} \dfrac{x^2y^2}{|x^3| + |y^3|} & \text{if } (x,y) \neq (0,0) \\ 0 & \text{if } (x,y) = (0,0) \end{cases}$

9. Prove Theorem 22.4.7.

In Exercises 10 through 19, determine the region of continuity of f and draw a sketch showing as a shaded region in E^2 the region of continuity of f.

10. $f(x,y) = y\sqrt{x^2 - y^2 - 4}$

11. $f(x,y) = \dfrac{xy}{\sqrt{16 - x^2 - y^2}}$

12. $f(x,y) = \dfrac{x^2 + y^2}{\sqrt{9 - x^2 - y^2}}$

13. $f(x,y) = x\sqrt{4x^2 + 9y^2 - 36}$

14. $f(x,y) = \ln (x^2 + y^2 - 9) - \ln (1 - x^2 - y^2)$

15. $f(x,y) = x \ln (xy)$

16. $f(x,y) = \sin^{-1} (xy)$

17. $f(x,y) = \tan^{-1} \dfrac{x}{y} + \sec^{-1} (xy)$

18. $f(x,y) = \begin{cases} \dfrac{x^2 - y^2}{x - y} & \text{if } x \neq y \\ x - y & \text{if } x = y \end{cases}$

19. $f(x,y) = \begin{cases} \dfrac{\sin (x + y)}{x + y} & \text{if } x + y \neq 0 \\ 1 & \text{if } x + y = 0 \end{cases}$

20. If a function f of two variables is discontinuous at the point (x_0, y_0) but $\lim\limits_{(x,y) \to (x_0,y_0)} f(x,y)$ exists, then f is said to have a *removable discontinuity* at (x_0, y_0), since if f is redefined at (x_0, y_0) so that $f(x_0, y_0) = \lim\limits_{(x,y) \to (x_0,y_0)} f(x,y)$, then f becomes continuous at (x_0, y_0). If the discontinuity is not removable, then it is called an *essential discontinuity*. For each of the following functions, determine whether the discontinuity is removable or essential, at the origin. (*a*) $f(x,y) = (x + y) \sin (x/y)$; (*b*) $f(x,y) = \sqrt{xy}/(x + y)$; (*c*) $f(x,y) = x^2y^2/(x^2 + y^2)$; (*d*) $f(x,y) = x^3y^2/(x^6 + y^4)$.

21. (*a*) Give a definition of continuity at a point for a function of three variables, similar to Definition 22.4.2. (*b*) State theorems for functions of three variables similar to Theorems 22.4.3 and 22.4.7. (*c*) Define a polynomial function of three variables and a rational function of three variables.

In Exercises 22 through 25, use the definitions and theorems of Exercise 21 to discuss the continuity of the given function.

22. $f(x,y,z) = \ln (36 - 4x^2 - y^2 - 9z^2)$

23. $f(x,y,z) = \dfrac{xz}{\sqrt{x^2 + y^2 + z^2 - 1}}$

24. $f(x,y,z) = \begin{cases} \dfrac{xz - y^2}{x^2 + y^2 + z^2} & \text{if } (x,y,z) \neq (0,0,0) \\ 0 & \text{if } (x,y,z) = (0,0,0) \end{cases}$

25. $f(x,y,z) = \begin{cases} \dfrac{3xyz}{x^2 + y^2 + z^2} & \text{if } (x,y,z) \neq (0,0,0) \\ 0 & \text{if } (x,y,z) = (0,0,0) \end{cases}$

(22.5)   Partial derivatives

We shall now discuss differentiation of real-valued functions of n variables. We proceed by reducing the discussion to the one-dimensional case by treating a function of n variables as a function of one variable at a time, holding the others fixed. This leads us to the concept of *partial derivative*. We first define the partial derivative of a function of two variables.

22.5.1 DEFINITION   Let f be a function of two variables, x and y. The *partial derivative of f with respect to x* is that function, denoted by $D_1 f$, such that its function value at any point (x,y) in the domain of f is given by

(1) $$D_1 f(x,y) = \lim_{\Delta x \to 0} \frac{f(x + \Delta x, y) - f(x,y)}{\Delta x}$$

if this limit exists. Similarly, the *partial derivative of f with respect to y* is that function, denoted by $D_2 f$, such that its function value at any point (x,y) in the domain of f is given by

(2) $$D_2 f(x,y) = \lim_{\Delta y \to 0} \frac{f(x, y + \Delta y) - f(x,y)}{\Delta y}$$

if this limit exists.

The process of finding a partial derivative is called *partial differentiation*. $D_1 f$ is read "D sub 1 of f," and this denotes the partial-derivative function. $D_1 f(x,y)$ is read "D sub 1 of f of x and y," and this denotes the partial-derivative function value at the point (x,y). Other notations for the partial-derivative function $D_1 f$ are f_1, f_x, and $\partial f / \partial x$. Other notations for the partial-derivative function value $D_1 f(x,y)$ are $f_1(x,y)$, $f_x(x,y)$, and $\partial f(x,y)/\partial x$. Similarly, other notations for $D_2 f$ are f_2, f_y, and $\partial f / \partial y$, and other notations for $D_2 f(x,y)$ are $f_2(x,y)$, $f_y(x,y)$, and $\partial f(x,y)/\partial y$. If $z = f(x,y)$, we may write $\partial z / \partial x$ for $D_1 f(x,y)$ and $\partial z / \partial y$ for $D_2 f(x,y)$. It should be pointed out that even though the notation $\partial f / \partial x$ is used quite frequently, a partial derivative may not be thought of as a ratio of ∂f and ∂x, as neither of these symbols has a meaning separately. The notation dy/dx may be thought of as the quotient of two differentials when y is a function of the single variable x, but there is not a similar interpretation for $\partial z/\partial x$.

EXAMPLE 1: *Given:* $f(x,y) = 3x^2 - 2xy + y^2$. *Find:* $D_1f(x,y)$ *and* $D_2f(x,y)$ by applying Definition 22.5.1.

Solution:

$$D_1f(x,y) = \lim_{\Delta x \to 0} \frac{f(x + \Delta x, y) - f(x,y)}{\Delta x}$$

$$= \lim_{\Delta x \to 0} \frac{3(x + \Delta x)^2 - 2(x + \Delta x)y + y^2 - (3x^2 - 2xy + y^2)}{\Delta x}$$

$$= \lim_{\Delta x \to 0} \frac{3x^2 + 6x\,\Delta x + 3\,(\Delta x)^2 - 2xy - 2y\,\Delta x + y^2 - 3x^2 + 2xy - y^2}{\Delta x}$$

$$= \lim_{\Delta x \to 0} \frac{6x\,\Delta x + 3\,(\Delta x)^2 - 2y\,\Delta x}{\Delta x}$$

$$= \lim_{\Delta x \to 0} (6x + 3\,\Delta x - 2y)$$

$$= 6x - 2y$$

$$D_2f(x,y) = \lim_{\Delta y \to 0} \frac{f(x, y + \Delta y) - f(x,y)}{\Delta y}$$

$$= \lim_{\Delta y \to 0} \frac{3x^2 - 2x(y + \Delta y) + (y + \Delta y)^2 - (3x^2 - 2xy + y^2)}{\Delta y}$$

$$= \lim_{\Delta y \to 0} \frac{3x^2 - 2xy - 2x\,\Delta y + y^2 + 2y\,\Delta y + (\Delta y)^2 - 3x^2 + 2xy - y^2}{\Delta y}$$

$$= \lim_{\Delta y \to 0} \frac{-2x\,\Delta y + 2y\,\Delta y + (\Delta y)^2}{\Delta y}$$

$$= \lim_{\Delta y \to 0} (-2x + 2y + \Delta y)$$

$$= -2x + 2y$$

If (x_0, y_0) is a particular point in the domain of f, then

$$(3) \qquad D_1f(x_0, y_0) = \lim_{\Delta x \to 0} \frac{f(x_0 + \Delta x, y_0) - f(x_0, y_0)}{\Delta x}$$

if this limit exists, and

$$(4) \qquad D_2f(x_0, y_0) = \lim_{\Delta y \to 0} \frac{f(x_0, y_0 + \Delta y) - f(x_0, y_0)}{\Delta y}$$

if this limit exists.

Alternate formulas to (3) and (4) for $D_1 f(x_0, y_0)$ and $D_2 f(x_0, y_0)$ are given by

$$(5) \qquad D_1 f(x_0, y_0) = \lim_{x \to x_0} \frac{f(x, y_0) - f(x_0, y_0)}{x - x_0}$$

if this limit exists, and

$$(6) \qquad D_2 f(x_0, y_0) = \lim_{y \to y_0} \frac{f(x_0, y) - f(x_0, y_0)}{y - y_0}$$

if this limit exists.

EXAMPLE 2: For the function f of Example 1, find $D_1 f(3, -2)$ in three ways: (a) apply (3); (b) apply (5); (c) substitute $(3, -2)$ for (x, y) in the expression for $D_1 f(x, y)$ found in Example 1.

(a) $D_1 f(3, -2) = \lim\limits_{\Delta x \to 0} \dfrac{f(3 + \Delta x, -2) - f(3, -2)}{\Delta x}$

$\qquad = \lim\limits_{\Delta x \to 0} \dfrac{3(3 + \Delta x)^2 - 2(3 + \Delta x)(-2) + (-2)^2 - (27 + 12 + 4)}{\Delta x}$

$\qquad = \lim\limits_{\Delta x \to 0} \dfrac{27 + 18\,\Delta x + 3\,(\Delta x)^2 + 12 + 4\,\Delta x + 4 - 43}{\Delta x}$

$\qquad = \lim\limits_{\Delta x \to 0} (18 + 3\,\Delta x + 4)$

$\qquad = 22$

(b) $D_1 f(3, -2) = \lim\limits_{x \to 3} \dfrac{f(x, -2) - f(3, -2)}{x - 3}$

$\qquad = \lim\limits_{x \to 3} \dfrac{3x^2 + 4x + 4 - 43}{x - 3}$

$\qquad = \lim\limits_{x \to 3} \dfrac{3x^2 + 4x - 39}{x - 3}$

$\qquad = \lim\limits_{x \to 3} \dfrac{(3x + 13)(x - 3)}{x - 3}$

$\qquad = \lim\limits_{x \to 3} (3x + 13)$

$\qquad = 22$

(c) From Example 1,

$\qquad D_1 f(x, y) = 6x - 2y$

Therefore,

$\qquad D_1 f(3, -2) = 18 + 4 = 22$

To distinguish derivatives of functions of more than one variable from derivatives of functions of one variable, we call the latter derivatives *ordinary derivatives*.

Comparing Definition 22.5.1 with the definition of an ordinary derivative (6.3.1), we see that $D_1 f(x, y)$ is the ordinary derivative of f if f is considered as a function of one variable x (that is, y is held constant), and $D_2 f(x, y)$ is the ordinary derivative of f if f is considered as a function of one variable y (and x is held constant). So the results in Example 1 could have been obtained more easily by applying the theorems for ordinary differentiation, considering y constant when finding $D_1 f(x,y)$ and considering x constant when finding $D_2 f(x,y)$. The following example illustrates this.

EXAMPLE 3: *Given:* $f(x,y) = 3x^3 - 4x^2y + 3xy^2 + 7x - 8y$. *Find:* $D_1 f(x,y)$ and $D_2 f(x,y)$.

Solution: Considering f as a function of x and holding y constant, we have

$$D_1 f(x,y) = 9x^2 - 8xy + 3y^2 + 7$$

Considering f as a function of y and holding x constant, we have

$$D_2 f(x,y) = -4x^2 + 6xy - 8$$

EXAMPLE 4: *Given:*

$$f(x,y) = \begin{cases} \dfrac{xy(x^2 - y^2)}{x^2 + y^2} & \text{if } (x,y) \neq (0,0) \\ 0 & \text{if } (x,y) = (0,0) \end{cases}$$

Find: (a) $f_1(0,y)$ for all y; (b) $f_2(x,0)$ for all x.

Solution: (a) If $y \neq 0$, from (5) we have

$$f_1(0,y) = \lim_{x \to 0} \frac{f(x,y) - f(0,y)}{x - 0} = \lim_{x \to 0} \frac{[xy(x^2 - y^2)]/(x^2 + y^2) - 0}{x}$$

$$= \lim_{x \to 0} \frac{y(x^2 - y^2)}{x^2 + y^2} = -\frac{y^3}{y^2} = -y$$

If $y = 0$, we have

$$f_1(0,0) = \lim_{x \to 0} \frac{f(x,0) - f(0,0)}{x - 0} = \lim_{x \to 0} \frac{0 - 0}{x} = 0$$

Since $f_1(0,y) = -y$ if $y \neq 0$ and $f_1(0,0) = 0$, we may conclude that $f_1(0,y) = -y$ for all y.

(b) If $x \neq 0$, from (6) we have

$$f_2(x,0) = \lim_{y \to 0} \frac{f(x,y) - f(x,0)}{y - 0} = \lim_{y \to 0} \frac{[xy(x^2 - y^2)]/(x^2 + y^2) - 0}{y}$$

$$= \lim_{y \to 0} \frac{x(x^2 - y^2)}{x^2 + y^2} = \frac{x^3}{x^2} = x$$

If $x = 0$, we have

$$f_2(0,0) = \lim_{y \to 0} \frac{f(0,y) - f(0,0)}{y - 0} = \lim_{y \to 0} \frac{0 - 0}{y} = 0$$

Since $f_2(x,0) = x$, if $x \neq 0$ and $f_2(0,0) = 0$, we may conclude that $f_2(x,0) = x$ for all x.

Geometric interpretations of the partial derivatives of a function of two variables are similar to those of a function of one variable. The graph of a function f of two variables is a surface having equation $z = f(x,y)$. If y is held constant — say, $y = y_0$ — then $z = f(x,y_0)$ is the equation of the trace of this surface in the plane $y = y_0$. The curve may be represented by the two equations

(7) $y = y_0$ and $z = f(x,y)$

$D_1f(x_0,y_0)$ then is the slope of the tangent line to the curve given by equations (7) at the point $P_0(x_0,y_0,f(x_0,y_0))$ in the plane $y = y_0$. Analogously, $D_2f(x_0,y_0)$ represents the slope of the tangent line to the curve having equations

$$x = x_0 \qquad \text{and} \qquad z = f(x,y)$$

at the point P_0 in the plane $x = x_0$. Figure 22.5.1 (*a* and *b*) shows the curves and the tangent lines.

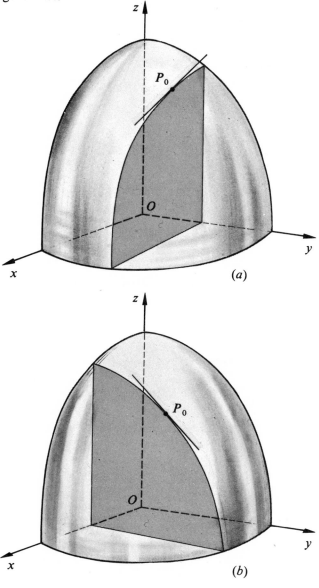

Figure 22.5.1

EXAMPLE 5: Find the slope of the tangent line to the curve of intersection of the surface $z = \frac{1}{2}\sqrt{24 - x^2 - 2y^2}$ with the plane $y = 2$ at the point $(2,2,\sqrt{3})$.

Solution: The required slope will be the value of $\partial z/\partial x$ at the point $(2,2,\sqrt{3})$.

$$\frac{\partial z}{\partial x} = \frac{-x}{2\sqrt{24 - x^2 - 2y^2}}$$

So at $(2,2,\sqrt{3})$,

$$\frac{\partial z}{\partial x} = \frac{-2}{2\sqrt{12}} = -\frac{1}{2\sqrt{3}}$$

We now extend the concept of partial derivative to functions of n variables.

22.5.2 DEFINITION   Let $P(x_1,x_2,\ldots x_n)$ be a point in E^n, and let f be a function of the n variables $x_1, x_2, \ldots, x_n$. Then the partial derivative of f with respect to x_k is that function, denoted by $D_k f$, such that its function value at any point P in the domain of f is given by

$$D_k f(x_1,x_2,\ldots,x_n)$$

$$= \lim_{\Delta x_k \to 0} \frac{f(x_1, x_2, \ldots, x_{k-1}, x_k + \Delta x_k, x_{k+1}, \ldots, x_n) - f(x_1,x_2,\ldots,x_n)}{\Delta x_k}$$

if this limit exists.

In particular, if f is a function of the three variables x, y, and z, then the partial derivatives of f are given by

$$(8) \qquad D_1 f(x,y,z) = \lim_{\Delta x \to 0} \frac{f(x + \Delta x, y, z) - f(x,y,z)}{\Delta x},$$

$$(9) \qquad D_2 f(x,y,z) = \lim_{\Delta y \to 0} \frac{f(x, y + \Delta y, z) - f(x,y,z)}{\Delta y}$$

and

$$(10) \qquad D_3 f(x,y,z) = \lim_{\Delta z \to 0} \frac{f(x, y, z + \Delta z) - f(x, y, z)}{\Delta z}$$

if these limits exist.

EXAMPLE 6: *Given:* $f(x,y,z) = x^2 y + yz^2 + z^3$.

Verify: $xf_1(x,y,z) + yf_2(x,y,z) + zf_3(x,y,z) = 3f(x,y,z)$.

Solution: Holding y and z constant, we get

$$f_1(x,y,z) = 2xy$$

Holding x and z constant, we get

$$f_2(x,y,z) = x^2 + z^2$$

Holding x and y constant, we obtain

$$f_3(x,y,z) = 2yz + 3z^2$$

Therefore,

$$xf_1(x,y,z) + yf_2(x,y,z) + zf_3(x,y,z) = x(2xy) + y(x^2 + z^2) + z(2yz + 3z^2)$$
$$= 2x^2y + x^2y + yz^2 + 2yz^2 + 3z^3$$
$$= 3(x^2y + yz^2 + z^3)$$
$$= 3f(x,y,z)$$

Exercises 22.5

In Exercises 1 through 6, apply Definition 22.5.1 to find each of the partial derivatives.

1. $f(x,y) = 6x + 3y - 7$; $D_1 f(x,y)$

2. $f(x,y) = 4x^2 - 3xy$; $D_1 f(x,y)$

3. $f(x,y) = 3xy + 6x - y^2$; $D_2 f(x,y)$

4. $f(x,y) = xy^2 - 5y + 6$; $D_2 f(x,y)$

5. $f(x,y) = \sqrt{x^2 + y^2}$; $D_1 f(x,y)$

6. $f(x,y) = \dfrac{x + 2y}{x^2 - y}$; $D_2 f(x,y)$

In Exercises 7 through 10, apply Definition 22.5.2 to find each of the partial derivatives.

7. $f(x,y,z) = x^2y - 3xy^2 + 2yz$; $D_2 f(x,y,z)$

8. $f(x,y,z) = x^2 + 4y^2 + 9z^2$; $D_1 f(x,y,z)$

9. $f(x,y,z,r,t) = xyr + yzt + yrt + zrt$; $D_4 f(x,y,z,r,t)$

10. $f(r,s,t,u,v,w) = 3r^2st + st^2v - 2tuv^2 - tvw + 3uw^2$; $D_5 f(r,s,t,u,v,w)$

11. *Given:* $f(x,y) = x^2 - 9y^2$. *Find:* $D_1 f(2,1)$ by (*a*) applying formula (3); (*b*) applying formula (5); (*c*) applying formula (1) and then replacing x and y by 2 and 1, respectively.

12. For the function in Exercise 11, find $D_2 f(2,1)$ by (*a*) applying formula (4); (*b*) applying formula (6); (*c*) applying formula (2) and then replacing x and y by 2 and 1, respectively.

In Exercises 13 through 24, find the indicated partial derivatives by holding all but one of the variables constant and applying theorems for ordinary differentiation.

13. $f(x,y) = y + \sqrt{x^2 + y^2}$; $D_1 f(x,y)$

14. $f(x,y) = \dfrac{x + y}{\sqrt{y^2 - x^2}}$; $D_2 f(x,y)$

15. $f(\theta,\phi) = \sin 3\theta \cos 2\phi;\ D_2 f(\theta,\phi)$

16. $f(r,\theta) = r^2 \cos \theta - 2r \tan \theta;\ D_2 f(r,\theta)$

17. $z = e^{y/x} \ln \dfrac{x}{y};\ \dfrac{\partial z}{\partial y}$

18. $r = e^{-\theta} \cos(\theta + \phi);\ \dfrac{\partial r}{\partial \theta}$

19. $u = (x^2 + y^2 + z^2)^{-1/2};\ \dfrac{\partial u}{\partial z}$

20. $u = \tan^{-1}(xyzw);\ \dfrac{\partial u}{\partial w}$

21. $f(x,y,z) = xyz + \ln(xyz);\ f_3(x,y,z)$

22. $f(x,y,z) = e^{xy}\sinh z - e^{xy} \cosh z;\ f_3(x,y,z)$

23. $f(x,y,z) = e^{xyz} + \tan^{-1} \dfrac{xy}{z};\ f_2(x,y,z)$

24. $f(r,\theta,\phi) = r^2 \sin \theta + e^r \cos \theta \sin \phi - \cos \phi;\ f_2(r,\theta,\phi)$

25. *Given:* $u = \sin \dfrac{r}{t} + \ln \dfrac{t}{r}.$ *Verify:* $t \dfrac{\partial u}{\partial t} + r \dfrac{\partial u}{\partial r} = 0$

26. *Given:* $w = x^2 y + y^2 z + z^2 x.$ *Verify:* $\dfrac{\partial w}{\partial x} + \dfrac{\partial w}{\partial y} + \dfrac{\partial w}{\partial z} = (x + y + z)^2$

27. Find the slope of the tangent line to the curve of intersection of the surface $z = x^2 + y^2$ with the plane $y = 1$ at the point $(2,1,5)$. Draw a sketch.

28. Find the slope of the tangent line to the curve of intersection of the surface $36x^2 - 9y^2 + 4z^2 + 36 = 0$ with the plane $x = 1$ at the point $(1,\sqrt{12},-3)$.

29. Find equations of the tangent line to the curve of intersection of the surface $x^2 + y^2 + z^2 = 9$ with the plane $y = 2$ at the point $(1,2,2)$.

30. Find equations of the tangent line to the curve of intersection of the surface $z = 3x^2 + y^2 + 1$ with the plane $x = 2$ at the point $(2,-1,14)$.

31. *Given:* $f(x,y) = \begin{cases} \dfrac{x^3 + y^3}{x^2 + y^2} & \text{if } (x,y) \neq (0,0) \\ 0 & \text{if } (x,y) = (0,0) \end{cases}$
    Find: (a) $f_1(0,0)$; (b) $f_2(0,0)$

32. *Given:* $f(x,y) = \begin{cases} \dfrac{x^2 - xy}{x + y} & \text{if } (x,y) \neq (0,0) \\ 0 & \text{if } (x,y) = (0,0) \end{cases}$
    Find: (a) $f_1(0,y)$ if $y \neq 0$; (b) $f_1(0,0)$

33. For the function of Exercise 32, find (a) $f_2(x,0)$ if $x \neq 0$; (b) $f_2(0,0)$.

(22.6)   Increments of functions of more than one variable

In Sec. 7.6, we showed that if f is a differentiable function of the single variable x and $y = f(x)$, then the increment Δy of the dependent variable can be expressed as

$$\Delta y = f'(x)\, \Delta x + \epsilon\, \Delta x$$

where ϵ depends upon Δx and $\epsilon \to 0$ as $\Delta x \to 0$.

From the above, it follows that if the function f is differentiable at x_0, the increment of f at x_0, denoted by $\Delta f(x_0)$, is given by

(1) $$\Delta f(x_0) = f'(x_0)\, \Delta x + \epsilon\, \Delta x$$

In this section, we shall obtain a similar formula for the increment of a function of more than one variable. We shall give the details for a function of two variables. We need to make use of the following theorem, which is the mean-value theorem for a function of a single variable applied to a function of two variables.

22.6.1 THEOREM   Let f be a function of two variables defined for all x in the closed interval $[a,b]$ and all y in the closed interval $[c,d]$. Suppose $D_1 f(x,y_0)$ exists for some y_0 in $[c,d]$ and for all x in $[a,b]$. Then there is a number ξ_1 in the open interval (a,b) such that

(2) $$f(b,y_0) - f(a,y_0) = (b - a)\, D_1(\xi_1,y_0)$$

Proof: Let g be the function of one variable x defined by

$$g(x) = f(x,y_0)$$
$$\text{Then} \quad g'(x) = D_1 f(x,y_0)$$

Since $D_1 f(x,y_0)$ exists for all x in $[a,b]$, it follows that $g'(x)$ exists for all x in $[a,b]$, and therefore g is continuous on $[a,b]$. So, by the mean-value theorem (8.5.1) for ordinary derivatives, there exists a number ξ_1 in (a,b) such that

$$g'(\xi_1) = \frac{g(b) - g(a)}{b - a}$$

or, equivalently,

$$D_1 f(\xi_1,y_0) = \frac{f(b,y_0) - f(a,y_0)}{b - a}$$

from which we obtain

$$f(b,y_0) - f(a,y_0) = (b - a)\, D_1 f(\xi_1,y_0) \qquad \text{Q.E.D.}$$

Equation (2) may be written in the form

(3) $$f(x_0 + h,\, y_0) - f(x_0,y_0) = h\, D_1 f(\xi_1,y_0)$$

where ξ_1 is between x_0 and $x_0 + h$ and h is either positive or negative (see Exercise 2 at the end of this section).

The following theorem is analogous to Theorem 22.6.1.

22.6.2 THEOREM   Let f be a function of two variables defined for all x in the closed interval $[a,b]$ and all y in the closed interval $[c,d]$. Suppose $D_2f(x_0,y)$ exists for some x_0 in $[a,b]$ and for all y in $[c,d]$. Then there is a number ξ_2 in the open interval (c,d) such that

(4) $$f(x_0,d) - f(x_0,c) = (d - c)\,D_2f(x_0,\xi_2)$$

The proof is similar to the proof of Theorem 22.6.1 and is left for the reader (see Exercise 1 at the end of this section).

Equation (4) may be written in the form

(5) $$f(x_0,\,y_0 + k) - f(x_0,y_0) = k\,D_2f(x_0,\xi_2)$$

where ξ_2 is between y_0 and $y_0 + k$ and k is either positive or negative (see Exercise 3 at the end of this section).

EXAMPLE 1:   *Given:* $f(x,y) = 2xy/(3 + x)$. *Find:* a ξ_1 required by Theorem 22.6.1 if x is in $[2,5]$ and $y = 4$.

Solution: By Theorem 22.6.1, there is a number ξ_1 in the open interval $(2,5)$ such that

$$f(5,4) - f(2,4) = (5 - 2)\,D_1f(\xi_1,4)$$

So,
$$5 - \frac{16}{5} = 3 \cdot \frac{24}{(3 + \xi_1)^2}$$

or
$$\frac{9}{5} = \frac{72}{(3 + \xi_1)^2}$$

or
$$(3 + \xi_1)^2 = 40$$

Therefore,
$$3 + \xi_1 = \pm 2\sqrt{10}$$

But since $2 < \xi_1 < 5$, we take only the "+" sign, and we obtain

$$\xi_1 = 2\sqrt{10} - 3$$

22.6.3 THEOREM   Let f be a function of two variables x and y defined on an open disk $B(P_0;r)$ where P_0 is the point (x_0,y_0). Suppose D_1f and D_2f exist on $B(P_0;r)$ and D_1f and D_2f are continuous at P_0. Furthermore, suppose that the point $(x_0 + \Delta x, y_0 + \Delta y)$ is in $B(P_0;r)$. Then,

(6) $$f(x_0 + \Delta x,\, y_0 + \Delta y) - f(x_0,y_0) = D_1f(x_0,y_0)\,\Delta x + D_2f(x_0,y_0)\,\Delta y$$
$$+ \epsilon_1\,\Delta x + \epsilon_2\,\Delta y$$

where ϵ_1 and ϵ_2 are functions of both Δx and Δy such that $\epsilon_1 \to 0$ and $\epsilon_2 \to 0$ as $(\Delta x, \Delta y) \to (0,0)$.

Proof: Subtracting and adding $f(x_0 + \Delta x,\, y_0)$ to $f(x_0 + \Delta x,\, y_0 + \Delta y) - f(x_0,y_0)$, we get

(7) $$f(x_0 + \Delta x, y_0 + \Delta y) - f(x_0,y_0)$$
$$= [f(x_0 + \Delta x, y_0 + \Delta y) - f(x_0 + \Delta x, y_0)] + [f(x_0 + \Delta x, y_0) - f(x_0,y_0)]$$

Since $D_1 f$ and $D_2 f$ exist on $B(P_0;r)$ and $(x_0 + \Delta x, y_0 + \Delta y)$ is in $B(P_0;r)$, it follows from (5) that

(8) $f(x_0 + \Delta x, y_0 + \Delta y) - f(x_0 + \Delta x, y_0) = (\Delta y) D_2 f(x_0 + \Delta x, \xi_2)$

where ξ_2 is between y_0 and $y_0 + \Delta y$.

From (3) it follows that

(9) $f(x_0 + \Delta x, y_0) - f(x_0, y_0) = (\Delta x) D_1 f(\xi_1, y_0)$

where ξ_1 is between x_0 and $x_0 + \Delta x$.

Substituting from (8) and (9) in (7), we obtain

(10) $f(x_0 + \Delta x, y_0 + \Delta y) - f(x_0, y_0) = (\Delta y) D_2 f(x_0 + \Delta x, \xi_2)$
$$+ (\Delta x) D_1 f(\xi_1, y_0)$$

Since $D_1 f$ and $D_2 f$ are continuous at P_0, $(x_0 + \Delta x, y_0 + \Delta y)$ is in $B(P_0;r)$, and ξ_2 is between y_0 and $y_0 + \Delta y$, it follows that

(11) $\lim_{(\Delta x, \Delta y) \to (0,0)} D_2 f(x_0 + \Delta x, \xi_2) = D_2 f(x_0, y_0)$

and, since ξ_1 is between x_0 and $x_0 + \Delta x$, it follows that

(12) $\lim_{(\Delta x, \Delta y) \to (0,0)} D_1 f(\xi_1, y_0) = D_1 f(x_0, y_0)$

Letting

(13) $D_1 f(\xi_1, y_0) = D_1 f(x_0, y_0) + \epsilon_1$

it follows from (12) that $\epsilon_1 \to 0$ as $(\Delta x, \Delta y) \to (0,0)$. Letting

(14) $D_2 f(x_0 + \Delta x, \xi_2) = D_2 f(x_0, y_0) + \epsilon_2$

it follows from (11) that $\epsilon_2 \to 0$ as $(\Delta x, \Delta y) \to (0,0)$. Substituting from (13) and (14) into (10), we get

$$f(x_0 + \Delta x, y_0 + \Delta y) - f(x_0, y_0) = \Delta y [D_2 f(x_0, y_0) + \epsilon_2]$$
$$+ \Delta x [D_1 f(x_0, y_0) + \epsilon_1]$$

from which we obtain

$$f(x_0 + \Delta x, y_0 + \Delta y) - f(x_0, y_0) = D_1 f(x_0, y_0) \Delta x + D_2 f(x_0, y_0) \Delta y$$
$$+ \epsilon_1 \Delta x + \epsilon_2 \Delta y$$

which is (6), and so the theorem is proved.

The expression on the left-hand side of (6) is called the *increment* of the function f at the point (x_0, y_0) and is denoted by $\Delta f(x_0, y_0)$. So, we have

(15) $\Delta f(x_0, y_0) = f(x_0 + \Delta x, y_0 + \Delta y) - f(x_0, y_0)$

22.6.4 DEFINITION   If f is a function of two variables x and y and the increment of f at (x_0, y_0) can be written as

(16) $\Delta f(x_0, y_0) = D_1 f(x_0, y_0) \Delta x + D_2 f(x_0, y_0) \Delta y + \epsilon_1 \Delta x + \epsilon_2 \Delta y,$

where $\epsilon_1 \to 0$ and $\epsilon_2 \to 0$ as $(\Delta x, \Delta y) \to (0,0)$, then f is said to be *differentiable* at (x_0, y_0).

EXAMPLE 2: *Given:* $f(x,y) = 3x - xy^2$. *(a) Find:* $\Delta f(x_0,y_0)$; *(b) find:* an ϵ_1 and an ϵ_2 so that equation (16) holds; *(c) show:* the ϵ_1 and the ϵ_2 found in *(b)* both approach zero as $(\Delta x, \Delta y) \to (0,0)$.

Solution:

$$\Delta f(x_0,y_0) = f(x_0 + \Delta x, y_0 + \Delta y) - f(x_0,y_0)$$

$$= 3(x_0 + \Delta x) - (x_0 + \Delta x)(y_0 + \Delta y)^2 - (3x_0 - x_0 y_0^2)$$

$$= 3\,\Delta x - 2x_0 y_0\,\Delta y - x_0\,(\Delta y)^2 - y_0^2\,\Delta x - 2y_0\,\Delta x\,\Delta y - \Delta x (\Delta y)^2$$

$$D_1 f(x_0,y_0) = 3 - y_0^2 \quad \text{and} \quad D_2 f(x_0,y_0) = -2x_0 y_0$$

Therefore,

$$\Delta f(x_0,y_0) - D_1 f(x_0,y_0)\,\Delta x - D_2 f(x_0,y_0)\,\Delta y$$
$$= -x_0\,(\Delta y)^2 - 2y_0\,\Delta x\,\Delta y - \Delta x\,(\Delta y)^2$$

The right-hand side of the above may be written in the following ways:

$$[-2y_0\,\Delta y - (\Delta y)^2]\,\Delta x + (-x_0\,\Delta y)\,\Delta y$$

or $\quad (-2y_0\,\Delta y)\,\Delta x + (-\Delta x\,\Delta y - x_0\,\Delta y)\,\Delta y$

or $\quad [-(\Delta y)^2]\,\Delta x + (-2y_0\,\Delta x - x_0\,\Delta y)\,\Delta y$

or $\quad 0 \cdot \Delta x + [-2y_0\,\Delta x - \Delta x\,\Delta y - x_0\,\Delta y]\,\Delta y$

So, we have four possible pairs of values for ϵ_1 and ϵ_2:

$$\epsilon_1 = -2y_0\,\Delta y - (\Delta y)^2 \quad \text{and} \quad \epsilon_2 = -x_0\,\Delta y$$

or $\quad \epsilon_1 = -2y_0\,\Delta y \quad \text{and} \quad \epsilon_2 = -\Delta x\,\Delta y - x_0\,\Delta y$

or $\quad \epsilon_1 = -(\Delta y)^2 \quad \text{and} \quad \epsilon_2 = -2y_0\,\Delta x - x_0\,\Delta y$

or $\quad \epsilon_1 = 0 \quad \text{and} \quad \epsilon_2 = -2y_0\,\Delta x - \Delta x\,\Delta y - x_0\,\Delta y$

For each pair, we see that $\epsilon_1 \to 0$ and $\epsilon_2 \to 0$ as $(\Delta x, \Delta y) \to (0,0)$.

22.6.5 THEOREM   If a function f of two variables is differentiable at a point, it is continuous at that point.

Proof: If f is differentiable at the point (x_0,y_0), it follows from Definition 22.6.4 that

$$f(x_0 + \Delta x, y_0 + \Delta y) - f(x_0,y_0) = D_1 f(x_0,y_0)\,\Delta x + D_2 f(x_0,y_0)\,\Delta y$$
$$+ \epsilon_1\,\Delta x + \epsilon_2\,\Delta y$$

where $\epsilon_1 \to 0$ and $\epsilon_2 \to 0$ as $(\Delta x, \Delta y) \to (0,0)$. Therefore,

$$f(x_0 + \Delta x, y_0 + \Delta y) = f(x_0,y_0) + D_1 f(x_0,y_0)\,\Delta x + D_2 f(x_0,y_0)\,\Delta y$$
$$+ \epsilon_1\,\Delta x + \epsilon_2\,\Delta y$$

Taking the limit of both sides of the above as $(\Delta x, \Delta y) \to (0,0)$, we obtain

$$(17) \qquad \lim_{(\Delta x, \Delta y) \to (0,0)} f(x_0 + \Delta x, y_0 + \Delta y) = f(x_0,y_0)$$

Letting $x_0 + \Delta x = x$ and $y_0 + \Delta y = y$, "$(\Delta x, \Delta y) \to (0,0)$" is equivalent to "$(x,y) \to (x_0,y_0)$," and so we have from (17)

$$\lim_{(x,y)\to(x_0,y_0)} f(x,y) = f(x_0,y_0)$$

which proves that f is continuous at (x_0,y_0).

Theorem 22.6.5 states that for a function of two variables *differentiability implies continuity*. However, it should be pointed out that the mere existence of the partial derivatives $D_1 f$ and $D_2 f$ at a point does not imply differentiability of the function at that point. We illustrate this by considering the function f defined by

$$f(x,y) = \begin{cases} \dfrac{xy}{x^2 + y^2} & \text{if } (x,y) \neq (0,0) \\ 0 & \text{if } (x,y) = (0,0) \end{cases}$$

$$D_1 f(0,0) = \lim_{x\to 0} \frac{f(x,0) - f(0,0)}{x - 0} = \lim_{x\to 0} \frac{0 - 0}{x} = 0$$

$$D_2 f(0,0) = \lim_{y\to 0} \frac{f(0,y) - f(0,0)}{y - 0} = \lim_{y\to 0} \frac{0 - 0}{y} = 0$$

Therefore, both $D_1 f(0,0)$ and $D_2 f(0,0)$ exist. However, in Example 3, Sec. 22.3, we showed that $\lim\limits_{(x,y)\to(0,0)} f(x,y)$ does not exist, and hence f is not continuous at $(0,0)$. Since f is not continuous at $(0,0)$, by Theorem 22.6.5 we may conclude that f is not differentiable at $(0,0)$. So, even though the existence of a derivative of a function of a single variable at a point implies differentiability and continuity of the function at that point, this does not hold for functions of more than one variable.

22.6.6 DEFINITION   Let f be a function of two variables x and y and P_0 be the point (x_0,y_0). Then if f, $D_1 f$, and $D_2 f$ exist on an open disk $B(P_0;r)$ and $D_1 f$ and $D_2 f$ are continuous at P_0, f is said to be *continuously differentiable* at P_0.

Since the conditions for a function of two variables to be continuously differentiable at a point P_0 are the same as the hypothesis of Theorem 22.6.3, we may conclude that for a function of two variables, *continuous differentiability implies differentiability*.

Suppose now that f is a function of the n variables $x_1, x_2, \ldots, x_n$. Let $\overline{P}$ be the point $(\overline{x}_1, \overline{x}_2, \ldots, \overline{x}_n)$. Then the increment of f at $\overline{P}$ is given by

$$(18) \qquad \Delta f(\overline{P}) = f(\overline{x}_1 + \Delta x_1, \overline{x}_2 + \Delta x_2, \ldots, \overline{x}_n + \Delta x_n) - f(\overline{P})$$

22.6.7 DEFINITION   If f is a function of the n variables $x_1, x_2, \ldots, x_n$, and the increment of f at the point $\overline{P}$ can be written as

$$(19) \qquad \Delta f(\overline{P}) = D_1 f(\overline{P}) \, \Delta x_1 + D_2 f(\overline{P}) \, \Delta x_2 + \cdots + D_n f(\overline{P}) \, \Delta x_n$$
$$+ \epsilon_1 \, \Delta x_1 + \epsilon_2 \, \Delta x_2 + \cdots + \epsilon_n \, \Delta x_n$$

where $\epsilon_1 \to 0$, $\epsilon_2 \to 0$, $\ldots$, $\epsilon_n \to 0$, as $(\Delta x_1, \Delta x_2, \ldots, \Delta x_n) \to (0,0,\ldots,0)$, then f is said to be *differentiable* at $\overline{P}$.

Analogous to Theorem 22.6.3, it can be proved that sufficient conditions for a function of n variables to be differentiable at a point $\overline{P}$ are that f, $D_1 f$, $D_2 f$, $\ldots$, $D_n f$ all exist on an open ball $B(\overline{P};r)$; $D_1 f$, $D_2 f$, $\ldots$, $D_n f$ are continuous at $\overline{P}$; and $(\overline{x}_1 + \Delta x_1, \overline{x}_2 + \Delta x_2, \ldots, \overline{x}_n + \Delta x_n)$ is a point in $B(\overline{P}; r)$. If these conditions are satisfied by a function f at $\overline{P}$, then f is said to be *continuously differentiable* at $\overline{P}$. As was the case for functions of two variables, it follows that for functions of n variables, continuous differentiability implies differentiability, and differentiability implies continuity. However, the existence of the partial derivatives $D_1 f$, $D_2 f$, $\ldots$, $D_n f$ at a point does not imply differentiability of the function at the point.

Exercises 22.6

1. Prove Theorem 22.6.2.

2. Show that equation (2) may be written in the form (3) where ξ_1 is between x_0 and $x_0 + h$.

3. Show that equation (4) may be written in the form (5) where ξ_2 is between y_0 and $y_0 + k$.

In Exercises 4 through 7, find either a ξ_1 required by Theorem 22.6.1 or a ξ_2 required by Theorem 22.6.2, whichever applies.

4. $f(x,y) = x^2 + 3xy - y^2$; x is in $[1,3]$; $y = 4$.

5. $f(x,y) = x^3 - y^2$; x is in $[2,6]$; $y = 3$.

6. $f(x,y) = \dfrac{4x}{x + y}$; y is in $[-2,2]$; $x = 4$.

7. $f(x,y) = \dfrac{2x - y}{2y + x}$; y is in $[0,4]$; $x = 2$.

In Exercises 8 through 11, do each of the following: (a) find $\Delta f(x_0, y_0)$ for the given function; (b) find an ϵ_1 and an ϵ_2 so that equation (16) holds; (c) show that the ϵ_1 and the ϵ_2 found in (b) both approach zero as $(\Delta x, \Delta y) \to (0,0)$.

8. $f(x,y) = 2x^2 + 3y^2$

9. $f(x,y) = x^2 y - 2xy$

10. $f(x,y) = \dfrac{y}{x}$

11. $f(x,y) = \dfrac{x^2}{y}$

12. *Given:* $f(x,y) = \begin{cases} \dfrac{3x^2 y^2}{x^4 + y^4} & \text{if } (x,y) \neq (0,0) \\ 0 & \text{if } (x,y) = (0,0) \end{cases}$

Prove: $D_1 f(0,0)$ and $D_2 f(0,0)$ exist, but f is not differentiable at $(0,0)$.

13. *Given:* $f(x,y) = \begin{cases} x + y - 2 & \text{if } x = 1 \text{ or } y = 1 \\ 2 & \text{if } x \neq 1 \text{ and } y \neq 1 \end{cases}$

   Prove: $D_1 f(1,1)$ and $D_2 f(1,1)$ exist, but f is not differentiable at $(1,1)$.

14. *Given:* $f(x,y) = \begin{cases} \dfrac{3x^2 y}{x^2 + y^2} & \text{if } (x,y) \neq (0,0) \\ 0 & \text{if } (x,y) = (0,0) \end{cases}$

   This function is continuous at $(0,0)$ (see Example 4, Sec. 22.3, and Exercise 3, Sec. 22.4). *Prove:* $D_1 f(0,0)$ and $D_2 f(0,0)$ exist but f is not continuously differentiable at $(0,0)$.

15. *Given:* $f(x,y) = \begin{cases} \dfrac{xy(x^2 - y^2)}{x^2 + y^2} & \text{if } (x,y) \neq (0,0) \\ 0 & \text{if } (x,y) = (0,0) \end{cases}$

   Prove: f is differentiable at $(0,0)$.

16. *Given:* $f(x,y) = \begin{cases} \dfrac{x^2 y^2}{x^2 + y^2} & \text{if } (x,y) \neq (0,0) \\ 0 & \text{if } (x,y) = (0,0) \end{cases}$

   Prove: f is continuously differentiable at $(0,0)$.

In Exercises 17 and 18 do each of the following: (*a*) find $\Delta f(x_0,y_0,z_0)$; (*b*) find the ϵ_1, ϵ_2, and ϵ_3, so that equation (19) holds; (*c*) show that the ϵ_1, ϵ_2, and ϵ_3 found in (*b*) all approach zero as $(\Delta x, \Delta y, \Delta z)$ approaches $(0,0,0)$.

17. $f(x,y,z) = xy - xz + z^2$ 18. $f(x,y,z) = 2x^2 z - 3yz^2$

19. *Given:* $f(x,y,z) = \begin{cases} \dfrac{xy^2 z}{x^4 + y^4 + z^4} & \text{if } (x,y,z) \neq (0,0,0) \\ 0 & \text{if } (x,y,z) = (0,0,0) \end{cases}$

   (*a*) Show that $D_1 f(0,0,0)$, $D_2 f(0,0,0)$, and $D_3 f(0,0,0)$ exist; (*b*) make use of the fact that differentiability implies continuity to prove that f is not differentiable at $(0,0,0)$.

20. *Given:* $f(x,y,z) = \begin{cases} \dfrac{xyz^2}{x^2 + y^2 + z^2} & \text{if } (x,y,z) \neq (0,0,0) \\ 0 & \text{if } (x,y,z) = (0,0,0) \end{cases}$

   Prove: f is differentiable at $(0,0,0)$.

21. *Given:* $f(x,y,z) = \begin{cases} \dfrac{x^2 y^2 z^2}{(x^2 + y^2 + z^2)^2} & \text{if } (x,y,z) \neq (0,0,0) \\ 0 & \text{if } (x,y,z) = (0,0,0) \end{cases}$

   Prove: f is continuously differentiable at $(0,0,0)$.

(22.7) The chain rule

In Sec. 7.2 we had the following chain rule (Theorem 7.2.1) for functions of a single variable: If y is a function of u, defined by $y = f(u)$, and $D_u y$ exists; and u is a function of x, defined by $u = g(x)$, and $D_x u$ exists; then y is a function of x, and $D_x y$ exists and is given by

$$D_x y = D_u y \, D_x u$$

or, equivalently,

$$(1) \qquad \frac{dy}{dx} = \frac{dy}{du} \frac{du}{dx}$$

We shall now consider the chain rule for a function of two variables, where each of these variables is also a function of two variables.

22.7.1 THEOREM (*The Chain Rule*)   If u is a differentiable function of x and y, defined by $u = f(x,y)$, and $x = F(r,s)$, and $y = G(r,s)$, and $\partial x/\partial r$, $\partial x/\partial s$, $\partial y/\partial r$, and $\partial y/\partial s$ all exist, then u is a function of r and s and

$$(2) \qquad \frac{\partial u}{\partial r} = \left(\frac{\partial u}{\partial x}\right)\left(\frac{\partial x}{\partial r}\right) + \left(\frac{\partial u}{\partial y}\right)\left(\frac{\partial y}{\partial r}\right)$$

$$(3) \qquad \frac{\partial u}{\partial s} = \left(\frac{\partial u}{\partial x}\right)\left(\frac{\partial x}{\partial s}\right) + \left(\frac{\partial u}{\partial y}\right)\left(\frac{\partial y}{\partial s}\right)$$

Proof: We shall prove (2). The proof of (3) is similar and is left for the reader (see Exercise 1 at the end of this section).

If s is held fixed and r is changed by an amount Δr, then x is changed by an amount Δx and y is changed by an amount Δy. So we have

$$\Delta x = F(r + \Delta r, s) - F(r,s)$$

$$\text{and} \qquad \Delta y = G(r + \Delta r, s) - G(r,s)$$

Since f is differentiable,

$$(4) \qquad \Delta f(x,y) = D_1 f(x,y)\, \Delta x + D_2 f(x,y)\, \Delta y + \epsilon_1\, \Delta x + \epsilon_2\, \Delta y$$

where ϵ_1 and ϵ_2 both approach zero as $(\Delta x, \Delta y)$ approaches $(0,0)$. Furthermore, we require that $\epsilon_1 = 0$ and $\epsilon_2 = 0$ when $\Delta x = \Delta y = 0$. We make this requirement so that ϵ_1 and ϵ_2, which are functions of Δx and Δy, will be defined as continuous at $(\Delta x, \Delta y) = (0,0)$.

If in (4) we replace $\Delta f(x,y)$ by Δu, $D_1 f(x,y)$ by $\partial u/\partial x$, and $D_2 f(x,y)$ by $\partial u/\partial y$ and divide both sides by $\Delta r (\Delta r \neq 0)$, we obtain

$$\frac{\Delta u}{\Delta r} = \frac{\partial u}{\partial x}\frac{\Delta x}{\Delta r} + \frac{\partial u}{\partial y}\frac{\Delta y}{\Delta r} + \epsilon_1 \frac{\Delta x}{\Delta r} + \epsilon_2 \frac{\Delta y}{\Delta r}$$

Taking the limit of both sides of the above as Δr approaches zero, we get

$$(5) \quad \lim_{\Delta r \to 0} \frac{\Delta u}{\Delta r} = \left(\frac{\partial u}{\partial x}\right) \lim_{\Delta r \to 0} \frac{\Delta x}{\Delta r} + \left(\frac{\partial u}{\partial y}\right) \lim_{\Delta r \to 0} \frac{\Delta y}{\Delta r} + \left(\lim_{\Delta r \to 0} \epsilon_1\right) \lim_{\Delta r \to 0} \frac{\Delta x}{\Delta r}$$

$$+ \left(\lim_{\Delta r \to 0} \epsilon_2\right) \lim_{\Delta r \to 0} \frac{\Delta y}{\Delta r}$$

Since u is a function of x and y and both x and y are functions of r and s, u is a function of r and s. Since s is held fixed and r is changed by an amount Δr, we have

(6)
$$\lim_{\Delta r \to 0} \frac{\Delta u}{\Delta r} = \lim_{\Delta r \to 0} \frac{u(r + \Delta r, s) - u(r,s)}{\Delta r} = \frac{\partial u}{\partial r}$$

Also,

(7)
$$\lim_{\Delta r \to 0} \frac{\Delta x}{\Delta r} = \lim_{\Delta r \to 0} \frac{F(r + \Delta r, s) - F(r,s)}{\Delta r} = \frac{\partial x}{\partial r}$$

and

(8)
$$\lim_{\Delta r \to 0} \frac{\Delta y}{\Delta r} = \lim_{\Delta r \to 0} \frac{G(r + \Delta r,s) - G(r,s)}{\Delta r} = \frac{\partial y}{\partial r}$$

Since $\partial x/\partial r$ and $\partial y/\partial r$ exist, F and G are each continuous with respect to the variable r. (NOTE: The existence of the partial derivatives of a function does not imply continuity with respect to all of the variables simultaneously, as we saw in the previous section, but as with functions of a single variable it does imply continuity of the function with respect to each variable separately.) Therefore as Δr approaches zero, both Δx and Δy approach zero. Since ϵ_1 approaches zero and ϵ_2 approaches zero as $(\Delta x, \Delta y)$ approaches $(0,0)$, we may conclude that

(9)
$$\lim_{\Delta r \to 0} \epsilon_1 = 0 \qquad \text{and} \qquad \lim_{\Delta r \to 0} \epsilon_2 = 0$$

If, for certain Δr, $\Delta x = \Delta y = 0$, then since we required that $\epsilon_1 = 0$ and $\epsilon_2 = 0$ in such a case, the limits in (9) are still zero.

Substituting (6), (7), (8), and (9) into (5), we obtain

$$\frac{\partial u}{\partial r} = \left(\frac{\partial u}{\partial x}\right)\left(\frac{\partial x}{\partial r}\right) + \left(\frac{\partial u}{\partial y}\right)\left(\frac{\partial y}{\partial r}\right)$$

which proves (2).

EXAMPLE 1: *Given:* $u = \ln \sqrt{x^2 + y^2}$; $x = re^s$; $y = re^{-s}$. *Find:* $\partial u/\partial r$ and $\partial u/\partial s$.

Solution:

$$\frac{\partial u}{\partial x} = \frac{x}{x^2 + y^2} \qquad \frac{\partial u}{\partial y} = \frac{y}{x^2 + y^2} \qquad \frac{\partial x}{\partial r} = e^s$$

$$\frac{\partial x}{\partial s} = re^s \qquad \frac{\partial y}{\partial r} = e^{-s} \qquad \frac{\partial y}{\partial s} = -re^{-s}$$

From (2) we get

$$\frac{\partial u}{\partial r} = \frac{x}{x^2 + y^2}\,(e^s) + \frac{y}{x^2 + y^2}\,(e^{-s}) = \frac{xe^s + ye^{-s}}{x^2 + y^2}$$

From (3) we get

$$\frac{\partial u}{\partial s} = \frac{x}{x^2 + y^2}\,(re^s) + \frac{y}{x^2 + y^2}\,(-re^{-s}) = \frac{r(xe^s - ye^{-s})}{x^2 + y^2}$$

As we mentioned earlier the symbols $\partial u/\partial r$, $\partial u/\partial s$, $\partial u/\partial x$, $\partial u/\partial y$, and so forth *must not* be considered as fractions. The symbols ∂u, ∂x, etc. have no meaning by themselves. For functions of one variable, the chain rule, given by equation (1), is easily remembered by thinking of an ordinary derivative as the quotient of two differentials. There is no similar interpretation for partial derivatives. Another troublesome notational problem arises when considering u as a function of x and y and then as a function of r and s. If $u = f(x,y)$, $x = F(r,s)$, and $y = G(r,s)$, then $u = f(F(r,s), G(r,s))$. [NOTE: It is incorrect to write $u = f(r,s)$]. If we let $f(F(r,s), G(r,s)) = h(r,s)$, then equations (2) and (3) may be written as

$$h_1(r,s) = f_1(x,y)F_1(r,s) + f_2(x,y)G_1(r,s)$$

and

$$h_2(r,s) = f_1(x,y)F_2(r,s) + f_2(x,y)G_2(r,s)$$

respectively.

In Theorem 22.7.1, the independent variables are r and s, and u is the dependent variable. The variables x and y may be called the *intermediate variables*. We now extend the chain rule to n intermediate variables and m independent variables.

22.7.2 THEOREM (*The General Chain Rule*)   Suppose u is a differentiable function of the n variables $x_1, x_2, \ldots, x_n$ and each of these variables is in turn a function of the m variables $y_1, y_2, \ldots, y_m$. Suppose further that each of the partial derivatives $\partial x_i/\partial y_j$ ($i = 1, 2, \ldots, n; j = 1, 2, \ldots, m$) exist. Then u is a function of $y_1, y_2, \ldots, y_m$, and

$$\frac{\partial u}{\partial y_1} = \left(\frac{\partial u}{\partial x_1}\right)\left(\frac{\partial x_1}{\partial y_1}\right) + \left(\frac{\partial u}{\partial x_2}\right)\left(\frac{\partial x_2}{\partial y_1}\right) + \cdots + \left(\frac{\partial u}{\partial x_n}\right)\left(\frac{\partial x_n}{\partial y_1}\right)$$

$$\frac{\partial u}{\partial y_2} = \left(\frac{\partial u}{\partial x_1}\right)\left(\frac{\partial x_1}{\partial y_2}\right) + \left(\frac{\partial u}{\partial x_2}\right)\left(\frac{\partial x_2}{\partial y_2}\right) + \cdots + \left(\frac{\partial u}{\partial x_n}\right)\left(\frac{\partial x_n}{\partial y_2}\right)$$

$$\cdot \quad \cdot \quad \cdot \quad \cdot \quad \cdot \quad \cdot \quad \cdot \quad \cdot \quad \cdot \quad \cdot \quad \cdot \quad \cdot \quad \cdot \quad \cdot$$

$$\frac{\partial u}{\partial y_m} = \left(\frac{\partial u}{\partial x_1}\right)\left(\frac{\partial x_1}{\partial y_m}\right) + \left(\frac{\partial u}{\partial x_2}\right)\left(\frac{\partial x_2}{\partial y_m}\right) + \cdots + \left(\frac{\partial u}{\partial x_n}\right)\left(\frac{\partial x_n}{\partial y_m}\right)$$

The proof is an extension of the proof of Theorem 22.7.1.

Note that in the general chain rule, there are as many terms on the right-hand side of each equation as there are intermediate variables.

EXAMPLE 2: *Given:* $u = xy + xz + yz$; $x = r$; $y = r \cos t$; $z = r \sin t$. *Find:* $\partial u/\partial r$ and $\partial u/\partial t$.

Solution: By applying the chain rule, we obtain

$$\frac{\partial u}{\partial r} = \left(\frac{\partial u}{\partial x}\right)\left(\frac{\partial x}{\partial r}\right) + \left(\frac{\partial u}{\partial y}\right)\left(\frac{\partial y}{\partial r}\right) + \left(\frac{\partial u}{\partial z}\right)\left(\frac{\partial z}{\partial r}\right)$$

$$= (y + z)(1) + (x + z)(\cos t) + (x + y)(\sin t)$$

$$= y + z + x \cos t + z \cos t + x \sin t + y \sin t$$

$$= r \cos t + r \sin t + r \cos t + (r \sin t)(\cos t) + r \sin t + (r \cos t)(\sin t)$$

$$= 2r (\cos t + \sin t) + r(2 \sin t \cos t)$$

$$= 2r (\cos t + \sin t) + r \sin 2t$$

$$\frac{\partial u}{\partial t} = \left(\frac{\partial u}{\partial x}\right)\left(\frac{\partial x}{\partial t}\right) + \left(\frac{\partial u}{\partial y}\right)\left(\frac{\partial y}{\partial t}\right) + \left(\frac{\partial u}{\partial z}\right)\left(\frac{\partial z}{\partial t}\right)$$

$$= (y + z)(0) + (x + z)(-r \sin t) + (s + y)(r \cos t)$$

$$= (r + r \sin t)(-r \sin t) + (r + r \cos t)(r \cos t)$$

$$= -r^2 \sin t - r^2 \sin^2 t + r^2 \cos t + r^2 \cos^2 t$$

$$= r^2 (\cos t - \sin t) + r^2 (\cos^2 t - \sin^2 t)$$

$$= r^2 (\cos t - \sin t) + r^2 \cos 2t$$

Now, suppose that u is a differentiable function of the two variables x and y and both x and y are differentiable functions of the single variable t. Then u is a function of the single variable t, and so instead of the *partial* derivative of u with respect to t, we have the *ordinary* derivative of u with respect to t, which is given by

(10)
$$\frac{du}{dt} = \left(\frac{\partial u}{\partial x}\right)\left(\frac{dx}{dt}\right) + \left(\frac{\partial u}{\partial y}\right)\left(\frac{dy}{dt}\right)$$

We call du/dt given by equation (10) the *total derivative* of u with respect to t. If u is a differentiable function of the n variables $x_1, x_2, \ldots, x_n$ and each x_i is a differentiable function of the single variable t, then u is a function of t and the total derivative of u with respect to t is given by

$$\frac{du}{dt} = \left(\frac{\partial u}{\partial x_1}\right)\left(\frac{dx_1}{dt}\right) + \left(\frac{\partial u}{\partial x_2}\right)\left(\frac{dx_2}{dt}\right) + \cdots + \left(\frac{\partial u}{\partial x_n}\right)\left(\frac{dx_n}{dt}\right)$$

EXAMPLE 3: *Given:* $u = x^2 + 2xy + y^2$; $x = t \cos t$; $y = t \sin t$. *Find:* du/dt by two methods: (a) using the chain rule; (b) expressing u in terms of t before differentiating.

Solution: (a) $\partial u/\partial x = 2x + 2y$; $\partial u/\partial y = 2x + 2y$; $dx/dt = \cos t - t \sin t$; $dy/dt = \sin t + t \cos t$. So, from (10) we have

$$\frac{du}{dt} = (2x + 2y)(\cos t - t \sin t) + (2x + 2y)(\sin t + t \cos t)$$

$$= 2(x + y)(\cos t - t \sin t + \sin t + t \cos t)$$

$$= 2(t \cos t + t \sin t)(\cos t - t \sin t + \sin t + t \cos t)$$

$$= 2t (\cos^2 t - t \sin t \cos t + \sin t \cos t + t \cos^2 t + \sin t \cos t$$
$$\qquad\qquad\qquad - t \sin^2 t + \sin^2 t + t \sin t \cos t)$$

$$= 2t[1 + 2 \sin t \cos t + t (\cos^2 t - \sin^2 t)]$$

$$= 2t(1 + \sin 2t + t \cos 2t)$$

(b)
$$u = (t \cos t)^2 + 2(t \cos t)(t \sin t) + (t \sin t)^2$$

$$= t^2 \cos^2 t + t^2(2 \sin t \cos t) + t^2 \sin^2 t$$

$$= t^2 + t^2 \sin 2t$$

So, $$\frac{du}{dt} = 2t + 2t \sin 2t + 2t^2 \cos 2t$$

EXAMPLE 4: If f is a differentiable function and a and b are constants, prove that $z = f((b/2)x^2 - (a/3)y^3)$ satisfies the equation

$$ay^2 \frac{\partial z}{\partial x} + bx \frac{\partial z}{\partial y} = 0$$

Solution: Let $u = (b/2)x^2 - (a/3)y^3$. We wish to show that $z = f(u)$ satisfies the given equation. By the chain rule we get

$$\frac{\partial z}{\partial x} = \frac{\partial z}{\partial u} \frac{\partial u}{\partial x} = f'(u)(bx) \qquad \text{and} \qquad \frac{\partial z}{\partial y} = \frac{\partial z}{\partial u} \frac{\partial u}{\partial y} = f'(u)(-ay^2)$$

Therefore,

$$ay^2 \frac{\partial z}{\partial x} + bx \frac{\partial z}{\partial y} = ay^2 \left[f'(u)(bx) \right] + bx \left[f'(u)(-ay^2) \right] = 0$$

which is what we wished to prove.

The following example illustrates the application of the chain rule to a problem involving related rates.

EXAMPLE 5: At a given instant the altitude of a right circular cone is 60 in. and is decreasing at the rate of 5 in./sec, and the radius of the base of the cone is 30 in. and is increasing at the rate of 2 in./sec. At what rate is the volume of the cone changing at this instant?

Solution:

Let t = the number of seconds in the time

Let r = the number of inches in the radius of the base of the cone at t sec

Let h = the number of inches in the altitude of the cone at t sec

Let V = the number of cubic inches in the volume of the cone at t sec

$$V = \frac{1}{3}\pi r^2 h$$

At the given instant, $r = 30$, $h = 60$, $dr/dt = 2$, and $dh/dt = -5$. Using the chain rule, we obtain

$$\frac{dV}{dt} = \frac{\partial V}{\partial r} \frac{dr}{dt} + \frac{\partial V}{\partial h} \frac{dh}{dt} = \frac{2}{3}\pi r h \frac{dr}{dt} + \frac{1}{3}\pi r^2 \frac{dh}{dt}$$

So at the given instant

$$\frac{dV}{dt} = \frac{2}{3}\pi(1,800)(2) + \frac{1}{3}\pi(900)(-5) = 900\pi$$

Therefore the volume is increasing at the rate of 900π in.^{3}/sec at the given instant.

Exercises 22.7

In Exercises 1 through 4, find the indicated partial derivative by two methods: (*a*) use the chain rule; (*b*) make the substitutions for x and y before differentiating.

1. $u = x^2 - y^2$; $x = 3r - s$; $y = r + 2s$; $\dfrac{\partial u}{\partial r}$; $\dfrac{\partial u}{\partial s}$

2. $u = 3x^2 + xy - 2y^2 + 3x - y$; $x = 2r - 3s$; $y = r + s$; $\dfrac{\partial u}{\partial r}$; $\dfrac{\partial u}{\partial s}$

3. $u = e^{y/x}$; $x = r \cos t$; $y = r \sin t$; $\dfrac{\partial u}{\partial r}$; $\dfrac{\partial u}{\partial t}$

4. $u = x^2 + y^2$; $x = \cosh r \cos t$; $y = \sinh r \sin t$; $\dfrac{\partial u}{\partial r}$; $\dfrac{\partial u}{\partial t}$

In Exercises 5 through 10, find the indicated partial derivative by using the chain rule.

5. $u = \sin^{-1}(3x + y)$; $x = r^2 e^s$; $y = \sin rs$; $\dfrac{\partial u}{\partial r}$; $\dfrac{\partial u}{\partial s}$

6. $u = xe^{-y}$; $x = \tan^{-1}(rst)$; $y = \ln(rs + st)$; $\dfrac{\partial u}{\partial r}$; $\dfrac{\partial u}{\partial s}$; $\dfrac{\partial u}{\partial t}$

7. $u = \cosh \dfrac{y}{x}$; $x = r^2 s$; $y = se^r$; $\dfrac{\partial u}{\partial r}$; $\dfrac{\partial u}{\partial s}$

8. $u = xy + xz + yz$; $x = rs$; $y = r^2 - s^2$; $z = (r - s)^2$; $\dfrac{\partial u}{\partial r}$; $\dfrac{\partial u}{\partial s}$

9. $u = x^2 + y^2 + z^2$; $x = r \sin \phi \cos \theta$; $y = r \sin \phi \sin \theta$; $z = r \cos \phi$;

$$\dfrac{\partial u}{\partial r}; \dfrac{\partial u}{\partial \phi}; \dfrac{\partial u}{\partial \theta}$$

10. $u = x^2 yz$; $x = \dfrac{r}{s}$; $y = re^s$; $z = re^{-s}$; $\dfrac{\partial u}{\partial r}$; $\dfrac{\partial u}{\partial s}$

In Exercises 11 through 14, find the total derivative du/dt by two methods: (*a*) use the chain rule; (*b*) make the substitutions for x and y or for x, y, and z before differentiating.

11. $u = ye^x + xe^y$; $x = \cos t$; $y = \sin t$

12. $u = \ln xy + y^2$; $x = e^t$; $y = e^{-t}$

13. $u = \sqrt{x^2 + y^2 + z^2}$; $x = \tan t$; $y = \cos t$; $z = \sin t$; $0 < t < \dfrac{\pi}{2}$

14. $u = \dfrac{t + e^x}{y - e^t}$; $x = 3 \sin t$; $y = \ln t$

In Exercises 15 through 18, find the total derivative du/dt by using the chain rule; do not express u as a function of t before differentiating.

15. $u = \tan^{-1}(y/x)$; $x = \ln t$; $y = e^t$

16. $u = xy + xz + yz$; $x = t \cos t$; $y = t \sin t$; $z = t$

17. $u = \dfrac{x+t}{y+t}$; $x = \ln t$; $y = \ln \dfrac{1}{t}$

18. $u = \ln(x^2 + y^2 + t^2)$; $x = t \sin t$; $y = \cos t$

19. If f is a differentiable function of the variable u, let $u = bx - ay$ and prove that $z = f(bx - ay)$ satisfies the equation $a(\partial z/\partial x) + b(\partial z/\partial y) = 0$, where a and b are constants.

20. If f is a differentiable function of the variable u, let $u = x^2 + y^2$ and prove that $z = xy + f(x^2 + y^2)$ satisfies the equation $y(\partial z/\partial x) - x(\partial z/\partial y) = y^2 - x^2$.

21. If f is a differentiable function of two variables u and v, let $u = x - y$ and $v = y - x$ and prove that $z = f(x - y, y - x)$ satisfies the equation $\partial z/\partial x + \partial z/\partial y = 0$.

22. If f is a differentiable function of x and y and $u = f(x,y)$, $x = r \cos \theta$, and $y = r \sin \theta$, show that

$$\frac{\partial u}{\partial x} = \frac{\partial u}{\partial r} \cos \theta - \frac{\partial u}{\partial \theta} \frac{\sin \theta}{r}$$

$$\frac{\partial u}{\partial y} = \frac{\partial u}{\partial r} \sin \theta + \frac{\partial u}{\partial \theta} \frac{\cos \theta}{r}$$

23. If f is a differentiable function of x and y and $u = f(x,y)$, $x = r \cos \theta$, and $y = r \sin \theta$, show that

$$\left(\frac{\partial u}{\partial r}\right)^2 + \frac{1}{r^2}\left(\frac{\partial u}{\partial \theta}\right)^2 = \left(\frac{\partial u}{\partial x}\right)^2 + \left(\frac{\partial u}{\partial y}\right)^2$$

24. If f and g are differentiable functions of x and y and $u = f(x,y)$ and $v = g(x,y)$, such that $\partial u/\partial x = \partial v/\partial y$ and $\partial u/\partial y = -\partial v/\partial x$, then if $x = r \cos \theta$ and $y = r \sin \theta$, show that

$$\frac{\partial u}{\partial r} = \frac{1}{r}\frac{\partial v}{\partial \theta} \quad \text{and} \quad \frac{\partial y}{\partial r} = -\frac{1}{r}\frac{\partial u}{\partial \theta}$$

25. Suppose f is a differentiable function of x and y and $u = f(x,y)$. Then if $x = \cosh v \cos w$ and $y = \sinh v \sin w$, express $\partial u/\partial v$ and $\partial u/\partial w$ in terms of $\partial u/\partial x$ and $\partial u/\partial y$.

26. Suppose f is a differentiable function of x, y, and z and $u = f(x,y,z)$. Then if $x = r \sin \phi \cos \theta$, $y = r \sin \phi \sin \theta$, and $z = r \cos \phi$, express $\partial u/\partial r$, $\partial u/\partial \phi$, and $\partial u/\partial \theta$ in terms of $\partial u/\partial x$, $\partial u/\partial y$, and $\partial u/\partial z$.

27. At a given instant, the length of one leg of a right triangle is 10 ft and it is increasing at the rate of 1 ft/min and the length of the other leg of the right triangle is 12 ft and it is decreasing at the rate of 2 ft/min. Find the rate of change of the acute angle opposite the leg of length 12 ft at the given instant.

28. At a given instant, the length of one side of a rectangle is 6 ft and it is increasing at the rate of 1 ft/sec and the length of another side of the rectangle is 12 ft and it is decreasing at the rate of 2 ft/sec. Find the rate of change of the area of the rectangle at the given instant.

29. Water is flowing into a tank in the form of a right-circular cylinder at the rate of $4\pi/5$ ft^3/min. The tank is stretching in such a way that even though it remains cylindrical, its radius is increasing at the rate of 0.002 ft/min. How fast is the depth of the water rising when the radius is 2 ft and the volume of water in the tank is 20π ft^3?

30. A vertical wall makes an angle of 120° with the ground. A ladder of length 20 ft is leaning against the wall and its top is sliding down the wall at the rate of 3 ft/sec. How fast is the area of the triangle formed by the ladder, the wall, and the ground changing when the ladder makes an angle of 30° with the ground?

(22.8)   Directional derivatives and the gradient

We shall now generalize the definition of a partial derivative to obtain the rate of change of a function with respect to distance in any direction. This leads to the concept of a *directional derivative*.

Let f be a function of the two variables x and y and let $P(x,y)$ be a point in the xy plane. Suppose **U** is the unit vector making an angle of θ with the positive side of the x axis. Then

$$\mathbf{U} = \cos \theta \mathbf{i} + \sin \theta \mathbf{j}$$

Figure 22.8.1 shows the representation of **U** having its initial point at the point $P(x,y)$.

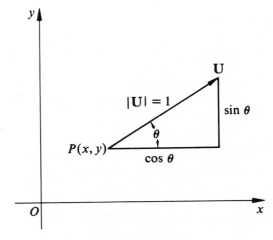

Figure 22.8.1

22.8.1 DEFINITION   Let f be a function of two variables x and y. If $\mathbf{U}$ is the unit vector $\cos \theta \mathbf{i} + \sin \theta \mathbf{j}$, then the *directional derivative* of f in the direction of $\mathbf{U}$, denoted by $D_{\mathbf{U}}f$, is given by

$$D_{\mathbf{U}}f(x,y) = \lim_{h \to 0} \frac{f(x + h \cos \theta, y + h \sin \theta) - f(x,y)}{h}$$

if this limit exists.

The directional derivative gives the rate of change of the function values $f(x,y)$ with respect to distance in the xy plane measured in the direction of the unit vector $\mathbf{U}$. This is illustrated in Fig. 22.8.2. The equation of the surface S in

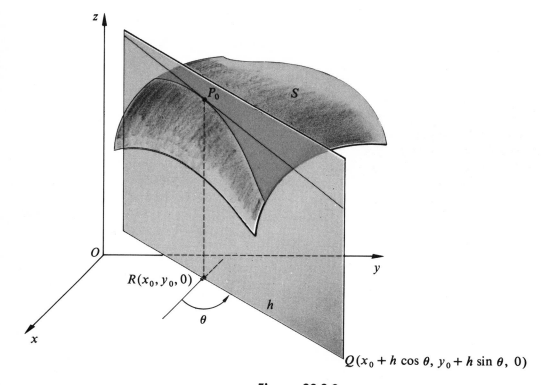

Figure 22.8.2

the figure is $z = f(x,y)$. $P_0(x_0,y_0,z_0)$ is a point on the surface, and the points $R(x_0,y_0,0)$ and $Q(x_0 + h \cos \theta, y_0 + h \sin \theta, 0)$ are points in the xy plane. The plane through R and Q parallel to the z axis makes an angle of θ with the positive direction on the x axis, and this plane intersects the surface S in the curve C. The directional derivative $D_{\mathbf{U}}f$, evaluated at P_0, is the slope of the tangent line to the curve C at P_0 in the plane of R, Q, and P_0.

If $\mathbf{U} = \mathbf{i}$, then $\cos \theta = 1$ and $\sin \theta = 0$, and we have from Definition 22.8.1

$$D_{\mathbf{i}}f(x,y) = \lim_{h \to 0} \frac{f(x + h, y) - f(x,y)}{h},$$

which is the partial derivative of f with respect to x.

If $\mathbf{U} = \mathbf{j}$, then $\cos \theta = 0$ and $\sin \theta = 1$, and we have

$$D_{\mathbf{j}} f(x,y) = \lim_{h \to 0} \frac{f(x, y + h) - f(x,y)}{h}$$

which is the partial derivative of f with respect to y.

So we see that f_x and f_y are special cases of the directional derivative in the directions of the unit vectors $\mathbf{i}$ and $\mathbf{j}$, respectively.

EXAMPLE 1: *Given:* $f(x,y) = 3x^2 - y^2 + 4x$, and $\mathbf{U}$ is the unit vector in the direction $\pi/6$. *Find:* $D_{\mathbf{U}} f$ by applying Definition 22.8.1.

Solution: $\mathbf{U} = \cos(\pi/6)\mathbf{i} + \sin(\pi/6)\mathbf{j} = (\sqrt{3}/2)\mathbf{i} + (1/2)\mathbf{j}$.

So, from 22.8.1 we have

$D_{\mathbf{U}} f(x,y)$

$$= \lim_{h \to 0} \frac{f(x + (\sqrt{3}/2)h, y + (1/2)h) - f(x,y)}{h}$$

$$= \lim_{h \to 0} \frac{3[x + (\sqrt{3}/2)h]^2 - [y + (1/2)h]^2 + 4[x + (\sqrt{3}/2)h] - (3x^2 - y^2 + 4x)}{h}$$

$$= \lim_{h \to 0} \frac{3x^2 + 3\sqrt{3}hx + (9/4)h^2 - y^2 - hy - (1/4)h^2 + 4x + 2\sqrt{3}h - 3x^2 + y^2 - 4x}{h}$$

$$= \lim_{h \to 0} \frac{3\sqrt{3}hx + (9/4)h^2 - hy - (1/4)h^2 + 2\sqrt{3}h}{h}$$

$$= \lim_{h \to 0} [3\sqrt{3}x + (9/4)h - y - (1/4)h + 2\sqrt{3}] = 3\sqrt{3}x - y + 2\sqrt{3}$$

We shall now proceed to obtain a formula which will enable us to calculate a directional derivative in a way that is shorter than if we used the definition. Let g be a function of the single variable t and, keeping x, y, and θ fixed, let

$$(1) \qquad\qquad g(t) = f(x + t \cos \theta, y + t \sin \theta)$$

and $\mathbf{U} = \cos \theta \mathbf{i} + \sin \theta \mathbf{j}$. Then, by the definition of an ordinary derivative, we have

$$g'(0) = \lim_{h \to 0} \frac{f(x + (0 + h)\cos \theta, y + (0 + h)\sin \theta) - f(x + 0 \cos \theta, y + 0 \sin \theta)}{h}$$

or

$$g'(0) = \lim_{h \to 0} \frac{f(x + h \cos \theta, y + h \sin \theta) - f(x,y)}{h}$$

Since the right-hand side of the above is $D_{\mathbf{U}} f(x,y)$, we have

$$(2) \qquad\qquad g'(0) = D_{\mathbf{U}} f(x,y)$$

We shall now find $g'(t)$ by applying the chain rule to the right-hand side of (1). We get

$$g'(t) = f_1(x + t \cos \theta, y + t \sin \theta) \frac{\partial(x + t \cos \theta)}{\partial t} + f_2(x + t \cos \theta, y + t \sin \theta) \frac{\partial(y + t \sin \theta)}{\partial t}$$

$$= f_1(x + t \cos \theta, y + t \sin \theta) \cos \theta + f_2(x + t \cos \theta, y + t \sin \theta) \sin \theta$$

Therefore,

(3) $$g'(0) = f_x(x,y) \cos \theta + f_y(x,y) \sin \theta$$

From (2) and (3) we obtain the following theorem.

22.8.2 THEOREM   If f is a differentiable function of x and y, and $\mathbf{U} = \cos \theta \mathbf{i} + \sin \theta \mathbf{j}$, then

$$D_{\mathbf{U}} f(x,y) = f_x(x,y) \cos \theta + f_y(x,y) \sin \theta$$

EXAMPLE 2: For the function f and the unit vector $\mathbf{U}$ of Example 1, find $D_{\mathbf{U}} f$ by Theorem 22.8.2.

Solution: Since $f(x,y) = 3x^2 - y^2 + 4x$, $f_x(x,y) = 6x + 4$ and $f_y(x,y) = -2y$. Since $\mathbf{U} = \cos(\pi/6)\mathbf{i} + \sin(\pi/6)\mathbf{j}$, we have from Theorem 22.8.2

$$D_{\mathbf{U}} f(x,y) = (6x+4)\frac{\sqrt{3}}{2} + (-2y)\frac{1}{2} = 3\sqrt{3}x + 2\sqrt{3} - y$$

which agrees with the answer in Example 1.

The directional derivative may be written as the dot product of two vectors. Since

$$f_x(x,y) \cos \theta + f_y(x,y) \sin \theta = (\cos \theta \mathbf{i} + \sin \theta \mathbf{j}) \cdot [f_x(x,y)\mathbf{i} + f_y(x,y)\mathbf{j}]$$

we have from Theorem 22.8.2

(4) $$D_{\mathbf{U}} f(x,y) = (\cos \theta \mathbf{i} + \sin \theta \mathbf{j}) \cdot [f_x(x,y)\mathbf{i} + f_y(x,y)\mathbf{j}]$$

The second vector on the right-hand side of (4) is a very important one, and it is called the *gradient vector* of the function f. The symbol which we shall use for the gradient vector of f is ∇f, where ∇ is an inverted capital delta and is read "del." Sometimes the symbol *grad f* is used.

22.8.3 DEFINITION   If f is a function of two variables x and y and f_x and f_y exist, then the *gradient vector* of f, denoted by ∇f (read: "del f"), is defined by

$$\nabla f(x,y) = f_x(x,y)\mathbf{i} + f_y(x,y)\mathbf{j}$$

Therefore, we may write (4) as

(5) $$D_{\mathbf{U}} f(x,y) = \mathbf{U} \cdot \nabla f(x,y)$$

If α is the angle between the two vectors $\mathbf{U}$ and ∇f, then

(6) $$\mathbf{U} \cdot \nabla f = |\mathbf{U}| \, |\nabla f| \cos \alpha$$

From (5) and (6) it follows that

(7) $$D_{\mathbf{U}} f = |\mathbf{U}| \, |\nabla f| \cos \alpha$$

We see from (7) that $D_{\mathbf{U}} f$ will be a maximum when $\cos \alpha = 1$, or when $\mathbf{U}$ is in the direction of ∇f, and in this case, $D_{\mathbf{U}} f = |\nabla f|$.

EXAMPLE 3: *Given:* $f(x,y) = 2x^2 - y^2 + 3x - y$. *Find:* the maximum value of $D_U f$ at the point where $x = 1$ and $y = -2$.

Solution: $f_x(x,y) = 4x + 3$ and $f_y(x,y) = -2y - 1$. So,

$$\nabla f(x,y) = (4x + 3)\mathbf{i} + (-2y - 1)\mathbf{j}$$

Therefore, $\nabla f(1,-2) = 7\mathbf{i} + 3\mathbf{j}$

So, the maximum value of $D_U f$ at the point $(2,-1)$ is

$$|\nabla f(1,-2)| = \sqrt{49 + 9} = \sqrt{58}$$

We extend the definition of a directional derivative to a function of three variables. In E^3 the direction of a vector is determined by its direction cosines. So we shall let $\cos \alpha$, $\cos \beta$, and $\cos \gamma$ be the direction cosines of the unit vector $\mathbf{U}$; therefore, $\mathbf{U} = \cos \alpha \mathbf{i} + \cos \beta \mathbf{j} + \cos \gamma \mathbf{k}$.

22.8.4 DEFINITION   Suppose f is a function of three variables x, y, and z. If $\mathbf{U}$ is the unit vector $\cos \alpha \mathbf{i} + \cos \beta \mathbf{j} + \cos \gamma \mathbf{k}$, then the *directional derivative* of f in the direction of $\mathbf{U}$, denoted by $D_U f$, is given by

$$D_U f(x,y,z) = \lim_{h \to 0} \frac{f(x + h \cos \alpha,\ y + h \cos \beta,\ z + h \cos \gamma) - f(x,y,z)}{h}$$

if this limit exists.

The directional derivative of a function of three variables gives the rate of change of the function values $f(x,y,z)$ with respect to distance in three-dimensional space measured in the direction of the unit vector $\mathbf{U}$.

The following theorem, which gives us a method for calculating a directional derivative for a function in E^3, is proved in a manner similar to the proof of Theorem 22.8.2.

22.8.5 THEOREM   If f is a differentiable function of x, y, and z and

$$\mathbf{U} = \cos \alpha\, \mathbf{i} + \cos \beta \mathbf{j} + \cos \gamma \mathbf{k},$$

then

$$D_U f(x,y,z) = f_x(x,y,z) \cos \alpha + f_y(x,y,z) \cos \beta + f_z(x,y,z) \cos \gamma$$

22.8.6 DEFINITION   If f is a function of three variables x, y, and z and the first partial derivatives f_x, f_y, and f_z exist, then the *gradient vector* of f, denoted by ∇f, is defined by

$$\nabla f(x,y,z) = f_x(x,y,z)\mathbf{i} + f_y(x,y,z)\mathbf{j} + f_z(x,y,z)\mathbf{k}$$

Just as for functions of two variables, it follows from Theorem 22.8.5 and Definition 22.8.6 that if $\mathbf{U} = \cos \alpha \mathbf{i} + \cos \beta \mathbf{j} + \cos \gamma \mathbf{k}$, then

(8) $D_U f(x,y,z) = \mathbf{U} \cdot \nabla f(x,y,z)$

Also, the directional derivative is a maximum when $\mathbf{U}$ is in the direction of the gradient vector, and the maximum directional derivative is the magnitude of the gradient vector.

EXAMPLE 4: *Given:* $f(x,y,z) = 3x^2 + xy - 2y^2 - yz + z^2$. *Find:* the rate of change of $f(x,y,z)$ at $(1,-2,-1)$ in the direction of the vector $2\mathbf{i} - 2\mathbf{j} - \mathbf{k}$.

Solution: The unit vector in the direction of $2\mathbf{i} - 2\mathbf{j} - \mathbf{k}$ is given by

$$\mathbf{U} = \frac{2}{3}\mathbf{i} - \frac{2}{3}\mathbf{j} - \frac{1}{3}\mathbf{k}$$

Also,

$$f(x,y,z) = (6x + y)\mathbf{i} + (x - 4y - z)\mathbf{j} + (-y + 2z)\mathbf{k}$$

So, from (8),

$$D_{\mathbf{U}}f(x,y,z) = \frac{2}{3}(6x + y) - \frac{2}{3}(x - 4y - z) - \frac{1}{3}(-y + 2z)$$

Therefore, the rate of change of $f(x,y,z)$ at $(1,-2,-1)$ in the direction of $\mathbf{U}$ is given by

$$D_{\mathbf{U}}f(1,-2,-1) = \frac{2}{3}(4) - \frac{2}{3}(10) - \frac{1}{3}(0) = -4$$

Exercises 22.8

In Exercises 1 through 4, find the directional derivative of the given function in the direction of the given unit vector $\mathbf{U}$ by using either Definition 22.8.1 or Definition 22.8.4, and then verify your result by applying either Theorem 22.8.2 or Theorem 22.8.5, whichever one applies.

1. $f(x,y) = x^2 + y^2$; $\mathbf{U} = \cos\frac{\pi}{4}\mathbf{i} + \sin\frac{\pi}{4}\mathbf{j}$

2. $f(x,y) = \dfrac{1}{x^2 + y^2}$; $\mathbf{U} = \frac{3}{5}\mathbf{i} - \frac{4}{5}\mathbf{j}$

3. $f(x,y,z) = x^2 + y^2 - z^2$; $\mathbf{U} = \cos\frac{\pi}{3}\mathbf{i} + \cos\frac{\pi}{4}\mathbf{j} + \cos\frac{2\pi}{3}\mathbf{k}$

4. $f(x,y,z) = x^2 - xy + yz$; $\mathbf{U} = \frac{3}{7}\mathbf{i} + \frac{2}{7}\mathbf{j} + \frac{6}{7}\mathbf{k}$

In Exercises 5 through 10, find the value of the directional derivative at the particular point P_0 for the given function in the direction of $\mathbf{U}$.

5. $g(x,y) = y^2 \tan^2 x$; $\mathbf{U} = -\dfrac{\sqrt{3}}{2}\mathbf{i} + \frac{1}{2}\mathbf{j}$; $P_0 = \left(\dfrac{\pi}{3}, 2\right)$.

6. $f(x,y) = xe^y$; $\mathbf{U} = \dfrac{1}{2}\mathbf{i} + \dfrac{\sqrt{3}}{2}\mathbf{j}$; $P_0 = (2,0)$.

7. $f(x,y,z) = \cos(xy) + \sin(yz)$; $\mathbf{U} = -\dfrac{1}{3}\mathbf{i} + \frac{2}{3}\mathbf{j} + \frac{2}{3}\mathbf{k}$; $P_0 = (2,0,-3)$.

8. $f(x,y,z) = \ln(x^2 + y^2 + z^2)$; $\mathbf{U} = \dfrac{1}{\sqrt{3}}\mathbf{i} - \dfrac{1}{\sqrt{3}}\mathbf{j} - \dfrac{1}{\sqrt{3}}\mathbf{k}$; $P_0 = (1,3,2)$.

9. $f(x,y) = e^{-3x} \cos 3y$; $\mathbf{U} = \cos\left(-\dfrac{\pi}{12}\right)\mathbf{i} + \sin\left(-\dfrac{\pi}{12}\right)\mathbf{j}$; $P_0 = \left(-\dfrac{\pi}{12}, 0\right)$.

10. $f(x,y,z) = \cos 2x \cos 3y \sinh 4z$; $\mathbf{U} = \dfrac{1}{\sqrt{3}}\mathbf{i} - \dfrac{1}{\sqrt{3}}\mathbf{j} + \dfrac{1}{\sqrt{3}}\mathbf{k}$; $P_0 = \left(\dfrac{\pi}{2}, 0, 0\right)$.

In Exercises 11 through 14, find $D_{\mathbf{U}}f$ at the given point P for which $\mathbf{U}$ is a unit vector in the direction of $\overrightarrow{PQ}$. Also at P find $D_{\mathbf{U}}f$, if $\mathbf{U}$ is a unit vector for which $D_{\mathbf{U}}f$ is a maximum.

11. $f(x,y,z) = x - 2y + z^2$; $P(3,1,-2)$, $Q(10,7,4)$.

12. $f(x,y,z) = x^2 + y^2 - 4xz$; $P(3,1,-2)$, $Q(-6,3,4)$.

13. $f(x,y) = e^x \tan^{-1} y$; $P(0,1)$, $Q(3,5)$.

14. $f(x,y) = e^x \cos y + e^y \sin x$; $P(1,0)$, $Q(-3,3)$.

15. Find the direction from the point $(1,3)$ for which the function values $f(x,y)$, given by $f(x,y) = e^{2y} \tan^{-1}(y/3x)$, are not changing.

16. The temperature T at any point (x,y) of a rectangular plate lying in the xy plane is given by $T = x^2 + y^2$. (*a*) Find the rate of change of the temperature at the point $(3,4)$ in the direction making an angle of $\pi/3$ with the positive x direction; (*b*) find the direction for which the rate of change of the temperature at the point $(-3,1)$ is a maximum.

17. The electric potential V at any point (x,y) of the xy plane is given by $V = e^{-2x} \cos 2y$. (*a*) Find the rate of change of the potential at the point $(0,\pi/4)$ in the direction making an angle of $\pi/6$ with the positive x direction; (*b*) if the electric intensity vector $\mathbf{E}$ is given by $\mathbf{E} = -\nabla V$, find $\mathbf{E}$ at $(0,\pi/4)$.

18. The density ρ at any point (x,y) of a rectangular plate lying in the xy plane is given by $\rho = 1/\sqrt{x^2 + y^2 + 3}$. (*a*) Find the rate of change of the density at the point $(3,2)$ in the direction making an angle of $2\pi/3$ with the positive x direction; (*b*) find the direction for which the rate of change of the density at $(3,2)$ is a maximum.

19. The electric potential V at any point (x,y,z) in three-dimensional space is given by $V = 1/\sqrt{x^2 + y^2 + z^2}$. (*a*) Find the rate of change of the potential at the point $(2,2,-1)$ in the direction of the vector $2\mathbf{i} - 3\mathbf{j} + 6\mathbf{k}$; (*b*) if the electric intensity vector $\mathbf{E}$ is given by $\mathbf{E} = -\nabla V$, find $\mathbf{E}$ at $(2,2,-1)$.

(22.9) Tangent planes and normals to surfaces

Let S be the surface having the equation

(1) $$F(x,y,z) = 0$$

and suppose $P_0(x_0,y_0,z_0)$ is a point on S. Then $F(x_0,y_0,z_0) = 0$. Suppose further that C is a curve on S through P_0 and a set of parametric equations of C is

(2) $$x = f(t) \qquad y = g(t) \qquad z = h(t)$$

Let the value of the parameter t at the point P_0 be t_0. A vector equation of C is

(3) $$\mathbf{R}(t) = f(t)\mathbf{i} + g(t)\mathbf{j} + h(t)\mathbf{k}$$

Since curve C is on surface S, we have, upon substituting (2) in (1),

(4) $$F(f(t),g(t),h(t)) = 0$$

Let $G(t) = F(f(t),g(t),h(t))$. If F_x, F_y, and F_z are continuous and not all zero at P_0, and if $f'(t_0)$, $g'(t_0)$, and $h'(t_0)$ exist, then the total derivative of F with respect to t at P_0 is given by

$$G'(t_0) = F_x(x_0,y_0,z_0)f'(t_0) + F_y(x_0,y_0,z_0)g'(t_0) + F_z(x_0,y_0,z_0)h'(t_0),$$

which may also be written as

$$G'(t_0) = \nabla F(x_0,y_0,z_0) \cdot D_t R(t_0)$$

Since $G'(t) = 0$ for all t under consideration, $G'(t_0) = 0$, and so it follows from the above that

(5) $$\nabla F(x_0,y_0,z_0) \cdot D_t R(t_0) = 0$$

From Sec. 21.8, we know that $D_t R(t_0)$ has the same direction as the unit tangent vector to curve C at P_0. Therefore, from (5) we may conclude that the gradient vector of F at P_0 is orthogonal to the unit tangent vector of every curve C on S through the point P_0. We are led, then, to the following definition.

22.9.1 DEFINITION   A vector which is orthogonal to the unit tangent vector of every curve C through a point P_0 on a surface S is called a *normal vector* to S at P_0.

From this definition and the preceding discussion we have the following theorem.

22.9.2 THEOREM   If an equation of a surface S is $F(x,y,z) = 0$, and F_x, F_y, and F_z are continuous and not all zero at the point $P_0(x_0,y_0,z_0)$ on S, then a normal vector to S at P_0 is $\nabla F(x_0,y_0,z_0)$.

We are now in a position to define the tangent plane to a surface at a point.

22.9.3 DEFINITION   If an equation of a surface S is $F(x,y,z) = 0$, then the *tangent plane* of S at a point $P_0(x_0,y_0,z_0)$ is the plane through P_0 having as a normal vector $\nabla F(x_0,y_0,z_0)$.

An equation of the tangent plane of the above definition is

(6) $$F_x(x_0,y_0,z_0)(x - x_0) + F_y(x_0,y_0,z_0)(y - y_0) + F_z(x_0,y_0,z_0)(z - z_0) = 0$$

Refer to Fig. 22.9.1, which shows the tangent plane to the surface S at P_0 and the representation of the gradient vector having its initial point at P_0.

A vector equation of the tangent plane given by (6) is

(7) $$\nabla F(x_0,y_0,z_0) \cdot [(x - x_0)\mathbf{i} + (y - y_0)\mathbf{j} + (z - z_0)\mathbf{k}] = 0$$

EXAMPLE 1: Find an equation of the tangent plane to the elliptic paraboloid $4x^2 + y^2 - 16z = 0$ at the point $(2,4,2)$.

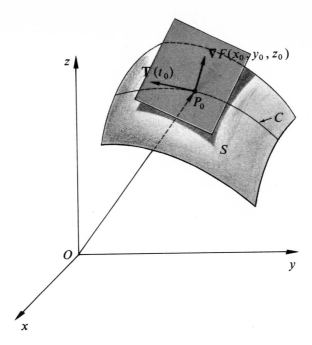

z

$\nabla F(x_0, y_0, z_0)$

$\mathbf{T}(t_0)$

P_0

C

S

O

y

x

Figure 22.9.1

Solution: Let $F(x,y,z) = 4x^2 + y^2 - 16z$. Then $\nabla F(x,y,z) = 8x\mathbf{i} + 2y\mathbf{j} - 16\mathbf{k}$, and so $\nabla F(2,4,2) = 16\mathbf{i} + 8\mathbf{j} - 16\mathbf{k}$. From (7) it follows that an equation of the tangent plane is

$$16(x - 2) + 8(y - 4) - 16(z - 2) = 0$$

or $\qquad\qquad\qquad 2x + y - 2z - 4 = 0$

22.9.4 DEFINITION   The *normal line* to a surface *S* at a point P_0 on *S* is the line through P_0 having as a set of direction numbers the components of any normal vector to *S* at P_0.

If an equation of a surface *S* is $F(x,y,z) = 0$, symmetric equations of the normal line to *S* at $P_0(x_0,y_0,z_0)$ are

(8) $$\frac{x - x_0}{F_x(x_0,y_0,z_0)} = \frac{y - y_0}{F_y(x_0,y_0,z_0)} = \frac{z - z_0}{F_z(x_0,y_0,z_0)}$$

The denominators in (8) are components of $\nabla F(x_0,y_0,z_0)$, which is a normal vector to *S* at P_0, and so (8) follows from Definition 22.9.4.

The normal line at a point on a surface is perpendicular to the tangent plane there.

EXAMPLE 2: Find symmetric equations of the normal line to the surface of Example 1 at (2,4,2).

Solution: Since $\nabla F(2,4,2) = 16\mathbf{i} + 8\mathbf{j} - 16\mathbf{k}$, it follows that symmetric equations of the required normal line are

$$\frac{x-2}{2} = \frac{y-4}{1} = \frac{z-2}{-2}$$

22.9.5 DEFINITION   The *tangent line* to a curve C at a point P_0 is the line through P_0 having as a set of direction numbers the components of the unit tangent vector to C at P_0.

From Definitions 22.9.3 and 22.9.5, we see that all the tangent lines at the point P_0 to the curves lying on a given surface lie in the tangent plane to the surface at P_0.

Consider a curve C which is the intersection of two surfaces having equations

(9) $$F(x,y,z) = 0$$

and

(10) $$G(x,y,z) = 0$$

respectively. We shall show how to obtain equations of the tangent line to C at a point $P_0(x_0,y_0,z_0)$. Since this tangent line lies in each of the tangent planes to the given surfaces at P_0, it is the line of intersection of the two tangent planes. A normal vector at P_0 to the surface having equation (9) is given by

$$\mathbf{N}_1 = \nabla F(x_0,y_0,z_0) = F_x(x_0,y_0,z_0)\mathbf{i} + F_y(x_0,y_0,z_0)\mathbf{j} + F_z(x_0,y_0,z_0)\mathbf{k}$$

and a normal vector at P_0 to the surface having equation (10) is given by

$$\mathbf{N}_2 = \nabla G(x_0,y_0,z_0) = G_x(x_0,y_0,z_0)\mathbf{i} + G_y(x_0,y_0,z_0)\mathbf{j} + G_z(x_0,y_0,z_0)\mathbf{k}$$

Both $\mathbf{N}_1$ and $\mathbf{N}_2$ are orthogonal to the unit tangent vector to C at P_0, and so if $\mathbf{N}_1$ and $\mathbf{N}_2$ are not parallel, it follows from Theorem 21.3.10 that the unit tangent vector has the direction which is the same as, or opposite to, the direction of $\mathbf{N}_1 \times \mathbf{N}_2$. Therefore, the components of $\mathbf{N}_1 \times \mathbf{N}_2$ will serve as a set of direction numbers of the tangent line. From this set of direction numbers and the coordinates of P_0 we may obtain symmetric equations of the required tangent line. This is illustrated in the following example.

EXAMPLE 3: Find symmetric equations of the tangent line to the curve of intersection of the surfaces $3x^2 + 2y^2 + z^2 = 49$ and $x^2 + y^2 - 2z^2 = 10$ at the point $(3,-3,2)$.

Solution: Let $F(x,y,z) = 3x^2 + 2y^2 + z^2 - 49 = 0$

and $G(x,y,z) = x^2 + y^2 - 2z^2 - 10$

Then $\nabla F(x,y,z) = 6x\,\mathbf{i} + 4y\,\mathbf{j} + 2z\,\mathbf{k}$ and $\nabla G(x,y,z) = 2x\,\mathbf{i} + 2y\,\mathbf{j} - 4z\,\mathbf{k}$ So,

$$\mathbf{N}_1 = \nabla F(3,-3,2) = 18\mathbf{i} - 12\mathbf{j} + 4\mathbf{k} = 2(9\mathbf{i} - 6\mathbf{j} + 2\mathbf{k})$$

and

$$\mathbf{N}_2 = \nabla G(3,-3,2) = 6\mathbf{i} - 6\mathbf{j} - 8\mathbf{k} = 2(3\mathbf{i} - 3\mathbf{j} - 4\mathbf{k})$$

$$\mathbf{N}_1 \times \mathbf{N}_2 = 4(9\mathbf{i} - 6\mathbf{j} + 2\mathbf{k}) \times (3\mathbf{i} - 3\mathbf{j} - 4\mathbf{k})$$

$$= 4(30\mathbf{i} + 42\mathbf{j} - 9\mathbf{k}) = 12(10\mathbf{i} + 14\mathbf{j} - 3\mathbf{k})$$

Therefore, a set of direction numbers of the required tangent line is $[10,14,-3]$. Symmetric equations of the line are, then,

$$\frac{x-3}{10} = \frac{y+3}{14} = \frac{z-2}{-3}$$

If two surfaces have a common tangent plane at a point, the two surfaces are said to be *tangent* at that point.

Exercises 22.9

In Exercises 1 through 12, find an equation of the tangent plane and equations of the normal line to the given surface at the indicated point.

1. $x^2 + y^2 + z^2 = 17; (2,-2,3)$

2. $4x^2 + y^2 + 2z^2 = 26; (1,-2,3)$

3. $x^2 + y^2 - 3z = 2; (-2,-4,6)$

4. $x^2 + y^2 - z^2 = 6; (3,-1,2)$

5. $y = e^x \cos z; (1,e,0)$

6. $z = e^{3x} \sin 3y; (0,\pi/6,1)$

7. $x^2 = 12y; (6,3,3)$

8. $z = x^{1/2} + y^{1/2}; (1,1,2)$

9. $x^{1/2} + y^{1/2} + z^{1/2} = 4; (4,1,1)$

10. $zx^2 - xy^2 - yz^2 = 18; (0,-2,3)$

11. $x^{2/3} + y^{2/3} + z^{2/3} = 14; (-8,27,1)$

12. $x^{1/2} + z^{1/2} = 8; (25,2,9)$

In Exercises 13 through 18, if the two given surfaces intersect in a curve, find equations of the tangent line to the curve of intersection at the given point; if the two given surfaces are tangent at the given point, prove it.

13. $x^2 + y^2 - z = 8, x - y^2 + z^2 = -2; (2,-2,0)$

14. $x^2 + y^2 - 2z + 1 = 0, x^2 + y^2 - z^2 = 0; (0,1,1)$

15. $y = x^2, y = 16 - z^2; (4,16,0)$

16. $x = 2 + \cos \pi yz, y = 1 + \sin \pi xz; (3,1,2)$

17. $x^2 + z^2 + 4y = 0, x^2 + y^2 + z^2 - 6z + 7 = 0; (0,-1,2)$

18. $x^2 + y^2 + z^2 = 8, yz = 4; (0,2,2)$

19. Prove that every normal line to the sphere $x^2 + y^2 + z^2 = a^2$ passes through the center of the sphere.

(22.10) Higher-order partial derivatives

If f is a function of two variables, then in general D_1f and D_2f are also functions of two variables, and if the partial derivatives of these functions exist, they are called *second partial derivatives* of f. In contrast, D_1f and D_2f are called *first partial derivatives* of f. There are four second partial derivatives of a function of two variables. If f is a function of the two variables x and y, the notations

$$D_2(D_1f) \quad D_{12}f \quad f_{12} \quad f_{xy} \quad \frac{\partial^2 f}{\partial y\, \partial x}$$

all denote the second partial derivative of f, which we obtain by first partial differentiating f with respect to x and then partial differentiating the result with respect to y. This second partial derivative is defined by

$$(1) \qquad f_{12}(x,y) = \lim_{\Delta y \to 0} \frac{f_1(x, y + \Delta y) - f_1(x,y)}{\Delta y}$$

if this limit exists. The notations

$$D_1(D_1f) \quad D_{11}f \quad f_{11} \quad f_{xx} \quad \frac{\partial^2 f}{\partial x^2}$$

all denote the second partial derivative of f, which is obtained by differentiating twice with respect to x, and we have the definition

$$(2) \qquad f_{11}(x,y) = \lim_{\Delta x \to 0} \frac{f_1(x + \Delta x, y) - f_1(x,y)}{\Delta x}$$

if this limit exists. We define the other two second partial derivatives in an analogous way, and we have

$$(3) \qquad f_{21}(x,y) = \lim_{\Delta x \to 0} \frac{f_2(x + \Delta x, y) - f_2(x,y)}{\Delta x}$$

and

$$(4) \qquad f_{22}(x,y) = \lim_{\Delta y \to 0} \frac{f_2(x, y + \Delta y) - f_2(x,y)}{\Delta y}$$

if these limits exist.

The definitions of higher-order partial derivatives are similar, and again we have various notations for a specific derivative. For example,

$$D_{112}f \quad f_{112} \quad f_{xxy} \quad \frac{\partial^3 f}{\partial y\, \partial x\, \partial x} \quad \frac{\partial^3 f}{\partial y\, \partial x^2}$$

all stand for the third partial derivative of f, which is obtained by partial differentiating twice with respect to x and then once with respect to y. Note that in the subscript notation, the order of partial differentiation is from left to right and in the notation $\partial^3 f / \partial y\, \partial x\, \partial x$, the order is from right to left.

EXAMPLE 1: *Given:* $f(x,y) = e^x \sin y + \ln xy$. *Find:* (a) $D_{11}f(x,y)$; (b) $D_{12}f(x,y)$; (c) $\partial^3 f/\partial x\partial y^2$.

Solution: $D_1 f(x,y) = e^x \sin y + (1/xy)y = e^x \sin y + 1/x$. So, (a) $D_{11} f(x,y)$
$= e^x \sin y - 1/x^2$;   and   (b) $D_{12} f(x,y) = e^x \cos y$. (c) To find $\partial^3 f / \partial x\, \partial y^2$,
we partial differentiate twice with respect to y and then once with respect
to x. This gives us

$$\frac{\partial f}{\partial y} = e^x \cos y + \frac{1}{y} \qquad \frac{\partial^2 f}{\partial y^2} = -e^x \sin y - \frac{1}{y^2} \qquad \frac{\partial^3 f}{\partial x\, \partial y^2} = -e^x \sin y$$

Higher-order partial derivatives of a function of n variables have definitions
which are analogous to the definitions of higher-order partial derivatives of a
function of two variables. If f is a function of n variables, there may be n^2
second partial derivatives of f at a particular point. That is, for a function of
three variables, if all the second-order partial derivatives exist, there are nine
of them and they are $f_{11}, f_{12}, f_{13}, f_{21}, f_{22}, f_{23}, f_{31}, f_{32}$, and f_{33}.

EXAMPLE 2: *Given:* $f(x,y,z) = \sin (xy + 2z)$. *Find:* $D_{132} f(x,y,z)$.
  Solution: $D_1 f(x,y,z) = y \cos (xy + 2z)$. $D_{13} f(x,y,z) = -2y \sin (xy + 2z)$.
$D_{132} f(x,y,z) = -2 \sin (xy + 2z) - 2xy \cos (xy + 2z)$.

EXAMPLE 3: *Given:* $f(x,y) = x^3 y - y \cosh xy$.   *Find:* (a) $D_{12} f(x,y)$; (b)
$D_{21} f(x,y)$.
  Solution:

(a) $D_1 f(x,y) = 3x^2 y - y^2 \sinh xy$
$\quad D_{12} f(x,y) = 3x^2 - 2y \sinh xy - xy^2 \cosh xy$
(b) $D_2 f(x,y) = x^3 - \cosh xy - xy \sinh xy$
$\quad D_{21} f(x,y) = 3x^2 - y \sinh xy - y \sinh xy - xy^2 \cosh xy$
$\qquad\qquad = 3x^2 - 2y \sinh xy - xy^2 \cosh xy$

We see from the above results that for the function of Example 3, the
"mixed" partial derivatives $D_{12} f(x,y)$ and $D_{21} f(x,y)$ are equal. So, for this
particular function, when finding the second partial derivative with respect to
x and then y, the order of differentiation is immaterial. This condition holds
for many functions. However, the following example shows that it is not
always true.

EXAMPLE 4: Let f be the function defined by

$$f(x,y) = \begin{cases} (xy)\dfrac{x^2 - y^2}{x^2 + y^2} & \text{if } (x,y) \neq (0,0) \\ 0 & \text{if } (x,y) = (0,0) \end{cases}$$

Find: $f_{12}(0,0)$ and $f_{21}(0,0)$.
  Solution: In Example 4, Sec. 22.5, we showed that for this function

(5) $\qquad\qquad f_1(0,y) = -y \qquad$ for all y

and

(6) $\qquad\qquad f_2(x,0) = x \qquad$ for all x

From formula (1) we obtain

$$f_{12}(0,0) = \lim_{\Delta y \to 0} \frac{f_1(0, 0 + \Delta y) - f_1(0,0)}{\Delta y}$$

But from (5), $f_1(0,\Delta y) = -\Delta y$ and $f_1(0,0) = 0$, and so we have

$$f_{12}(0,0) = \lim_{\Delta y \to 0} \frac{-\Delta y - 0}{\Delta y} = \lim_{\Delta y \to 0} (-1) = -1$$

From formula (3), we get

$$f_{21}(0,0) = \lim_{\Delta x \to 0} \frac{f_2(0 + \Delta x, 0) - f_2(0,0)}{\Delta x}$$

From (6), $f_2(\Delta x,0) = \Delta x$ and $f_2(0,0) = 0$ and therefore

$$f_{21}(0,0) = \lim_{\Delta x \to 0} \frac{\Delta x - 0}{\Delta x} = \lim_{\Delta x \to 0} 1 = 1$$

We see then that for the function of Example 4, the mixed partial derivatives $f_{12}(x,y)$ and $f_{21}(x,y)$ are not equal if $(x,y) = (0,0)$. The following theorem gives a set of conditions for which $f_{12}(x_0,y_0)$ and $f_{21}(x_0,y_0)$ are equal.

22.10.1 THEOREM   Suppose f is a function of two variables x and y defined on an open disk $B((x_0,y_0);r)$ and f_x, f_y, f_{xy}, f_{yx} are also defined on B. Furthermore, suppose that f_{xy} and f_{yx} are continuous on B. Then

$$f_{xy}(x_0,y_0) = f_{yx}(x_0,y_0)$$

Proof: Consider a square having its center at (x_0,y_0) and the length of its side $2|h|$, such that $0 < \sqrt{2}|h| < r$. Then all the points in the interior of the square and on the sides of the square are in the open disk B — see Fig. 22.10.1.

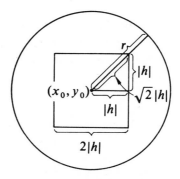

Figure 22.10.1

Then the points $(x_0 + h, y_0 + h)$, $(x_0 + h, y_0)$, and $(x_0, y_0 + h)$ are in B. Let Δ be defined by

(7) $\Delta = f(x_0 + h, y_0 + h) - f(x_0 + h, y_0) - f(x_0, y_0 + h) + f(x_0,y_0)$

We define a function G by

(8) $G(x) = f(x, y_0 + h) - f(x, y_0)$

    Then $G(x + h) = f(x + h, y_0 + h) - f(x + h, y_0)$

So, (7) may be written as

(9) $\Delta = G(x_0 + h) - G(x_0)$

From (8) we obtain

(10) $G'(x) = f_x(x, y_0 + h) - f_x(x, y_0)$

Now, since $f_x(x, y_0 + h)$ and $f_x(x, y_0)$ are defined on B, $G'(x)$ exists if x is in the closed interval having end points at x_0 and $x_0 + h$. Hence G is continuous if x is in this closed interval. By the mean-value theorem (8.5.1), there is a number c_1 between x_0 and $x_0 + h$ such that

(11) $G(x_0 + h) - G(x_0) = hG'(c_1)$

Substituting from (11) into (9), we get

(12) $\Delta = hG'(c_1)$

From (12) and (10) we obtain

(13) $\Delta = h[f_x(c_1, y_0 + h) - f_x(c_1, y_0)]$

Now if we let g be the function defined by

(14) $g(y) = f_x(c_1, y)$

we may write (13) as

(15) $\Delta = h[g(y_0 + h) - g(y_0)]$

From (14) we obtain

(16) $g'(y) = f_{xy}(c_1, y)$

Since $f_{xy}(c_1, y)$ is defined on B, $g'(y)$ exists if y is in the closed interval having end points at y_0 and $y_0 + h$, and hence g is continuous if y is in this closed interval. Therefore, by the mean-value theorem, there is a number d_1 between y_0 and $y_0 + h$ such that

(17) $g(y_0 + h) - g(y_0) = hg'(d_1)$

Substituting from (17) into (15), we get $\Delta = h^2 g'(d_1)$, and so from (16) we have

(18) $\Delta = h^2 f_{xy}(c_1, d_1)$

for some point (c_1, d_1) in the open disk B.

    We now define a function ϕ by

(19) $\phi(y) = f(x_0 + h, y) - f(x_0, y)$

and so $\phi(y + h) = f(x_0 + h, y + h) - f(x_0, y + h)$. Therefore, (7) may be written as

(20) $\Delta = \phi(y_0 + h) - \phi(y_0)$

From (19) we get

(21) $$\phi'(y) = f_y(x_0 + h, y) - f_y(x_0, y)$$

ϕ' exists if y is in the closed interval having y_0 and $y_0 + h$ as end points, since by hypothesis each term on the right-hand side of (21) exists on B. Therefore ϕ is continuous on this closed interval, and so by the mean-value theorem, there is a number d_2 between y_0 and $y_0 + h$ such that

(22) $$\phi(y_0 + h) - \phi(y_0) = h\phi'(d_2)$$

From (20), (21), and (22) it follows that

(23) $$\Delta = h[f_y(x_0 + h, d_2) - f_y(x_0, d_2)]$$

Define the function χ by

(24) $$\chi(x) = f_y(x, d_2)$$

and write (23) as

(25) $$\Delta = h[\chi(x_0 + h) - \chi(x_0)]$$

From (24) we get

(26) $$\chi'(x) = f_{yx}(x, d_2)$$

and by the mean-value theorem we may conclude that there is a number c_2 between x_0 and $x_0 + h$ such that

(27) $$\chi(x_0 + h) - \chi(x_0) = h\chi'(c_2)$$

From (25), (26), and (27) we obtain

(28) $$\Delta = h^2 f_{yx}(c_2, d_2)$$

Equating the right-hand sides of (18) and (28), we get

$$h^2 f_{xy}(c_1, d_1) = h^2 f_{yx}(c_2, d_2)$$

and since $h \neq 0$, we may divide by h^2, which gives us

(29) $$f_{xy}(c_1, d_1) = f_{yx}(c_2, d_2)$$

where (c_1, d_1) and (c_2, d_2) are in B.

Since c_1 and c_2 are each between x_0 and $x_0 + h$, we may write $c_1 = x_0 + \epsilon_1 h$, where $0 < \epsilon_1 < 1$, and $c_2 = x_0 + \epsilon_2 h$, where $0 < \epsilon_2 < 1$. Similarly, since both d_1 and d_2 are between y_0 and $y_0 + h$, we may write $d_1 = y_0 + \epsilon_3 h$, where $0 < \epsilon_3 < 1$, and $d_2 = y_0 + \epsilon_4 h$, where $0 < \epsilon_4 < 1$. Making these substitutions in (29), we get

(30) $$f_{xy}(x_0 + \epsilon_1 h, y_0 + \epsilon_3 h) = f_{yx}(x_0 + \epsilon_2 h, y_0 + \epsilon_4 h).$$

Since f_{xy} and f_{yx} are continuous on B, upon taking the limit of both sides of (30) as h approaches zero, we obtain

$$f_{xy}(x_0, y_0) = f_{yx}(x_0, y_0)$$

which is what we wished to prove.

As a result of this theorem, if the function f of two variables has continuous partial derivatives on some open disk, then the order of partial differentiation may be changed without affecting the result; that is,

$$D_{112}f = D_{121}f = D_{211}f$$

$$D_{1122}f = D_{1212}f = D_{1221}f = D_{2112}f = D_{2121}f = D_{2211}f$$

and so forth. In particular, to prove that $D_{211}f = D_{112}f$, under the assumption that all of the partial derivatives are continuous on some open disk, we apply Theorem 22.10.1 repeatedly, and we have

$$D_{211}f = D_1(D_{21}f) = D_1(D_{12}f) = D_1[D_2(D_1f)] = D_2[D_1(D_1f)]$$
$$= D_2(D_{11}f) = D_{112}f$$

Exercises 22.10

In Exercises 1 through 8, do each of the following: (a) find $D_{11}f(x,y)$; (b) find $D_{22}f(x,y)$; (c) show that $D_{12}f(x,y) = D_{21}f(x,y)$.

1. $f(x,y) = \dfrac{x^2}{y} - \dfrac{y}{x^2}$

2. $f(x,y) = 2x^3 - 3x^2y + xy^2$

3. $f(x,y) = e^{2x} \sin y$

4. $f(x,y) = e^{-x/y} + \ln \dfrac{y}{x}$

5. $f(x,y) = (x^2 + y^2) \tan^{-1} \dfrac{y}{x}$

6. $f(x,y) = \sin^{-1} \dfrac{y}{x}$

7. $f(x,y) = x \sinh y + y \cosh x$

8. $f(x,y) = x \cos y - ye^x$

In Exercises 9 through 14, find the indicated partial derivatives.

9. $f(x,y,z) = ye^x + ze^y + e^z$; (a) $f_{xz}(x,y,z)$; (b) $f_{yz}(x,y,z)$

10. $g(x,y,z) = \sin(xyz)$; (a) $g_{23}(x,y,z)$; (b) $g_{12}(x,y,z)$

11. $f(r,s) = r^3s + r^2s^2 - rs^3$; (a) $f_{121}(r,s)$; (b) $f_{221}(r,s)$

12. $f(u,v) = \ln \cos(u - v)$; (a) $f_{uuv}(u,v)$; (b) $f_{vuv}(u,v)$

13. $g(r,s,t) = \ln(r^2 + s^2 + t^2)$; (a) $g_{132}(r,s,t)$; (b) $g_{122}(r,s,t)$

14. $f(x,y,z) = \tan^{-1}(xyz)$; (a) $f_{113}(x,y,z)$; (b) $f_{123}(x,y,z)$

In Exercises 15 through 18, show that $u(x,y)$ satisfies the equation

$$\partial^2 u/\partial x^2 + \partial^2 u/\partial y^2 = 0,$$

which is known as Laplace's equation in E^2.

15. $u(x,y) = \ln(x^2 + y^2)$

16. $u(x,y) = e^x \sin y + e^y \cos x$

17. $u(x,y) = \tan^{-1} \dfrac{y}{x} + \dfrac{x}{x^2 + y^2}$

18. $u(x,y) = \tan^{-1} \dfrac{2xy}{x^2 - y^2}$

19. Laplace's equation in E^3 is $\partial^2 u/\partial x^2 + \partial^2 u/\partial y^2 + \partial^2 u/\partial z^2 = 0$. Show that $u(x,y,z) = (x^2 + y^2 + z^2)^{-1/2}$ satisfies this equation.

20. For the function of Example 4, show that f_{12} is discontinuous at $(0,0)$ and hence that the hypothesis of Theorem 22.10.1 is not satisfied if $(x_0,y_0) = (0,0)$.

In Exercises 21 through 23, find $f_{12}(0,0)$ and $f_{21}(0,0)$, if they exist.

21. $f(x,y) = \begin{cases} \dfrac{2xy}{x^2 + y^2} & \text{if } (x,y) \neq (0,0) \\ 0 & \text{if } (x,y) = (0,0) \end{cases}$

22. $f(x,y) = \begin{cases} \dfrac{x^2y^2}{x^4 + y^4} & \text{if } (x,y) \neq (0,0) \\ 0 & \text{if } (x,y) = (0,0) \end{cases}$

23. $f(x,y) = \begin{cases} x^2 \tan^{-1} \dfrac{y}{x} - y^2 \tan^{-1} \dfrac{x}{y} & \text{if} \quad x \neq 0 \text{ and } y \neq 0 \\ 0 & \text{if} \quad \text{either } x = 0 \text{ or } y = 0 \end{cases}$

24. *Given:* $u = f(x,y)$, $x = F(t)$, and $y = G(t)$. *Assume:* $f_{xy} = f_{yx}$. *Prove by using the chain rule that*

$$\frac{d^2u}{dt^2} = f_{xx}\left(\frac{dx}{dt}\right)^2 + 2f_{xy}\frac{dx}{dt}\frac{dy}{dt} + f_{yy}\left(\frac{dy}{dt}\right)^2 + f_x\frac{d^2x}{dt^2} + f_y\frac{d^2y}{dt^2}$$

25. *Given:* $u = f(x,y)$, $x = F(t,s)$, and $y = G(t,s)$. *Assume:* $f_{xy} = f_{yx}$. *Prove by using the chain rule that*

$$\frac{\partial^2u}{\partial t^2} = f_{xx}\left(\frac{\partial x}{\partial t}\right)^2 + 2f_{xy}\frac{\partial x}{\partial t}\frac{\partial y}{\partial t} + f_{yy}\left(\frac{\partial y}{\partial t}\right)^2 + f_x\frac{\partial^2x}{\partial t^2} + f_y\frac{\partial^2y}{\partial t^2}$$

26. *Given:* $u = f(x,y)$, $x = F(t,s)$, and $y = G(t,s)$. *Assume:* $f_{xy} = f_{yx}$. *Prove by using the chain rule that*

$$\frac{\partial^2u}{\partial s\,\partial t} = f_{xx}\frac{\partial x}{\partial s}\frac{\partial x}{\partial t} + f_{xy}\left(\frac{\partial x}{\partial s}\frac{\partial y}{\partial t} + \frac{\partial y}{\partial s}\frac{\partial x}{\partial t}\right) + f_{yy}\frac{\partial y}{\partial s}\frac{\partial y}{\partial t} + f_x\frac{\partial^2x}{\partial s\,\partial t} + f_y\frac{\partial^2y}{\partial s\,\partial t}$$

27. *Given:* $u = e^y \cos x$, $x = 2t$, $y = t^2$. Find d^2u/dt^2 in three ways: (a) by first expressing u in terms of t; (b) by using the formula of Exercise 24; (c) by using the chain rule.

28. *Given:* $u = 3xy - 4y^2$, $x = 2se^t$, $y = se^{-t}$. *Find:* $\partial^2u/\partial t^2$ in three ways: (a) by first expressing u in terms of s and t; (b) by using the formula of Exercise 25; (c) by using the chain rule.

29. For u, x, and y as given in Exercise 28, find $\partial^2u/\partial s\,\partial t$ in three ways; (a) by first expressing u in terms of s and t; (b) by using the formula of Exercise 26; (c) by using the chain rule.

30. *Given:* $u = 9x^2 + 4y^2$, $x = r \cos \theta$, $y = r \sin \theta$. *Find:* $\partial^2u/\partial r^2$ in three ways: (a) by first expressing u in terms of r and θ; (b) by using the formula of Exercise 25; (c) by using the chain rule.

31. For u, x, and y as given in Exercise 30, find $\partial^2u/\partial\theta^2$ in three ways: (a) by first expressing u in terms of r and θ; (b) by using the formula of Exercise 25; (c) by using the chain rule.

32 For u, x and y as given in Exercise 30, find $\partial^2 u/\partial r\ \partial\theta$ in three ways: (*a*) by first expressing u in terms of r and θ; (*b*) by using the formula of Exercise 26; (*c*) by using the chain rule.

33. If $u = f(x,y)$ and $v = g(x,y)$, then the equations

$$\frac{\partial u}{\partial x} = \frac{\partial v}{\partial y} \quad \text{and} \quad \frac{\partial v}{\partial x} = -\frac{\partial u}{\partial y}$$

are called the *Cauchy-Riemann* equations. If f and g and their first and second partial derivatives are continuous, prove that if u and v satisfy the Cauchy-Riemann equations, they also satisfy Laplace's equation.

34. The one-dimensional heat-conduction partial differential equation is

$$\frac{\partial u}{\partial t} = k^2 \frac{\partial^2 u}{\partial x^2}$$

Show that if f is a function of x satisfying the equation

$$\frac{d^2 f}{dx^2} + \lambda^2 f = 0,$$

and g is a function of t satisfying the equation $dg/dt + k^2\lambda^2 g = 0$, then if $u = f(x)g(t)$, the partial differential equation is satisfied. k and λ are constants.

35. The partial differential equation for a vibrating string is

$$\frac{\partial^2 u}{\partial t^2} = a^2 \frac{\partial^2 u}{\partial x^2}$$

Show that if f is a function of x satisfying the equation $d^2f/dx^2 + \lambda^2 f = 0$ and g is a function of t satisfying the equation $d^2g/dt^2 + a^2\lambda^2 g = 0$, then if $u = f(x)g(t)$, the partial differential equation is satisfied. a and λ are constants.

36. Prove that if f and g are two arbitrary functions of a real variable having continuous second derivatives and $u = f(x + at) + g(x - at)$, then u satisfies the partial differential equation of the vibrating string given in Exercise 35. HINT: Let $v = x + at$ and $w = x - at$; then u is a function of v and w and v and w are in turn functions of x and t.

37. Prove that if f is a function of two variables and all the partial derivatives of f up to the fourth order are continuous on some open disk, then

$$D_{1122}f = D_{2121}f.$$

23 Multiple integration

(23.1)   The double integral

The definite integral of a function of a single variable, discussed in Chap. 10, may be extended to a function of several variables. We shall call an integral of a function of a single variable a *single integral*, to distinguish it from a *multiple integral*, which involves a function of several variables. The physical and geometrical applications of multiple integrals are analogous to those given in Chap. 11 for an integral of a function on E^1.

In the discussion of a single integral, we required that the function be defined on a closed interval in E^1. For the double integral of a function of two variables, we shall require that the function be defined on a closed region in E^2. By a closed region we shall mean that the region includes its boundary. In this chapter, when we refer to a region, it will be assumed to be closed. The simplest kind of closed region in E^2 is a closed rectangle, which we now proceed to define. Let us consider two points, $A(a_1, a_2)$ and $B(b_1, b_2)$, such that $a_1 \leq b_1$ and $a_2 \leq b_2$. These two points determine a rectangle having sides parallel to the

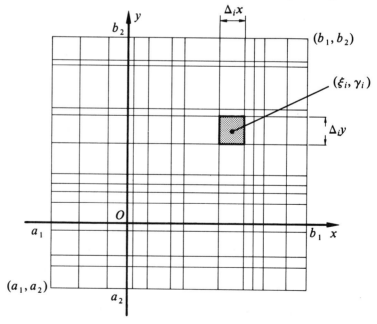

Figure 23.1.1

coordinate axes — refer to Fig. 23.1.1. The two points, together with the points (b_1,a_2) and (a_1,b_2), are called the *vertices* of the rectangle and the line segments joining consecutive vertices are called the *edges* of the rectangle. The set of all points interior to the rectangle is called an *open rectangle*. The set of all points in the open rectangle, together with the points on the edges of the rectangle, is called a *closed rectangle*.

Let us denote the closed rectangular region of Fig. 23.1.1 by R. This region R may be considered as a *region of integration*. It corresponds to the interval of integration for a function defined on E^1. So our first step is to define a *partition*, Δ, of this region R. We draw lines parallel to the coordinate axes and obtain a network of rectangular subregions which cover R. The *norm* of this partition, denoted by $\|\Delta\|$, is the length of the longest diagonal of a rectangular subregion of the partition. We number the subregions in some arbitrary way (such as by starting in the upper left-hand corner of R). Let the number of subregions be n, and we shall denote the width of the ith subregion by $\Delta_i x$ and its height by $\Delta_i y$ Therefore the product $\Delta_i x\, \Delta_i y$ is the area of the ith rectangular subregion. Denoting the area by $\Delta_i A$, we have

$$\Delta_i A = \Delta_i x\, \Delta_i y$$

Let (ξ_i, γ_i) be an arbitrary point in the ith subregion. Compute the function value $f(\xi_i, \gamma_i)$ and form the product $f(\xi_i, \gamma_i)\, \Delta_i A$. Associated with each of the n subregions is such a product, and we form the sum

(1)
$$\sum_{i=1}^{n} f(\xi_i, \gamma_i)\, \Delta_i A$$

There are many sums of the form (1), since the norm of the partition may be any positive number and each point (ξ_i, γ_i) may be any point in the ith subregion. However, if the function f is continuous on the region R, all the sums formed by taking partitions with small enough norms will be close to one number, and this number is defined to be the limit of the sum in (1) as the norm of the partition of the region R approaches zero. We have then the following definition.

23.1.1 DEFINITION   The number L is said to be the *limit* of sums of form (1) if the number L satisfies the property that for any $\epsilon > 0$, there exists a $\delta > 0$ such that

$$\left| \sum_{i=1}^{n} f(\xi_i, \gamma_i)\Delta_i A - L \right| < \epsilon$$

for every partition Δ for which $\|\Delta\| < \delta$ and for all possible selections of the point (ξ_i, γ_i) in the ith rectangle, $i = 1, 2, \ldots, n$.

If Definition 23.1.1 holds, we write

$$\lim_{\|\Delta\| \to 0} \sum_{i=1}^{n} f(\xi_i, \gamma_i)\, \Delta_i A = L$$

If the number L of Definition 23.1.1 exists, it can be shown that it is unique.

23.1.2 DEFINITION   A function f of two variables is said to be *integrable* on a rectangular region R if f is defined on R and the number L of Definition 23.1.1 exists. This number L is called the *double integral* of the function f on R. We write

(2)
$$\int\int_R f(x,y)\, dA = \lim_{||\Delta||\to 0} \sum_{i=1}^{n} f(\xi_i,\gamma_i)\, \Delta_i A$$

Other symbols for the double integral in (2) are

$$\int\int_R f(x,y)\, dx\, dy \quad \text{and} \quad \int\int_R f(x,y)\, dy\, dx$$

The following example illustrates the approximation of the value of a double integral directly from the definition.

EXAMPLE 1: Let R be the rectangular region having vertices $(-1,1)$ and $(2,3)$. Find an approximate value of the double integral

$$\int\int_R (2x^2 - 3y)\, dA$$

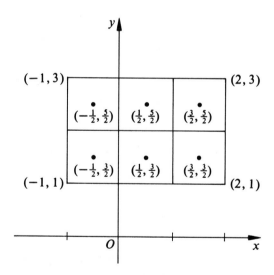

Figure 23.1.2

Solution: Refer to Fig. 23.1.2, which shows the region R partitioned into six subregions by the lines $x = 0$, $x = 1$, and $y = 2$. Each of the subregions is a square of side one unit, and so for each i, $\Delta_i A = 1$. In each of the square subregions we select as the point (ξ_i,γ_i) the center of the square. Therefore an approximation to the given double integral is given by

$$\iint\limits_R (2x^2 - 3y)\, dA \approx f\left(-\frac{1}{2},\frac{3}{2}\right)\cdot 1 + f\left(\frac{1}{2},\frac{3}{2}\right)\cdot 1 + f\left(\frac{3}{2},\frac{3}{2}\right)\cdot 1$$

$$+ f\left(\frac{3}{2},\frac{5}{2}\right)\cdot 1 + f\left(\frac{1}{2},\frac{5}{2}\right)\cdot 1 + f\left(-\frac{1}{2},\frac{5}{2}\right)\cdot 1$$

$$= -4\cdot 1 - 4\cdot 1 + 0\cdot 1 - 3\cdot 1 - 7\cdot 1 - 7\cdot 1$$

$$= -25$$

In Example 1 of the next section, we shall see that the exact value of the double integral is -24.

Just as the integral of a function of a single variable was interpreted geometrically as the area of a plane region, the geometric interpretation of a double integral is as the volume of a three-dimensional solid. Suppose that the function f is defined on a rectangular region R in E^2. Furthermore, for simplicity in this discussion, assume $f(x,y)$ is positive on R. The graph of the equation $z = f(x,y)$ is a surface, which lies above the xy plane. This is shown in Fig. 23.1.3. In the

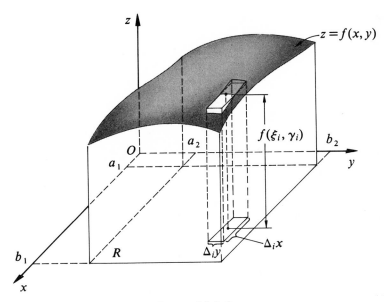

Figure 23.1.3

figure is shown a particular rectangular subregion of R, having dimensions $\Delta_i x$ and $\Delta_i y$, and a rectangular solid having this subregion as base and $f(\xi_i,\gamma_i)$ as altitude where (ξ_i,γ_i) is any point in the ith subregion. The volume of the rectangular solid is given by

(3) $$\Delta_i V = f(\xi_i,\gamma_i)\, \Delta_i A = f(\xi_i,\gamma_i)\, \Delta_i x\, \Delta_i y$$

The number given in (3) is the volume of the thin rectangular solid whose base is the rectangle having sides of lengths $\Delta_i x$ and $\Delta_i y$ and whose altitude is $f(\xi_i,\gamma_i)$. The sum given in (1) is the sum of volumes of such solids, and this sum approximates the volume of the three-dimensional solid which is bounded by region R, the planes perpendicular to the xy plane that contain the edges of R, and the graph of f.

The sum given by (1) also approximates the number given by the double integral

$$\int\int_R f(x,y)\,dA$$

It can be proved that the volume of the three-dimensional solid under the graph of f is the value of the double integral. This is stated in the following theorem, for which a formal proof will not be given.

23.1.3 THEOREM If f is a function of two variables which is continuous on a closed rectangular region R, then f is integrable on R, and furthermore if $f(x,y) \geq 0$ for (x,y) in R, then if $V(S)$ is the volume of the solid S bounded by R, the graph of f, and the planes perpendicular to the xy plane which contain the edges of R, then

$$V(S) = \int\int_R f(x,y)\,dA$$

We shall now consider the double integral of a function f over a more general region. We must first define some terms. By a *smooth function*, we mean one which has a continuous derivative. A *smooth curve* is a curve which consists of a finite number of arcs of graphs of smooth functions. Examples of smooth curves are straight lines, ellipses, and parabolas. Geometrically, a smooth curve has a continuously turning tangent line. Let R be a closed region whose boundary consists of a finite number of arcs of smooth curves which are joined together to form a closed curve. As we did with a rectangular region, we draw lines parallel to the coordinate axes, which gives us a rectangular partition of the region R. Some of the rectangular subregions will be entirely in R and others will contain points which are not in R. We shall discard the subregions which contain points not in R and consider only those which lie entirely in R (these are shaded in Fig. 23.1.4). Letting the number of these shaded subregions be n, we proceed in a manner analogous to the procedure we used for a rectangular region R. Definitions 23.1.1 and 23.1.2 apply when the region R is the more general one described above. It should be intuitive to the reader that as the norm of the partition approaches zero, n approaches $+\infty$ and the area of the region omitted (that is, the discarded rectangles) approaches zero. Actually it can be proved in advanced calculus that if a function is integrable on a region R, the limit of the approximating sums of the form (1) is the same no matter how we subdivide the region R, as long as each subregion has a shape to which an area may be assigned. Analogous to properties of the definite integral of a function of a single variable are several properties of the double integral. The most important properties are given in the following theorems.

23.1.4 THEOREM   If c is a constant and the function f is integrable on a closed region R, then cf is integrable on R and

$$\int\int_R cf(x,y)\,dA = c\int\int_R f(x,y)\,dA$$

23.1.5 THEOREM   If the functions f and g are integrable on a closed region R, then

$$\int\int_R [f(x,y) + g(x,y)]\,dA = \int\int_R f(x,y)\,dA + \int\int_R g(x,y)\,dA$$

The result of Theorem 23.1.5 may be extended to any finite number of functions which are integrable.

The proofs of Theorems 23.1.4 and 23.1.5 follow directly from the definition of a double integral and they are left for the reader (see Exercises 11 and 12 at the end of this section).

23.1.6 THEOREM   If the functions f and g are integrable on the closed region R and $f(x,y) \geq g(x,y)$ for all (x,y) in R, then

$$\int\int_R f(x,y)\,dA \geq \int\int_R g(x,y)\,dA$$

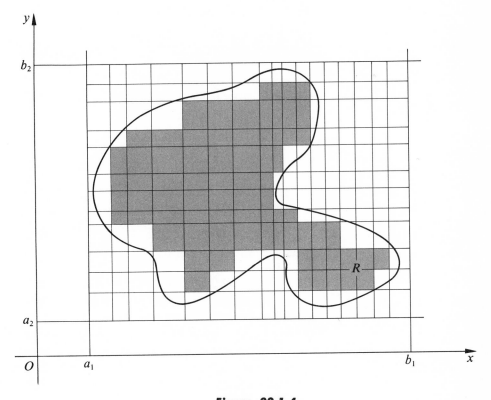

Figure 23.1.4

This theorem is analogous to Theorem 10.4.8 for the definite integral of a function of a single variable, and the proof is similar and is left for the reader (see Exercise 13 at the end of this section).

23.1.7 THEOREM   Let the function f be integrable on a closed region R and suppose m and M are two numbers such that $m \leq f(x,y) \leq M$ for all (x,y) *in* R. Then, if $A(R)$ denotes the area of region R, we have

$$mA(R) \leq \int\int_R f(x,y)\, dA \leq MA(R)$$

The proof of this theorem is left for the reader (see Exercise 14 at the end of this section). The proof is similar to that of Theorem 10.5.2 and is based on Theorem 23.1.6.

23.1.8 THEOREM   Suppose the function f is continuous on the closed region R and region R is composed of the two subregions R_1 and R_2 which have no points in common, except for points on parts of their boundaries.

$$\int\int_R f(x,y)\, dA = \int\int_{R_1} f(x,y)\, dA + \int\int_{R_2} f(x,y)\, dA$$

The proof of this theorem is also left for the reader. It depends upon the definition of a double integral and limit theorems (see Exercise 15 at the end of this section).

Exercises 23.1

In Exercises 1 through 6, find an approximate value of the given double integral where R is the rectangular region having the vertices P and Q, Δ is a regular partition of R, and (ξ_i, γ_i) is the midpoint of each subregion.

1. $\int\int_R (x^2 + y)\ dA$; $P(0,0)$; $Q(4,2)$; Δ: $x_1 = 0,\ x_2 = 1,\ x_3 = 2,\ x_4 = 3,$ $y_1 = 0,\ y_2 = 1$.

2. $\int\int_R (2 - x - y)\ dA$; $P(0,0)$; $Q(6,4)$; Δ: $x_1 = 0,\ x_2 = 2,\ x_3 = 4,\ y_1 = 0,$ $y_2 = 2$.

3. $\int\int_R (xy + 3y^2)\, dA$; $P(-2,0)$, $Q(4,6)$; Δ: $x_1 = -2, x_2 = 0, x_3 = 2, y_1 = 0,$ $y_2 = 2,\ y_3 = 4$.

4. $\int\int_R (xy + 3y^2)\, dA$; $P(0,-2)$, $Q(6,4)$; Δ: $x_1 = 0, x_2 = 2, x_3 = 4, y_1 = -2,$ $y_2 = 0,\ y_3 = 2$.

5. $\int\int_R (x^2y - 2xy^2)\, dA$; $P(-3,-2)$; $Q(1,6)$; Δ: $x_1 = -3, x_2 = -1, y_1 = -2,$ $y_2 = 0,\ y_3 = 2,\ y_4 = 4$.

6. $\int\int_R (x^2y - 2xy^2)\, dA$; $P(-3,-2)$; $Q(1,6)$; Δ: $x_1 = -3, x_2 = -2, x_3 = -1,$ $x_4 = 0, y_1 = -2, y_2 = -1, y_3 = 0, y_4 = 1, y_5 = 2, y_6 = 3, y_7 = 4, y_8 = 5$.

In Exercises 7 through 10, find an approximate value of the given double integral where R is the rectangular region having the vertices P and Q, Δ is a regular partition of R, and (ξ_i, γ_i) is an arbitrary point in each subregion.

7. The double integral, P, Q, and Δ are the same as in Exercise 1; $(\xi_1, \gamma_1) = (1/4, 1/2)$; $(\xi_2, \gamma_1) = (7/4, 0)$; $(\xi_3, \gamma_1) = (5/2, 1/4)$, $(\xi_4, \gamma_1) = (4, 1)$; $(\xi_1, \gamma_2) = (3/4, 7/4)$; $(\xi_2, \gamma_2) = (5/4, 3/2)$; $(\xi_3, \gamma_2) = (5/2, 2)$; $(\xi_4, \gamma_2) = (3, 1)$.

8. The double integral, P, Q, and Δ are the same as in Exercise 2; $(\xi_1, \gamma_1) = (1/2, 3/2)$; $(\xi_2, \gamma_1) = (3, 1)$; $(\xi_3, \gamma_1) = (11/2, 1/2)$; $(\xi_1, \gamma_2) = (2, 2)$; $(\xi_2, \gamma_2) = (2, 2)$, $(\xi_3, \gamma_2) = (5, 3)$.

9. The double integral, P, Q, and Δ are the same as in Exercise 3; $(\xi_1, \gamma_1) = (-1/2, 1/2)$; $(\xi_2, \gamma_1) = (1, 3/2)$; $(\xi_3, \gamma_1) = (5/2, 2)$; $(\xi_1, \gamma_2) = (-3/2, 7/2)$; $(\xi_2, \gamma_2) = (0, 3)$; $(\xi_3, \gamma_2) = (4, 4)$; $(\xi_1, \gamma_3) = (-1, 9/2)$; $(\xi_2, \gamma_3) = (1, 9/2)$; $(\xi_3, \gamma_3) = (3, 9/2)$.

10. The double integral, P, Q, and Δ are the same as in Exercise 3; $(\xi_1, \gamma_1) = (-2, 0)$; $(\xi_2, \gamma_1) = (0, 0)$; $(\xi_2, \gamma_1) = (2, 0)$; $(\xi_1, \gamma_2) = (-2, 2)$; $(\xi_2, \gamma_2) = (0, 2)$; $(\xi_2, \gamma_2) = (2, 2)$; $(\xi_1, \gamma_3) = (-2, 4)$; $(\xi_2, \gamma_3) = (0, 4)$; $(\xi_3, \gamma_3) = (2, 4)$.

11. Prove Theorem 23.1.4.

12. Prove Theorem 23.1.5.

13. Prove Theorem 23.1.6.

14. Prove Theorem 23.1.7.

15. Prove Theorem 23.1.8.

(23.2) Evaluation of double integrals and iterated integrals

For functions of a single variable, the fundamental theorem of integral calculus provided us with a method for evaluating a definite integral by means of finding an antiderivative (or indefinite integral) of the integrand. We have a corresponding method for evaluating a double integral, which involves performing successive single integrations. A rigorous development of this method belongs to a course in advanced calculus. Our discussion will be an intuitive one, and we shall make use of the geometrical interpretation of the double integral as a volume. We shall first develop the method for the double integral on a rectangular region.

Let f be a given function that is integrable on a closed rectangular region R in the xy plane bounded by the lines $x = a_1$, $x = b_1$, $y = a_2$, $y = b_2$. We shall assume that $f(x, y) \geq 0$ for all (x, y) in R. Refer to Fig. 23.2.1, which shows a sketch of the graph of the equation $z = f(x, y)$ when (x, y) is in R. The number which represents the value of the double integral

$$\iint\limits_R f(x, y) \, dA$$

is the volume of the solid between the surface and the region R. We shall find

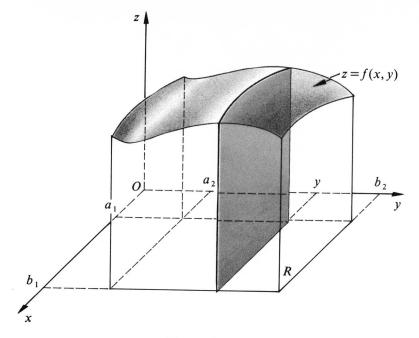

Figure 23.2.1

this volume by the method of parallel plane sections, which we discussed in Sec. 11.9.

Let y be a point in $[a_2,b_2]$. Consider the plane which is parallel to the xz plane through the point $(0,y,0)$. Let $A(y)$ be the area of the plane region of intersection of this plane with the solid. By the method of parallel plane sections, as discussed in Sec. 11.9, we express the volume of the solid by

$$\int_{a_2}^{b_2} A(y)\, dy$$

Since the volume of the solid is also given by the double integral, we have

(1)
$$\iint_R f(x,y)\, dA = \int_{a_2}^{b_2} A(y)\, dy$$

By using (1), we can find the value of the double integral of the function f on R by evaluating a single integral of $A(y)$. We now must find $A(y)$ when y is given. Since $A(y)$ is the area of a plane region, we may find it by integration. In Fig. 23.2.1, notice that the upper boundary of the plane region is the graph of the equation $z = f(x,y)$ when x is in $[a_1,b_1]$. Therefore, $A(y) = \int_{a_1}^{b_1} f(x,y)\, dx$. If we substitute this into equation (1), we obtain

(2)
$$\iint_R f(x,y)\, dA = \int_{a_2}^{b_2}\left[\int_{a_1}^{b_1} f(x,y)\, dx\right] dy$$

The integral on the right-hand side of (2) is called an *iterated integral*. Usually the brackets are omitted when writing an iterated integral. So we write (2) as

(3) $$\iint_R f(x,y)\, dA = \int_{a_2}^{b_2} \int_{a_1}^{b_1} f(x,y)\, dx\, dy$$

In evaluating the "inner integral" in equation (3), remember that x is the variable of integration and y is considered as a constant in this integration. This is analogous to considering y as a constant when finding the partial derivative of $f(x,y)$ with respect to x.

By considering plane sections parallel to the yz plane, we may develop the following formula, which interchanges the order of integration.

(4) $$\iint_R f(x,y)\, dA = \int_{a_1}^{b_1} \int_{a_2}^{b_2} f(x,y)\, dy\, dx$$

A sufficient condition for formulas (3) and (4) to be valid is that the function be continuous on the rectangular region R.

EXAMPLE 1: Evaluate the double integral

$$\iint_R (2x^2 - 3y)\, dA$$

if R is the region consisting of all points (x,y) for which $-1 \le x \le 2$ and $1 \le y \le 3$.

Solution: $a_1 = -1$, $b_1 = 2$, $a_2 = 1$, and $b_2 = 3$. So we have from (3)

$$\iint_R (2x^2 - 3y)\, dA = \int_1^3 \int_{-1}^2 (2x^2 - 3y)\, dx\, dy$$

$$= \int_1^3 \left[\int_{-1}^2 (2x^2 - 3y) \right] dx\, dy$$

$$= \int_1^3 \left[\frac{2}{3}x^3 - 3xy \right]_{-1}^2 dy$$

$$= \int_1^3 (6 - 9y)\, dy = -24$$

In Example 1 of the previous section we found an approximate value of this double integral to be -25.

EXAMPLE 2: Find the volume of the solid bounded by the surface $f(x,y) = 4 - x^2/9 - y^2/16$, the planes $x = 3$ and $y = 2$, and the three coordinate planes.

Solution: The solid is shown in Fig. 23.2.2. From Theorem 23.1.3, we have

$$V(S) = \iint_R f(x,y)\, dA = \int_0^3 \int_0^2 \left(4 - \frac{x^2}{9} - \frac{y^2}{16} \right) dy\, dx$$

$$= \int_0^3 \left[4y - \frac{x^2 y}{9} - \frac{y^3}{48} \right]_0^2 dx = \int_0^3 \left(\frac{47}{6} - \frac{2}{9}x^2 \right) dx$$

$$= \frac{47}{6}x - \frac{2}{27}x^3 \Big]_0^3 = 21\frac{1}{2}$$

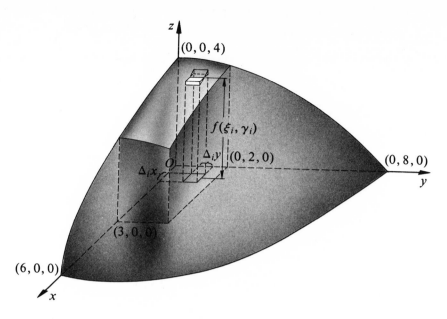

Figure 23.2.2

Suppose now R is a region in the xy plane which is bounded by the lines $x = a$ and $x = b$, where $a < b$, and by the curves $y = \phi_1(x)$ and $y = \phi_2(x)$, where ϕ_1 and ϕ_2 are two functions which are continuous on the closed interval $[a,b]$, and furthermore $\phi_1(x) \leq \phi_2(x)$ whenever $a \leq x \leq b$ — see Fig. 23.2.3. Let Δ be a partition of the interval $[a, b]$ defined by Δ: $a = x_0 < x_1 < \cdots < x_n = b$. Consider the region R of Fig. 23.2.3 to be divided into vertical strips of widths $\Delta_i x$. A particular strip is shown in the figure. The intersection of the surface $z = f(x,y)$ and a plane $x = \bar{x}$, where $x_{i-1} \leq \bar{x} \leq x_i$, is a curve, and a segment

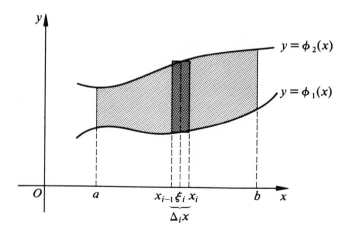

Figure 23.2.3

of this curve is over the vertical strip of width $\Delta_i x$. The area of the region under this curve segment and above the xy plane is given by

$$\int_{\phi_1(\bar{x})}^{\phi_2(\bar{x})} f(\bar{x},y)\, dy$$

Interpreting a double integral as a volume, the double integral of f on this vertical strip is approximately equal to

$$\left[\int_{\phi_1(\bar{x})}^{\phi_2(\bar{x})} f(\bar{x},y)\, dy \right] \Delta_i x$$

If we take the limit as the norm of Δ approaches zero of the sum of these double integrals for all the vertical strips of R from $x = a$ to $x = b$, it seems reasonable that we would obtain the double integral of f on R; that is,

$$(5)\ \lim_{\|\Delta\|\to 0}\sum_{i=1}^{n}\left[\int_{\phi_1(\bar{x})}^{\phi_2(\bar{x})} f(\bar{x},y)\, dy\right]\Delta_i x = \int_a^b\int_{\phi_1(x)}^{\phi_2(x)} f(x,y)\, dy\, dx = \int_R\int f(x,y)\, dy\, dx$$

If the region R is bounded by the curves $x = \lambda_1(y)$ and $x = \lambda_2(y)$ and the lines $y = c$ and $y = d$, where $c < d$, and λ_1 and λ_2 are two functions continuous on the closed interval $[c,d]$ for which $\lambda_1(y) \leq \lambda_2(y)$ whenever $c \leq y \leq d$, then consider a partition Δ of the interval $[c,d]$ and divide the region into horizontal strips of widths $\Delta_i y$. See Fig. 23.2.4, which shows a particular horizontal strip.

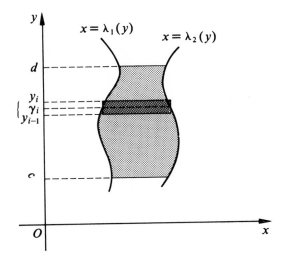

Figure 23.2.4

The intersection of the surface $z = f(x,y)$ and a plane $y = \bar{y}$, where $y_{i-1} \leq \bar{y} \leq y_i$, is a curve, and a segment of this curve is over the vertical strip of width $\Delta_i y$. Then, as above, the double integral of f over the horizontal strip is approximately equal to

$$\left[\int_{\lambda_1(\bar{y})}^{\lambda_2(\bar{y})} f(x,\bar{y})\, dx \right] \Delta_i y$$

Taking the limit as $\|\Delta\|$ approaches zero of the sum of these double integrals for all the horizontal strips of R from $y = c$ to $y = d$, again it seems reasonable that we would obtain the double integral of f on R, and so we have

$$(6) \qquad \lim_{\|\Delta\| \to 0} \sum_{i=1}^{n} \left[\int_{\lambda_1(\bar{y})}^{\lambda_2(\bar{y})} f(x,\bar{y}) \, dx \right] \Delta_i y = \int_c^d \int_{\lambda_1(y)}^{\lambda_2(y)} f(x,y) \, dx \, dy$$

$$= \iint_R f(x,y) \, dx \, dy$$

Sufficient conditions for formula (5) to be valid are that f be continuous on the closed region R and that ϕ_1 and ϕ_2 be smooth functions. Similarly formula (6) is valid if λ_1 and λ_2 are smooth functions and f is continuous on R. In some cases, it may be necessary to subdivide a region R into subregions on which the above conditions hold.

If in either (5) or (6), $f(x,y) = 1$ for all x and y, the double integral is the area of the region R in the xy plane.

EXAMPLE 3: Find by using double integrals the area of the region in the xy plane bounded by the curves $y = x^2$ and $y = -x^2 + 4x$.

Solution: The region is shown in Fig. 23.2.5. Let $A = $ the number of square units in the area of the region. Applying (5) we have

$$A = \int_0^2 \int_{x^2}^{-x^2+4x} dy \, dx = \int_0^2 (-x^2 + 4x - x^2) \, dx = 2\tfrac{2}{3}$$

EXAMPLE 4: Find the volume of the solid above the xy plane bounded by the elliptic paraboloid $z = x^2 + 4y^2$ and the cylinder $x^2 + 4y^2 = 4$.

Solution: The solid is shown in Fig. 23.2.6.

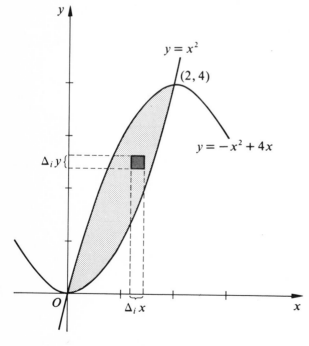

Figure 23.2.5

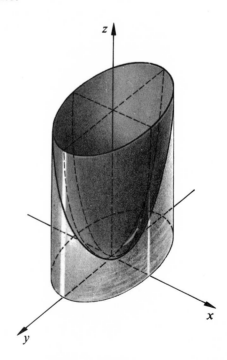

Figure 23.2.6

Using symmetry properties, we find the volume in the first octant which is one-fourth of the required volume. We have then

$$\frac{V}{4} = \int\int_R (x^2 + 4y^2)\, dA = \int_0^1 \int_0^{2\sqrt{1-y^2}} (x^2 + 4y^2)\, dx\, dy$$

$$= \int_0^1 \left[\frac{x^3}{3} + 4y^2x\right]_0^{2\sqrt{1-y^2}} dy$$

$$= \int_0^1 \left[\frac{8}{3}(1 - y^2)^{3/2} + 8y^2(1 - y^2)^{1/2}\right] dy$$

$$= \frac{8}{3}\int_0^1 [(1 - y^2)^{1/2} (2y^2 + 1)\, dy] = \pi$$

Therefore the volume is 4π cubic units.

EXAMPLE 5: Find the volume of the solid of Example 4 by reversing the order of integration.

Solution:

$$\frac{V}{4} = \int\int_R (x^2 + 4y^2)\, dA = \int_0^2 \int_0^{\sqrt{4-x^2}/2} (x^2 + 4y^2)\, dy\, dx$$

$$= \int_0^2 \left[x^2y + \frac{4}{3}y^3\right]_0^{\sqrt{4-x^2}/2} dx$$

$$= \int_0^2 \left[\frac{1}{2}x^2\sqrt{4 - x^2} + \frac{1}{6}(4 - x^2)^{3/2}\right] dx$$

$$= \frac{1}{6}\int_0^2 \sqrt{4 - x^2}(2x^2 + 4)\, dx = \pi$$

Hence the volume is 4π cubic units, which agrees with the answer of Example 4.

Exercises 23.2

In Exercises 1 through 5, find the exact value of the double integral.

1. Same as Exercise 1 in Exercises 23.1.

2. Same as Exercise 2 in Exercises 23.1.

3. Same as Exercise 3 in Exercises 23.1.

4. Same as Exercise 4 in Exercises 23.1.

5. Same as Exercise 5 in Exercises 23.1.

6. Find the volume bounded by the planes $x = y + 2z + 1$, $y = 0$, $z = 0$, and $3y + z - 3 = 0$. Draw a sketch of the solid.

7. Find the volume of the solid under the plane $z = 4x$ and above the circle $x^2 + y^2 = 16$ in the xy plane. Draw a sketch of the solid.

8. Find the volume of the solid in the first octant bounded by the paraboloid $z = 9 - x^2 - 3y^2$. Draw a sketch of the solid.

9. Find the volume of the solid in the first octant bounded by the two cylinders $x^2 + y^2 = 4$ and $x^2 + z^2 = 4$. Draw a sketch of the solid.

10. Find by double integration the volume of the portion of the sphere $x + y^2 + z^2 = 16$ which lies in the first octant. Draw a sketch of the solid.

11. Find the volume in the first octant bounded by the surfaces $x + z^2 = 1$, $x = y$, and $x = y^2$. Draw a sketch of the solid.

In Exercises 12 through 15, find the area of the region bounded by the given curves in the xy plane, using double integrals. Draw a sketch of the region.

12. $y^2 = 4x$ and $x^2 = 4y$ 14. $x^2 + y^2 = 16$ and $y^2 = 6x$

13. $y = x^3$ and $y = x^2$ 15. $y = x^2 - 9$ and $y = 9 - x^2$

16. Given the iterated integral

$$\int_0^a \int_0^x \sqrt{a^2 - x^2} \, dy \, dx$$

(a) Draw a sketch of the solid whose volume is represented by the given iterated integral; (b) evaluate the iterated integral; (c) write the iterated integral which gives the volume of the same solid as the given integral but for which the order of integration is reversed.

17. Given the iterated integral

$$\frac{2}{3} \int_0^a \int_0^{\sqrt{a^2 - x^2}} (2x + y) \, dy \, dx$$

Follow the same instructions as for Exercise 16.

18. Use double integration to find the area of the region in the first quadrant bounded by the parabola $y^2 = 4x$, the circle $x^2 + y^2 = 5$, and the x axis by two methods: (a) integrate first with respect to x; (b) integrate first with respect to y. Compare the two methods of solution.

19. Find, by two methods, the volume of the solid in the first octant bounded by the plane $3x + 8y + 6z = 24$, the xz and yz planes, and the region in the xy plane bounded by the parabola $y^2 = 2x$, the line $2x + 3y = 10$, and the x axis: (a) integrate first with respect to x; (b) integrate first with respect to y. Compare the two methods of solution.

20. Use double integration to find the volume of the solid common to two right-circular cylinders of radius r, whose axes intersect at right angles (see Exercise 10 in Exercises 11.9).

21. Express the volume of the ellipsoid $x^2/a^2 + y^2/b^2 + z^2/c^2 = 1$ as an iterated integral.

(23.3)   Center of mass and moments of inertia

In Chap. 11 we used single integrals to find the center of mass of a homogeneous lamina. In using single integrals we could consider only laminae of constant density. With double integrals we may find the center of mass of either a homogeneous or a nonhomogeneous lamina.

Suppose we are given a lamina which has the shape of a region R in the xy plane. Let $\rho(x,y)$ be the density of the lamina at any point (x,y) of R where ρ is continuous on R. To find the total mass of the lamina we proceed as follows. Let Δ be a partition of R into n rectangles. If (ξ_i, γ_i) is any point in the ith rectangle having area $\Delta_i A$, then an approximation to the mass of the ith rectangle is given by $\rho(\xi_i, \gamma_i)\, \Delta_i A$, and the total mass of the lamina is approximated by

$$\sum_{i=1}^{n} \rho(\xi_i, \gamma_i)\, \Delta_i A$$

Taking the limit of the above sum as the norm of Δ approaches zero, the mass M of the lamina is given by

$$M = \lim_{\|\Delta\| \to 0} \sum_{i=1}^{n} \rho(\xi_i, \gamma_i)\, \Delta_i A$$

or, equivalently,

$$M = \int \int_R \rho(x,y)\, dA$$

The moment of mass of the ith rectangle with respect to the x axis is approximated by $\gamma_i \rho(\xi_i, \gamma_i)\, \Delta_i A$. The sum of the moments of mass of the n rectangles with respect to the x axis is then approximated by the sum of n such terms and the moment of mass with respect to the x axis of the entire lamina is given by

$$M_x = \lim_{\|\Delta\| \to 0} \sum_{i=1}^{n} \gamma_i \rho(\xi_i, \gamma_i)\, \Delta_i A$$

or, equivalently,

$$M_x = \int \int_R y\rho(x,y)\, dA$$

Analogously, its moment of mass with respect to the y axis is given by

$$M_y = \int \int_R x\rho(x,y)\, dA$$

The center of mass of the lamina is denoted by the point $(\bar{x}, \bar{y})$ and

$$\bar{x} = \frac{M_y}{M} \quad \text{and} \quad \bar{y} = \frac{M_x}{M}$$

EXAMPLE 1: A lamina in the shape of an isosceles right triangle has a density which varies as the square of the distance from the vertex of the right angle. Find the mass and the center of mass of the lamina.

Solution: Choose the coordinate axes so that the vertex of the right triangle

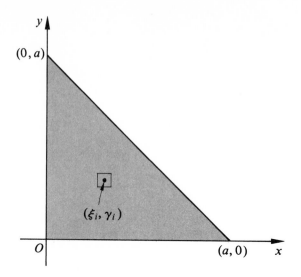

Figure 23.3.1

is at the origin and the sides of length a of the triangle are along the coordinate axes — see Fig. 23.3.1. The density is given by

$$\rho = k(x^2 + y^2)$$

Therefore,

$$M = k \iint\limits_{R} (x^2 + y^2) \, dA$$

$$= k \int_0^a \int_0^{a-x} (x^2 + y^2) \, dy \, dx = k \int_0^a \left[yx^2 + \frac{1}{3}y^3 \right]_0^{a-x} dx$$

$$= k \int_0^a \left(\frac{1}{3}a^3 - a^2x + 2ax^2 - \frac{4}{3}x^3 \right) dx$$

$$= k\left(\frac{1}{3}a^4 - \frac{1}{2}a^4 + \frac{2}{3}a^4 - \frac{1}{3}a^4 \right) = \frac{1}{6}ka^4$$

To find the center of mass, we observe that because of symmetry it must lie on the line $y = x$. Therefore if we find $\bar{x}$, we shall also have $\bar{y}$. We have

$$M_y = k \iint\limits_{R} x(x^2 + y^2) \, dA = k \int_0^a \int_0^{a-x} x(x^2 + y^2) \, dy \, dx$$

$$= k \int_0^a \left(\frac{1}{3}a^3x - a^2x^2 + 2ax^3 - \frac{4}{3}x^4 \right) dx$$

$$= k\left[\frac{1}{6}a^5 - \frac{1}{3}a^5 + \frac{1}{2}a^5 - \frac{4}{15}a^5 \right] = \frac{k}{15}a^5$$

Since $M\bar{x} = ka^5/15$ and $M = ka^4/6$, we get $\bar{x} = 2a/5$. Therefore the center of mass is at the point $(2a/5, 2a/5)$.

23.3.1 DEFINITION   The *moment of inertia* of a particle of mass m about an axis is defined to be the product mr^2, where r is the perpendicular distance from the particle to the axis.

If we have a system of n particles of masses $m_1, m_2, \ldots, m_n$ at distances of $r_1, r_2, \ldots, r_n$, respectively, the moment of inertia about the axis is given by

(1)
$$I = m_1 r_1^2 + m_2 r_2^2 + \cdots + m_n r_n^2$$

Extending this concept of moment of inertia to continuous distributions of masses in a plane such as rods or laminae by processes similar to those previously used, we have the following definition.

23.3.2 DEFINTION   Suppose we are given a distribution of masses occupying a region R in the xy plane and suppose the density of this distribution at the point (x,y) is given by $\rho(x,y)$, where ρ is continuous on R. Then the moment of inertia about the x axis of this distribution of masses is given by

(2)
$$I_x = \int\int_R y^2 \rho(x,y)\, dA$$

Similarly, the moment of inertia about the y axis is given by

(3)
$$I_y = \int\int_R x^2 \rho(x,y)\, dA$$

and the moment of inertia about the origin, or the z axis, is given by

(4)
$$I_O = \int\int_R (x^2 + y^2)\rho(x,y)\, dA$$

I_O, given by formula (4), is called the *polar moment of inertia.*

EXAMPLE 2: Find the moment of inertia of a homogeneous straight wire about an axis perpendicular to the wire and passing through one end.

Solution: Let the wire be of length a and suppose it extends along the x axis from the origin. We shall find its moment of inertia about the y axis. Divide the wire into segments of lengths $\Delta_1 x, \Delta_2 x, \ldots, \Delta_n x$, and consider the mass of the ith segment to be $\rho \Delta_i x$, where the density ρ is a constant. The moment of inertia of this segment is $\rho x_i^2\, \Delta_i x$ if all the masses are concentrated at a single point at a distance of x_i from the origin. The moment of inertia I then is given by

$$I = \lim_{\|\Delta\| \to 0} \sum_{i=1}^{n} \rho x_i^2\, \Delta_i x = \int_0^a \rho x^2\, dx = \tfrac{1}{3}\rho a^3$$

EXAMPLE 3: Find the moment of inertia of a homogeneous rectangular lamina about one corner.

Solution: Suppose the lamina is bounded by the lines $x = a$, $y = b$, the x axis, and the y axis. The moment of inertia about the origin is then given by

$$I_O = \int\int_R \rho(x^2 + y^2)\, dA = \rho \int_0^b \int_0^a (x^2 + y^2)\, dx\, dy = \rho \frac{ab}{3}(a^2 + b^2)$$

Let us imagine the total mass M of a lamina as being concentrated at one point; that is, suppose a particle at this point has the same mass M as the lamina. Then if this particle is at a distance r from a given axis L, the moment of inertia about L of this particle is Mr^2. This number r is called the *radius of gyration* of the given lamina about L. We have the following definition.

23.3.3 DEFINITION   If I is the moment of inertia about an axis L of a distribution of masses in a plane and M is the total mass of the distribution, then the *radius of gyration r* of the distribution about L is given by

$$r^2 = \frac{I}{M}$$

EXAMPLE 4: Suppose a lamina is in the shape of a semicircle and the density of the lamina at any point is proportional to the distance of the point from the diameter. Find the radius of gyration of the lamina about the x axis.

Solution: An equation of the circle is $x^2 + y^2 = a^2$ and the density of the lamina at the point (x,y) is given by $\rho(x,y) = ky$. Then

$$M = \lim_{\|\Delta\|\to 0} \sum_{i=1}^{n} \rho(\xi_i,\gamma_i)\,\Delta_i A = \int\int_R \rho(x,y)\,dA$$

$$= \int_0^a \int_{-\sqrt{a^2-y^2}}^{\sqrt{a^2-y^2}} ky\,dx\,dy = k\int_0^a \left[yx\right]_{-\sqrt{a^2-y^2}}^{\sqrt{a^2-y^2}}\,dy$$

$$= 2k\int_0^a y\sqrt{a^2 - y^2}\,dy = \frac{2}{3}ka^3$$

$$I_x = \lim_{\|\Delta\|\to 0} \sum_{i=1}^{n} \gamma_i{}^2\rho(\xi_i,\gamma_i)\,\Delta_i A = \int\int_R y^2\rho(x,y)\,dA$$

$$= \int_{-a}^{a}\int_0^{\sqrt{a^2-x^2}} ky^3\,dy\,dx = \frac{k}{4}\int_{-a}^{a}(a^2 - x^2)^2 = \frac{4}{15}ka^5$$

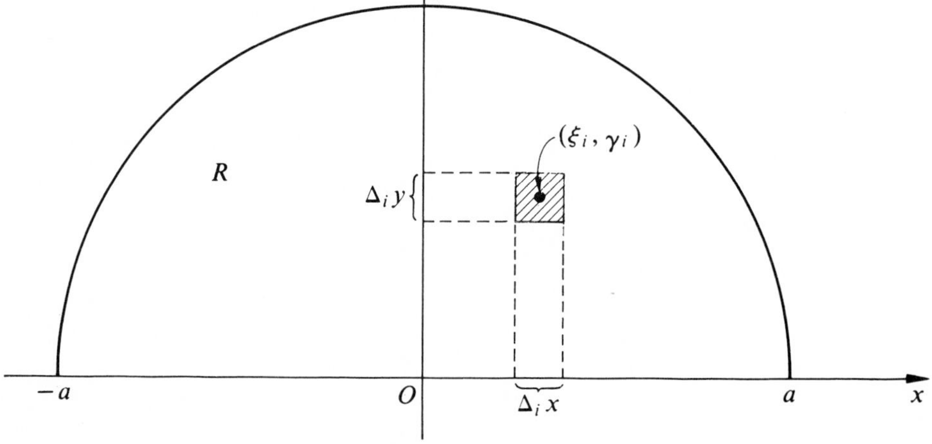

Figure 23.3.2

Therefore, if r is the radius of gyration,

$$r^2 = \left(\frac{4}{15} ka^5 \right) \Big/ \left(\frac{2}{3} ka^3 \right) = \frac{2}{5} a^2$$

and hence

$$r = \frac{\sqrt{10}}{5} a$$

Exercises 23.3

In Exercises 1 through 6, find the mass and center of mass of the given lamina if the density varies as indicated.

1. A lamina in the shape of a square of side a units, and the density varies as the square of the distance from one vertex.

2. A lamina in the shape of an isosceles right triangle and the density varies as the distance from one of the equal sides.

3. A lamina in the shape of the region bounded by $x^2 = 8y$, $x = 0$, $y = 2$, and the density varies as the distance from the line $y = -1$.

4. A lamina in the shape of the triangle which is cut from the first quadrant by the line $3x + 2y = 18$, and the density varies as the product of the distances from the coordinate axes.

5. A lamina in the shape of the region bounded by the curve $y = e^x$, the line $x = 1$, and the coordinate axes, and the density varies as the distance from the x axis.

6. A lamina in the shape of a quarter circle of radius a units, and the density varies as the sum of the distances from the two straight edges.

In Exercises 7 through 12, find the moment of inertia of the given homogeneous lamina about the indicated axis.

7. The lamina in the shape of the triangle bounded by $4y = 3x$, $x = 4$, and the x axis, about the y axis.

8. The lamina of Exercise 7 about the line $x = 4$.

9. The lamina in the shape of a circle of radius r units, about its center.

10. The lamina in the shape of the region bounded by the parabola $x^2 = 4 - 4y$ and the x axis, about the x axis.

11. The lamina of Exercise 10 about the origin.

12. The lamina in the shape of a triangle of sides of lengths a, b, and c about the side of length a.

13. *Given:* The lamina bounded by the curve $y = \sin x$ and the x axis from $x = 0$ to $x = \pi$. The density at any point is proportional to the distance of the point from the x axis. Find: (*a*) the mass; (*b*) the center of mass; (*c*) the

moment of inertia about the x axis; (d) the radius of gyration about the x axis.

14. For the lamina of Exercise 13, find: (a) the moment of inertia about the y axis; (b) the polar moment of inertia.

15. Given the lamina bounded by the curve $y = \sqrt{x}$ and the line $y = x$. The density at any point is proportional to the distance of the point from the y axis. Find: (a) the mass; (b) the center of mass; (c) the moment of inertia about the y axis; (d) the radius of gyration about the y axis.

16. For the lamina of Exercise 15, find: (a) the moment of inertia about the x axis; (b) the polar moment of inertia.

17. A homogeneous lamina is in the shape of an isosceles triangle having a base of length b and an altitude h. Find the radius of gyration of the lamina about its line of symmetry.

18. A lamina is enclosed by the parabola $y = 2x - x^2$ and the x axis. Find the moment of inertia of the lamina about the line $y = 4$ if the density at any point is proportional to the distance of the point from the line $y = 4$.

(23.4)   The double integral in polar coordinates

We shall now show how we may define the double integral of a function on a region in the polar coordinate plane. We shall begin by considering the simplest kind of region.

Let R be the region bounded by the lines $\theta = \alpha$ and $\theta = \beta$ and by the circles $r = a$ and $r = b$. Then let Δ be a *partition* of this region which is obtained by drawing lines through the pole and circles having centers at the pole. This is shown in Fig. 23.4.1. We obtain a network of subregions which we shall call

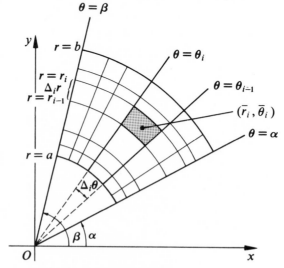

Figure 23.4.1

"curved" rectangles. The norm $||\Delta||$ of the partition is the length of the longest of the diagonals of the "curved" rectangles. Let the number of the subregions be n and let $\Delta_i A$ denote the area of the ith subregion. Then

$$\Delta_i A \;=\; \tfrac{1}{2}\Delta_i\theta\,(r_i{}^2 - r_{i-1}{}^2) \;=\; \bar{r}_i\,\Delta_i r\,\Delta_i\theta$$

where $\Delta_i\theta = \theta_i - \theta_{i-1}$, $\Delta_i r = r_i - r_{i-1}$, and $\bar{r}_i = (r_{i-1} + r_i)/2$. Let us take the point $(\bar{r}_i,\bar{\theta}_i)$ as the center of the ith subregion and form the sum

(1)
$$\sum_{i=1}^{n} f(\bar{r}_i,\bar{\theta}_i)\,\Delta_i A \;=\; \sum_{i=1}^{n} f(\bar{r}_i,\bar{\theta}_i)\bar{r}_i\,\Delta_i r\,\Delta_i\theta$$

It can be shown that if f is continuous on the region R, then the limit of the sum in (1), as $||\Delta||$ approaches zero, exists and that this limit will be the double integral of f on R. We write either

(2)
$$\lim_{||\Delta||\to 0} \sum_{i=1}^{n} f(\bar{r}_i,\bar{\theta}_i)\,\Delta_i A \;=\; \int\!\!\int_{R} f(r,\theta)\,dA$$

or

(3)
$$\lim_{||\Delta||\to 0} \sum_{i=1}^{n} f(\bar{r}_i,\bar{\theta}_i)\bar{r}_i\,\Delta_i r\,\Delta_i\theta \;=\; \int\!\!\int_{R} f(r,\theta)r\,dr\,d\theta$$

Note that in formula (3), we have $\bar{r}_i\,\Delta_i r\,\Delta_i\theta$, instead of $\Delta_i A$ and $r\,dr\,d\theta$, instead of dA.

The double integral may be shown to be equal to an iterated integral having one of two possible forms:

$$\int\!\!\int_{R} f(r,\theta)\,dA \;=\; \int_{\alpha}^{\beta}\!\int_{a}^{b} f(r,\theta)r\,dr\,d\theta \;=\; \int_{a}^{b}\!\int_{\alpha}^{\beta} f(r,\theta)\,r\,d\theta\,dr$$

We may define the double integral of a continuous function f of two variables on regions of the polar coordinate plane other than the one previously considered. For example, consider the region R bounded by $r = \phi_1(\theta)$ and $r = \phi_2(\theta)$ where ϕ_1 and ϕ_2 are smooth functions, and by the lines $\theta = \alpha$ and $\theta = \beta$. See Fig. 23.4.2. In the figure, $\phi_1(\theta) \leq \phi_2(\theta)$ for all θ in the closed interval $[\alpha,\beta]$. Then

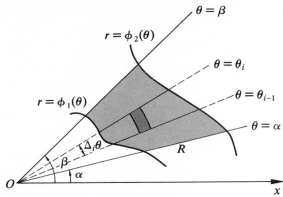

Figure 23.4.2

it may be shown that the double integral of f on R exists and equals an iterated integral, and we have

(4)
$$\iint\limits_{R} f(r,\theta)\, dA = \int_{\alpha}^{\beta} \int_{\phi_1(\theta)}^{\phi_2(\theta)} f(r,\theta) r\, dr\, d\theta$$

If the region R is bounded by the curves $\theta = \chi_1(r)$ and $\theta = \chi_2(r)$, where χ_1 and χ_2 are smooth functions, and by the circles $r = a$ and $r = b$, as shown in Fig. 23.4.3, where $\chi_1(r) \leq \chi_2(r)$ for all r in the closed interval $[a,b]$, then

(5)
$$\iint\limits_{R} f(r,\theta)\, dA = \int_{a}^{b} \int_{\chi_1(r)}^{\chi_2(r)} f(r,\theta) r\, d\theta\, dr$$

EXAMPLE 1: Find the mass of a lamina whose face is the first loop of the rose $r = \sin 3\theta$ and whose density at any point is proportional to its distance from the pole.

Solution: Refer to Fig. 23.4.4.

The density is given by $f(r,\theta) = kr$ and R is the region enclosed by one leaf of the rose. If M denotes the mass, we have

$$M = \iint\limits_{R} f(r,\theta) r\, dr\, d\theta = \iint\limits_{R} kr^2\, dr\, d\theta$$

$$= 2k \int_{0}^{\pi/6} \int_{0}^{\sin 3\theta} r^2\, dr\, d\theta = \frac{2k}{3} \int_{0}^{\pi/6} \sin^3 3\theta\, d\theta$$

$$= \frac{2k}{3} \int_{0}^{\pi/6} (1 - \cos^2 3\theta) \sin 3\theta\, d\theta$$

$$= \frac{2k}{3} \left[-\frac{\cos 3\theta}{3} + \frac{\cos^3 3\theta}{9} \right]_{0}^{\pi/6} = \frac{4k}{27}$$

Sometimes it is easier to evaluate a double integral in the polar coordinate system than in the cartesian coordinate system.

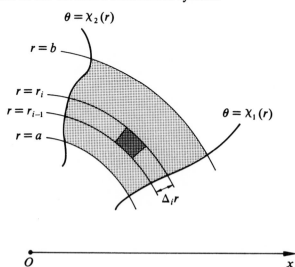

Figure 23.4.3

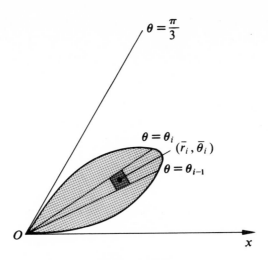

Figure 23.4.4

EXAMPLE 2: Evaluate the double integral

$$\int\int_R \frac{1}{x^2 + y^2}\, dx\, dy$$

where the region R is in the first quadrant and is bounded by the two circles $x^2 + y^2 = 1$ and $x^2 + y^2 = 4$.

Solution: If we evaluate this double integral in polar coordinates, taking as the equations of the circle that bound the region R, $r = 1$ and $r = 2$, and as the lines, $\theta = 0$ and $\theta = \pi/2$, we have

$$\int\int_R \frac{1}{x^2 + y^2}\, dx\, dy = \int\int_R \frac{1}{r}\, dr\, d\theta = \int_0^{\pi/2}\int_1^2 \frac{1}{r}\, dr\, d\theta$$

$$= \ln 2 \int_0^{\pi/2} d\theta = \frac{\pi}{2} \ln 2$$

We made the substitutions $dx\, dy = dA = r\, dr\, d\theta$ and $x^2 + y^2 = r^2$.

EXAMPLE 3: A homogeneous lamina is in the shape of a circle. Find the moment of inertia about a diameter.

Solution: Taking the center of the circle at the pole and the radius as a, an equation of the circle in polar coordinates is $r = a$. We can find the moment of inertia about the polar axis (or x axis) by using the formula

$$I_x = \int\int_R \rho y^2\, dA$$

Substituting $r \sin \theta$ for y and using formula (4), we have

$$I_x = \int\int_R \rho r^2 \sin^2 \theta\, dA = \rho \int_0^{2\pi}\int_0^a r^3 \sin^2 \theta\, dr\, d\theta = \tfrac{1}{4}\pi\rho a^4$$

Since the mass of the lamina is given by $M = \pi\rho a^2$, we may write $I_x = \tfrac{1}{4}Ma^2$.

Exercises 23.4

In Exercises 1 through 4, find the areas of the indicated region by using double integrals.

1. The region inside the cardioid $r = 2(1 + \sin \theta)$.

2. One leaf of the rose $r = a \cos 2\theta$.

3. The region inside the cardioid $r = a(1 + \cos \theta)$ and outside the circle $r = a$.

4. The region inside the circle $r = 1$ and outside the lemniscate $r^2 = \cos 2\theta$.

In Exercises 5 through 8, find the mass and the center of mass of the given lamina if the density varies as indicated.

5. The lamina in the shape of the circle $r = a \cos \theta$, and the density varies as the distance from the pole.

6. The lamina in the shape of the region inside the limaçon $r = 2 - \cos \theta$, and the density varies as the reciprocal of the distance from the pole.

7. The lamina in the shape of the region bounded by $r = 2 + \cos \theta, 0 \leq \theta \leq \pi$, and the polar axis, and the density varies as $\sin \theta$.

8. The lamina of Exercise 7, if the density varies as $r \sin \theta$.

In Exercises 9 through 12, find the moment of inertia of the given homogeneous lamina about the indicated axis or point.

9. The lamina in the shape of the circle $r = \sin \theta$ about the polar axis.

10. The lamina of Exercise 9 about the $\pi/2$ axis.

11. The lamina in the shape of the region bounded by the cardioid $r = a (1 - \cos \theta)$, about the pole.

12. The lamina in the shape of the region bounded by the cardioid $r = a (1 + \cos \theta)$ and the circle $r = 2a \cos \theta$, about the pole.

(23.5)   The triple integral

The extension of the double integral to the triple integral is analogous to the extension of the single integral to the double integral. The simplest type of region in E^3 is a rectangular parallelepiped which is bounded by six planes $x = a_1$, $x = a_2$, $y = b_1$, $y = b_2$, $z = c_1$, and $z = c_2$. Let f be a function of three variables and suppose f is continuous on such a region. A partition of this region is formed by dividing R into rectangular boxes by drawing planes parallel to the coordinate planes. Denote such a partition by Δ and suppose n is the number of boxes. Let $\Delta_i V$ be the volume of the ith box. Choose an arbitrary point (ξ_i, γ_i, μ_i) in the ith box. Form the sum

(1)
$$\sum_{i=1}^{n} f(\xi_i, \gamma_i, \mu_i) \, \Delta_i V$$

Refer to Fig. 23.5.1, which shows the rectangular parallelepiped together with the ith box.

The *norm* of the partition is the length of the longest diagonal of the boxes. The sums of form (1) will approach a limit as the norms of the partitions approach zero for any choices of the points (ξ_i, γ_i, μ_i), if f is continuous on R, and then we call this limit the *triple integral* of f on R. We write

$$\lim_{\|\Delta\| \to 0} \sum_{i=1}^{n} f(\xi_i, \gamma_i, \mu_i) \, \Delta_i V = \int \int_R \int f(x,y,z) \, dV$$

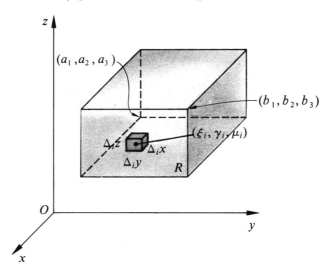

Figure 23.5.1

Analogous to a double integral being equal to a twice-iterated integral, the triple integral is equal to a threefold-iterated integral. When R is the rectangular parallelepiped described above, and f is continuous on R, we have

$$\int \int_R \int f(x,y,z) \, dV = \int_{a_1}^{a_2} \int_{b_1}^{b_2} \int_{c_1}^{c_2} f(x,y,z) \, dz \, dy \, dx$$

EXAMPLE 1: Evaluate the triple integral

$$\int \int_R \int xy \sin yz \, dV$$

if R is the rectangular parallelepiped bounded by the planes $x = \pi$, $y = \pi$, $z = \pi$, and the three coordinate planes.

Solution:

$$\iiint\limits_{R} xy \sin yz \, dV = \int_0^\pi \int_0^\pi \int_0^\pi xy \sin yz \, dz \, dy \, dx$$

$$= \int_0^\pi \int_0^\pi -x \cos yz \Big]_0^\pi dy \, dx$$

$$= \int_0^\pi \int_0^\pi x(1 - \cos \pi y) \, dy \, dx$$

$$= \int_0^\pi x\left(y - \frac{1}{\pi} \sin \pi y\right)\Big]_0^\pi dx$$

$$= \int_0^\pi x\left(\pi - \frac{\sin \pi^2}{\pi}\right) dx = \frac{\pi^3 - \pi \sin \pi^2}{2}$$

We now discuss how to define the triple integral of a continuous function f of three variables on a region in E^3 other than a rectangular parallelepiped.

Suppose that R is a region in the xy plane. Let S be the closed three-dimensional region which is bounded by R, the planes $x = a$ and $x = b$, the cylinders $y = \phi_1(x)$ and $y = \phi_2(x)$, and the surfaces $z = F_1(x,y)$ and $z = F_2(x,y)$ where the functions ϕ_1, ϕ_2, F_1, and F_2 are smooth. See Fig. 23.5.2.

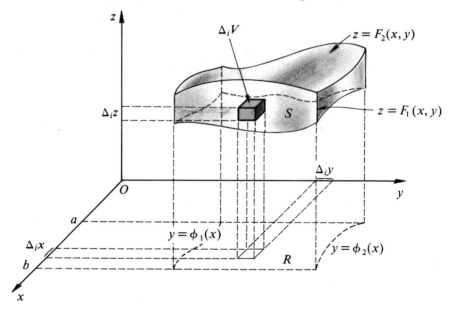

Figure 23.5.2

Construct planes parallel to the coordinate planes, forming a set of rectangular parallelepipeds which completely cover S. The parallelepipeds which are entirely inside S or on the boundary of S form a *partition* Δ of S. Choose some system of numbering so that they are numbered from 1 to n. The norm $||\Delta||$ of this partition of S is the length of the longest diagonal of any parallelepiped belonging to the partition.

Let the volume of the ith parallelepiped be $\Delta_i V$. This is also shown in Fig. 23.5.2. Let f be a function of three variables which is continuous on S and let (ξ_i, γ_i, μ_i) be an arbitrary point in the ith parallelepiped. Form the sum

(2) $$\sum_{i=1}^{n} f(\xi_i, \gamma_i, \mu_i)\, \Delta_i V$$

If the sums of form (1) have a limit as $\|\Delta\|$ approaches zero, and if this limit is independent of the choice of the partitioning planes and the choices of the arbitrary point (ξ_i, γ_i, μ_i) in each parallelepiped, then this limit is called the triple integral of f on S and we write

$$\lim_{\|\Delta\| \to 0} \sum_{i=1}^{n} f(\xi_i, \gamma_i, \mu_i)\, \Delta_i V = \int \int_{S} \int f(x,y,z)\, dV$$

It can be proved in advanced calculus that a sufficient condition for the above limit to exist is that f be continuous on S. Furthermore, under the condition imposed upon the functions ϕ_1, ϕ_2, F_1, and F_2 that they be smooth, it can also be proved that the triple integral may be evaluated by the iterated integral

$$\int_{a}^{b} \int_{\phi_1(x)}^{\phi_2(x)} \int_{F_1(x,y)}^{F_2(x,y)} f(x,y,z)\, dz\, dy\, dx$$

Just as the double integral can be interpreted as the area of a plane region, the triple integral can be interpreted as the volume of a three-dimensional region.

EXAMPLE 2: Find the volume of the solid bounded by the sphere

$$x^2 + y^2 + z^2 = 9$$

and below by the plane $z = 3 - y$.

Solution: The solid is shown in Fig. 23.5.3.

If we eliminate z between the two given equations, we obtain

$$x^2 + y^2 + (3 - y)^2 = 9,$$

or, equivalently,

$$x^2 = 6y - 2y^2$$

The volume of the solid S is given by

$$\int \int_{S} \int dV$$

To evaluate this triple integral by means of an iterated integral, we notice that the limits of integration for z are $3 - y$ to $\sqrt{9 - x^2 - y^2}$ and that those of the other two variables are those of the plane region R which is the projection of S onto the xy plane. We integrate with respect to y from 0 to 3 and with respect

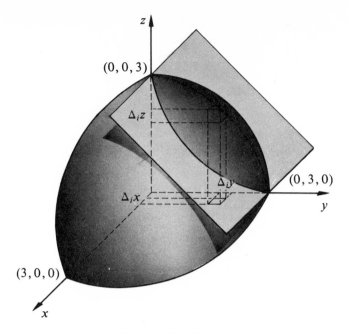

Figure 23.5.3

to x from $-\sqrt{6y - 2y^2}$ to $\sqrt{6y - 2y^2}$. So, if V is the volume of the solid, we have

$$V = \int \int_S \int dV = \int_0^3 \int_{-\sqrt{6y-2y^2}}^{\sqrt{6y-2y^2}} \int_{3-y}^{\sqrt{9-x^2-y^2}} dz \, dx \, dy$$
$$= \frac{2}{3}\pi$$

Some physical applications of the triple integral will be taken up in the next section using cylindrical and spherical coordinates.

Exercises 23.5

In Exercises 1 through 6, evaluate the given triple integral.

1. $\int \int_R \int y \, dV$ if R is the region bounded by the tetrahedron formed by the plane $12x + 20y + 15z = 60$ and the coordinate planes.

2. $\int \int_R \int (x^2 + z^2) \, dV$ if R is the same region as in Exercise 1.

3. $\int \int_R \int z \, dV$ if R is the region bounded by the tetrahedron having vertices $(0,0,0)$, $(1,1,0)$, $(1,0,0)$, and $(1,0,1)$.

4. $\int \int_R \int yz \, dV$ if R is the same region as in Exercise 3.

5. $\int \int_R \int (xz + 3z) \, dV$ if R is the region bounded by the cylinder $x^2 + z^2 = 9$ and the planes $x + y = 3$, $z = 0$, and $y = 0$.

6. $\int \int\limits_{R} \int xyz \, dV$, if R is the region bounded by the cylinders $x^2 + y^2 = 4$ and $x^2 + z^2 = 4$.

In Exercises 7 through 12, find the volume of the given solid by triple integration. Draw a sketch of the solid.

7. The solid in the first octant bounded below by the xy plane, above by the plane $z = y$, and laterally by the cylinder $y^2 = x$ and the plane $x = 1$. Set up the six iterated integrals with their limits for a triple integral over this solid.

8. The solid in the first octant bounded by the cylinder $x^2 + z^2 = 16$, the plane $x + y = 2$, and the three coordinate planes.

9. The solid in the first octant bounded by the cylinders $x^2 + y^2 = 4$ and $x^2 + 2z = 4$ and the three coordinate planes.

10. The solid bounded by the elliptic cone $4x^2 + 9y^2 - 36z^2 = 0$ and the plane $z = 1$.

11. The volume of the sphere $x^2 + y^2 + z^2 = a^2$.

12. The volume of the ellipsoid $x^2/a^2 + y^2/b^2 + z^2/c^2 = 1$.

(23.6)   Cylindrical and spherical coordinates.

If a region S in E^3 has an axis of symmetry, triple integrals on S are easier to evaluate if *cylindrical coordinates* are used, and if there is symmetry with respect to a point, it is often convenient to choose that point as the origin and to use *spherical coordinates*. In this section we shall introduce these two coordinate systems and apply triple integration to physical applications using these coordinates.

The cylindrical coordinates of a point P in three-dimensional space are r, θ,

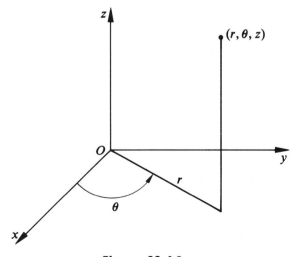

Figure 23.6.1

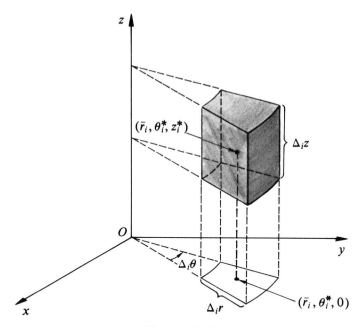

Figure 23.6.2

and z, where (r,θ) is the polar-coordinate representation of the projection of P onto a polar plane and z is the directed distance from this polar plane to P. See Fig. 23.6.1.

Construct a partition of the region S by drawing planes through the z axis, planes perpendicular to the z axis, and right-circular cylinders having the z axis as axis. A typical subregion is shown in Fig. 23.6.2. The elements of the constructed partition lie entirely in S. We call this partition a *cylindrical partition*. The length of the longest "diagonal" of any of the subregions is the *norm* of the partition. Let n be the number of subregions of the partition and $\Delta_i V$ be the volume of the ith subregion.

The volume of the ith subregion is equal to the area of its base times its altitude. The area of the base is $\bar{r}_i\,\Delta_i r\,\Delta_i\theta$, where $\bar{r}_i = (r_i + r_{i-1})/2$. Hence if $\Delta_i z$ is the altitude of the ith subregion, $\Delta_i V = \bar{r}_i\,\Delta_i r\,\Delta_i\theta\,\Delta_i z$.

Let f be a function of r, θ, and z, and suppose that f is continuous on S. Let $(\bar{r}_i, \theta_i^*, z_i^*)$ be the cylindrical coordinate representation of an arbitrary point in the ith subregion such that $\theta_{i-1} \leq \theta_i^* \leq \theta_i$ and $z_{i-1} \leq z_i^* \leq z_i$. Form the sum

$$(1) \qquad \sum_{i=1}^{n} f(\bar{r}_i, \theta_i^*, z_i^*)\bar{r}_i\,\Delta_i r\,\Delta_i\theta\,\Delta_i z$$

As the norm of Δ approaches zero, it can be shown, under suitable conditions on S, that the limit of the sums of form (1) exist. This limit is called the *triple integral in cylindrical coordinates* of the function f on S, and we write

$$(2) \qquad \lim_{\|\Delta\|\to 0} \sum_{i=1}^{n} f(\bar{r}_i, \theta_i^*, z_i^*)\bar{r}_i\,\Delta_i r\,\Delta_i\theta\,\Delta_i z = \int\!\!\int_S\!\!\int f(r,\theta,z)r\,dr\,d\theta\,dz$$

We may evaluate the triple integral in (2) by an iterated integral. Let the region S in E^3 be bounded by the planes $\theta = \alpha$ and $\theta = \beta$, with $\alpha < \beta$, the cylinders $r = \phi_1(\theta)$ and $r = \phi_2(\theta)$ where ϕ_1 and ϕ_2 are smooth on $[\alpha,\beta]$ and $\phi_1(\theta) \leq \phi_2(\theta)$ for $\alpha \leq \theta \leq \beta$, and by the surfaces $z = F_1(r,\theta)$ and $z = F_2(r,\theta)$ where F_1 and F_2 are functions of two variables which are smooth on some region R in the polar plane which is bounded by the curves $r = \phi_1(\theta)$, $r = \phi_2(\theta)$, $\theta = \alpha$, and $\theta = \beta$. Furthermore, let $F_1(r,\theta) \leq F_2(r,\theta)$ for every point (r,θ) in R. Then the triple integral may be evaluated by an iterated integral by the formula

$$(3) \qquad \iiint\limits_{S} f(r,\theta,z)r\,dr\,d\theta\,dz = \int_{\alpha}^{\beta} \int_{\phi_1(\theta)}^{\phi_2(\theta)} \int_{F_1(r,\theta)}^{F_2(r,\theta)} rf(r,\theta,z)\,dz\,dr\,d\theta$$

There are five other iterated integrals which can be used to evaluate the triple integral in (3) since there are six possible permutations of the three variables r, θ, and z.

EXAMPLE 1: Find the center of mass of a solid hemisphere of radius a having constant density.

Solution: If we choose our coordinate axes so that the origin is at the center of the sphere, then an equation of the hemispherical surface which is above the xy plane is $z = \sqrt{a^2 - x^2 - y^2}$. Figure 23.6.3 shows this surface and the solid

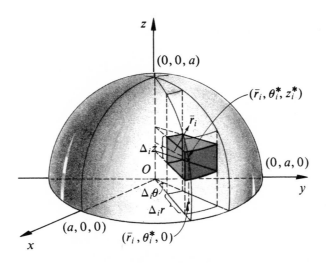

Figure 23.6.3

together with an element of volume. Because of symmetry, $\bar{x} = \bar{y} = 0$. So we calculate $\bar{z}$. Expressing the equation of the hemisphere in cylindrical coordinates we have

$$z = \sqrt{a^2 - r^2}$$

Hence if M_{xy} is the moment of mass with respect to the xy plane,

$$M_{xy} = \iiint\limits_{S} \rho z\,dV = \rho\int_{0}^{2\pi} \int_{0}^{a} \int_{0}^{\sqrt{a^2-r^2}} z\,dz\,r\,dr\,d\theta = (1/4)\rho\pi a^4$$

Since the mass of the hemisphere is $(2/3)\rho\pi a^3$, we get

$$\bar{z} = \frac{M_{xy}}{(2/3)\rho\pi a^3} = \frac{3a}{8}$$

Suppose we have a distribution of masses of variable density distributed over a region S in three-dimensional space. Let the density be $\rho(x,y,z)$ at the point (x,y,z) in S. Then if M denotes the total mass, $(\bar{x},\bar{y},\bar{z})$ denotes the center of mass, and I_x, I_y, and I_z, denote the moments of inertia with respect to the x, y, and z axes, respectively, their values are given by

$$M = \iiint_S \rho(x,y,z)\, dV \qquad \bar{x} = \frac{\iiint_S x\rho(x,y,z)\, dV}{M}$$

$$\bar{y} = \frac{\iiint_S y\rho(x,y,z)\, dV}{M} \qquad \bar{z} = \frac{\iiint_S z\rho(x,y,z)\, dV}{M}$$

$$I_x = \iiint_S (y^2 + z^2)\rho(x,y,z)\, dV \qquad I_y = \iiint_S (x^2 + z^2)\rho(x,y,z)\, dV$$

$$I_z = \iiint_S (x^2 + y^2)\rho(x,y,z)\, dV$$

The integrals in the above equations may be evaluated either by letting $dV = dz\, dy\, dx$ or by using cylindrical coordinates, in which case $dV = dz\, r\, dr\, d\theta$.

EXAMPLE 2: Find the moment of inertia of the homgeneous right-circular cylinder bounded by the xy plane, the plane $z = 4$, and the cylindrical surface $x^2 + y^2 = 4$ with respect to the z axis.

Solution: Figure 23.6.4 shows the portion of the right-circular cylinder in the first octant, together with an element of volume. Using cylindrical coordinates and letting $x^2 + y^2 = r^2$, the formula for I_z is

$$I_z = \iiint_S r^2\rho\, dz\, r\, dr\, d\theta$$

There are six different possible orders of integration. Figure 23.6.4 shows the order $dz\, dr\, d\theta$. Replacing the triple integral by the iterated integral, we get

$$I_z = 4 \int_0^{\pi/2} \int_0^2 \int_0^4 r^3\rho\, dz\, dr\, d\theta$$

In the first integration, the block is summed from $z = 0$ to $z = 4$; the block becomes a column. In the second integration, the column is summed from $r = 0$ to $r = 2$; the column becomes a wedge-shaped slice of the cylinder. In the third integration, the wedge-shaped slice is rotated from $\theta = 0$ to $\theta = \pi/2$; this sweeps the wedge about the entire volume in the first octant. We multiply by 4 to get the entire volume. After performing the integration, we obtain

$$I_x = 32\pi\rho$$

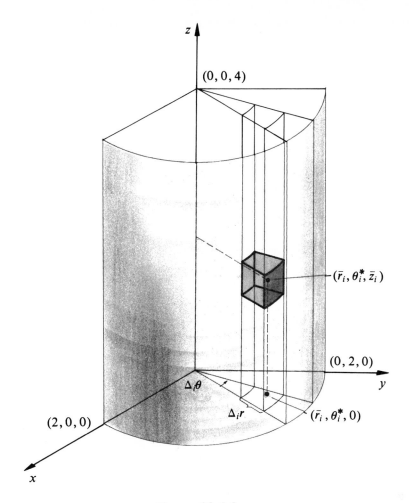

Figure 23.6.4

We illustrate the summation of the element in two other orders. Figure 23.6.5 represents the order $dr\ dz\ d\theta$. It shows the block summed from $r = 0$ to $r = 2$ to give a wedge-shaped sector; this is summed from $z = 0$ to $z = 4$ to give a wedge-shaped slice; the slice is rotated from $\theta = 0$ to $\theta = \pi/2$ to cover the first octant.

Figure 23.6.6 represents the order $d\theta\ dr\ dz$. It shows the block summed from $\theta = 0$ to $\theta = \pi/2$ to give a hollow ring inside the cylinder; this hollow ring is summed from $r = 0$ to $r = 2$ to give a horizontal slice of the cylinder; the horizontal slice is summed from $z = 0$ to $z = 4$.

You will note that triple integrals and cylindrical coordinates are especially useful in finding the moment of inertia of a solid with respect to the z axis, since the distance from the z axis to the element of volume is the coordinate r.

In a spherical coordinate system, there is a polar coordinate plane and a z axis perpendicular to the polar plane at the pole. A point is located by three

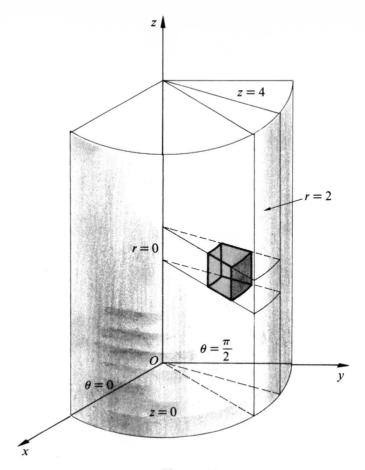

Figure 23.6.5

numbers, and the spherical coordinate representation of a point P is (ρ,θ,ϕ) where $\rho = |\overline{OP}|$, θ is the polar angle of the projection of P on the polar plane, and ϕ is the smallest nonnegative angle from the positive side of the z axis to the line OP. See Fig. 23.6.7.

A partition of the solid region S is formed by planes containing the z axis, spheres with centers at the origin, and circular cones having vertices at the origin and the z axis as the axis. A typical subregion of the partition, having volume $\Delta_i V$, is shown in Fig. 23.6.8. The element of volume is approximated by $\bar{\rho}_i^2 \sin \bar{\phi}_i \Delta_i \rho \, \Delta_i \theta \, \Delta_i \phi$. The triple integral in spherical coordinates of a function f of three variables over a region S in E^3 is given by

$$\lim_{||\Delta|| \to 0} \sum_{i=1}^{n} f(\bar{\rho}_i \bar{\theta}_i \bar{\phi}_i) \bar{\rho}_i^2 \sin \bar{\phi}_i \Delta_i \rho \, \Delta_i \theta \Delta_i \phi = \iint_S \int f(\rho,\theta,\phi) \rho^2 \sin \phi \, d\rho \, d\theta \, d\phi$$

and it is evaluated by an iterated integral. Spherical coordinates are especially useful in some problems involving spheres. The following example illustrates this.

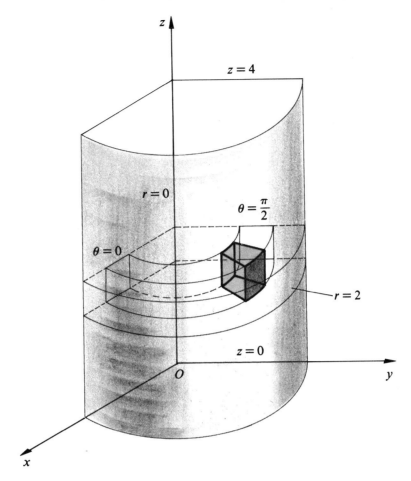

Figure 23.6.6

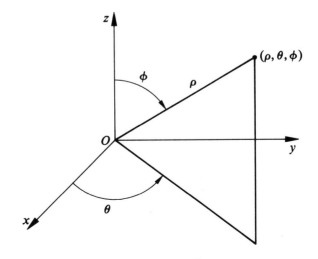

Figure 23.6.7

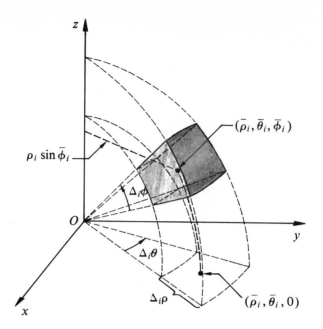

Figure 23.6.8

EXAMPLE 3: Find the mass, the center of mass, and the moment of inertia about the z axis of the homogeneous solid bounded above by the sphere $\rho = a$ and below by the cone $\phi = \alpha$, where $0 < \phi < \pi/2$.

   Solution: Since the solid is homogeneous, its density is a constant; call it k Also, the center of mass is on the axis of symmetry, which is the z axis. The

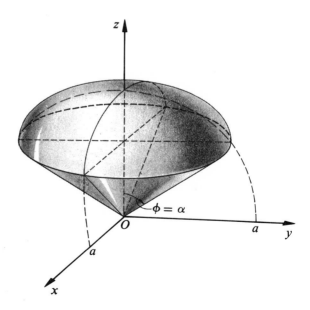

Figure 23.6.9

solid is shown in Fig. 23.6.9. Let M equal the mass of the given solid. We have then

$$M = \int_0^{2\pi} \int_0^\alpha \int_0^a k\rho^2 \sin\phi \, d\rho \, d\phi \, d\theta = \frac{2}{3}\pi a^3 k(1 - \cos\alpha)$$

Let M_p be the moment of mass about the polar plane p. Then, since $z = \rho \cos\phi$, we have

$$M_p = \int_0^{2\pi} \int_0^\alpha \int_0^a k(\rho \cos\phi)\rho^2 \sin\phi \, d\rho \, d\phi \, d\theta$$

$$= \frac{a^4 k}{4} \int_0^{2\pi} \int_0^\alpha \sin\phi \cos\phi \, d\phi = \frac{a^4}{8}k \sin^2\alpha \int_0^{2\pi} d\theta = \frac{1}{4}k\pi a^4 \sin^2\alpha$$

$$\bar{z} = \frac{M_p}{M} = \frac{3}{8}a(1 + \cos\alpha)$$

Therefore the center of mass of the solid is at the point $(3a(1 + \cos\alpha)/8, 0, 0)$.

Since the distance of a point (ρ, θ, ϕ) from the vertical z axis is given by $\rho \sin\phi$, the moment of inertia about the z axis of a particle at the point (ρ, θ, ϕ) of mass m is given by $m\rho^2 \sin^2\phi$. Therefore the moment of inertia of the given solid about the z axis is given by

$$I_z = \int_0^{2\pi} \int_0^\alpha \int_0^a k(\rho^2 \sin^2\phi)\rho^2 \sin\phi \, d\rho \, d\phi \, d\theta$$

$$= k\frac{a^5}{5} \int_0^{2\pi} \int_0^\alpha \sin^3\phi \, d\phi \, d\theta = \frac{2}{15}\pi a^5 k(\cos^3\alpha - 3\cos\alpha + 2)$$

Exercises 23.6

1. Find the moment of inertia of the tetrahedron bounded by the coordinate planes and the plane $2x + 3y + 4z = 12$, about the x axis.

2. Find the moment of inertia of the solid bounded by the cylinder $x = 4 - y^2$ and the planes $y = z$, $x = 0$, and $z = 0$, about the z axis.

3. Find the moment of inertia of a right-circular cone of base radius a, altitude h, and mass M about an axis through the vertex and parallel to the base.

4. Find the mass and center of mass of the solid hemisphere $r = a$ above the xy plane if its density varies as the distance from the origin.

5. Find the mass and center of mass of the solid hemisphere of Exercise 4 if its density varies as the square of the distance from the origin.

6. Find the mass of the solid between two concentric spheres having radii a and $2a$ if the density varies inversely as the square of the distance from the center.

7. Find the moment of inertia of the solid in Exercise 6 about a diameter.

8. Use spherical coordinates to find the volume of a right-circular cone having vertex angle α and altitude h.

9. Find the mass of the solid in Exercise 8 if the density varies as the distance from the vertex.

10. Find the moment of inertia of the solid of Exercise 8 with respect to the axis.

11. A torus is generated by revolving a circle of radius a about an axis in its plane at a distance b from the center of the circle ($b > a$). If the mass of the torus is M, find its moment of inertia about the axis of revolution.

12. A tetrahedron has its faces in the planes $x = y$, $x = z$, $z = a$, and $y = 0$. The density of the tetrahedron varies inversely as the distance from the z axis. Find its mass in two ways: (a) express the equations of the planes $x = z$ and $z = a$ in spherical coordinates; (b) express the equations of the planes $x = z$ and $z = a$ in cylindrical coordinates.

24 Infinite series

(24.1) Sequences

The reader has undoubtedly encountered sequences of numbers in his previous study of mathematics. For example, the numbers, 5, 7, 9, 11, 13, 15 form a sequence. This sequence is said to be *finite*, since there is a first and last number. If a sequence does not have both a first and last number, the sequence is said to be *infinite*. For example, the sequence

(1)
$$\frac{1}{3}, \frac{2}{5}, \frac{3}{7}, \frac{4}{9}, \ldots$$

is infinite, since the three dots with no number following indicate that there is no last number. We shall be concerned here with infinite sequences, and when we use the word sequence it will be understood that we are referring to an "infinite" sequence. We define a sequence as a particular kind of function.

24.1.1 DEFINITION   A *sequence* is a function whose domain is the set of positive integers.

The numbers in the range of the sequence, which are called the *elements* of the sequence, will be restricted to real numbers in this book.

If the function f is defined by $f(n) = n/(2n + 1)$, where n is a positive integer, we have for function values the following:

$$f(1) = \frac{1}{3} \quad f(2) = \frac{2}{5} \quad f(3) = \frac{3}{7} \quad f(4) = \frac{4}{9} \quad \text{etc.}$$

and we see that the range of f consists of the elements of the sequence (1). Usually the nth element, $f(n)$, of the sequence is stated when the elements are listed in order. So, for the sequence (1) we would write

$$\frac{1}{3}, \frac{2}{5}, \frac{3}{7}, \frac{4}{9}, \ldots, \frac{n}{2n + 1}, \ldots$$

A sequence is then a set of ordered pairs of the form $(n, f(n))$, where n is any positive integer. Since the domain of any sequence is the same, we may use the notation $\{f(n)\}$ to denote a sequence. So the sequence (1) may be denoted by $\{n/(2n + 1)\}$. We also use the subscript notation $\{a_n\}$ to denote the sequence for which $f(n) = a_n$.

The reader should distinguish between the elements of a sequence and the sequence itself. For example, the sequence $\{1/n\}$ has as its elements the reciprocals of the positive integers,

(2) $$1, \frac{1}{2}, \frac{1}{3}, \frac{1}{4}, \cdots, \frac{1}{n}, \cdots$$

The sequence for which

$$f(n) = \begin{cases} 1 & \text{if } n \text{ is odd} \\ \dfrac{2}{n+2} & \text{if } n \text{ is even} \end{cases}$$

has as its elements

(3) $$1, \frac{1}{2}, 1, \frac{1}{3}, 1, \frac{1}{4}, \cdots$$

The elements of sequences (2) and (3) are the same; however, the sequences are different.

If there is a number L such that $|L - a_n|$ is arbitrarily small, for n sufficiently large, we say that the sequence $\{a_n\}$ has the limit L. Following is the precise definition of the *limit* of a sequence.

24.1.2 DEFINITION   A sequence $\{a_n\}$ is said to have the limit L if for every $\epsilon > 0$, there exists a number $N > 0$ such that $|a_n - L| < \epsilon$ for every integer $n > N$; and we write

$$\lim_{n \to +\infty} a_n = L$$

The reader should compare this definition with Definition 4.4.1 of the limit of $f(x)$ as x approaches positive infinity. The two definitions are almost identical; however, when we state that $\lim\limits_{x \to +\infty} f(x) = L$, the function f is defined for all real numbers greater than some real number R, while when we consider $\lim\limits_{n \to +\infty} a_n$, n is restricted to positive integers. We have, however, the following theorem which follows immediately from Definition 4.4.1.

24.1.3 THEOREM   If $\lim\limits_{x \to +\infty} f(x) = L$, and f is defined for every positive integer, then also $\lim\limits_{n \to +\infty} f(n) = L$ when n is any positive integer.

The proof is left for the reader (see Exercise 13 at the end of this section).

24.1.4 DEFINITION   If a sequence $\{a_n\}$ has a limit, the sequence is said to be *convergent* and we say that a_n *converges* to that limit. If a sequence is not convergent, it is said to be *divergent*.

EXAMPLE 1: Prove that if $|r| < 1$, the sequence $\{r^n\}$ is convergent and that r^n converges to zero.

Proof: First of all, if $r = 0$, the sequence is $\{0\}$ and $\lim\limits_{n \to +\infty} 0 = 0$, and so the theorem holds. If $0 < |r| < 1$, we shall consider the function f defined by $f(x) = r^x$, where x is any positive number, and show that $\lim_{x \to +\infty} r^x = 0$. Then from Theorem 24.1.3 it will follow that $\lim_{n \to +\infty} r^n = 0$ when n is any positive integer.

To prove that $\lim_{x \to +\infty} r^x = 0$ $(0 < |r| < 1)$, we shall show that for any $\epsilon > 0$, there exists a number $N > 0$ such that

(4) $$|r^x - 0| < \epsilon \quad \text{whenever} \quad x > N$$

Statement (4) is equivalent to

$$|r|^x < \epsilon \quad \text{whenever} \quad x > N$$

which will be true if and only if

$$\ln |r|^x < \ln \epsilon \quad \text{whenever} \quad x > N$$

or, equivalently,

(5) $$x \ln |r| < \ln \epsilon \quad \text{whenever} \quad x > N$$

Since $0 < |r| < 1$, $\ln |r| < 0$, and so (5) is equivalent to

$$x > \frac{\ln \epsilon}{\ln |r|} \quad \text{whenever} \quad x > .N$$

Therefore, if we take $N = \ln \epsilon / \ln |r|$, we may conclude (4). Consequently, $\lim_{x \to +\infty} r^x = 0$, and so $\lim_{n \to +\infty} r^n = 0$ if n is any positive integer. Hence, by Definitions 24.1.2 and 24.1.4, $\{r^n\}$ is convergent and r^n converges to zero.

We have limit theorems for sequences, which are analogous to limit theorems for functions given in Chap. 4. We shall state these theorems using the terminology of sequences. The proofs are omitted since they are almost identical to the proofs of the corresponding theorems given in Chap. 4.

24.1.5 THEOREM If $\{a_n\}$ and $\{b_n\}$ are convergent sequences and c is a constant, then

(i) the constant sequence $\{c\}$ has c as its limit

(ii) $\lim_{n \to +\infty} c\, a_n = c \lim_{n \to +\infty} a_n$

(iii) $\lim_{n \to +\infty} (a_n \pm b_n) = \lim_{n \to +\infty} a_n \pm \lim_{n \to +\infty} b_n$

(iv) $\lim_{n \to +\infty} a_n b_n = (\lim_{n \to +\infty} a_n)(\lim_{n \to +\infty} b_n)$

(v) $\lim_{n \to +\infty} \dfrac{a_n}{b_n} = \dfrac{\lim_{n \to +\infty} a_n}{\lim_{n \to +\infty} b_n}$ if $\lim_{n \to +\infty} b_n \neq 0$

EXAMPLE 2: Determine if the sequence $\left\{ \dfrac{n^2}{2n^2 - 1} \right\}$ is convergent or divergent.

Solution: We shall investigate $\displaystyle\lim_{n\to+\infty}\frac{n^2}{2n^2-1}$.

$$\lim_{n\to+\infty}\frac{n^2}{2n^2-1}=\lim_{n\to+\infty}\frac{1}{2-1/n^2}=\frac{1}{2-\displaystyle\lim_{n\to+\infty}1/n^2}=\frac{1}{2}$$

NOTE: Theorem 4.4.4(ii) states that $\displaystyle\lim_{x\to+\infty}1/x^2=0$ if x is a real number; so, by Theorem 24.1.3 it follows that $\displaystyle\lim_{n\to+\infty}1/n^2=0$ when n is a positive integer.

We conclude that the given sequence is convergent and that $n^2/(2n^2-1)$ converges to $1/2$.

EXAMPLE 3: Determine if the sequence $\{(-1)^n+1\}$ is convergent or divergent.

Solution: The terms of this sequence are $0, 2, 0, 2, 0, 2, \ldots, (-1)^n+1, \ldots$. Since $a_n=0$ if n is odd, and $a_n=2$ if n is even, it appears that the sequence is divergent. To prove this, let us assume that the sequence is convergent and show that this assumption leads to a contradiction. If the sequence has the limit L, then by Definition 24.1.2, for every $\epsilon>0$, there exists a number $N>0$ such that $|a_n-L|<\epsilon$ for every integer $n>N$. In particular, taking $\epsilon=1/2$, there exists a number $N>0$ such that

$$|a_n-L|<1/2 \qquad \text{for every integer } n>N$$

or, equivalently,

(6) $\qquad -1/2<a_n-L<1/2 \qquad \text{for every integer } n>N$

Since $a_n=0$ if n is odd and $a_n=2$ if n is even, it follows from (6) that

$$-1/2<-L<1/2 \qquad \text{and} \qquad -1/2<2-L<1/2$$

But if $-L>-1/2$, then $2-L>3/2$, and hence $2-L$ cannot be less than $1/2$. So, we have a contradiction, and therefore the given sequence is divergent.

EXAMPLE 4: Determine if the sequence $\{n\sin(\pi/n)\}$ is convergent or divergent.

Solution: We wish to determine if $\displaystyle\lim_{n\to+\infty}n\sin(\pi/n)$ exists. Let $f(x)=x\sin(\pi/x)$ and investigate $\displaystyle\lim_{x\to+\infty}f(x)$. Since $f(x)$ may be written as $[\sin(\pi/x)]/(1/x)$ and $\displaystyle\lim_{x\to+\infty}\sin(\pi/x)=0$ and $\displaystyle\lim_{x\to+\infty}(1/x)=0$, we may apply L'Hôpital's rule, and we have

$$\lim_{x\to+\infty}f(x)=\lim_{x\to+\infty}\frac{-(\pi/x^2)\cos(\pi/x)}{-1/x^2}=\lim_{x\to+\infty}\pi\cos(\pi/x)=\pi$$

Therefore $\displaystyle\lim_{n\to+\infty}f(n)=\pi$ when n is a positive integer. So the given sequence is convergent and $n\sin(\pi/n)$ converges to π.

We shall be concerned with certain kinds of sequences, which are given special names.

24.1.6 DEFINITION   A sequence $\{a_n\}$ is said to be *monotonic* and

- (i)   *nondecreasing* if $a_n \leq a_{n+1}$

- (ii) *strictly increasing* if $a_n < a_{n+1}$

- (iii) *nonincreasing* if $a_n \geq a_{n+1}$

- (iv) *strictly decreasing* if $a_n > a_{n+1}$

Sequence (1) is an example of a strictly increasing sequence, (2) is an example of a strictly decreasing sequence, and (3) is a sequence which is not monotonic.

24.1.7 DEFINITION   The number C is called a *lower bound* of the sequence $\{a_n\}$ if $C \leq a_n$ for all positive integers n, and the number D is called an *upper bound* of the sequence $\{a_n\}$ if $a_n \leq D$ for all positive integers n.

The number zero is a lower bound of the sequence (1). Another lower bound of this sequence is $1/3$. Actually any number which is less than or equal to $1/3$ is a lower bound of sequence (1). For the sequence (2), 1 is an upper bound; 26 is also an upper bound. Any number which is greater than or equal to 1 is an upper bound of sequence (2). Any nonpositive number will serve as a lower bound of sequence (2). We see then that a sequence may have many upper or lower bounds.

24.1.8 DEFINITION   If A is a lower bound of a sequence $\{a_n\}$ and if A has the property that for every lower bound C of $\{a_n\}$, $C \leq A$, then A is called the *greatest lower bound* of the sequence. Similarly, if B is an upper bound of a sequence $\{a_n\}$ and if B has the property that for every upper bound D of $\{a_n\}$, $B \leq D$, then B is called the *least upper bound* of the sequence.

The greatest lower bound of sequence (1) is $1/3$, and the least upper bound of sequence (2) is 1.

24.1.9 DEFINITION   A sequence $\{a_n\}$ is said to be *bounded* if and only if it has an upper bound and a lower bound.

We now state a very important property of the real-number system, namely, the *axiom of completeness*. We shall need to make use of this axiom to prove Theorem 24.1.11.

24.1.10 THE AXIOM OF COMPLETENESS.   Every set of real numbers which has a lower bound has a greatest lower bound, and every set of real numbers which has an upper bound has a least upper bound.

We are now in a position to prove a theorem which will be useful to us later when discussing infinite series.

24.1.11 THEOREM   A necessary and sufficient condition for a monotonic sequence to be convergent is that it be bounded.

Proof: We shall prove the theorem for the case when the monotonic sequence is nondecreasing. Let the sequence be $\{a_n\}$. There are two parts to the proof. We shall first prove the sufficiency part; that is, if $\{a_n\}$ is a nondecreasing sequence which is bounded, it must be convergent.

Since $\{a_n\}$ is bounded, there is an upper bound for the sequence. By the axiom of completeness (24.1.10), $\{a_n\}$ has a least upper bound, which we shall call B. Then if ϵ is a positive number, $B - \epsilon$ can not be an upper bound of the sequence since $B - \epsilon < B$ and B is the least upper bound of the sequence. So, for some positive integer — say, N —

$$(7) \qquad\qquad B - \epsilon < a_N$$

Since B is the least upper bound of $\{a_n\}$, by Definition 24.1.7 it follows that

$$(8) \qquad\qquad a_n \leq B \qquad \text{for every positive integer } n$$

Since $\{a_n\}$ is a nondecreasing sequence, we have from Definition 24.1.6(i) that

$$a_n \leq a_{n+1} \qquad \text{for every positive integer } n$$

and so

$$(9) \qquad\qquad a_N \leq a_n \qquad \text{whenever} \qquad n \geq N$$

From (7), (8), and (9), it follows that

$$B - \epsilon < a_N \leq a_n \leq B < B + \epsilon \qquad \text{whenever} \qquad n \geq N$$

from which we get

$$B - \epsilon < a_n < B + \epsilon \qquad \text{whenever} \qquad n \geq N$$

or, equivalently,

$$-\epsilon < a_n - B < \epsilon \qquad \text{whenever} \qquad n \geq N$$

which may be written as

$$(10) \qquad\qquad |a_n - B| < \epsilon \qquad \text{whenever} \qquad n \geq N$$

But by Definition 24.1.2, (10) is the condition that $\lim\limits_{n \to +\infty} a_n = B$. Therefore, the sequence $\{a_n\}$ is convergent.

Now we shall prove the necessity part; that is, if $\{a_n\}$ is a nondecreasing sequence which is convergent, it is bounded. To prove that a sequence is bounded, we must show that it has a lower bound and an upper bound.

Since $\{a_n\}$ is a nondecreasing sequence, its first element will serve as a lower bound. We must now find an upper bound. Since $\{a_n\}$ is convergent, the sequence has a limit; call this limit L. Therefore, $\lim\limits_{n \to +\infty} a_n = L$, and so by Definition 24.1.2, for any $\epsilon > 0$, there exists a number $N > 0$ such that

$$|a_n - L| < \epsilon \qquad \text{for every positive integer } n > N$$

or, equivalently,

$$-\epsilon < a_n - L < \epsilon \qquad \text{whenever} \qquad n > N$$

or, equivalently,

$$L - \epsilon < a_n < L + \epsilon \qquad \text{whenever} \qquad n > N$$

Since $\{a_n\}$ is nondecreasing, we may conclude that

$$a_n < L + \epsilon \qquad \text{for all positive integers } n$$

Therefore, $L + \epsilon$ will serve as an upper bound of the sequence $\{a_n\}$.

To prove the theorem when $\{a_n\}$ is a nonincreasing sequence, we consider the sequence $\{-a_n\}$, which will be nondecreasing, and apply the above results. We leave it to the reader to fill in the steps (see Exercise 14 below).

Theorem 24.1.11 states in part that if a monotonic sequence is bounded, it is convergent. That is, the theorem tells us that if $\{a_n\}$ is a bounded monotonic sequence, there exists a number L such that $\lim\limits_{n \to +\infty} a_n = L$, but it does not tell us how to find L. For this reason, Theorem 24.1.11 is called an *existence theorem*. Many important concepts in mathematics are based on existence theorems. In particular, there are many sequences for which we cannot find the limit by direct use of the definition or by using limit theorems. However, the knowledge that such a limit exists can be of great value to a mathematician.

The following two theorems are corollaries of Theorem 24.1.11 and their proofs are left for the reader (see Exercises 21 and 22 at the end of this section).

24.1.12 THEOREM Let $\{a_n\}$ be a monotonic nondecreasing sequence, and suppose that D is an upper bound of this sequence. Then $\{a_n\}$ is convergent and

$$\lim_{n \to +\infty} a_n \leq D$$

24.1.13 THEOREM Let $\{a_n\}$ be a monotonic nonincreasing sequence, and suppose that C is a lower bound of this sequence. Then $\{a_n\}$ is convergent and

$$\lim_{n \to +\infty} a_n \geq C$$

Exercises 24.1

In Exercises 1 through 12, determine if the sequence is convergent or divergent. If the sequence converges, find its limit.

1. $\left\{\dfrac{n+1}{2n-1}\right\}$

2. $\left\{\dfrac{2n^2+1}{3n^2-n}\right\}$

3. $\left\{\dfrac{n^2+1}{n}\right\}$

4. $\left\{\dfrac{3n^3+1}{2n^2+n}\right\}$

5. $\left\{\dfrac{\ln n}{n^2}\right\}$

9. $\left\{\dfrac{1}{\sqrt{n^2+1}-n}\right\}$

6. $\left\{\dfrac{e^n}{n}\right\}$

10. $\{\sqrt{n+1}-\sqrt{n}\}$

7. $\{\tanh n\}$

11. $\left\{\left(1+\dfrac{1}{3n}\right)^n\right\}$

HINT: Use $\displaystyle\lim_{x\to 0}(1+x)^{1/x}=e$.

8. $\left\{\dfrac{\sinh n}{\sin n}\right\}$

12. $\left\{\left(1+\dfrac{2}{n}\right)^n\right\}$

See Hint for Exercise 11.

13. Prove Theorem 24.1.3.

14. Use the fact that Theorem 24.1.11 holds for a nondecreasing sequence to prove that the theorem holds when $\{a_n\}$ is a nonincreasing sequence. HINT: Consider the sequence $\{-a_n\}$.

In Exercises 15 through 20, determine whether or not the given sequence is monotonic. If it is monotonic, determine whether it is (a) nondecreasing; (b) strictly increasing; (c) nonincreasing; or (d) strictly decreasing.

15. $\left\{\dfrac{n}{2^n}\right\}$

18. $\{n^2+(-1)^n n\}$

16. $\left\{\dfrac{n!}{3^n}\right\}$

19. $\left\{\dfrac{n^n}{n!}\right\}$

17. $\left\{\dfrac{n!}{1\cdot 3\cdot 5\cdots(2n-1)}\right\}$

20. $\left\{\dfrac{1\cdot 3\cdot 5\cdots(2n-1)}{2^n\cdot n!}\right\}$

21. Prove Theorem 24.1.12.

22. Prove Theorem 24.1.13.

In Exercises 23 through 26, prove that the given sequence is convergent by using Theorem 24.1.11.

23. The sequence of Exercise 15.

25. The sequence of Exercise 17.

24. $\left\{\dfrac{n^2}{2^n}\right\}$

26. $\left\{\dfrac{2^n}{n!}\right\}$

27. Prove that if the sequence $\{a_n\}$ is convergent and $\displaystyle\lim_{n\to+\infty}a_n=L$, then the sequence $\{|a_n|\}$ is also convergent and $\displaystyle\lim_{n\to+\infty}|a_n|=|L|$.

28. Prove that if the sequence $\{a_n\}$ is convergent and $\displaystyle\lim_{n\to+\infty}a_n=L$, then the sequence $\{a_n{}^2\}$ is also convergent and $\displaystyle\lim_{n\to+\infty}a_n{}^2=L^2$.

29. Prove that if the sequence $\{a_n\}$ converges, then $\lim\limits_{n \to +\infty} a_n$ is unique. HINT: Assume that $\lim\limits_{n \to +\infty} a_n$ has two different values, L and M, and show that this is impossible by taking $\epsilon = \frac{1}{2}|L - M|$ in Definition 24.1.2.

(24.2)   Infinite series of constant terms

24.2.1 DEFINITION   If $\{u_n\}$ is a sequence and

$$s_n = \sum_{i=1}^{n} u_i = u_1 + u_2 + u_3 + \cdots + u_n$$

then the sequence $\{s_n\}$ is called an *infinite series*.

The numbers $u_1, u_2, u_3, \ldots$ are called the *terms* of the infinite series. We use the following symbolism to denote an infinite series:

(1)
$$\sum_{n=1}^{+\infty} u_n = u_1 + u_2 + u_3 + \cdots + u_n + \cdots$$

Given the infinite series denoted by (1), $s_1 = u_1$, $s_2 = u_1 + u_2$, $s_3 = u_1 + u_2 + u_3$, and in general

(2)
$$s_k = \sum_{i=1}^{k} u_i = u_1 + u_2 + u_3 + \cdots + u_k$$

s_k, defined by (2), is called the kth partial sum of the given series, and the sequence $\{s_n\}$ is a *sequence of partial sums*.

Since $s_{n-1} = u_1 + u_2 + \cdots + u_{n-1}$ and $s_n = u_1 + u_2 + \cdots + u_{n-1} + u_n$, we have the formula

(3)
$$s_n = s_{n-1} + u_n$$

EXAMPLE 1: *Given:* the infinite series $\sum\limits_{n=1}^{+\infty} u_n = \sum\limits_{n=1}^{+\infty} 1/n(n+1)$. *Find:* the first four terms of the sequence of partial sums $\{s_n\}$, and find a formula for s_n in terms of n.

Solution: Applying formula (3), we get

$$s_1 = u_1 = \frac{1}{1 \cdot 2} = \frac{1}{2}$$

$$s_2 = s_1 + u_2 = \frac{1}{2} + \frac{1}{2 \cdot 3} = \frac{2}{3}$$

$$s_3 = s_2 + u_3 = \frac{2}{3} + \frac{1}{3 \cdot 4} = \frac{3}{4}$$

$$s_4 = s_3 + u_4 = \frac{3}{4} + \frac{1}{4 \cdot 5} = \frac{4}{5}$$

By partial fractions, we see that $u_k = 1/k(k + 1) = 1/k - 1/(k + 1)$. Therefore, $u_1 = 1 - 1/2$; $u_2 = 1/2 - 1/3$; $u_3 = 1/3 - 1/4$; $\cdots$; $u_{n-1} = 1/(n - 1) - 1/n$; $u_n = 1/n - 1/(n + 1)$. So, since $s_n = u_1 + u_2 + \cdots + u_{n-1} + u_n$, we have

$$s_n = \left(1 - \frac{1}{2}\right) + \left(\frac{1}{2} - \frac{1}{3}\right) + \left(\frac{1}{3} - \frac{1}{4}\right) + \cdots + \left(\frac{1}{n - 1} - \frac{1}{n}\right) + \left(\frac{1}{n} - \frac{1}{n + 1}\right)$$

Upon removing parentheses and combining terms, we obtain

$$s_n = 1 - \frac{1}{n + 1} = \frac{n}{n + 1}$$

Taking $n = 1, 2, 3$, and 4, we see that our previous results agree.

It should be noted that the method of solution of the above example applies only to a special case, and in general it is not possible to obtain such an expression for s_n.

We now define what we mean by the "sum" of an infinite series.

24.2.2 DEFINITION   Let $\sum_{n=1}^{+\infty} u_n$ be a given infinite series, and let $\{s_n\}$ be the sequence of partial sums defining this infinite series. Then if $\lim_{n \to +\infty} s_n$ exists and is equal to S, we say that the given series is *convergent* and that S is the *sum* of the given infinite series. If $\lim_{n \to +\infty} s_n$ does not exist, the series is said to be *divergent* and the series does not have a sum.

If an infinite series has a sum S, we also say that the series *converges* to S.

EXAMPLE 2: Determine if the infinite series of Example 1 has a sum.
   Solution: In the solution of Example 1, we showed that the sequence of partial sums for the given series is $\{s_n\} = \{n/(n + 1)\}$. Therefore,

$$\lim_{n \to +\infty} s_n = \lim_{n \to +\infty} \frac{n}{n + 1} = \lim_{n \to +\infty} \frac{1}{1 + 1/n} = 1$$

So, we conclude that the infinite series has a sum equal to 1. We may write

$$\sum_{n=1}^{+\infty} \frac{1}{n(n + 1)} = \frac{1}{2} + \frac{1}{6} + \frac{1}{12} + \frac{1}{20} + \cdots + \frac{1}{n(n + 1)} + \cdots = 1$$

As we mentioned above, in most cases it is not possible to obtain an expression for s_n in terms of n, and so we must have other methods for determining whether or not a given infinite series has a sum, or, equivalently, whether a given infinite series is convergent or divergent.

24.2.3 THEOREM   If the infinite series $\sum_{n=1}^{+\infty} u_n$ is convergent, then $\lim_{n \to +\infty} u_n = 0$.

Proof: Letting $\{s_n\}$ be the sequence of partial sums for the given series, and denoting the sum of the series by S, we have, from Definition 24.2.2, $\lim_{n \to +\infty} s_n = S$. Therefore, for any $\epsilon > 0$, there exists a number $N > 0$ such that

$|S - s_n| < \epsilon/2$ for every integer $n > N$. Also for these integers $n > N$, we know that $|S - s_{n+1}| < \epsilon/2$. We have then

$$|u_{n+1}| = |s_{n+1} - s_n| = |S - s_n + s_{n+1} - S| \leq |S - s_n| + |s_{n+1} - S|$$

So, $|u_{n+1}| < \dfrac{\epsilon}{2} + \dfrac{\epsilon}{2}$

$$= \epsilon \qquad \text{for every integer } n > N$$

Therefore, $\lim\limits_{n \to +\infty} u_n = 0$.

The following theorem is a corollary of the preceding one.

24.2.4 THEOREM   If $\lim\limits_{n \to +\infty} u_n \neq 0$, then $\sum\limits_{n=1}^{+\infty} u_n$ is divergent.

Proof: Assume $\sum\limits_{n=1}^{+\infty} u_n$ is convergent. Then, by Theorem 24.2.3, $\lim\limits_{n \to +\infty} u_n = 0$. But this contradicts the hypothesis. Therefore the series is divergent.

The condition of Theorem 24.2.3 is a necessary one for convergence but not a sufficient one. That is, if for a given infinite series $\lim\limits_{n \to +\infty} u_n \neq 0$, we may conclude that the series is divergent; however, if $\lim\limits_{n \to +\infty} u_n = 0$, no conclusion regarding the convergence of the series may be made. That is, it is possible to have a divergent series for which $\lim\limits_{n \to +\infty} u_n = 0$. An example of such a series is the one known as the *harmonic series*, which is

(3) $$1 + \frac{1}{2} + \frac{1}{3} + \frac{1}{4} + \cdots + \frac{1}{n} + \cdots$$

Clearly, $\lim\limits_{n \to +\infty} 1/n = 0$. In order to prove that the harmonic series diverges, we shall need to make use of the following theorem.

24.2.5 THEOREM   Let $\{s_n\}$ be the sequence of partial sums for a given convergent series $\sum\limits_{n=1}^{+\infty} u_n$. Then for any $\epsilon > 0$, there exists a number N such that

$$|s_R - s_T| < \epsilon \qquad \text{whenever} \qquad R > N \text{ and } T > N$$

Proof: Since $\sum\limits_{n=1}^{+\infty} u_n$ is convergent, call its sum S. Then for any $\epsilon > 0$, there exists an $N > 0$ such that $|S - s_n| < \epsilon/2$ whenever $n > N$. Therefore, if $R > N$ and $T > N$,

$$|s_R - s_T| = |s_R - S + S - s_T| \leq |s_R - S| + |S - s_T| < \frac{\epsilon}{2} + \frac{\epsilon}{2}$$

So, $|s_R - s_T| < \epsilon \qquad \text{whenever} \qquad R > N \text{ and } T > N$ \hfill Q.E.D.

We shall now prove that the harmonic series (3) is divergent. For this series, $s_n = 1 + \frac{1}{2} + \cdots + 1/n$ and $s_{2n} = 1 + \frac{1}{2} + \cdots + 1/n + 1/(n+1) + \cdots + 1/2n$. So,

(4) $$s_{2n} - s_n = \frac{1}{n+1} + \frac{1}{n+2} + \frac{1}{n+3} + \cdots + \frac{1}{2n}$$

If $n > 1$,

(5) $$\frac{1}{n+1} + \frac{1}{n+2} + \frac{1}{n+3} + \cdots + \frac{1}{2n} > \frac{1}{2n} + \frac{1}{2n} + \frac{1}{2n} + \cdots + \frac{1}{2n}$$

There are n terms on each side of the inequality sign in (5); so the right-hand side is $n(1/2n) = 1/2$. Therefore, from (4) and (5) we have

(6) $$s_{2n} - s_n > \frac{1}{2} \qquad \text{whenever} \qquad n > 1$$

But Theorem 24.2.5 states that if the given series is convergent, then $s_{2n} - s_n$ may be made as small as we please by taking n large enough; that is, if we take $\epsilon = \frac{1}{2}$, there exists an N such that $s_{2n} - s_n < \frac{1}{2}$ whenever $2n > N$ and $n > N$. But this would contradict (6). We may therefore conclude that the harmonic series is divergent, even though $\lim_{n \to +\infty} 1/n = 0$.

A geometric series is a series of the form

(7) $$\sum_{n=1}^{+\infty} ar^{n-1} = a + ar + ar^2 + \cdots + ar^{n-1} + \cdots$$

The nth partial sum of this series is given by

(8) $$s_n = a(1 + r + r^2 + \cdots + r^{n-1})$$

From the identity

$$1 - r^n = (1 - r)(1 + r + r^2 + \cdots + r^{n-1})$$

we may write (8) as

(9) $$s_n = \frac{a(1 - r^n)}{1 - r} \qquad \text{if } r \neq 1$$

24.2.6 THEOREM   The geometric series converges to the sum $a/(1 - r)$ if $|r| < 1$, and the geometric series diverges if $|r| \geq 1$.

Proof: In Example 1, Sec. 24.1, we showed that $\lim_{n \to +\infty} r^n = 0$ if $|r| < 1$. Therefore, from (9), we may conclude that if $|r| < 1$,

$$\lim_{n \to +\infty} s_n = \frac{a}{1 - r}$$

So, if $|r| < 1$, the geometric series converges, and its sum is $a/(1 - r)$.

If $r = 1$, $s_n = na$; then $\lim_{n \to +\infty} s_n = +\infty$ if $a > 0$, and $\lim_{n \to +\infty} s_n = -\infty$ if $a < 0$. If $r = -1$, the geometric series becomes $a - a + a - \cdots + (-1)^{n-1}a + \cdots$; so that $s_n = 0$ if n is even, and $s_n = a$ if n is odd. Therefore, $\lim_{n \to +\infty} s_n$ does not exist. So the geometric series diverges when $|r| = 1$.

If $|r| > 1$, $\lim\limits_{n\to+\infty} ar^{n-1} = a \lim\limits_{n\to+\infty} r^{n-1}$. Clearly, $\lim\limits_{n\to+\infty} r^{n-1} \neq 0$, since we can make $|r^{n-1}|$ as large as we please by taking n large enough. Therefore, by Theorem 24.2.4, the series is divergent. This completes the proof.

The following example illustrates how Theorem 24.2.6 may be used to express a nonterminating repeating decimal as a rational number.

EXAMPLE 3: Express the decimal .3333 ... as a rational number.
Solution:

$$.333\cdots = 3/10 + 3/100 + 3/1{,}000 + 3/10{,}000 + \cdots + 3/10^n + \cdots.$$

We have a geometric series in which $a = 3/10$ and $r = 1/10$. Since $r < 1$, it follows from Theorem 24.2.6 that the series converges and its sum is $a/(1 - r)$. Therefore,

$$.3333\ldots = \frac{3/10}{1 - 1/10} = \frac{1}{3}$$

24.2.7 THEOREM   If $\sum\limits_{n=1}^{+\infty} a_n$ and $\sum\limits_{n=1}^{+\infty} b_n$ are two infinite series, differing only in their first m terms (that is, $a_k = b_k$, if $k > m$), then either both series converge or both series diverge.

Proof: Let $\{s_n\}$ and $\{t_n\}$ be the sequences of partial sums of the series $\sum\limits_{n=1}^{+\infty} a_n$ and $\sum\limits_{n=1}^{+\infty} b_n$, respectively. Then,

$$s_n = a_1 + a_2 + \cdots + a_m + a_{m+1} + a_{m+2} + \cdots + a_n$$

and $$t_n = b_1 + b_2 + \cdots + b_m + b_{m+1} + b_{m+2} + \cdots + b_n$$

Since $a_k = b_k$ if $k > m$, then if $n \geq m$, we have

$$s_n - t_n = (a_1 + a_2 + \cdots + a_m) - (b_1 + b_2 + \cdots + b_m)$$

So, $$s_n - t_n = s_m - t_m \qquad \text{whenever} \qquad n \geq m$$

Therefore, $$s_n = t_n + (s_m - t_m) \qquad \text{whenever} \qquad n \geq m$$

and $$\lim_{n\to+\infty} s_n = \lim_{n\to+\infty} t_n + (s_m - t_m)$$

So, either both $\lim\limits_{n\to+\infty} s_n$ and $\lim\limits_{n\to+\infty} t_n$ exist or do not exist, and the theorem is proved.

Theorem 24.2.7 tells us that the convergence or divergence of an infinite series is not affected by changing a finite number of terms. In particular, for a given infinite series, we can add or subtract a finite number of terms without affecting its convergence or divergence.

24.2.8 THEOREM   If c is any nonzero constant and the series $\sum\limits_{n=1}^{+\infty} u_n$ is convergent, the series $\sum\limits_{n=1}^{+\infty} cu_n$ is also convergent and its sum is $c \sum\limits_{n=1}^{+\infty} u_n$. If the series $\sum\limits_{n=1}^{+\infty} u_n$ is divergent, then the series $\sum\limits_{n=1}^{+\infty} cu_n$ is also divergent.

Proof: Let the nth partial sum of the series $\sum\limits_{n=1}^{+\infty} u_n$ be s_n; so,

$$s_n = u_1 + u_2 + \cdots + u_n$$

The nth partial sum of the series $\sum\limits_{n=1}^{+\infty} cu_n$ is $c(u_1 + u_2 + \cdots + u_n) = cs_n$. So, if $\lim\limits_{n\to+\infty} s_n$ exists, $\lim\limits_{n\to+\infty} cs_n$ also exists and $\lim\limits_{n\to+\infty} cs_n = c \lim\limits_{n\to+\infty} s_n$. If $\lim\limits_{n\to+\infty} s_n$ does not exist, then $\lim\limits_{n\to+\infty} cs_n$ does not exist. So, the theorem is proved.

The above theorem states that if an infinite series is multiplied, term by term, by a nonzero constant, its convergence or divergence is not affected.

24.2.9 THEOREM   If $\sum\limits_{n=1}^{+\infty} a_n$ and $\sum\limits_{n=1}^{+\infty} b_n$ are two convergent series, then $\sum\limits_{n=1}^{+\infty} (a_n + b_n)$ and $\sum\limits_{n=1}^{+\infty} (a_n - b_n)$ are also convergent, and

$$\sum_{n=1}^{+\infty} (a_n \pm b_n) = \sum_{n=1}^{+\infty} a_n \pm \sum_{n=1}^{+\infty} b_n$$

The proof of this theorem is left for the reader (see Exercise 11 at the end of this section).

The following examples illustrate how we make use of the results of this section to determine the convergence or divergence of a given infinite series.

EXAMPLE 4: Determine whether the infinite series $\sum\limits_{n=1}^{+\infty} (2n - 1)/(3n + 2)$ is convergent or divergent.

  Solution: $\lim\limits_{n\to+\infty} [(2n - 1)/(3n + 2)] = \lim\limits_{n\to+\infty} [(2 - 1/n)/(3 + 2/n)] = 2/3 \neq 0$. Therefore, by Theorem 24.2.4, the series is divergent.

EXAMPLE 5: Determine whether the infinite series $\sum\limits_{n=1}^{+\infty} 1/3n$ is convergent or divergent.

Solution:

$$\sum_{n=1}^{+\infty} \frac{1}{3n} = \frac{1}{3} + \frac{1}{6} + \frac{1}{9} + \frac{1}{12} + \cdots + \frac{1}{3n} + \cdots$$

Since $\sum_{n=1}^{+\infty} 1/n$ is the harmonic series, which is divergent, then by Theorem 24.2.8,

with $c = 1/3$, the given series is divergent.

EXAMPLE 6: Determine whether the infinite series $\sum_{n=1}^{+\infty} 1/2^n$ is convergent or divergent.

Solution:

$$\sum_{n=1}^{+\infty} \frac{1}{2^n} = \frac{1}{2} + \frac{1}{4} + \frac{1}{8} + \cdots + \frac{1}{2^n} + \cdots$$

which is the geometric series, with $a = \frac{1}{2}$ and $r = \frac{1}{2}$, and therefore, by Theorem 24.2.6, it is convergent.

Exercises 24.2

In Exercises 1 through 6, find the first four terms of the sequence of partial sums $\{s_n\}$ and find a formula for s_n in terms of n; also, determine if the infinite series is convergent or divergent, and if it is convergent, find its sum.

1. $\sum_{n=1}^{+\infty} \dfrac{1}{(2n-1)(2n+1)}$

4. $\sum_{n=1}^{+\infty} n$

2. $\sum_{n=1}^{+\infty} \dfrac{2}{(4n-3)(4n+1)}$

5. $\sum_{n=1}^{+\infty} \dfrac{2n+1}{n^2(n+1)^2}$

3. $\sum_{n=1}^{+\infty} \ln \dfrac{n}{n+1}$

6. $\sum_{n=1}^{+\infty} \dfrac{2^{n-1}}{3^n}$

In Exercises 7 through 10, find the infinite series which is the given sequence of partial sums; also determine if the infinite series is convergent or divergent, and if it is convergent, find its sum.

7. $\{s_n\} = \left\{\dfrac{2n}{3n+1}\right\}$

9. $\{s_n\} = \left\{\dfrac{1}{2^n}\right\}$

8. $\{s_n\} = \left\{\dfrac{n^2}{n+1}\right\}$

10. $\{s_n\} = \{3^n\}$

11. Prove Theorem 24.2.9.

In Exercises 12 through 25, write the first four terms of the given infinite series and determine if the series is convergent or divergent. If the series is convergent, find its sum.

12. $\displaystyle\sum_{n=1}^{+\infty} \frac{n}{n+1}$

13. $\displaystyle\sum_{n=1}^{+\infty} \frac{2n+1}{3n+2}$

14. $\displaystyle\sum_{n=1}^{+\infty} \frac{2}{3n}$

15. $\displaystyle\sum_{n=1}^{+\infty} \left(\frac{2}{3}\right)^n$

16. $\displaystyle\sum_{n=1}^{+\infty} \frac{2}{3^{n-1}}$

17. $\displaystyle\sum_{n=1}^{+\infty} (-1)^{n+1}\frac{3}{2^n}$

18. $\displaystyle\sum_{n=1}^{+\infty} \ln\frac{1}{n}$

19. $\displaystyle\sum_{n=1}^{+\infty} e^{-n}$

20. $\displaystyle\sum_{n=1}^{+\infty} \sin \pi n$

21. $\displaystyle\sum_{n=1}^{+\infty} \cos \pi n$

22. $\displaystyle\sum_{n=1}^{+\infty} \frac{\sinh n}{n}$

23. $\displaystyle\sum_{n=1}^{+\infty} (2^{-n} + 3^{-n})$

24. $\displaystyle\sum_{n=1}^{+\infty} [1 + (-1)^n]$

25. $\displaystyle\sum_{n=1}^{+\infty} \left(\frac{1}{2n} - \frac{1}{3n}\right)$

In Exercises 26 through 29, express the given nonterminating repeating decimal as a rational number.

26. 0.27 27 27 ...

27. 1.234 234 234 ...

28. 2.045 45 45 ...

29. 0.4653 4653 4653 ...

30. A ball is dropped from a height of 12 ft. Each time it strikes the ground, it bounces back to a height of three-fourths the distance from which it fell. Find the total distance traveled by the ball before it comes to rest.

(24.3)   Infinite series of positive terms

If all the terms of an infinite series are positive, the sequence of partial sums is monotonic and increasing. The following theorem then follows immediately from Theorem 24.1.11.

24.3.1 THEOREM   A necessary and sufficient condition for an infinite series of positive terms to be convergent is that its sequence of partial sums have an upper bound.

This theorem enables us to prove the theorem known as the comparison test, which is one of the most important tests for determining the convergence or divergence of an infinite series.

24.3.2 THEOREM (*Comparison Test*)   Let the series $\sum\limits_{n=1}^{+\infty} u_n$ be a series of positive terms.

(i)   If $\sum\limits_{n=1}^{+\infty} v_n$ is a series of positive terms which is known to be convergent, and

$u_n \leq v_n$ for all positive integers n, then $\sum\limits_{n=1}^{+\infty} u_n$ is convergent.

(ii)   If $\sum\limits_{n=1}^{+\infty} w_n$ is a series of positive terms which is known to be divergent, and

$u_n \geq w_n$ for all positive integers n, then $\sum\limits_{n=1}^{+\infty} u_n$ is divergent.

Proof of (i): Let $\{s_n\}$ be the sequence of partial sums for the series $\sum\limits_{n=1}^{+\infty} u_n$ and $\{t_n\}$

be the sequence of partial sums for the series $\sum\limits_{n=1}^{+\infty} v_n$. Since $\sum\limits_{n=1}^{+\infty} v_n$ is a series of

positive terms which is convergent, it follows from Theorem 24.3.1 that the sequence $\{t_n\}$ has an upper bound; call it B. Since $u_n \leq v_n$ for all positive integers n, we may conclude that $s_n \leq t_n \leq B$ for all positive integers n. Therefore, B is an upper bound of the sequence $\{s_n\}$, and since the terms of the series $\sum\limits_{n=1}^{+\infty} u_n$ are all positive, it follows from Theorem 24.3.1 that $\sum\limits_{n=1}^{+\infty} u_n$ is convergent.

Proof of (ii): Assume that $\sum\limits_{n=1}^{+\infty} u_n$ is convergent. Then since both $\sum\limits_{n=1}^{+\infty} u_n$ and

$\sum\limits_{n=1}^{+\infty} w_n$ are infinite series of positive terms and $w_n \leq u_n$ for all positive integers

n, it follows from part (i) that $\sum\limits_{n=1}^{+\infty} w_n$ is convergent. However, this contradicts

the hypothesis, and so our assumption is false. Therefore, $\sum\limits_{n=1}^{+\infty} u_n$ is divergent.

As we stated in Sec. 24.2, as a result of Theorem 24.2.7, the convergence or divergence of an infinite series is not affected by discarding a finite number of terms or by adding a finite number of terms. Therefore, when applying the comparison test, if $u_i \leq v_i$ or $u_i \geq w_i$ when $i > m$, the test is valid regardless of how the first m terms of the two series compare.

EXAMPLE 1: Determine whether the infinite series $\sum\limits_{n=1}^{+\infty} 3/(2^n + 1)$ is convergent or divergent.

    Solution: The given series is

$$\frac{3}{3} + \frac{3}{5} + \frac{3}{9} + \frac{3}{17} + \cdots + \frac{3}{2^n + 1} + \cdots$$

Comparing the nth term of this series with the nth term of the convergent geometric series

$$\frac{3}{2} + \frac{3}{4} + \frac{3}{8} + \frac{3}{16} + \cdots + \frac{3}{2^n} + \cdots \qquad r = \frac{1}{2} < 1$$

we have $\quad \dfrac{3}{2^n + 1} < \dfrac{3}{2^n} \quad$ for every positive integer n

Therefore, by the comparison test, Theorem 24.3.2(i), the given series $\sum\limits_{n=1}^{+\infty} 3/(2^n + 1)$ is convergent.

EXAMPLE 2: Determine whether the infinite series $\sum\limits_{n=1}^{+\infty} 1/\sqrt{n}$ is convergent or divergent.

Solution: The given series is

$$\sum_{n=1}^{+\infty} \frac{1}{\sqrt{n}} = \frac{1}{\sqrt{1}} + \frac{1}{\sqrt{2}} + \frac{1}{\sqrt{3}} + \cdots + \frac{1}{\sqrt{n}} + \cdots$$

Comparing the nth term of this series with the nth term of the divergent harmonic series, we have

$$\frac{1}{\sqrt{n}} \geq \frac{1}{n} \qquad \text{for every positive integer } n$$

So, by Theorem 24.3.2(ii), the given series $\sum\limits_{n=1}^{+\infty} 1/\sqrt{n}$ is divergent.

In order to apply the comparison test, we need to make use of a series whose convergence or divergence is known. In the above two examples, we used a geometric series and the harmonic series. Before obtaining other series that are frequently used for comparison, we shall state and prove two theorems which we shall need as we proceed. These two theorems state properties of the sum of a convergent series of positive terms that are similar to the properties which hold for the sum of a finite number of terms.

24.3.3 THEOREM If $\sum\limits_{n=1}^{+\infty} u_n$ is a given convergent series of positive terms, its terms may be grouped in any manner, and the resulting series will also be convergent and will have the same sum as the given series.

Proof: Let $\{s_n\}$ be the sequence of partial sums for the given convergent series of positive terms. Then $\lim\limits_{n \to +\infty} s_n$ exists, and let this limit be S. Consider a series $\sum\limits_{n=1}^{+\infty} v_n$, whose terms are obtained by grouping the terms of $\sum\limits_{n=1}^{+\infty} u_n$ in some manner. In particular, suppose that $\sum\limits_{n=1}^{+\infty} v_n$ is the series

(1) $u_1 + (u_2 + u_3) + (u_4 + u_5 + u_6) + (u_7 + u_8 + u_9 + u_{10}) + \cdots$

Let $\{t_m\}$ be the sequence of partial sums for the series (1). Each partial sum of the sequence $\{t_m\}$ is also a partial sum of the sequence $\{s_n\}$. Therefore, as m increases without bound, so does n. Since $\lim\limits_{n\to+\infty} s_n = S$, we may conclude that $\lim\limits_{m\to+\infty} t_m = S$. A similar argument may be made for any grouping of the terms of the given series.

24.3.4 THEOREM   If $\sum\limits_{n=1}^{+\infty} u_n$ is a given convergent series of positive terms, the order of the terms may be rearranged and the resulting series will also be convergent and will have the same sum as the given series.

   Proof: Let $\{s_n\}$ be the sequence of partial sums for the given convergent series of positive terms, and let $\lim\limits_{n\to+\infty} s_n = S$. Let $\sum\limits_{n=1}^{+\infty} v_n$ be a series formed by rearranging the order of the terms of $\sum\limits_{n=1}^{+\infty} u_n$. For example, suppose $\sum\limits_{n=1}^{+\infty} v_n$ is the series

(2) $u_4 + u_3 + u_7 + u_1 + u_9 + u_5 + \cdots$

Let $\{t_n\}$ be the sequence of partial sums for series (2). Each partial sum of the sequence $\{t_n\}$ will be less than S, since it is the sum of n terms of the infinite series $\sum\limits_{n=1}^{+\infty} u_n$. Therefore S is an upper bound of the sequence $\{t_n\}$. Furthermore, since all the terms of series (2) are positive, it is a monotonic increasing sequence. Hence by Theorem 24.1.12 the sequence $\{t_n\}$ is convergent and then $\lim\limits_{n\to+\infty} t_n = T \leq S$. Now, since the given series $\sum\limits_{n=1}^{+\infty} u_n$ may be obtained from series (2) by rearranging the order of the terms, we can use the same argument and conclude that $S \leq T$. If both inequalities, $T \leq S$ and $S \leq T$, must hold, it follows that $S = T$. This proves the theorem.

   A series which is often used in the comparison test is the one known as the *p series*, or the *hyperharmonic series*. It is

(3) $\dfrac{1}{1^p} + \dfrac{1}{2^p} + \dfrac{1}{3^p} + \cdots + \dfrac{1}{n^p} + \cdots$ where p is a constant

EXAMPLE 3: Prove that the p series diverges if $p \leq 1$ and converges if $p > 1$.

   Solution: If $p = 1$, the p series is the harmonic series, which diverges. If $p < 1$, then $n^p \leq n$, and so

$$\frac{1}{n^p} \geq \frac{1}{n} \qquad \text{for every positive integer } n$$

So, by Theorem 24.3.2(ii), the p series is divergent if $p < 1$.

If $p > 1$, we shall group the terms as follows:

(4) $\dfrac{1}{1^p} + \left(\dfrac{1}{2^p} + \dfrac{1}{3^p}\right) + \left(\dfrac{1}{4^p} + \dfrac{1}{5^p} + \dfrac{1}{6^p} + \dfrac{1}{7^p}\right) + \left(\dfrac{1}{8^p} + \dfrac{1}{9^p} + \cdots + \dfrac{1}{15^p}\right) + \cdots$

Consider the series

(5) $\qquad\qquad \dfrac{1}{1^p} + \dfrac{2}{2^p} + \dfrac{4}{4^p} + \dfrac{8}{8^p} + \cdots + \dfrac{2^{n-1}}{(2^{n-1})^p} + \cdots$

which is a geometric series whose ratio is $2/2^p = 1/2^{p-1}$, which is a positive number less than 1. Hence, series (5) is convergent. Rewriting the terms of series (5), we get

(6) $\dfrac{1}{1^p} + \left(\dfrac{1}{2^p} + \dfrac{1}{2^p}\right) + \left(\dfrac{1}{4^p} + \dfrac{1}{4^p} + \dfrac{1}{4^p} + \dfrac{1}{4^p}\right) + \left(\dfrac{1}{8^p} + \dfrac{1}{8^p} + \cdots + \dfrac{1}{8^p}\right) + \cdots$

Comparing series (4) and series (6), we see that the group of terms in each set of parentheses after the first group is less in sum for (4) than it is for (6). Therefore, by the comparison test, series (4) is convergent. Since (4) is merely a re-grouping of the terms of the p series when $p > 1$, we may conclude from Theorem 24.3.3 that the p series is convergent if $p > 1$.

Note that the series in Example 2 is the p series where $p = \frac{1}{2} < 1$, and therefore it is divergent.

Additional series which may be used for the comparison test are provided by the *integral test*, which is given in the next theorem.

24.3.5 THEOREM (*Integral Test*)   Let f be a function which is continuous, nonincreasing, and positive-valued for all $x \geq 1$. Then the infinite series

$$\sum_{n=1}^{+\infty} f(n) = f(1) + f(2) + f(3) + \cdots + f(n) + \cdots$$

is convergent if the improper integral

$$\int_1^{+\infty} f(x)\, dx$$

exists, and is divergent if the improper integral is infinite.

Proof: If i is a positive integer, by the mean-value theorem for integrals (10.5.2), there exists a number X such that $i - 1 \leq X \leq i$ and

(7) $\qquad\qquad \int_{i-1}^{i} f(x)\, dx = f(X) \cdot 1$

Since f is a nonincreasing function,

$$f(i - 1) \geq f(X) \geq f(i)$$

and so from (7) we have

$$f(i - 1) \geq \int_{i-1}^{i} f(x)\, dx \geq f(i)$$

Therefore if n is any positive integer,

$$\sum_{i=2}^{n} f(i-1) \geq \sum_{i=2}^{n} \int_{i-1}^{i} f(x)\, dx \geq \sum_{i=2}^{n} f(i)$$

or, equivalently,

(8)
$$\sum_{i=1}^{n-1} f(i) \geq \int_{1}^{n} f(x)\, dx \geq \sum_{i=1}^{n} f(i) - f(1)$$

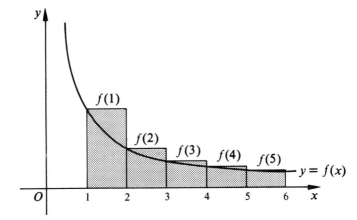

Figure 24.3.1

Figures 24.3.1 and 24.3.2 show the geometric interpretation of the above discussion for the case when $n = 6$. In Fig. 24.3.1, we have a sketch of the graph of a function f satisfying the hypothesis. The sum of the areas of the shaded rectangles is $f(1) + f(2) + f(3) + f(4) + f(5)$, which is the left member of the inequality (8) when $n = 6$. Clearly, the sum of the areas of these rectangles is greater than the area given by the definite integral when $n = 6$. in Fig. 24.3.2 the sum of the areas of the shaded rectangles is $f(2) + f(3) +$

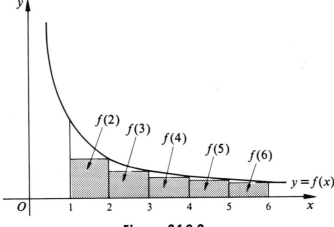

Figure 24.3.2

$f(4) + f(5) + f(6)$ which is the right member of the inequality (8) when $n = 6$, and this sum is less than the value of the definite integral when $n = 6$.

If the given improper integral exists, let L be its value. Then

(9)
$$\int_1^n f(x)\, dx \leq L$$

From the second and third members of the inequality (8) and from (9), we obtain

(10)
$$\sum_{i=1}^n f(i) \leq f(1) + \int_1^n f(x)\, dx \leq f(1) + L$$

Consider now the infinite series $\displaystyle\sum_{n=1}^{+\infty} f(n)$. Let the sequence of partial sums of this series be $\{s_n\}$ where $s_n = \displaystyle\sum_{i=1}^n f(i)$. From (10) we see that $\{s_n\}$ has an upper bound of $f(1) + L$. Also, $\{s_n\}$ is a monotonic nondecreasing sequence, and so by Theorem 24.1.12 we may conclude that $\displaystyle\sum_{n=1}^{+\infty} f(n)$ is convergent.

Suppose the given improper integral is infinite. From (8) we have

$$\sum_{i=1}^{n-1} f(i) \geq \int_1^n f(x)\, dx$$

for all positive integers n, and so $\displaystyle\lim_{n\to+\infty} \sum_{i=1}^{n-1} f(i)$ must also be infinite. Therefore, $\displaystyle\sum_{n=1}^{+\infty} f(n)$ is divergent.

EXAMPLE 4: Use the integral test to show that the p series diverges if $p \leq 1$ and converges if $p > 1$.

Solution: The p series is $\displaystyle\sum_{n=1}^{+\infty} 1/n^p$. The function f, defined by $f(x) = 1/x^p$, satisfies the hypothesis of Theorem 24.3.5. So, considering the improper integral, we have

$$\int_1^{+\infty} \frac{dx}{x^p} = \lim_{b\to+\infty} \int_1^b \frac{dx}{x^p}$$

If $p = 1$, the above integral gives us

$$\lim_{b\to+\infty} \ln x \Big]_1^b = \lim_{b\to+\infty} \ln b = +\infty$$

If $p \neq 1$, the integral gives us

$$\lim_{b\to+\infty} \frac{x^{1-p}}{1-p}\Big]_1^b = \lim_{b\to+\infty} \frac{b^{1-p} - 1}{1-p}$$

This limit is $+\infty$ when $p < 1$, and it is $-1/(1 - p)$ if $p > 1$. Therefore, by the integral test, it follows that the p series converges for $p > 1$ and diverges for $p \leq 1$.

Exercises 24.3

In Exercises 1 through 20, determine if the given series is convergent or divergent.

1. $\displaystyle\sum_{n=1}^{+\infty} \frac{1}{n2^n}$

2. $\displaystyle\sum_{n=1}^{+\infty} \frac{1}{n!}$

3. $\displaystyle\sum_{n=1}^{+\infty} ne^{-n}$

4. $\displaystyle\sum_{n=1}^{+\infty} \frac{1}{\sqrt{2n+1}}$

5. $\displaystyle\sum_{n=1}^{+\infty} \frac{\ln n}{n}$

6. $\displaystyle\sum_{n=2}^{+\infty} \frac{1}{n \ln n}$

7. $\displaystyle\sum_{n=2}^{+\infty} \frac{1}{n(\ln n)^2}$

8. $\displaystyle\sum_{n=1}^{+\infty} \frac{\ln n}{n^2}$

9. $\displaystyle\sum_{n=2}^{+\infty} \frac{1}{n\sqrt{\ln n}}$

10. $\displaystyle\sum_{n=1}^{+\infty} \frac{n^2}{4n^3+1}$

11. $\displaystyle\sum_{n=1}^{+\infty} \frac{\tan^{-1} n}{n^2+1}$

12. $\displaystyle\sum_{n=1}^{+\infty} ne^{-n^2}$

13. $\displaystyle\sum_{n=1}^{+\infty} \frac{1}{\sqrt{n^3+1}}$

14. $\displaystyle\sum_{n=1}^{+\infty} \frac{2^n}{n!}$

15. $\displaystyle\sum_{n=1}^{+\infty} \frac{n!}{(2n)!}$

16. $\displaystyle\sum_{n=1}^{+\infty} \frac{|\csc n|}{n}$

17. $\displaystyle\sum_{n=2}^{+\infty} \frac{1}{n\sqrt{n^2-1}}$

18. $\displaystyle\sum_{n=1}^{+\infty} \frac{1}{n+\sqrt{n}}$

19. $\displaystyle\sum_{n=1}^{+\infty} \cot^{-1} n$

20. $\displaystyle\sum_{n=1}^{+\infty} \frac{1}{(n+2)(n+4)}$

21. If S_k is the kth partial sum of the harmonic series, prove that

$$\ln(k+1) < S_k < 1 + \ln k$$

HINT: $1/(m+1) \leq 1/x \leq 1/m$ if $0 < m \leq x \leq m + 1$. Integrate each member of the inequality from m to $m + 1$; let m take on successively the values $1, 2, \ldots, n - 1$, and add the results.

22. Use the result of Exercise 21 to estimate the sum $1/50 + \cdots + 1/100$.

(24.4) Infinite series of positive and negative terms

In this section we shall consider infinite series having both positive and negative terms. The first type of such a series which we shall discuss is one whose terms are alternately positive and negative — an *alternating series.*

24.4.1 DEFINITION   If $a_n > 0$ for all positive integers n, then the series

$$\sum_{n=1}^{+\infty} (-1)^{n+1} a_n = a_1 - a_2 + a_3 - a_4 + \cdots + (-1)^{n+1} a_n + \cdots$$

and the series

$$\sum_{n=1}^{+\infty} (-1)^n a_n = -a_1 + a_2 - a_3 + a_4 - \cdots + (-1)^n a_n + \cdots$$

are called *alternating series.*

The following theorem gives a test for the convergence of an alternating series.

24.4.2 THEOREM (*Alternating-series Test*)   If the numbers $u_1, u_2, u_3, \ldots, u_n, \ldots$ are alternately positive and negative, $|u_{n+1}| < |u_n|$ for all positive integers n, and $\lim\limits_{n \to +\infty} u_n = 0$, then the alternating series $\sum\limits_{n=1}^{+\infty} u_n$ is convergent.

Proof: Let us assume that the odd-numbered terms of the given series are positive and the even-numbered terms are negative. This is not a loss of generality since if this is not the case, then we may consider the series whose first term is u_2, because discarding a finite number of terms does not affect the convergence of the series. So, $u_{2n-1} > 0$ and $u_{2n} < 0$ for every positive integer n. Consider the partial sum

(1) $s_{2n} = (u_1 + u_2) + (u_3 + u_4) + \cdots + (u_{2n-1} + u_{2n})$

The first term of each quantity in parentheses in (1) is positive and the second term is negative, and since by hypothesis $|u_{n+1}| < |u_n|$, we may conclude that each quantity in parentheses is positive. Therefore,

(2) $0 < s_2 < s_4 < s_6 < \cdots < s_{2n} < \cdots$

We may also write s_{2n} as

(3) $s_{2n} = u_1 + (u_2 + u_3) + (u_4 + u_5) + \cdots + (u_{2n-2} + u_{2n-1}) + u_{2n}$

Each quantity in parentheses in (3) is negative and so also is u_{2n}. Therefore,

(4) $s_{2n} < u_1$ for every positive integer n

From (2) and (4) we have

$0 < s_{2n} < u_1$ for every positive integer n

So the sequence $\{s_{2n}\}$ is bounded. Furthermore, from (2) the sequence $\{s_{2n}\}$ is monotonic. Therefore, by Theorem 24.1.11 the sequence $\{s_{2n}\}$ is convergent. Let $\lim\limits_{n \to +\infty} s_{2n} = S$, and from Theorem 24.1.12 we know that $S \le u_1$.

Since $s_{2n+1} = s_{2n} + u_{2n+1}$, we have

$$\lim_{n \to +\infty} s_{2n+1} = \lim_{n \to +\infty} s_{2n} + \lim_{n \to +\infty} u_{2n+1}$$

but, by hypothesis, $\lim\limits_{n \to +\infty} u_{2n+1} = 0$, and so $\lim\limits_{n \to +\infty} s_{2n+1} = \lim\limits_{n \to +\infty} s_{2n}$. Therefore the sequence of partial sums of the even-numbered terms and the sequence of partial sums of the odd-numbered terms have the same limit S. Therefore, $\lim\limits_{n \to +\infty} s_n = S$ for every positive integer n, which proves the theorem.

EXAMPLE 1: Prove that the alternating series $\sum\limits_{n=1}^{+\infty} (-1)^{n+1}/n$ is convergent.

Solution: The given series is

$$\sum_{n=1}^{+\infty} (-1)^{n+1} \frac{1}{n} = 1 - \frac{1}{2} + \frac{1}{3} - \frac{1}{4} + \cdots + (-1)^{n+1} \frac{1}{n} + (-1)^{n+2} \frac{1}{n+1} + \cdots$$

Since $1/(n+1) < 1/n$ for all positive integers n, and $\lim\limits_{n \to +\infty} (1/n) = 0$, it follows from Theorem 24.4.2 that the given alternating series is convergent.

24.4.3 DEFINITION   If an infinite series $\sum\limits_{n=1}^{+\infty} u_n$ is convergent and its sum is S, then the *remainder* obtained by approximating the sum of the series by the kth partial sum s_k is denoted by R_k and

$$R_k = S - s_k$$

24.4.4 THEOREM   If $\sum\limits_{n=1}^{+\infty} u_n$ is an alternating series, $|u_{n+1}| < |u_n|$, and $\lim\limits_{n \to +\infty} u_n = 0$, then if R_k is the remainder obtained by approximating the sum of the series by the sum of the first k terms, $|R_k| < |u_{k+1}|$.

Proof: Assume that the odd-numbered terms of the given series are positive and the even-numbered terms are negative. Then, from (2) in the proof of Theorem 24.4.2, we see that the sequence $\{s_{2n}\}$ is monotonic and increasing. So, if S is the sum of the given series, we have

(5) $s_{2k} < s_{2k+2} < S$ for all $k \ge 1$

To show that the sequence $\{s_{2n-1}\}$ is monotonic and decreasing, we write

(6) $s_{2n-1} = u_1 + (u_2 + u_3) + (u_4 + u_5) + \cdots + (u_{2n-2} + u_{2n-1})$

The first term of each quantity in parentheses in (6) is negative and the second term is positive, and since $|u_{n+1}| < |u_n|$, it follows that each quantity in parentheses is negative. Therefore, since $u_1 > 0$, we conclude that

$s_1 > s_3 > s_5 > \cdots > s_{2n-1} > \cdots$, and so the sequence $\{s_{2n-1}\}$ is monotonic and decreasing. Therefore,

$$(7) \qquad\qquad S < s_{2k+1} < s_{2k-1} \qquad \text{for all } k \geq 1$$

From (7) we have $S - s_{2k} < s_{2k+1} - s_{2k} = u_{2k+1}$, and from (5) we have $0 < S - s_{2k}$. Therefore,

$$(8) \qquad\qquad 0 < S - s_{2k} < u_{2k+1} \qquad \text{for all } k \geq 1$$

From (5) we have $-S < -s_{2k}$, and so $s_{2k-1} - S < s_{2k-1} - s_{2k} = -u_{2k}$. Since from (7) it follows that $0 < s_{2k-1} - S$, we have

$$(9) \qquad\qquad 0 < s_{2k-1} - S < -u_{2k} \qquad \text{for all } k \geq 1$$

Since from Definition 24.4.3, $R_k = S - s_k$, (8) may be written as $0 < |R_{2k}| < |u_{2k+1}|$ and (9) may be written as $0 < |R_{2k-1}| < |u_{2k}|$. Hence, we have $|R_k| < |u_{k+1}|$ for all $k \geq 1$, and the theorem is proved.

EXAMPLE 2: A series for computing $\ln(1 - x)$ if x is in the open interval $(-1,1)$ is

$$\ln(1 - x) = -x - \frac{x^2}{2} - \frac{x^3}{3} - \frac{x^4}{4} - \cdots - \frac{x^n}{n} - \cdots$$

Find an estimate of the error when the first three terms of this series are used to approximate the value of $\ln 1.1$.

Solution: Using the given series with $x = -0.1$, we get

$$\ln 1.1 = 0.1 - \frac{(0.1)^2}{2} + \frac{(0.1)^3}{3} - \frac{(0.1)^4}{4} + \cdots$$

This series satisfies the conditions of Theorem 24.4.4, and so if R_3 is the difference between the actual value of $\ln 1.1$ and the sum of the first three terms,

$$|R_3| < |u_4| = 0.000025$$

So we know that the sum of the first three terms will yield a value of $\ln 1.1$ accurate at least to four decimal places. Using the first three terms, we get

$$\ln 1.1 = 0.0953.$$

Associated with each infinite series is the series whose terms are the absolute values of the terms of that series.

24.4.5 DEFINITION   The infinite series $\sum_{n=1}^{+\infty} u_n$ is said to be *absolutely convergent* if the series $\sum_{n=1}^{+\infty} |u_n|$ is convergent.

EXAMPLE 3: Determine if the series $\sum\limits_{n=1}^{+\infty} (-1)^{n+1}/n!$ is absolutely convergent

Solution: The given series is

$$\sum_{n=1}^{+\infty} (-1)^{n+1} \frac{1}{n!} = \frac{1}{1} - \frac{1}{1\cdot 2} + \frac{1}{1\cdot 2\cdot 3} - \frac{1}{1\cdot 2\cdot 3\cdot 4} + \cdots$$
$$+ (-1)^{n+1} \frac{1}{1\cdot 2\cdot 3\cdot \,\cdots\, \cdot n} + \cdots$$

This series will be absolutely convergent if the series

$$(10) \quad \sum_{n=1}^{+\infty} \frac{1}{n!} = \frac{1}{1} + \frac{1}{1\cdot 2} + \frac{1}{1\cdot 2\cdot 3} + \frac{1}{1\cdot 2\cdot 3\cdot 4} + \cdots + \frac{1}{1\cdot 2\cdot 3\cdot \,\cdots\, \cdot n} + \cdots$$

is convergent. Comparing series (10) with the geometric series for which $a = 1$, and $r = \frac{1}{2}$, namely,

$$1 + \frac{1}{2} + \frac{1}{2\cdot 2} + \frac{1}{2\cdot 2\cdot 2} + \cdots + \frac{1}{2^{n-1}} + \cdots$$

we see that the first two terms of each series are the same, while each of the remaining terms of series (10) is less than the corresponding term of the geometric series. Therefore, since the geometric series is convergent when $|r| < 1$, and since $1/n! \leq 1/2^{n-1}$ (see Exercise 29 at the end of this section), we may conclude from the comparison test that series (10) is convergent and, therefore, the given series is absolutely convergent.

The following theorem gives an important test for the convergence of a series whose terms are positive and negative.

24.4.6 THEOREM   If the infinite series $\sum\limits_{n=1}^{+\infty} u_n$ is absolutely convergent, it is convergent and

$$\left| \sum_{n=1}^{+\infty} u_n \right| \leq \sum_{n=1}^{+\infty} |u_n|$$

Proof: Consider the three infinite series $\sum\limits_{n=1}^{+\infty} u_n$, $\sum\limits_{n=1}^{+\infty} |u_n|$, and $\sum\limits_{n=1}^{+\infty} (u_n + |u_n|)$, and let their sequences of partial sums be, respectively, $\{s_n\}$, $\{t_n\}$, and $\{r_n\}$. For every positive integer n, $u_n + |u_n|$ is either 0 or $2|u_n|$, and so we have the inequality

$$(11) \qquad\qquad 0 \leq u_n + |u_n| \leq 2|u_n|$$

Since $\sum\limits_{n=1}^{+\infty} |u_n|$ is convergent, it has a sum, which we shall denote by T. $\{t_n\}$ is a nondecreasing sequence of positive numbers, and so $t_n \leq T$ for all positive integers n. From (11), it follows that

$$0 \leq r_n \leq 2t_n \leq 2T$$

Therefore, the sequence $\{r_n\}$ has an upper bound of $2T$, and so by Theorem 24.3.1, the series $\sum\limits_{n=1}^{+\infty} (u_n + |u_n|)$ is convergent, and we may call its sum R. Since from (11), $\{r_n\}$ is a monotonic nondecreasing sequence, it may be concluded from Theorem 24.1.12 that $R \leq 2T$.

Each of the series $\sum\limits_{n=1}^{+\infty} (u_n + |u_n|)$ and $\sum\limits_{n=1}^{+\infty} |u_n|$ is convergent, and hence from Theorem 24.2.9, the series

$$\sum_{n=1}^{+\infty} [(u_n + |u_n|) - |u_n|] = \sum_{n=1}^{+\infty} u_n$$

is also convergent.

Let the sum of the series $\sum\limits_{n=1}^{+\infty} u_n$ be S. Then, also from Theorem 24.2.9, $S = R - T$, and since $R \leq 2T$, $S \leq 2T - T = T$.

Since $\sum\limits_{n=1}^{+\infty} u_n$ is convergent and has the sum S, it follows from Theorem 24.2.8 that $\sum\limits_{n=1}^{+\infty} (-u_n)$ is convergent and has the sum $-S$. Since $\sum\limits_{n=1}^{+\infty} |-u_n| = \sum\limits_{n=1}^{+\infty} |u_n| = T$, we may replace $\sum\limits_{n=1}^{+\infty} u_n$ by $\sum\limits_{n=1}^{+\infty} (-u_n)$ in the above discussion and show that $-S \leq T$.

Because $S \leq T$ and $-S \leq T$, we have $|S| \leq T$, and therefore $\left| \sum\limits_{n=1}^{+\infty} u_n \right| \leq \sum\limits_{n=1}^{+\infty} |u_n|$ and the theorem is proved.

The converse of Theorem 24.4.6 is not true in general. That is, it doesn't necessarily follow that if a series is convergent, it is also absolutely convergent. An example of this is the series of Example 1 of this section. We proved that $\sum\limits_{n=1}^{+\infty} (-1)^{n+1}/n$ is convergent; however, the series of absolute values is the harmonic series, which is divergent.

24.4.7 DEFINITION   A series which is convergent, but not absolutely convergent, is said to be *conditionally convergent*.

So, the series of Example 1 is conditionally convergent.

EXAMPLE 4: Determine if the series $\sum\limits_{n=1}^{+\infty} \cos (n\pi/3)/n^2$ is convergent or divergent.

Solution: Denote the given series by $\sum\limits_{n=1}^{+\infty} u_n$. Therefore,

$$\sum_{n=1}^{+\infty} u_n = \frac{\frac{1}{2}}{1^2} - \frac{\frac{1}{2}}{2^2} - \frac{1}{3^2} - \frac{\frac{1}{2}}{4^2} + \frac{\frac{1}{2}}{5^2} + \frac{1}{6^2} + \frac{\frac{1}{2}}{7^2} - \cdots + \frac{\cos(n\pi/3)}{n^2} + \cdots$$

$$= \frac{1}{2} - \frac{1}{8} - \frac{1}{9} - \frac{1}{32} + \frac{1}{50} + \frac{1}{36} + \frac{1}{98} - \cdots$$

We have a series of positive and negative terms. We can prove this series is convergent if we can show that it is absolutely convergent.

$$\sum_{n=1}^{+\infty} |u_n| = \sum_{n=1}^{+\infty} \frac{|\cos(n\pi/3)|}{n^2}$$

Since $\quad |\cos(n\pi/3)| \leq 1 \quad$ for all n

$$\frac{|\cos(n\pi/3)|}{n^2} \leq \frac{1}{n^2} \quad \text{for all positive integers } n$$

The series $\sum\limits_{n=1}^{+\infty} 1/n^2$ is the p series, with $p = 2$, and is therefore convergent. So,

by the comparison test, $\sum\limits_{n=1}^{+\infty} |u_n|$ is convergent, and therefore the given series is

absolutely convergent, and hence by Theorem 24.4.6, it is convergent.

You will note that the terms of the series $\sum\limits_{n=1}^{+\infty} |u_n|$ neither increase mono-

tonically nor decrease monotonically. For example, $|u_4| = 1/32$, $|u_5| = 1/50$, $|u_6| = 1/36$, and so $|u_5| < |u_4|$; but $|u_6| > |u_5|$.

The *ratio test*, given in the next theorem, is used frequently to determine whether or not a given series is absolutely convergent.

24.4.7 THEOREM (*Ratio Test*)   Let $\sum\limits_{n=1}^{+\infty} u_n$ be a given infinite series for which every u_n is nonzero. Suppose that

$$\lim_{n \to +\infty} \left| \frac{u_{n+1}}{u_n} \right| \text{ is either } L \text{ or } +\infty$$

Then,

    (i)   if $L < 1$, the given series is absolutely convergent

    (ii) if $L > 1$ or if $\lim\limits_{n \to +\infty} |u_{n+1}/u_n| = +\infty$, the series is divergent

    (iii) if $L = 1$, no conclusion regarding convergence may be made

Proof of (i): If $L < 1$, let R be a number such that $L < R < 1$. Suppose that $R - L = \epsilon < 1$. Since $\lim\limits_{n \to +\infty} |u_{n+1}/u_n| = L$, there exists an integer $N > 0$ such that

$$\left| \left| \frac{u_{n+1}}{u_n} \right| - L \right| < \epsilon \qquad \text{whenever} \qquad n \geq N$$

or, equivalently,

(12) $$0 < \frac{|u_{n+1}|}{|u_n|} < L + \epsilon = R \qquad \text{whenever} \qquad n \geq N$$

Letting n take on the sucessive values $N, N + 1, N + 2, \ldots$, etc., we obtain from (12)

$$|u_{N+1}| < R|u_N|$$
$$|u_{N+2}| < R|u_{N+1}| < R^2|u_N|$$
$$|u_{N+3}| < R|u_{N+2}| < R^3|u_N|$$

$$\cdots \cdots \cdots \cdots \cdots \cdots$$

In general, we have

(13) $$|u_{N+k}| < R^k|u_N| \qquad \text{for every positive integer } k$$

The series

$$\sum_{k=1}^{+\infty} |u_N|R^k = |u_N|R + |u_N|R^2 + \cdots + |u_N|R^n + \cdots$$

is convergent since it is a geometric series whose ratio is less than 1. So from (13) and the comparison test, it follows that the series $\sum_{k=1}^{+\infty} |u_{N+k}|$ is convergent. The series $\sum_{k=1}^{+\infty} |u_{N+k}|$ differs from the series $\sum_{n=1}^{+\infty} |u_n|$ in only the first N terms. Therefore $\sum_{n=1}^{+\infty} |u_n|$ is convergent, and so the given series is absolutely convergent.

Proof of (ii): If $\lim_{n \to +\infty} |u_{n+1}/u_n| = L > 1$ or $\lim_{n \to +\infty} |u_{n+1}/u_n| = +\infty$, then in either case there is an integer $N > 0$ such that $|u_{n+1}/u_n| > 1$ for all $n \geq N$. Letting n take on the successive values $N, N + 1, N + 2, \ldots$, etc., we obtain

$$|u_{N+1}| > |u_N|$$
$$|u_{N+2}| > |u_{N+1}| > |u_N|$$
$$|u_{N+3}| > |u_{N+2}| > |u_N|$$

$$\cdots \cdots \cdots \cdots \cdots \cdots$$

So, we may conclude that $|u_n| > |u_N|$ for all $n > N$. Hence $\lim_{n \to +\infty} u_n \neq 0$, and so the given series is divergent.

Proof of (iii): If we apply the ratio test to the p series, we have

$$\lim_{n \to +\infty} \left| \frac{u_{n+1}}{u_n} \right| = \lim_{n \to +\infty} \left| \frac{1/(n+1)^p}{n^p} \right| = \lim_{n \to +\infty} \left| \left(\frac{n}{n+1} \right)^p \right| = 1$$

Since the p series diverges if $p \leq 1$ and converges if $p > 1$, we have shown that it is possible to have both convergent and divergent series for which we have $\lim_{n \to +\infty} |u_{n+1}/u_n| = 1$. This proves part (iii).

EXAMPLE 5: Determine if the series $\sum_{n=1}^{+\infty} (-1)^{n+1} n/2^n$ is convergent or divergent.

    Solution: $u_n = (-1)^{n+1} n/2^n$ and $u_{n+1} = (-1)^{n+2}(n+1)/2^{n+1}$.

Therefore,
$$\left|\frac{u_{n+1}}{u_n}\right| = \frac{n+1}{2^{n+1}} \cdot \frac{2^n}{n} = \frac{n+1}{2n}$$

So
$$\lim_{n \to +\infty} \left|\frac{u_{n+1}}{u_n}\right| = \lim_{n \to +\infty} \frac{1 + 1/n}{2} = \frac{1}{2} < 1$$

Therefore, by the ratio test, the given series is absolutely convergent and hence, by Theorem 24.4.6, is convergent.

EXAMPLE 6: Determine if the series

$$\sum_{n=1}^{+\infty} (-1)^n \frac{n+2}{n(n+1)} = -\frac{3}{1 \cdot 2} + \frac{4}{2 \cdot 3} - \frac{5}{3 \cdot 4} + \cdots + (-1)^n \frac{n+2}{n(n+1)} + \cdots$$

is absolutely convergent, conditionally convergent, or divergent. Prove your answer.

    Solution: To test for absolute convergence, we shall apply the ratio test.

$$u_n = (-1)^n \frac{n+2}{n(n+1)} \qquad \text{and} \qquad u_{n+1} = (-1)^{n+1} \frac{n+3}{(n+1)(n+2)}$$

Therefore,

$$\left|\frac{u_{n+1}}{u_n}\right| = \frac{n+3}{(n+1)(n+2)} \cdot \frac{n(n+1)}{n+2} = \frac{n(n+3)}{(n+2)^2} = \frac{n^2 + 3n}{n^2 + 4n + 4}$$

$$\lim_{n \to +\infty} \left|\frac{u_{n+1}}{u_n}\right| = \lim_{n \to +\infty} \frac{1 + 3/n}{1 + 4/n + 4/n^2} = 1$$

So, the ratio test fails.

Since
$$|u_n| = \frac{n+2}{n(n+1)} = \frac{n+2}{n+1} \cdot \frac{1}{n} > \frac{1}{n}$$

we may apply the comparison test, and since the series $\sum_{n=1}^{+\infty} 1/n$ is the harmonic series, which diverges, we conclude that the series $\sum_{n=1}^{+\infty} |u_n|$ is divergent and hence $\sum_{n=1}^{+\infty} u_n$ is not absolutely convergent.

    Since the given series satisfies the hypothesis of the alternating-series test (Theorem 24.4.2), the given series is convergent. Since it is convergent but not absolutely convergent, we conclude that the given series is conditionally convergent.

    It should be noted that the ratio test does not include all possibilities for $\lim_{n \to +\infty} |u_{n+1}/u_n|$, as it is possible that the limit does not exist and is not $+\infty$. The discussion of such cases is beyond the scope of this book.

To conclude our discussion of infinite series of constant terms, we suggest a possible procedure to follow for determining the convergence or divergence of a given series. First of all, if $\lim\limits_{n\to+\infty} u_n \neq 0$, we may conclude that the series is divergent. If $\lim\limits_{n\to+\infty} u_n = 0$ and the series is an alternating series, then try the alternating-series test. If this test is not applicable, then try the ratio test. If in applying the ratio test, $L = 1$, then another test must be used. The integral test may work when the ratio test does not; this was shown in the case of the p series. Also, the comparison test may be tried.

Exercises 24.4

In Exercises 1 through 8, determine if the given alternating series is convergent or divergent.

1. $\displaystyle\sum_{n=1}^{+\infty} (-1)^n \frac{1}{\ln n}$

2. $\displaystyle\sum_{n=1}^{+\infty} (-1)^{n+1} \sin \frac{\pi}{n}$

3. $\displaystyle\sum_{n=1}^{+\infty} (-1)^{n+1} \frac{n^2}{n^3 + 2}$

4. $\displaystyle\sum_{n=1}^{+\infty} (-1)^{n+1} \frac{\ln n}{n}$

5. $\displaystyle\sum_{n=1}^{+\infty} (-1)^{n+1} \frac{\ln n}{n^2}$

6. $\displaystyle\sum_{n=1}^{+\infty} (-1)^n \frac{e^n}{n}$

7. $\displaystyle\sum_{n=1}^{+\infty} (-1)^n \frac{n}{2^n}$

8. $\displaystyle\sum_{n=1}^{+\infty} (-1)^n \frac{\sqrt{n}}{3n - 1}$

In Exercsies 9 through 12, find the error if the sum of the first four terms is used as an approximation to the sum of the given infinite series.

9. $\displaystyle\sum_{n=1}^{+\infty} (-1)^{n+1} \frac{1}{n}$

10. $\displaystyle\sum_{n=1}^{+\infty} (-1)^n \frac{1}{n!}$

11. $\displaystyle\sum_{n=1}^{+\infty} (-1)^{n+1} \frac{1}{(2n - 1)^2}$

12. $\displaystyle\sum_{n=1}^{+\infty} (-1)^{n+1} \frac{1}{n^n}$

In Exercises 13 through 16, find the sum of the given infinite series, accurate to three decimal places.

13. $\displaystyle\sum_{n=1}^{+\infty} (-1)^{n+1} \frac{1}{(2n)^3}$

14. $\displaystyle\sum_{n=1}^{+\infty} (-1)^{n+1} \frac{1}{(2n)!}$

15. $\displaystyle\sum_{n=1}^{+\infty} (-1)^{n+1} \frac{1}{n2^n}$

16. $\displaystyle\sum_{n=1}^{+\infty} (-1)^n \frac{1}{(2n + 1)^3}$

In Exercises 17 through 28, determine if the given series is absolutely convergent, conditionally convergent, or divergent. Prove your answer.

17. $\displaystyle\sum_{n=1}^{+\infty} (-1)^{n+1} \frac{2^n}{n!}$

23. $\displaystyle\sum_{n=1}^{+\infty} (-1)^{n+1} \frac{3^n}{n!}$

18. $\displaystyle\sum_{n=1}^{+\infty} (-1)^{n+1} \frac{1}{(2n-1)!}$

24. $\displaystyle\sum_{n=1}^{+\infty} (-1)^n \frac{n^2+1}{n^3}$

19. $\displaystyle\sum_{n=1}^{+\infty} \frac{n^2}{n!}$

25. $\displaystyle\sum_{n=2}^{+\infty} (-1)^{n+1} \frac{1}{n(\ln n)^2}$

20. $\displaystyle\sum_{n=1}^{+\infty} n \left(\frac{2}{3}\right)^n$

26. $\displaystyle\sum_{n=1}^{+\infty} (-1)^n \frac{\cos n}{n^2}$

21. $\displaystyle\sum_{n=1}^{+\infty} (-1)^n \frac{n!}{2^{n+1}}$

27. $\displaystyle\sum_{n=1}^{+\infty} \frac{n^n}{n!}$

22. $\displaystyle\sum_{n=1}^{+\infty} (-1)^{n+1} \frac{1}{n(n+2)}$

28. $\displaystyle\sum_{n=1}^{+\infty} \frac{1\cdot3\cdot5\cdots(2n-1)}{1\cdot4\cdot7\cdots(3n-2)}$

29. Prove by mathematical induction that $1/n! \le 1/2^{n-1}$.

30. Prove that if $\displaystyle\sum_{n=1}^{+\infty} u_n$ is absolutely convergent and $u_n \ne 0$ for all n, then $\displaystyle\sum_{n=1}^{+\infty} 1/|u_n|$ is divergent.

31. Prove that if $\displaystyle\sum_{n=1}^{+\infty} u_n$ is absolutely convergent, then $\displaystyle\sum_{n=1}^{+\infty} u_n^2$ is convergent.

32. Show by means of an example that the converse of Exercise 31 is not true.

(24.5)   Power series

24.5.1 DEFINITION   A *power series* in $(x-a)$ is a series of the form

(1) $c_0 + c_1(x-a) + c_2(x-a)^2 + \cdots + c_n(x-a)^n + \cdots$

We shall use the notation $\displaystyle\sum_{n=0}^{+\infty} c_n(x-a)^n$ to represent the series (1). [Note that we take $(x-a)^0 = 1$, even when $x = a$, for convenience in writing the general term.] If x is a particular number, the power series (1) becomes an infinite series of constant terms, as was discussed in previous sections. A special case of (1) is obtained when $a = 0$ and the series becomes a power series in x, which is

(2) $\displaystyle\sum_{n=0}^{+\infty} c_n x^n = c_0 + c_1 x + c_2 x^2 + \cdots + c_n x^n + \cdots$

In addition to power series in $(x - a)$ and x, there are power series of the form

$$\sum_{n=0}^{+\infty} c_n[\phi(x)]^n = c_0 + c_1\phi(x) + c_2[\phi(x)]^2 + \cdots + c_n[\phi(x)]^n + \cdots$$

where ϕ is a function of x. Such a series is called a power series in $\phi(x)$. In this book, we shall be concerned exclusively with power series of the forms (1) and (2), and when we use the term "power series," we shall mean either of these forms. In discussing the theory of power series, we shall confine ourselves to series (2). The more general power series (1) may be obtained from (2) by the translation $x = \bar{x} - a$, and therefore our results may be applied to series (1) as well.

In dealing with an infinite series of constant terms, we were concerned with the question of convergence or divergence of the series. In considering a power series, the question we ask is: *For what values of x, if any, does the power series converge?* For each value of x for which the power series converges, the series represents the number which is the sum of the series. Therefore, we may think of a power series as defining a function. The function f, having function values

(3) $$f(x) = \sum_{n=0}^{+\infty} c_n x^n$$

has as its domain all values of x for which the power series in (3) converges.

The following two examples illustrate how the ratio test may be used to determine the values of x for which a power series is convergent. Note that when $n!$ is used in representing the nth term of a power series (as in Example 2), we take $0! = 1$, so that the expression for the nth term will hold when $n = 0$.

EXAMPLE 1: Find the values of x for which the power series

$$\sum_{n=1}^{+\infty} (-1)^{n+1} \frac{2^n x^n}{n3^n}$$

is convergent.

Solution: For the given series,

$$u_n = (-1)^{n+1} \frac{2^n x^n}{n3^n} \quad \text{and} \quad u_{n+1} = (-1)^{n+2} \frac{2^{n+1} x^{n+1}}{(n+1)\,3^{n+1}}$$

So,

$$\lim_{n \to +\infty} \left| \frac{u_{n+1}}{u_n} \right| = \lim_{n \to +\infty} \left| \frac{2^{n+1} x^{n+1}}{(n+1)\,3^{n+1}} \cdot \frac{n3^n}{2^n x^n} \right| = \lim_{n \to +\infty} \frac{2}{3} |x| \frac{n}{n+1} = \frac{2}{3} |x|$$

So, the power series is absolutely convergent when $2|x|/3 < 1$ or, equivalently, when $|x| < 3/2$. The series is divergent when $2|x|/3 > 1$ or, equivalently, when $|x| > 3/2$. When $2|x|/3 = 1$, that is, when $x = \pm 3/2$, the ratio test fails. When $x = 3/2$, the given power series becomes

$$\frac{1}{1} - \frac{1}{2} + \frac{1}{3} - \frac{1}{4} + \cdots + (-1)^{n+1} \frac{1}{n} + \cdots$$

which is convergent, as was shown in Example 1, Sec. 24.4. When $x = -3/2$, we have

$$-\frac{1}{1} - \frac{1}{2} - \frac{1}{3} - \frac{1}{4} - \cdots - \frac{1}{n} - \cdots$$

which by Theorem 24.2.8 is divergent. We conclude then that the given power series is convergent when $-3/2 < x \leq 3/2$. The series is absolutely convergent when $-3/2 < x < 3/2$ and is conditionally convergent when $x = 3/2$. If $x \leq -3/2$ or $x > 3/2$, the series is divergent.

EXAMPLE 2: Find the values of x for which the power series $\sum_{n=0}^{+\infty} x^n/n!$ is convergent.

Solution: For the given series, $u_n = x^n/n!$ and $u_{n+1} = x^{n+1}/(n+1)!$. So, applying the ratio test, we have

$$\lim_{n \to +\infty} \left| \frac{u_{n+1}}{u_n} \right| = \lim_{n \to +\infty} \left| \frac{x^{n+1}}{(n+1)!} \cdot \frac{n!}{x^n} \right| = |x| \lim_{n \to +\infty} \frac{1}{n+1} = 0 < 1$$

We conclude that the given power series is absolutely convergent for all values of x.

24.5.2 THEOREM If the power series $\sum_{n=0}^{+\infty} c_n x^n$ is convergent for $x = x_1$ ($x_1 \neq 0$), then it is absolutely convergent for all values of x for which $|x| < |x_1|$.

Proof: If $\sum_{n=0}^{+\infty} c_n x_1^n$ is convergent, then $\lim_{n \to +\infty} c_n x_1^n = 0$. Therefore, if we take $\epsilon = 1$ in Definition 4.4.1, there exists an integer $N > 0$ such that

$$|c_n x_1^n| < 1 \qquad \text{whenever} \qquad n \geq N$$

Now, if x is any number such that $|x| < |x_1|$, we have

$$(4) \qquad |c_n x^n| = \left| c_n x_1^n \frac{x^n}{x_1^n} \right| = |c_n x_1^n| \left| \frac{x}{x_1} \right|^n < \left| \frac{x}{x_1} \right|^n \qquad \text{whenever } n \geq N$$

The series

$$(5) \qquad \sum_{n=N}^{+\infty} \left| \frac{x}{x_1} \right|^n$$

is convergent, since it is a geometric series with $r = |x/x_1| < 1$ (because $|x| < |x_1|$). Comparing the series $\sum_{n=N}^{+\infty} |c_n x^n|$, where $|x| < |x_1|$, with series (5), we see from (4) and the comparison test that $\sum_{n=N}^{+\infty} |c_n x^n|$ is convergent for $|x| < |x_1|$. So the given power series is absolutely convergent for all values of x for which $|x| < |x_1|$.

A corollary of the above theorem is the following one.

24.5.3 THEOREM If the power series $\sum_{n=0}^{+\infty} c_n x^n$ is divergent for $x = x_2$, then it is divergent for all values of x for which $|x| > |x_2|$.

Proof: Suppose the given power series is convergent for some number x for which $|x| > |x_2|$. Then by Theorem 24.5.2, the series must converge when $x = x_2$. However, this contradicts the hypothesis. Therefore, the given power series is divergent for all values of x for which $|x| > |x_2|$.

From Theorems 24.5.2 and 24.5.3, we may prove the following important theorem regarding the convergence and divergence of a power series of the form $\sum_{n=0}^{+\infty} c_n x^n$.

24.5.4 THEOREM Let $\sum_{n=0}^{+\infty} c_n x^n$ be a given power series. Then exactly one of the following conditions holds.

(i)   The series converges only when $x = 0$

(ii) The series is absolutely convergent for all values of x

(iii) There exists a number $R > 0$ such that the series is absolutely convergent for all values of x for which $|x| < R$ and is divergent for all values of x for which $|x| > R$.

Proof: If we replace x by zero in the given power series, we have $c_0 + 0 + 0 + \ldots$, which is obviously convergent. Therefore, every power series of the form $\sum_{n=0}^{+\infty} c_n x^n$ is convergent when $x = 0$. If this is the only value of x for which the series converges, then condition (i) holds.

Suppose the given series is convergent for $x = x_1$ where $x_1 \neq 0$. Then it follows from Theorem 24.5.2 that the series is absolutely convergent for all values of x for which $|x| < |x_1|$. Now, if in addition there is no value of x for which the given series is divergent, we may conclude that the series is absolutely convergent for all values of x. This is condition (ii).

If the given series is convergent for $x = x_1$ where $x_1 \neq 0$, and is divergent for $x = x_2$ where $|x_2| > |x_1|$, then it follows from Theorem 24.5.3 that the series is divergent for all values of x for which $|x| > |x_2|$. Hence, $|x_2|$ is an upper bound of the set of values of $|x|$ for which the series is absolutely convergent. Therefore, by the axiom of completeness (24.1.10), this set of numbers has a least upper bound, which is the number R of condition (iii). This proves that exactly one of the three conditions holds.

If instead of the power series $\sum_{n=0}^{+\infty} c_n x^n$, we have the series $\sum_{n=0}^{+\infty} c_n (x - a)^n$, in conditions (i) and (iii) of Theorem 24.5.4 we replace x by $x - a$, and the conditions become

(i)   The series converges only when $x = a$

(iii) There exists a number $R > 0$ such that the series is absolutely convergent for all values of x for which $|x - a| < R$ and is divergent for all values of x for which $|x - a| > R$

The set of all values of x for which a given power series is convergent is called the *interval of convergence* of the power series. The number R of condition (iii) of Theorem 24.5.4 is called the *radius of convergence* of the power series. If condition (i) holds, we take $R = 0$, and if condition (ii) holds, we write $R = +\infty$.

For the power series of Example 1 of this section, $R = 3/2$ and the interval of convergence is $(-3/2, 3/2]$. In Example 2, $R = +\infty$ and we write the interval of convergence as $(-\infty, +\infty)$.

If R is the radius of convergence of the power series $\displaystyle\sum_{n=0}^{+\infty} c_n x^n$, then the interval of convergence is one of the following intervals: $(-R, R)$, $[-R, R]$, $(-R, R]$, or $[-R, R)$. For the more general power series $\displaystyle\sum_{n=0}^{+\infty} c_n(x - a)^n$, the interval of convergence is one of the following:

$$(a - R, a + R),\ [a - R, a + R],\ (a - R, a + R],\ \text{or}\ [a - R, a + R).$$

A given power series defines a function having the interval of convergence as its domain. The most useful method at our disposal for determining the interval of convergence of a power series is the ratio test. However, the ratio test will not tell us anything regarding the convergence or divergence of the power series at the end points of the interval of convergence. At an end point, a power series may be either absolutely convergent, conditionally convergent, or divergent. If a power series converges at both end points, then it follows from the definition of absolute convergence that the series is absolutely convergent at each end point (see Exercise 21 at the end of this section). If a power series converges at one end point and diverges at the other, the series is conditionally convergent at the end point at which it converges (see Exercise 22 at the end of this section). There are cases for which the convergence or divergence of a power series at the end points can not be determined by the methods of elementary calculus.

EXAMPLE 3: Determine the interval of convergence of the power series

$$\sum_{n=1}^{+\infty} n(x - 2)^n.$$

Solution: The given series is

$$(x - 2) + 2(x - 2)^2 + 3(x - 2)^3 + \cdots + n(x - 2)^n + (n + 1)(x - 2)^{n+1} + \cdots$$

Applying the ratio test, we have

$$\lim_{n \to +\infty} \left| \frac{u_{n+1}}{u_n} \right| = \lim_{n \to +\infty} \left| \frac{(n + 1)(x - 2)^{n+1}}{n(x - 2)^n} \right| = |x - 2| \lim_{n \to +\infty} \frac{n + 1}{n} = |x - 2|$$

The given series then will be absolutely convergent if $|x - 2| < 1$ or equivalently, $-1 < x - 2 < 1$ or, equivalently, $1 < x < 3$.

When $x = 1$, the series is $\displaystyle\sum_{n=1}^{+\infty} (-1)^n n$, which is divergent, since $\displaystyle\lim_{n \to +\infty} u_n \neq 0$.

When $x = 3$, the series is $\displaystyle\sum_{n=1}^{+\infty} n$, which is also divergent because $\displaystyle\lim_{n \to +\infty} u_n \neq 0$.

Therefore, the interval of convergence is $(1,3)$. So, the given power series defines a function having the interval $(1,3)$ as its domain.

EXAMPLE 4: Determine the interval of convergence of the power series

$$\sum_{n=1}^{+\infty} \frac{x^n}{2 + n^2}$$

Solution: The given series is

$$\frac{x}{2 + 1^2} + \frac{x^2}{2 + 2^2} + \frac{x^3}{2 + 3^2} + \cdots + \frac{x^n}{2 + n^2} + \frac{x^{n+1}}{2 + (n + 1)^2} + \cdots$$

Applying the ratio test, we have

$$\lim_{n \to +\infty} \left| \frac{u_{n+1}}{u_n} \right| = \lim_{n \to +\infty} \left| \frac{x^{n+1}}{2 + (n + 1)^2} \cdot \frac{2 + n^2}{x^n} \right| = |x| \lim_{n \to +\infty} \frac{2 + n^2}{2 + n^2 + 2n + 1} = |x|$$

So, the given series will be absolutely convergent if $|x| < 1$ or, equivalently, $-1 < x < 1$. When $x = 1$, we have the series

$$\frac{1}{2 + 1^2} + \frac{1}{2 + 2^2} + \frac{1}{2 + 3^2} + \cdots + \frac{1}{2 + n^2} + \cdots$$

Since $1/(2 + n^2) < 1/n^2$ for all positive integers n, and since $\displaystyle\sum_{n=1}^{+\infty} 1/n^2$ is a convergent p-series, it follows from the comparison test that the given power series is convergent when $x = 1$. When $x = -1$, we have the series $\displaystyle\sum_{n=1}^{+\infty} (-1)^n/(2 + n^2)$, which is convergent since we have just seen that it is absolutely convergent. Hence, the interval of convergence of the given power series is $[-1,1]$.

Exercises 24.5

In Exercises 1 through 20, find the interval of convergence of the given power series.

1. $\displaystyle\sum_{n=1}^{+\infty} (-1)^{n+1} \frac{x^{2n-1}}{(2n - 1)!}$

2. $\displaystyle\sum_{n=0}^{+\infty} \frac{x^n}{n + 1}$

3. $\displaystyle\sum_{n=1}^{+\infty} \frac{2^n x^n}{n^2}$

4. $\displaystyle\sum_{n=1}^{+\infty} (-1)^n \frac{x^{2n}}{(2n)!}$

5. $\displaystyle\sum_{n=1}^{+\infty} n!x^n$

13. $\displaystyle\sum_{n=2}^{+\infty} (-1)^{n+1}\frac{x^n}{n(\ln n)^2}$

6. $\displaystyle\sum_{n=0}^{+\infty} \frac{x^n}{(n+1)5^n}$

14. $\displaystyle\sum_{n=1}^{+\infty} \frac{(x+5)^{n-1}}{n^2}$

7. $\displaystyle\sum_{n=1}^{+\infty} (-1)^n\frac{x^n}{(2n-1)3^{2n-1}}$

15. $\displaystyle\sum_{n=1}^{+\infty} \frac{n!x^n}{n^n}$

8. $\displaystyle\sum_{n=1}^{+\infty} (-1)^{n+1}\frac{(n+1)x}{n!}$

16. $\displaystyle\sum_{n=1}^{+\infty} \frac{n^n}{n!}x^n$

9. $\displaystyle\sum_{n=1}^{+\infty} (-1)^{n+1}\frac{(x-1)^n}{n}$

17. $\displaystyle\sum_{n=1}^{+\infty} \frac{\ln n(x-5)^n}{n+1}$

10. $\displaystyle\sum_{n=1}^{+\infty} \frac{(x+2)^n}{(n+1)2^n}$

18. $\displaystyle\sum_{n=1}^{+\infty} n^n(x-3)^n$

11. $\displaystyle\sum_{n=0}^{+\infty} (\sinh 2n)x^n$

19. $\displaystyle\sum_{n=1}^{+\infty} (-1)^n\frac{1\cdot3\cdot5\cdots(2n-1)}{2\cdot4\cdot6\cdots2n}x^{2n+1}$

12. $\displaystyle\sum_{n=1}^{+\infty} \frac{x^n}{\ln(n+1)}$

20. $\displaystyle\sum_{n=1}^{+\infty} \frac{(-1)^{n+1}1\cdot3\cdot5\cdots(2n-1)}{2\cdot4\cdot6\cdots2n}x^n$

21. Prove that if a power series converges at both end points of its interval of convergence, then the power series is absolutely convergent at each end point.

22. Prove that if a power series converges at one end point of its interval of convergence and diverges at the other end point, then the power series is conditionally convergent at the end point at which it converges.

23. Prove that if the radius of convergence of the power series $\displaystyle\sum_{n=1}^{+\infty} u_n x^n$ is r, then the radius of convergence of the series $\displaystyle\sum_{n=1}^{+\infty} u_n x^{2n}$ is $\sqrt{r}$.

24. Prove that if $\displaystyle\lim_{n\to+\infty} \sqrt[n]{|u_n|} = L$ $(L\neq 0)$, then the radius of convergence of the power series $\displaystyle\sum_{n=1}^{+\infty} u_n x^n$ is $1/L$.

(24.6) Taylor's formula

We learned in the previous section that a power series defines a function whose domain is the interval of convergence of the power series. In Sec. 24.7 we shall consider the problem of representing a given function as a power series. However, before we can do this, we need to have at our disposal a very important formula, known as *Taylor's formula*, named in honor of the English mathematician Brook Taylor (1685–1731). The following theorem, which may be considered as a generalization of the mean-value theorem (8.5.1), gives us Taylor's formula.

24.6.1 THEOREM   Let f be a function such that f and its first n derivatives are continuous on the closed interval $[a,b]$. Furthermore, let $f^{(n+1)}(x)$ exist for all x in the open interval (a,b). Then there is a number ξ in the open interval (a,b) such that

$$(1) \quad f(b) = f(a) + \frac{f'(a)}{1!}(b-a) + \frac{f''(a)}{2!}(b-a)^2 + \cdots + \frac{f^{(n)}(a)}{n!}(b-a)^n$$

$$+ \frac{f^{(n+1)}(\xi)}{(n+1)!}(b-a)^{n+1}$$

(1) also holds if $b < a$; in which case, we replace $[a,b]$ by $[b,a]$, and (a,b) by (b,a).

Before proving this theorem, we note that when $n = 0$, (1) becomes

$$f(b) = f(a) + f'(\xi)(b-a)$$

where ξ is between a and b. This is the mean-value theorem (8.5.1).

There are several known proofs of Theorem 24.6.1, although none is very well motivated. The one following makes use of Cauchy's mean-value theorem (20.1.1).

Proof of Theorem 24.6.1: Let F and G be two functions defined by

$$(2) \quad F(x) = f(b) - f(x) - f'(x)(b-x) - \frac{f''(x)}{2!}(b-x)^2 - \cdots$$

$$- \frac{f^{(n-1)}(x)}{(n-1)!}(b-x)^{n-1} - \frac{f^{(n)}(x)}{n!}(b-x)^n$$

and

$$(3) \quad G(x) = \frac{(b-x)^{n+1}}{(n+1)!}$$

We see that $F(b) = 0$ and $G(b) = 0$. Differentiating (2), we get

$$F'(x) = -f'(x) + f'(x) - f''(x)(b-x) + \frac{2f''(x)(b-x)}{2!} - \frac{f'''(x)(b-x)^2}{2!}$$

$$+ \frac{3f'''(x)(b-x)^2}{3!} - \frac{f^{(iv)}(x)(b-x)^3}{3!} + \cdots$$

$$+ \frac{(n-1)f^{(n-1)}(x)(b-x)^{n-2}}{(n-1)!} - \frac{f^{(n)}(x)(b-x)^{n-1}}{(n-1)!}$$

$$+ \frac{nf^{(n)}(x)(b-x)^{n-1}}{n!} - \frac{f^{(n+1)}(x)(b-x)^n}{n!}$$

Combining terms, we see that the sum of every odd-numbered term with the following even-numbered term is zero, and so we have only the last term remaining. Therefore,

$$(4) \qquad\qquad F'(x) = -\frac{f^{(n+1)}(x)}{n!}(b-x)^n$$

Differentiating (3), we obtain

(5)
$$G'(x) = -\frac{1}{n!}(b - x)^n$$

Checking the hypothesis of Theorem 20.1.1, we see that

(i) F and G are continuous on $[a,b]$

(ii) F and G are differentiable on (a,b)

(iii) $G'(x) \neq 0$ for all x in (a,b)

So by the conclusion of Theorem 20.1.1 we have

$$\frac{F(b) - F(a)}{G(b) - G(a)} = \frac{F'(\xi)}{G'(\xi)}$$

where ξ is in (a,b). But $F(b) = 0$ and $G(b) = 0$. So, we have

(6)
$$F(a) = \frac{F'(\xi)}{G'(\xi)}G(a)$$

for some ξ in (a,b).

Letting $x = a$ in (3), $x = \xi$ in (4), and $x = \xi$ in (5) and substituting into (6), we obtain

$$F(a) = -\frac{f^{(n+1)}(\xi)}{n!}(b - \xi)^n\left[-\frac{n!}{(b - \xi)^n}\right]\frac{(b - a)^{n+1}}{(n + 1)!}$$

or, equivalently,

(7)
$$F(a) = \frac{f^{(n+1)}(\xi)}{(n + 1)!}(b - a)^{n+1}$$

If in (2) we let $x = a$, we obtain

(8) $$F(a) = f(b) - f(a) - f'(a)(b - a) - \frac{f''(a)}{2!}(b - a)^2 - \cdots$$
$$- \frac{f^{(n-1)}(a)}{(n - 1)!}(b - a)^{n-1} - \frac{f^{(n)}(a)}{n!}(b - a)^n$$

Substituting from (7) into (8), we get

$$f(b) = f(a) + f'(a)(b - a) + \frac{f''(a)}{2!}(b - a)^2 + \cdots + \frac{f^{(n)}(a)}{n!}(b - a)^n$$
$$+ \frac{f^{(n+1)}(\xi)}{(n + 1)!}(b - a)^{n+1}$$

which is the desired result. The theorem holds if $b < a$, since the conclusion of Theorem 20.1.1 is unaffected if a and b are interchanged.

If in (1) we replace b by x, we obtain Taylor's formula, which is

(9) $$f(x) = f(a) + \frac{f'(a)}{1!}(x - a) + \frac{f''(a)}{2!}(x - a)^2 + \cdots + \frac{f^{(n)}(a)}{n!}(x - a)^n$$
$$+ \frac{f^{(n+1)}(\xi)}{(n + 1)!}(x - a)^{n+1}$$

where ξ is between a and x.

The condition under which (9) holds is that f and its first n derivatives must be continuous on a closed interval containing a and x, and the $(n + 1)$st derivative of f must exist at all points of the corresponding open interval. Formula (9) may be written as

(10) $$f(x) = P_n(x) + R_n(x)$$

where

(11) $$P_n(x) = f(a) + \frac{f'(a)}{1!}(x - a) + \frac{f''(a)}{2!}(x - a)^2 + \cdots + \frac{f^{(n)}(a)}{n!}(x - a)^n$$

and

(12) $$R_n(x) = \frac{f^{(n+1)}(\xi)}{(n + 1)!}(x - a)^{n+1} \qquad \text{where } \xi \text{ is between } a \text{ and } x$$

$P_n(x)$ is called the nth-degree *Taylor polynomial* of the function f at the number a, and $R_n(x)$ is called the *remainder*. $R_n(x)$ as given in (12) is called the *Lagrange form* of the remainder, named in honor of the French mathematician Joseph L. Lagrange (1736–1813).

EXAMPLE 1: Find the third-degree Taylor polynomial of the cosine function at $\pi/4$ and the Lagrange form of the remainder.

Solution: Letting $f(x) = \cos x$, we have from (11)

$$P_3(x) = f\left(\frac{\pi}{4}\right) + f'\left(\frac{\pi}{4}\right)\left(x - \frac{\pi}{4}\right) + \frac{f''(\pi/4)}{2!}\left(x - \frac{\pi}{4}\right)^2 + \frac{f'''(\pi/4)}{3!}\left(x - \frac{\pi}{4}\right)^3$$

Since $f(x) = \cos x$, $f(\pi/4) = \sqrt{2}/2$; $f'(x) = -\sin x$, $f'(\pi/4) = -\sqrt{2}/2$; $f''(x) = -\cos x, f''(\pi/4) = -\sqrt{2}/2; f'''(x) = \sin x, f'''(\pi/4) = \sqrt{2}/2$. Therefore,

$$P_3(x) = \frac{\sqrt{2}}{2} - \frac{\sqrt{2}}{2}\left(x - \frac{\pi}{4}\right) - \frac{\sqrt{2}}{4}\left(x - \frac{\pi}{4}\right)^2 + \frac{\sqrt{2}}{12}\left(x - \frac{\pi}{4}\right)^3$$

Since $f^{(iv)}(x) = \cos x$, we obtain from (12)

$$R_3(x) = \frac{\cos \xi}{24}\left(x - \frac{\pi}{4}\right)^4 \qquad \text{where } \xi \text{ is between } \frac{\pi}{4} \text{ and } x$$

Since $|\cos \xi| \leq 1$, we may conclude that for all x, $|R_3(x)| \leq (x - \pi/4)^4/24$.

Taylor's formula may be used to approximate a function by means of a Taylor polynomial. From (10) we obtain

(13) $$|R_n(x)| = |f(x) - P_n(x)|$$

If $P_n(x)$ is used to approximate $f(x)$, we can obtain an upper bound for the error of this approximation if we can find a number $E > 0$ such that $|R_n(x)| \leq E$ or, because of (13), such that $|f(x) - P_n(x)| \leq E$ or, equivalently,

$$P_n(x) - E \leq f(x) \leq P_n(x) + E$$

EXAMPLE 2: Use the solution of Example 1 to compute an approximate value of $\cos 47°$ and determine the accuracy of the result.

Solution: $47° = 47\pi/180$ radians. So, in the solution of Example 1, we take $x = 47\pi/180$ and $x - \pi/4 = \pi/90$, and we have

$$\cos 47° = \frac{\sqrt{2}}{2}\left[1 - \frac{\pi}{90} - \frac{1}{2}\left(\frac{\pi}{90}\right)^2 + \frac{1}{6}\left(\frac{\pi}{90}\right)^3\right] + R_3\left(\frac{47\pi}{180}\right)$$

$$\text{where} \quad R_3\left(\frac{47\pi}{180}\right) = \frac{\cos \xi}{24}\left(\frac{\pi}{90}\right)^4 \quad \text{with } \frac{\pi}{4} < \xi < \frac{47\pi}{180}$$

Since $0 < \cos \xi < 1$,

$$0 < R_3\left(\frac{47\pi}{180}\right) < \frac{1}{24}\left(\frac{\pi}{90}\right)^4 < 0.00000004$$

Taking $\pi/90 \approx 0.034907$, we obtain

$$\cos 47° \approx 0.68200$$

which is accurate to five decimal places.

EXAMPLE 3: Use a Taylor polynomial at zero to find the value of $\sqrt{e}$, accurate to four decimal places.

Solution: Letting $f(x) = e^x$, all the derivatives of f at x are e^x and all the derivatives evaluated at zero are 1. Therefore, from (11) we have

$$P_n(x) = 1 + x + \frac{x^2}{2!} + \frac{x^3}{3!} + \cdots + \frac{x^n}{n!}$$

and from (12) we get

$$R_n(x) = \frac{e^\xi}{(n+1)!}\,x^{n+1} \quad \text{where } \xi \text{ is between 0 and } x$$

We want $|R_n(\frac{1}{2})|$ to be less than 0.00005. If we take $\xi = \frac{1}{2}$ in the above and since $e^{1/2} < 2$, we get

$$\left|R_n(\tfrac{1}{2})\right| < \frac{e^{1/2}}{2^{n+1}(n+1)!} < \frac{2}{2^{n+1}(n+1)!} = \frac{1}{2^n(n+1)!}$$

$|R_n(\frac{1}{2})|$ will be less than 0.00005 if $1/2^n(n+1)! < 0.00005$.
When $n = 5$,

$$\frac{1}{2^n(n+1)!} = \frac{1}{(32)(720)} = 0.00004 < 0.00005$$

So,

$$\sqrt{e} \approx P_5\left(\frac{1}{2}\right) = 1 + \frac{1}{2} + \frac{1}{8} + \frac{1}{48} + \frac{1}{384} + \frac{1}{3,840}$$

from which we obtain $\sqrt{e} \approx 1.64870$.

A special case of Taylor's formula is obtained by taking $a = 0$ in (9), and we get

$$(14)\, f(x) = f(0) + \frac{f'(0)}{1!}\,x + \frac{f''(0)}{2!}\,x^2 + \cdots + \frac{f^{(n)}(0)}{n!}\,x^n + \frac{f^{(n+1)}(\xi)}{(n+1)!}\,x^{n+1}$$

where ξ is between 0 and x. Formula (14) is called Maclaurin's formula, named in honor of the Scotch mathematician Colin Maclaurin (1698–1746). However, the formula was obtained earlier by Taylor and by another English mathematician, James Stirling (1692–1770).

There are other forms of the remainder in Taylor's formula. Depending upon the function, one form of the remainder may be more desirable to use than another. The following theorem expresses the remainder as an integral, and it is known as *Taylor's formula with integral form of the remainder*.

24.6.2 THEOREM   If f is a function whose first $n + 1$ derivatives are continuous on a closed interval containing a and x, then $f(x) = P_n(x) + R_n(x)$, where $P_n(x)$ is the nth-degree Taylor polynomial of f at a and $R_n(x)$ is the remainder given by

$$(15) \qquad R_n(x) = \frac{1}{n!} \int_a^x (x - t)^n f^{(n+1)}(t) \, dt$$

The proof of this theorem is left for the reader (see Exercise 19 at the end of this section).

Exercises 24.6

In Exercises 1 through 10, find the Taylor polynomial of degree n with the Lagrange form of the remainder at the number a for the given function.

1. $f(x) = \sin x; \ a = \pi/6; \ n = 3$ 6. $f(x) = \sqrt{x}; \ a = 4; \ n = 4$

2. $f(x) = \tan x; \ a = 0; \ n = 3$ 7. $f(x) = \ln \cos x; \ a = \pi/3; \ n = 3$

3. $f(x) = \sinh x; \ a = 0; \ n = 4$ 8. $f(x) = e^{-x^2}; \ a = 0; \ n = 3$

4. $f(x) = \cosh x; \ a = 0; \ n = 4$ 9. $f(x) = (1 + x)^{3/2}; \ a = 0; \ n = 3$

5. $f(x) = \ln x; \ a = 1; \ n = 3$ 10. $f(x) = (1 - x)^{-1/2}; \ a = 0; \ n = 3$

11. Compute $\sin 31°$ accurate to three decimal places by using the Taylor polynomial at $\pi/6$. (Use the approximation $\pi/180 \approx 0.0175$.)

12. Use the Taylor polynomial found in Exercise 6 to compute $\sqrt{5}$, accurate to as many decimal places as is justified when R_4 is neglected.

13. Use a Taylor polynomial at $x = 0$ for the function defined by $f(x) = \ln(1 + x)$ to compute the value of $\ln 1.2$, accurate to four decimal places.

14. Use a Taylor polynomial at $x = 0$ for the function defined by

$$f(x) = \ln \frac{1 + x}{1 - x}$$

to compute the value of $\ln 1.2$ accurate to four decimal places. Compare the computation with that of Exercise 13.

15. Show that the formula

$$(1 + x)^{3/2} \approx 1 + \frac{3}{2}x$$

is accurate to three decimal places if $-0.03 \le x \le 0$.

16. Show that the formula

$$(1 + x)^{-1/2} \approx 1 - \frac{1}{2}x$$

is accurate to two decimal places if $-0.1 \le x \le 0$.

17. Draw sketches of the graphs of $y = \sin x$ and $y = mx$ on the same set of axes. Note that if m is positive and close to zero, then the graphs intersect at a point whose abscissa is close to π. By finding the second-degree Taylor polynomial for the function f defined by $f(x) = \sin x - mx$ at $x = \pi$, show that an approximate solution of the equation $\sin x = mx$, when m is positive and close to zero, is given by $x \approx \pi/(1 + m)$.

18. Use the method described in Exercise 17 to find an approximate solution of the equation $\cot x = mx$ when m is positive and close to zero.

19. Prove Theorem 24.6.2. HINT: Let

$$\int_a^x f'(t)\, dt = f(x) - f(a)$$

Solve for $f(x)$ and integrate

$$\int_a^x f'(t)\, dt$$

by parts by letting $u = f'(t)$ and $dv = dt$. Repeat this process, and the desired result follows by mathematical induction.

(24.7)   Differentiation of power series

A power series $\displaystyle\sum_{n=0}^{+\infty} c_n x^n$ defines a function whose domain is the interval of convergence of the series. In this section we shall prove that if R is the radius of convergence of the power series and $R \neq 0$, then the function is differentiable on the open interval $(-R, R)$ and the derivative of the function may be obtained by differentiating the power series term by term. We first need some preliminary theorems.

24.7.1 THEOREM   If $\displaystyle\sum_{n=0}^{+\infty} c_n x^n$ is a power series having a radius of convergence of $R > 0$, then the series $\displaystyle\sum_{n=1}^{+\infty} n c_n x^{n-1}$ also has R as its radius of convergence.

This theorem states that the series, obtained by differentiating term by term each term of a given power series, will have the same radius of convergence as the given series.

Proof: Let x be any number in the open interval $(-R, R)$. Then $|x| < R$. Choose a number x_1 so that $|x| < |x_1| < R$. Since $|x_1| < R$, $\displaystyle\sum_{n=0}^{+\infty} c_n x_1^n$ is convergent. Hence, $\lim\limits_{n \to +\infty} c_n x_1{}^n = 0$. So if we take $\epsilon = 1$ in Definition 4.4.1, there exists a number $N > 0$ such that

$$|c_n x_1{}^n| < 1 \qquad \text{whenever} \qquad n > N$$

Let M be the largest of the numbers $|c_1 x_1|$, $|c_2 x_1{}^2|$, $|c_3 x_1{}^3|$, $\ldots$, $|c_N x_1{}^N|$, 1. Then

(1) $\qquad\qquad\qquad |c_n x_1{}^n| \leq M \qquad$ for all positive integers n

Now

$$|n c_n x^{n-1}| = \left| n c_n \cdot \frac{x^{n-1}}{x_1{}^n} \cdot x_1{}^n \right| = n \frac{|c_n x_1{}^n|}{|x_1|} \left| \frac{x}{x_1} \right|^{n-1}$$

From (1) and the above, we get

(2) $\qquad\qquad\qquad |n c_n x^{n-1}| \leq n \frac{M}{|x_1|} \left| \frac{x}{x_1} \right|^{n-1}$

Applying the ratio test to the series

(3) $\qquad\qquad\qquad \dfrac{M}{|x_1|} \displaystyle\sum_{n=1}^{+\infty} n \left| \dfrac{x}{x_1} \right|^{n-1}$

we have

$$\lim_{n \to +\infty} \left| \frac{u_{n+1}}{u_n} \right| = \lim_{n \to +\infty} \left| \frac{(n+1)|x|^n}{|x_1|^n} \cdot \frac{|x_1|^{n-1}}{n|x|^{n-1}} \right| = \left| \frac{x}{x_1} \right| \lim_{n \to +\infty} \frac{n+1}{n} = \left| \frac{x}{x_1} \right| < 1$$

Therefore, series (3) is absolutely convergent, and so from (2) and the comparison test, the series $\displaystyle\sum_{n=1}^{+\infty} n c_n x^{n-1}$ is also absolutely convergent. Since x is any number in $(-R, R)$, it follows that if the radius of convergence of $\displaystyle\sum_{n=1}^{+\infty} n c_n x^{n-1}$ is R', then $R' \geq R$. To complete the proof we must show that R' cannot be greater than R. This is left for the reader (see Exercise 28, p. 918).

24.7.2 THEOREM If the radius of convergence of the power series $\displaystyle\sum_{n=0}^{+\infty} c_n x^n$ is $R > 0$, then R is also the radius of convergence of the series $\displaystyle\sum_{n=2}^{+\infty} n(n-1) c_n x^{n-2}$.

Proof: If we apply Theorem 24.7.1 to the series $\displaystyle\sum_{n=1}^{+\infty} n c_n x^{n-1}$, we have the desired result.

We are now in a position to prove the theorem regarding term-by-term differentiation of a power series.

24.7.3 THEOREM Let $\displaystyle\sum_{n=0}^{+\infty} c_n x^n$ be a power series whose radius of convergence is $R > 0$.

Then, if f is the function defined by

(4)
$$f(x) = \sum_{n=0}^{+\infty} c_n x^n$$

$f'(x)$ exists for every x in the open interval $(-R,R)$, and it is given by

$$f'(x) = \sum_{n=1}^{+\infty} n c_n x^{n-1}$$

Proof: Let x and a be two distinct numbers in the open interval $(-R,R)$. Then by Taylor's formula — formula (9), Sec. 24.6, with $n = 1$ — we have, for every positive integer n,

(5)
$$x^n = a^n + n a^{n-1}(x - a) + \frac{n(n-1)}{2}(\xi_n)^{n-2} (x - a)^2$$

where ξ_n is between a and x for every positive integer n.

From (4) we have

$$f(x) - f(a) = \sum_{n=0}^{+\infty} c_n x^n - \sum_{n=0}^{+\infty} c_n a^n$$

$$= c_0 + \sum_{n=1}^{+\infty} c_n x^n - c_0 - \sum_{n=1}^{+\infty} c_n a^n$$

$$= \sum_{n=1}^{+\infty} c_n(x^n - a^n)$$

Dividing by $x - a$ (since $x \neq a$) and using (5), we have from the above

$$\frac{f(x) - f(a)}{x - a} = \frac{1}{x - a} \sum_{n=1}^{+\infty} c_n \left[n a^{n-1}(x - a) + \frac{n(n-1)}{2} (\xi_n)^{n-2}(x - a)^2 \right]$$

So,

(6)
$$\frac{f(x) - f(a)}{x - a} = \sum_{n=1}^{+\infty} n c_n a^{n-1} + \frac{x - a}{2} \sum_{n=2}^{+\infty} n(n - 1)c_n (\xi_n)^{n-2}$$

Since a is in $(-R,R)$, it follows from Theorem 24.7.1 that $\sum_{n=1}^{+\infty} n c_n a^{n-1}$ is absolutely convergent.

Since both a and x are in $(-R,R)$, there is some number $K > 0$ such that $|a| < K < R$ and $|x| < K < R$. It follows from Theorem 24.7.2 that

$$\sum_{n=2}^{+\infty} n(n - 1)c_n K^{n-2}$$

is absolutely convergent. Then, since

(7) $$|n(n-1)c_n\,(\xi_n)^{n-2}| < |n(n-1)c_nK^{n-2}|$$

for each ξ_n, we may conclude from the comparison test that

$$\sum_{n=2}^{+\infty} n(n-1)c_n(\xi_n)^{n-2}$$

is absolutely convergent.

It follows from (6) that

(8) $$\left|\frac{f(x)-f(a)}{x-a} - \sum_{n=1}^{+\infty} nc_na^{n-1}\right| = \left|\frac{x-a}{2} \sum_{n=2}^{+\infty} n(n-1)c_n(\xi_n)^{n-2}\right|$$

However, from Theorem 24.4.6, we know that if $\sum_{n=1}^{+\infty} u_n$ is absolutely convergent, then

$$\left|\sum_{n=1}^{+\infty} u_n\right| \le \sum_{n=1}^{+\infty} |u_n|$$

Applying this to the right-hand side of (8), we obtain

(9) $$\left|\frac{f(x)-f(a)}{x-a} - \sum_{n=1}^{+\infty} nc_na^{n-1}\right| \le \frac{|x-a|}{2} \sum_{n=2}^{+\infty} n(n-1)|c_n|\,|\xi_n|^{n-2}$$

From (7) and (9) we get

(10) $$\left|\frac{f(x)-f(a)}{x-a} - \sum_{n=1}^{+\infty} nc_na^{n-1}\right| \le \frac{|x-a|}{2} \sum_{n=2}^{+\infty} n(n-1)|c_n|\,K^{n-2}$$

where $0 < K < R$. Since the series on the right-hand side of (10) is absolutely convergent, the limit of the right-hand side, as x approaches a, is zero. So it follows from (10) and the theorem of Exercise 2 of Sec. 4.6 that

$$\lim_{x \to a} \frac{f(x)-f(a)}{x-a} = \sum_{n=1}^{+\infty} nc_na^{n-1}$$

or, equivalently,

$$f'(a) = \sum_{n=1}^{+\infty} nc_na^{n-1}$$

and since a may be any number in the open interval $(-R,R)$, the theorem is proved.

It follows from Theorem 24.7.3 that if f is the function defined by

(11) $$f(x) = \sum_{n=0}^{+\infty} c_nx^n = c_0 + c_1x + c_2x^2 + c_3x^3 + c_4x^4 + \cdots + c_nx^n + \cdots$$

whose domain is the open interval $(-R, R)$, where $R \neq 0$, then f has derivatives of all orders. Successive differentiations of (11) give us

$$f'(x) = c_1 + 2c_2 x + 3c_3 x^2 + 4c_4 x^3 + \cdots + nc_n x^{n-1} + \cdots$$

$$f''(x) = 2c_2 + 2 \cdot 3c_3 x + 3 \cdot 4c_4 x^2 + \cdots + (n - 1)nc_n x^{n-2} + \cdots$$

$$f'''(x) = 2 \cdot 3c_3 + 2 \cdot 3 \cdot 4c_4 x + \cdots + (n - 2)(n - 1)nc_n x^{n-3} + \cdots$$

$$f^{(iv)}(x) = 2 \cdot 3 \cdot 4c_4 + \cdots + (n - 3)(n - 2)(n - 1)nc_n x^{n-4} + \cdots$$

and so forth. From Theorem 24.7.3 we know that the function f and its derivatives have the same radius of convergence. Letting $x = 0$ in the power-series representations of f and its derivatives, we get $c_0 = f(0)$, $c_1 = f'(0)$, $c_2 = f''(0)/2!$, $c_3 = f''(0)/3!$, and in general

$$(12) \qquad\qquad c_n = \frac{f^{(n)}(0)}{n!} \qquad \text{for every positive integer } n$$

Formula (12) also holds when $n = 0$ if we take $f^{(0)}(0)$ to be $f(0)$ and $0! = 1$. So, from (11) and (12), we may write the power series of f in x as

$$(13) \quad \sum_{n=0}^{+\infty} \frac{f^{(n)}(0)}{n!} x^n = f(0) + f'(0)x + \frac{f''(0)}{2!} x^2 + \cdots + \frac{f^{(n)}(0)}{n!} x^n + \cdots$$

If the function f is a power series in $(x - a)$, then we evaluate f and its derivatives at a and we obtain

$$(14) \quad \sum_{n=0}^{+\infty} \frac{f^{(n)}(a)}{n!} (x - a)^n = f(a) + f'(a)(x - a)$$

$$+ \frac{f''(a)}{2!} (x - a)^2 + \cdots + \frac{f^{(n)}(a)}{n!} (x - a)^n + \cdots$$

The series in (14) is called the *Taylor series* of f at a. The special case of (14), when $a = 0$, is equation (13), which is called the *Maclaurin series*.

We may deduce that a power-series representation of a function is unique. That is, if two functions have the same function values in some interval containing the number a, and if both functions have a power-series representation in $x - a$, then these series must be the same, since the coefficients in the series are obtained from the values of the functions and their derivatives at a. Therefore, if a function has a power-series representation in $x - a$, this series must be a Taylor series. A natural question that arises is: May we conclude that if a function has a Taylor series in $x - a$, this series represents the function for all values of x in the interval of convergence of the series? The answer is no, in general. In Example 2 of this section, we show this. However, for most elementary functions, if r is the radius of convergence of the Taylor series in $x - a$, then the series represents the function for all values of x for which $|x - a| < r$. A theorem that gives a test for determining whether or not a function is represented by its Taylor series is the following.

24.7.4 THEOREM   Let f be a function such that f and all of its derivatives exist in some interval $(a - r, a + r)$. Then the function is represented by its Taylor series

$$\sum_{n=0}^{+\infty} \frac{f^{(n)}(a)}{n!} (x - a)^n$$

for all x such that $|x - a| < r$ if and only if

$$\lim_{n \to +\infty} R_n(x) = \lim_{n \to +\infty} \frac{f^{(n+1)}(\xi_n)}{(n + 1)!} (x - a)^{n+1} = 0$$

where each ξ_n is between x and a.

Proof: In the interval $(a - r, a + r)$, the function f satisfies the hypothesis of Theorem 24.6.1 for which

$$f(x) = P_n(x) + R_n(x)$$

where $P_n(x)$ is the nth-degree Taylor polynomial of f at a and $R_n(x)$ is the remainder, given by

$$R_n(x) = \frac{f^{(n+1}(\xi_n)}{(n + 1)!} (x - a)^{n+1}$$

where each ξ_n is between x and a. So, $P_n(x) = f(x) - R_n(x)$ and

(15) $$\lim_{n \to +\infty} P_n(x) = f(x) - \lim_{n \to +\infty} R_n(x)$$

Now, $P_n(x)$ is the nth partial sum of the Taylor series of f at a. From (15) we see that $\lim_{n \to +\infty} P_n(x)$ exists and equals $f(x)$ if and only if $\lim_{n \to +\infty} R_n(x) = 0$, and so the theorem is proved.

Theorem 24.7.4 also holds for other forms of the remainder $R_n(x)$ besides the Lagrange form.

It is often difficult to apply Theorem 24.7.4 in practice, since the values of ξ_n are arbitrary. However, sometimes an upper bound for $R_n(x)$ may be found, and we may be able to prove that the limit of the upper bound is zero as n approaches $+\infty$. The following limit is helpful in some cases.

(16) $$\lim_{n \to +\infty} \frac{x^n}{n!} = 0 \qquad \text{for all } x$$

This follows from Example 2 of Sec. 24.5, where we showed that the power series $\sum_{n=0}^{+\infty} x^n/n!$ is convergent for all values of x and hence the limit of its nth term must be zero.

EXAMPLE 1: Find the Maclaurin series for e^x and prove that the series represents the function for all values of x.

Solution: If $f(x) = e^x$, $f^{(n)}(x) = e^x$ for all x, and therefore $f^{(n)}(0) = 1$ for all n. So, from (13) we have the Maclaurin series for e^x:

(17) $$1 + x + \frac{x^2}{2!} + \frac{x^3}{3!} + \cdots + \frac{x^n}{n!} + \cdots$$

To prove that (17) holds for all x, we shall show that $\lim\limits_{n \to +\infty} R_n(x) = 0$ for all x.

$$R_n(x) = \frac{e^{\xi_n}}{(n+1)!} x^{n+1}$$

where each ξ_n is between 0 and x. If $x > 0$, then $0 < \xi_n < x$, and hence $e^{\xi_n} < e^x$. So,

$$(18) \qquad\qquad 0 < \frac{e^{\xi_n}}{(n+1)!} x^{n+1} < e^x \frac{x^{n+1}}{(n+1)!}$$

From (16) it follows that $\lim\limits_{n \to +\infty} x^{n+1}/(n+1)! = 0$, and so

$$\lim\limits_{n \to +\infty} e^x \frac{x^{n+1}}{(n+1)!} = 0$$

So, from (18) we may conclude that if $x > 0$, then $\lim\limits_{n \to +\infty} R_n(x) = 0$. If $x < 0$, then $x < \xi_n < 0$ and $0 < e^{\xi_n} < 1$. Therefore,

$$0 < \frac{e^{\xi_n}}{(n+1)!} x^{n+1} < \frac{x^{n+1}}{(n+1)!}$$

and so $\lim\limits_{n \to +\infty} R_n(x) = 0$. If $x = 0$, the series obviously gives e^0. We may therefore conclude that the series in (17) represents e^x for all values of x.

From the results of the above example, we may write

$$(19) \qquad\qquad e^x = \sum_{n=0}^{+\infty} \frac{x^n}{n!} = 1 + x + \frac{x^2}{2!} + \frac{x^3}{3!} + \cdots$$

In a manner similar to the solution of Example 1, we may show that each of the following Maclaurin series represents the function for all values of x. The reader is asked to do so in Exercises 1, 2, 3, and 4 at the end of this section.

$$(20) \qquad \sin x = \sum_{n=0}^{+\infty} \frac{(-1)^n x^{2n+1}}{(2n+1)!} = x - \frac{x^3}{3!} + \frac{x^5}{5!} - \frac{x^7}{7!} + \cdots$$

$$(21) \qquad \cos x = \sum_{n=0}^{+\infty} \frac{(-1)^n x^{2n}}{(2n)!} = 1 - \frac{x^2}{2!} + \frac{x^4}{4!} - \frac{x^6}{6!} + \cdots$$

$$(22) \qquad \sinh x = \sum_{n=0}^{+\infty} \frac{x^{2n+1}}{(2n+1)!} = x + \frac{x^3}{3!} + \frac{x^5}{5!} + \frac{x^7}{7!} + \cdots$$

$$(23) \qquad \cosh x = \sum_{n=0}^{+\infty} \frac{x^{2n}}{(2n)!} = 1 + \frac{x^2}{2!} + \frac{x^4}{4!} + \frac{x^6}{6!} + \cdots$$

EXAMPLE 2: Let f be the function defined by

$$f(x) = \begin{cases} e^{-1/x^2} & \text{if } x \neq 0 \\ 0 & \text{if } x = 0 \end{cases}$$

Find the Maclaurin series for f and show that it converges for all values of x but that it represents $f(x)$ only when $x = 0$.

Solution: To find $f'(0)$ we use the definition of a derivative and we have

$$f'(0) = \lim_{x \to 0} \frac{e^{-1/x^2} - 0}{x - 0} = \lim_{x \to 0} \frac{1/x}{e^{1/x^2}}$$

Since the limit of both the numerator and denominator are $+\infty$, we use L'Hôpital's rule, and we get

$$f'(0) = \lim_{x \to 0} \frac{-1/x^2}{e^{1/x^2}(-2/x^3)} = \lim_{x \to 0} \frac{x}{2e^{1/x^2}} = 0$$

By a similar method, using the definition of a derivative and L'Hôpital's rule; we get 0 for every derivative. So $f^{(n)}(0) = 0$ for all n. Therefore, the Maclaurin series for the given function is $0 + 0 + 0 + \ldots + 0 + \ldots$. This series converges to 0 for all x; however, if $x \neq 0$, $f(x) \neq 0$.

In elementary algebra, the reader learned that the binomial theorem expresses $(a + b)^m$ as a sum of powers of a and b. However, at that time m was restricted to positive integers. Let us now take $a = 1$ and $b = x$, and apply the binomial theorem to the expression $(1 + x)^m$, where m is not a positive integer. We obtain the power series

$$(24) \quad 1 + mx + \frac{m(m-1)}{2!}x^2 + \frac{m(m-1)(m-2)}{3!}x^3 + \cdots$$
$$+ \frac{m(m-1)(m-2)\cdots(m-n+1)}{n!}x^n + \cdots$$

Series (24) is the Maclaurin series for $(1 + x)^m$. It is called a *binomial series*. To find the radius of convergence of series (24), we apply the ratio test and we have

$$\lim_{n \to +\infty} \left| \frac{u_{n+1}}{u_n} \right|$$

$$= \lim_{n \to +\infty} \left| \frac{m(m-1)\cdots(m-n+1)(m-n)}{(n+1)!} \cdot \frac{n!}{m(m-1)\cdots(m-n+1)} \cdot \frac{x^{n+1}}{x^n} \right|$$

$$= \lim_{n \to +\infty} \left| \frac{m-n}{n+1} \right| |x| = \lim_{n \to +\infty} \left| \frac{m/n - 1}{1 + 1/n} \right| |x| = |x|$$

So the series is convergent if $|x| < 1$. We shall now prove that series (24) represents $(1 + x)^m$ for all real numbers m if x is in the open interval $(-1, 1)$. We shall not do this by calculating $R_n(x)$ and showing that its limit is zero, because this is quite difficult, as the reader will soon see if he attempts to do so. Instead we shall use the following method. Let

$$(25) \quad f(x) = 1 + \sum_{n=1}^{+\infty} \frac{m(m-1)\cdots(m-n+1)}{n!}x^n \qquad |x| < 1$$

We wish to show that $f(x) = (1 + x)^m$ where $|x| < 1$. By Theorem 24.7.3 we have

$$(26) \quad f'(x) = \sum_{n=1}^{+\infty} \frac{m(m-1)\cdots(m-n+1)}{(n-1)!}x^{n-1} \qquad |x| < 1$$

Multiplying both sides of (26) by x, we get from Theorem 24.2.8

$$(27) \qquad xf'(x) = \sum_{n=1}^{+\infty} \frac{m(m-1)\cdots(m-n+1)}{(n-1)!} x^n$$

Rewriting the right-hand side of (26), we have

$$(28) \qquad f'(x) = m + \sum_{n=2}^{+\infty} \frac{m(m-1)\cdots(m-n+1)}{(n-1)!} x^{n-1}$$

Rewriting the summation in (28) by decreasing the lower limit by 1 and replacing n by $n+1$, we get

$$(29) \qquad f'(x) = m + \sum_{n=1}^{+\infty} (m-n)\frac{m(m-1)\cdots(m-n+1)}{n!} x^n$$

If in (27) we multiply numerator and denominator by n, we get

$$(30) \qquad xf'(x) = \sum_{n=1}^{+\infty} n\,\frac{m(m-1)\cdots(m-n+1)}{n!} x^n$$

Since the series in (29) and (30) are absolutely convergent for $|x| < 1$, then by Theorem 24.2.9 we may add them term by term, and the resulting series will be absolutely convergent for $|x| < 1$; when we do so, we get

$$(1+x)f'(x) = m\left[1 + \sum_{n=1}^{+\infty} \frac{m(m-1)\cdots(m-n+1)}{n!} x^n \right]$$

and since by (25) the expression in brackets is $f(x)$, we have

$$(1+x)f'(x) = mf(x)$$

or, equivalently,

$$\frac{f'(x)}{f(x)} = \frac{m}{1+x}$$

The left-hand side of the above is $D_x[\ln f(x)]$, and so we may write

$$D_x[\ln f(x)] = \frac{m}{1+x}$$

However, we also know that

$$D_x[\ln (1+x)^m] = \frac{m}{1+x}$$

Since $\ln f(x)$ and $\ln (1+x)^m$ have the same derivative, they differ by a constant. Hence,

$$\ln f(x) = \ln (1+x)^m + C$$

But when $x = 0$, we see from (25) that $f(x) = 1$. Therefore $C = 0$, and so we get

$$f(x) = (1+x)^m$$

So, we have proved the general binomial theorem, which is

$$(31) \quad (1 + x)^m = 1 + mx + \frac{m(m - 1)}{2!} x^2 + \cdots$$

$$+ \frac{m(m - 1) \cdots (m - n + 1)}{n!} x^n + \cdots$$

and this is true for every real number m and every x such that $|x| < 1$.

EXAMPLE 3: Use the binomial series to write $1/\sqrt{1 - x}$ as a power series in x.

Solution: From (31) we have

$$(1 - x)^{-1/2} = 1 - \frac{1}{2}x + \frac{(-1/2)(-1/2 - 1)}{2!} x^2$$

$$+ \frac{(-1/2)(-1/2 - 1)(-1/2 - 2)}{3!} x^3 + \cdots$$

$$+ \frac{(-1/2)(-3/2)(-5/2) \cdots (-1/2 - n + 1)}{n!} x^n + \cdots$$

$$= 1 - \frac{1}{2}x + \frac{1 \cdot 3}{2^2 \cdot 2!} x^2 - \frac{1 \cdot 3 \cdot 5}{2^3 \cdot 3!} x^3 + \cdots$$

$$+ (-1)^n \frac{1 \cdot 3 \cdot 5 \cdots (2n - 1)}{2^n n!} x^n + \cdots$$

Exercises 24.7

1. Prove that the series

$$\sum_{n=0}^{+\infty} \frac{(-1)^n x^{2n+1}}{(2n + 1)!}$$

represents $\sin x$ for all values of x.

2. Prove that the series

$$\sum_{n=0}^{+\infty} \frac{(-1)^n x^{2n}}{(2n)!}$$

represents $\cos x$ for all values of x.

3. Prove that the series

$$\sum_{n=0}^{+\infty} \frac{x^{2n+1}}{(2n + 1)!}$$

represents $\sinh x$ for all values of x.

4. Prove that the series

$$\sum_{n=0}^{+\infty} \frac{x^{2n}}{(2n)!}$$

represents $\cosh x$ for all values of x.

5. Differentiate the series in Exercise 1 for sin x and compare the result with the series in Exercise 2 for cos x.

6. Differentiate the series in Exercise 4 for cosh x and compare the result with the series in Exercise 3 for sinh x.

In Exercises 7 through 12, find a power-series expansion for the given function at the number a and determine its radius of convergence.

7. $f(x) = \ln x; a = 1$

8. $f(x) = \dfrac{1 + \cos x}{x}; a = 0$

9. $f(x) = \sin x; a = -\pi/4$

10. $f(x) = \cos x; a = \pi/3$

11. $f(x) = xe^x; a = 0$

12. $f(x) = \sin^2 x; a = 0$

   HINT: Use $\sin^2 x = (1 - \cos 2x)/2$.

In Exercises 13 through 18, use the binomial series to write the given function as a power series in x. Determine the radius of convergence of the resulting series.

13. $f(x) = \sqrt{1 + x}$ 16. $f(x) = (9 + x^4)^{-1/2}$

14. $f(x) = (1 - x)^{-1/2}$ 17. $f(x) = (4 + x^2)^{-1}$

15. $f(x) = (1 + x^2)^{-1/2}$ 18. $f(x) = (8 + x)^{1/3}$

In Exercises 19 through 24, use a power series in x to compute the value of the given quantity to the indicated accuracy.

19. cosh ½; to five decimal places

20. sin 33°; to four decimal places

21. $\sqrt{24}$; to three decimal places

22. $\sqrt[3]{29}$; to three decimal places

23. cos 42°30′; to four decimal places

24. $\sqrt[5]{e}$; to four decimal places

25. Compute the value of e, correct to seven decimal places, and prove that your answer has the required accuracy.

26. Derive the formula

$$\ln \frac{1 + x}{1 - x} = 2 \sum_{n=1}^{+\infty} \frac{x^{2n-1}}{2n - 1} \qquad |x| < 1$$

and justify your steps.

27. Use the series of Exercise 26 to compute the value of ln 2, correct to five decimal places, and prove that your answer has the required accuracy.

28. In the proof of Theorem 24.7.1, we showed that if R and R' are the radii of convergence of the series $\sum\limits_{n=0}^{+\infty} c_n x^n$ and $\sum\limits_{n=1}^{+\infty} n c_n x^{n-1}$, respectively, then $R' \geq R$. Prove that $R' > R$ is impossible. HINT: Assume $R' > R$ and obtain a contradiction by selecting an x such that $R < |x| < R'$, and show that when $n > |x|$, $|c_n x^n| < |n c_n x^{n-1}|$.

(24.8) Integration of power series

The theorem regarding the term-by-term integration of a power series is a consequence of Theorem 24.7.3, regarding the term-by-term differentiation of a power series.

24.8.1 THEOREM   Let $\sum\limits_{n=0}^{+\infty} c_n x^n$ be a power series whose radius of convergence is $r > 0$. Then if f is the function defined by

$$f(x) = \sum_{n=0}^{+\infty} c_n x^n$$

f is integrable on every closed subinterval of $(-r,r)$ and we evaluate the integral of f by integrating the given power series term by term; that is, if x is in $(-r,r)$, then

$$\int_0^x f(t)\,dt = \sum_{n=0}^{+\infty} \frac{c_n}{n+1} x^{n+1}$$

Furthermore, r is the radius of convergence of the resulting series.

Proof: Let g be the function defined by

$$g(x) = \sum_{n=0}^{+\infty} \frac{c_n}{n+1} x^{n+1}$$

Since the terms of the power-series representation of $f(x)$ are the derivatives of the terms of the power-series representation of $g(x)$, the two series have the same radius of convergence, by Theorem 24.7.1. By Theorem 24.7.3, it follows that

$$g'(x) = f(x) \qquad \text{for every } x \text{ in } (-r,r)$$

By Theorem 24.7.2, it follows that $f'(x) = g''(x)$ for every x in $(-r,r)$. Since f is differentiable on $(-r,r)$, f is continuous on $(-r,r)$, and consequently f is continuous on every closed subinterval of $(-r,r)$. From Theorem 10.6.2, it follows that if x is in $(-r,r)$ then

$$\int_0^x f(t)\,dt = g(x) - g(0) = g(x)$$

or, equivalently,

$$\int_0^x f(t)\,dt = \sum_{n=0}^{+\infty} \frac{c_n}{n+1} x^{n+1} \qquad\qquad \text{Q.E.D.}$$

We shall use Theorem 24.8.1 to obtain a power-series representation of $\ln(1 + x)$. We start with the function f defined by $f(x) = 1/(1 + x)$. The Maclaurin series for this function is $\sum\limits_{n=0}^{+\infty} (-1)^n x^n$, and it represents the function for all x in the interval $(-1,1)$. So we have

(1) $$\frac{1}{1 + x} = \sum_{n=0}^{+\infty} (-1)^n \, x^n \qquad \text{for } |x| < 1$$

Applying Theorem 24.8.1, we integrate term by term, and we obtain

$$\int_0^x \frac{1}{1 + t} \, dt = \sum_{n=0}^{+\infty} \frac{(-1)^n \, x^{n+1}}{n + 1} \qquad \text{for } |x| < 1$$

and so we have

$$\ln(1 + x) = \sum_{n=0}^{+\infty} \frac{(-1)^n \, x^{n+1}}{n + 1} \qquad \text{for } |x| < 1$$

EXAMPLE 1: Find a power-series representation of $\tan^{-1} x$ by using the Maclaurin series for $1/(1 + x)$.

Solution: Since the Maclaurin series for $1/(1+x)$ represents the function for $|x| < 1$, we have

$$\frac{1}{1 + x} = 1 - x + x^2 - x^3 + \cdots + (-1)^n \, x^n + \cdots \qquad \text{for } |x| < 1$$

Replacing x by x^2, we obtain

$$\frac{1}{1 + x^2} = 1 - x^2 + x^4 - x^6 + \cdots + (-1)^n x^{2n} + \cdots \qquad \text{for } |x| < 1$$

Applying Theorem 24.8.1 and integrating term by term, we get

$$\int_0^x \frac{1}{1 + t^2} \, dt = x - \frac{1}{3}x^3 + \frac{1}{5}x^5 - \cdots + (-1)^n \frac{x^{2n+1}}{2n + 1} + \cdots$$

Therefore,

$$\tan^{-1} x = \sum_{n=0}^{+\infty} (-1)^n \frac{x^{2n+1}}{2n + 1} \qquad \text{for } |x| < 1$$

EXAMPLE 2: Find a power-series representation of

$$\int_0^x e^{-t^2} \, dt$$

Solution: In Example 1, Sec. 24.7, we showed that

$$e^x = \sum_{n=0}^{+\infty} \frac{x^n}{n!} \qquad \text{for all values of } x$$

Replacing x by $-t^2$, we get

$$e^{-t^2} = \sum_{n=0}^{+\infty} (-1)^n \frac{t^{2n}}{n!} \qquad \text{for all values of } t$$

Therefore, by Theorem 24.8.1, we have

$$\int_0^x e^{-t^2} \, dt = \sum_{n=0}^{+\infty} \int_0^x (-1)^n \frac{t^{2n}}{n!} \, dt = \sum_{n=0}^{+\infty} (-1)^n \frac{x^{2n+1}}{n!(2n+1)}$$

The power series represents the integral for all values of x.

EXAMPLE 3: Using the result of Example 2, compute accurate to three decimal places, the value of

$$\int_0^{1/2} e^{-t^2} \, dt$$

Solution: Replacing x by $\frac{1}{2}$ in the power series obtained in Example 2, we have

$$\int_0^{1/2} e^{-t^2} \, dt = 1 - \frac{1}{24} + \frac{1}{320} - \frac{1}{5376} + \cdots$$

$$= 1 - 0.417 + 0.0031 - 0.0002 + \cdots$$

From the first three terms we get

$$\int_0^{1/2} e^{-t^2} \approx 0.961$$

Since the series is alternating, by Theorem 24.4.4 we know that the error is less than the absolute value of the fourth term.

Exercises 24.8

In Exercises 1 through 6, compute the value of the given integral, accurate to four decimal places, by using series.

1. $\int_{1/2}^1 \frac{e^x}{x} \, dx$

2. $\int_{1/4}^{1/2} \frac{\cos x - 1}{x} \, dx$

3. $\int_0^{1/2} \sin x^2 \, dx$

4. $\int_0^1 \sqrt{1 - x^3} \, dx$

5. $\int_0^{1/2} \frac{\sin x}{x} \, dx$

6. $\int_0^1 \frac{e^x - e^{-x}}{x} \, dx$

7. Prove that $\pi/4 = \tan^{-1}(1/2) + \tan^{-1}(1/3)$. Use this formula and a power series for $\tan^{-1} x$ to compute the value of π accurate to eight decimal places.

8. Use a power series for $\tan^{-1} x$ to derive the formula

$$\frac{\pi}{4} = 1 - \frac{1}{3} + \frac{1}{5} - \frac{1}{7} + \cdots + (-1)^{n+1} \frac{1}{2n-1} + \cdots$$

9. Find a series for xe^x by multiplying the Maclaurin series for e^x by x. Then

integrate the resulting series term by term from 0 to 1 and show that the sum of the series

$$\sum_{n=1}^{+\infty} \frac{1}{n!(n+2)}$$

is exactly equal to ½.

10. By using a method similar to that used in Exercise 9, show that the exact sum of the series

$$\sum_{n=1}^{+\infty} (-1)^{n+1} \frac{x^{2n+1}}{(2n-1)(2n+1)}$$

is

$$½[(x^2 + 1) \tan^{-1} x - x]$$

11. Find a power-series representation for $\tanh^{-1} x$ by using the Maclaurin series for $(1 - t^2)^{-1}$ and integrating term by term from 0 to x.

12. Find the power series in x of $f(x)$ if $f''(x) = -f(x)$ and $f(0) = 0$, and $f'(0) = 1$. Also, find the radius of convergence of the resulting series.

(24.9)   Extrema of functions of two variables

An important application of the derivatives of a function of one variable is in the study of extreme values of a function, which leads to a variety of problems involving maximum and minimum. We discussed this thoroughly in Chap. 8, where we proved theorems involving the first and second derivatives, which enabled us to determine relative maximum and minimum values of a function of a single variable. To prove a second-derivative test for maxima and minima of a function of two variables, we need to make use of Taylor's formula. This is the reason we postponed this discussion until now.

24.9.1 DEFINITION   The function f of two variables is said to have an *absolute maximum value* on a region R in the xy plane if there is some point (x_0,y_0) in R such that $f(x_0,y_0) \geq f(x,y)$ for all points (x,y) in R. In such a case, $f(x_0,y_0)$ is the absolute maximum value of f on R.

24.9.2 DEFINITION   The function f of two variables is said to have an *absolute minimum value* on a region R in the xy plane if there is some point (x_0,y_0) in R such that $f(x_0,y_0) \leq f(x,y)$ for all points (x,y) in R. In such a case, $f(x_0,y_0)$ is the absolute minimum value of f on R.

For functions of a single variable we assumed without proof the extreme-value theorem (8.2.9). We have a generalization of this theorem for functions of two variables. This is also assumed without proof, as it is beyond the scope of this book.

24.9.3 THEOREM (*The Extreme-value Theorem for Functions of Two Variables*)   Let R be a closed region in the xy plane (such as a closed rectangular region or a closed disk) and let f be a function of two variables which is continuous on R. Then there is at least one point in R where f has an absolute maximum value and there is at least one point in R where f has an absolute minimum value.

24.9.4 DEFINITION   The function f of two variables is said to have a *relative maximum value* at the point (x_0,y_0) if there exists an open disk $B((x_0,y_0);r)$ such that $f(x,y) < f(x_0,y_0)$ for all $(x,y) \neq (x_0,y_0)$ in the open disk.

24.9.5 DEFINITION   The function f of two variables is said to have a *relative minimum value* at the point (x_0,y_0) if there exists an open disk $B((x_0,y_0);r)$ such that $f(x,y) > f(x_0,y_0)$ for all $(x,y) \neq (x_0,y_0)$ in the open disk.

24.9.6 THEOREM   If $f(x,y)$ exists at all points in some open disk $B((x_0,y_0);r)$ and if f has a relative extremum at (x_0,y_0), then if $f_x(x_0,y_0)$ and $f_y(x_0,y_0)$ exist,

$$f_x(x_0,y_0) = f_y(x_0,y_0) = 0$$

Proof: We shall prove that if f has a relative maximum value at (x_0,y_0) and if $f_x(x_0,y_0)$ exists, then $f_x(x_0,y_0) = 0$. By the definition of a partial derivative,

$$f_x(x_0,y_0) = \lim_{\Delta x \to 0} \frac{f(x_0 + \Delta x, y_0) - f(x_0,y_0)}{\Delta x}$$

Since f has a relative maximum value at (x_0,y_0), by Definition 24.9.4 it follows that

$$f(x_0 + \Delta x, y_0) - f(x_0,y_0) < 0$$

whenever Δx is sufficiently small so that $(x_0 + \Delta x, y_0)$ is in B. If Δx approaches zero from the right, $\Delta x > 0$, and therefore

$$\frac{f(x_0 + \Delta x, y_0) - f(x_0,y_0)}{\Delta x} \leq 0$$

Hence, by Theorem 4.6.3, if $f_x(x_0,y_0)$ exists, $f_x(x_0,y_0) \leq 0$.
    Similarly, if Δx approaches zero from the left, $\Delta x < 0$, and so

$$\frac{f(x_0 + x, y_0) - f(x_0, y_0)}{\Delta x} \geq 0$$

Therefore, by Theorem 4.6.4, if $f_x(x_0,y_0)$ exists, $f_x(x_0,y_0) \geq 0$. We conclude then that since $f_x(x_0,y_0)$ exists, both inequalities, $f_x(x_0,y_0) \leq 0$ and $f_x(x_0,y_0) \geq 0$, must hold and consequently $f_x(x_0,y_0) = 0$.
    The proof that $f_y(x_0,y_0) = 0$ if $f_y(x_0,y_0)$ exists and f has a relative maximum value at (x_0,y_0) is analogous and is left for the reader (see Exercise 1 at the end of this section). The proof of the theorem when $f(x_0,y_0)$ is a relative minimum value is also left for the reader (see Exercise 2 at the end of this section).
    Theorem 24.9.6 states that a necessary condition for a function of two variables to have a relative extremum at a point where its first partial derivatives exist is that these partial derivatives be zero. It is possible for a function of two

variables to have a relative extremum at a point at which the partial derivatives do not exist, but we shall not consider this situation in this book. Furthermore, the vanishing of the first partial derivatives of a function of two variables is not a sufficient condition for the function to have a relative extremum at the point. Such a situation occurs at a point called a *saddle point.* A simple example of a function which has a saddle point is the one defined by

$$f(x,y) = x^2 - y^2$$

For this function we see that $f_x(x,y) = 2x$ and $f_y(x,y) = -2y$. Both $f_x(0,0)$ and $f_y(0,0)$ equal zero. Referring to Fig. 24.9.1, we see that the graph of the function

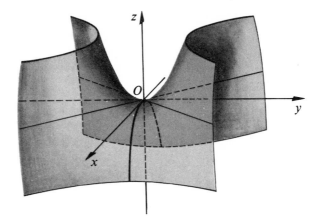

is "saddle shaped" at points close to the origin. It is apparent that this function f does not satisfy either Definition 24.9.4 or Definition 24.9.5 when $(x_0,y_0) = (0,0)$.

We shall have a second-derivative test which will give us conditions that guarantee a function to have a relative extremum at a point where the first partial derivatives vanish. However, sometimes it is possible to determine relative extrema of a function by the Definitions 24.9.4 and 24.9.5. This is illustrated in the following example.

EXAMPLE 1: *Given:* the function f, defined by

$$f(x,y) = 6x - 4y - x^2 - 2y^2$$

Determine if f has any relative extrema.

Solution: Since f and its first partial derivatives exist at all (x,y) in E^2, Theorem 29.9.6 is applicable. Differentiating, we get

$$f_x(x,y) = 6 - 2x \qquad \text{and} \qquad f_y(x,y) = -4 - 4y$$

Setting f_x and f_y equal to zero, we get $x = 3$ and $y = -1$. Since the graph of the equation

$$z = 6x - 4y - x^2 - 2y^2$$

is a paraboloid having a vertical axis, with vertex at $(3, -1, 11)$ and opening downward, we may conclude that $f(x,y) < f(-3, -1)$ for all $(x,y) \neq (-3, -1)$, and hence by Definition 24.9.4, $f(3, -1) = 11$ is a relative maximum function value. It follows from Definition 24.9.1 that 11 is the absolute maximum function value of f on E^2.

The basic test for determining relative maxima and minima for functions of two variables is the second-derivative test, which is given in the next theorem.

24.9.7 THEOREM (*Second-derivative Test*)   Let f be a function of two variables such that f and its first- and second-order partial derivatives are continuous on some open disk $B((a,b);r)$. Suppose further that $f_x(a,b) = f_y(a,b) = 0$. Then

(i) f has a relative minimum value at (a,b) if

$$f_{xx}(a,b)f_{yy}(a,b) - f_{xy}^2(a,b) > 0 \qquad \text{and} \qquad f_{xx}(a,b) > 0$$

(ii) f has a relative maximum value at (a,b) if

$$f_{xx}(a,b)f_{yy}(a,b) - f_{xy}^2(a,b) > 0 \qquad \text{and} \qquad f_{xx}(a,b) < 0$$

(iii) $f(a,b)$ is not a relative extremum if

$$f_{xx}(a,b)f_{yy}(a,b) - f_{xy}^2(a,b) < 0$$

(iv) We can make no conclusion if

$$f_{xx}(a,b)f_{yy}(a,b) - f_{xy}^2(a,b) = 0$$

Proof of (i): For simplicity of notation, let us define

$$\phi(x,y) = f_{xx}(x,y)f_{yy}(x,y) - f_{xy}^2(x,y)$$

We are given $\phi(a,b) > 0$ and $f_{xx}(a,b) > 0$, and we wish to prove that $f(a,b)$ is a relative minimum function value. Since f_{xx}, f_{xy}, and f_{yy} are continuous on $B((a,b);r)$, it follows that ϕ is also continuous on B. Hence, there exists an open disk $B'((a,b);r')$, where $r' \leq r$, such that $\phi(x,y) > 0$ and $f_{xx}(x,y) > 0$ for every point (x,y) in B'. Let h and k be constants, not both zero, such that the point $(a + h, b + k)$ is in B'. Then the parametric equations

$$x = a + ht \qquad \text{and} \qquad y = b + kt \qquad 0 \leq t \leq 1$$

define all the points on the line segment from (a,b) to $(a + h, b + k)$ and all these points are in B'. Let F be the function of one variable defined by

(1) $$F(t) = f(a + ht, b + kt)$$

By Taylor's formula (Theorem 24.6.1), we have

(2) $$F(t) = F(0) + F'(0)t + \frac{F''(\xi)}{2!}t^2$$

where ξ is between 0 and t. If $t = 1$ in equation (2), we get

(3) $$F(1) = F(0) + F'(0) + \frac{1}{2}F''(\xi)$$

where $0 < \xi < 1$. Since $F(0) = f(a,b)$ and $F(1) = f(a + h, b + k)$, it follows from equation (3) that

(4) $$f(a + h, b + k) = f(a,b) + F'(0) + \frac{1}{2} F''(\xi)$$

where $0 < \xi < 1$.

To find $F'(t)$ and $F''(t)$ from (1), we use the chain rule and we obtain

(5) $$F'(t) = hf_x(a + ht, b + kt) + kf_y(a + ht, b + kt)$$

and $$F''(t) = h^2 f_{xx} + hk f_{yx} + hk f_{xy} + k^2 f_{yy}$$

where each second partial derivative is evaluated at $(a + ht, b + kt)$. From Theorem 22.10.1, it follows that $f_{xy}(x,y) = f_{yx}(x,y)$ for all (x,y) in B'. So

(6) $$F''(t) = h^2 f_{xx} + 2hk f_{xy} + k^2 f_{yy}$$

where each second partial derivative is evaluated at $(a + ht, b + kt)$. Substituting 0 for t in equation (5) and ξ for t in equation (6), we get

(7) $$F'(0) = hf_x(a,b) + kf_y(a,b) = 0$$

and

(8) $$F''(\xi) = h^2 f_{xx} + 2hk f_{xy} + k^2 f_{yy}$$

where each second partial derivative is evaluated at $(a + h\xi, b + k\xi)$, where $0 < \xi < 1$. Substituting from (7) and (8) into (4), we obtain

(9) $$f(a + h, b + k) - f(a,b) = \frac{1}{2}(h^2 f_{xx} + 2hk f_{xy} + k^2 f_{yy})$$

The terms in parentheses on the right-hand side of equation (9) may be written as

$$h^2 f_{xx} + 2hk f_{xy} + k^2 f_{yy} = f_{xx}\left[h^2 + 2hk\frac{f_{xy}}{f_{xx}} + \left(k\frac{f_{xy}}{f_{xx}}\right)^2 - \left(k\frac{f_{xy}}{f_{xx}}\right)^2 + k^2\frac{f_{yy}}{f_{xx}}\right]$$

So, from (9) we have

(10) $$f(a + h, b + k) - f(a,b) = \frac{f_{xx}}{2}\left[\left(h + \frac{f_{xy}}{f_{xx}}k\right)^2 + \frac{f_{xx}f_{yy} - f_{xy}{}^2}{f_{xx}{}^2}k^2\right]$$

Since $f_{xx}f_{yy} - f_{xy}{}^2$ evaluated at $(a + h\xi, b + k\xi)$ equals $\phi(a + h\xi, b + k\xi) > 0$, it follows that the expression in brackets on the right-hand side of equation (10) is positive. Furthermore, since $f_{xx}(a + h\xi, b + k\xi) > 0$, it follows from equation (10) that $f(a + h, b + k) - f(a,b) > 0$, and hence we have proved that

$$f(a + h, b + k) > f(a,b)$$

for every point $(a + h, b + k) \neq (a,b)$ in B'. Therefore, by Definition 24.9.5, $f(a,b)$ is a relative minimum value of f.

The proof of part (ii) is similar and is left for the reader (see Exercise 3 below). The proof of part (iii) is also left for the reader (see Exercise 4 below). Part (iv) is included to cover all possible cases.

EXAMPLE 2: *Given: f is the function defined by* $f(x,y) = 2x^4 + y^2 - x^2 - 2y$. Determine the relative extrema of f if there are any.

Solution: $f_x(x,y) = 8x^3 - 2x$ and $f_y(x,y) = 2y - 2$. Setting $f_x(x,y) = 0$, we get $x = -\frac{1}{2}$, $x = 0$, and $x = \frac{1}{2}$. Setting $f_y(x,y) = 0$, we get $y = 1$. To apply the second-derivative test, we find the second partial derivatives of f, and we get $f_{xx}(x,y) = 24x^2 - 2$, $f_{yy}(x,y) = 2$, and $f_{xy}(x,y) = 0$.

f_x and f_y both vanish at the points $(-\frac{1}{2},1)$, $(0,1)$ and $(\frac{1}{2},1)$.

At $(-\frac{1}{2},1)$, $f_{xx} > 0$ and $f_{xx}f_{yy} - f_{xy}^2 > 0$, and so f has a relative minimum value there.

At $(0,1)$, $f_{xx}f_{yy} - f_{xy}^2 < 0$, and so f does not have a relative extremum there.

At $(\frac{1}{2},1)$, $f_{xx} > 0$ and $f_{xx}f_{yy} - f_{xy}^2 > 0$, and so f has a relative minimum value there.

Hence we conclude that f has a relative minimum value of $-9/8$ at each of the points $(-\frac{1}{2},1)$ and $(\frac{1}{2},1)$.

Exercises 24.9

1. Prove that $f_y(x_0,y_0) = 0$ if $f_y(x_0,y_0)$ exists and f has a relative maximum value at (x_0,y_0).

2. Prove Theorem 24.9.6 when $f(x_0,y_0)$ is a relative minimum value.

3. Prove Theorem 24.9.7(ii).

4. Prove Theorem 24.9.7(iii).

In Exercises 5 through 10, determine the relative extrema of f, if there are any.

5. $f(x,y) = 18x^2 - 32y^2 - 36x - 128y - 110$

6. $f(x,y) = \dfrac{1}{x} - \dfrac{64}{y} + xy$

7. $f(x,y) = \sin(x + y) + \sin x + \sin y$

8. $f(x,y) = x^3 + y^3 - 18xy$

9. $f(x,y) = 4xy^2 - 2x^2y - x$

10. $f(x,y) = \dfrac{2x + 2y + 1}{x^2 + y^2 + 1}$

11. Find three numbers whose sum is N such that their product is as great as possible.

12. Prove that the box having the largest volume that can be placed inside a sphere is in the shape of a cube.

13. Find the volume of the largest box that can be inscribed in the ellipsoid

$$\frac{x^2}{a^2} + \frac{y^2}{b^2} + \frac{z^2}{c^2} = 1$$

14. Prove that if a rectangular box, without a top, having a given volume, is to be made using the least amount of material, then the box should have a square base and an altitude whose length is half that of the base.

15. Prove that if a rectangular box without a top is to be made from a given amount of material, then the box will have the largest possible volume if it has a square base and an altitude whose length is half that of the base.

16. Find the point in the plane $Ax + By + Cz + D = 0$ that is closest to the origin.

17. Find the shortest distance between the two lines:

$$\frac{x + 2}{4} = \frac{y - 3}{1} = \frac{z + 1}{5}$$

and

$$\frac{x + 1}{-2} = \frac{y - 0}{3} = \frac{z - 3}{1}$$

Appendix: numerical tables

(1) Powers and roots

n	n^2	$\sqrt{n}$	n^3	$\sqrt[3]{n}$	n	n^2	$\sqrt{n}$	n^3	$\sqrt[3]{n}$
1	1	1.000	1	1.000	51	2,601	7.141	132,651	3.708
2	4	1.414	8	1.260	52	2,704	7.211	140,608	3.732
3	9	1.732	27	1.442	53	2,809	7.280	148,877	3.756
4	16	2.000	64	1.587	54	2,916	7.348	157,464	3.780
5	25	2.236	125	1.710	55	3,025	7.416	166,375	3.803
6	36	2.449	216	1.817	56	3,136	7.483	175,616	3.826
7	49	2.646	343	1.913	57	3,249	7.550	185,193	3.848
8	64	2.828	512	2.000	58	3,364	7.616	195,112	3.871
9	81	3.000	729	2.080	59	3,481	7.681	205,379	3.893
10	100	3.162	1,000	2.154	60	3,600	7.746	216,000	3.915
11	121	3.317	1,331	2.224	61	3,721	7.810	226,981	3.936
12	144	3.464	1,728	3.289	62	3,844	7.874	238,328	3.958
13	169	3.606	2,197	2.351	63	3,969	7.937	250,047	3.979
14	196	3.742	2,744	2.410	64	4,096	8.000	262,144	4.000
15	225	3.873	3,375	2.466	65	4,225	8.062	274,625	4.021
16	256	4.000	4,096	2.520	66	4,356	8.124	287,496	4.041
17	289	4.123	4,913	2.571	67	4,489	8.185	300,763	4.062
18	324	4.243	5,832	2.621	68	4,624	8.246	314,432	4.082
19	361	4.359	6,859	2.668	69	4,761	8.307	328,509	4.102
20	400	4.472	8,000	2.714	70	4,900	8.367	343,000	4.121
21	441	4.583	9,261	2.759	71	5,041	8.426	357,911	4.141
22	484	4.690	10,648	2.802	72	5,184	8.485	373,248	4.160
23	529	4.796	12,167	2.844	73	5,329	8.544	389,017	4.179
24	576	4.899	13,824	2.884	74	5,476	8.602	405,224	4.198
25	625	5.000	15,625	2.924	75	5,625	8.660	421,875	4.217
26	676	5.099	17,576	2.962	76	5,776	8.718	438,976	4.236
27	729	5.196	19,683	3.000	77	5,929	8.775	456,533	4.254
28	784	5.291	21,952	3.037	78	6,084	8.832	474,552	4.273
29	841	5.385	24,389	3.072	79	6,241	8.888	493,039	4.291
30	900	5.477	27,000	3.107	80	6,400	8.944	512,000	4.309
31	961	5.568	29,791	3.141	81	6,561	9.000	531,441	4.327
32	1,024	5.657	32,768	3.175	82	6,724	9.055	551,368	4.344
33	1,089	5.745	35,937	3.208	83	6,889	9.110	571,787	4.362
34	1,156	5.831	39,304	3.240	84	7,056	9.165	592,704	4.380
35	1,225	5.916	42,875	3.271	85	7,225	9.220	614,125	4.397
36	1,296	6.000	46,656	3.302	86	7,396	9.274	636,056	4.414
37	1,369	6.083	50,653	3.332	87	7,569	9.327	658,503	4.431
38	1,444	6.164	54,872	3.362	88	7,744	9.381	681,472	4.448
39	1,521	6.245	59,319	3.391	89	7,921	9.434	704,969	4.465
40	1,600	6.325	64,000	3.420	90	8,100	9.487	729,000	4.481
41	1,681	6.403	68,921	3.448	91	8,281	9.539	753,571	4.498
42	1,764	6.481	74,088	3.476	92	8,464	9.592	778,688	4.514
43	1,849	6.557	79,507	3.503	93	8,649	9.643	804,357	4.531
44	1,936	6.633	85,184	3.530	94	8,836	9.695	830,584	4.547
45	2,025	6.708	91,125	3.557	95	9,025	9.747	857,375	4.563
46	2,116	6.782	97,336	3.583	96	9,216	9.798	884,736	4.579
47	2,209	6.856	103,823	3.609	97	9,409	9.849	912,673	4.595
48	2,304	6.928	110,592	3.634	98	9,604	9.899	941,192	4.610
49	2,401	7.000	117,649	3.659	99	9,801	9.950	970,299	4.626
50	2,500	7.071	125,000	3.684	100	10,000	10.000	1,000,000	4.642

(2) Natural logarithms

N	0	1	2	3	4	5	6	7	8	9
1.0	0000	0100	0198	0296	0392	0488	0583	0677	0770	0862
1.1	0953	1044	1133	1222	1310	1398	1484	1570	1655	1740
1.2	1823	1906	1989	2070	2151	2231	2311	2390	2469	2546
1.3	2624	2700	2776	2852	2927	3001	3075	3148	3221	3293
1.4	3365	3436	3507	3577	3646	3716	3784	3853	3920	3988
1.5	4055	4121	4187	4253	4318	4383	4447	4511	4574	4637
1.6	4700	4762	4824	4886	4947	5008	5068	5128	5188	5247
1.7	5306	5365	5423	5481	5539	5596	5653	5710	5766	5822
1.8	5878	5933	5988	6043	6098	6152	6206	6259	6313	6366
1.9	6419	6471	6523	6575	6627	6678	6729	6780	6831	6881
2.0	6931	6981	7031	7080	7129	7178	7227	7275	7324	7372
2.1	7419	7467	7514	7561	7608	7655	7701	7747	7793	7839
2.2	7885	7930	7975	8020	8065	8109	8154	8198	8242	8286
2.3	8329	8372	8416	8459	8502	8544	8587	8629	8671	8713
2.4	8755	8796	8838	8879	8920	8961	9002	9042	9083	9123
2.5	9163	9203	9243	9282	9322	9361	9400	9439	9478	9517
2.6	9555	9594	9632	9670	9708	9746	9783	9821	9858	9895
2.7	9933	9969	*0006	*0043	*0080	*0116	*0152	*0188	*0225	*0260
2.8	1.0296	0332	0367	0403	0438	0473	0508	0543	0578	0613
2.9	0647	0682	0716	0750	0784	0818	0852	0886	0919	0953
3.0	1.0986	1019	1053	1086	1119	1151	1184	1217	1249	1282
3.1	1314	1346	1378	1410	1442	1474	1506	1537	1569	1600
3.2	1632	1663	1694	1725	1756	1787	1817	1848	1878	1909
3.3	1939	1969	2000	2030	2060	2090	2119	2149	2179	2208
3.4	2238	2267	2296	2326	2355	2384	2413	2442	2470	2499
3.5	1.2528	2556	2585	2613	2641	2669	2698	2726	2754	2782
3.6	2809	2837	2865	2892	2920	2947	2975	3002	3029	3056
3.7	3083	3110	3137	3164	3191	3218	3244	3271	3297	3324
3.8	3350	3376	3403	3429	3455	3481	3507	3533	3558	3584
3.9	3610	3635	3661	3686	3712	3737	3762	3788	3813	3838
4.0	1.3863	3888	3913	3938	3962	3987	4012	4036	4061	4085
4.1	4110	4134	4159	4183	4207	4231	4255	4279	4303	4327
4.2	4351	4375	4398	4422	4446	4469	4493	4516	4540	4563
4.3	4586	4609	4633	4656	4679	4702	4725	4748	4770	4793
4.4	4816	4839	4861	4884	4907	4929	4951	4974	4996	5019
4.5	1.5041	5063	5085	5107	5129	5151	5173	5195	5217	5239
4.6	5261	5282	5304	5326	5347	5369	5390	5412	5433	5454
4.7	5476	5497	5518	5539	5560	5581	5602	5623	5644	5665
4.8	5686	5707	5728	5748	5769	5790	5810	5831	5851	5872
4.9	5892	5913	5933	5953	5974	5994	6014	6034	6054	6074
5.0	1.6094	6114	6134	6154	6174	6194	6214	6233	6253	6273
5.1	6292	6312	6332	6351	6371	6390	6409	6429	6448	6467
5.2	6487	6506	6525	6544	6563	6582	6601	6620	6639	6658
5.3	6677	6696	6715	6734	6752	6771	6790	6808	6827	6845
5.4	6864	6882	6901	6919	6938	6956	6974	6993	7011	7029

N	0	1	2	3	4	5	6	7	8	9
5.5	1.7047	7066	7084	7102	7120	7138	7156	7174	7192	7210
5.6	7228	7246	7263	7281	7299	7317	7334	7352	7370	7387
5.7	7405	7422	7440	7457	7475	7492	7509	7527	7544	7561
5.8	7579	7596	7613	7630	7647	7664	7681	7699	7716	7733
5.9	7750	7766	7783	7800	7817	7834	7851	7867	7884	7901
6.0	1.7918	7934	7951	7967	7984	8001	8017	8034	8050	8066
6.1	8083	8099	8116	8132	8148	8165	8181	8197	8213	8229
6.2	8245	8262	8278	8294	8310	8326	8342	8358	8374	8390
6.3	8405	8421	8437	8453	8469	8485	8500	8516	8532	8547
6.4	8563	8579	8594	8610	8625	8641	8656	8672	8687	8703
6.5	1.8718	8733	8749	8764	8779	8795	8810	8825	8840	8856
6.6	8871	8886	8901	8916	8931	8946	8961	8976	8991	9006
6.7	9021	9036	9051	9066	9081	9095	9110	9125	9140	9155
6.8	9169	9184	9199	9213	9228	9242	9257	9272	9286	9301
6.9	9315	9330	9344	9359	9373	9387	9402	9416	9430	9445
7.0	1.9459	9473	9488	9502	9516	9530	9544	9559	9573	9587
7.1	9601	9615	9629	9643	9657	9671	9685	9699	9713	9727
7.2	9741	9755	9769	9782	9796	9810	9824	9838	9851	9865
7.3	9879	9892	9906	9920	9933	9947	9961	9974	9988	*0001
7.4	2.0015	0028	0042	0055	0069	0082	0096	0109	0122	0136
7.5	2.0149	0162	0176	0189	0202	0215	0229	0242	0255	0268
7.6	0281	0295	0308	0321	0334	0347	0360	0373	0386	0399
7.7	0412	0425	0438	0451	0464	0477	0490	0503	0516	0528
7.8	0541	0554	0567	0580	0592	0605	0618	0630	0643	0656
7.9	0669	0681	0694	0707	0719	0732	0744	0757	0769	0782
8.0	2.0794	0807	0819	0832	0844	0857	0869	0882	0894	0906
8.1	0919	0931	0943	0956	0968	0980	0992	1005	1017	1029
8.2	1041	1054	1066	1078	1090	1102	1114	1126	1138	1150
8.3	1163	1175	1187	1199	1211	1223	1235	1247	1258	1270
8.4	1282	1294	1306	1318	1330	1342	1353	1365	1377	1389
8.5	2.1401	1412	1424	1436	1448	1459	1471	1483	1494	1506
8.6	1518	1529	1541	1552	1564	1576	1587	1599	1610	1622
8.7	1633	1645	1656	1668	1679	1691	1702	1713	1725	1736
8.8	1748	1759	1770	1782	1793	1804	1815	1827	1838	1849
8.9	1861	1872	1883	1894	1905	1917	1928	1939	1950	1961
9.0	2.1972	1983	1994	2006	2017	2028	2039	2050	2061	2072
9.1	2083	2094	2105	2116	2127	2138	2148	2159	2170	2181
9.2	2192	2203	2214	2225	2235	2246	2257	2268	2279	2289
9.3	2300	2311	2322	2332	2343	2354	2364	2375	2386	2396
9.4	2407	2418	2428	2439	2450	2460	2471	2481	2492	2502
9.5	2.2513	2523	2534	2544	2555	2565	2576	2586	2597	2607
9.6	2618	2628	2638	2649	2659	2670	2680	2690	2701	2711
9.7	2721	2732	2742	2752	2762	2773	2783	2793	2803	2814
9.8	2824	2834	2844	2854	2865	2875	2885	2895	2905	2915
9.9	2925	2935	2946	2956	2966	2976	2986	2996	3006	3016

Use ln 10 = 2.30259 to find logarithms of numbers greater than 10 or less than 1. *Example:*
ln 220 = ln 2.2 + 2 ln 10 = 0.7885 + 2(2.30259) = 5.3937.

(3) Exponential and hyperbolic functions

x	e^x	e^{-x}	$\sinh x$	$\cosh x$	$\tanh x$
0	1.0000	1.0000	.00000	1.0000	.00000
0.1	1.1052	.90484	.10017	1.0050	.09967
0.2	1.2214	.81873	.20134	1.0201	.19738
0.3	1.3499	.74082	.30452	1.0453	.29131
0.4	1.4918	.67032	.41075	1.0811	.37995
0.5	1.6487	.60653	.52110	1.1276	.46212
0.6	1.8221	.54881	.63665	1.1855	.53705
0.7	2.0138	.49659	.75858	1.2552	.60437
0.8	2.2255	.44933	.88811	1.3374	.66404
0.9	2.4596	.40657	1.0265	1.4331	.71630
1.0	2.7183	.36788	1.1752	1.5431	.76159
1.1	3.0042	.33287	1.3356	1.6685	.80050
1.2	3.3201	.30119	1.5095	1.8107	.83365
1.3	3.6693	.27253	1.6984	1.9709	.86172
1.4	4.0552	.24660	1.9043	2.1509	.88535
1.5	4.4817	.22313	2.1293	2.3524	.90515
1.6	4.9530	.20190	2.3756	2.5775	.92167
1.7	5.4739	.18268	2.6456	2.8283	.93541
1.8	6.0496	.16530	2.9422	3.1075	.94681
1.9	6.6859	.14957	3.2682	3.4177	.95624
2.0	7.3891	.13534	3.6269	3.7622	.96403
2.1	8.1662	.12246	4.0219	4.1443	.97045
2.2	9.0250	.11080	4.4571	4.5679	.97574
2.3	9.9742	.10026	4.9370	5.0372	.98010
2.4	11.023	.09072	5.4662	5.5569	.98367
2.5	12.182	.08208	6.0502	6.1323	.98661
2.6	13.464	.07427	6.6947	6.7690	.98903
2.7	14.880	.06721	7.4063	7.4735	.99101
2.8	16.445	.06081	8.1919	8.2527	.99263
2.9	18.174	.05502	9.0596	9.1146	.99396
3.0	20.086	.04979	10.018	10.068	.99505
3.1	22.198	.04505	11.076	11.122	.99595
3.2	24.533	.04076	12.246	12.287	.99668
3.3	27.113	.03688	13.538	13.575	.99728
3.4	29.964	.03337	14.965	14.999	.99777
3.5	33.115	.03020	16.543	16.573	.99818
3.6	36.598	.02732	18.285	18.313	.99851
3.7	40.447	.02472	20.211	20.236	.99878
3.8	44.701	.02237	22.339	22.362	.99900
3.9	49.402	.02024	24.691	24.711	.99918
4.0	54.598	.01832	27.290	27.308	.99933
4.1	60.340	.01657	30.162	30.178	.99945
4.2	66.686	.01500	33.336	33.351	.99955
4.3	73.700	.01357	36.843	36.857	.99963
4.4	81.451	.01228	40.719	40.732	.99970
4.5	90.017	.01111	45.003	45.014	.99975
4.6	99.484	.01005	49.737	49.747	.99980
4.7	109.95	.00910	54.969	54.978	.99983
4.8	121.51	.00823	60.751	60.759	.99986
4.9	134.29	.00745	67.141	67.149	.99989
5.0	148.41	.00674	74.203	74.210	.99991

(4) Trigonometric functions

Degrees	Radians	Sin	Cos	Tan	Cot			
0	0.0000	0.0000	1.0000	0.0000		1.5708	90
1	0.0175	0.0175	0.9998	0.0175	57.290	1.5533	89
2	0.0349	0.0349	0.9994	0.0349	28.636	1.5359	88
3	0.0524	0.0523	0.9986	0.0524	19.081	1.5184	87
4	0.0698	0.0698	0.9976	0.0699	14.301	1.5010	86
5	0.0873	0.0872	0.9962	0.0875	11.430	1.4835	85
6	0.1047	0.1045	0.9945	0.1051	9.5144	1.4661	84
7	0.1222	0.1219	0.9925	0.1228	8.1443	1.4486	83
8	0.1396	0.1392	0.9903	0.1405	7.1154	1.4312	82
9	0.1571	0.1564	0.9877	0.1584	6.3138	1.4137	81
10	0.1745	0.1736	0.9848	0.1763	5.6713	1.3963	80
11	0.1920	0.1908	0.9816	0.1944	5.1446	1.3788	79
12	0.2094	0.2079	0.9781	0.2126	4.7046	1.3614	78
13	0.2269	0.2250	0.9744	0.2309	4.3315	1.3439	77
14	0.2443	0.2419	0.9703	0.2493	4.0108	1.3265	76
15	0.2618	0.2588	0.9659	0.2679	3.7321	1.3090	75
16	0.2793	0.2756	0.9613	0.2867	3.4874	1.2915	74
17	0.2967	0.2924	0.9563	0.3057	3.2709	1.2741	73
18	0.3142	0.3090	0.9511	0.3249	3.0777	1.2566	72
19	0.3316	0.3256	0.9455	0.3443	2.9042	1.2392	71
20	0.3491	0.3420	0.9397	0.3640	2.7475	1.2217	70
21	0.3665	0.3584	0.9336	0.3839	2.6051	1.2043	69
22	0.3840	0.3746	0.9272	0.4040	2.4751	1.1868	68
23	0.4014	0.3907	0.9205	0.4245	2.3559	1.1694	67
24	0.4189	0.4067	0.9135	0.4452	2.2460	1.1519	66
25	0.4363	0.4226	0.9063	0.4663	2.1445	1.1345	65
26	0.4538	0.4384	0.8988	0.4877	2.0503	1.1170	64
27	0.4712	0.4540	0.8910	0.5095	1.9626	1.0996	63
28	0.4887	0.4695	0.8829	0.5317	1.8807	1.0821	62
29	0.5061	0.4848	0.8746	0.5543	1.8040	1.0647	61
30	0.5236	0.5000	0.8660	0.5774	1.7321	1.0472	60
31	0.5411	0.5150	0.8572	0.6009	1.6643	1.0297	59
32	0.5585	0.5299	0.8480	0.6249	1.6003	1.0123	58
33	0.5760	0.5446	0.8387	0.6494	1.5399	0.9948	57
34	0.5934	0.5592	0.8290	0.6745	1.4826	0.9774	56
35	0.6109	0.5736	0.8192	0.7002	1.4281	0.9599	55
36	0.6283	0.5878	0.8090	0.7265	1.3764	0.9425	54
37	0.6458	0.6018	0.7986	0.7536	1.3270	0.9250	53
38	0.6632	0.6157	0.7880	0.7813	1.2799	0.9076	52
39	0.6807	0.6293	0.7771	0.8098	1.2349	0.8901	51
40	0.6981	0.6428	0.7660	0.8391	1.1918	0.8727	50
41	0.7156	0.6561	0.7547	0.8693	1.1504	0.8552	49
42	0.7330	0.6691	0.7431	0.9004	1.1106	0.8378	48
43	0.7505	0.6820	0.7314	0.9325	1.0724	0.8203	47
44	0.7679	0.6947	0.7193	0.9657	1.0355	0.8029	46
45	0.7854	0.7071	0.7071	1.0000	1.0000	0.7854	45
		Cos	Sin	Cot	Tan	Radians	Degrees

(5) Common logarithms

N	0	1	2	3	4	5	6	7	8	9
10	0000	0043	0086	0128	0170	0212	0253	0294	0334	0374
11	0414	0453	0492	0531	0569	0607	0645	0682	0719	0755
12	0792	0828	0864	0899	0934	0969	1004	1038	1072	1106
13	1139	1173	1206	1239	1271	1303	1335	1367	1399	1430
14	1461	1492	1523	1553	1584	1614	1644	1673	1703	1732
15	1761	1790	1818	1847	1875	1903	1931	1959	1987	2014
16	2041	2068	2095	2122	2148	2175	2201	2227	2253	2279
17	2304	2330	2355	2380	2405	2430	2455	2480	2504	2529
18	2553	2577	2601	2625	2648	2672	2695	2718	2742	2765
19	2788	2810	2833	2856	2878	2900	2923	2945	2967	2989
20	3010	3032	3054	3075	3096	3118	3139	3160	3181	3201
21	3222	3243	3263	3284	3304	3324	3345	3365	3385	3404
22	3424	3444	3464	3483	3502	3522	3541	3560	3579	3598
23	3617	3636	3655	3674	3692	3711	3729	3747	3766	3784
24	3802	3820	3838	3856	3874	3892	3909	3927	3945	3962
25	3979	3997	4014	4031	4048	4065	4082	4099	4116	4133
26	4150	4166	4183	4200	4216	4232	4249	4265	4281	4298
27	4314	4330	4346	4362	4378	4393	4409	4425	4440	4456
28	4472	4487	4502	4518	4533	4548	4564	4579	4594	4609
29	4624	4639	4654	4669	4683	4698	4713	4728	4742	4757
30	4771	4786	4800	4814	4829	4843	4857	4871	4886	4900
31	4914	4928	4942	4955	4969	4983	4997	5011	5024	5038
32	5051	5065	5079	5092	5105	5119	5132	5145	5159	5172
33	5185	5198	5211	5224	5237	5250	5263	5276	5289	5302
34	5315	5328	5340	5353	5366	5378	5391	5403	5416	5428
35	5441	5453	5465	5478	5490	5502	5514	5527	5539	5551
36	5563	5575	5587	5599	5611	5623	5635	5647	5658	5670
37	5682	5694	5705	5717	5729	5740	5752	5763	5775	5786
38	5798	5809	5821	5832	5843	5855	5866	5877	5888	5899
39	5911	5922	5933	5944	5955	5966	5977	5988	5999	6010
40	6021	6031	6042	6053	6064	6075	6085	6096	6107	6117
41	6128	6138	6149	6160	6170	6180	6191	6201	6212	6222
42	6232	6243	6253	6263	6274	6284	6294	6304	6314	6325
43	6335	6345	6355	6365	6375	6385	6395	6405	6415	6425
44	6435	6444	6454	6464	6474	6484	6493	6503	6513	6522
45	6532	6542	6551	6561	6571	6580	6590	6599	6609	6618
46	6628	6637	6646	6656	6665	6675	6684	6693	6702	6712
47	6721	6730	6739	6749	6758	6767	6776	6785	6794	6803
48	6812	6821	6830	6839	6848	6857	6866	6875	6884	6893
49	6902	6911	6920	6928	6937	6946	6955	6964	6972	6981
50	6990	6998	7007	7016	7024	7033	7042	7050	7059	7067
51	7076	7084	7093	7101	7110	7118	7126	7135	7143	7152
52	7160	7168	7177	7185	7193	7202	7210	7218	7226	7235
53	7243	7251	7259	7267	7275	7284	7292	7300	7308	7316
54	7324	7332	7340	7348	7356	7364	7372	7380	7388	7396

N	0	1	2	3	4	5	6	7	8	9
55	7404	7412	7419	7427	7435	7443	7451	7459	7466	7474
56	7482	7490	7497	7505	7513	7520	7528	7536	7543	7551
57	7559	7566	7574	7582	7589	7597	7604	7612	7619	7627
58	7634	7642	7649	7657	7664	7672	7679	7686	7694	7701
59	7709	7716	7723	7731	7738	7745	7752	7760	7767	7774
60	7782	7789	7796	7803	7810	7818	7825	7832	7839	7846
61	7853	7860	7868	7875	7882	7889	7896	7903	7910	7917
62	7924	7931	7938	7945	7952	7959	7966	7973	7980	7987
63	7993	8000	8007	8014	8021	8028	8035	8041	8048	8055
64	8062	8069	8075	8082	8089	8096	8102	8109	8116	8122
65	8129	8136	8142	8149	8156	8162	8169	8176	8182	8189
66	8195	8202	8209	8215	8222	8228	8235	8241	8248	8254
67	8261	8267	8274	8280	8287	8293	8299	8306	8312	8319
68	8325	8331	8338	8344	8351	8357	8363	8370	8376	8382
69	8388	8395	8401	8407	8414	8420	8426	8432	8439	8445
70	8451	8457	8463	8470	8476	8482	8488	8494	8500	8506
71	8513	8519	8525	8531	8537	8543	8549	8555	8561	8567
72	8573	8579	8585	8591	8597	8603	8609	8615	8621	8627
73	8633	8639	8645	8651	8657	8663	8669	8675	8681	8686
74	8692	8698	8704	8710	8716	8722	8727	8733	8739	8745
75	8751	8756	8762	8768	8774	8779	8785	8791	8797	8802
76	8808	8814	8820	8825	8831	8837	8842	8848	8854	8859
77	8865	8871	8876	8882	8887	8893	8899	8904	8910	8915
78	8921	8927	8932	8938	8943	8949	8954	8960	8965	8971
79	8976	8982	8987	8993	8998	9004	9009	9015	9020	9025
80	9031	9036	9042	9047	9053	9058	9063	9069	9074	9079
81	9085	9090	9096	9101	9106	9112	9117	9122	9128	9133
82	9138	9143	9149	9154	9159	9165	9170	9175	9180	9186
83	9191	9196	9201	9206	9212	9217	9222	9227	9232	9238
84	9243	9248	9253	9258	9263	9269	9274	9279	9284	9289
85	9294	9299	9304	9309	9315	9320	9325	9330	9335	9340
86	9345	9350	9355	9360	9365	9370	9375	9380	9385	9390
87	9395	9400	9405	9410	9415	9420	9425	9430	9435	9440
88	9445	9450	9455	9460	9465	9469	9474	9479	9484	9489
89	9494	9499	9504	9509	9513	9518	9523	9528	9533	9538
90	9542	9547	9552	9557	9562	9566	9571	9576	9581	9586
91	9590	9595	9600	9605	9609	9614	9619	9624	9628	9633
92	9638	9643	9647	9652	9657	9661	9666	9671	9675	9680
93	9685	9689	9694	9699	9703	9708	9713	9717	9722	9727
94	9731	9736	9741	9745	9750	9754	9759	9763	9768	9773
95	9777	9782	9786	9791	9795	9800	9805	9809	9814	9818
96	9823	9827	9832	9836	9841	9845	9850	9854	9859	9863
97	9868	9872	9877	9881	9886	9890	9894	9899	9903	9908
98	9912	9917	9921	9926	9930	9934	9939	9943	9948	9952
99	9956	9961	9965	9969	9974	9978	9983	9987	9991	9996

Answers

TO ODD-NUMBERED EXERCISES

EXERCISES 1.2 (PAGE 9)

1. $(-2,+\infty)$
3. $(-\infty,3/4)$
5. $[4,8]$
7. $(-2,1]$
9. all x not in $[0,20/3]$
11. all x not in $[-1/3,1]$
13. all x not in $[-2,2]$
15. all x not in $[-5,3]$

17. $[-1,1/2]$
19. $(-3,3/4)$
21. $((3-\sqrt{3})/2, (3+\sqrt{3})/2)$
23. $(-\infty,-1)$ and $(1/3,3)$
25. $(3/2,31/14)$ and $(7/3,+\infty)$
27. $(-\infty,2/3]$
29. all x not in $(-4,4)$
31. all x not in $(-1-\sqrt{2}, -1+\sqrt{2})$

EXERCISES 1.3 (PAGE 16)

1. $1, -5/2$
3. $-3, 8$
5. $-1/4, 4$
7. $-2/3, 1/2$
9. $4/3, 3$
11. $(-11,3)$

13. $[2/3,2]$
15. all x not in $[1,4]$
17. all x not in $(2/3,10)$
19. $[-9/2,3/2]$
21. all x not in $[10/9,2]$
23. all x not in $[5/13,1)$ and $x \neq -3$

EXERCISES 2.2 (PAGE 22)

1. (a) $(1,2)$; (b) $(-1,-2)$;
   (c) $(-1,2)$; (d) $(-2,1)$
3. (a) $(2,-2)$; (b) $(-2,2)$;
   (c) $(-2,-2)$; (d) does not apply
5. (a) $(-1,3)$; (b) $(1,-3)$;
   (c) $(1,3)$; (d) $(-3,-1)$

7. 2
9. $41/2$
13. $-2, 8$
15. $\sqrt{17}$
17. $77x^2 + 90xy + 21y^2 - 122x$
    $- 66y - 55 = 0$

EXERCISES 2.3 (PAGE 25)

3. $\sqrt{53}/2$; $\sqrt{89}/2$; $\sqrt{26}$
5. $(1,-1/2)$; $3\sqrt{5}/2$

7. $(-9/4,17/4)$; $(1/2,11/2)$;
   $(13/4,27/4)$

EXERCISES 2.4 (PAGE 32)

1. -1
3. $-1/7$

7. (a) yes; (b) yes; (c) no; (d) no
9. $-8/3$

EXERCISES 2.5 (PAGE 37)

27. (a) $x = 4$; (b) $y = -3$

29. (a) $x - 2y + 5 = 0$;
(b) $2x + y - 5 = 0$

EXERCISES 2.6 (PAGE 43)

1. $4x - y - 11 = 0$
3. $x = -3$
5. $4x - 3y + 12 = 0$
7. $\sqrt{3}x - y + 2\sqrt{3} - 5 = 0$
9. $x + y = 0$
11. $x/(8/5) + y/8 = 1$
13. $9x - 4y - 11 = 0$;
$9x + 4y - 19 = 0$; $y = 1$

15. $2x + 3y - 12 = 0$;
$(2 + 2\sqrt{2})x + (3 - 3\sqrt{2})y$
$-12 = 0$; $(2 - 2\sqrt{2})x +$
$(3 + 3\sqrt{2})y - 12 = 0$
17. $2x + 3y + 7 = 0$; $\sqrt{13}$
19. (a) $-A/B$; (b) $-C/B$; (c) $-C/A$;
(d) $Bx - Ay = 0$
23. $x + 5y - 5\sqrt{2} = 0$;
$x + 5y + 5\sqrt{2} = 0$

EXERCISES 2.7 (PAGE 47)

1. (a) $1/2$; (b) $10/11$; (c) $-7/4$;
(d) $7/31$; (e) $7/26$; (f) 1.3
3. $27°$; $45°$; $108°$
5. $27°$; $63°$; $90°$

7. $3x - y + 7 = 0$; $x + 3y - 11 = 0$
11. $52°$; $90°$; $106°$; $112°$
13. $-(19 + \sqrt{370})/3$

EXERCISES 2.8 (PAGE 53)

1. $(x - 4)^2 + (y + 3)^2 = 25$;
$x^2 + y^2 - 8x + 6y = 0$
3. $(x + 5)^2 + (y + 12)^2 = 9$;
$x^2 + y^2 + 10x + 24y + 160 = 0$
5. $x^2 + y^2 - 2x - 4y - 8 = 0$
7. $x^2 + y^2 + 6x + 10y + 9 = 0$
9. $x^2 + y^2 - 4x - 4y - 2 = 0$
11. $(3,4)$; 4

13. $(0, -2/3)$; $5/3$
15. circle
17. no real locus
19. circle
21. $x + y + 5 = 0$
23. $3x + 4y - 19 = 0$
27. $m^2r^2 + r^2 - b^2 = 0$

EXERCISES 2.9 (PAGE 57)

1. $(0,1)$; $y = -1$; 4
3. $(-2,0)$; $x = 2$; 8
5. $(0, -1/4)$; $y = 1/4$; 1
7. $(9/8,0)$; $x = -9/8$; $9/2$
9. $y^2 = 20x$
11. $x^2 = -8y$

13. $y^2 = 2x$
15. $y^2 = -6x$
19. $x^2 = -y$
21. 166 ft
23. $y^2 - 10x - 10y + 20 = 0$
25. $x^2 + y^2 + 10y = 0$

EXERCISES 2.10 (PAGE 64)

1. $x'^2 + y'^2 = 13$
3. $y'^2 = 6x'$
5. $x'^2 + 4y'^2 = 4$
7. $y' = 2x'^3$
9. $x'^2 + 4y'^2 = 16$
11. $3x'^2 - 2y'^2 = 6$
13. $(-3, 1/4)$; $(-3, -3/4)$; $x = -3$;
$y = 5/4$

15. $(1, -5)$; $(-1/2, -5)$; $y = -5$;
$x = 5/2$
17. $(2/3,1)$; $(7/24,1)$; $y = 1$;
$x = 25/24$
19. $y^2 + 20x - 8y - 24 = 0$
21. $x^2 + 2x - 8y + 41 = 0$
23. $x^2 - 6x - 6y - 3 = 0$;
$x^2 - 6x + 6y + 21 = 0$

25. $y^2 - 4x - 4y - 12 = 0$
27. $y^2 - 2x - 8y + 25 = 0$;
 $y^2 - 18x - 8y + 169 = 0$
29. $(-b/2a, (4ac - b^2)/4a$

31. $x^2 - 2x + 4y + 1 = 0$; $x^2 - 2x$
 $- 16y - 79 = 0$; $x^2 - 2x - 4y$
 $-31 = 0$; $x^2 - 2x + 16y + 49 = 0$
33. $x'^3 - y'^2 = 0$

EXERCISES 3.1 (PAGE 72)

1. domain: $(-\infty, +\infty)$;
 range: $(-\infty, +\infty)$
3. domain: $(-\infty, +\infty)$;
 range: $[-6, +\infty)$
5. domain: $[4/3, +\infty)$;
 range: $[0, +\infty)$
7. domain: all x not in $(-2, +2)$;
 range: $[0, +\infty)$
9. domain: $(-\infty, +\infty)$;
 range: $[0, +\infty)$
11. domain: $(-\infty, +\infty)$;
 range; -2 and 2
13. domain: $(-\infty, +\infty)$;
 range: all real numbers except 3

15. domain: $(-\infty, +\infty)$;
 range: $[-4, +\infty)$
17. domain: all real numbers
 except -5 and -1; range: all
 real numbers except -7 and -3
19. domain: all x not in $(-1, 4)$;
 range: $[0, +\infty)$
21. domain: all real numbers except
 2; range: all nonnegative real
 numbers
23. domain: all real numbers except
 -5; range: all real numbers
 in $[3, +\infty)$

EXERCISES 3.2 (PAGE 76)

1. (a) -5; (b) -6; (c) -3; (d) 30;
 (e) $2h^2 + 9h + 4$; (f) $8x^4 + 10x^2 - 3$; (g) $2x^4 - 7x^2$;
 (h) $2x^2 + 4hx + 5x + 2h^2 + 5h - 3$; (i) $2x^2 + 5x + 2h^2 + 5h - 6$; (j) $4x + 2h + 5$
3. (a) 1; (b) $\sqrt{11}$; (c) 2; (d) $3\sqrt{7}$;
 (e) $\sqrt{4x + 9}$;
 (f) $2/(\sqrt{2x + 2h + 3} + \sqrt{2x + 3})$
5. (a) $x^2 + x - 6$, domain:
 $(-\infty, +\infty)$;
 (b) $-x^2 + x - 4$, domain:
 $(-\infty, +\infty)$;
 (c) $x^3 - 5x^2 - x + 5$,
 domain: $(-\infty, +\infty)$;
 (d) $(x - 5)/(x^2 - 1)$, domain: all
 real numbers except -1 and 1;
 (e) $(x^2 - 1)/(x - 5)$, domain:
 all real numbers except 5;
 (f) $x^2 - 6$, domain: $(-\infty, +\infty)$;
 (g) $x^2 - 10x + 24$, domain:
 $(-\infty, +\infty)$
7. (a) $(x^2 + 2x - 1)/(x^2 - x)$,
 domain: all real numbers except
 0 and 1; (b) $(x^2 + 1)/(x^2 - x)$,

domain: all real numbers except
0 and 1; (c) $(x + 1)/(x^2 - x)$,
domain: all real numbers except
0 and 1; (d) $(x^2 + x)/(x - 1)$,
domain: all real numbers except
0 and 1; (e) $(x - 1)/(x^2 + x)$,
domain: all real numbers except
$-1, 0,$ and 1; (f) $(1 + x)/(1 - x)$,
domain: all real numbers except
0 and 1; (g) $(x - 1)/(x + 1)$,
domain: all real numbers except
-1 and 1
9. (a) $\sqrt{x^2 - 1} + \sqrt{x - 1}$, domain:
 $[1, +\infty)$; (b) $\sqrt{x^2 - 1} - \sqrt{x - 1}$,
 domain: $[1, +\infty)$;
 (c) $(x - 1)\sqrt{x + 1}$,
 domain: $[1, +\infty)$; (d) $\sqrt{x + 1}$,
 domain: $(1, +\infty)$; (e) $1/\sqrt{x + 1}$,
 domain: $(1, +\infty)$; (f) $\sqrt{x - 2}$,
 domain: $[2, +\infty)$;
 (g) $\sqrt{\sqrt{x^2 - 1} - 1}$,
 domain: $(-\infty, -\sqrt{2}]$ and
 $[\sqrt{2}, +\infty)$
11. (a) $f(x) = \sqrt{x}$; (b) $f(x) = -\sqrt{|x|}$
15. (a) even; (b) odd; (c) even; (d) even

EXERCISES 3.3 (PAGE 81)

1. domain: $(-\infty,+\infty)$; range: 0 and 1
3. domain: $(-\infty,+\infty)$; range: 0 and 1
5. domain: $(-\infty,+\infty)$; range: $[0,+\infty)$
7. domain: $(-\infty,+\infty)$; range: $[0,1]$
9. domain: $(-\infty,+\infty)$; range: $[0,+\infty)$

11. domain: $(-\infty,+\infty)$; range: $[0,1)$
13. domain: $(-\infty,+\infty)$; range: the nonnegative integers
15. domain: all real numbers except zero; range: $(-\infty,-1]$, 0, and $(1/2,1]$
17. domain: $(-\infty,+\infty)$; range: 1 and 3

EXERCISES 4.1 (PAGE 89)

1. 0.005
3. 0.005
5. 1/1,400
7. 0.01
9. $\delta = \epsilon/5$
11. $\delta = \epsilon$

13. $\delta = \min(1,\epsilon/3)$
15. $\delta = \min(1,\epsilon/2)$
17. $\delta = \min(1/2,\epsilon/4)$
19. $\delta = \min(1,\epsilon/8)$
21. $\delta = \min(1,\epsilon/6)$

EXERCISES 4.2 (PAGE 96)

1. 7
3. $-1/22$
5. 12
7. 1/7
9. 3/2

11. $\sqrt{30}/5$
13. $\sqrt{2}/4$
15. 1/3
17. 11/17
23. (a) 0

EXERCISES 4.3 (PAGE 101)

1. (a) 0; (b) does not exist; (c) does not exist
3. (a) does not exist; (b) 0; (c) does not exist

5. (a) -3; (b) 2; (c) does not exist
7. (a) 7; (b) 7; (c) 7
9. (a) 5; (b) 5; (c) 5
11. (a) 0; (b) 0; (c) 0

EXERCISES 4.4 (PAGE 113)

1. 2/5
3. 0
5. 1
7. $-\infty$
9. ∞
11. $+\infty$

13. $+\infty$
15. 1/2
17. $-\infty$
19. 0
27. Take $\delta = \sqrt{3/N}$

EXERCISES 4.5 (PAGE 120)

1. $y = 0$; $x = 5$
3. $y = 0$; $x = -2$
5. $y = 0$; $x = -6$; $x = 1$
7. $y = 4$; $x = 3$; $x = -3$
9. $y = 0$; $x = -2$; $x = 2$
11. $y = -3$; $y = 3$

13. $x = -\sqrt{2}$; $x = \sqrt{2}$
15. $y = 2/3$; $x = 4/3$
17. $y = -1$; $y = 1$
19. $y = -1$; $y = 1$; $x = 3$
21. $y = 1$; $x = -3$

EXERCISES 5.1 (PAGE 128)

1. 4
3. -3
5. -3
7. $-3/2$
9. $-3; 2$
11. 0

13. continuous everywhere
15. 3
17. 2
19. all integers; (ii)
21. continuous everywhere
23. 0

EXERCISES 5.2 (PAGE 136)

5. continuous on $(3,7)$, $(-5,+\infty)$, $[-10,-5)$
7. continuous on $(-\infty,-3)$, $(-\infty,-3]$, $(3,+\infty)$, $[3,+\infty)$
9. continuous on $(-\infty,1)$, $(1,+\infty)$
11. continuous on $(-2,2)$, $[-2,2]$, $[-2,2)$, $(-2,2]$
13. continuous on $(-1,3)$
15. continuous on $(-3,3)$, $[-3,3]$, $[-3,3)$, $(4,+\infty)$
17. 5
19. $c = -3$ and $k = 4$
21. no; f will be continuous on

$[a,c]$ if $g(b)$ exists and $g(b) = h(b)$
23. all real numbers
25. all x in $(-4,4)$
27. all x not in $[-4,4]$
29. all x in $(0,+\infty)$
31. all noninteger real numbers
33. $x^{3/2}$; all positive integers
35. $1/(\sqrt{x} - 2)$; continuous at all x in $(2,+\infty)$
37. $1/(\sqrt{x} - 2)$; continuous at all x in $(0,4)$ and $(4,+\infty)$
39. $(\sqrt{x} + 1)/(\sqrt{x} - 1)$; continuous at all x in $(0,1)$ and $(1,+\infty)$

EXERCISES 6.1 (PAGE 142)

1. $-2x_1$
3. $-6 - 2x_1$
5. $3x_1^2 - 3$
7. $12x_1^2 - 26x_1 + 4$
9. $8x + y + 9 = 0$; $x - 8y + 58 = 0$
11. $6x - y - 16 = 0$; $x + 6y - 52 = 0$
13. $2x + 5y - 17 = 0$; $5x - 2y + 30 = 0$

15. $2x + 3y - 12 = 0$; $3x - 2y - 5 = 0$
17. $x - 12y + 16 = 0$; $12x + y - 98 = 0$
19. $8x - y - 5 = 0$
21. $2x - y - 2 = 0$
23. $(12 - 2\sqrt{30})x - y + 4\sqrt{30} - 30 = 0$;
$(12 + 2\sqrt{30})x - y - 4\sqrt{30} - 30 = 0$

EXERCISES 6.2 (PAGE 149)

3. $6t_1$; 18
5. $1/2\sqrt{t_1 + 1}$; $1/4$
7. $-5/(5t_1 + 6)^{3/2}$; $-5/64$
9. $t < -3$, moving to right; $-3 < t < 1$, moving to left; $t > 1$, moving to right; changes direction when $t = -3$ and $t = 1$

11. $t < -1 - \sqrt{5}$, moving to left; $-1 - \sqrt{5} < t < -1 + \sqrt{5}$, moving to right; $t > -1 + \sqrt{5}$, moving to left; changes direction when $t = -1 \pm \sqrt{5}$
13. (a) -32 ft/sec; (b) -64 ft/sec; (c) 4 sec; (d) -128 ft/sec

EXERCISES 6.3 (PAGE 154)

1. $8x + 5$
3. $1/2\sqrt{x}$

5. $-1/(x + 1)^2$
7. $-2/x^3 - 1$

9. $-1/2(x + 1)^{3/2}$
11. -6
13. $-1/216$
15. $5/4$
17. 3

19. -12
21. $-\sqrt{5}/25$
23. $f'(x) = 1/3(x - 1)^{2/3}$; f is not differentiable at 1

EXERCISES 6.4 (PAGE 156)

1. (a) 8.6; (b) 8.3; (c) 8.1; (d) 8
3. $-1/16$
5. $4\pi r^2$

7. 64π in.^{2}/in.
9. 32π in.^{3}/in.
11. 11.2 knots

EXERCISES 6.5 (PAGE 160)

1. (b) yes; (c) 1, -1; (d) no
3. (b) yes; (c) -1, 1; (d) no
5. (b) yes; (c) 0, 1; (d) no
7. (b) yes; (c) 0, 0; (d) yes
9. (b) yes; (c) does not exist, 0;

(d) no
11. (b) yes; (c) neither exist; (d) no
13. (b) yes; (c) -6, -6; (d) yes
17. $f'_+(0) = 0$
19. $f'(x_1) = 0$, if x_1 is not an integer

EXERCISES 7.1 (PAGE 167)

1. $3x^2 - 6x + 5$
3. $x^7 - 4x^3$
5. $t^3 - t$
7. $4\pi r^2$
9. $2x + 3 - 2x^{-3}$
11. $-6x^{-3} - 20x^{-5}$
13. $3\sqrt{3}s^2 - 2\sqrt{3}s$
15. $70x^6 + 60x^4 - 15x^2 - 6$
17. $-4(x + 1)(x - 1)^{-3}$
19. $-(x - 1)^{-2}$
21. $5(1 - 2x^2)(1 + 2x^2)^{-2}$

23. $48x^2(x^3 + 8)^{-2}$
25. $6(x^2 + 10x + 1)(x + 5)^{-2}$
29. $2(3x + 2)(6x^2 + 2x - 3)$
31. $3(4x + 1)(2x^2 + x + 1)^2$
33. $x + (4\sqrt{6} - 10)y - 8\sqrt{6} + 21 = 0$;
$x - (4\sqrt{6} + 10)y + 8\sqrt{6} + 21 = 0$
35. $4°40'$
37. $3(9 - t_1^2)(9 + t_1^2)^{-2}$ ft/sec; .24 ft/sec; 3 sec

EXERCISES 7.2 (PAGE 170)

1. $6(x + 2)(x^2 + 4x - 5)^2$
3. $2(8t^3 - 21t^2 + 2) \times (2t^4 - 7t^3 + 2t - 1)$
5. $-2(x + 4)^{-3}$
7. $6(3u - 1)(3u^2 + 5)^2 \times (12u^2 - 3u + 5)$
9. $2(-12x + 17)(2x - 5)^{-2} \times (4x + 3)^{-3}$
11. $18(y - 7)(y + 2)^{-3}$

13. $-2(14x + 3)(7x^2 + 3x - 1)^{-2}$
15. $2(r^2 + 1)^2(2r + 5) \times (8r^2 + 15r + 2)$
17. $2z(z^2 - 5)^2(z^2 + 22)(z^2 + 4)^{-3}$
19. $4(4x - 1)^2(x^2 + 2)^3 \times (21x^4 - 3x^3 + 49x^2 - 4x + 30) \times (3x^2 + 5)^{-3}$
21. $15x - 4y - 6 = 0$
23. $x + 16y - 35 = 0$

EXERCISES 7.3 (PAGE 173)

1. $2(3x + 5)^{-1/3}$
3. $(17/2)(2x - 5)^{-1/2}(3x + 1)^{-3/2}$
5. $2x^{-1/2} - (5/2)x^{-3/2}$
7. $(1/3)(6x^2 - 10x + 1) \times (2x^3 - 5x^2 + x)^{-2/3}$

9. $(\sqrt{2}/2)t^{-3/2}(t - 1)$
11. $x^{-2}(x^2 - 1)^{-1/2}$
13. $(1/6)(x + 5)(x - 1)^{-1/2}(x + 1)^{-4/3}$
15. $(x/3)(5x^2 - 1)(x^2 - 5)^{-1/2} \times (x^2 + 3)^{-2/3}$

17. $(-1/4)(9 - x)^{-1/2} \times$
    $[9 + (9 - x)^{1/2}]^{-1/2}$
19. $4x - 5y + 9 = 0$
21. $x + 4y = 0$
23. (a) 0; (b) 1/2; (c) no t
25. $[f(x)/|f(x)|] f'(x)$

27. $(4/3)(12x^2 + 2x - 9)(3x + 2)^3 \times$
    $(x^2 - 1)^{-1/3}$
29. $(1/6)(31t^4 + 29t^3 + 109t^2 - 18t$
    $- 88)(t^3 - 2t + 1)^{1/2} \times$
    $(t^2 + t + 5)^{-2/3}$

EXERCISES 7.4 (PAGE 176)

1. $5x^4 - 6x^2 + 1; 20x^3 - 12x$
3. $8s^3 - 12s^2 + 7; 24s^2 - 24s$
5. $x/\sqrt{x^2 + 1}; (x^2 + 1)^{-3/2}$
7. $(5/2)x^{3/2} - 5; (15/4)x^{1/2}$
9. $-2x(3 + 2x^2)^{-3/2}; 2(4x^2 - 3) \times$
    $(3 + 2x^2)^{-5/2}$

11. $24x$
13. $6(x + 3)(1 - x)^{-5}$
15. $(15/16)x^{-7/2}(7x^3 + 2x^2 - 1)$
17. $-7/4$ at $(1/2, -9/16)$; 5 at $(-1, -3)$
19. 1/2 sec; 249/80 ft; $-11/8$ ft/sec
21. 3/2 sec; $4\sqrt{6}/3$ ft; $2\sqrt{6}/3$ ft/sec

EXERCISES 7.5 (PAGE 180)

1. $-x/y$
3. $(8y - 3x^2)/(3y^2 - 8x)$
5. $(y - 1)/(1 - x)$
7. $-y^{1/2}x^{-1/2}$
9. $(x - xy^2)/(x^2y - y)$
11. $(3x^2 - 4y)/(4x - 3y^2)$
13. $(3x^2 - 2xy + 2)/(x^2 + 3)$
15. $(y + 4\sqrt{xy})/(\sqrt{x} - x)$
19. $-3a^4x^2y^{-7}$
21. $2x + y = 4$
25. (a) $f_1(x) = 2\sqrt{x - 2}$,

$f_2(x) = -2\sqrt{x - 2}$; (d) $f_1'(x) =$
$(x - 2)^{-1/2}, f_2'(x) = -(x-2)^{-1/2}$;
(e) $2/y$; (f) $x - y - 1 = 0$,
$x + y - 1 = 0$
27. (a) $f_1(x) = \sqrt{x^2 - 9}, f_2(x) =$
$-\sqrt{x^2 - 9}$;
(d) $f_1'(x) = x(x^2 - 9)^{-1/2}$,
$f_2'(x) = -x(x^2 - 9)^{-1/2}$;
(e) x/y;
(f) $5x + 4y + 9 = 0$,
$5x - 4y + 9 = 0$

EXERCISES 7.6 (PAGE 184)

1. (a) $3x^2 \Delta x + 3x (\Delta x)^2 + (\Delta x)^3$;
   (b) $3x^2 \Delta x$; (c) $3x (\Delta x)^2 + (\Delta x)^3$
3. (a) $\sqrt{x + \Delta x} - \sqrt{x}$; (b) $\Delta x/2\sqrt{x}$;
   (c) $(-1/2)x^{-1/2}(\sqrt{x} - \sqrt{x + \Delta x})^2$
5. (a) $(6x^2 + 6x) \Delta x +$
   $(6x + 3) (\Delta x)^2 + 2 (\Delta x)^3$;
   (b) $(6x^2 + 6x) \Delta x$; (c) $(6x + 3)$
   $(\Delta x)^2 + 2 (\Delta x)^3$
7. (a) 0.0309; (b) 0.03; (c) 0.0009

9. (a) -0.875; (b) -1.5; (c) 0.625
11. (a) -0.00248; (b) -0.00250;
    (c) 0.00002
13. 6.125
15. 9.056
17. 0.205
19. 108 in.²
21. 2.88π in.³

EXERCISES 7.7 (PAGE 188)

1. $6(3x - 1)(3x^2 - 2x + 1)^2 dx$
3. $(2/3)(7x^2 + 9x)(2x + 3)^{-2/3} dx$
5. $(x - 1)^{-1/2}(x + 1)^{-3/2} dx$
7. $2(x^2 + 1)^{-3/2} dx$
9. $-9x^2/8y$
11. $-y^{1/2}x^{-1/2}$
13. $(4x^3 - 9x^2y + 4y^3) \div$
    $(3x^3 - 12xy^2 - 4y^3)$

15. $(9x^2 - 2xy + 2y^2 - 6x) \div$
    $(x^2 - 4xy + 3y^2 - 2y)$
17. $18t^5 - 56t^3 + 38t$
19. $(2t - 1)(2\sqrt{t^2 - t + 4} - 3) \div$
    $\sqrt{t^2 - t + 4}$
21. $6t^5 - 4t^3 - 2t - 9t(t^2 + 1)^{1/2}$
    $+ 6t(t^2 + 1)^{-1/2}$
23. $8t(16t^4 - 8t^2y + 8t^2 - 2y + 1)$
    $\div (16t^4 + 8t^2 - y^2 + 1)$

EXERCISES 8.1 (PAGE 192)

1. 9/5 ft/sec
3. $1/2\pi$ ft/min
5. $5/8\pi$ ft/min
7. 25/3 ft/sec
9. $6/25\pi$ ft/min
11. 1/6 ft/min

13. 14 ft/sec
15. $(3\sqrt{97} + 97)/194 \approx 0.65$ ft/sec
17. decrease at the rate of 4 in./min
19. $(8 - 4\pi/3)$ ft^3/min
21. 32 ft^3/min

EXERCISES 8.2 (PAGE 203)

1. $-5, 1/3$
3. $-3, -1, 1$
5. 0, 2
7. $-2, 0, 2$
9. $-3, 3$
11. $f(2) = -2$, abs. min.
13. no absolute extrema
15. $f(-3) = 0$, abs. min.
17. $f(5) = 1$, abs. min.
19. $f(4) = 1$, abs. min.
21. $f(5) = 2$, abs. max.
23. $f(2) = 0$, abs. min.

25. $f(-3) = -46$, abs. min.;
    $f(-1) = -10$, abs. max.
27. $f(-2) = 0$, abs. min.;
    $f(-4) = 144$, abs. max.
29. $f(2) = 0$, abs. min.;
    $f(3) = 25$, abs. max.
31. $f(-1) = -1$, abs. min.;
    $f(2) = 1/2$, abs. max.
33. $f(-1) = 0$, abs. min.;
    $f(1) = \sqrt[3]{4}$, abs. max.
35. $f(-3) = -13$, abs. min.;
    $f(3) = 7$, abs. max.

EXERCISES 8.3 (PAGE 209)

1. 2,500 ft^2
3. 25 yd by 50 yd
5. $(10 + 4\sqrt{3})$ ft
7. 8 miles from point B
9. 3.40, 9.43
11. radius $= 3\sqrt{2}$ in.; altitude
    $= 6\sqrt{2}$ in.

13. radius of circle $= 5/(\pi + 4)$
    ft; length of side of square $=$
    $10/(\pi + 4)$ ft
15. length of side of triangle $=$
    $10(9 - 4\sqrt{3})/11$ ft; length of
    side of square $=$
    $10(3\sqrt{3} - 4)/11$ ft

EXERCISES 8.4 (PAGE 214)

1. 2
3. $(2 + \sqrt{7})/3$ or $(2 - \sqrt{7})/3$
5. $(-6 - \sqrt{39})/6$ in $[-3, -1/2]$;
   $(-6 \pm \sqrt{39})/6$ in $[-3, 1/2]$;
   $(-6 + \sqrt{39})/6$ in $[-1/2, 1/2]$
7. $c = 3/4$

9. f is discontinuous at 2
11. f is not differentiable at 2
13. f is discontinuous at 3
15. f is not differentiable at 1
17. $c = 0$

EXERCISES 8.5 (PAGE 218)

1. 1/2
3. 8/27
5. $(3 + 4\sqrt{3})/2$
7. 1
9. (i) fails to hold

11. 4
13. $3 + \sqrt{2}/10 \approx 3.14$
15. $\pm\sqrt{39}/3$
17. f is discontinuous at 3
19. f is not differentiable at 4

EXERCISES 8.6 (PAGE 228)

1. (a) and (b) $f(2) = -5$, rel. min.; (c) $[2,+\infty)$; (d) $(-\infty,2]$

3. (a) and (b) no relative extrema; (c) $(-\infty,+\infty)$; (d) nowhere

5. (a) and (b) $f(2) = -50$, rel. min.; $f(-2) = 64$, rel. max.; (c) $(-\infty,-2), [2,+\infty)$; (d) $[-2,2]$

7. (a) and (b) no relative extrema; (c) $(0,+\infty)$; (d) nowhere

9. (a) and (b) $f(2) = 4$, rel. max.; (c) $(-\infty,2]$; (d) $[2,3]$

11. (a) and (b) $f(1/5) = 3{,}456/625$, rel. max.; $f(1) = 0$, rel. min.; (c) $(-\infty,1/5]$, $[1,+\infty)$; (d) $[1/5,1]$

13. (a) and (b) $f(4) = 2$, rel. max (c) $(-\infty,4]$; (d) $[4,+\infty)$

15. (a) and (b) $f(4) = 9$, rel. max.; (c) $(-\infty,4]$; (d) $[4,+\infty)$

17. (a) and (b) $f(-2) = 5$ rel. max.; $f(0) = 1$, rel. min.;

(c) $(-\infty,-2], [0,+\infty)$; (d) $[-2,0]$

19. (a) and (b) $f(2) = -3$, rel. min.; (c) $[2,+\infty)$; (d) $(-\infty,2]$

21. (a) and (b) $f(-1) = 2$, rel. max.; $f(0) = 1$, rel. min.; $f(2) = 5$, rel. max.; (c) $(-\infty,-1], [0, 2]$; (d) $[-1,0]$, $[2,+\infty)$

23. (a) and (b) $f(-9) = -8$, rel. min.; $f(-4) = 0$, rel. max.; $f(2) = -7$, rel. min.; (c) $[-9,-4], [2,+\infty)$; (d) $(-\infty,-9], [0,2]$

25. (a) and (b) no relative extrema; (c) $[0,+\infty)$; (d) nowhere

27. (a) and (b) $f(-1) = 0$, rel. max.; $f(1) = -\sqrt[3]{4}$, rel. min.; (c) $(-\infty,-1], [1,+\infty)$; (d) $[-1,1]$

29. (a) and (b) $f(4) = \sqrt[3]{4}/4$, rel. max.; (c) $(-4,4]$; (d) $(-\infty,-4)$, $[4,+\infty)$

31. $a = 9, b = -36, c = 34$

EXERCISES 8.7 (PAGE 233)

1. $f(1/3) = 2/3$, rel. min.

3. $f(3/2) = 81/4$, rel. max.; $f(-1) = -11$, rel. min.

5. $f(4) = 0$, rel. min.

7. $G(3) = 0$, rel. min.

9. $h(-2) = -2$, rel. min.

11. $f(1) = 8$, rel. min.

13. $F(27) = 9$, rel. max.

EXERCISES 8.8 (PAGE 237)

1. $f(0) = 0$, abs. min.

3. no absolute extrema

5. $g(1/4) = 3/4$, abs. min.

7. $f(0) = 0$, abs. min.; $f(\sqrt{2}) = \sqrt{3}/18$, abs. max.

9. 4 in. by 8 in. by 16/3 in.

11. altitude = 3/4 the width of the base

13. a cube of edge 5 yd

15. $\sqrt{2}$

17. $2\sqrt{2}$

19. ratio of height of rectangle to radius of semicircle = $(4 + \pi)/4$

21. $(0,1)$

23. $27{,}225$

25. 225

EXERCISES 8.9 (PAGE 246)

1. concave downward for $x < 0$; concave upward for $x > 0$; $(0,0)$, pt. of infl.

3. concave upward everywhere

5. concave downward for $x<-1$ and $0<x<1$; concave upward for

$-1<x<0$ and $x>1$; $(0,0)$, pt. of infl.

7. concave upward for $x<2$; concave downward for $x>2$; $(2,0)$, pt. of infl.

9. $a = -1, b = 3$

11. $a = 2, b = -6, c = 0, d = 3$

EXERCISES 8.10 (PAGE 250)

1. $f(-1) = 5$, rel. max.; $f(1) = -3$, rel. min.; $(0,1)$, pt. of infl.; f increasing on $(-\infty, -1]$ and $[1, +\infty)$; f decreasing on $[-1,1]$; graph concave downward for $x < 0$; graph concave upward for $x > 0$

3. $f(3/2) = -27/16$, rel. min.; $(0,0)$, $(1,-1)$, pts. of infl.; f increasing on $[3/2, +\infty)$; f decreasing on $(-\infty, 3/2]$; graph concave upward for $x < 0$ and $x > 1$; graph concave downward for $0 < x < 1$

5. $f(-3) = 5$, rel. max.; $f(-1/3) = -121/27$, rel. min.; $(-5/3, 7/27)$, pt. of infl.; f increasing on $(-\infty, -3]$ and $[-1/3, +\infty)$; f decreasing on $[-3, -1/3]$; graph concave downward for $x < -5/3$; graph concave upward for $x > -5/3$

7. $f(0) = 1$, rel. min.; $(1/2, 23/16)$, $(1, 2)$, pts. of infl.; f decreasing on $(-\infty, 0]$; f increasing on $[0, +\infty)$; graph concave upward for $x < 1/2$ and $x > 1$; graph concave downward for $1/2 < x < 1$

9. $f(-1) = 7/12$, rel. min.; $f(0) = 1$, rel. max.; $f(2) = -5/3$, rel. min.; pts. of infl. at $x = (1 \pm \sqrt{7})/3$; f decreasing on $(-\infty, -1]$ and $[0,2]$; f increasing on $[-1,0]$ and $[2, +\infty)$; graph concave upward for $x < (1 - \sqrt{7})/3$ and $x > (1 + \sqrt{7})/3$; graph concave downward for $(1 - \sqrt{7})/3 < x < (1 + \sqrt{7})/3$

11. $f(4/5) = 26{,}244/3{,}125$, rel. max.; $f(2) = 0$, rel. min.; pts of infl. at $(-1,0)$ and $x = (8 \pm 3\sqrt{6})/10$; f increasing on $(-\infty, 4/5]$ and $[2, +\infty)$; f decreasing on $[4/5, 2]$; graph concave downward for $x < -1$ and $(8 - 3\sqrt{6})/10 < x < (8 + 3\sqrt{6})/10$; graph concave upward for $-1 < x < (8 - 3\sqrt{6})/10$ and $x > (8 + 3\sqrt{6})/10$

13. $f(-4/3) = 256/81$, rel. max.; $f(0) = 0$, rel. min.; $(-1,2)$, pt. of infl.; f increasing on $(-\infty, -4/3]$ and $[0, +\infty)$; f decreasing on $[-4/3, 0]$; graph concave downward for $x < -1$; graph concave upward for $x > -1$

15. $f(0) = 0$, rel. min.: $f(1) = 1$, rel. max.; f decreasing on $(-\infty, 0)$ and $[1, +\infty)$; f increasing on $(0,1]$; graph concave downward for $x < 0$ and $x > 0$

17. $f(-1/8) = -3/8$, rel. min.; $(0,0)$, $(1/4, 3\sqrt[3]{2}/4)$, pts. of infl.; f decreasing on $(-\infty, -1/8]$; f increasing on $[-1/8, +\infty)$; graph concave upward for $x < 0$ and $x > 1/4$; graph concave downward for $0 < x < 1/4$

19. no relative extrema; $(3,2)$, pt. of infl.; f increasing on $(-\infty, +\infty)$; graph concave downward for $x < 3$; graph concave upward for $x > 3$

21. no relative extrema; $(3,2)$, pt. of infl. with horizontal tangent; f increasing on $(-\infty, +\infty)$ graph concave downward for $x < 3$; graph concave upward for $x > 3$

23. $f(-1) = 3$, rel. min.; f decreasing on $(-\infty, -1]$; f increasing on $[-1, +\infty)$; graph concave upward for all x

25. $f(0) = 0$, rel. min.; $f(16/5) = 512\sqrt{5}/125$, rel. max.; pt. of infl. at $x = (48 - 8\sqrt{6})/15$; f decreasing on $(-\infty, 0]$ and $[16/5, 4]$; f increasing on $[0, 16/5]$; graph concave upward

for $x < (48 - 8\sqrt{6})/15$; graph concave downward for $(48 - 8\sqrt{6})/15 < x < 4$

$x > 1 + \sqrt{2}$; graph concave downward for $1 - \sqrt{2} < x < 1 + \sqrt{2}$

27. $f(1) = 2$, rel. max.; pts. of infl. at $x = 1 \pm \sqrt{2}$; f increasing on $(-\infty, 1]$; f decreasing on $[1, +\infty)$; graph concave upward for $x < 1 - \sqrt{2}$ and

29. $f(-2/3) = 4\sqrt{6}/9$, rel. max.; f increasing on $(-\infty, -2/3]$; f decreasing on $[-2/3, 0]$; graph concave downward for $x < 0$

EXERCISES 9.1 (PAGE 257)

1. $3x^5/5 + C$
3. $3t - t^2 + t^3/3 + C$
5. $-1/x^2 - 3/x + 5x + C$
7. $(2x)^{3/2}/3 - \sqrt{2x} + C$
9. $2(x^3 - 1)^{3/2}/9 + C$
11. $\sqrt{3s^2 + 1}/3 + C$
13. $(-4/3)(1 + 1/2x)^{3/2} + C$
15. $-x^9/9 + 12x^7/7 - 48x^5/5 + 64x^3/3 + C$

17. $2(t + 3)^{3/2}/3 - 6\sqrt{t + 3} + C$
19. $-6(3 - x)^{3/2} + 12(3 - x)^{5/2}/5 - 2(3 - x)^{7/2}/7 + C$
21. $2\sqrt{x^3 + 3x^2 + 1}/3 + C$
23. $-27(3 - 2y)^{1/3}/4 + 3(3 - 2y)^{4/3}/16 + C$
25. $3(r^{1/3} + 2)^5/5 + C$
27. (a) $2x^4 + 4x^3 + 3x^2 + x + C$; (b) $(2x + 1)^4/8 + C$

EXERCISES 9.2 (PAGE 264)

1. $y = x^3 + x^2 - 7x + C$
3. $3x^2y + Cy + 2 = 0$
5. $2\sqrt{1 + y^2} = 3x^2 + C$
7. $12y = 5x^4 + 6x^2 + C_1x + C_2$
9. $3y = x^3 - 3x^2 - 12x + 18$
11. $x^2 = 4y^2$
13. $12y = -x^4 + 6x^2 - 20x + 27$
15. $y = x^2 - 3x + 2$
17. $3y = -2x^3 + 3x^2 + 2x + 6$

19. $12y = -x^4 + 6x^2 - 20x + 27$
21. $v = -t^2 + 5t + 2, s = -t^3/3 + 5t^2/2 + 2t$
23. $1,600s = v^2 + 1,200$
25. 5.9 sec; 188 ft/sec
27. 3.4 sec; 99 ft/sec
29. 77/18 ft/sec²
31. 4½ ft

EXERCISES 10.1 (PAGE 270)

1. 51
3. 73/12
5. 63/4
7. 7/12
17. 32,500

19. $10(10^n - 1)$
21. 100/101
23. $n^4 - 2n^3/3 - 3n^2 - 4n/3$
25. $3^{2n} - 3^{-2n}/9 - 20n/9 - 8/9$

EXERCISES 10.2 (PAGE 277)

1. 8/3
3. 15
5. 9
7. 3/5

9. $\frac{1}{2}m(b^2 - a^2)$
11. 9
13. 15

EXERCISES 10.3 (PAGE 286)

1. 247/32
3. 1,469/1,320
5. 0.835

7. 8/3
9. 15/4
11. 66

13. 4
15. 20

17. 5/3
19. 305/6

EXERCISES 10.5 (PAGE 300)

1. $c = (1 + \sqrt{5})/2$
3. $c = -4$
5. doesn't hold because f is discontinuous at -2
7. doesn't hold because f is discontinuous at 1

9. $\sqrt[3]{30}/2$
11. $-2 + \sqrt{21}$
13. 0
15. $28/3; 2\sqrt{21}/3$
17. $7\pi/4$

EXERCISES 10.6 (PAGE 309)

1. 200/3
3. 140/3
5. 7/240
7. -8
9. 0
11. $2 - \sqrt[3]{2}$
13. 104/5
15. 27/4
17. 11/6

19. 22/3
21. 15
23. 52/3
25. 98/3
27. 7/3
29. $32/3; 4(3 - \sqrt{3})/3$
31. $14/9; 196/81$
33. 42,304/175

EXERCISES 11.1 (PAGE 321)

1. 32/3
3. 32/3
5. 12/5
7. 9/2
9. $8\sqrt{2}/3$
11. 5/12

13. 27/10
15. 64/3
17. 253/12
19. 12
21. 128/5

EXERCISES 11.2 (PAGE 328)

1. 64π
3. $704\pi/5$
5. $384\pi/7$
7. $3,456\pi/35$
9. $4\pi r^3/3$

11. $64\pi/5$
13. $\pi a^2 h/3$
15. 180π
17. $16\pi/3$

EXERCISES 11.3 (PAGE 335)

9. $\pi/2$
11. $3\pi/10$
13. $5\pi/6$
15. $49\pi/30$

17. $32\pi a^3/15$
19. $7\pi/2$
21. $4\pi(r^2 - a^2)^{3/2}/3$

EXERCISES 11.4 (PAGE 340)

1. 180 in.-lb
3. 12,000 in.-lb
5. 6,562.5w ft-lb

7. $4w$ ft-lb
9. $256\pi w$ ft-lb

EXERCISES 11.5 (PAGE 344)

1. $320w$ lb
3. $2.25w$ lb
5. $1250w/3$ lb

7. 6,000 lb
9. $250\sqrt{409}\ w$ lb

EXERCISES 11.6 (PAGE 350)

1. $(4,0)$
3. $(6,0)$
5. 5.92 in. from one end

7. 16/3 ft from the left end
9. 16 lb

EXERCISES 11.7 (PAGE 361)

1. $(2,1/3)$
5. $(0,8/5)$
7. $(0,12/5)$
9. $(6,7)$
11. $(16/15,64/21)$
13. $(1/2,-3/2)$
15. $5p/3$

17. $2.25w$ lb
19. $100,000w$ ft-lb
23. The point on the bisecting radius whose distance from the center of the circle is $4/3\pi$ times the radius
25. $4\pi r^3/3$
27. $(3\sqrt{2}\pi^2 + 4\sqrt{2}\pi)r^3/6$

EXERCISES 11.8 (PAGE 372)

1. $(0,8/5,0)$
3. $(1/2,0,0)$
5. $(16/5,0,0)$
7. $(2,10/7,0)$
9. $(0,7/3,0)$

11. $(0,13/5,0)$
13. $(5/16,4,0)$
15. $(2,5p/8,0)$
17. On axis, $3h/4$ units from vertex
19. $(44/13,0,0)$

EXERCISES 11.9 (PAGE 377)

1. $4\sqrt{3}r^3/3$
3. $8r^3/3$
5. $ah/6$

7. $2r^3/3$ in.^{3}
9. 1,944 in.^{3}

EXERCISES 11.10 (PAGE 384)

1. $14/3$
3. $33/8$
5. $(97^{3/2} - 125)/27$

7. $4\sqrt{3}$
9. $[8a^3 - (3b^2 + a^2)^{3/2}] / 8(a^2 - b^2)$

EXERCISES 12.2 (PAGE 395)

1. $2x/(1 + x^2)$
3. $x/(x^2 - 4)$
5. $(2 \ln x + 1)/x \ln x$
7. $(8 \ln x)/x$
9. $1/2(1 + \sqrt{x + 1})$
11. $\dfrac{x^9 - 18x^7 + 15x^2 + 10}{10(x^3 + 2x)^{1/2}(x^7 + 1)^{6/5}}$
13. $\dfrac{3(3x + 4)}{2(x + 1)^{3/2}(x + 2)^{3/2}}$

15. $\dfrac{(x^3 - x) \ln (x^2 - 1) + 2x^3 + 2x}{(x^2 - 1)\sqrt{x^2 + x}}$
17. $(-xy - y)/(xy + x)$
19. $-\ln |3 - 2x|/2 + C$
21. $\ln |\ln x| + C$
23. $\ln^3 3x/3 + C$
25. $x^2 + 4 \ln |x^2 - 4| + C$
27. $\ln 5$
29. $(1/2) \ln (4/7)$

EXERCISES 12.3 (PAGE 400)

11. $2x + 4y + \ln 16 - 1 = 0$

13. $\ln 4$

15. $(8 - 6 \ln 3)\pi$

17. $\ln x = -1/2$

EXERCISES 12.4 (PAGE 412)

1. $f^{-1}(x) = \sqrt[3]{x}$; domain: $(-\infty, +\infty)$

3. no inverse

5. $f^{-1}(x) = 1/(2 - x)$; domain: all real numbers except 2

7. $f(x) = \sqrt[3]{(8 - x)/x}$; domain: all real numbers except 0

9. no inverse

11. (a) $f_1(x) = \sqrt{9 - x^2}, f_2(x) = -\sqrt{9 - x^2}$; (b) neither has an inverse; (c) $D_x y = -x/y$, $D_y x = -y/x$

13. (a) $f(x) = 4/x$; (b) $f^{-1}(x) = 4/x$, domain: all real numbers except 0; (c) $D_x y = -y/x$, $D_y x = -x/y$

15. (a) $f(x) = (2x^2 + 1)/3x$; (b) no inverse; (c) $D_x y = (4x - 3y)/3x$, $D_y x = 3x/(4x - 3y)$

17. domain of f^{-1}: $[0, +\infty)$; range of f^{-1}: $[4, +\infty)$

19. domain of f^{-1}: $(-\infty, +\infty)$; range of f^{-1}: $(0, +\infty)$

21. domain of f^{-1}: $(-\infty, +\infty)$; range of f^{-1}: $(-\infty, +\infty)$

23. $f'^{(-1)}(x) = 1/\sqrt{1 - [f^{-1}(x)]^4}$

EXERCISES 12.5 (PAGE 419)

5. $-6xe^{-3x^2}$

7. $2e^{2x}(x - 1)/x^3$

9. $4/(e^x + e^{-x})^2$

11. $2x$

13. $(3 - e^{2x})/(e^x + e^{-x})^3$

15. $x^x(\ln x + 1)$

17. $-e^{y-x}$

19. $-(2ye^{2x} + y^2)/(2e^{2x} + 3xy)$

21. $-e^{2-5x}/5 + C$

23. $e^x - e^{-x} + C$

25. $1/6(1 - 2e^{3x}) + C$

27. $e^{2x^2-4x}/4 + C$

29. $e^x - 3 \ln(e^x + 3) + C$

31. e^2

33. $(e^4 - 1)/2$

35. $e^4/4 + e^2 - 1/4$

37. $f(1) = e^{-1}$, rel. max.; $(2, 2e^{-2})$, pt. of infl.; f increasing on $[1, +\infty)$; f decreasing on $(-\infty, 1]$; graph concave upward for $x > 2$; graph concave downward for $x < 2$

39. $(3 - e)/2$

43. $\pi(1 - e^{-2b})/2$; $\pi/2$

EXERCISES 12.6 (PAGE 425)

9. $3^{5x}5 \ln 3$

11. $2^{5x}3^{4x^2}(8x \ln 3 + 5 \ln 2)$

13. $(\log_{10} e - \log_{10} x)/x^2$

15. $\log_a e/2x\sqrt{\log_a x}$

17. $(\log_{10} e)^2/(x + 1) \log_{10}(x + 1)$

19. $x^{\sqrt{x}}(2 + \ln x)/2\sqrt{x}$

21. $x^{e^x-1}e^x(x \ln x + 1)$

23. 0

25. $2x(e^x)^x$

27. $3^{2x}/2 \ln 3 + C$

29. $a^x e^x/(1 + \ln a) + C$

31. $10^{x^3}/3 \ln 10 + C$

33. $10^{\ln x^2}/\ln 100 + C$

35. $2e^x3^{e^x}/\ln 6 + C$

39. $(4 \ln 2 + 1)x - (8 \ln 2 + 4)y + 4 = 0$

EXERCISES 12.7 (PAGE 428)

1. 11,300

3. 13.9

5. 5.13 per cent

7. 40

9. 42.1°

EXERCISES 13.1 (PAGE 435)

1. cosine and secant are even; others are odd
9. $3 \sin \theta - 4 \sin^3 \theta$
11. (a) $\sqrt{2}(\sqrt{3} - 1)/4$;
    (b) $\sqrt{2}(\sqrt{3} + 1)/4$; (c) $2 - \sqrt{3}$

13. (a) $\sqrt{2}(\sqrt{3} + 1)/4$;
    (b) $\sqrt{2}(\sqrt{3} - 1)/4$; (c) $2 + \sqrt{3}$
15. (a) $\sin \theta$; (b) $-\cos \theta$;
    (c) $-\sin \theta$; (d) $-\cos \theta$

EXERCISES 13.2 (PAGE 439)

1. 4
3. 0
5. 3/5

7. 1/2
9. 12

EXERCISES 13.3 (PAGE 443)

3. $6 \cos 2x$
5. $\cos 2x$
7. 0
9. $-\csc^2 r/2\sqrt{\cot r}$
11. $\sin x (1 + \sec^2 x)$
13. $\cot x$
15. $-3t^2 \csc (t^3 + 1) \cot (t^3 + 1)$
17. $(1 + 2 \cos x)/(2 + \cos x)^2$
19. $y^2(3 + \sin y)$
21. $-2 \cot x \times$
    $[2(1 + x^2)\csc^2 2x + x \cot 2x] \div$
    $(1 + x^2)^2$
23. $(\sin x)^x[\ln (\sin x) + x \cot x]$

25. $x^{\sin x-1}[\sin x + x \cos x (\ln x)]$
27. $(\sin x)^{\sin x} \cos x \times$
    $[1 + \ln (\sin x)]$
29. $\dfrac{\sin x\sqrt{1 + \cos^2 x}}{\tan^3 x}\left[\cot x - \right.$
    $\left. \dfrac{\sin x \cos x}{1 + \cos^2 x} - \dfrac{3}{\sin x \cos x} \right]$
31. $-3 \sin^2 x(5 \cos^2 x - 2 \cos x + 1)$
    $\div 2(1 - 3 \cos x)^{3/2}$
33. $\sin (x - y)/[\sin (x - y) - 1]$
35. $-(1 + y^{-2})$
37. $-y/x$

EXERCISES 13.4 (PAGE 447)

1. (a) no relative extrema;
   (b) $((2n - 1)\pi/2,0)$ where n is any integer, pts. of infl.;
   (c) -1
3. (a) $(n\pi,1)$ where n is an odd integer, rel. max.; $(n\pi,0)$ where n is an even integer, rel. min.;
   (b) $((2n - 1)\pi/2,1/2)$ where

   n is any integer, pts. of infl.;
   (c) 1/2 and $-1/2$
5. (a) $(n\pi,-2)$ where n is an odd integer, rel. max.; $(n\pi,0)$ where n is an even integer, rel. min.; (b) no pts. of infl.
15. $((1 + 4n)\pi/4,\sqrt{2}/2)$ where n is any integer; $109°30'$
17. $12x - 6\sqrt{3}y = 3\sqrt{3} + 8\pi$

EXERCISES 13.5 (PAGE 453)

1. $25\pi/36$ in.^{2}/sec
3. decreasing at rate of 1/48 radians/sec
5. $(x^{2/3} + y^{2/3})^{3/2}$ ft

7. $4a/3$
9. $5\sqrt{5}$ ft
11. k

EXERCISES 13.6 (PAGE 456)

1. $\ln |\sec 2x|/2 + C$
3. $-\cos 3x/3 + \sin 2x/2 + C$

5. $\ln |\sin (3x + 1)|/3 + C$
7. $-e^{\cos x} + C$

9. $\ln |\csc 5x^2 - \cot 5x^2|/10 + C$

11. $\cos (\cos x) + C$

13. $1/2$

15. $\ln 2/2$

17. $(\ln 3 - \ln 16)/12$

19. $3 \ln (\sqrt{2} + 1)/2$

23. 2

25. $2\sqrt{2}$

27. $\ln (2 + \sqrt{3})$

29. $\ln (2 + \sqrt{3})$

EXERCISES 13.7 (PAGE 460)

1. $\cos^3 x/3 - \cos x + C$

3. $3x/8 - \sin 2x/4 + \sin 4x/32 + C$

5. $(x + \sin x)/2 + C$

7. $\sin^3 x/3 - 2 \sin^5 x/5 + \sin^7 x/7 + C$

9. $t/8 - \sin 12t/96 + C$

11. $x/16 - \sin^3 x/24 - \sin 2x/32 + C$

13. $9x/2 + 4 \cos x - \sin 2x/4 + C$

15. $\frac{1}{2}\sqrt[3]{\sin^2 3x}(1 - \frac{1}{4}\sin^2 3x) + C$

17. $(4 \cos 2x - \cos 8x)/16 + C$

19. $(7 \sin x + \sin 7x)/14 + C$

21. $x - \sin 6x/12 + \sin 5x/5 - \sin 4x/8 - \sin x + C$

23. $2/3$

25. $3/8$

27. $5/9$

29. $(3\pi + 32)/32$

37. $\pi/2$

39. $5\pi^2/8$

EXERCISES 13.8 (PAGE 463)

1. $-\cot^2 x/2 - \ln |\sin x| + C$

3. $-\cot 6x/6 + C$

5. $\tan^9 x/9 + \tan^7 x/7 + C$

7. $-\cot^5 3x/15 - \cot^3 3x/9 + C$

9. $(\tan 3x - \cot 3x)/3 + C$

11. $x - 2 \tan \frac{1}{2}x + 2 \tan^3 \frac{1}{2}x/3 + C$

13. $-\cot^5 2t/10 + \cot^3 2t/6 - \cot 2t/2 - t + C$

15. $-\csc^3 x/3 + C$

17. $-2 \cot 2x + C$

19. $(1 - \ln 2)/2$

21. $56/15$

23. $848/105$

25. $1/5$

27. π

29. $(4 - \pi)/4$

31. $(\pi - 2)/2$

35. $(\cot^{n-1} x)/(1 - n) - \int \cot^{n-2} x \, dx$

EXERCISES 13.9 (PAGE 472)

1. (a) $-\pi/2$; (b) π; (c) $-\pi/4$; (d) $3\pi/4$; (e) π; (f) $-\pi/2$

3. (a) $2\sqrt{2}/3$; (b) $\sqrt{2}/4$; (c) $2\sqrt{2}$; (d) $3\sqrt{2}/4$; (e) 3

5. (a) $-2\sqrt{5}/5$; (b) $\sqrt{5}/5$; (c) $-1/2$; (d) $\sqrt{5}$; (e) $-\sqrt{5}/2$

7. (a) $\sqrt{3}$; (b) $\sqrt{21}/7$

9. (a) $\pi/2$; (b) $-\pi/4$; (c) π; (d) $3\pi/4$

11. $119/169$

13. $2(\sqrt{10} + 1)/9$

15. $(48 - 25\sqrt{3})/39$

17. $(4\sqrt{10} + \sqrt{5})/15$

EXERCISES 13.10 (PAGE 477)

3. $1/\sqrt{4 - x^2}$

5. $1/|t|\sqrt{25t^2 - 1}$

7. $4/(4 + x^2)$

9. $\sin^{-1} 2y + 2y/\sqrt{1 - 4y^2}$

11. $\csc^{-1} (1/x) + x/\sqrt{1 - x^2}$

13. $2\sqrt{4 - x^2}$

15. $(a - t)/\sqrt{a^2 - t^2}$

17. $-\cos x/|\cos x|$

19. 0

21. $\cot^{-1} x$

23. $-e^x - 1/\sqrt{1 - x^2}$

25. $(1 + y^2)(\sin y + 3x^2) \div [(1 - x \cos y)(1 + y^2)]$

27. $52\pi/3$ miles/min

29. 0.078 radians/sec

31. 8 ft/sec

EXERCISES 13.11 (PAGE 480)

7. $\tan^{-1} (x/5)/5 + C$

9. $\sin^{-1} (\sqrt{5}x/2)/\sqrt{5} + C$

11. $\sin^{-1} (3r^2/4)/6 + C$

13. $\tan^{-1} (e^x/\sqrt{7})/\sqrt{7} + C$

15. $2 \tan^{-1} \sqrt{x} + C$

17. $2 \tan^{-1} [(2x - 1)/\sqrt{7}]/\sqrt{7} + C$

19. $\sin^{-1} [(x - 1)/4] + C$

21. $-\sqrt{3 - 2x - x^2} -$
$\sin^{-1} \frac{1}{2}(x + 1) + C$

23. $\sin^{-1} [(x + 1)/\sqrt{5}] -$

$\sqrt{4 - 2x - x^2} + C$

25. $x^2/2 + 5 \ln |2x^2 - 4x + 3|/4 -$
$\sqrt{2} \tan^{-1} \sqrt{2}(x - 1)/4 + 2x + C$

27. $\pi/4$

29. $\frac{1}{2} \ln 2 + \frac{1}{4}\pi$

31. $\pi/3$

33. $2\pi/3 + \sqrt{3} - 2$

35. $\pi/4$

37. π

39. $4 \ln 2/\pi$

EXERCISES 14.2 (PAGE 487)

1. $x(\ln x - 1) + C$

3. $x \tan x + \ln |\cos x| + C$

5. $x \sin^{-1} x + \sqrt{1 - x^2} + C$

7. $\frac{1}{2}(x^2 + 1) \tan^{-1} x - \frac{1}{2}x + C$

9. $\frac{1}{2}e^x(\sin x + \cos x) + C$

11. $-x^2\sqrt{1 - x^2} -$
$2(1 - x^2)^{3/2}/3 + C$

13. $x(\ln x)^2 - 2x \ln x + 2x + C$

15. $\sec^3 x \tan x/4 + 3(\sec x \tan x$

$+ \ln |\sec x + \tan x|)/8 + C$

17. $9/16$

19. $(3e^4 + 1)/4$

21. $8/25$

23. $(4\pi - 3\sqrt{3})/3$

25. $e^2 + 1$

27. $\pi(3e^4 + 1)/2$

29. $(\pi/2, \pi/8)$

31. $\pi^4/6 - \pi^2/4$

EXERCISES 14.3 (PAGE 492)

1. $-\sqrt{4 - x^2}/4x + C$

3. $-\sqrt{9 - x^2}/x - \sin^{-1} (x/3) + C$

5. $\ln |x|/5 - \ln (5 + \sqrt{25 - x^2})/5 + C$

7. $\frac{1}{2} \sin^{-1} u + \frac{1}{2}u\sqrt{1 - u^2} + C$

9. $-\frac{1}{4}x(16 - x^2)^{3/2} +$
$2x\sqrt{16 - x^2} + 32 \sin^{-1} \frac{1}{4}x + C$

11. $-x/9\sqrt{4x^2 - 9} + C$

13. $\ln |x + 2 + \sqrt{4x + x^2}| + C$

15. $(x + 2)/9\sqrt{5 - 4x - x^2} + C$

17. $\tan x/4\sqrt{4 - \tan^2 x} + C$

19. $88/3$

21. $(6 - 2\sqrt{3})/27$

23. $(3 \sec^{-1} 3 - \pi)/6$

25. $75\pi/16$

27. $\pi/8$

29. $(3/2)[\sqrt{65} - \sqrt{17} +$
$\ln (\sqrt{65} - 1) +$
$\ln (\sqrt{17} + 1) - 10 \ln 2]$

31. $2\pi[4 - 3 \sec^{-1} (5/3)] \approx 7.70$

33. $M_{xz} = 8\pi/25 + \ln (3/5) \approx 0.495;$
centroid: $(0,0.064,0)$

EXERCISES 14.4 (PAGE 498)

1. $\frac{1}{4} \ln \left|\dfrac{x - 2}{x + 2}\right| + C$

3. $\ln |C(x - 2)^2(x + 2)^3|$

5. $\frac{1}{4} \ln |Cx^4(2x + 1)^3/(2x - 1)|$

7. $\dfrac{1}{9} \ln \left|\dfrac{x + 3}{x}\right| - \dfrac{1}{3x} + C$

9. $-1/2(x + 2)^2 + C$

11. $\frac{1}{2} \ln |C(x + 1)^2/(2x + 3)| +$
$3/(x + 1)$

13. $\frac{1}{2}x^2 + 2x - 3/(x - 1) -$
$\ln |x^2 + 2x - 3| + C$

15. $-\ln |(x - 1)^2(3x + 2)^{2/3}| -$
$3/(x - 1) - 1/3(3x + 2) + C$

17. $4 \ln (4/3) - 3/2$

19. $\ln (27/4) - 2$

21. $13 \ln 2 - 4 \ln 5$

23. $\ln (7/2) - 5/3$

25. $\ln 4.5$

27. $2\pi(6 \ln 3 - 2 \ln 2 + 2)$

29. $4\pi/9$

31. $\ln (9/2)$ ft

EXERCISES 14.5 (PAGE 504)

1. $\frac{1}{2}\ln|Cx^2/(2x^2+1)|$

3. $(1/8)\ln|C(2x-1)/(2x+1)|$ $-(1/4)\ \tan^{-1}2x$

5. $\ln|x-1|+\tan^{-1}x+C$

7. $\frac{1}{2}\ln|Cx^2/(x^2+x+1)|$

9. $\ln[x^2/(x^2+1)]-\frac{1}{2}\tan^{-1}x-$ $x/2(x^2+1)+C$

11. $\dfrac{1}{162}\ln\left|\dfrac{(9x^2+3x+1)^5}{(3x-1)^4}\right|$ $+\dfrac{5\sqrt{3}}{27}\tan^{-1}\left(\dfrac{6x+1}{\sqrt{3}}\right)+C$

13. $x/(4x^2+9)+$ $\tan^{-1}(2x/3)/6+C$

15. $\ln|\tan x+1|+(2/\sqrt{3})$ $\tan^{-1}[(2\tan x-1)/\sqrt{3}]+C$

17. $3\ln 4$

19. $\ln(12/5)+3\ln(20/13)/2$

21. $\pi/4$

23. $3(\ln 2)/4+5\pi/8$

25. $(\ln 2+\pi)/3$

27. $(\sqrt{3}\pi-3\ln 2)/18$

EXERCISES 14.6 (PAGE 506)

1. $\frac{2}{3}\tan^{-1}\left(\frac{1}{3}\tan\frac{x}{2}\right)+C$

3. $-\ln|1-\tan(x/2)|+C$

5. $\frac{1}{2}\ln|\tan(x/2)|-\frac{1}{4}\tan^2(x/2)$ $+C$

7. $\dfrac{x}{3}-\dfrac{5}{6}\tan^{-1}\left(2\tan\dfrac{x}{2}\right)+C$

9. $2\tan^{-1}\left(\tan\frac{x}{2}\right)+$

$\frac{4}{3}\ln\left|\left(\tan\frac{x}{2}-3\right)\Big/\left(\tan\frac{x}{2}+3\right)\right|$ $+C$

11. $2\tan^{-1}\left(2+\tan\frac{x}{2}\right)+C$

13. $\frac{1}{4}\ln 3$

15. $2\sqrt{3}\ln(1+\sqrt{3})$

17. $\dfrac{\sqrt{3}}{2}\ln\left(1+\dfrac{\sqrt{3}}{2}\right)$

EXERCISES 14.7 (PAGE 509)

1. $2x^{3/2}/3-3x+18\sqrt{x}-$ $54\ln(3+\sqrt{x})+C$

3. $\ln|(\sqrt{1+4x}-1)\div$ $(\sqrt{1+4x}+1)|+C$

5. $2\sqrt{2}\ln|(\sqrt{1+x}+\sqrt{2})/(1-x)|$ $-\sqrt{2}\sqrt{1+x}+C$

7. $3(x-2)^{2/3}/2-3(x-2)^{1/3}+$ $3\ln|1+\sqrt[3]{x-2}|+C$

9. $2\sqrt{x+4}+2\sqrt{2x}+$ $4\sqrt{2}\ln|(\sqrt{x}-2\sqrt{x+4}+4\sqrt{2})$ $\div(x-4)|+C$

11. $3\tan^{-1}\sqrt[6]{x}+3\sqrt[6]{x}/(1+\sqrt[3]{x})+$ C

13. $2\tan^{-1}(x+\sqrt{x^2+2x-1})+C$

15. $-\frac{1}{2}\sin^{-1}[(2-x)/\sqrt{2}x]+C$

17. $4-2\ln 3$

19. $\ln(11/10)$

21. $(54-2\sqrt[3]{3})/9$

EXERCISES 14.8 (PAGE 510)

1. $x/8-\sin 16x/128+C$

3. $2\sqrt{4-e^x}+C$

5. $(x+1)\tan^{-1}\sqrt{x}-\sqrt{x}+C$

7. $x/2+3\sin(2x/3)/4+C$

9. $\ln|x-1|-2/(x-1)-$ $1/(x-1)^2+C$

11. $\cos x\sin 3x/8-$ $3\sin x\cos 3x/8+C$

13. $3\ln|x^{1/3}/(1+x^{1/3})|+C$

15. $\tan 3x/3-\cot 3x/3+$ $2\ln|\csc 6x-\cot 6x|/3+C$

17. $2\ln t-3/(t+2)+C$

19. $x+\frac{1}{2}\ln|(x+1)(x^2+1)^2\div$ $(x-1)|+C$

21. $x/16-\sin 12x/192-$ $\sin^3 6x/144+C$

23. $\sin^{-1}[(r+2)/\sqrt{7}]+C$

25. $\dfrac{x^{n+1}}{n+1}\left(\ln x-\dfrac{1}{n+1}\right)+C$

27. $2e^{t/2}(4\sin 2t+\cos 2t)/17+C$

29. $\frac{1}{4}\tan^{-1}(\frac{1}{2}\sin^2 x)+C$

31. $-\cos x/n+2\cos^3 x/3n-$ $\cos^5 x/5n+C$

33. $(1/8)[-2 \csc^3 \theta \cot \theta - 3 \csc \theta \cot \theta + 3 \ln |\csc \theta - \cot \theta|] + C$

35. $2 \ln |y - 2| - 8/(y - 2) - 9/2(y - 2)^2 + C$

37. $-\tan^{-1} (\cos x) + C$

39. $\frac{1}{2}(t - 2)\sqrt{4t - t^2} + 2 \sin^{-1} \frac{1}{2}(t - 2) + C$

41. $\ln \left| \dfrac{x^3 - x^2 + x}{(x + 1)^2} \right| + \dfrac{2}{\sqrt{3}} \tan^{-1} \left(\dfrac{2x - 1}{\sqrt{3}} \right) + C$

43. $\frac{1}{3} \sin^{-1} (3e^x/2) + C$

45. $-\cot^5 3x/15 - \cot^3 3x/9 + C$

47. $(x^3 \sin^{-1} x)/3 + (x^2 + 2)\sqrt{1 - x^2} \div 9 + C$

49. $\tan^{-1} (\cos x) + C$

51. $2 \sec^{-1} |2 \sin 3t|/3 + C$

53. $-(x^2 + a^2)^{3/2}/3a^2x^3 + C$

55. $\sqrt{2t} - \sqrt{1 - 2t} \sin^{-1} \sqrt{2t} + C$

57. $4\sqrt{2 + \sqrt{x - 1}}(\sqrt{x - 1} - 4)/3 + C$

59. $\dfrac{\sqrt{2}}{4} \ln \left| \dfrac{\tan x - \sqrt{2 \tan x} + 1}{\tan x + \sqrt{2 \tan x} + 1} \right| + \dfrac{\sqrt{2}}{2} \tan^{-1} (\sqrt{2 \tan x} - 1) + \dfrac{\sqrt{2}}{2} \tan^{-1} (\sqrt{2 \tan x} + 1) + C$

61. 4

63. $2 \ln (6/5) + 1/2$

65. $8(2 - \sqrt{2})/3$

67. $4\sqrt{3}/3 - \pi/2$

69. $256/15$

71. $(2 - \ln 2)/4$

73. $(4\pi - 9\sqrt{3})a^2/8$

75. $[\ln (9/2) - \pi/3]/2$

77. 5

79. $\ln (3/2) + 1/6$

81. $4/3$

83. $2 - \frac{1}{2} \ln 3$

85. $\pi/24$

87. π

89. $(\ln 3 - \ln 2)/5$

EXERCISES 15.2 (PAGE 517)

1. approx: 0.696; exact: $\ln 2 \approx 0.693$

3. approx: 4.500; exact: 4

5. approx: 0.880; exact: $\ln (1 + \sqrt{2}) \approx 0.881$

7. approx: 1.954; exact: 2

9. 0.248

11. 1.545

13. 3.694

15. $-1/150 \leq \epsilon_T \leq -1/1,200$

17. $-1/2 \leq \epsilon_T \leq 0$

19. $-e/50 \leq \epsilon_T \leq -1/150$

21. 2.717

EXERCISES 15.3 (PAGE 524)

1. by Simpson's rule: $8/3$; exact: $8/3$

3. by Simpson's rule: 0.881; exact: $\ln (1 + \sqrt{2}) \approx 0.881$

5. by Simpson's rule: 0.6045; exact: $\pi\sqrt{3}/9 \approx 0.6046$

7. $\epsilon_S = 0$

9. $-\pi^5/233,280 \leq \epsilon_S \leq 0$

11. 0.237

13. 0.836

15. 1.359

17. $\pi r^2 h$

19. $\pi h_1(r_1{}^2 + r_2{}^2 + r_1 r_2)/3$

21. (a) -0.0962; (b) -0.0950; (c) -0.0991

EXERCISES 16.1 (PAGE 532)

1. (a) $(-4, 5\pi/4)$; (b) $(4, -7\pi/4)$; (c) $(-4, -3\pi/4)$

3. (a) $(-2, 3\pi/2)$; (b) $(2, -3\pi/2)$; (c) $(-2, -\pi/2)$

5. (a) $(-\sqrt{2}, 3\pi/4)$; (b) $(\sqrt{2}, -\pi/4)$; (c) $(-\sqrt{2}, -5\pi/4)$

7. $(3, 4\pi/3)$; $(-3, \pi/3)$

9. $(-4, 7\pi/6)$; $(4, 11\pi/6)$

11. $(-2,3\pi/4)$; $(2,7\pi/4)$

13. (a) $(-3,0)$; (b) $(-1,-1)$;
    (c) $(2,-2\sqrt{3})$; (d) $(0,2)$;
    (e) $(-\sqrt{2},\sqrt{2})$; (f) $(\sqrt{3}/2,-1/2)$

15. $r = a$

17. $r = 2/(1 - \cos\theta)$

19. $r^2 = 4\cos 2\theta$

21. $r = 9\cos\theta - 8\sin\theta$

23. $(x^2 + y^2)^2 = 4xy$

25. $(x^2 + y^2)^3 = x^2$

27. $(x^2 + y^2)^2 = 4(x^2 - y^2)$

29. $4x^4 + 8x^2y^2 + 4y^4 + 36x^3 + 36xy^2 - 81y^2 = 0$

EXERCISES 16.3 (PAGE 542)

41. $\theta = 2\pi/3$; $\theta = 5\pi/3$

43. $\theta = \pi/4$; $\theta = 3\pi/4$

45. $\theta = \pi/4$; $\theta = 3\pi/4$

47. -1

49. $r = \pi^2/(\sin\theta - \pi\cos\theta)$

EXERCISES 16.4 (PAGE 547)

1. $(3/2,\pi/6)$, $(3/2,5\pi/6)$

3. $(\sqrt{2},\pi/4)$, pole

5. $(\pi/2,\pi/8)$

7. $(-1/2,\pi/3)$, $(-1,\pi/2)$,
   $(-1,3\pi/2)$, $(-1/2,11\pi/6)$, pole

9. $(\sqrt{15},75°31')$, $(-\sqrt{15},284°29')$,

pole

11. $(6,\pi/6)$, $(6,5\pi/6)$, $(2,7\pi/6)$,
    $(2,11\pi/6)$

13. $(\sqrt{2}/2,\pi/6)$, $(\sqrt{2}/2,\pi/2)$,
    $(\sqrt{2}/2,5\pi/6)$, $(\sqrt{2}/2,7\pi/6)$,
    $(\sqrt{2}/2,3\pi/2)$, $(\sqrt{2}/2,11\pi/6)$, pole

EXERCISES 16.5 (PAGE 551)

1. $3\pi/4$

3. $153°26'$

5. $38°9'$

7. $5\pi/6$

9. $\pi/2$

11. $2\pi/3$

13. $0, \pi/2$

15. $0, 79°6'$

EXERCISES 16.6 (PAGE 556)

1. $9\pi/4$

3. 4π

5. 4

7. $9\pi/8$

9. $11\pi/4 - 11\sin^{-1}(1/3)/2 - 3\sqrt{2}$

11. $19\pi/3 - 11\sqrt{3}/2$

13. $9(\pi - 2)/2$

15. $(8 - \pi)a^2/4$

17. $(\pi + 1)/2$

19. 4 square units

EXERCISES 17.1 (PAGE 562)

3. $e = 1$: $y = 0$; $e < 1$: $x^2/a^2 + y^2/b^2 = 1$; $e > 1$: $x^2/a^2 - y^2/b^2 = 1$

EXERCISES 17.2 (PAGE 567)

5. (a) 1; (b) parabola;
   (c) $r\cos\theta = -2$

7. (a) 1/2; (b) ellipse;
   (c) $r\sin\theta = 5$

9. (a) 2/3; (b) ellipse;
   (c) $r\cos\theta = -3$

11. (a) 6/5; (b) hyperbola;
    (c) $2r\sin\theta = -3$

13. (a) 2/7; (b) ellipse;
    (c) $r\sin\theta = -5$

15. $r = 4/(1 - \sin\theta)$

17. $r = 3/(1 + 2\sin\theta)$

19. $r = 4/(2 + \cos\theta)$,
    $r = 12/(2 - \cos\theta)$

21. $16\sqrt{3}\pi/3$

25. $r^2 = a^2(1 - e^2)/(1 - e^2\cos^2\theta)$

EXERCISES 17.3 (PAGE 575)

1. vertices: $(-3,0)$, $(3,0)$;
   foci: $(-\sqrt{5},0)$, $(\sqrt{5},0)$;
   directrices: $x = \pm 9/\sqrt{5}$; $e = \sqrt{5}/3$; extremities of minor
   axis: $(0,-2)$, $(0,2)$

3. vertices: $(-3,0)$, $(3,0)$;
   foci: $(-\sqrt{3},0)$, $(\sqrt{3},0)$;
   directrices: $x = \pm 3\sqrt{3}$; $e = \sqrt{3}/3$; extremeties of minor
   axis: $(0,-\sqrt{6})$, $(0,\sqrt{6})$

5. vertices: $(-2,0)$, $(2,0)$;
   foci: $(-\sqrt{13},0)$, $(\sqrt{13},0)$;
   directrices: $x = \pm 4/\sqrt{13}$; $e =$

$\sqrt{13}/2$; $2a = 4$; $2b = 6$

7. vertices: $(-1/3,0)$, $(1/3,0)$;
   foci: $(-5/12,0)$, $(5/12,0)$;
   directrices: $x = \pm 4/15$; $e = 5/4$; $2a = 2/3$; $2b = 1/2$

9. $9x^2 - 4y^2 = 36$

11. $16x^2 + 25y^2 = 100$

13. $32x^2 - 33y^2 = 380$

15. $2x + 3y - 12 = 0$

17. $7x^2 - 4y^2 = 28$

19. $24\sqrt{3}$ ft

23. 535.9 in.³

25. $4\sqrt{3}\pi ab$

EXERCISES 17.4 (PAGE 585)

1. $e = \sqrt{3}/3$; center: $(2,3)$;
   foci: $(2 \pm \sqrt{3},3)$;
   directrices: $x = 2 \pm 3\sqrt{3}$

3. $e = \sqrt{10}/5$; center: $(0,1/2)$;
   foci: $(0, (5 \pm \sqrt{170})/10)$;
   directrices: $y = (2 \pm \sqrt{170})/4$

5. point-circle: $(-5/2,4)$

7. $e = \sqrt{3}$; center: $(-3,-1)$;
   foci: $(-3, (-3 \pm 2\sqrt{6})/3)$;
   directrices: $y = (-9 \pm 2\sqrt{6})/9$

9. $e = \sqrt{7}/2$; center: $(-1,4)$;

foci: $(-1,-3)$, $(-1,11)$;
directrices: $y = 0$, $y = 8$

11. $e = \sqrt{13}/3$; center: $(1,-2)$;
    foci: $(1, -2 \pm \sqrt{13})$;
    directrices: $y = (-26 \pm 9\sqrt{13})/13$

13. $3x^2 + 4y^2 = 300$

15. $(x - 4)^2/25 + (y + 2)^2/9 = 1$

17. $(y - 3)^2/64 - (x + 1)^2/48 = 1$

19. $25x^2 - 144y^2 = 14{,}400$

21. $(y + 1)^2/144 - (x + 2)^2/81 = 1$

23. $9(x + 3)^2 - 4(y - 1)^2 = 324$

EXERCISES 17.5 (PAGE 592)

3. $16\bar{y}^2 - 9\bar{x}^2 = 36$

5. $\bar{y}^2 - \bar{x}^2 = 16$

7. $9\bar{x}^2 + 4\bar{y}^2 = 36$

9. $3\bar{x}'^2 + \bar{y}'^2 = 18$

11. $\bar{x}'^2 + 4\bar{y}'^2 = 16$

13. $\bar{x}'^2 - 4\bar{y}'^2 = 16$

EXERCISES 18.2 (PAGE 599)

1. $|\mathbf{A}| = 5$

3. $|\mathbf{A}| = 2$

5. $|\mathbf{A}| = \sqrt{11}$

7. $(3,9)$

9. $(3,0)$

11. $(1/6,-1/6)$

13. $\langle 2,-3 \rangle$

15. $\langle -2,-7 \rangle$

17. $\langle 5,6 \rangle$

19. $(-4,3)$

21. $(12,-5)$

EXERCISES 18.3 (PAGE 607)

1. $\langle -1,9 \rangle$

3. $\langle 1,-5 \rangle$

5. $\langle -2,2 \rangle$

7. $\langle 7,3 \rangle$

9. $\langle -9,-4 \rangle$

11. $\langle \sqrt{2},\sqrt{3} \rangle$

15. $\langle 1,-2 \rangle$

21. $\langle -2,7 \rangle$

23. $\sqrt{74}$
25. $\sqrt{229}$
27. $-2\mathbf{i} + 4\mathbf{j}$
29. $\sqrt{221}$
31. $\sqrt{13} + \sqrt{17}$
33. $3\sqrt{13} - 2\sqrt{17}$

35. $(5/\sqrt{41})\mathbf{i} + (4/\sqrt{41})\mathbf{j}$
37. $h = 2, k = 3$
39. (a) $(1/\sqrt{2})\mathbf{i} - (1/\sqrt{2})\mathbf{j}$;
   (b) $(-1/2)\mathbf{i} + (\sqrt{3}/2)\mathbf{j}$;
   (c) $-\mathbf{i}$; (d) $\mathbf{j}$

EXERCISES 18.4 (PAGE 615)

1. 10
3. -1
11. $\sqrt{2}/10$
13. $-16/65$

15. $10, -2/5$
17. $-4/3$
19. $(-240 + \sqrt{85{,}683})/407$

EXERCISES 18.5 (PAGE 622)

1. $(-\infty, 0)$ and $(0,4]$
3. $[-1,1]$
5. all real numbers not in $(-4,3)$
7. $4t/3$; $4/9$
9. b/a; 0
11. $(\ln t + 1)/te^t(2 + t)$;
   $[2 + t - (\ln t + 1) \times$
   $(2 + 4t + t^2)]/t^3 e^{2t}(2 + t)^3$

13. $y^2 - x - 2y + 1 = 0, x \geq 0$
15. $xy = 1, x > 0$ and $y > 0$
17. $y = 1, x = -1$
19. $5\sqrt{3}x + 2y = 20$
21. $dy/dx = 0$; $d^2y/dx^2 = -1/4a$: $d^3y/dx^3 = 0$
23. $x^{2/3} + y^{2/3} = a^{2/3}$

EXERCISES 18.6 (PAGE 626)

1. $4\mathbf{j}$
3. $2\mathbf{i}$
5. $2t\mathbf{i} + 2\mathbf{j}$; $2\mathbf{i}$
7. $2e^{2t}\mathbf{i} + (1/t)\mathbf{j}$; $4e^{2t}\mathbf{i} - (1/t^2)\mathbf{j}$
9. $[1/(t^2 + 1)]\mathbf{i} + 2^t \ln 2\mathbf{j}$;
   $[-2t/(t^2 + 1)^2]\mathbf{i} + 2^t(\ln 2)^2\mathbf{j}$
11. $(2t - 3)/\sqrt{2t^2 - 6t + 5}$
13. $20t$
15. $8 \sin 4t$
19. $x^2 + y^2 = 1$; 0

EXERCISES 18.7 (PAGE 634)

1. $(1/\sqrt{2}) \ln (1 + \sqrt{2}) + 1$
3. $2[(40)^{3/2} - (13)^{3/2}]/27$
5. $6a$
7. $8a$
9. πa

11. 12
13. $\frac{1}{2}a[2\pi\sqrt{4\pi^2 + 1} +$ $\ln (\sqrt{4\pi^2 + 1} + 2\pi)] \approx 21.3a$
15. $\frac{1}{2}a[\theta_1 - 3 \sin (2\theta_1/3)]$

EXERCISES 18.8 (PAGE 638)

1. (a) $2t\mathbf{i} + \mathbf{j}$; (b) $2\mathbf{i}$;
   (c) $\sqrt{37}$; (d) 2
3. (a) $\mathbf{i} + \tan t\mathbf{j}$; (b) $\sec^2 t\mathbf{j}$;
   (c) $\sqrt{2}$; (d) 2
5. (a) $\cos t\mathbf{i} + \sec^2 t\mathbf{j}$;
   (b) $-\sin t\mathbf{i} + 2 \sec^2 t \tan t\mathbf{j}$;

   (c) $\sqrt{91}/6$; (d) $\sqrt{849}/18$
7. (a) $2\mathbf{i} + 6\mathbf{j}$; (b) $2\mathbf{j}$;
   (c) $2\sqrt{10}$; (d) 2
9. (a) $3\mathbf{j}$; (b) $4\mathbf{i}$; (c) 3; (d) 4
11. (a) $\mathbf{i} + \sqrt{3}\mathbf{j}$; (b) $-\sqrt{3}\mathbf{i} + \mathbf{j}$;
   (c) 2; (d) 2

EXERCISES 18.9 (PAGE 640)

1. $\ln| \sec t|\mathbf{i} - \ln| t|\mathbf{j} + \mathbf{C}$
3. $\frac{1}{4}(2t - \sin 2t)\mathbf{i} +$ $\frac{1}{2}(2t + \sin 2t)\mathbf{j} + \mathbf{C}$

5. $(t \ln |t| - t)\mathbf{i} + (t^3/3)\mathbf{j} + \mathbf{C}$
7. $[(2t - 3)/(t - 1)]\mathbf{i} +$ $\frac{1}{2}(4 - 2t - t^2)\mathbf{j}$

EXERCISES 18.10 (PAGE 644)

1. range: 36.7 miles; max. ht.: 48,500 ft; velocity at impact: $1{,}250\sqrt{2}\mathbf{i} - 1{,}250\sqrt{2}\mathbf{j}$
3. 6 sec; $4{,}800\sqrt{3}$ ft $\approx 8{,}313.6$ ft

5. yes; $40°8'$
7. $v_0^2 \sin^2 \alpha/2g$
9. 283 ft/sec.

EXERCISES 18.11 (PAGE 650)

1. $\mathbf{T}(t) = \dfrac{t^2 - 1}{t^2 + 1}\mathbf{i} + \dfrac{2t}{t^2 + 1}\mathbf{j};$

   $\mathbf{N}(t) = \dfrac{2t}{t^2 + 1}\mathbf{i} + \dfrac{1 - t^2}{t^2 + 1}\mathbf{j}$

3. $\mathbf{T}(t) = \dfrac{e^{2t}}{\sqrt{e^{4t} + 1}}\mathbf{i} + \dfrac{1}{\sqrt{e^{4t} + 1}}\mathbf{j};$

   $\mathbf{N}(t) = \dfrac{1}{\sqrt{e^{4t} + 1}}\mathbf{i} - \dfrac{e^{2t}}{\sqrt{e^{4t} + 1}}\mathbf{j}$

5. $\mathbf{T}(t) = -\sin kt\,\mathbf{i} + \cos kt\,\mathbf{j};$
   $\mathbf{N}(t) = -\cos kt\,\mathbf{i} - \sin kt\,\mathbf{j}$

7. $\mathbf{T}(t) = -(1+ \cot^4 t)^{-1/2}\mathbf{i}+(1+ \tan^4 t)^{-1/2}\mathbf{j}$

   $\mathbf{N}(t) = \dfrac{\cos^2 t}{\sqrt{\sin^4 t + \cos^4 t}}\mathbf{i} - \dfrac{\sin^2 t}{\sqrt{\sin^4 t + \cos^4 t}}\mathbf{j}$

9. $\cos^{-1}(27/5\sqrt{37})$
13. $x = 2 + \cos s,\ y = 3 + \sin s$
15. $x = a(1 - s)^{3/2},\ y = as^{3/2}$

EXERCISES 18.12 (PAGE 661)

1. $K = \sqrt{2}/8$
3. $K = \sqrt{2}/4$
5. $K(t) = 4(1 - t^2)^4 \div |1 - t|[(1 - t)^4 + (1 + t)^4]^{3/2};$
   $K(0) = \sqrt{2}$
7. $K = 1/2$
9. $K = \sqrt{2}/4$
11. $K = 4\sqrt{7}/49$
13. $(2 - x^2)^{3/2}/|x|$
15. $2(x + y)^{3/2}/a^{1/2}$

17. $4a\,|\sin \tfrac{1}{2}t|$
19. $(3,9)$
21. $(-3,-1)$
25. $K = 23\sqrt{7}/98$
27. $K = 1/16a$
29. $K = 2;\ (x_c,y_c) = (0,-1/2)$
31. $K = \sqrt{2}/4;\ (x_c,y_c) = (3,-2)$
33. $((3y^2 + 8p^2)/4p,\ -y^3/4p^2)$
35. $((a^2 - b^2)\cos^3 t/a,\ (b^2 - a^2) \times \sin^3 t/b)$

EXERCISES 18.13 (PAGE 665)

1. $\mathbf{V}(t) = 2\mathbf{i} + 2t\mathbf{j};\ \mathbf{A}(t) = 2\mathbf{j};$

   $\mathbf{T}(t) = \dfrac{1}{\sqrt{1 + t^2}}\mathbf{i} + \dfrac{t}{\sqrt{1 + t^2}}\mathbf{j};$

   $\mathbf{N}(t) = \dfrac{-t}{\sqrt{t^2 + 1}}\mathbf{i} + \dfrac{1}{\sqrt{t^2 + 1}}\mathbf{j};$

   $|\mathbf{V}(t)| = 2\sqrt{1 + t^2};$

   $A_T = \dfrac{2t}{\sqrt{1 + t^2}};\ A_N = \dfrac{2}{\sqrt{1 + t^2}};$

   $K(t) = \dfrac{1}{2(1 + t^2)^{3/2}}$

3. $\mathbf{V}(t) = -15 \sin 3t\,\mathbf{i} + 15 \cos 3t\,\mathbf{j};$
   $\mathbf{A}(t) = -45 \cos 3t\,\mathbf{i} - 45 \sin 3t\,\mathbf{j};$
   $\mathbf{T}(t) = -\sin 3t\,\mathbf{i} + \cos 3t\,\mathbf{j};$
   $\mathbf{N}(t) = -\cos 3t\,\mathbf{i} - \sin 3t\,\mathbf{j};$
   $|\mathbf{V}(t)| = 15;\ A_T = 0;\ A_N = 45;$
   $K(t) = 1/5$

5. $\mathbf{V}(t) = e^t\mathbf{i} - e^{-t}\mathbf{j};$
   $\mathbf{A}(t) = e^t\mathbf{i} + e^{-t}\mathbf{j};\ \mathbf{T}(t) = \dfrac{e^{2t}}{\sqrt{e^{4t} + 1}}\mathbf{i} - \dfrac{1}{\sqrt{e^{4t} + 1}}\mathbf{j};$

   $\mathbf{N}(t) = \dfrac{1}{\sqrt{e^{4t} + 1}}\mathbf{i} + \dfrac{e^{2t}}{\sqrt{e^{4t} + 1}}\mathbf{j};$

   $|\mathbf{V}(t)| = \sqrt{e^{4t} + 1}/e^t;\ A_T = (e^{4t} - 1)/e^t\sqrt{e^{4t} + 1};$
   $A_N = 2e^t/\sqrt{e^{4t} + 1};$
   $K(t) = 2e^{3t}/(e^{4t} + 1)^{3/2}$

7. if k = constant speed, $\mathbf{V} = \dfrac{k}{\sqrt{2}}\mathbf{i} + \dfrac{k}{\sqrt{2}}\mathbf{j},\ \mathbf{A} = \dfrac{k^2}{16}\mathbf{i} - \dfrac{k^2}{16}\mathbf{j},$

   $\mathbf{T} = \dfrac{1}{\sqrt{2}}\mathbf{i} + \dfrac{1}{\sqrt{2}}\mathbf{j},$

   $\mathbf{N} = \dfrac{1}{\sqrt{2}}\mathbf{i} - \dfrac{1}{\sqrt{2}}\mathbf{j},$

   $A_T = 0,\ A_N = k^2\sqrt{2}/16$

EXERCISES 19.1 (PAGE 673)

25. $\dfrac{4}{5}\operatorname{sech}^2 \dfrac{4x + 1}{5}$

27. $e^r \sinh (e^r)$

29. $e^x(\cosh x + \sinh x)$

31. $2 \operatorname{sech} 2t$

33. $2x \operatorname{sech} x^2$

35. $x^{\sinh x - 1}(x \cosh x \ln x + \sinh x)$

41. $\sinh^5 x/5 + \sinh^7 x/7 + C$

43. $\ln^2 \cosh x + C$

45. $3x/8 + \sinh 2x/4 + \sinh 4x/32 + C$

47. $\tanh 3x/3 - \tanh^3 3x/9 + C$

49. $\tfrac{1}{2} \sin x \cosh x - \tfrac{1}{2} \cos x \sinh x + C$

51. $\tfrac{1}{3} \cosh^3 2 - \cosh 2 + 2/3$

53. $\ln \cosh 1$

61. $\bar{x} = (\cosh 1 - \sinh 1) \div (\cosh 1 - 1), \bar{y} = (\sinh 2 - 2) \div 8(\cosh 1 - 1)$

63. $a^2 \sinh (x_1/a)$

65. $\tfrac{1}{4}\pi a^2(a \sinh (2x_1/a) + 2x_1)$

EXERCISES 19.2 (PAGE 682)

17. $\ln [(1 + \sqrt{17})/4]$

19. $\tfrac{1}{2} \ln 3$

21. $2x/\sqrt{x^4 + 1}$

23. $4/(1 - 16x^2)$

25. $-1/(3x^2 + 2x)$

27. $2x \cosh^{-1} x^2 + 2x^3/\sqrt{x^4 - 1}$

29. $|\sec x|$

31. $-\csc x \cot x/|\cot x|$

33. $\sinh^{-1} x$

35. $\sinh^{-1} \tfrac{1}{2}x + C = \ln \tfrac{1}{2}(x + \sqrt{x^2 + 4}) + C$

37. $\tfrac{1}{2} \cosh^{-1} x^2 + C = \tfrac{1}{2} \ln (x^2 + \sqrt{x^4 - 1}) + C$

39. $\begin{cases} -(1/12) \tanh^{-1} (3x/4) + C \text{ if } |x| < 4/3 \\ -(1/12) \coth^{-1} (3x/4) + C \text{ if } |x| > 4/3 \end{cases} = \dfrac{1}{24} \ln \left|\dfrac{4 - 3x}{4 + 3x}\right| + C$

41. $\sinh^{-1} (\sin x/\sqrt{3}) + C = \ln (\sin x + \sqrt{4 - \cos^2 x}) - \tfrac{1}{2} \ln 3 + C$

43. $\begin{cases} \dfrac{1}{\sqrt{6}} \tanh^{-1} \dfrac{x + 2}{\sqrt{6}} + C \text{ if } |x + 2| < \sqrt{6} \\ \dfrac{1}{\sqrt{6}} \coth^{-1} \dfrac{x + 2}{\sqrt{6}} + C \text{ if } |x + 2| > \sqrt{6} \end{cases} = \dfrac{1}{2\sqrt{6}} \ln \left|\dfrac{\sqrt{6} + 2 + x}{\sqrt{6} - 2 - x}\right| + C$

45. $\ln \left(\dfrac{5 + \sqrt{21}}{3 + \sqrt{5}}\right)$

47. $\ln 3$

49. $\tfrac{1}{3} \ln \left(\dfrac{7 + \sqrt{40}}{4 + \sqrt{7}}\right)$

EXERCISES 20.2 (PAGE 695)

1. 1

3. 0

5. 2

7. 0

9. ∞

11. $\ln (2/3)$

13. $1/6$

15. 1

17. 2

19. 0

21. $+\infty$

23. $3/5$

25. 1

27. -1

EXERCISES 20.3 (PAGE 698)

1. $1/2$

3. $1/2$

5. 1

7. $1/2$

9. 1

11. $1/3$

13. e^a

15. e^2

17. $e^{-1/3}$

19. 0

EXERCISES 20.4 (PAGE 702)

1. 1
3. 1
5. 2
7. divergent

9. 1
11. divergent
13. $\pi/2$
15. $\pi/2$

EXERCISES 20.5 (PAGE 705)

1. 2
3. divergent
5. divergent
7. divergent
9. $\pi/4$
11. divergent

13. divergent
15. divergent
17. 0
19. $\pi/3$
21. divergent

EXERCISES 21.1 (PAGE 715)

1. (7,0,0), (7,2,0), (0,2,0), (0,2,3), (0,0,3), (7,0,3)
3. (2,1,2), (2,3,2), (−1,3,2), (−1,3,5), (−1,1,5), (2,1,5)
5. (b) $3\sqrt{77}$; (c) (0,0,0), (15,18,12), (15,0,0), (15,18,0), (0,18,0), (0,18,12), (0,0,12), (15,0,12)
9. (a) 13/2; (b) (5/4,−1,2)
11. (a) 23/2; (b) (3/2,1/4,1/2)
13. ($4\sqrt{6}$,4,2), ($−4\sqrt{6}$, 4,2)
15. sphere, center at (4,−2,−1), radius 5
17. point sphere: (0,0,3)

19. no real locus
21. $x^2 + (y - 1)^2 + (z + 4)^2 = r^2$, $r > 0$
23. (−4,2,6), (2,0,4), (4,4,2)
25. cylinder whose elements are parallel to the y axis and which intersects the xz plane in the circle with center at the origin and radius 2
27. the x axis
29. the plane, perpendicular to the xy plane and which intersects the xy plane in the line $x = y$

EXERCISES 21.2 (PAGE 721)

15. $\langle 5,-1,2 \rangle$
17. $\langle -19,0,37 \rangle$
19. $\langle 7,13,-11 \rangle$
21. −1
23. $\langle 26,-7,-4 \rangle$
25. $\langle 32,20,44 \rangle$

27. −1/8
29. 181
31. $\langle 9,-1,-23 \rangle$
33. $15\sqrt{1,582}$
35. −185

EXERCISES 21.3 (PAGE 729)

5. $4/\sqrt{89}, 3/\sqrt{89}, 8/\sqrt{89}$
7. $-6/\sqrt{86}, -1/\sqrt{86}, -7/\sqrt{86}$
9. $3[(2/3) + (-2/3)\mathbf{j} + (1/3)\mathbf{k}]$
11. $\sqrt{14}[(-2/\sqrt{14})\mathbf{i} + (1/\sqrt{14})\mathbf{j} + (-3/\sqrt{14})\mathbf{k}]$
13. $13\sqrt{7}/70$

19. $5\sqrt{29}/27$
21. 17
23. $\sqrt{89}$
25. $9\sqrt{29}$
27. $(\mathbf{i} + \mathbf{j} - \mathbf{k})/\sqrt{3}$
31. 20

EXERCISES 21.4 (PAGE 738)

1. $x + 2y - 3z + 1 = 0$
3. $x - 3y - 4z - 3 = 0$
5. $3x + 2y + 6z - 23 = 0$
7. $5x - 2y + 7z = 0$
9. $\frac{2}{3}\mathbf{i} - \frac{1}{3}\mathbf{j} + \frac{2}{3}\mathbf{k}; -\frac{2}{3}\mathbf{i} + \frac{1}{3}\mathbf{j} - \frac{2}{3}\mathbf{k}$
11. $\frac{4}{13}\mathbf{i} + \frac{3}{13}\mathbf{j} - \frac{12}{13}\mathbf{k}; -\frac{4}{13}\mathbf{i} - \frac{3}{13}\mathbf{j} + \frac{12}{13}\mathbf{k}$

13. $\frac{3}{\sqrt{13}}\mathbf{i} + \frac{2}{\sqrt{13}}\mathbf{k}; -\frac{3}{\sqrt{13}}\mathbf{i} - \frac{2}{\sqrt{13}}\mathbf{k}$
15. $5x - 3y + 7z + 14 = 0$
17. $2x - y - z + 1 = 0$
19. $4y - 3z - 1 = 0$ and $z = 1$
21. $16/45$
23. $16\sqrt{6}/15$
25. $3/2$

EXERCISES 21.5 (PAGE 741)

1. $(x - 1)/4 = (y - 2)/-3, \ z = 1$
3. $(x - 4)/1 = (y + 5)/3 = (z - 20)/-6$
5. $x/13 = y/-12 = z/-8$
7. $8x - y = 66, 13x - 5z = 102, 13y - 40z = -42$

9. $4x + y = -3, 3x - z = -4, 3y + 4z = 7$
11. $5\sqrt{6}/18$
13. $4x + 7y - 3z + 7 = 0$
15. $x = y/2 = z - 1$
17. $x = y = -z$

EXERCISES 21.6 (PAGE 748)

9. $x^2 + z^2 = 4y$
11. $x^2 + 4y^2 + 4z^2 = 16$
13. $y^2 + z^2 = \sin^2 x$
15. axis is the z axis; generating curve is either $y^2 - z^2 = 4$

in yz plane or $x^2 - z^2 = 4$ in xz plane
17. axis is the y axis; generating curve is either $|y| = x^2$ in xy plane or $|y| = z^2$ in yz plane

EXERCISES 21.7 (PAGE 753)

1. ellipsoid
3. elliptic hyperboloid of one sheet
5. elliptic paraboloid

7. hyperbolic paraboloid
9. elliptic cone

EXERCISES 21.8 (PAGE 759)

3. $(\mathbf{i} + 2t\mathbf{j} + 3t^2\mathbf{k})/\sqrt{1 + 4t^2 + 9t^4}$
5. $[(\cos t - \sin t)\mathbf{i} + (\sin t + \cos t)\mathbf{j} + \mathbf{k}]/\sqrt{3}$
9. $\sqrt{3}(e^3 - 1)$
11. $\pi\sqrt{\pi^2 + 8}/8 + \ln(\pi + \sqrt{\pi^2 + 8}) - (3/2)\ln 2$
13. $\mathbf{T} = (\mathbf{i} + 2\mathbf{j} + 3\mathbf{k})/\sqrt{14}$, $\mathbf{N} = (-11\mathbf{i} - 8\mathbf{j} + 9\mathbf{k})/\sqrt{266}$, $\mathbf{B} = (3\mathbf{i} - 3\mathbf{j} + \mathbf{k})/\sqrt{19}$, $K = \sqrt{266}/98$

15. $\mathbf{T} = (\mathbf{i} + \mathbf{j} + \mathbf{k})/\sqrt{3}$, $\mathbf{N} = (-\mathbf{i} + \mathbf{j})/\sqrt{2}$, $\mathbf{B} = -\mathbf{i} - \mathbf{j} + 2\mathbf{k}, K = \sqrt{2}/3$
17. $\mathbf{V}(\pi/2) = -a\mathbf{i} + \mathbf{k}, \mathbf{A}(\pi/2) = -a\mathbf{j}, |\mathbf{V}(\pi/2)| = \sqrt{a^2 + 1}$
19. $\mathbf{V}(\pi/2) = -\frac{1}{2}\pi\mathbf{i} + \mathbf{j} + \mathbf{k}$, $\mathbf{A}(\pi/2) = -2\mathbf{i} - \frac{1}{2}\pi\mathbf{j}, |\mathbf{V}(\pi/2)| = \frac{1}{2}\sqrt{\pi^2 + 8}$

EXERCISES 22.2 (PAGE 766)

1. (a) $-1/7$; (b) $(x^2 + y^2) \div (x^2 - y^2)$; (c) $(x^2 + 2xy + y^2) \div (x^2 - 2xy + y^2)$; (d) 0; (e) set

of all points (x,y) in E^2 except those on line $x = y$; (f) $(-\infty, +\infty)$

3. domain: set of all points (x,y) in E^2 except those on line $x = y$; range: $(-\infty, +\infty)$

5. domain: set of all points (x,y) in E^2 interior to the circle $x^2 + y^2 = 4$ and all points on the y axis except $(0,2)$ and $(0,-2)$; range: $(-\infty, +\infty)$

7. domain: set of all points (x,y) in E^2 interior to and on the circumference of the circle $x^2 + y^2 = 1$; range: $[0, \pi/2]$

9. domain: set of all points (x,y) in E^2 for which $xy > 1$; range: $(-\infty, +\infty)$

11. domain: set of all points (x,y,z) in E^3 in and above the plane $z = 2$; range: $(-\infty, +\infty)$

13. domain: set of all points (x,y,z) in E^3 for which $|x| \le 1$ and $|y| \le 1$; range: $(-\pi, 2\pi)$

15. domain: set of all points in E^2; range: $[0, +\infty)$

17. domain: set of all points (x,y) in E^2 lying on or above the x axis or on the y axis; range: $(-\infty, +\infty)$

19. (a) 2; (b) 6; (c) $\sqrt{x - y^2}$; (d) $|x - y|$

EXERCISES 22.3 (PAGE 775)

1. $\delta = \epsilon/7$
3. $\delta = \min(1, \epsilon/6)$
5. $\delta = \min(1, \epsilon/8)$
17. 0

19. 2
21. exists and equals 0
23. does not exist
25. exists and equals 0

EXERCISES 22.4 (PAGE 781)

1. continuous at every point $(x,y) \ne (0,0)$ in E^2
3. continuous at every point in E^2
5. continuous at every point $(x,y) \ne (0,0)$ in E^2
7. continuous at every point in E^2
11. all points (x,y) in E^2 which are interior to the circle $x^2 + y^2 = 16$
13. all points (x,y) in E^2 which are exterior to the ellipse

$4x^2 + 9y^2 = 36$

15. all points (x,y) in E^2 which are in either the first or third quadrant
17. all points (x,y) in E^2 for which $|xy| > 1$
19. all points in E^2
23. continuous at every point in E^3 which is exterior to the sphere $x^2 + y^2 + z^2 = 1$
25. continuous at all points in E^3

EXERCISES 22.5 (PAGE 789)

1. 6
3. $3x - 2y$
5. $x/\sqrt{x^2 + y^2}$
7. $x^2 - 6xy + 2z$
9. $xy + yt + zt$
11. 4
13. $x/\sqrt{x^2 + y^2}$
15. $-2 \sin 3\theta \sin 2\phi$

17. $[ye^{y/x} \ln(x/y) - xe^{y/x}]/xy$
19. $z(x^2 + y^2 + z^2)^{-3/2}$
21. $xy + 1/z$
23. $xze^{xyz} + xz/(x^2y^2 + z^2)$
27. 4
29. $x + 2z - 5 = 0,\ y = 2$
31. (a) 1; (b) 1
33. (a) -2; (b) 0

EXERCISES 22.6 (PAGE 796)

5. $\xi_1 = \sqrt{156}/3$
7. $\xi_2 = \sqrt{5} - 1$

9. (a) $\Delta f(x_0, y_0) = 2(x_0 y_0 - y_0)\,\Delta x + (x_0^2 - 2x_0)\,\Delta y +$

$(y_0 \Delta x + \Delta x \Delta y) \Delta x +$
$2(x_0 \Delta x - \Delta x) \Delta y$
(b) $\epsilon_1 = y_0 \Delta x + \Delta x \Delta y$ and
$\epsilon_2 = 2(x_0 \Delta x - \Delta x)$

11. (a) $\Delta f(x_0, y_0) = \dfrac{2x_0}{y_0 + \Delta y} (\Delta x) +$

$\dfrac{1}{y_0 + \Delta y} (\Delta x)^2 - \dfrac{x_0}{y_0^2 + y_0 \Delta y} (\Delta y)$

$= \dfrac{2x_0}{y_0} (\Delta x) + \dfrac{-x_0^2}{y_0^2} (\Delta y) +$

$\left(\dfrac{2x_0}{y_0 + \Delta y} - \dfrac{2x_0}{y_0} + \dfrac{\Delta x}{y_0 + \Delta y} \right) (\Delta x)$

$+ \left(\dfrac{x_0^2}{y_0^2} - \dfrac{x_0^2}{y_0^2 + y_0 \Delta y} \right) (\Delta y)$

(b) $\epsilon_1 = 2x_0/(y_0 + \Delta y) -$
$2x_0/y_0 + \Delta x/(y_0 + \Delta y)$;
$\epsilon_2 = x_0^2/y_0^2 - x_0^2/(y_0^2 + y_0 \Delta y)$

13. $D_1 f(1,1) = 1,\ D_2 f(2,2) = 1$

17. (a) $\Delta f(x_0, y_0, z_0) = (y_0 - z_0) \Delta x$
$+ x_0 \Delta y + (-x_0 + 2z_0) \Delta z +$
$(-\Delta z) \Delta x + (\Delta x)(\Delta y) + (\Delta z)(\Delta z)$
(b) $\epsilon_1 = -\Delta z,\ \epsilon_2 = \Delta x,\ \epsilon_3 = \Delta z$

19. $D_1 f(0,0,0) = D_2 f(0,0,0) =$
$D_3 f(0,0,0) = 0$

EXERCISES 22.7 (PAGE 803)

1. $\partial u/\partial r$: (a) $6x - 2y$,
   (b) $16r - 10s$; $\partial u/\partial s$:
   (a) $-2x - 4y$, (b) $-10r - 6s$
3. $\partial u/\partial r$: (a) $e^{y/x} \times$
   $[x \sin t - y \cos t]/x^2 = 0$,
   (b) 0; $\partial u/\partial t$: (a) $re^{y/x} \times$
   $[x \cos t + y \sin t]/x^2$,
   (b) $e^{\tan t} \sec^2 t$
5. $\partial u/\partial r = (6re^s + s \cos rs) \div$
   $\sqrt{1 - (3x + y)^2}$
   $\partial u/\partial s = (3r^2 e^s + r \cos rs) \div$
   $\sqrt{1 - (3x + y)^2}$
7. $\partial u/\partial r = \sinh (y/x) \times$
   $(-2rsy + se^r x)/x^2$
   $\partial u/\partial s = \sinh (y/x) \times$
   $(-r^2 y + e^r x)/x^2$
9. $\partial u/\partial r = 2x \sin \phi \cos \theta +$
   $2y \sin \phi \sin \theta + 2z \cos \phi$
   $\partial u/\partial \phi = 2xr \cos \phi \cos \theta +$
   $2yr \cos \phi \sin \theta - 2zr \sin \phi$
   $\partial u/\partial \theta = -2xr \sin \phi \sin \theta +$
   $2yr \sin \phi \cos \theta$

11. (a) $e^x(\cos t - y \sin t) +$
    $e^y(x \cos t - \sin t)$
    (b) $e^{\cos t}(\cos t - \sin^2 t) +$
    $e^{\sin t}(\cos^2 t - \sin t)$
13. (a) $(x^2 + y^2 + z^2)^{-1/2} \times$
    $(x \sec^2 t - y \sin t + z \cos t)$
    (b) $\tan t \sec t$
15. $(txe^t - y)/t(x^2 + y^2)$
17. $(x + y + 2t)/t(y + t)^2$
25. $\dfrac{\partial u}{\partial v} = (\sinh v \cos w) \dfrac{\partial u}{\partial x} +$

    $(\cosh v \sin w) \dfrac{\partial u}{\partial y}$

    $\dfrac{\partial u}{\partial w} = (-\cosh v \sin w) \dfrac{\partial u}{\partial x} +$

    $(\sinh v \cos w) \dfrac{\partial u}{\partial y}$

27. decreasing at the rate of 8/61
    radians/min
29. 0.19 ft/min

EXERCISES 22.8 (PAGE 810)

1. $\sqrt{2}x + \sqrt{2}y$
3. $x + \sqrt{2}y + z$
5. -42
7. -2
9. $-3e^{\pi/4} \cos (\pi/12)$

11. $-29/11;\ \sqrt{21}$
13. $(3\pi + 8)/20;\ \sqrt{\pi^2 + 4}/4$
15. $\theta = \tan^{-1}[3/(3\pi + 1)]$
17. (a) -1; (b) $2\mathbf{j}$
19. (a) $8/189$; (b) $(2\mathbf{i} + 2\mathbf{j} - \mathbf{k})/27$

EXERCISES 22.9 (PAGE 815)

1. $2x - 2y + 3z - 17 = 0$;
   $(x - 2)/2 = (y + 2)/-2 =$
   $(z - 3)/3$

3. $4x + 8y + 3z + 22 = 0$;
   $(x + 2)/4 = (y + 4)/8 =$
   $(z - 6)/3$

5. $ex - y = 0; (x - 1)/-e = (y - e)/1, z = 0$
7. $x - y - 3 = 0; (x - 6)/1 = (y - 3)/-1, z = 3$
9. $x + 2y + 2z - 8 = 0; (x - 4)/1 = (y - 1)/2 = (z - 1)/2$

11. $3x - 2y - 6z + 84 = 0;$ $(x + 8)/-3 = (y - 27)/2 = (z - 1)/6$
13. $(x - 2)/4 = (y + 2)/-1 = z/20$
15. $x = 4, y = 16$
17. surfaces are tangent

EXERCISES 22.10 (PAGE 821)

1. (a) $2/y - 6y/x^4$; (b) $2x^2/y^3$
3. (a) $4e^{2x} \sin y$; (b) $-e^{2x} \sin y$
5. (a) $2 \tan^{-1}(y/x) - 2xy/(x^2 + y^2)$; (b) $2 \tan^{-1}(y/x) + 2xy/(x^2 + y^2)$
7. (a) $y \cosh x$; (b) $x \sinh y$
9. (a) 0; (b) e^y
11. (a) $6r + 4s$; (b) $4r - 6s$
13. (a) $16rst/(r^2 + s^2 + t^2)^3$;

(b) $4r(3s^2 - t^2 - r^2) \div (r^2 + s^2 + t^2)^3$
21. neither exists
23. $f_{12}(0,0) = -1; f_{21}(0,0) = 1$
27. $4t^2 e^{t^2} \cos 2t - 8te^{t^2} \sin 2t - 2e^{t^2} \cos 2t$
29. $16se^{-2t}$
31. $-10r^2 \cos 2\theta$

EXERCISES 23.1 (PAGE 830)

1. 50
3. 1,368
5. 704

7. 50 3/4
9. 1,376

EXERCISES 23.2 (PAGE 837)

1. $50\frac{2}{3}$
3. 1,404
5. $746\frac{2}{3}$
7. 512/3
9. 16/3
11. $(15\pi - 32)/120$
21. $\dfrac{8c}{ab}\displaystyle\int_0^b \int_0^{a\sqrt{b^2-y^2}/b} \sqrt{a^2b^2 - b^2x^2 - a^2y^2}\, dx\, dy$

13. 1/12
15. 72
17. (b) $5a^3/9$;

(c) $\dfrac{2}{3}\displaystyle\int_0^a \int_0^{\sqrt{a^2-y^2}} (2x + y)\, dx\, dy$
19. 356/15

EXERCISES 23.3 (PAGE 843)

1. $M = 2ka^4/3; \bar{x} = 5a/8; \bar{y} = 5a/8$
3. $M = 176k/15; \bar{x} = 35/22, \bar{y} = 108/77$
5. $M = k(e^2 - 1)/4$
7. 48ρ
9. $\frac{1}{2}\pi\rho a^4$

11. $196\rho/45$
13. (a) $\pi k/4$; (b) $\bar{x} = \pi/2, \bar{y} = 16/9\pi$; (c) $3\pi k/32$; (d) $\sqrt{6}/4$
15. (a) $k/15$; (b) $\bar{x} = 15/28, \bar{y} = 5/8$; (c) $k/45$; (d) $\sqrt{3}/3$
17. $\sqrt{6}\, b/12$

EXERCISES 23.4 (PAGE 848)

1. 6π
3. $(\pi + 8)/a^2$
5. $M = 2\pi ka^3/9, \bar{x} = 3a/10, \bar{y} = 0$

7. $M = 13k/3, \bar{x} = 42/65, \bar{y} = 19\pi/52$
9. $5\pi\rho/64$
11. $35\pi\rho a^4/16$

EXERCISES 23.5 (PAGE 852)

1. $15/2$
3. $1/24$
5. $648/5$

7. $1/4$
9. $3\pi/2$
11. $4\pi a^3/3$

EXERCISES 23.6 (PAGE 861)

1. 30
3. $3(a^2 + 4h^2)M/20$
5. $2\pi ka^5/5$; $(0,0,5a/24)$

7. $56\pi ka^3/9$
9. $\pi kh^4 (\sec^3 \alpha - 1)/6$
11. $M(3a^2 + 4b^2)/4$

EXERCISES 24.1 (PAGE 869)

1. convergent; $1/2$
3. divergent
5. convergent; 0
7. convergent; 1
9. divergent

11. convergent; $\sqrt[3]{e}$
15. nonincreasing
17. strictly decreasing
19. increasing

EXERCISES 24.2 (PAGE 877)

1. $s_n = n/(2n + 1)$; convergent; $1/2$
3. $s_n = \ln(1/n - 1)$; divergent
5. $s_n = (n^2 + 2n)/(n + 1)^2$;
   convergent; 1
7. $\displaystyle\sum_{n=1}^{+\infty} \frac{2}{(3n - 2)(3n + 1)}$;
   convergent; $2/3$
9. $\displaystyle\frac{1}{2} - \sum_{n=1}^{+\infty} \frac{1}{2^{n+1}}$; convergent; 0

13. divergent
15. convergent; 2
17. convergent; -3
19. convergent; $1/(e - 1)$
21. divergent
23. convergent; $3/2$
25. divergent
27. $137/111$
29. $47/101$

EXERCISES 24.3 (PAGE 885)

1. convergent
3. convergent
5. divergent
7. convergent
9. divergent

11. convergent
13. convergent
15. convergent
17. convergent
19. divergent

EXERCISES 24.4 (PAGE 894)

1. convergent
3. convergent
5. convergent
7. convergent
9. $|R_4| < 0.2$
11. $|R_4| < 1/81$
13. 0.113

15. 0.406
17. absolutely convergent
19. convergent
21. divergent
23. absolutely convergent
25. absolutely convergent
27. divergent

EXERCISES 24.5 (PAGE 900)

1. $(-\infty, +\infty)$
3. $[-1/2, 1/2]$
5. $x = 0$
7. $(-9, 9]$
9. $(0, 2]$

11. $(-1/e^2, 1/e^2)$
13. $(-1, 1]$
15. $(-e, e)$
17. $[4, 6)$
19. $[-1, 1]$

EXERCISES 24.6 (PAGE 906)

1. $P_3(x) = 1/2 + \sqrt{3}(x - \pi/6)/2 - (x - \pi/6)^2/4 - \sqrt{3}(x - \pi/6)^3/12$; $R_3(x) = \sin \xi (x - \pi/6)^4/24$, ξ between $\pi/6$ and x
3. $P_4(x) = x - x^3/6$; $R_4(x) = x^5 \cosh \xi/120$, ξ between 0 and x
5. $P_3(x) = x - 1 - (x - 1)^2/2 + (x - 1)^3/3$; $R_3(x) = (x - 1)^4/4\xi^4$, ξ between 1 and x
7. $P_3(x) = -\ln 2 - \sqrt{3}(x - \pi/3) -$

$2(x - \pi/3)^2 - 8\sqrt{3}(x - \pi/3)^3/3$; $R_3(x) = -\sec^3 \xi(1 + 4 \tan^3 \xi)(x - \pi/3)^4/12$, ξ between $\pi/3$ and x
9. $P_3(x) = 1 + 3x/2 + 3x^2/8 - x^3/16$; $R_3(x) = 3x^4/128(1 + \xi)^{5/2}$, ξ between 0 and x
11. 0.515
13. 0.1823

EXERCISES 24.7 (PAGE 916)

7. $\sum\limits_{n=1}^{+\infty} (x - 1)^n/n$; $r = 1$
9. $\dfrac{\sqrt{2}}{2}[-1 + (x + \pi/4) + (x + \pi/4)/2! - (x + \pi/4)^3/3! - (x + \pi/4)^4/4! + (x + \pi/4)^5/5! + (x + \pi/4)^6/6! - \cdots]$; $r = +\infty$
11. $\sum\limits_{n=1}^{+\infty} x^n/(n - 1)!$; $r = +\infty$
13. $1 + \sum\limits_{n=1}^{+\infty} \dfrac{(-1)^{n+1}(2n - 2)! x^n}{2^{2n-1} n!(n - 1)!}$; $r = 1$

15. $1 + \sum\limits_{n=1}^{+\infty} \dfrac{(-1)^n 1 \cdot 3 \cdots (2n - 1) x^{2n}}{2^n n!}$; $r = 1$
17. $\frac{1}{4} \sum\limits_{n=0}^{+\infty} (-1)^n x^n/2^n$; $r = 2$
19. 1.12763
21. 4.899
23. 0.7373
25. 2.7182818
27. 0.69315

EXERCISES 24.8 (PAGE 920)

1. 1.4409
3. 0.0419
5. 0.4931

7. 3.14159265
11. $\sum\limits_{n=1}^{+\infty} x^{2n-1}/(2n - 1)$

EXERCISES 24.9 (PAGE 926)

5. no relative extrema; $(1, -2)$ is a saddle point
7. $3\sqrt{3}/2$, rel. max. at $(\pi/3, \pi/3)$; $-3\sqrt{3}/2$, rel. min. at $(5\pi/3, 5\pi/3)$

9. no relative extrema
11. $N/3$, $N/3$, $N/3$
13. $8abc/3\sqrt{3}$
17. $2\sqrt{3}$

Index

970

Continuity (*Cont.*)
of a vector-valued function, 623, 755
Continuous differentiability, 795
Continuous function, 123
Convergence, interval of, 899
radius of, 899
Convergent improper integral, 700, 704
Convergent infinite series, 872
Convergent, sequence, 864
Coordinates, cylindrical, 853–862
polar, 526–557
rectangular cartesian, 17, 18
spherical, 853–862
Cosecant function, 432
derivative of, 442
inverse, 469
Cosine function, 432
derivative of, 441
inverse, 467
Cosines, direction, 724
Cotangent function, 432
derivative of, 441
inverse, 469
Critical number, 197
Cross multiplication of vectors, 718
Cross product of vectors, 718
Cross section of a surface in a plane, 744
Cubic, twisted, 760
Cubic function, 78
Curvature, 651–662
center of, 662
circle of, 657
of plane curve, 654
radius of, 657
of space curve, 756
vector, 656, 756
Curve(s), 34
smooth, 828
in three-dimensional space, 753–761
Cycloid, 620
Cylinder, as a solid, 373
as a surface, 742
directrix of, 743
elliptic, 743
generator of, 743
height of, 373
hyperbolic, 743
parabolic, 743
Cylinder, right-circular, 373
ruling of, 743
Cylindrical coordinates, 853–862
Cylindrical partition, 854
Cylindrical shell method for volumes, 330–335

Decreasing function, 220
Definite integral, 266–310
applications of, 311–385
definition of, 282

properties of, 287–294
Degenerate cases of the conic sections, 559
Degenerate circle, 577
Degenerate ellipse, 577
Degenerate hyperbola, 582
Degenerate parabola, 582
Del (∇), 808
Delta (Δ) notation, 19, 20, 279
Delta (δ), 84
Density, 348
Dependent variables, 67, 765
Derivative(s), 138, 161
applications of, 190–250
of a composite function, 168–171
chain rule, 168, 798
of a constant, 162
of a constant times a function, 163
of cos u, 441
of cos^{-1} u, 473
of cosh u, 671
of cosh^{-1} u, 681
of cot u, 441
of cot^{-1} u, 474
of coth u, 671
of coth^{-1} u, 681
of csc u, 442
of csc^{-1} u, 475
of csch u, 671
of csch^{-1} u, 681
definition of, 150
directional, 805–811
of exponential functions, 416, 422
first through nth, 174
of a function, 150–155
of inverse function, 410
of higher-order, 174–177
of hyperbolic functions, 671, 672
of inverse hyperbolic functions, 680, 681
of inverse trigonometric functions, 473–478
from the left, 159
of logarithmic function, 422
of natural logarithmic function, 392
notation, 150, 186
one-sided, 158
ordinary, 785
partial, 783–790
definition of, 783
of the power function for negative integer exponents, 166
positive integer exponents, 162,
rational exponents, 171–174
real exponents, 424
of the product of two functions, 164, 165

of the quotient of two functions, 165, 166
as a rate of change, 155–157
from the right, 158
of sec u, 441
of sec^{-1} u, 775
of sech u, 671
of sech^{-1} u, 681
of sin u, 440
of sin^{-1} u, 473
of sinh u, 671
of sinh^{-1} u, 680
of the sum of a finite number of functions, 164
of the sum of two functions, 164
of tan u, 441
of tan^{-1} u, 474
of tanh u, 671
of tanh^{-1} u, 681
total, 801
of trigonometric functions, 440–442
of a vector-valued function, 623–627, 755
See also Differentiation
Descartes, René, 17
Differentiability, 154, 793
and continuity, 157–161
continuous, 795
of a vector-valued function, 625
Differential(s), 181–185
formulas, 185–189
theorems on, 186
Differential calculus of functions of several variables, 762–823
Differential equations, 258
first-order, 258
second-order, 260
with variables separable, 258–265
Differential geometry, 758
Differentiation, 162
of algebraic functions, 162–189
implicit, 177–180
inverse of, 251–258
logarithmic, 394, 424
partial, 781
of power series, 907–918
of trigonometric functions, 440–443
applications of, 449–454
See also Derivative(s)
Directed distances, 18–23
Directed line segment, 593
Direction angles, 723
Direction cosines, 724
Direction numbers, 740
Directional derivative, 805–811
Directrix (directrices), 54
of a conic, 560
of a cylinder, 743
of a parabola, 54

$$\frac{-b \pm \sqrt{b^2 - 4AC}}{2a}$$